GEOMORPHOLOGY

GEOMORPHOLOGY

with special reference
to Australia

C. R. Twidale M.Sc. Ph.D.

*Reader in Geography in the
University of Adelaide*

NELSON

THOMAS NELSON (AUSTRALIA) LIMITED
597 Little Collins Street, Melbourne 3000
403 George Street, Sydney 2000

THOMAS NELSON AND SONS LTD
36 Park Street, London W1Y 4DE

THOMAS NELSON AND SONS (SOUTH AFRICA) PTY LTD
P.O. Box 7331, Johannesburg

THOMAS NELSON AND SONS (CANADA) LTD
81 Curlew Drive, Don Mills, Ontario

© Thomas Nelson (Australia) Ltd 1968

SBN 17 004707 5

Reprinted 1968, 1970, 1971

Typesetting by The Universities Press, North Melbourne
Printed by Dai Nippon Printing Co., (International) Ltd. Hong Kong.

Acknowledgements

The writer wishes to thank Dr B. Daily, Department of Geology, University of Adelaide, Mr R. S. Coggins, Bedford Park Teachers' College, Adelaide, and Messrs. N. F. Alley and D. G. Tulloch, members of the South Australian Department of Education, for their assistance in reading all or part of the finished manuscript; Miss Janet Saies and Miss Anne Lillingston for help with proof-reading and indexing, Max Foale for meticulously and patiently drafting many of the illustrations; and his wife Kate for her forbearance during the writing of this book and for reading the finished manuscript and making numerous helpful suggestions.

Acknowledgements are due also the the Council, Royal Society of South Australia, for permission to reproduce Figs. 8, 14, 41, 55, 58, 62, 107, 162, 174, 177, 200, 224, 226, 227(e), 249; Council, Royal Society of N.S.W. (Fig. 253); Council, Linnean Society of N.S.W. (Fig. 218); Editor, American Geographical Society (Fig. 201); Editor, *Australian Journal of Science* (Fig. 219); Editor, *Bulletin Volcanologique* (Fig. 165); Editor, Institute of British Geographers (Figs. 95, 96, 97); Editor, Geological Society of Australia (Figs. 9, 25, 29, 31, 33, 36, 52, 175); Editor, The Geological Society of America (Fig. 247); Editor, *Geological Magazine* (Fig. 243); Editor, *Australian Geographer* (Figs. 133, 196, 197); Editors, *Revue de Géomorphologie Dynamique* (Figs. 100, 101, 102); Editor, *The Geographical Review* (Fig. 217); Editor, The Association of American Geographers (Fig. 1); The University of Chicago Press for permission to reproduce Fig. 171, which originally appeared in the *Journal of Geology*; A.N.U. Press for Figs. 66 and 105, which originally appeared in *Landform Studies from Australia and New Guinea* (Ed. Jennings & Mabbutt) and Fig. 198, which originally appeared in Bird, *Coastal Landforms: an introduction to coastal geomorphology with Australian examples*; Arctic Institute of North America (Fig. 202); Royal Geographical Society, London (Fig. 214(c)); Department of National Development, Canberra (Fig. 65); C.S.I.R.O., Melbourne (Figs. 39, 225); Chief Geologist, Bureau of Mineral Resources, Geology and Geophysics (Figs. 30, 63); Director of Mines, South Australia (Figs. 6(c), 18, 27, 42, 56, 59, 64, 78, 80, 89, 110, 111, 199, 240, 251, 252, 257); Director, Geological Survey of Victoria (Fig. 47); Gebrüder Borntraeger (Fig. 109); Macmillan & Co. Ltd. for Fig. 209, which originally appeared in Wright, *The Quaternary Ice Age*; Methuen & Co. Ltd.

for Fig. 35, which originally appeared in Hills, *Elements of Structural Geology*, and Fig. 230, which appeared in Hills, *Arid Lands*; Longmans, Green & Co. Ltd. for Fig. 166, which originally appeared in Shackleton, *Europe*; W. H. Freeman & Co. for permission to reproduce Figs. 204 and 212, which originally appeared in Gilluly, Waters and Woodford, *Principles of Geology*, 2nd ed. Copyright 1959, and, in their capacity as book-publishing affiliate of Scientific American Inc., Figs. 195, 222 and 223; John Murray for Fig. 211, which originally appeared in Gregory, *Nature and Origin of Fiords*; Hulton Educational Publications Ltd. for Fig. 202, which originally appeared in Greswell, *Glaciers and Glaciation*; Whitcombe & Tombs for Figs. 23, 37, 48, 147, which originally appeared in Hills, *Physiography of Victoria*; Cooper Square Publishers Inc. for Fig. 121, which originally appeared in Sharpe, *Landslides and Related Phenomena*; Professor J. A. Mabbutt and the Trustees of the Australian Museum (Fig. 169); Professor C. Wahrhaftig and The Geological Society of America (Fig. 242); Professor G. H. Dury and Penguin Books Australia Ltd. for Figs. 114 and 214, which originally appeared in *The Face of the Earth*; Professor J. Tricart (Fig. 2); Mr. R. C. Sprigg (Fig. 53); Surveyors Office, City of Adelaide (Fig. 43); Mrs. E. M. Campbell (Figs. 184(a) and (b)); Department of Geology, University of Adelaide (Fig. 220). Fig. 215 is taken from the unfortunately discontinued *Journal of Geomorphology*, a casualty of World War II.

South Australia Government Tourist Bureau for permission to reproduce Plates 2 and 25; Queensland Government Railways (Pl. 4); South Australia Lands Department (Pls. 7, 54, 55); Director, Division of National Mapping, Department of National Development, Canberra (Pls. 9, 13, 28, 53); Division of Land Research, C.S.I.R.O. (Pls. 10, 11, 12, 21, 36, 56, 72); Geological Survey of South Australia, Department of Mines (Pls. 26, 64); Professor C. Wahrhaftig (Pls. 27, 35); Professor J. N. Jennings (Pl. 37); Hunting Aerosurveys, Aerofilms Ltd. (Pl. 58); Mr. R. C. Sprigg (Pl. 63).

While every effort has been made to trace and acknowledge copyright holders, in some cases this has not been possible. Should any infringement have occurred the author and publishers tender their apologies.

Contents

Preface		xi
PART A	INTRODUCTION	
Chapter 1	Some General Concepts	1
PART B	THE INFLUENCE OF STRUCTURE	
Chapter 2	Geological Background	9
Chapter 3	Tectonic Landforms	46
Chapter 4	Structural Landforms	78
PART C	GEOMORPHOLOGICAL PROCESSES	
Chapter 5	Weathering	134
Chapter 6	Rivers and Valleys	148
Chapter 7	The Arid Lands	204
Chapter 8	Coastal Processes and Forms	236
PART D	HISTORICAL GEOMORPHOLOGY	
Chapter 9	The Quaternary: Direct Effects of Glaciation	256
Chapter 10	The Quaternary: Indirect Effects of Glaciation	283
Chapter 11	Surfaces of Low Relief	306
Chapter 12	Cyclic and Non-cyclic Landscape Development	320
Chapter 13	The Work of Man–Anthropogenic Influences	341
Chapter 14	Conclusion	347
References and Suggested Further Reading		351
Appendix	A Regional Subdivision of South Australia	368
	B The Adelaide District	386
Index		400

List of Plates

Plate		
1	Minor domes and basins	25
2	Wilpena Pound, S.A.	25
3	Eden fault scarp, S.A.	57
4	Glasshouse Mountains, Queensland	68
5	Columnar jointing in the Gawler Range porphyry	69
6	Mt Schank from the northwest	69
7	Mt Schank from the air	71
8	Stratified ash exposed in Mt Schank quarry	72
9	Mt Tabletop, north Queensland, from the air	76
10	Mt Tabletop from the southeast	76
11	Porcupine or Galah Gorge, north Queensland	77
12	Weathering and erosion of sandstone	84
13	Mueller plateau, Northern Territory	84
14	Dissected pediment north of Brachina Gorge	94
15	Cliffs of the River Murray, S.A.	98
16	Joint blocks in granite, Granite Island, near Victor Harbour	98
17	Corestone and spheroidally weathered granite	99
18	Cluster of tors near Palmer, Queensland	99
19	Tors near Palmer	100
20	Corestones in gruss, Jindabyne, N.S.W.	102
21	Tor in upper Herbert River valley, north Queensland	103
22	Onion weathering near Tooma dam, Snowy Mountains, N.S.W.	103
23	Split tor from the Kosciusko area, N.S.W.	104
24	Granite landscape, north Flinders Ranges	106
25	Ayers Rock, Northern Territory	107
26	Domes of the Olgas	108
27	Olgas, Northern Territory, from the air	108
28	Mt Lindsay, northwestern S.A.	109
29	Dome of Pildappa Hill, Northwest Eyre Peninsula	113
30	Ucontitchie Hill, northwest Eyre Peninsula	113
31	Pit on Pildappa Hill	120
32	Pan, or flat floored depression	120
33	Rillen or gutters	122
34	Tafoni or caverns	122
35	Kangaroo Tail, Ayers Rock	125
36	Fluted surface (Rillenkarren), North Queensland	130
37	Limestone cliffs, Australian Bight	130
38	Flaking induced by bushfire, Wilpena Pound	139
39	Pitting of granite surface	139
40	Blocky disintegration of quartzite, Mt Conner, N.T.	141
41	Frost shattered phyllites and shales near Knob Lake, Labrador	141
42	'Boss and shield' forms	145
43	Overhanging slope at Ucontitchie Hill	146
44	Slumping of gully banks	159

List of Plates

Plate		
45	Intensely gullied Tertiary sands South of Adelaide	159
46	Small puffs of turf and soil, Birdwood, S.A.	163
47	Bank cracking near Sellicks Hill, S.A.	166
48	Land slip in weathered Permian clays and sands, S.A.	167
49	Earthflows near Yankalilla, S.A.	167
50	Deep gully eroded in unconsolidated clays and gravels of alluvial fans	168
51	Deep V-shaped gorge of the Onkaparinga, S.A.	169
52	Narrow V-shaped gorges, north of Brachina Gorge	173
53	Arm Creek, Northern Territory	182
54	River meanders and ox bow lakes, Murray River, S.A.	183
55	Braided and distributary stream northeast of S.A.	184
56	Einasleigh River, northern Queensland, a braided river	195
57	Shallow former stream channel preserved on terrace remnant	195
58	Alluvial fans deposited by streams emerging from upland region, Zagros Mountains, Iran	208
59	Gibber plain near Wilpena	210
60	Pediments and inselbergs, Broken Hill, N.S.W.	210
61	Salina of Lake Gairdner on eastern side	217
62	Wind erosion on Lake Torrens plain	217
63	Convergent longitudinal sand dunes, Simpson Desert	223
64	Longitudinal sand dunes, Great Victoria Desert	224
65	Shore platform cut in gneisses, Lake Greenly, S.A.	234
66	Cliff, notch and platform, Cape Northumberland, S.A.	244
67	Coastal cliffs and shore platform at Halletts Cove, S.A.	244
68	Detail of serrated platform at Halletts Cove	245
69	Raised sea platform near Cape Northumberland	245
70	Overhanging slope and weathering front, Minnipa, S.A.	312
71	Unconformity, Boolcunda, S.A.	312
72	Mesa and butte, northwest Queensland	340
73	Erosion surface near Dutchmans Stern	340
74	Eroded track near Nonning, Gawler Ranges	342
75	Deep gully in unconsolidated clays and gravels	344
76	Old plough furrows deep enough to channel-run off	345
77	Exploitation of furrows to form gullies	345
78	Deep gully in Permian shale, Yankalilla, S.A.	346

List of Tables

Table		
1	Morphogenetic regions	3
2	A. Geological and B. Cainozoic time-scales	43
3	Some river catchments and discharges	152
4	Quaternary stratigraphy	266
5	The traditional scheme of Quaternary high sea levels	287
6	Postulated Pleistocene high sea levels in southeastern Australia	294
7	Interplay of uplift, incision, and wasting	329

For O. D. Kendall

Preface

DURING THE PAST FEW YEARS, the theoretical framework of geomorphology has changed considerably. More important is the emergence of a new body of factual material about Australia and its several parts. This dramatic advance in knowledge—and it is no less—is due in considerable measure to the air photographic coverage provided by the R.A.A.F., Department of National Mapping, and the several State Lands Departments (Photogrammetric Branches) and to some extent, to the general expansion of scientific exploration and investigation. The cover of stereoscopic air photographs of large scale is nearing completion and, besides providing in themselves a vast treasury of data, make possible many other works of geomorphological significance. The aerial photographs and the mosaics (at a scale of about 1 inch to the mile) compiled from them do not replace the urgent need for detailed topographical maps. But they at least meet part of that necessity and in some ways are more valuable than maps which are inherently incomplete in the detail recorded on them. The availability of aerial photographs has enabled several institutions, particularly the Federal and State Geological Surveys, the Land Research, and Soils, Divisions of the C.S.I.R.O., and private concerns, such as Geosurveys in South Australia, to compile geological, geomorphological and soils maps far more accurate and detailed than anything previously produced in Australia. The extensive and increasing coverage of regional map sheets is an invaluable aid to geomorphological investigations. University research also has progressed with some significant results, though the pace of research in Australia is not all that it could or should be.

For these reasons, the conceptual advances and the sheer accumulation of factual data, much of the earlier geomorphological work can now be improved upon; many of the regional descriptions can be elaborated, while many of the old interpretations have had to be abandoned or drastically modified. Nevertheless, the more one examines the work of scientists like Griffith Taylor, Charles Fenner, and other pioneers in the field (notably the geologists J. T. Jutson and R. Lockhart Jack), the more one is filled with admiration for their perspicacity and insight, and for their acute observation and deduction. They worked in a period lacking detailed maps of any description, and under conditions of transport and communications which would deter most modern travellers from venturing far from home. It is a tribute to these early workers that the best topographical map of South Australia, for instance, is still that of L. K. Ward, produced in 1917. The reinterpretations outlined in this book are offered not in carping spirit, but as necessitated by progress in both the factual and theoretical fields. The reader would do well to bear in mind the words of Lord Macaulay, who in his *Essay on Milton* wrote:

> Ages are spent on collecting materials, ages more in separating and combining them. Even when a system has been formed there is still something to add, to alter or to reject. Every generation enjoys the use of a vast hoard bequeathed to it by antiquity, and transmits that hoard, augmented by fresh acquisitions, to the future ages. In these pursuits, therefore, the first speculators be under great disadvantages, and when they fail be entitled to praise.

Though I have long wanted and intended to write this book, there has been a natural tendency to wait until more facts are available. But there are always gaps in our knowledge of even an area as limited as Australia. Now the book has been produced, I am still more conscious of its shortcomings, particularly of the unevenness of the coverage accorded to various parts of the continent. In considerable measure, it is based on South Australian experience, although many examples have been cited from other parts of Australia. I am also aware that, such is the rate of scientific advance, the book could be out of date before it leaves the presses. However, there has long been a need for a textbook which uses local examples, and in this way demonstrates that the theoretical concepts of geomorphology are not abstractions, but are as valid in Australia as in every other continent.

The book is aimed at three principal groups. It is intended as a textbook for use in upper Secondary and elementary University courses. It is hoped it will provide further reading and useful examples at lower levels not only to Geography students but in General Science courses too. Further it is hoped that the substance of the book will be of interest and value to geomorphologists not only in Australia but also overseas. Lastly, the material should be of interest to the layman who travels around Australia, uses his eyes, and sees much which is intriguing but not readily explicable.

The organisation of the book is simple. An introductory chapter outlines the principles which underlie the work. There follow sections concerned with the earth's crust and its role in determining the form of the land surface; with the processes shaping the surface in Australia; and with the effects of past conditions on the present form of the land.

PART A: INTRODUCTION

1. Some General Concepts

(a) STRUCTURE, PROCESS AND TIME

IN HIS CLASSIC ESSAY, *The Geographical Cycle*, William Morris Davis wrote:
> All the varied forms of the land are dependent upon—or, as the mathematician would say, are functions of—three variable quantities which may be called structure, process and time (*Geographical Essays* (1954) p. 249).

This quotation provides at once the theme of this book and its organisation. The form of the land surface varies widely from one part of the world to another, and to a lesser though still considerable degree within the borders of Australia. These variations are not a matter of chance and consequently the distribution of the various groups, families, suites, associations or *assemblages* of landforms is not fortuitous. The form of the land surface at any given place can be analysed and explained in a logical manner, as can the distributional pattern of the landform assemblages. The reasons behind the varied forms of the land surface are most often complex and still not completely understood, but in theory, and in many instances in practice, landforms can be explained rationally.

The three main reasons for morphological variation are, as suggested in the quotation cited above, the differences in structure of the earth's crust from place to place, contrasts in the processes at work at and near the earth's surface from one area to another, and changes in these two factors in the context of geological time. Thus, the three principal parts of this book are concerned with these three subjects, with particular reference to each as it applies in Australia.

(b) GEOMORPHOLOGICAL MEANING OF THE TERM 'STRUCTURE'

For the purpose of geomorphology the term *structure* includes any feature of the earth's crust which influences landform development. The term includes such rock characteristics (see Chapter 2) as mineralogical composition (lithology), the textures of the rock (grain or particle size, patterns of crystal arrangement), its joints and bedding planes, cleavage, the attitude or disposition of the strata, and the pattern of folds and faults. Although its relative importance varies from place to place, structure is always significant and in many areas is the most important single factor determining surface form.

(c) MORPHOGENETIC REGIONS

The nature of the processes at work in weathering and eroding the rocks exposed at the surface and occurring near the surface is determined by the structural characteristics of the outcrops and by climate, acting not only through such obvious features as the amount and incidence of precipitation, and temperature regime, but also through the control exerted by climate on the vegetational cover. So important is the climatic control of landforms that this long-recognised relationship has been elaborated into a concept of *morphogenetic regions* (Figs. 1, 2; Table 1).

Fig 1 Theoretical morphogenetic regions (*after Peltier*).

Table 1 Morphogenetic Regions

Morphogenetic region	Estimated Range of Average Annual Temperature (°F)	Estimated Range of Average Annual Rainfall (inches)	Morphological characteristics
Glacial	0–20	0–45	glacial erosion; nivation; wind action
Periglacial	5–30	5–55	strong mass movement; moderate to strong wind action; weak effect of running water
Boreal	15–38	10–60	moderate frost action; moderate to slight wind action; moderate effect of running water
Maritime	35–70	50–75	strong mass movement; moderate to strong action of running water;
Selva	60–85	55–90	strong mass movement; slight effect of slope wash; no wind action
Moderate	38–85	35–60	maximum effect of running water; moderate mass movement; frost action slight in colder part of the region; no significant wind action except on coasts
Savanna	10–85	25–50	strong to weak action of running water; moderate wind action
Semi-arid	35–85	10–25	strong wind action; moderate to strong action of running water;
Arid	55–85	0–15	strong wind action; slight action of running water and mass movement

Source: After *Peltier*.

The basic assumption on which this concept is founded is that in each climatic region, a certain complex of climatically induced and conditioned processes of weathering and erosion (the *morphogenetic system* or *system of erosion*) gives rise to a characteristic family or assemblage of landforms, which is peculiar to one specific climatic region and to no other. Several such morphogenetic regions have long been known. Davis, in his *Geographical Essays*, considered landform development in *humid temperate* regions (the *normal* of some workers), in *arid* lands and in *glaciated* regions. The *humid tropical lands* were partially described in the 1930s though they remain in considerable measure unknown. Subsequently the forms developed under *periglacial* or sub-arctic conditions, and in *semi-arid* and *savannah* regions have been described, and a case has been made for the recognition of a *Mediterranean*-type geomorphological region.

Fig 2 World distribution of morphogenetic regions (*after Tricart*):
1. Glaciated regions; 2. Periglacial (subarctic) regions with permafrost (permanently frozen subsoil); 3. Periglacial regions without permafrost; 4. Forests on (relict) Pleistocene permafrost; 5. Mid-latitude forests, maritime or with mild winters; 6. As for 5 but with severe winters; 7. As for 5 but with Mediterranean climate; 8. Steppes and semi desert plains; 8a. As for 8 but with severe winters; 9. Deserts and degraded steppes with mild winters; 10. As for 9 but with severe winters; 11. Savanna; 12. Rain forest; 13. Latitudinally anomalous regions where elevation exerts a controlling influence.

In terms of Tricart's classification (Fig. 2), three morphogenetic regions occur extensively within Australia—the semi-desert steppes, and the true deserts, in the centre and west, and the mid-latitude forest zone, with wind and mass movement less important and running water more consistently active, occupying large areas in the east. In addition savanna and rain forest occupy much of northern Australia. In Australia, however, we are principally concerned with the desert and semi-desert morphogenetic regions, the shaping of which is dominated by running water and wind, and with regions where river work is more significant.

In addition to guiding the *types* of landforms developed, climate determines the *rate* at which the land surface is changed by weathering and erosion, and, by implication, deposition. All land surfaces are constantly changing, but in most areas these changes are slow. However, even small amounts of erosion acquire great significance in the context of geological time: erosion at a rate of one tenth of an inch a year would result in the lowering of the land surface by more than 8,000 feet in a million years, a period which though immense to us, is in fact a mere moment of geological time.

Reliable data on rates of erosion is scarce, but the information to hand suggests that as one would expect, erosion is very much greater in mountainous areas than on lowlands, and that there are wide variations in these rates from one climatic region to another. The most rapid changes occur in cold mountain and hot dry mountain areas, where vegetation is scarce; erosion is least on arid lowlands, both hot and cold.

The concept of morphogenetic regions undoubtedly has its usefulness as is evidenced by the organisation of many text books, including this, and particularly as a basis for the classification of landform assemblages. It is necessary however to point out difficulties which arise from the complexities of the land surface. There are problems of gradational boundaries, uncertainties relating to the relations of process and landform, and from the unsophisticated use of climatic data. It is not sufficient, for instance, to consider total annual rainfall alone, for its seasonal distribution and incidence in detail are important geomorphologically and have to be borne in mind. Several important groups of landforms are associated with particular structures or rock types: the features developed through faulting, and those evolved on limestone and granite, for instance, are quite characteristic, as is described below, and these forms are found in a wide variety of climatic regimes. Such forms have an *azonal* distribution, in contrast to those which evolve only under certain climatic conditions, occur typically in certain morphogenetic regions, and are *zonal* in their distribution.

Far more difficult, however, is the possibility of *inheritance*. Many important landforms developed in the past when climatic conditions were different from those now experienced. These forms have persisted, modified to a greater or lesser degree by the action of modern processes of weathering and erosion, but nevertheless recognisable as alien to their present situation. Many land surfaces are of *palimpsest* type, that is, they bear the imprint of more than one climate. In Europe, Britain and North America the glacial origin of many forms prominent in the present landscape is clear; but elsewhere the age and origin of weathering features is controversial, and it is difficult to be certain whether a given set of forms is developing under existing conditions or whether they have been inherited from conditions which were prevalent x thousands or millions of years ago.

(d) HILLSLOPES
The interplay of climate and structure is expressed in slope form and development. Slopes are of course the basic elements of which all landforms are composed. They are of two types, faceted and non-faceted or

graded. The *faceted* comprise several units (Fig. 3a) and through the extension of the upper, debris and waning slopes, and the concurrent diminution of the bluff, can be converted to the sigmoidal smooth or *graded* slope (Fig. 3b). Conversely, the graded type can be changed to the faceted through a renewal of vigorous erosion and the development of a bluff.

Fig 3   Slope units on (a) faceted and (b) graded hillslopes.

How a given slope evolves in time depends on the relative loss or gain of material on each unit of the slope—the *slope budget*—which in turn varies with structure and the localisation and effectiveness of weathering and erosion. These in their turn vary with climate and structure.

Some General Concepts

For the sake of simplicity let us consider a graded slope under conditions which favour powerful attack of the lower slope and little or no erosion of the upper. Such conditions may prevail where particularly resistant rock outcrops on the upper slope, or where a winding river impinges directly upon the base of a slope. In these circumstances the lower slope is steepened causing a bluff to be developed. Such steepening and undermining causes more material to fall from the bluff thus providing first a protective covering for the lower slope and secondly, debris which has to be removed by the erosive agencies. The stronger the attack, the more debris is supplied. Thus a stage is reached when the supply of material from the bluff balances the ability of the erosive forces to remove it, and stability of form is achieved. Hereafter storms cause the renewal of erosion and the retreat or recession of the slope, but the morphology remains constant in the long term. In this circumstance therefore, a steep slope is developed and maintained, and the slope recedes, maintaining a constant form and inclination: this is *parallel retreat* or slope recession (Fig. 4a).

However, if erosion of the upper slope exceeds that of the lower, the course of slope development is different. Obviously the whole slope will be lowered, and a series of ever more gentle slopes will be evolved: *slope lowering* or decline, as shown on Fig. 4b.

Fig 4 (a) Recession and (b) decline of hillslopes.

On slopes which are structurally homogeneous, climate is the important determinant of the slope budget and of slope behaviour, but most slopes are, in some measure, structurally controlled. The factors which govern slope behaviour are referred to in detail in several places in the text below; but it will be clear that these two contrasted styles of slope behaviour, controlled by the slope budget, and resulting in either the backwearing, or the downwearing, of slopes, result in pronounced differences in landscape morphology and development through time (Fig. 5).

(e) TIME AND STAGE
Time itself has no effect on the land surface, but is the medium in which various geomorphological changes take place. Not only have climatic conditions changed from time to time with widespread direct and indirect results, and as clearly implied in the discussion of morphogenetic regions, but the crust of the earth has not been, and is not, stable.

Fig 5   Contrasted landscapes resulting from varied slope behaviour.

The effects of some such changes remain imprinted on the earth's form for many years even in the geological context. Moreover, in addition to long-term climatic variations such as are implicit in the phrase 'climatic change', the effects of *storms* are extremely important geomorphologically. Such climatic catastrophies—a flash flood, a major coastal storm, a devastating landslide, a marauding tornado—cause changes to the land surface which are only slowly repaired by processes working at more usual rates or levels of activity. They remain for a long time as important, commonly spectacular, features of the landscape. In considering storm effects, frequency of occurrence has to be measured against effectiveness. Analysis suggests that it is not the storm of a millenium which is geomorphologically most significant, because such storms occur too infrequently, but rather the storm of a century, which is both damaging and common enough to be significant.

Another important aspect of time in geomorphology is the concept of stage. For it is implicit in the brief preliminary treatment of slope form and behaviour presented above that though there are significant variations according to structural and climatic environment, landform assemblages evolve through time. They undergo an orderly sequence of changes, which if allowed to run its full course without significant interruption, causes the landscape to return to an assemblage resembling the original (Fig. 5). Such an evolutionary sequence is termed a *geomorphic cycle*. Not all geomorphologists believe that landscape development is cyclic in all instances, the alternative view being that in some conditions, at any rate, landscapes attain equilibrium, and though changing dynamically remain morphologically stable.

These three factors of structure, process, and time are dealt with in some detail in the following pages, but, throughout, the reader is asked to remember the concepts briefly outlined above.

PART B: INFLUENCE OF STRUCTURE

2. Geological Background

MANY IMPORTANT MAJOR AND MINOR GEOMORPHOLOGICAL features of the surface of Australia owe their origin either directly or indirectly to the nature of the underlying crust. In this chapter, rock types, their structures and ages, are briefly discussed.

(a) ROCK TYPES

The rocks which form the earth's crust are of three types. *Igneous* rocks are emplaced in molten form either intrusively, at depth, as is the case with granite[1], for instance, or are poured out or extruded at the surface in the form of a lava flow. All *volcanic* rocks, of which basalt is a common example, are of this second type.[2] The rocks intruded deep in the crust are known as *plutonic* rocks. As they cool slowly, there has been time for considerable aggregates of the various rock-forming minerals to come together and so the average size of crystals is large: these rocks are coarse grained. Volcanic rocks, on the other hand, cool rapidly as the lavas come in contact with the atmosphere, and so these rocks are fine textured, featuring crystals so small that they can be discerned often only under the microscope. Igneous rocks intruded at *intermediate* depths, in dykes and sills, for example, exhibit crystals of a size intermediate between these two extremes.

Igneous rocks are the primary materials of the earth's crust and outcrop over very large areas of the earth's surface. But many other regions are underlain by rocks derived from igneous rocks. The weathering and erosion (the disintegration and wearing away of the rocks—see Chapters 4–8) of these crystalline rocks provides materials which, after transportation by water, wind and ice, are laid down either on the land or, more commonly, in water to form *sedimentary* rocks. These may be regarded as forming a veneer or blanket overlying a crystalline basement in many areas. They are characteristically layered, bedded or stratified, commonly display sorting or grading, and commonly contain fossils. Sandstone, shale and siltstone are common examples of *clastic* sediments, built of particles derived from other rocks. Other sediments such as limestone, bog iron ore and coal, originate as *chemical* precipitates or through *organic* agencies.

Both igneous and sedimentary rocks may be subjected to heat or pressure and thereby changed to a rock of quite different structure and mineralogical character. Some such *metamorphic* rocks are associated with intrusions or extrusions of igneous rocks. The rocks in the immediate vicinity of an intrusion of granite or immediately beneath a lava flow are baked, and for obvious reasons this type of alteration is often known as *contact* metamorphism. It is found only in a narrow zone known as the metamorphic *aureole*. *Regional* metamorphism, however, is much more important and occurs when large areas suffer compression and associated heating. The more intense the compression, the more marked are the changes brought about, but it is not unusual for all trace of the original bedding of a sediment, for instance, to be lost and replaced by a new set of fractures — the *cleavage*, disposed normal to the direction of greatest stress — and for extensive recrystallisation of the rock to occur.

(b) COMMON STRUCTURES
(i) Bends and breaks in rocks
Each of these three types of rock may be subjected to tectonism or earth movements (indeed metamorphism is commonly associated with earth movements) and as a result, either *folded* or *faulted*.

It is clear from detailed studies of rocks, both in the field and in the laboratory, that some bend more easily than others, whilst others fracture more readily than they bend. Some rocks are inherently stronger than others, some are brittle, some plastic. In addition, the environment and thickness of the stratum and the time factor are important in determining whether a bed will bend (fold) or break (fracture). Limestone and sandstone, for instance, tend to fracture or to form only broad folds because they are strong and rather brittle, but if either of these is interbedded in a thick sequence of shales, which tend to be soft and plastic and hence to fold easily, the flow form of the shale is imposed upon the interbedded sandstone. Again, where the overlying thickness of rocks is great, limestones and sandstones tend to fold rather than fracture, and with any rock type a long term stress results in fracture. Rocks like massive limestones and sandstones which have a high inherent strength and possess the strength to lift overlying strata are said to be *competent*, while rocks which flow easily and are weak are *incompetent*.

(ii) Dip and strike
It will be recalled that sedimentary rocks are laid down in layers or strata. These beds may have a slight initial inclination, but usually are horizontally disposed, or nearly so. The outcrop of a stratum which is precisely

Geological Background

horizontal follows round the contours and a whole succession of beds is exposed in a valley or hill side.

An outcrop of younger rocks preserved on a hill top and surrounded by older strata is called an *outlier* (Fig. 6a), and an exposure of older rocks, say in an isolated hill or in a valley floor, surrounded by younger rocks is an *inlier* (Fig. 6b). Mt Babbage, in the northern Flinders Ranges,[3] is an example of an outlier of Cretaceous rocks surrounded by Precambrian strata (Fig. 6c), and many of the Permian outcrops of the southern Mt Lofty Ranges occur in basins bounded by Precambrian or early Palaeozoic strata, and thus form outliers also. The Peake and Denison Ranges are an example of an inlier, consisting of Precambrian rocks which emerge from a sea of Mesozoic and later strata (Fig. 9).

Strata which have been compressed, however slightly, are inclined and the bedding planes are said to dip. The dip, or *true dip*, of a stratum (Fig. 10) is the maximum angle between the bedding plane and the horizontal. On geological maps the direction of dip of a stratum is indicated by an arrow and the amount in degrees. Note that younger beds appear at the surface down dip or in the direction of dip. The direction at right angles to true dip measured in the horizontal plane is the *strike*. Just as the form of a hill can be indicated by the use of contours, so the behaviour or form of a stratum can be shown by *structure* or *stratum contours* (Fig. 11); and as is the case with topographical contours, the distance apart of the contours indicates the dip of the stratum, the amount of which can be obtained precisely by the use of simple trigonometry (Fig. 11). The dip of a stratum is rarely constant, for beds usually follow irregular or curved planes, but the attitude and behaviour can be reconstructed very easily from a study of the stratum contours. If there is a *monocline* or simple flexure or bend in a stratum, for instance, it is expressed in the stratum contours as shown in Fig. 12. An example of stratum contours used on a geological map is shown in Fig. 9.

(iii) Folds

Sediments which have been subjected to equal forces from opposite directions are pushed into symmetrical folds, the most common examples of which are the *anticline* and *syncline* (Fig. 13a). The bisector of such folds is called the *axial plane* and in symmetrical folds is vertical, but in the more generally found asymmetrical folds, due to unequal and opposite forces, the axial plane is inclined to the vertical. The angle between the two is called the *hade* of the axial plane (Fig. 13b). In addition, the crest of a fold, the trace of the axial plane at the top of a bed, more often than not is tilted, and the angle between the two is the *pitch* (Fig. 13c). Such folds whose outcrops narrow and widen, appear and disappear, are described as *pitching* or *plunging* folds. They are very common in the Flinders Ranges, for example in the areas north of Quorn and south of

Fig 6 (a) Outlier and (b) inlier; (c) Mt Babbage area, northern Flinders Ranges, showing outliers of Cretaceous rocks (white) surrounded by Precambrian (stippled) (*adapted from Moolawatana 1-mile geological sheet, Geol. Surv. S.A.*).

Fig 7   Location and drainage map.   Ex = exoreic, En = endoreic, A = Areic.

Hawker (Fig. 14) where the outcrops of two prominent sandstone formations display Z- and W-shaped outcrops, and also in the Waterhouse, James and Krichauff Ranges of the Northern Territory (Fig. 15).

Within some broad anticlines (and synclines), minor anticlines and synclines are developed. Such structures are called *anticlinoria* and *synclinoria* (Fig. 16). Elsewhere folding is so intense that folds are *overturned* and become *recumbent* (Fig. 17a), while in others the compression is so great that the axial planes of adjacent anticlines and synclines are parallel, producing *isoclinal folding* (Fig. 17b).

Anticlines and synclines are formed through the activity of tangential or lateral pressures, but if in addition to the two sets of opposed forces there are other, possibly less intense, pressures from another direction, domes and basins develop (Pl. 1). Similar structures result from upthrusts in the crust, for instance in the vicinity of igneous intrusions. Domes and basins formed in this manner tend to be more regular than those related to complex pressure distributions. *Cross folding*, or folding involving two sets of opposed pairs of compressive stresses, has resulted in the prominent natural amphitheatre and basin structure known as Wilpena Pound (Pl. 2). This structure (Fig. 18) lies adjacent to large anticlinal and

Fig 8 Map of South Australia showing geomorphological regions (*after D. King, adapted*).

dome structures in which the beds dip *quaquaversally*, or outward in all directions from a central point. The crest of the anticlinal structure has been eroded away (a *denuded anticline*), exposing older rocks in the core. Unequal stresses, or successive compression from different directions may also result in domes and basins being arranged *en échelon* in plan (Fig. 19).

Fig 9   Stratum contours of the base of the Mesozoic in a portion of the Lake Eyre Basin. Precambrian outcrops stippled (*adapted from Tectonic Map of Australia, Geol. Soc. Austr.*).

x = angle of true dip
(a)

as shown on geological map
(b)

Fig 10   Dip and strike of a sedimentary stratum.

Geomorphology

stratum contour for <u>top</u> of bed A

800
700
600
500

(a) in section

Dip can be calculated from a simple trigonometrical ratio :—

x = angle of dip
a = distance between stratum contours, measured from map and converted for scale
y = vertical interval of stratum contours

$\tan x = y/a$

800 700 600 500

(b) in plan

Fig 11 Stratum contours and the calculation of dip.

$x < y$

(a) Monoclinal Flexure in section

700   600 500 400 300 200   100

(b) on map, as expressed in Stratum Contours

Fig 12 Monocline shown in section and by stratum contours.

Geological Background

(a) **Anticline & Syncline**

h = Hade of axial plane
$x < y$

(b) **Asymmetrical folds**

Fig 13 Simple folds in rocks: (a) a single stratum folded into anticline and syncline; (b) and (c) some simple geometrical features of folds, asymmetrical folds and pitch or plunge of an anticlinal structure. x = angle of pitch.

Fig 14 Simple folds in the southern Flinders Ranges.

Fig 15 Part of the Mt Lewis anticline, south of the Krichauff Range, N.T., showing hogbacks and cuestas developed on part of a denuded dome (*drawn from photograph*).

Geological Background 19

Fig 16 Anticlinorium and synclinorium shown developed in a single stratum: (a) General; (b) Diagrammetic section across the southern Flinders Ranges just north of Quorn showing synclinorium.

Fig 17 More complex folding patterns: (a) recumbent and (b) isoclinal folds. ap = axial plane.

Fig 18 Geological sketch of the Wilpena Pound area, central Flinders Ranges. Sandstone outcrops stippled, faults shown by heavy lines, strike of strata shown by dashed lines (*adapted from Parachilna 4-mile Geological Sheet, Geol. Surv. S.A.*).

Fig 19 *En échelon* fold pattern, showing minor structures trending north-south arrayed *en échelon* along the main northwest-southeast structural axis.

Neither faults (see below) nor folds should be regarded as static features, for structures of both types are still developing. The continued development of folds is difficult to demonstrate, but it is possible where precise surveys have been made repeatedly. In the Long Beach area of California a comparison of surveys made (with great accuracy in connection with the search for, and development of, oilfields) before and after the earthquake of 1931 showed that the plain to the east of the city had been bowed upward in a structure 7 inches high and 4 miles across. The Inglewood area of the Los Angeles plain is rising at about 3 feet-a-century, and in the Cajon Pass, north of San Bernadino, where surveys were taken in 1906, 1924, and 1944, the crest of the arch structure in the area rose 8 inches between the first and last surveys, a rate of 20 inches-a-century. These amounts may seem negligible, but are highly significant in the context of geological time: if the Inglewood area cited above continues to rise at its present rate for, say, 25,000 years (insignificant in the context of geological time) then at the end of that period it will stand 750 feet higher than it is at present.

(iv) Faults and joints

There are two major types of fracture in rocks—faults and joints. A *fault* is a fracture in a rock along which there has been differential movement, with one side moving relative to the other along the fracture. Faults may be, and commonly are, large scale structures, and generally occur in *zones* rather than in isolation. Faulting and folding are commonly associated, and in practice it is in many places difficult to distinguish, for example, between faulting and monoclinal flexing (hence their common association in geological legends).

Joints, on the other hand, are small scale fractures along which there has been either no movement or the same amount of movement along the fracture; in other words, no differential movement along the fracture. Some joints are due to cooling (in igneous rocks) or dehydration and shrinkage (in sediments), but many are of tectonic origin; and many fractures called joints are, in reality, faults along which, however, no differential movement can be demonstrated.

Faults are due to either tension or compression. In regions where the crust is being stretched and where other conditions are right for faulting (see earlier), *normal* (also called gravity, or tensional) faults are formed (Fig. 20a). Note that younger rocks occur on the *downthrow* side which is that side of the fault indicated on geological maps by a small bar drawn at right angles to the thick line indicative of the trace of the fault. Faults running parallel to the direction of dip are known as *dip faults* (Fig. 20b), those running along the strike as *strike faults* (Fig. 20c), and those intermediate between these two as *oblique faults* (Fig. 20d). Some aspects of the geometry of faults are shown in Fig. 20e.

Faults due to compression are of two types. Those with a high angle of dip (or low hade between the fault plane and the vertical) are known as *reverse faults* (Fig. 21a), but those with a large hade (more than 45°) are called *thrust faults* (Fig. 21b, c). In *normal thrusts* (Fig. 21b) the upper block is thrust over the bottom, but in *lag thrusts* (Fig. 21c) the lower area moves up and under the upper part. *Imbricate* zones with complex zones of reversed faults, indicative of intense localised compression and distortion, are commonly seen within the zones of thrust faults (Fig. 21d).

Geological Background

(a) Normal or Gravity fault – section

(b) Dip fault – plan

(c) Strike fault – plan

(d) Oblique fault – plan

d = dip of stratum
x = "   " fault
y = hade of fault
A—B = <u>throw</u> of fault – vertical movement
A—C = <u>slip</u> of fault – movement along fault plane
B—C = <u>heave</u> of fault – horizontal movement
O P = <u>displacement</u> along the fault

The younger rocks appear in outcrop on the <u>downthrow</u> side, shown on maps by a small tick.

(e) Geometry of faults

Fig 20 Some simple types of faults; and (e) some aspects of the geometry of faults.

(a) Reverse fault — hade (x) $<45°$

(b) Thrust fault – normal — hade (x) $>45°$

(c) Thrust fault – lag

(d) Imbricate structure

each small fault is a reverse fault

Fig 21 Reverse and thrust faults; and (d) imbricate zone.

hinge or pivot
monoclinal flexure
fault plane
the throw of the fault increases from **A** to **B**

Fig 22 Hinge fault.

Plate 1 Minor domes and basins, anticlines and synclines exposed between Neepabunna Homestead and Italowie Gorge, northern Flinders Ranges.

Plate 2 Wilpena Pound from the southeast. This basin structure is preserved in the massive Pound Sandstone, a resistant formation which stands high above the adjacent plains and valleys. (*South Australian Tourist Bureau*)

Fig 23 The fracture pattern of Port Phillip Bay and environs (*after Hills*)
Key 1 Rowsley Fault   2 Lovely Banks Monocline
     3 Barrabool Fault   4 Curlewis Fault
     5 Torquay Fault   6 Selwyn's Fault
     7 Tyabb Fault   8 Heath Hill Fault
     9 Bass Fault   10 Kongwak Fault

Fig 24 Wrench fault: the San Andreas fault in the San Francisco area.

Geological Background

Both normal and reverse faults are common, and their geometry is simple, but more complex *hinge* and *pivotal* faults with varied downthrow and resulting from rotational movements are not rare (Fig. 22). They occur, for instance, in the Adelaide area (see Chapter 3), and south of Melbourne (Fig. 23) where dislocation along the Selwyn fault increases to the south, but disappears to the north.

Finally, some very important faults display little or no vertical displacement, but very large horizontal movements. Such structures with predominantly lateral dislocation are known as *tear* or *wrench* faults. Along the San Andreas fault (Fig. 24), for instance, during the 1906 earthquake there was a lateral displacement of some 21 feet in the centre of the faulted zone near Tomales Bay, with the Pacific side moving northward relative to the rest of the continent. Also of the wrench type is the Berridale fault in southern New South Wales (Fig. 25). Along this fracture, lateral dislocation of some 7 miles has been measured with respect to a granite mass and its associated metamorphic aureole.

Fig 25 The Berridale fault in southeastern N.S.W. The granite outcrop is stippled (*after Lambert and White*).

Faults also may be offset in plan and arranged *en échelon* as a result of unequal and opposed stresses, for example in the area south of Adelaide (see Chapter 3). Many earthquakes are due to movements along fault planes and repeated movements along the same zone of weakness are general. The Adelaide earthquake of 1954 resulted in a maximum movement of 2–3 inches along the Eden fault. In the Buena Vista oil field, in the

San Joaquin valley of California, a fault block is rising at about 4 feet a century. Faulting is of a *recurrent* character and therefore all faults must be regarded as four-dimensional structures which possess length and breadth as well as depth, and change in time.

(v) Field evidence for faulting

This takes several forms. When rocks adjacent to each other or a fault plane are moved relative to each other, the plane surfaces are gouged and scratched, resulting in the formation of scratches or striations called *slickensides*, or distinct ridges and furrows, called *mullion structures*. The opposed surfaces may also be polished and plucked, causing the development of *fault steps*. Movement along the fault also generates frictional heat, so that a skin of rocks immediately adjacent to the fault is cooked or recrystallised, that is to say, metamorphosed.

There may also be intense shattering of rocks along fault planes forming aggregates of angular fragments of the country rock which, when consolidated, are known as *fault breccias*. Some rocks do not, however, disintegrate into sufficiently large fragments to form a breccia, but into a powder of flour-like consistency which, when consolidated, forms a fine grained *fault gouge*. Such a gouge, if silicified, is called a mylonite. The presence of any of these indicates that a fault is not far away.

Strata are abruptly displaced and are repeated or disappear. They are commonly distorted in the immediate vicinity of fault planes, and such *fault drag* can be used to detect the sense of movement (Fig. 26a). Such drag of beds is exposed in the Eocene[4] strata just north of the outlet of the Torrens Gorge (M.R.[5] Adelaide, S.A., 723940) where they come into contact with the Eden fault (Fig. 26b).

Faults are commonly expressed in the topography and are readily detected. The displacement of beds causes either *fault* or *fault-line scarps* to be formed. Fault scarps are directly due to differential movement, but fault-line scarps result from the differential erosion of a softer bed brought into juxtaposition with a resistant stratum by faulting. There are many fault scarps in the vicinity of Adelaide, in northeast Eyre Peninsula and in other parts of Australia (see Chapter 3). Escarpments and ridges due to the outcrop of a hard rock are displaced or terminated by faulting. In the southern Flinders Range, for instance, several upstanding ridges are terminated in this manner. The eastern end of the Bluff, 8 miles north of Quorn, for instance, ends abruptly in a zone where there is much fault breccia and fragments displaying slickensides, and where, moreover, streams are straight. Although the fault plane is not exposed, it is safe to attribute the topographic feature to faulting (Fig. 27).

Two important major landforms as well as numerous minor features, are directly related to faulting: horsts and grabens or rift valleys. A *horst* is a long, relatively narrow ridge bounded by faults and due to upthrusting (Fig. 28). The Mt Lofty Ranges in the vicinity of Adelaide is a

Fig 26 (a) Fault drag as seen in quarry face; (b) as seen in relation to the Eden fault scarp, just north of the Torrens Gorge; (c) as observed in Rocky River Gorge, east of Port Pirie, S.A.

Fig 27 Geological sketch of the Big Ben area, north of Quorn, showing topographical features attributed to faulting. Sandstone outcrop stippled, faults marked by heavy lines and *f* (*adapted from Willochra 1-mile Geological Sheet, Geol. Surv. S.A.*).

Geological Background

Fig 28 A horst block.

Fig 29 The Cullarin horst (*after Stauffer and Rickards*).

Fig 30 Tectonic map of the Canberra district (*after Öpik*).

good example (Chapter 3), as are the Cullarin horst, in N.S.W. and A.C.T. (Fig. 29), the Black Mt horst in Canberra (Fig. 30), and the Leeuwin horst in the far southwest of Western Australia (Fig. 31).

In eastern Australia generally, many linear features formerly attributed to faulting later came to be regarded as due to differential erosion; certainly caution is necessary in the interpretation of such features, but recent work has brought a return to earlier interpretations, and has shown that many are indeed associated with faults. Many, such as the eastern face of the Mt Clear Range (Fig. 32), at the base of which the Murrumbidgee River flows, are regarded as fault-line erosional scarps. The Cotter horst (A.C.T.) is interpreted as having increased in relative elevation through gradual erosion and etching out of the fault lines. But many of these features are due to geologically recent, though relatively minor movements, and it is increasingly apparent that, in some measure at least, the present topography is due to late tectonic movements. The horst and graben topography of the Lake George area (Fig. 29), for example, is attributed to recent minor earth movements along faults which originated during the early Palaeozoic. At the other end of the continent, in northern Queensland, the important Palmerville fault (Fig. 33), for instance, has been active at least four times since the Silurian, including one phase of activity during the late Cainozoic. Reversals of the sense of movement along the fault are evidenced.

If the structures mentioned are at all typical of the region as a whole, there is no doubt that many of the ridges are horsts; the intervening 'corridors', or long narrow depressions and valleys, are grabens, or rift valleys; and faults in general play a major role in determining the location of rivers, and hence of valleys and uplands.

A *rift valley* is a long, narrow depression which has suffered subsidence and is bounded by essentially parallel faults. Rifts may be either tensional or compressional, as we might well expect, for if there is tension in one place, there is likely to be compression in neighbouring areas. In Oslo fjord and the Rhine rift, the structures are tensional (Fig. 34) but in the great East African rifts (Fig. 35), examples of both types of structure appear to be present. In Australia, Lake George occupies part of a rift valley (Fig. 29). The fault on the western side of the rift is difficult to locate, but a short distance to the south, east of Queanbeyan, the Lake George fault has been shown to dip steeply westward, i.e. is of reverse type, and moreover is paralleled by other, similar, structures. The Fortesque River valley in the Pilbara district of Western Australia is a rift valley (Fig. 36) bounded on the northern side by the West Pilbara and Nullagine fault scarps, and on the south by the Hamersley scarp. Further north, the Fitzroy River–Christmas Creek valley is of similar character (Fig. 36). The Latrobe valley of Gippsland lacks the narrowness and parallel scarps of the true graben, but nevertheless occupies a downfaulted structure (Fig. 37).

Geological Background

Streams take advantage of the lines of weakness caused by faults, and like fault and fault-line scarps, are readily identified by their unusually straight patterns in plan. The Crackenback River, west of Jindabyne, in N.S.W., is a superb example of a major stream, the course of which is closely related to a major fracture zone (Fig. 38). The course of the Murrumbidgee south of Canberra has already been mentioned; other examples include the Towamba in the far southeast of N.S.W. (Fig. 25), the Norman in northwest Queensland (Fig. 39), and, near Adelaide, a tributary of the Little Para river which follows the trace of a fault (M.R. Adelaide, S.A., 784038–782017). Lines of springs also can form along faults, for groundwater 'trapped' in an aquifer by an impervious cap rock can find its way to the surface along such zones of weakness (Fig. 40). Such is the case with some mound springs, formed by the accumulation of chemical precipitates where artesian waters reach the surface on the beds of Lakes Eyre and Frome. Their association with faults is betrayed by their alignment.

Finally, drainage can be disturbed by faulting. A fault block may be uplifted across the normal drainage direction, causing water to be ponded back to form a lake or swamp (Fig. 41). Lake Bumbunga (M.R. Burra, S.A., 1:253440, 621810) near Lochiel occupies a downfaulted depression as does Diamond Lake (Fig. 42). On the other hand, a river downstream from an upfaulted area will be able to erode deeply into the new block (it is said to be rejuvenated—see Chapter 6) and excavate a gorge-like valley. Examples of both rejuvenation and ponding back caused by faulting have been described from northeast Eyre Peninsula (see Chapter 3) while the Torrens Lake in Adelaide is, in its natural state, the valley of a river rejuvenated along a known fault line (Fig. 43)—that of the Para fault. The Torrens Gorge, above the Eden fault, is doubtless also due to rejuvenation associated with fault dislocation.

Far more spectacular examples of drainage disturbance due to faulting, however, are known from the eastern States. Many of the dramatic deep gorges excavated by the short rivers flowing to the Pacific have been cut in response to a rejuvenation (see Chapter 6) of streams caused by the upthrust of the eastern uplands and by former lower stands of the sea. It is likely that the major gorges of north Queensland are of this origin, as are the Macleay gorges of New England and the many deep gorges west of Sydney, such as that of the Grose (M.R. Windsor, N.S.W., 639457 and westwards), the latter related to the fault or monoclinal fold just west of the Nepean. In Victoria, the Werribee Gorge upstream from the Rowsley fault, and the Tarrago, north of Drouin (M.R. Drouin, Vic., 840037 and eastwards) are of similar origin and type.

Just as the erosion related to faulting is on an altogether greater scale in the eastern states compared with South Australia, so is drainage impedence. Though many of the lakes of the so-called Great Dividing Range, lakes like Pelican, Louisa, Galilee and Buchanan in northern and central Queensland, are due to warping rather than faulting, there are some large lakes which undoubtedly originated in this way. Lake George has already been cited; Lake Omeo, near Benambra in eastern Victoria (M.R. Tallangatta, Vic., 1:253,440, at 36° 58′ S, 147° 40′ E) is another example of drainage disturbed by faulting.

What is unquestionably one of the most spectacular examples in the world of drainage disturbance associated with faulting, derives from the Echuca district of Victoria. At present the River Murray turns sharply southwards to the south of Deniliquin (Fig. 44). This deflection was caused by the Cadell fault block rising across the course of the river. The Murray was unable to maintain its bed across the rising block, and was diverted around its southern end. It is interesting that on the gentle western slope of the tilted fault block is a depression known as Green Gully. Harris, to whom is due the interpretation of this area, describes the Gully as one of several 'well-marked tortuous depressions with a general east-west direction...'. Where Green Gully 'is best shown it is a wide shallow valley with relatively steep sides, and with every appearance

Fig 31   Fracture pattern in the southwest of W.A. (*after Stratigraphy of W.A.*).

of being a disused, partly infilled river course'. It is undoubtedly the channel, or one of the channels, of the earlier Murray.

The line of the Cadell fault continues southward after some local complications in the vicinity of Echuca. It gives rise to a distinct ridge, with an east-facing escarpment, which has not only influenced the course of the Campaspe River, but has impeded the local drainage and caused the formation of Lake Cooper (Fig. 44).

Fig 32 Fault-controlled escarpment south of Canberra—the area shown in Fig 30 is indicated in the north.

(c) THE DATING OF ROCKS

Rocks can be dated in two ways, relatively and absolutely, or at least within narrow limits on the absolute scale.

The *Law of Superposition* is obvious, but fundamental. It states that in a sequence of rocks which is not overturned by tectonism, the lower one goes in the sequence, the older the rocks are, and conversely the higher in the sequence, the younger. In other words, the order of rocks is a reflection of their relative ages. Thus, in Fig. 45 stratum A is clearly older than B, but the granite and related sills and dykes are obviously younger than both because they intrude the sediments which must have been already there when the vulcanicity took place.

As has been mentioned, sediments commonly contain fossils which are the skeletons, imprints, or vestiges of any type of organism which lived in the past (the imprint of the dinosaur's foot is just as much a fossil as a complete skeleton of, say, a fish).

Generally speaking, both fossil flora and fauna preserved in the geological column evolved closer and closer to modern forms as time passed.

Fig 33   The Palmerville fault in north Queensland (*after de Keyser*).

Fig 34 Section of rift valley showing normal or tensional faults.

Fig 35 Sketch map of the African rift system (*after Hills*); Lake Nyasa is now Lake Malawi.

Fig 36 The rift valleys of the Fitzroy and Fortescue river areas (*after Jutson*, and *Stratigraphy of W.A.*).

Fig 37 Fault pattern of the Latrobe valley, Vic. (*after Hills*).

Geological Background 39

Fig 38 Straight fracture-guided course of the Crackenback River, west of Jindabyne, N.S.W.

Fig 39 Fault controlled Norman River, northwest Queensland.

Fig 40 Spring line formed along a fault. The sandstone aquifer is sealed by an impermeable caprock such as shale.

Fig 41 Blocking of drainage by faulting. This minor but quite clear instance comes from the Whyalla region of northeast Eyre Peninsula (*after Miles*).

Fig 42 Fault blocks in the Port Wakefield area (*adapted from Wakefield 1-mile Geological Sheet, Geol. Surv. S.A.*).

Geological Background

Fig 43 Sections across the Torrens valley just north of the City of Adelaide, showing a younger valley countersunk in an older, broader valley (*from map by City of Adelaide Surveyors*).

Fig 44 Fault and river patterns in the Echuca district, Vic. (*from information in Hills*, and *Bowler and Harford*).

Many modern organisms do not appear until late in the geological record, whilst others, abundant in the past, are now extinct. Some fossil forms have a restricted time range, others are widespread and continued, almost unchanged, for many millions of years; but by considering groups or assemblages of fossils as characteristic of, and peculiar to, limited time spans, and bearing in mind the laws of superposition, a relative time scale can be arbitrarily constructed (Column 2 of Table 2A) for sediments, and from their relations with igneous and metamorphic rocks for the latter also.

Many attempts were made to give absolute values to this widely used and very useful relative scale, but until the discovery of radioactivity, this was not satisfactorily accomplished. About the turn of the present century, it was recognised that many elements are unstable, and in course of time lose particles. Through this decomposition which is called radioactivity, they lose weight and are transmuted to new substances. Thus uranium, with atomic weight 238, gradually loses particles of helium to become other sorts of uranium, then omnium, radium, polonium and finally uranium-lead (atomic weight 206). The rate of decay is constant and can be determined. Thus, by measuring the proportional amounts of uranium 238 to uranium-lead, the time can be calculated during which decay has been progressing which is the same as the age of the minerals in which the elements genetically occur.

Table 2 A. Geological Time-Scale (millions of years)

Era (1)	Period (2)	Duration (3)	Millions of years ago (4)
Cainozoic	Quaternary	1*	
	Tertiary	68	70 ± 2
Mesozoic	Cretaceous	65	135 ± 5
	Jurassic	45	180 ± 5
	Triassic	45	225 ± 5
Palaeozoic	Permian	45	270 ± 5
	Carboniferous	80	350 ± 10
	Devonian	50	400 ± 10
	Silurian	40	440 ± 10
	Ordovician	60	500 ± 15
	Cambrian	100	600 ± 20
Precambrian	Proterozoic	?	
	Archaean		

B. Cainozoic Time-Scale (millions of years)

Quaternary	Recent	10,000 years	
	Pleistocene*	1	
	Pliocene	10	11
	Miocene	14	25
Tertiary	Oligocene	15	40
	Eocene	20	60
	Paleocene	10	70 ± 2

* The Pleistocene may be as short as 600,000 years, or as long as 3–3½ million years duration, with the latter the more probable.

Other common and useful pairs of elements linked in chains of disintegration are potassium-argon, strontium-rubidium, and thorium-actinium. Great care has to be taken with the application of the principle, but consistent results have been obtained which enable absolute limits to be given to the various periods and epochs listed in Table 2. The methods mentioned can be used on materials about a million years old or more. A similar and especially interesting method, since it can be used to date geologically recent events beyond the limits of accuracy of the radioactive decay methods already described, concerns carbon-14 (C14). Ordinary carbon has an atomic weight of 12, but carbon with an atomic weight of 14 forms from nitrogen in the upper atomsphere through interaction with cosmic rays. Once formed, C14 diffuses into the lower atmosphere and some is absorbed by and incorporated in the cells of plants and animals. There is a fixed ratio of C14 to C12 in the air, and in organisms also the two are in equilibrium, for the intake of new C14 is balanced by the loss of electrons from the C14 already there, which is thus re-converted to nitrogen of the same atomic weight. When an organism dies, however, the accession of new C14 stops, while that already in it continues to disintegrate. Thus, the proportion of C14 to C12 decreases. The rate of decay of C14 has been carefully measured and is found to be constant, so that a measure is provided of the age of the organic material in which the C14 occurs. Half of the C14 disappears in about 5568 ± 30 years (a value known as the half life of C14) and in another 5,568 years, half the remainder will have disintegrated, and so on.

Thus, by measuring the radioactivity of living matter, and the radioactivity of the sample of fossil material, the ratio of activity between the two can be determined. Bearing in mind the half life of C14, the material from which the sample was taken can be dated within close limits. If we imagine that a sample, when measured, yields 3·825 disintegrations a minute compared with the $15·3 \pm 0·1$ general for living matter. The sample is only one-fourth as active as modern material, which means that the C14 in the sample has used two half-lives; in the first the radioactivity was reduced by half, and in the second the remaining half would be halved, to a quarter of the original; the material in question is $2 \times 5568 \pm 30$ or $11,136 \pm 60$ years old. C14 dates are expressed in years before present (B.P.) or years before Christ (B.C.).

For technical reasons, the method is at present only valid for material up to 50,000–60,000 years old, and for certain types of sample has a still shorter span. Thus there is a vital and frustrating gap in our absolute dating techniques between say, 50,000 years (C14) and about 1 million years, beyond which the other radioactive methods can be used.

It should also be appreciated that the C14 and fossil methods of dating can be applied only to sedimentary rocks, and that the radiometric techniques also can be used only with certain rocks. The potassium-argon method is applied extensively to determine ages of glauconites in sedimentary rocks, but radiometric methods generally are most commonly applied to igneous rocks. Great care must be taken in evaluating the results of such determinations, for there are many pitfalls. An age obtained in this way may, for example, not be that of the rock but only of the last phase of equilibrium of the minerals in the rock. In many respects ages derived from fossil evidence are still the most reliable and in every case the radiometric date should conform to the limits imposed by stratigraphic (including fossil) evidence.

Fig 45   Age relations of various rocks.

Absolute methods provide only milestones, and traditional methods are still essential for their application and extrapolation, and for testing their validity. In Fig. 45, for instance, the relative ages of the two units can be readily determined. The geological age of the sediments can be determined from fossils, and the absolute age of the igneous unit by radioactive methods. These should be consistent: for instance, the determined age of C cannot be less than that of A, for C intrudes A. Similarly, the ages of A and B should be consistent with the law of superposition.

Notes

[1] Note however that some granites are of metamorphic origin.
[2] The term *vulcanism* includes all igneous activity, but *volcanicity* pertains to extrusive phenomena only.
[3] For principal locations and regions see Figs. 7 and 8.
[4] See Geological time-scale, Table 2A, p. 43.
[5] Unless otherwise stated all Map References (M.R.) are to the one-mile military Sheet indicated.

3. Tectonic Landforms

(a) TECTONIC AND STRUCTURAL LANDFORMS

TWO DISTINCT TYPES OF RELIEF and landform, the development of which are strongly controlled by geological factors, can be distinguished.

The term *tectonics* includes all forms of earth movements, and a *tectonic landform* is one which owes its origin directly to earth movements. Thus a fault may be expressed in the landscape as a fault scarp. The plane of dislocation is here exposed in the landscape to form an escarpment. In similar fashion a monoclinal fold may be directly expressed in the form of the land surface. But a *structural landform* is one due to the etching out of structures, of whatever type or magnitude, by agencies of weathering and erosion. A fault may bring into juxtaposition rocks which vary greatly in their resistance to weathering and erosion.[1] The softer outcrop is eroded more rapidly than the harder, exposing the fault plane and bringing the line of dislocation into relief. Such a scarp is called a fault-line scarp and, though of similar form to its tectonic counterpart, is clearly of different origin.

Many escarpments in eastern Australia associated with faults are generally regarded as of fault-line erosional type, though it is usually rather difficult to prove such an interpretation. In Victoria, however, Hills (*Physiography of Victoria*) provides some well-documented examples. The eastern scarp of Futters Range (Fig. 46), some 4-5 miles west of Wangaratta (M.R. Wangaratta, Vic., 212270-224977) is of the fault-line type, Permian tillites (glacial deposits), having been faulted against Lower Palaeozoic rocks, and subsequently eroded to reveal the fault line. The Rowsley scarp, which is south of Bacchus Marsh, and which borders the Brisbane ranges on their western side, is also a fault-line scarp, as is the eastern scarp of the Grampians. According to Hills, westerly dipping sandstones of late Palaeozoic age which predominantly form the Grampians (see Fig. 47) were deposited on a basement of metamorphic rocks and then subjected to monoclinal folding and faulting (Fig. 48a). During the Cretaceous the whole area was planated (Fig. 48b) and, during subsequent weathering and erosion, the more susceptible metamorphic rocks were worn away more rapidly than the sandstone outcrops, which thus became a distinct upland region (Fig. 48c).

During this differential erosion the ancient line of faulting was etched out as a fault-line scarp. More recent and detailed mapping shows that the main eastern escarpment is now some little distance west of the suspected line of faulting, but this could be due to dissection and retreat of

Tectonic Landforms

Fig 46 Futters Range, the eastern border of which is a fault-line scarp.

Fig 47 Simplified geological section through the Grampians of western Victoria (*adapted from section on Geological Map of Grampians, Geol. Surv. Vic.*).

the rampart from the original, tectonically determined, line of demarcation between upland and plain (Fig. 47).

Folds in sedimentary rocks are frequently brought into relief by erosion, but these are structural landforms, a fact which is demonstrated dramatically when, as is found in some areas, there is an inverse relationship between structure and topography, when downfolds or synclines are found high in the relief, or when upfolded arches or anticlines underlie plains.

Fig 48 Suggested evolution of the Grampians and of a fault-line scarp on the eastern margin (*modified, after Hills*).

Structural landforms are exceedingly common and their detailed morphology depends upon the agency or agencies responsible for the weathering and erosion of the forms (see Chapters 4–9). Structural landforms can be classified as of *destructional* origin, because they are due to the wearing away of the land surface. On the other hand some of the debris that results from erosion is deposited on the land, forming definite features such as sand dunes, moraines, and alluvial fans; these, like tectonic forms, may be considered *constructional* in origin, in the first case having been built up by agencies active at the earth's surface, in the second by internal forces.

The principal tectonic forms involve faults and folds and, closely associated with these in some areas, volcanic activity. Faults, the mineralogical and textural character of the rocks, their attitude or disposition, and the nature and spacing of fractures such as joints and bedding planes, are exploited by weathering and erosion to give structural forms.

(b) THE TECTONIC FRAMEWORK OF AUSTRALIA

Australia is usually considered to consist of three distinct tectonic and physiographic regions—the Western Shield, the Central Basins and the Eastern Uplands.

The *Shield* is a resistant mass or craton in which crystalline rocks are common, and which, physiographically, takes the form of a tableland. The Eastern Uplands, a region of high rugged relief, though including extensive tablelands, are built of thick sequences of sedimentary rocks deposited in a gigantic trough or *geosyncline* and subsequently compressed, folded, faulted and subjected to vulcanism. Such areas are called *orogens*, or orogenic fold belts, and the whole process of deposition, compression and uplift is known as *orogenesis* or mountain building. The extensive plains of the Central Basins are underlain by relatively young, undisturbed sediments. Though thick in many places, the sedimentary cover rests on a basement of crystalline rocks which are subsurface extensions of the Shield area. Such areas are known as *platforms*.

Thus the Australian continent is built of a Shield, a Platform and an Orogen (Fig. 49). This regional subdivision is valid but is, in a sense, an oversimplification. Within the confines of the Shield are platform areas which, though much smaller, are structurally similar in character to those of the Central Basins. However, even the size contrast diminishes when it is considered that the Central Basins themselves consist of a number of major sub-basins (including the Carpentaria and Lake Eyre basins) and each of these, in turn, includes a number of minor basin structures, the sub-basins and their subsidiary structures being of a size comparable with the basins within and fringing the Shield. Nevertheless, the distinction between the Shield and the central basins appears to be important for the border between the two tectonic regions has been developing for at least the past 150 million years and possibly as much as 250 million years. It is still actively in motion (see below).

The Shield is traversed by fractures which take the form of steeply dipping faults or major joints called *lineaments*. In many places they

Geomorphology

1 Kimberley Block	2 Bonaparte Basin
3 Arnhem Land	4 Georgina Basin
5 Isa Highlands Block	6 Carpentaria Basin
7 Lake Eyre Basin	8 Murray Basin
9 Shatter Belt	10 Gawler Block
11 Eucla Basin	12 Yilgarn Block
13 Carnarvon Basin	14 Pilbara (Hammersley Ranges)
15 Canning or Desert Basin	

Fig 49 Principal tectonic regions of Australia, with diagrammatic cross-section.

occur parallel to fold axes, are traceable over very long distances and in plan are gently arcuate or rectilinear. They strike in a few limited directions and form a framework of fractures running northwest to southeast, northeast to southwest, east to west, and north to south across the continent, which is thus effectively subdivided into a number of more or less rhomboidal blocks (Fig. 49). Some, like the Kimberleys, the Hamersley Ranges and the Isa Highlands, appear to have suffered repeated uplift, that is, to have been *positive* tectonic regions through geological history. Others, of which the Eucla, Canning, Georgina and Bonaparte basins are examples, have consistently been areas of subsidence, and are *negative* tectonic regions.

Australia is not the only continent to display such a pattern of lineaments, for Africa and, indeed, all Shield areas apparently exhibit similar structural patterns. The framework is of ancient origin, having been established by the end of the Precambrian, but recurrent movements along the fractures have occurred throughout subsequent geological history, and continue at the present time.

Though not so obvious at first glance, the platform and orogenic regions of Australia are also profoundly affected by the development of lineaments. For instance block faulted mountains or horsts trending north to south are clearly expressed in many parts of the Eastern Uplands and in the alignment and shape of offshore islands, which are partially drowned horsts. In each of the three major Central Basins—the Carpentaria, Eyre and Murray—the drainage pattern is markedly asymmetrical, with the major rivers flowing to the western side of each of the basins (Fig. 50). In the case of the Carpentaria and Lake Eyre basins, this is a direct reflection of the asymmetry of the subsurface structures which display their greatest depths, steepest dips, and greatest instability on their western sides.

Thus the major relief features within Australia, as well as the outline of the continent, are primarily determined by these structures. In detail also, drainage and relief display guidance either by lineaments or by joints or faults which run parallel to local lineament trends (Fig. 50). The courses of the Darling, Georgina, Diamantina and Flinders Rivers are all remarkably straight and all are closely related to the trace of major faults in the underlying strata. The regional, as opposed to the continental control of major relief exerted by lineaments may be illustrated by reference to South Australia.

(c) THE FRAMEWORK OF LINEAMENTS IN SOUTH AUSTRALIA

Several types of structural region lie within the borders of South Australia but the most important feature of the tectonic framework is that the State is located astride the unstable boundary between the Shield to the west and the Basins to the east. Throughout the State, however, the pattern

Fig 50 Drainage systems of the Central Basins, and some important lineaments.

of lineaments is an important factor determining major and minor relief. The possible fracture pattern is shown in Fig. 51; included here are known faults and major fold axes, prominent trend lines, topographical and drainage features, and major geological boundaries. It will be noted that the suggested lineaments are far more abundant in the platform areas than within the Shield. This contrast may be real, but it may be also explicable in terms of an essential ignorance of large areas of the Shield in South Australia.

The Shield proper is represented by the Gawler block (Fig. 49) of which Yorke Peninsula is geologically an inherent part. The southern part of the Gawler block underlies Eyre Peninsula and it extends to the northwest for a distance as yet unknown. Some suggestion of the likely termination of the structure is, however, provided by the angular eastern margin of the Eucla basin (see Fig. 52). This block is outlined by lineaments. The Lincoln fault zone delineates the block on the southeast and though, on the southwest and, northeast, the structures are as yet not demonstrated in the field, they are strongly suggested by the trend of the coastlines on the southwest and southeast, by seismic data on the southwest (Fig. 51), and by the trend of the contact between Archaean and Proterozoic rocks in the northeast.

To the east and north of this nucleus are the worn-down roots of ancient mountain ranges or orogens. Those of the northwest of South Australia are intensely metamorphosed, and the associated igneous cores also are widely exposed, but in the Mt Lofty–Olary Upland–Flinders Ranges, crystalline rocks form relatively small outcrops. The massive accumulation of sediments represented by the rocks of Kangaroo Island, Mt Lofty Ranges, Olary Upland, Flinders Ranges and Peake and Denison Ranges formed in a deep trough, the Adelaide geosyncline, located on the continental shelf offshore from the Proterozoic and early Palaeozoic West Australian (or Westralian) Shield continent.

To the west, the Eucla basin is a platform, and in the east the western parts of the Lake Eyre and Murray basins, including such subsidiary structures as the Frome basin, are also platform structures. In the Lake Eyre basin, the lower Cretaceous sediments are marine, but the Cainozoic strata are all terrestrial. In the Murray basin, sedimentation is lacustrine or swampy through to the end of the Tertiary. Marine sedimentation in the Eucla basin is evidenced during the Permian, Cretaceous, Eocene and Miocene. Within the orogens and platform areas, as with the Shield, major features are determined by lineaments. The outlines of the Mt Lofty horst, of the Olary Upland, and even of the curious hourglass shape of the Flinders Ranges, all appear to be closely related to faults, monoclines and major joints which are either known or which can be inferred from the unusually rectilinear topographical boundaries. The exposed and buried ridges of crystalline rocks which form boundaries between the platform region, all follow lineament trends: the Wilcannia threshold

Fig 51 South Australia—fracture pattern.

Fig 52 Stratum contours of the base of the marine Tertiary at the eastern end of the Eucla Basin (*adapted from the Tectonic Map of Australia, Geol. Soc. Austr.*).

between the Lake Eyre and Murray basins is known to be fault-bounded in parts, and the same can be said of the Padthaway ridge (which has been called a horst), between the Murray basin and the coastal area and ocean.
The fault system is most pronounced, however, both geologically and physiographically at the Shield-Basin junction (Fig. 51). The Flinders–Mt Lofty Ranges, although commonly represented on topographical maps as having curved outlines, in reality consist of a number of distinct juxtaposed blocks with straight borders, coincident with faults trending mainly northwest to southeast and southwest to northeast, though in the south, especially, north to south and east to west trends are apparent. To the west of the upland are a number of rift valleys and down-faulted blocks arranged like an inverted and somewhat distorted letter Y. The two southern arms of the Y are inundated by the ocean and form the Spencer and St Vincent Gulfs, delineated in part by the Lincoln fault zone, the Kulpara fault and the complex system of faults about Adelaide (see below). To the north of the Gulfs area the single stem of the Y is the downfaulted Lake Torrens depression, the western margin of which is coincident with a prominent north to south trending fault zone. The eastern margin of the depression is less well known, but appears to be controlled in the north by the northwest to southeast trending Norwest fault, and in the south possibly by a northeasterly extension of the Lincoln fault.

Still further to the north, the Shield-Basin border is especially active. Not only is the Lake Eyre depression a negative tectonic area, but the Lake Eyre salina itself is very likely a downfaulted block. The eastern border of the Peake and Denison Ranges is faulted, with the downthrow to the east. The whole of the Lake Eyre depression has been since the middle Mesozoic, and still is, a negative tectonic region.

This zone of dislocation extending north to south through the centre of South Australia is only one of several probable major lineaments. Others are the Lincoln Fault zone, the southwesterly-northeasterly trending faults within the Flinders, the Paralana fault zone, which extends further to the northeast and is suggested by the remarkably straight course of the Strzelecki (Fig. 51; see also Fig. 53).

Many other fractures which apparently influence topography and drainage lie adjacent to these two major zones; the Warburton and Cooper rivers both run straight, in a northeast to southwest direction, parallel with the Strzelecki–Paralana structure and in the case of the Cooper, aligned with a known fault, as well as with several fold axes in the far northeast of the State. The Murray, south of Morgan, runs parallel to the north to south Morgan fault (see Chapter 6). The shapes of Lakes Eyre, Frome, Torrens and Gairdner, and the location and in some small measure the shapes of Lakes Gregory, Blanche and Callabonna, also appear to be influenced by prominent faults.

As is the case with Australia as a whole, the framework of lineaments is

Fig 53   The northeast region of South Australia showing principal topographic features, the duricrusted (silcrete) remnants, and important structural axes (*after Sprigg*).

ancient, but many of its constituent faults are recurrent. Many of the fault scarps are so little dissected that they can only be geologically youthful; and many are the foci of earthquakes and earth tremors. Furthermore, late Cainozoic (including Pleistocene) strata in several places have been dislocated by faults, proving beyond doubt their recent activity. In addition to these instances of tectonic control of topography, of which some evidence is known, many more possible cases are suggested from an inspection of Fig. 51. The northeast margin of the Eucla Basin, the west coast of Eyre Peninsula and the western termination of Kangaroo Island all fall in a single northwesterly-southeasterly trending zone. The same is true of the western terminus of the Gawler Range, a gap in the eastern uplands of Eyre Peninsula near Cleve, the fault zone traversing the 'ankle' of Yorke Peninsula, the seismically active Backstairs Passage, and the southeast coast between Robe and the Victorian border.

(d) EXAMPLES OF FAULTED LANDSCAPES

Several specific instances of faults expressed in the landscape have already been cited. Here, a few areas are considered in greater detail.

(i) The Gulfs region of South Australia

Although, in the Adelaide district, there are important features due to erosion and deposition during the Cainozoic, it has long been appreciated that the major topographical features of the area are directly consequent upon structure. The contorted bedrock which underlies the area is block-faulted (Figs. 54, 55) and the topography is a direct reflection of this underlying structure.

The Mount Lofty Ranges in the vicinity of Adelaide attain a general elevation of some 1200–1800 feet, and a maximum of 2,384 feet in Mt Lofty itself. They are underlain by Proterozoic and lower Palaeozoic rocks, as well as by limited areas of possible Archaean rocks preserved in anticlinal cores. Within the ranges there are many major faults. But apart from guiding the pattern of drainage in limited areas, for instance, in the headwaters of the Little Para (see earlier), most have no topographical expression. However, zones of particularly deep weathering, of

Plate 3 The Eden fault scarp, looking southward from Anstey Hill. This prominent feature has strongly influenced the eastward spread of the Adelaide metropolitan area, for besides providing steep building sites, a reticulated water supply is difficult to maintain on the upper half of two-thirds of the escarpment.

Fig 54 Tectonic sketch of the Mt Lofty Ranges showing principal faults and fault blocks.

Fig 55 Block diagram of Adelaide region (*after Sprigg*).

commercial significance, are found in the masses of friable sand and kaolinitic clays associated with the major faults.

The ranges are bounded on both east and west by known fault zones which run almost parallel to one another and border a relatively long and narrow upland, which can therefore be termed a horst. On the east are the Palmer and Milendella faults, on the west the Eden fault zone which runs north to south to the northeast of Adelaide but which to the south swings to a southwesterly strike before it disappears beneath the sea at Brighton (Fig. 54). The fault scarp of the Eden is a conspicuous feature (Pl. 3) and besides being clearly detectable in bore logs, the fault plane is exposed just north of the Gorge mouth (M.R. Adelaide, S.A., 723940), in a quarry cut into the scarp face (Fig. 26b) where the fault appears to be of reverse type. The general setting however (see below) suggests that this is a local feature and that the overall behaviour of the faults is consistent with their being of normal type.

To the west of the Eden fault lies the Para block which is bounded on the west by a low, but distinct, west-facing fault escarpment, with a surface which falls from about 700 feet east of Elizabeth to about 125 feet immediately north of the City of Adelaide, where the structure disappears beneath the Cainozoic sediments of the Adelaide plains. The last exposed remnant of the fault scarp runs immediately to the west of the City. Bore-log evidence shows that the Para fault zone includes two major parallel faults. The gradual slope of the surface of the Para block to the south and the decline in the fault scarp suggests that the whole fault block is tilted to the south. The Eden fault also is not a simple structure: in the vicinity of Crouch Hill (M.R. Adelaide, S.A., 762022), near Golden Grove, the fault scarp disappears, and in the coastal cliffs near Brighton, little or no vertical displacement is discernible, yet due east of the city the scarp is some 600 feet high. The structure appears to be a pivotal or rotational fault with hinges in the vicinity of the coast and Golden Grove.

Both the Eden and Para faults are of recurrent character. The Eden was active in post Eocene—pre Pliocene times, and is still active. Movements along the Para fault are recorded before and during the Miocene, the throw between Croydon and Kent Town being about 1,300 feet, but reached maximum regional intensity during the late Pliocene or early Pleistocene when displacement along the Para fault amounted to at least 600 feet.

On the eastern side of the main horst block, a complex system of faults borders the ranges. Near Palmer, the Milendella fault (Fig. 56) is offset about 2 miles to the east with respect to the Palmer fault. Nowhere are the structures exposed though their presence cannot be doubted: the prominent escarpment and the occurrence of similar granites and gneisses, both within the ranges and beneath the adjacent Murray plains, are strongly suggestive of faulting. As is the case in the Adelaide region,

Fig 56   Geological sketch map of Palmer district showing main areas of granite outcrop and principal fault zones (*adapted from Mannum 1-mile Geological Sheet, Geol. Surv. S.A.*).

there is some evidence in the form of platforms perched between the main plateau of the Ranges and the plain below, for instance just south of Harrisons Creek (M.R. Mannum, S.A., 156901; see Fig. 57), that the faulting took place in more than one phase. There is, however, no evidence of the age of faulting in this area. The undisturbed nature of the Miocene calcarenite which underlies the Murray basin and which rests on the granites and gneisses may indicate a pre Miocene age for a major phase of faulting. On the other hand, these strata are not preserved close to the scarp and, as on the western side of the Ranges fault drag and other distortions occur only in a narrow zone, it could be that such structures, if they affected the Miocene rocks, have been removed by erosion. Thus there is no unequivocal evidence on this point.

To the south are a number of tilted fault blocks (Fig. 54), of similar age and character to those just described. The topography of the area is a direct reflection of this underlying structure; the tilted fault blocks find expression in pronounced northwesterly-facing escarpments, and gentler back slopes lead down to fault basins like those which underlie the Noarlunga and Willunga plains. The main axis of dislocation, viewed regionally, runs from north to south, but the individual fault zones are aligned obliquely to this, and overlap one another (Fig. 54), i.e. are arranged *en échelon*. This reflects a marked change of direction in the

Tectonic Landforms

Fig 57 Perched platform near Harrisons Creek, close to the original site of Palmer township.

overall tectonic pattern from north to south in the Mt Lofty Ranges to east-west in Kangaroo Island.

The fault scarps of the Adelaide area are striking in their elevation. Those of northeast Eyre Peninsula are much lower, but are equally as distinct as those just described. They run for the most part from north to south and delineate a number of tilted rectangular blocks (Fig. 58). The scarps are low, and originated during the late Tertiary, for deposited along the base of some of them are marine Pliocene limestones. As already described (Chapter 2), these small features have clearly influenced the sparse drainage of the area, causing widespread stream rejuvenation, and, with the Ash Reef fault which is unusual in that it downthrows to the west, some impedence to drainage (see Fig. 41).

Similar features (Fig. 59), also running meridionally, occur on Yorke Peninsula. They are low and are considered due to Tertiary faulting, though they have also been interpreted as shoreline features related to Pleistocene high stands of the sea. In the Wakefield area too (Fig. 42), there are ridges which are bounded on the eastern side by precipitous, though dissected, scarps, and which are the result of Tertiary faulting.

Though there are local variations, the fault blocks of the Mt Lofty

62   Geomorphology

Fig 58   Faults and fault blocks in northeast Eyre Peninsula (*after Miles*).

Ranges in the vicinity of Adelaide are tilted down to the east and to the south so that most of the fault scarps face west. On the Yorke and Eyre peninsulas, again with local anomalies, they are tilted down to the west and the scarps face east. Thus it is possible to interpret the Gulfs region as a whole as an arch whose crestal area has suffered rather complex downfaulting (Fig. 60).

The Gulfs region provides one of the best examples of fault-controlled topography in Australia, but it is not the only area owing its major outlines to fracturing in the crust.

Tectonic Landforms

Fig 59 The pattern of faults on Yorke Peninsula (*after* Crawford).

Fig 60 Section showing suggested regional structure of the Gulfs region.

Fig 61 Section across Betoota and Curalle anticlines, northeast of South Australia (*after Wopfner*).

(ii) S.W. Western Australia
Between Perth and Geraldton a narrow coastal plain is enclosed between the ocean and an abrupt escarpment. The scarp, which is remarkably linear in plan, rises 800–1,000 feet from the lowland and leads up to the plateau which occupies much of the southwest of the Australian continent. This major relief feature is due to faulting: the scarp is due to movement along the Darling fault, a fracture zone in granitic rocks. The fault zone is of ancient origin but has suffered recurrent movement. To the south of Bunbury, the lowland corridor is a rift valley bordered on the east by the Darling fault and on the west by the Dunsborough fault, which in turn demarcates the Cape Leeuwin horst on its eastern side (Fig. 31).

(iii) The Canberra City area
According to Öpik, the major relief features of the Canberra area are due to faulting and to the relative resistance of ancient volcanic rocks (Fig. 30). The entire Canberra plain occupies a downfaulted depression above which rise the complex Black Mt horst, and the old volcanic masses of Ainslie, Majura, and Gooroo. Öpik further asserts that, in essence, the outlines of relief are of great antiquity, a matter which is again referred to in Chapter 12.

(iv) Port Phillip Bay
Port Phillip Bay occupies a sunkland, the outlines of which are in considerable measure determined by known faults (Fig. 23) which were active during the Cainozoic. A similar downfaulted area lies to the east.

(e) FOLDED LAND SURFACES
Most of the northeast of South Australia is underlain by only gently folded Cretaceous rocks, which have been eroded to form extensive plains traversed by sand dunes or mantled with pavements of stones—the stony desert or gibber plain. But in several areas, and particularly on the low divide or interfluve between the Diamantina–Warburton and Cooper Creek drainage lines, there are extensive areas of low hills (Fig. 53). These are capped by a rock indurated with silica, and called silcrete or 'billy'. During the early Tertiary this area was worn down by streams and, as a result of the weathering of the surface and near surface rocks of the plain of low relief, an aggregate of heavily siliceous material developed. The silcrete, which is very tough and resistant to weathering and erosion, was gently folded into a series of broad domes and basins in the late Tertiary, and it is these structures, partially dissected, which now form the low uplands of the northeast. The strata in the flanks or limbs of the folds are gently dipping, at angles of up to 20° though generally much lower. Sand washed from the flanks and blown in by the wind has accumulated in the floors of the basins. In places rivers have breached

Tectonic Landforms

the structures. They have eroded the crests of the domes, where the rocks are stretched, where the joints are open and allow rapid weathering, and which are therefore especially susceptible to erosion. Where this has occurred, the limbs of the anticlines take the form of asymmetrical ridges called cuestas, with a long gentle slope coinciding with the dip of the strata and a steeper escarpment facing inwards toward the centre of the structure (Fig. 61). Cuestas develop also on the limbs of synclines, but there the escarpments face outwards.

Thus, though dissected, these landforms of the northeast of South Australia are directly related to a period of folding which took place some millions of years ago; they are thus examples of tectonic forms.

It is difficult to prove that land surfaces have suffered warping or folding particularly where repeated and precise topographical surveys have not been made. In the silcrete (or siliceous duricrust) of arid South Australia, N.S.W., and Queensland the old weathering horizon closely approximates the former land surface, and its distortion is thus a measure of the folding that has taken place since the duricrust developed.

In the Exmouth Gulf region of northwest Western Australia, the relief is also directly related to local structures. The peninsula of North West Cape is underlain by an anticline, and the gulf by a tectonic low (Fig. 62).

Fig 62   Structures in the North West Cape area (*after Condon, et al.*).

In N.W. Queensland, the geologically recent warping of the headwater regions of the Flinders and Diamantina river basins is suggested from the drainage patterns themselves (Fig. 63). Taylor long ago argued that a warping of the plains just north of the original divide (marked by the lateritic Kynuna plateau) between the Gulf of Carpentaria and Lake Eyre catchments caused the headwaters of the Flinders river system to be diverted into the Diamantina, thus giving rise to the peculiar pattern of the latter. This same warping, and the resultant increased stream gradients, caused the northward flowing streams to change from a meandering to a braided habit.

Fig 63 Evolution of drainage in the Kynuna area involving capture of headwaters of the Gulf drainage by the Diamantina, after warping. The left-hand diagram shows the late Tertiary situation; the right-hand, the present.

(f) VOLCANIC LANDSCAPES

Volcanic activity is closely related in both space and time with earth movements. It may be that volcanic activity is the cause of some warping and faulting, and it is certainly located in areas rendered weak and unstable by tectonism. It will be recalled that vulcanism includes any igneous activity at and near the earth's surface, and thus embraces the intrusion of large masses of granite in batholiths, as well as the intrusion of smaller sills and dykes. Volcanic activity includes only those eruptions of molten rock or magma that occur at the surface of the earth.

Volcanoes are a reflection of the instability of the earth, and especially of certain parts of the earth's crust. They are symptoms of great activity deep in the earth's crust. Active volcanoes are concentrated in certain limited areas—in the young fold-mountain belts. These zones are also those of earthquake activity, and seismic and volcanic activity are associated in these zones of weakness and instability.

A volcano is usually pictured as a cone with a crater from which is blasted glowing debris from the country rock, through which the molten lava has passed together with molten bombs of lava, gases and steam, and from which emerge flows of lava or molten rock. In general this is correct, but there are many kinds of volcano. Not all lava emerges from craters, for in some areas such as Iceland, fissures are important in this respect.

Volcanic eruptions give rise to very characteristic landforms. Due to the release of pressure, molten rock surges to the surface where it is extruded. The nature of the volcanic activity, and the forms resulting from the activity, depend very much on the chemistry of the molten lava. Lavas rich in free silica (*acid* lavas) tend to be sticky or viscous, and do not flow readily. In contrast, *basic* lavas, such as basalt, which are lacking in free silica, are non-viscous and fluid and flow easily. Acid lavas tend to coagulate and block their own vents, so that pressure increases beneath the surface: a dangerous explosive-type of activity is associated with such lavas. About 200,000 people have lost their lives through volcanic activity during the past 400 years mostly through such explosive activity. In 1815, a single gigantic explosion destroyed Tamboro in the East Indies, killing about 56,000 people. Acid lavas build spectacular acicular forms rather like toothpaste being squeezed out of a tube. They are, however, particularly vulnerable to erosion and are short-lived. Perhaps the best known example of such a form is the slender needle pushed up to a height of 1,000 feet at Mt Pelée (Martinique, West Indies) in 1902.

In Australia the best known and most spectacular landforms associated with alkaline volcanic rocks are the Glass House Mountains, north of Brisbane. These ancient volcanic stocks, plugs and necks are considered by some workers to be Tertiary, though they are probably of early Mesozoic age. They form steep-sided domes (Pl. 4) and needles; many display columnar jointing, and some rise to 1800 feet above the level of the surrounding plain. Similar features are displayed in the Warrumbungle Range of northeastern N.S.W.

On the other hand, fluid basalts build flat cones and plateaux of great extent. Basalt magma flows at speeds up to 20 mph and spreads over huge areas. The Deccan of India and the Antrim plateau of Northern Ireland are basalt plateaux of this type and the Columbia River plateau of northwestern U.S.A. is more than 200,000 square miles in area. The Hawaiian islands are typical of low angle volcanic cones of great extent. In detail, the surface of such basalt areas is extremely rough, consisting of broken masses of jagged blocks of lava. Fresh lava areas are little weathered and there is no soil, but where the rock has been exposed to the atmosphere, soil has collected in pockets and depressions. Caverns are common, and surface drainage is sparse in many places, though the relationship of surface and water table is important in this respect. In broad view, the basalt surface is even and may be described as a plain or plateau, but in detail there are broad areas of even ground separated by low, steep rises or low escarpments, some of which are due to erosion by the few rivers, but most of which are due to the occurrence of separate lava flows. There are also low cones or vents, indicating the sites of former volcanoes. The centres of some are occupied by lakes. Some of the craters are due to explosive activity. Others are due to subsidence (*calderas*), and are larger than the average explosion crater.

Plate 4 Part of the Glasshouse Mountains, Queensland—angular, needle-like volcanic mountains. (*Queensland Government Railways*)

In South Australia there are two small areas of geologically recent volcanic activity; one small, in the northeast of Kangaroo Island, and one, slightly more extensive in the Southeast (Fig. 64), though in the Wooltana area and in the Gawler Ranges there was widespread volcanic activity during the Precambrian. In the latter, areas of columnar jointing are commonplace (Pl. 5).

The volcanic area in the Southeast is a westward extension of the much larger Western Districts volcanic area of Victoria. The activity was of basic type and basalt was extruded from the Mt Schank vents, but most of the material is ash, and ejectamenta, usually well stratified, rather than basalt. The volcanic areas of the Southeast fall into two groups, representing two more-or-less distinct periods of activity. The older set of vents, extending between and including Mt Graham and Mt Bluff, consist of imperfect conical forms, with the exception of Boyce Hill, which has a conical shape. Mt Graham and Mt McIntyre are elongate ridges comprising a number of separate vents, and Lakes Leake and Edwards are very small calderas due to subsidence in and around volcanic craters. This older group, which appear to be arranged in three northwest to southeast trending zones (Fig. 64), have been affected by high sea levels

Plate 5 Columnar jointing in the Gawler Range porphyry. Such clusters of columns are commonly exposed in this ancient volcanic region.

Plate 6 Mt Schank, a volcanic vent, seen from the northwest. Its appearance is deceptive for although it stands prominently above the otherwise gently rolling plain, the mount is a rim enclosing a deep, steep-sided depression, the floor of which is about the same level as the plain outside.

of the Quaternary (see Chapter 9). In turn, they have influenced the configuration of these ancient elevated coastlines. The cones and ridges were present before or during the early part of the Quaternary and must therefore be of earlier date. On the other hand, the igneous rocks are extruded through early Tertiary strata, and this older phase of volcanicity is generally considered of late Tertiary—early Quaternary age.

Fig 64 Volcanic vents in the south east of South Australia (*after Sprigg*).

The younger group of cones in the Mt Gambier and Mt Schank (Pls. 6, 7, 8) areas is little affected by weathering and erosion. They have not been involved in the high Quaternary sea levels evidenced by the numerous old dunes, and therefore they essentially post date the period of high sea levels. Ash from the Mt Gambier area has been dated at about 4,700 years old and about 1,400 years old, indicating that the vents were certainly active at these times, though possibly for a considerable period before and after.

Tectonic Landforms

This younger group is clearly of Recent age, and aboriginal men must have witnessed the later phases of vulcanicity in the Southeast, for they have been present in the area for at least 8,000 years, and most probably very much longer.

Plate 7 Mt Schank from the air. This vertical air photograph shows the characteristic circular form in plan, as well as the conical shape of this double vent. The two craters together measure about ⅓ mile in a N.-S. direction. (*S.A. Lands Department*)

Mt Schank is a deep depression, the bottom of which is about level with the plain outside the crater. The Mt Gambier complex includes three major vents, plus a number of subsidiary or secondary outlets. Blue Lake is about 260 feet deep. Some faulting is visible in the craters. The lakes of the Mt Gambier area are simply subsidence features that have sunk below the regional water table and are therefore permanently filled with water.

Within both older and younger volcanic phases there were pauses when weathering and erosion occurred and we must visualise two major phases, each of spasmodic or interrupted activity.

Plate 8   Stratified ash exposed in quarry face on the east side of Mt Schank. The layers of ash, of which the mountain is largely composed, can be clearly seen. They are due to the gradual build up, layer by layer, of debris flung from the volcano. The steep sides of the hill are not easy to climb on account of the loose ash on the surface.

Across the border in Victoria, basalts of late Cainozoic age occupy about 5,800 square miles (in addition, early Cainozoic basalts extend over large areas both east and south of Melbourne). In this area well over 100 distinct vents have been recognised. Most of them rise less than 300 feet above the surrounding lava plains, and some are less than 50 feet high; a few rise more than 650 feet above plain level. The nature and morphology of the vents varies: some are typical lava cones (e.g. Mt Hamilton, some 30 miles west-southwest of Ballarat), some few, like Tower Hill (M.R. Port Fairy, Vic., 300750), are calderas, others are *maars*, with very gentle outer slopes of tuffaceous material leading up to a vertical sided vent (e.g. Terang, about 10 miles west of Camperdown), and yet others are complex spatter cones, for example, in the vicinity of Mt Eccles, 30 miles northeast of Portland. Some vents are dry, others contain lakes.

The plains display distinct steps and extensive treads due to the weathering and erosion of individual lava flows. The fronts are rocky and on the intervening plains are stony rises and soil-filled depressions. Caves are fairly common, and, at the margins of the basalt uplands, rivers flow in deep gorges, into which they tumble by way of spectacular waterfalls, particularly where the river has excavated through the basalt into softer rocks beneath. One of the best known marginal basalt falls is the Trentham Falls (M.R. Daylesford, Vic., 378895), where the Coliban River leaves the lava area.

Basalt plains and plateaux displaying similar assemblages of forms are commonplace in the eastern uplands, including Tasmania (Fig. 65). Extensive outcrops occur, for instance, in northwest Tasmania, in the Kiandra and Monaro regions of southeastern N.S.W., in the Hunter valley, New England, the Toowoomba, Springsure and Clermont areas of southern and central Queensland, and in several areas of northern Queensland. These lavas are not all of the same age (those of southern N.S.W., are early Tertiary) and consequently display differences in the degree to which they are weathered and eroded. The degree of dissection, to take one criterion, varies from place to place, partly as a function of age, though the presence of underlying soft bedrock, such as the easily eroded Cretaceous shales north of Hughenden and Richmond, northwest Queensland, causes rapid undermining and retreat of the basalt margins. Another contrast is in the number of vents surviving: again, duration of weathering and erosion is important, but it has to be remembered that the lavas may have emerged from fissures rather than orifices. Wherever they occur, the basalts give rise to plains and plateaux with distinct steps and treads, stony rises and soil-filled depressions, caverns and, where the relief amplitude permits, deep, narrow gorges.

In the Hunter valley (Fig. 66) basalts of two distinct ages occur. Both are of the Tertiary, but it is the earlier which is the more widespread and forms extensive plateaux. The basalt is in several places more than 2,000 feet thick (e.g. in Barrington Tops) and beneath the Liverpool Range

Fig 65 Distribution of basalt and granitic outcrops in eastern Australia (*from Geology map, 'Atlas of Australian Resources'*).

Fig 66 Basalt plateaux in the Hunter Valley (*after Galloway*).

probably approaches 3,000 feet thickness. Both here and in New England the basalt has been subjected to planation, deep weathering, including lateritisation (see Chapter 5), and subsequent deep dissection.

In north Queensland, basalt occupies some 12,000 square miles of plains and plateaux in a number of distinct lava fields in the general area of Hughenden, Einasleigh and Mt Garnet. Several distinct periods of volcanicity can be distinguished but the nature and degree of weathering and erosion suggest that all are late Cainozoic; however, the latest lava flows are very recent. The landforms developed on these areas are similar to those described from Victoria and South Australia (Pls. 9, 10, 11); some of the drainage diversions are, however, worthy of note (see Chapter 6).

Many of the manifestations of volcanism described above are clearly and directly expressed in the relief and are tectonic forms. Some, such as the gorges and other features are due to weathering and erosion.

76   *Geomorphology*

Plate 9   Aerial photograph of Mt Tabletop, a complex basalt cone in North Queensland. Besides the main vent in the southwest, four secondary or adventive cones occur to the northeast; there is little surface drainage on the basalt plains, but note the radial pattern of gullies on the main dome. (*Dept National Development*)

Plate 10   Mt Tabletop from the southeast. The main dome and three of the secondary vents are visible. (*C.S.I.R.O.*)

Tectonic Landforms

Plate 11 Porcupine or Galah Gorge, 30 miles north of Hughenden, northern Queensland. The river has eroded some 200 feet through the various flows of lava into sandstone and siltstone. The structural benches are due to the differential erosion of the layered flows. (*C.S.I.R.O.*)

Note

[1] They are said to be 'hard' or 'soft', but this refers to their relative resistance to these agencies rather than to their physical hardness.

4. Structural Landforms

SEVERAL ROCK CHARACTERISTICS are significant in determining the progress of weathering and erosion. Mineral composition, grain size and other textural features, attitude or disposition of beds (whether they are horizontal, gently dipping, steeply dipping or vertical), and their fracture pattern, are all important, either individually or in combination. Some rocks, like quartzite, are everywhere resistant to weathering and erosion, and thus form uplands. Others, like shales and siltstones are uniformly weak and are easily weathered and eroded to form valleys or plains. Massively jointed and bedded rocks, like the Miocene calcarenite (or sandy limestone) exposed in the river bluffs of the Murray valley, are more resistant than finely bedded shales. Many similar structural effects are exemplified throughout the text; in this chapter detailed consideration is given to the influence of lithology, disposition of strata, and jointing, in the shaping of the land surface.

(a) DISPOSITION OR ATTITUDE OF STRATA

(i) General

Dissected, flat-lying sediments, near-horizontal lava flows and duricrusts[1] formed on rocks of any disposition give rise to plateaux, mesas and buttes, depending on the degree of dissection. A mesa is a small plateau, and technically a mesa becomes a butte when the area of the preserved upper surface is reduced to such an extent that its maximum diameter is less than its elevation above the surrounding plain. In Australia, such plateau forms are commonly known as *tent hills* (Fig. 67) . Good examples occur between Port Augusta and Whyalla, in the Lincoln Gap area, and west of Lake Torrens, in the Arcoona Plateau. The plateau forms of these areas are developed on sandstones lithologically similar and stratigraphicaly equivalent to strata which crop out to the east, in the Flinders Ranges. Yet in the latter area, the landforms developed are very different.

During later Precambrian and early Palaeozoic times the present Westralian Shield was the Australian continent. On its southeastern border, a great thickness of sediments was deposited in the Adelaide geosyncline. The thickness of sediments was less at the margin than toward the centre of the geosyncline, and thus the Pound Sandstone Formation which attains thicknesses of up to 9,000 feet in the Flinders Ranges, is very thin in places to the west of the Ranges, for instance near Lincoln Gap, though it is more substantially represented west of Lake Torrens.

Structural Landforms

Sometime during the early or middle Palaeozoic these sediments suffered compression and, as a result, were folded and faulted and raised into fold mountains. This orogenesis took place after the deposition of fossiliferous Cambrian sediments in the geosyncline, but before the Permian glaciation which affected the southern part of the fold mountain belt (Cambrian sediments were involved in the folding, while the Permian glacial deposits were not). However, near Leigh Creek and in the southern Flinders, Triassic lacustrine beds are gently folded, suggesting that compression did not cease abruptly, but continued at least locally, into the Mesozoic.

Fig 67 (a) Tent hills underlain by flat-lying Precambrian sandstone at Lincoln Gap, southwest of port Augusta; (b) East of Coober Pedy in flat-lying Cretaceous sediments with a capping of gibber.

Fig 68 Diagrammatic section of the shield/orogen junction in the vicinity of Port Augusta.

The folding and faulting are especially well developed in an elongate zone running roughly north to south from Lake Eyre to the Southern Ocean. In the north, the distorted zone terminates abruptly along a line running submeridionally along the western edge of Lake Torrens, where there is known to be a fault zone. It appears that to the east of this line, the geosynclinal sediments were squeezed against the resistant mass of the Shield, while those stratigraphically equivalent, lithologically similar rocks to the west, overlapping on to the border of the Shield, were not affected and remain horizontally disposed, or essentially so (Fig. 68). This structural contrast, developed long ago, is now reflected in the different landforms of the two zones.

(ii) Flat-lying strata
In the plateau regions the degree of dissection and the relative extent of plateau and plain varies from place to place (Fig. 69), but the assemblage of landforms and the slope profiles are similar everywhere.

The plateau surface gives way abruptly to an escarpment which leads down to the plains below (Fig. 70). The scarp includes several distinct facets and breaks of gradient. Such slopes are called *faceted* slopes. Though over considerable areas a given massive bed forms the surface, the *plateau* viewed as a whole cuts across several strata and must therefore be of erosional character. On it rests a thin discontinuous mantle of stony soil. The scarp is comprised of two major elements—the *bluff* and the *debris slope*. In the bluff, the exposed ends of strata are revealed, the various facets displayed there being joint planes; in detail, the bluff is irregular, but is closely controlled by structure. The upper part of the bluff is generally slightly rounded to form a distinct, though in these areas insignificant, unit—the *upper slope* (also known as the waxing slope). Below the bluff the debris slope extends to the plains. At the junction between debris slope and bluff, caverns or shelters are commonly formed. These caverns are very important in slope development for they are the principal means whereby the bluff is undermined, maintained and made to retreat. The reason for the initiation of caverns is related to the level of the water table; at some point on a slope there is a concentration of soil moisture coincident with the 'outcrop' of the water table. At this level, a cavern is initiated and a bluff is developed or maintained through undermining. The debris from the bluff fails to give a protective veneer to the slope below, though as the slope retreats under attack from weathering and erosion the *debris slope* comes to be essentially a bedrock unit with only a veneer of debris (Fig. 70). The debris slope suffers dissection by rills, gullies and streams, some of which extend headward and directly attack the base of the bluff. The pattern of scarp streams is closely controlled by the joint pattern in the sandstone (Fig. 69).

Mass movement of debris (see Chapter 6), particularly *soil creep*, is also important here and is evidenced by small terraces or *terracettes* of fine debris impounded behind large obstacles, such as blocks of rock fallen from the bluff (Fig. 71), chance outcrops, or tree trunks. The debris slope is the lowest of the steep slope units, and its size, both absolute and in relation to the bluff, varies with the intensity of erosion at the base of the steep slope (see also Chapters 1, 6 and 11). Around Lincoln Gap, streams are sparsely distributed but some impinge against the base of the scarp, causing the erosion and reduction of the debris slope and, as a result, the extension of the bluff. In some areas the steep slope is rather more complex and, instead of displaying one bluff and one debris slope, alternations of harder and softer sandstones has caused the development of numerous small bluffs and *structural benches* coincident with the harder strata, separated by more easily weathered and eroded strata which form debris slopes (Fig. 72).

The scarp gives way to the plains quite abruptly in a narrow zone of curvature. The plains are broadly rolling, due to stream dissection and, although underlain at shallow depth by bedrock, carry a veneer of alluvium, colluvium (slope debris) and wind blown materials, with fixed dunes (see Chapter 7) developed around shrubs and bushes. The thickness of unconsolidated debris increases downslope and here the plains are of *depositional* type; but forming discontinuous fringes around the plateaux and plateau-remnants are smooth plains developed essentially on bedrock and called *pediments* (see below, Chapters 7 and 11).

At Lincoln Gap and in many other parts of South Australia the morphology of the scarps is essentially uniform, though certain exceptions have been noted. The reason is that the main attack by weathering and erosion affects the lower part of the slope. Because water tends to spread as the run-off radiates off the plateaux and hence slows down and percolates into the subsurface, it causes weathering; and because rills and streams increase in volume downstream, the reduction of lower slopes takes place more quickly than on the upper part of the scarp. The bluff is an expression of this fact. Such contrasted attack is known as *differential* weathering and erosion, as opposed to the equally common *selective* weathering and erosion in which inherent weaknesses in the rock outcrops are exploited by various agencies. Because of differential erosion, losses from the lower slope are greater than from the upper; the *budgets*, or net gains and losses, of the two areas differ. Where the slope budget is such that erosion is strongest on lower slopes, bluffs are prominent morphological features and the form and inclination of slopes tend to be constant even during recession, so that extensive plateaux and small buttes are bounded by similar slopes.

Such behaviour is referred to as scarp or slope *retreat* in contradistinction to situations where the upper slope is reduced more rapidly than the lower, when slope *decline* takes place. Because the upper slope is protected by the presence of a resistant capping (in the area cited, the tough sandstone), the development of constant, steep slope forms and parallel recession (Fig. 4a) are promoted.

Similar forms are in evidence wherever the local bedrock is horizontal or nearly so. Basalt plateaux have already been described from several areas of eastern Australia: basalt forms a good caprock and slopes of the faceted type are developed where dissection has occurred. The assemblage of plateau, mesa or butte bounded by faceted slopes is also commonly evolved on flat-lying and resistant sandstones similar to those of the Lincoln Gap and Arcoona plateau areas. The Blue Mountains,

Fig 69 Morphological map of Lincoln Gap area.

Structural Landforms

Fig 70 Typical hillslope in the Lincoln Gap area.

Fig 71 Scarp with minor terraces developed.

Fig 72 Structural benches. (b) = bluff; (d) = debris slope.

Plate 12 The weathering and erosion of sandstone in many places gives rise to odd forms. In the Gilberton plateau of northern Queensland a 'beehive' has been etched out of the level-bedded country rock. The fretted surface is due to the detailed exploitation of minor joints and bedding planes. (*C.S.I.R.O.*)

Plate 13 The Mueller plateau, Northern Territory, inland from the Nicholson River. The gently dipping sandstone is very well jointed and bedded. Both sets of fractures are well expressed in the details of the cliffs and in the minor stream patterns. (*Dept. National Development*)

Structural Landforms

west of Sydney, provide excellent examples of such forms (for a comparison of plateaux in various stages of dissection see the St Albans and Kiama, N.S.W. one inch survey sheets). The plateau, which rises to more than 3,500 feet in some areas and commonly exceeds 2,500 feet above sea level is underlain by the massively jointed, bedded, sub-horizontally disposed Hawkesbury sandstone. It is deeply dissected by such rivers as the Colo, Grose and Cox, which have eroded quite broad valleys separated by relatively narrow divides. Rocky bluffs, dominated by huge joint blocks and marked structural benches, coincident with the outcrop of especially hard beds, dominate the valley walls, though they give way at lower elevations to debris slopes strewn with coarse, angular sandstone blocks. Rivers which rise on the plateau tumble over these scarps in high, commonly spectacular falls, and odd conformations of the sandstone bluffs add to their scenic attractiveness here and elsewhere (Fig. 73).

In the Gilberton plateau of northern Queensland, which is developed on Cretaceous sandstones, the plateau remnants are more extensive, the

Fig 73 (a) Field sketch of the Three Sisters, Katoomba, N.S.W. Sandstone cliffs and deep, steep-sided valleys are shown; (b) Field sketch of sandstone bluffs on south side Mt Conner, N.T.; (c) Plateaux and mesa in level bedded sandstone, Barrow Creek, N.T.

Fig 74 Wittenoom Gorge, Pilbara, W.A. (*from photograph*).

valleys narrower and fewer, probably because of the interior (and hence protected) location, lower rainfall and only intermittent river activity, and possibly the more recent commencement of dissection. But the detailed forms of the valley walls are the same as those described (Pl. 12). Also, much of the Nullagine and Hamersley plateaux, formed on level bedded Proterozoic sandstones, are relatively undissected (Fig. 74), as is the Mueller plateau, on the divide between the Gulf and Barkly drainage in the Northern Territory (Pl. 13), but the Kimberley and Arnhem Land areas are in many parts greatly eroded and the plateau character is here less evident.

Plateau, mesas and buttes are also eroded where resistant cappings have formed not from primary strata, as it were, but as a result of weathering and erosion—duricrusts of various compositions and including ferricrete, bauxite, silcrete and calcrete (see Chapter 5) as well as the less common gypcrete (a layer of gypsum which, despite its physical softness, is in some areas sufficiently resistant to form a hard capping) and lags and concentrations of coarse debris, including gibber. Various examples are shown in Fig. 75 (see also Fig. 67b).

(iii) Folded sediments

In the fold mountain belt to the east of Lincoln Gap and Arcoona Plateau, similar faceted slope forms are found in many places, but the relative development of each of the slope units is much more varied (Fig. 76) and the landform assemblages differ also. Within the Flinders Ranges folding generally was not severe. Overthrust faults indicative of severe local compression in the Adelaide geosyncline occur in the Willouran Ranges (Norwest fault), in the northeast (part of the Paralana fault complex), in the Olary upland (Outalpa thrust), and in northern Yorke Peninsula (Yararoo thrust), but overall compression was not great and, as a result, the basin and dome structures, the anticlines and synclines are simple and open.

After the original sediments had been folded, there must have been variations in lithology exposed, if only because of primary sorting and grading of sediments, but the exploitation of structural weaknesses in the folds must have added further variety and eventually become the sole cause of exposure of different strata.

Initially, topography may reflect the disposition of the underlying bedrock. But such situations do not persist for very long. The original drainage is concentrated in the synclines and depressions, but the crests of the domes and anticlines offered areas of particular weaknesses for subsequent exploitation by the agencies of weathering and erosion. They are weak because, high in the structures, the strata are in tension (Fig. 77) and thus the joints are open and susceptible to atmospheric agencies. Thus the anticlinal structures would have been weathered and eroded more quickly than the synclines, where superficially at any rate, the strata are compressed.

For these reasons, the anticlines would be etched out, while synclines would be left eventually to become high points in the topography, causing *inversion of relief*. In the southern Flinders, the Willochra plain occupies an anticlinal structure, while the higher ground to east and west is underlain by complex synclinoria (Fig. 16b). Note, however, (Fig. 77), that when erosion penetrates deeply into folded structures the stress conditions are reversed, becoming compressional in anticlines and tensional in synclines. Eventually, therefore, one might anticipate a reversion to the original relationship between relief and structure.

Various types of sediment were deposited in the Adelaide geosyncline. They include several massive sandstone and limestone formations, both resistant to weathering and erosion. They therefore tend to form upstanding ridges and, since both are affected by folding together with the rest of the sedimentary sequences, their distribution in plan is a direct reflection of the geometry of folding at the level to which erosion has penetrated to the present. Thus the W- and Z-shaped patterns of sandstone ridges north of Quorn and south of Hawker respectively are a direct reflection of plunging anticlinal and synclinal structures (Fig. 14). The same formation recurs many times over in the landscape due to folding sandstone. The amphitheatre of Wilpena Pound is underlain by a basin (Fig. 18); the Aroona Valley, bordered on both east and west by high ranges, is due to the erosion of soft argillaceous strata which strike north-south and lie between resistant sandstones and limestones (Fig. 78); the multiple ridge which forms the border of the ranges around Brachina is associated with westward dipping limestone and sandstone outcrops (Pl. 14); the intricate pattern of upland and lowland around Mt Serle is directly related to the pattern of outcrop formed by faulting and folding (Fig. 80). Many other examples of this direct relationship between structure and surface could be cited from the Flinders Ranges, but examples just as clear and spectacular come from the James, Krichauff, Waterhouse and MacDonnell Ranges of the Northern Territory (Fig. 15).

Even in detail the attitude of strata is expressed in the morphology of individual ridges and hills. Gently dipping, resistant strata form ridges and hills called *cuestas* which are asymmetrical in cross section (Figs. 81, 82). Wilpena Pound is oval in plan and the bounding ridges are cuestas with the steeper scarps facing outwards and the long, gentle dip slopes all leading down to the centre of the basin (Fig. 18). In domes like that around Blinman, or at Betoota, in the northeast of South Australia, this arrangement is reversed: the scarps face inwards and the dip slopes outwards (Fig. 61).

Gently dipping dykes or sills also give rise to cuestas; for example in the Everard Ranges moderately dipping dolerite dykes intruding the granitic bedrock form asymmetrical ridges of which Black Hill is an example. Roughly triangular facets, called *flatirons* (Fig. 84), form as the result of stream dissection of cuestas. In the Grampians of Western Victoria the upper Palaeozoic sandstones dip predominantly westward and give rise to markedly asymmetrical ridges, the scarps of which face east and the gentler dip slopes, west (Figs. 47, 85). But the narrow gorges, the rather bizarre isolated blocks of the outcrops, the waterfalls, structural benches and the details of weathering are those of sandstone, whether level-bedded or tilted (Fig. 86).

Cuestas occur in many parts of Australia, including the central uplands near Ormiston Gorge and the James Range (Fig. 55a). Where strata are steeply inclined, as in many parts of the MacDonnell Ranges of central Australia, *hogbacks* are found which are symmetrical in cross section. At Warrens and Buckaringa Gorges, north of Quorn in the southern Flinders Ranges, the A.B.C. Range quartzite dips east at 75°–80° and the ridge is of the hogback type. The east-facing scarp is an exposed bedding plane on which the pattern of joints is seen in plan view (Fig. 76e). To the northeast, however, this same ridge changes in form; the dip of the A.B.C. quartzite decreases to about 30°–33°, for example where the Willochra and Kanyaka Creeks breach the ridge, and here a cuesta has been developed (Fig. 87).

Fig 75 (a) Laterite (ferricrete) capped residual, Cue, W.A. (*from photograph*); (b) Silcrete capped residuals west of Oodnadatta; (c) Lateritised granite dissected to form mesa, south of Cloncurry, northwestern Queensland.

Fig 76 Characteristic hillslopes in the Flinders Ranges: (a) Steeply dipping shales near Buckaringa Gorge; (b) Mt Chambers Gorge, showing bluffs associated with level bedded sandstones; (c) Low limestone bluffs south of Blinman; (d) East-facing scarp, north of Buckaringa Gorge (the sandstone is nearly vertical and the bedding plane forms the bluff); (e) The Bluff, north of Quorn (the sandstone is dipping to the right).

Structural Landforms

(a)

(b)

(c)

(d)

(e)

Geomorphology

Fig 77 Tension and compression in folded rocks.

Fig 78 Diagrammatic geological map of the Aroona valley (*from Parachilna 4-mile Geological Sheet, Geol. Surv. S.A.*).
Fig 79 Generalised section of A–B in Fig 78.

Structural Landforms

Fig 80 Map showing complex faulting and folding in the Mt Serle region. The topography directly reflects the intricacies of structure, for wherever it occurs the sandstone is resistant and thus forms ridges (*adapted from Angepena 1-mile Geological Sheet, Geol. Surv. S.A.*).

Fig 81 The folded sediments of the Krichauff Ranges, N.T., give rise to alternations of ridge and valley coincident with the outcrop of hard and soft rocks (*from photograph*).

Fig 82   Central Mt Wedge, N.T., a cuesta in sandstone.

Fig 83   Cuestas with the scarp showing structural benches, MacDonnell Ranges, N.T.

Fig 84   Flatirons in sandstone near Puttapa Gap, south of Copley.

Fig 85   Mt Abrupt, Grampians, Vic.

Fig 86 (a) and (b) Weathering forms in sandstone, Grampians, Vic. (*drawn from photographs supplied by D. Moss*).

Fig 87 Change of ridge profile with dip of strata in the southern Flinders Ranges (*adapted from Willochra 1-mile Geological Sheet, Geol. Surv. S.A.*).

Fig 88 Ridge and cleft in sandstone at Warrens Gorge, southern Flinders Ranges. The two features are underlain by sandstone but that in which the cleft is eroded is finely bedded, in contrast to the massive rock of the ridge.

Plate 14 Dissected pediment just north of the Brachina Gorge. Note its remarkable smoothness, the remnants standing higher (in the distance) and lower (in the foreground) than the pediment specifically referred to here, and the multiple escarpment of the Flinders Range. The first and lower scarp is underlain by Cambrian limestone, the second and higher by the Pound Sandstone.

(b) THE INFLUENCE OF JOINTING: GRANITE LANDFORMS
(i) General
Joints are fractures in rocks along which no movement can be proved. Many are undoubtedly faults and are related geometrically to the regional pattern of stresses and lineaments. These are of tectonic origin, but others are due to cooling or, in the case of sediments, to dehydration and compression during consolidation (*diagenesis*). But whatever their origin and in whatever type of rock they occur, joints are important geomorphologically because they form lines of weakness which can be exploited by weathering agencies including water and wind. For this reason the pattern and spacing (or texture) of the joint pattern are commonly imposed upon the pattern of relief.

The geometry and spacing of joints varies greatly from one rock type to another, within the same rock type and even within the same outcrop or quarry exposure. The Miocene calcarenite (sandy limestone) which is widely exposed in the cliffs bordering the valley of the River Murray in South Australia, the Palaeozoic sandstone of the Grampians and the Hawkesbury sandstone of the Blue Mountains, are massively jointed. The large cubic blocks delineated by the joints and bedding places are clearly expressed, not only in the morphology of the cliffs but also in the courses of the rivers which in detail are controlled by the patterns of joints (Pl. 15). In many siltstones and shales, on the other hand, the joints are so close to one another that the joint blocks are so small they scarcely warrant the term. In Warrens Gorge, in the southern Flinders Ranges, variations in the spacing of bedding planes are directly expressed in minor ridges and vales, the former coincident with massive outcrops, the latter with strata of fissile character (Fig. 88).

The influence of joints in the development of karst is made clear in a later section, but their effects are even more apparent in granitic rocks. Rocks of granitic character form no really large outcrops in South Australia, but are widely distributed (Fig. 89). In the Eastern Uplands, granites occur as numerous batholiths (large masses emplaced discordantly in the surrounding country rock) and are exposed over very large areas (Fig. 65). In Western Australia, Tasmania and the Northern Territory, granite rocks also occur extensively. These granitic rocks display a wide variety of joint pattern and texture, ranging from very fine through medium to very coarse, and the landform assemblage developed on these mineralogically similar rocks varies correspondingly.

(ii) Moderately spaced joints—the development of tors
In many areas the joint blocks delineated by the joint fractures are between one and ten feet diameter (Pl. 16). At Palmer, some 35 miles east of Adelaide, for example, the blocks exposed in road cuttings and in quarries are of this range. The Palmer outcrop is not large, measuring about 3 miles from north to south and 1 mile from east to west (Fig. 56),

but in the northern part displays characteristic granite features and forms. In both road cuttings and quarry faces, it is clear that while the rocks are beneath the surface, water penetrates along the joints and causes the weathering of the rocks adjacent to the fractures. The result is that the marginal areas of each block, and particularly the corners of each, display a series of curved, discontinuous fractures separating very thin elongated layers or lenses of rock. This type of concentric fracturing is called *spheroidal weathering*. The weathered zone encloses a more-or-less spherical mass of fresh rock called a *corestone* or kernel (Pl. 17). Thus each joint block is differentially weathered with a central corestone surrounded by a mass of laminated or finely banded and weathered rock. If subsequently the land surface is lowered and such differentially weathered blocks are subjected to erosion by wind, and especially by running water, it is evident that the weathered and friable marginal zones will be much more readily and rapidly eroded than will the fresh corestones. Thus as a result of differential weathering beneath the land surface there is differential erosion upon exposure to the elements. The laminated and disintegrated rock is washed away and the corestones are exposed to form essentially rounded boulders known in Australia as *tors* but called *boulders of weathering*, or of *disintegration* elsewhere. Tors are strewn over the northern part of the Palmer outcrop (Pl. 18), and are even more abundant than at first seems apparent, for many are buried beneath a veneer of sand washed into valleys from the crests of the ridges (Pl. 19). Similar tors are also found at Victor Harbour and in several areas of the Upper South East. They are abundant on the Monaro Upland of N.S.W.

In the Kosciusko region, where granitic rocks are widespread, tors are well developed, and corestones clearly exposed in the numerous road cuttings (Pl. 20). Many of the granite joint blocks in the higher areas have suffered intense frost shattering and the fragments are angular, but at lower levels the tors and corestones are well rounded. The Victorian granitic outcrops are well documented: tors are widely distributed in such areas and outcrops as Mt Buffalo (near which Big Gun Hill displays little-rounded joint blocks), Tarago, where corestones are well developed and Tallarook. Small but notable isolated outcrops displaying strong jointing, tors and massive, bold, rounded surfaces protrude above the alluvial plains of the Murray valley for instance in Pyramid Hill and Bald Rock, some 30 miles west-northwest of Echuca.

Tor fields have been described from the Armidale district of northern N.S.W., and also occur in northern Queensland near Charters Towers; the Georgetown district, south of Croydon; near Cloncurry and in the hinterland of Cairns (Pl. 21). They are so typical that in many areas, tors identify the granite bedrock.

The marginal weathering of joint blocks does not everywhere take the form of spheroidal weathering. Within the Palmer outcrop large tetrahedral cornerstones are separated from the corestones by a single fracture

Structural Landforms

(Fig. 90). In the Snowy Mountain area of southern N.S.W. the marginal zones of dioritic[2] blocks (Pl. 22) display thick, concentric layers (*onion weathering*). Some granite corestones are surrounded by masses of disintegrated rock (*granular disintegration*) and at one site near the Tooma Dam the marginal area of dioritic rocks displays concentric bands of different minerals.

Obviously the size and geometry of the corestones varies with the geometry of the joint pattern. Many joint blocks are roughly cubic and the corestones and tors weathered from them are spherical, but at Palmer some joint blocks are elongated in one direction and the corestones and tors are ovoid.

Fig 89 Distribution of granitic rocks in South Australia (*adapted from Geol. Surv. S.A.* map, 1953).

Plate 15 Cliffs of the River Murray, near Walkers Flat, South Australia. The river is actively undercutting the cliff in which massively jointed Miocene calcarenite is exposed. The angularity of the cliff in detail is directly related to these exposed joint blocks.

Plate 16 Joint blocks in granite, exposed in a sea cliff on the southern side of Granite Island, near Victor Harbour. Note the three sets of joints, two vertical and one horizontal, disposed at right angles to one another—the orthogonal system.

Structural Landforms

Plate 17 Corestone and spheroidally weathered granite exposed in a road cutting just west of Palmer. The fresh, essentially unweathered granite of the corestone is surrounded by granite which has been weathered to form thin laminae or lenses which easily crumble in the hand. Tors are exposed on the hillslope above.

Plate 18 Cluster of tors near Palmer.

Plate 19 Tors near Palmer, revealed through the removal by streams of fine sand which formerly covered those on lower slopes and in depressions.

As described here tors develop in two stages (Fig. 91), the first involving differential subsurface weathering, and the second differential erosion. The two-stage origin of granite residuals has been recently and forcefully advocated by Linton with particular reference to the tors (in Britain used of massive hills comprising numerous large and little-weathered joint blocks) of Dartmoor, in southwestern England, though the theory was stated in essence, with respect to the same area, almost a century before.

The size of joint blocks which develop into tors varies from place to place. In the Palmer region, corestones and tors vary between $1\frac{1}{2}$ and 10 feet diameter. At the lower limit, joint blocks weather slowly enough to survive as tors only where the granite is fine grained and resistant, as, for instance, the fine grey granite which underlies all the higher parts of the Palmer outcrop. At the other end of the scale very large tors like those at the Devil's Marbles, in the Northern Territory, are up to 40 feet diameter, yet on northwestern Eyre Peninsula there are joint blocks 10 and 15 feet diameter respectively which have not been weathered differentially, and which therefore do not give rise to tors. The reason is that not all joints are equally susceptible to weathering. Some are open and, so, readily exploitable, but others are tight and immune to all but the slowest weathering and are detected in the field only with great difficulty.

Some of these tight, latent, joints occur in the tor blocks at Palmer (Fig. 92), but they have played no part in determining the primary outlines of the blocks and are only brought into relief by weathering very much later, when they cause the tors to split into two parts along remarkably rectilinear fractures. Every stage in the exploitation of these latent

Structural Landforms

Fig 90 Types of marginal weathering in granite joint blocks.

Fig 91 Two stage development of granite residuals: (a) Joint pattern; (b) Differential, subsurface weathering of blocks to form corestones; (c) Lowering of land surface and removal of weathered debris, leaving the corestones as residual boulders—tors, in the Australian sense.

Plate 20 Corestones in gruss, or weathered granite, Jindabyne area, N.S.W. Note the spheroidal weathering of the two nearer blocks, and the polygonal pattern of cracking on some of those beyond.

Structural Landforms   103

Plate 21 Tor, 20–25 feet maximum diameter, in the valley of the upper Herbert River, north Queensland. (*C.S.I.R.O.*)

Plate 22 Onion weathering near Tooma Dam, Snowy Mountains, N.S.W. Here the spherical corestones are surrounded by thick leaves or layers of rock.

joints, terminating in the separation of the two parts, is seen at Palmer, and similar features are displayed elsewhere (Pl. 23).

(iii) Close jointing in granites

Although the northern part of the Palmer outcrop displays very good tors which, from the local evidence, clearly originate in the two-stage fashion described above, the southern two-thirds of the outcrop have no particular characteristics associated with this particular rock type. This is because the southern part of the mass is greatly shattered and fissured; the joints (or faults) are very closely spaced, with the result that the joint blocks are very small and have weathered through completely. Thus there is no differential weathering, and, consequently no

Plate 23   Split tor from the Kosciusko area, N.S.W.

corestones of relatively resistant fresh rock, no differential erosion, and no tors. The landscape developed is a rather featureless rolling plateau which is deeply dissected by streams like Harrisons Creek, flowing to the Murray. Similar contrasting landform assemblages developed on granitic rocks occur in the north Flinders, in the Mt Painter region. Here granites of at least two different ages are exposed. The older has been affected by intense earth movements and is, as a result, intensely fractured. Despite

Fig 92 Exploitation by weathering agencies of secondary or latent joints within a tor at Palmer.

the present low average rainfall (about 9 inches a year), the landscape is greatly dissected; the closely shattered older granite is weathered through and offers uniform resistance (or lack of resistance) to erosion and, despite the present low average rainfall, an intense network of streams has evolved closely dissecting the landscape and producing a region of all slopes, with steep slopes everywhere, deep V-shaped valleys meeting in knife-edged ridges, and with no significant areas of flat land either in the valley floors or on the top of the hills (Pl. 24). Like the dissected plateau of the Palmer region, this north Flinders landscape could have developed on any uniformly, moderately resistant bedrock and could not be described as typical of granitic outcrops. Such is not the case with the second and younger granite of the Mt Painter area, which post-dates the main period of tectonism in the area, and subsequently is only moderately jointed. In consequence, as might be expected from a comparison with the Palmer area, tors are well developed and exposed in valley walls, and are scattered abundantly over the surface of this upland.

(iv) Widely spaced jointing in granites: giant tors or inselbergs
In arid lands many residuals rise abruptly from the plains. They are called *inselbergs (Germ.*—island mountain), and take the form of isolated ranges, ridges or hills. Unquestionably the most spectacular inselbergs are the dome-shaped monoliths known as *bornhardts*, of which examples are known from every continent save Antarctica but which are best developed, and most clearly and abundantly displayed in the tropical lands.

Inselbergs have been sculptured from a variety of rock types. In central Australia, for instance, in the areas adjoining the border between the Northern Territory and South Australia, many ridges, ranges and massive monolithic rocks protrude above the vast sand and gibber plains. Some, such as the Indulkana Ranges, are built of tilted or subhorizontal sedimentary rocks; others, like the western Everards are underlain by granitoid complexes, or, as in the Musgraves, by complexes of igneous and metamorphic crystalline rocks. There are three justly famous isolated inselbergs in the southern part of the Northern Territory, each standing more than 1,000 feet above the central plain level. Mt Conner is a flat-topped hill formed of gently dipping quartzites; to the west is Ayers Rock (Pl. 25) which is a massive, monolithic flattish-topped dome of arkosic sandstone, a sedimentary rock, and still further westward is perhaps the most fantastic and strange of them all, the Olgas, a group of weirdly shaped domes composed of massive conglomerate (see Pls. 26, 27).

Although inselberg ridges and ranges are underlain by a wide variety of resistant rock types, domed inselbergs are especially common in granitic terrain. Examples have been described from such diverse areas as Newfoundland and Lappland; the American west and southwest, Georgia and New England; the deserts of northern Chile and the humid coastlands of Brazil; Korea, Siam and Corsica; and many climatically contrasted regions of the African continent. Inselbergs were first named from arid Africa and the 'sugarloafs' of the Rio area of coastal southern Brazil are renowned. In the U.S.A. the Yosemite region is famous for

Plate 24 Granite landscape, northern Flinders Ranges. The granite here is closely fractured and despite the sparse rainfall offers uniformly low resistance to weathering and stream dissection. Hence the 'all-slopes' landscape with deep gorges and no flat areas either high or low in the relief.

its gigantic domes; Stone Mountain, Georgia, and Looking Glass Rock, North Carolina, are other well-known domed inselbergs. In part the reason for the widespread occurrence of the form on granite is that it is a common and extensively outcropping constituent of the continental areas, but the structure of granite also renders it especially prone to inselberg development. The morphology and development of granite inselbergs illustrates many general points which are true of non-granitic forms also.

Although they are dome-shaped and give the impression of roundness in plan, many granite bornhardts are in fact composed of a single, or of a number of, massive rectangular or rhomboidal blocks bounded by major joints. In South Australia it can be shown that major joints, which determine the outlines of the domes in plan, but which are not the only joints in the rock mass, run parallel to the lineaments (Chapter 3). Joints paralleling lineament trends also play a significant part in determining the detailed sculpture of the domes. Viewed from the side, the morphology of many domes is determined by the development of several more-or-less concentric and massive rock *sheets* or shells, which vary in thickness between one and several scores of feet.

Plate 25 Ayers Rock, Northern Territory—a monolithic inselberg of arkosic sandstone. (*South Australian Tourist Bureau*)

108   *Geomorphology*

Plate 26   The dramatic domes of the Olgas. Built of coarse conglomerate, these domes display the effects of differential etching of joints and bedding planes, as well as sheet structures. (*Photograph: Clyde Wahrhaftig*)

Plate 27   Vertical aerial photograph of the Olgas, showing the well developed rectangular joint pattern. (*Dept National Development*)

Structural Landforms

Inselbergs are the tropical equivalents of the *monadnocks* of humid temperate lands (see Chapter 12). Indeed some residuals termed inselbergs are morphologically identical with monadnocks and it is confusing, to say the least, to differentiate forms solely on the basis of present climatic conditions. However typical inselbergs rise more abruptly from the plains than do typical monadnocks.

There are two principal schools of thought concerning the origin of inselbergs. Some consider that they develop simply through 'scarp retreat and pedimentation': steep slopes recede, leaving behind smooth planate pediplains and enclosing steep-sided residuals or inselbergs. Evidence from several areas, including Eyre Peninsula suggests, on the other hand, that differential subsurface weathering, strongly controlled by structural factors, such as jointing, occurs before the inselbergs are brought out in the relief by erosion.

(v) Inselbergs in South Australia

In the Everard Ranges of the northwest of the State, in northwestern Eyre Peninsula and near Mannum, the granite bedrock consists effectively of massive blocks. In fact, the rock in these areas is demonstrably greatly jointed but the fractures are tight and, as far as exploitation by weathering is concerned, most of them may as well not be there.

The Everard Ranges (Figs. 89, 93) are located in the northwest of South Australia and consist of two main ranges and a large number of

Plate 28   Mt Lindsay, an isolated dome in the northwest of South Australia. (*Geol. Surv. S.A.*)

minor ranges and isolated hills. The uplands stand abruptly above the level of the particularly flat plains. The amplitude of relief is about 1,000 feet, the plain level is 2,000 feet or a little less and the highest peak—Mt Illbillie—rises to little more than 3,000 feet. The plains are not underlain directly by bedrock but by several score feet of alluvium and wind-blown material (Fig. 93).

Although the overall topographic grain runs from east to west, within each of the uplands the grain is diagonal to this. Each of the ridges is subdivided into massive blocks (some up to a mile in diameter) by a system of joints, the dominant components of which run northwest to southeast and northeast to southwest. Each of these joint blocks forms a great dome (Fig. 94) subdivided into massive slabs or sheets of rock several feet thick. The sheets at the surface have broken down into a large number of more or less cubic blocks (Figs. 93, 94), some of which are rounded and are morphologically indistinguishable from the tors formed by the two-stage process described above. Thus tors identical in form can develop in more than one way. Some of the tors are weathered on the undersides, forming hollows or caverns, and in some this differential, weathering has proceeded to such an extent that only a thin crust remains the former top and sides of the block. On the upper flattish surfaces of the domes, there are flat-floored gnammas or weather pits; and scaling or flaking of the heavily indurated superficial zone of the rock is prominent over the entire surface.

A similar assemblage of gross forms is found in the Gawler Ranges. These are built of a Precambrian porphyry, a volcanic rock, in which major joints or faults run from east to west but within the east-west ranges the low, rounded hills are formed by massive blocks delineated by northeast to southwest and northwest to southeast trending joints.

Away from the main ranges of the northwest, there are isolated hills corresponding to isolated joint blocks. Similar forms are found fringing the Mann Ranges (Pl. 28), which are to the west of the Everards and upon which are found similar sheet structures, tors, weather pits, and superficial flaking. Ayers Rock and the Olgas group, though not granitic, are similar forms from the adjacent region of the Northern Territory.

Central and northwestern Eyre Peninsula is a broadly rolling plain underlain by a discontinuous sheet of calcrete (or massive superficial limestone) and traversed by sand dunes. These largely cover the underlying bedrock, but in several well defined zones running parallel to the local lineament trend (Figs. 51, 95), granite is exposed (Pl. 29) in low, rounded whalebacks and platforms, or steep-sided isolated hills called inselbergs. Whether low or high, the granite rises have basically the same rounded or domed form: some are well exposed, others but little, and yet others may have been worn down. All consist of masses of very large blocks of rock, 15 feet and more in diameter. Moreover, the joints are tight, so that weathering agents, particularly water, can less readily pene-

Structural Landforms 111

Fig 93 Diagrammatic section of an intermontane valley in the Everard Ranges.

Fig 94 Field sketch of massive domes in the Everard Ranges.

Fig 95 Distribution of granite inselbergs on northwest Eyre Peninsula.

trate the massive rock, which for the main part remains unaltered. The granite of the adjacent plains, however, is more closely jointed, has been more weathered and, in consequence, has been worn down far more than the massive rock which remains upstanding (Fig. 96). This is the fundamental reason for the survival of the inselbergs—the widely spaced, tight joints, giving very large zones or *compartments* which are resistant to weathering.

The hills themselves consist of a single massive block, or an aggregate of such rectangular or rhomboidal blocks (*Fig 97*) delineated by joints, which run parallel to the regional lineaments trends. The highest of the residuals is Wudinna Hill, which is also the largest in area. It stands about 300 feet above the level of the surrounding plain. Most of the inselbergs, however, rise only 50–110 feet above the plains.

How have these features developed? The available evidence suggests that the residuals are local areas of especially massive and resistant granite. At present the plain areas marginal to the hills are intensely weathered, and it may be that such subsurface differential weathering

Fig 96 Hill-plain junction as observed at Ucontitchie Hill, south of Wudinna, Eyre Peninsula: (a) section; (b) field sketch.

Structural Landforms

Plate 29 The dome of Pildappa Hill, seen from the west.

Plate 30 Ucontitchie Hill, south of Wudinna, northwestern Eyre Peninsula, displaying one of the massive sheets of rock which subdivide this bornhardt.

Fig 97 Examples of inselbergs whose form in plan is determined by major fractures trending parallel to the regional lineament directions: (a) Chilpuddie Hill; (b) Ucontitchie Hill; (c) Yarwondutta Rocks; (d) Podinna Rocks; (e) Little Wudinna Hill; (f) Pildappa Hill; (g) Wudinna Hill; (h) and (i) Polda Rocks; (j) Minnipa Hill; (k) an island in the Investigator Group, Australian Bight; (l) Ayers Rock, N.T. All but (k) and (l) are on N.W. Eyre Peninsula.

has occurred beneath ancient, now uplifted and dissected erosional surfaces of low relief, evidenced in eastern, southern and central Eyre Peninsula, and in the Gawler Ranges to the north (see Chapter 12). In this view, these hills are simply massive tors, developing in essentially the two-stage manner. The elevation of the residuals above the plain is compatible with the possible depth of weathering beneath plains of extended life-span; and the development could take place in several, rather than in two, stages (Fig. 98a, b).

Field evidence in South Australia, as well as in other parts of Australia, eastern and western Africa and Brazil, to name but a few regions, supports this two-stage theory of inselberg development, involving deep differential weathering of large masses or compartments of rock and their subsequent differential erosion. Elsewhere, however, and particularly in southern Africa, evidence of deep weathering beneath the plains which separate the residual hills is apparently not forthcoming. Here it is possible that the inselbergs have developed through stream incision (guided by major fractures in the granite bedrock), followed by scarp retreat to an advanced stage (cf. Fig. 4a).

Seen from the ground many of the hills appear dome-shaped. Their gross morphology is determined by massive sheets (Pl. 30) or lenses.

Fig 98 Two-stage origin of inselbergs: (a) and (b) without sheet structures; (c) and (d) with sheet structures concentrated in monolithic rock masses.

The thick sheets of rock which are characteristic of the domes are well known in massive granites, but occur in other rock types also, (for instance, in the Gawler Range porphyry, sedimentary rocks as well as metamorphic) and are commonly attributed to *offloading*. Granites and many metamorphic rocks originate deep in the earth's crust under conditions of great pressure. Sediments may be deeply buried and again subjected to very high pressures. If, as a result of erosion, the overlying rocks are removed, the weight of rocks pressing down on the (say) granite is gradually reduced. Under the conditions of lower pressure, the granite tends to expand, principally in an upward direction. On this interpretation the sheeting is a result of this pressure release.

On Eyre Peninsula, however, there is some suggestion that the sheeting is of another origin. The distribution of the domes in restricted zones which are geometrically related to the regional tectonic framework, the delineation of the features by major joints running parallel to lineaments, the reason for the localised variation in state of jointing, all remain unexplained by the offloading hypothesis. In addition, the incidence of possible imbrication within some of the sheets (Fig. 99), the restriction of some sheets within major joint blocks, the occurrence of synclinal sheeting in some granite hills on Dartmoor in southwestern England, and in the Yosemite area of California, and the presence of features suggestive of compression require explanation. It has been suggested that the domes are the foci of compressive stresses and that this is the reason for the tightness of the joints in these areas: this is why the inselberg masses are resistant and have survived. These same lateral forces could have caused the rocks to acquire a tendency to arching which is expressed when the overlying and adjacent rocks are eroded. Thus the features may be interpreted as due to tectonics and erosion together, i.e. as structural forms (Fig. 98c, d).

On the surface of the inselbergs, whalebacks and rock platforms, there are many distinctive weathering and erosional features. One of the most common is the *gnamma* or *weather pit*, a circular or elliptical hollow etched from solid granite. Some, which are not common, are deep and semi-circular in cross section, and are called *pits* (Pl. 31). On Pildappa Hill, north of Minnipa, there are pits 3–3½ feet deep, but one at least 9 feet deep (and 3 × 6 feet in cross section) is known from the country between Minnipa and Mount Sturt, in the Gawler Ranges. Most common is the *pan* which is relatively hollow and flat-floored (Pl. 32). They are up to 3 feet deep, up to 12 feet across, their shape is in some measure determined by jointing (Fig. 100), and they usually have overhanging sides around part of their circumference. On steep slopes the depressions are asymmetrical, with the higher wall on the upslope side, and are called *armchair shaped hollows*. The different forms of gnammas develop because of different rocks and slopes. Both pits and pans are found only on flat rock surfaces (Fig. 101). The pits are found only on fresh rock;

Fig 99 Possible imbrication in massive sheet of granite, Ucontitchie Hill.

they are deep relative to their area because water, which accomplishes the disintegration and decay of the granite, obviously persists longer in the lower parts of the hollows. The *pans*, however, occur in granite, the upper few inches of which are fractured, presumably by water weathering and insolational heating, parallel to the surface. This fracturing enables water to penetrate most rapidly laterally and thus grow in this direction rather than downwards (Fig. 102). Thus structure is an important morphological control even in detail.

The armchair shaped hollows, on the other hand, occur on slopes and their asymmetry is merely a reflection of this.

The sides of many of the inselbergs are very deep and in some areas, overhanging, There is evidence that this is due to marked weathering of the granite around the base of the hills and subsequent erosion. The borders of many hills are also scored by gutters (or *Rillen*) up to 2 feet deep (Pl. 33), which are caused by a combination of weathering and erosion.

The lower surfaces of many tors and the edges of the massive sheets have been hollowed out by weathering (Pl. 34). The caves or *tafoni* which result are quite large in some places. Near the top of Ucontitchie Hill, for example, southwest of Wudinna, there is a huge tor which has been hollowed out and there is a cave some 12 feet high inside the block. In some instances there and on Granite Island, near Victor Harbour,

Fig 100 Morphological map of Pildappa Hill showing distribution of pit and pans, and joint control of form of latter (*after Twidale and Corbin*).

Structural Landforms

Fig 101 Distribution of various types of gnammas or weather pit on Pildappa Hill, north of Minnipa (*after Twidale and Corbin*).

Fig 102 Suggested evolution of pits and pans (*after Twidale and Corbin*).

Plate 31 Pit on Pildappa Hill. This hollow is about 3½ feet deep, oval in plan, and roughly hemispherical in shape. It is developed wholly in massive, unweathered granite.

Plate 32 Pan, or flat floored depression, on a granite dome in the Kulgera Hills, Northern Territory.

Fig 103 Field sketch of quarry face in granite, near Mannum.

Fig 104 Bald Rock, northern Vic., showing the massive granite domes (*from photograph in Hills, 'Physiography of Victoria'*).

only a mere shell of rock remains. Such rocks have been called *tortoiseshell rocks* in Western Australia.

The inselbergs, which are being reduced by very marked scaling, especially on northern aspects, were formerly very important on account of the opportunity they offered for water conservation schemes, and many of the bare hills have been enclosed by low stone walls which prevent water from running into the sands of the surrounding plains, but divert it into tanks or excavated reservoirs. Before the Tod River was piped to the northwestern area, such water supplies (e.g. in Wudinna, Ucontitchie and Pildappa Hills and Yarwondutta Rocks) were very important, and the granite hills formed local early foci of settlement.

Closer to Adelaide a granite dome of particular interest is exposed near Mannum (Fig. 56). Two miles upstream from this river town, on the left, or east bank of the Murray, there is a granite quarry whose face is traversed by many joints (Fig. 103). All however are tight, and have not been affected by weathering to any significant extent. The general domelike character of the occurrence is clearly seen in the quarry face as well as in the natural outcrop immediately to the north, where weather pits and gutters score the surface. But overlying the granite are beds of the widespread marine Miocene limestone; the granite dome existed as such before the transgression of the Miocene sea, it was made first an island, and was later inundated and buried, and has only been re-exposed in relatively recent times by excavation by the river Murray of its present

Plate 33 *Rillen* or gutters which score the sides of Yarwondutta Rocks, near Minnipa, northwestern Eyre Peninsula.

Plate 34 *Tafoni* or caverns developed on the underside of a massive rock sheet at Ucontitchie Hill, northwestern Eyre Peninsula.

relatively deep and narrow trench. Such forms which have suffered burial and re-exposure are called *exhumed* landforms (see Chapter 11). Although there is no sign of weathering along the numerous joints displayed in this outcrop, tors have developed from it, and possibly still are evolving. Thus, as was the case with those boulders resulting from the breakdown of massive rock sheets, it may be suggested that some tors form without preparation by subsurface weathering.

Another group of granite forms of particular interest is at Caloote (Fig. 56). At first sight the outcrop seems commonplace, consisting of a large number of grouped tors. But on the flat top of one is preserved a weather pit of pan type and, on another, a number of quite deep gutters, or *Rillen*. Now both pans and gutters are typical of the rather extensive, flattish upper surfaces of domed inselbergs. They do not develop on the very limited and characteristically rounded surfaces of tors; and the occurrence of these at Caloote suggests that the outcrop once took the form of a dome which has suffered disintegration. It has been noted that the massive sheets of rock which are such a feature of the domes in the Everards and Eyre Peninsula break down to tor forms, and there is no reason why, quite fortuitously, some of the surviving tor blocks should not include one with remnants of gutters and one with a pan.

(vi) Other examples of domed inselbergs and associated forms

As has been described, domed inselbergs are well displayed in certain parts of South Australia, where, moreover, the existence of marginal excavations has brought to light evidence which clearly points to their two-stage origin. Comparable forms are developed in other parts of Australia, though not always on granitic bedrock; the essential feature seems to be that the rock is massively jointed and resistant to weathering and erosion.

Thus, Bald Rock (M.R. Bendigo, Vic., 1:253,440, 224552) in northern Victoria, is composed of massive joint blocks some of which present bold, rounded faces (Fig. 104). Vertical joints are strongly displayed on Mt Buffalo, giving this prominence the aspect of a half dome. It is, from this, only a short step to fully developed domed inselbergs which apparently occur some 3 miles west of Moonbi, near Armidale, N.S.W., and which certainly are present in the southwest of Western Australia, for instance, near Hyden, 180 miles east of Perth. Ayers Rock and the Olgas group (Pls. 25, 26, 27) in the southern part of the Northern Territory, are splendid and spectacular examples of domed inselbergs, but are developed on arkosic sandstone and massive conglomerate, respectively. But the Kulgera Hills, east of these two, are granitic domes, as are those of the Harts Range, in central Australia.

The minor features described from the Eyre Peninsula domes occur also on these other examples. Sheeting is for instance well developed on both the Olgas and Ayers Rock (the so-called Kangaroo Tail—Pl. 35).

Steepened basal slopes have been noted on the southern side of Ayers Rock in many parts of the Olgas, on the Kulgera Hills, and in Western Australia ('The Great Wave', near Hyden). Weather pits, which were long ago described by the pioneer Western Australian geologists, are well formed on the Kulgera Hills and have been observed in the Kosciusko region. Tafoni have a similar distribution though apparently are missing from the colder regions, but split rocks and tors derived from the disintegration of sheets are widespread.

Just as domed inselbergs are not exclusively formed on granitic rocks, so it may be mentioned that weather pits have been observed on sandstones at Mt Conner (southern Northern Territory) and also in the southern Flinders Ranges. They occur also on Ayers Rock. Caverns or tafoni, of course, are very well developed on sandstones.

(c) ROCK TYPE AND JOINTING: KARST TOPOGRAPHY

(i) General

'Karst' is a general term applied to limestone areas which possess an assemblage of landforms resulting from the subsurface diversion of drainage and underground solution of the country rock. The term derives from the limestone plateau in Jugoslavia adjacent to the Adriatic sea. In Australia extensive limestone outcrops are restricted to the Nullarbor plain and lower Murray valley, but there are many minor occurrences. The limestone morphology of the Fitzroy Basin, Western Australia, is spectacular; others, equally interesting but less dramatic, occur in the Cooleman plain, Jenolan and Wee Jasper areas of N.S.W., the Buchan Caves area of Victoria, the Mole Creek area of northern Tasmania, the dolomitic limestone of the Barkly basin, fairly extensive coastal areas underlain by dune sands indurated with lime (aeolianite) in Victoria, South Australia and Western Australia, and innumerable other minor areas throughout the continent.

In South Australia, limestone outcrops are common. It is a common and important outcrop in the Flinders Ranges (where cave systems have developed) and the Mt Lofty Ranges, but the two most extensive areas are in the Murray plains and the adjacent Southeast, and in the Nullarbor plain. Underlain by sediments in which limestones and impure limestones are prominent, both the Murray plains and the Southeast display a marked lack of surface drainage. At the northwest and western margins of the region, there are intermittently flowing streams. Apart from these, a few very small streams near the coast and the Glenelg, which is predominantly a Victorian stream and only winds into South Australia, the Murray is the only surface stream. It is an example of an *allogenic* or *exotic stream*, which rises and derives its water beyond the arid region, where the water budget is one of net loss. The rest of the drainage is *cryptoreic*, or subsurface. The limestones are, for

Plate 35 The Kangaroo Tail, Ayers Rock, a sheet structure in arkosic sandstone. (*Photograph: Clyde Wahrhaftig*) the most part, too impure and physically weak for karst forms to be well represented, but they are weakly developed. A few sink holes, mostly filled with soil and sand and other debris, and better seen on air photographs than on the ground, are present as are a very few enclosed depressions due to solution and collapse. Over most of the region, the karst nature of the terrain is not obvious. In the lower Southeast however, and especially in the Naracoorte and Tantanoola districts where a purer and more cohesive limestone occurs, there are small, if shallow, caves in which there are stalactites, stalagmites, drip curtains and other minor limestone forms.

The development of karst forms is dependent upon four conditions being fulfilled. Karst can develop where one or more of these conditions do not occur, but the best karst forms are found where all apply. The optimum conditions for karst development are:

(1) There must be present near the surface a soluble rock, such as limestone. Dolomite and chalk fulfil this condition, but not others. Limestone is not soluble in water but reacts strongly with weak acids to form the bicarbonate, which is soluble in water:

$$CaCO_3 + H_2O + CO_2 \rightarrow Ca(HCO_3)_2$$
lime or   carbonic acid   calcium bicarbonate
calcite

(2) The soluble rock must be highly jointed, dense, and preferably thinly bedded. The rock should be strong and compact. There should be joints which allow water to pass, but the rock itself should be impenetrable to water.

(3) Groundwater should be able to descend through the rock, accomplish its solutional work and then emerge: in other words, there should be conditions which permit ground-waters approaching carbonate saturation point to be evacuated from the limestone area. Normally this is accomplished by means of deeply intrenched surface streams.

(4) There should be a moderate or heavy rainfall, otherwise karst development is retarded. A reasonable rainfall also ensures that there is a vegetation cover sufficient to supply on decomposition the humic acids so necessary for the solution of limestone.

Where all these conditions are not met, karst development is not marked, though some typical forms may be present.

Probably the most significant feature of karst regions is notable by virtue of its absence: the lack of surface drainage. Dry valleys are common (see Fig. 105) and the few rivers that flow, do so in gorges cut to the deep water table. Rainwater seeps downwards along joints and bedding plains which are enlarged by solution in the process. The vertical shafts formed in this way vary in size from a few feet diameter to a hundred feet and more, and in depth from ten to thirty feet. In a well developed karst there are thousands of such sinkholes; some are apparently due wholly to solution and are called *dolines*, while others owe their origin to a combination of solution and collapse—*collapse dolines*. Examples are fairly common, but a collapse doline from Wee Jasper (N.S.W.) has been described in the literature (*Australian Geographer*, Sept. 1963). Run-off usually enters sinkholes by slow percolation, but some streams enter sinkholes through openings called *swallow holes*.

At the surface, exposed limestone becomes pitted, grooved (Pl. 36), etched and fluted to give a very rough and intricately detailed relief called *lapies* (Karren), an important component of which is the *limestone pavement*, with *clints* or blocks separated by open crevices or *grikes*. Solution

Fig 105 Dry valleys and gorges in the limestone Cooleman Plain area, N.S.W. (*adapted from Jennings*).

pans are small shallow flat-floored depressions due to solution of the rock. Very commonly the solution of limestone at and near the surface causes an insoluble residue of clays to be left behind as a soil mantle. This is usually red coloured and is called *terra rossa*.

At certain levels, bedding planes are enlarged to become *caves*, such as those at Mole Creek, Jenolan and Wee Jasper. The origin of these is complex, open to debate, and is discussed below. The roofs of caves occasionally collapse causing deep depressions to occur at the surface. They are called *karst windows*, large examples of which are called *uvalas*. Where solution, collapse and faulting have combined to form a very large depression of regional extent, it is called a *polje*. Isolated limestone hills standing above the level of the floor of the polje, or indeed, of any karst plain, are called *hums* (cf. = inselberg, monadnock, pyramidal peak). *Stalactites*, *stalagmites*, and associated forms such as *drip curtains*, are some of the best known limestone features, and are well known from Jenolan.[3] They form in caves and are due to the evaporation of water and the precipitation of limestone in columns and sheets. Some of these forms are shown diagrammatically in Fig. 106.

(ii) The Nullarbor plain

The Nullarbor plain occupies some 77,000 square miles of Western and South Australia (Fig. 107). The plain is approximately co-extensive with the Eucla basin, a large shallow depression in the surface of the Precambrian rocks of the great West Australian Shield which, during the Permian, later Mesozoic and much of the Tertiary, was invaded by the sea in which sediments were deposited. The deepest known section of the basin is at Madura, where crystalline Precambrian rocks were encountered at just below 2,000 feet in a bore. The floor of the basin rises from this area in all directions, save southward, for the basin structure continues beneath the Bight.

The typical sequence of rocks encountered in bores put down in the basin is:

Surface soil	about 2 feet thick at most.
Nullarbor Limestone	50–200 feet of grey or brown crystalline limestone deposited in a shallow sea during lower Miocene times.
Unnamed limestone	thin, impure, chalky limestone.
Wilson Bluff Limestone	almost 200 feet thick. A white, friable, chalky and pure limestone of upper Eocene age.
Cretaceous beds	conglomerates, shales, clays deposited in massive swamp.
Permian beds	shale and clay.

Fig 106 Some common karst forms.

Fig 107 The Nullarbor plain (*after Jennings*).

Thus, the sediments record a gradual deepening of the basin. Even at its deepest, however, the basin was only shallow and received very little debris from the surrounding land which, in the early and middle Tertiary, must have had either very little relief or few streams, or both.

The Nullarbor Limestone crops out over the whole surface of the plain. It varies in thickness between 50 and 200 feet, is virtually horizontal and is well jointed and bedded. There may be a gentle southerly dip but, if so, it is very slight. The only area where the strata may be disrupted by faulting is to the west of Ooldea, where there are three west-facing scarps, each 30–50 feet high and trending parallel to each other. The major joints in the Nullarbor Limestone are aligned northwest to southeast and northeast to southwest.

The present climate of the plain is hot and arid to semi-arid. On average, there are ten days with temperatures of 100° each year in the south of the

Plate 36 Fluted surface (*Rillenkarren*) developed by solution of the surface of Palaeozoic limestones, N. Queensland. (*C.S.I.R.O.*)

Plate 37 Limestone cliffs at the southern margin of the Nullarbor plain. (*Photograph: J. N. Jennings*) region, and thirty in the north. Winter means range between 50–55°F, though frosts are experienced, and summer means between 70–75°F. Annual average rainfall varies from about 10 inches a year in the west to rather less than 5 inches in the far north. Cook may be taken as typical of the region; the mean annual rainfall of 6·01 inches is received on 42 raindays. But the high temperatures decrease the effectiveness of the little rain that is received: Cook, for instance, has a potential evaporation of 180 inches per year. Yet the plains can be flooded and rail traffic temporarily dislocated or halted.

As the name of the region implies, vegetation is not abundant. Only a scattering of shrubs and bushes covers the plain.

Because of the aridity and the well structured nature of the surface rocks there are no surface streams on the Nullarbor at present; any surface waters are rapidly swallowed by the rock, for they disappear down joints. The plain is flat and featureless. It rises to the north, but save at and near the coast, gradients are so slight as to be imperceptible. The highest point of the plains, more than 1,000 feet above sea level, is about 75 miles northeast of Loongana, but the average elevation of the plains is about 500–600 feet. To the south, the plains terminate in spectacular cliffs (Pl. 37) which are about 140 feet high at the Head of Bight, rising to 250 feet at Wilson Bluff and 300 feet to the west of Twilight Cove. Between Wilson Bluff and Twilight Cove there is a narrow coastal plain with a maximum width of 25 miles, and called the Roe plain. Behind it, the old coastal cliffs continue as the 200–250 feet high Hampton Range. On the plain there is slight local change in elevation, mainly very broad undulations; and in the vicinity of sinkholes, of course, there is considerable relief; but in general the plain is flat and featureless.

The fact that the Nullarbor Limestone is so thin and yet outcrops over the whole of the plain, strongly suggests that the surface we see today is essentially the upper surface of deposition in the basin structure. Had there been much erosion, some of the rocks underlying the Nullarbor Limestone would surely be exposed at the surface. The Nullarbor Limestone has no doubt been slightly eroded, but there has been very little change due to the aridity of the climate and nature of the surface strata. The surface is a sedimentary plain (or *sediplain*) which has survived almost unchanged since the Miocene.

Over most of the Nullarbor plain the Nullarbor limestone, though close to the surface, is covered by 2 to 3 feet of soil. In depressions, the thickness of cover increases up to 10 feet. Mostly, therefore, the Nullarbor plain is *covered karst*. In the relatively small areas of outcrop, solutional features are not well developed. On flattish rock surfaces small solution pans occur, 1 to 2 feet across, up to 2 inches deep and round or oval in shape. There are, however, many tiny solution pits, small depressions up to 2 inches across, though usually about $\frac{1}{2}$ inch diameter, and separated by knife-edged walls up to $1\frac{1}{2}$ inches high and culminating in tiny points: similar pitted limestone surfaces occur in coastal areas and walking over them in bare feet is very painful.

Beneath the surface of the plain, sinkholes and collapse dolines lead down to caves. Despite claims to the contrary, and with the necessary proviso that few parts of the plain are as yet explored in detail, it appears that cave development in the area is relatively meagre. The caves are naturally divided into two categories—the shallow and the deep, though there are a few at intermediate levels. The shallow caves attain depths of up to 70 feet below the surface and are thus restricted to the Nullarbor and the unnamed limestone. They are of limited lateral extent, one or two hundred feet being typical, though one or two are known to be up to 700 feet long and include quite large chambers. The shallow caves include vertical shafts, narrow fissures, small openings leaving the sides of dolines, small karst windows, and large lateral passages leaving collapse dolines.

The caves reveal that the upper 10 to 20 feet of the Nullarbor Limestone is massive. Below this zone of solid limestone the rock is intensely perforated: the walls of caves are riddled with tubes 2 to 4 inches diameter which appear to penetrate the whole rock.

At the present time the cave walls appear to be collapsing; large blocks litter the floors of the caves, and there are reliable accounts, a comparison of which indicates that roof collapse has occurred during the past century.

Several deep caves have been discovered, all close to the coast. All are entered by way of narrow apertures through the overlying Nullarbor beds, spacious cave development being restricted to the deep lying Wilson Bluff Limestone. They are simple and massive: their lengths vary between 800 and 3,000 feet, and they consist of large passages or halls 40–60 feet high and 80 to 120 feet wide, though in places there are great vaults in which the caves are both higher and wider—80 to 160 feet high and 150–200 feet wide. The deep caves penetrate below the level of groundwater saturation and in several there are deep lakes. The limestone of the cave walls is generally smooth and massive, perforation being present, and then only to a minor extent, close to the top of the Wilson Bluff Limestone. As in the shallow caves, there are many indications of roof and wall collapse.

Theories of cave formation fall into two major categories:
(1) Those which place great emphasis upon the erosion and solution accomplished by diverted surface waters (*vadose* waters).
(2) Those which consider the solutional effects of groundwater below the level of the water table (*phreatic* waters) to be all important.

There are of course many variations of these. Some authors attribute major effects to laterally flowing water at the level of the water table, i.e., vadose waters flowing laterally.

Although there are difficulties inherent in the theory it seems most likely that the Nullarbor caves were initiated by groundwater solution. When water can escape from the karst (at the coast), the solution cavities are enlarged, and moreover, the upper part of the limestone is drained of water due to the lowering of the water table. Vadose waters assume a considerable significance, not only in the fashioning of the shallow caves, but also by materially assisting in the enlargement of cavities to form the large deep caves in the zone where surface and groundwaters meet and where, moreover, there are fluctuations in the level of the water table.

According to this hypothesis, the shallow caves must have formed in relation to one high stand of the water table (higher sea level) and the extensive horizontal chambers of some of the deep caves in relation to another higher stand of the sea; for even they are higher than the present level of the table. There are uncertainties concerning, in particular, the relation of various cave systems to possible higher stands of the water table related to former periods of higher rainfall. However the type of explanation outlined here involving both vadose and phreatic waters satisfies most of the field evidence.

The low rainfall and lack of vegetation suggests that today the caves are inactive. True, the caves are increasing in size, but only by collapse and disintegration. It has been suggested that the caves formed during slightly wetter phases of the Pleistocene, for which there is some evidence adjacent to the limestone outcrops in the shape of old stream courses now defunct, partly obliterated and represented by long strings of salinas. In the Lake Eyre Basin (see Chapter 7) there is evidence of higher rainfall in the Pleistocene or Recent and both here and at Balladonia Soak have been found the fossil remains of giant marsupials, fauna which could not have existed under the present arid conditions. Further, there is a general case to be made for wetter phases (or pluvials) in the Pleistocene, on the basis of evidence from other areas.

Thus the Nullarbor plain is essentially an original sedimentary surface. It is featureless because of its simple geological structure, the 'resistant' nature of the surface strata, and the low rainfall. The plain is a covered karst. Both on and below the surface, karst development is retarded and poorly developed. This is not due to lack of time, but to the arid climate and poor vegetation. What development there has been is attributed to phases in the Pleistocene, when rainfall was slightly higher. Today, the caves, which are comparatively few in number, are disintegrating and inactive.

NOTES

[1] Duricrusts are durable layers which form as crusts, pans or horizons in or on soils. They vary in composition, some consisting of concentrations of iron (laterite or ferricrete—a tough rock rich in iron) others of silica (*silcrete*, widely known in Australia as 'billy'), and yet others of lime (*calcrete*, caliche, kunkar, or kankar). All form resistant cappings in some areas of Australia. West of Lake Eyre, gypsum, a physically soft mineral, forms a relatively resistant capping to the underlying unconsolidated silts, and in many parts of the arid north, mantles of coarse debris have been cemented by dried clays to form tough protective carapaces.

[2] Diorites are of the same general origin and nature as granites but are mineralogically different, containing more dark minerals rich in Fe. and Mg.

[3] Note that forms morphologically similar to stalactites and drip curtains can form in other ways, as a result of strong differential weathering and in volcanic caves.

PART C: GEOMORPHOLOGICAL PROCESSES

5. Weathering

(a) GENERAL REMARKS

STRUCTURAL LANDSCAPES ARE THOSE in which inherent contrasts in the underlying bedrock are brought into relief by processes of weathering and erosion. In this and subsequent chapters, these processes are discussed.

Both weathering and erosion are strongly influenced by climate. A given set of climatic conditions causes the development of certain complex of weathering and erosional processes. These mould the land surface in such a way that a distinctive suite or family of landforms is evolved. The merits and weaknesses of the concept of morphogenetic regions were discussed in the introductory chapter, but provided the limitations are appreciated, climate can be used as a convenient basis on which to classify landscapes.

In all areas, however, weathering is an important precursor to transportation and erosion, and in all areas mass movement of weathered rock and soil (see Chapter 6) is a significant factor contributing to the total transportation of material to lower levels.

Weathering, for convenience, may be defined as the disintegration or decomposition of rocks *in situ* at or near the ground surface. This definition is not as precise as one might wish, but it roughly indicates the type of process under discussion. Weathering is concerned with the reduction of a rock mass to a form and size susceptible to *erosion* (the wearing away or lowering of the land surface), which is accomplished by such agencies as mass movement, running water, glaciers, the wind and wind-driven waves. The evacuation of material in solution may however eventually cause such a reduction in volume of the rock mass that the surface is lowered for this reason alone, so that weathering here effectively simulates erosion (see below, Chapter 11). Conversely debris carried along a stream bed simultaneously causes that bed to be worn away and may itself suffer disintegration through impact. Thus the complex of processes known as weathering is more difficult to define than is apparent from a preliminary consideration.

In contrast with metamorphic processes, weathering occurs within the range of temperatures found at and near the earth's surface. A rock undergoing weathering is not static: on the contrary, in certain weathering processes some minerals and elements are lost, others gained, and yet others redeposited at other levels at the same site. There is considerable movement of material beneath the ground surface. But the main mass of the rock remains *in situ*, and is not transported.

Many weathering processes are known in outline and in theory, but in many instances what actually takes place in nature is obscure. It is in any case rather unreal to define and explain most weathering processes in isolation, for several processes commonly combine to cause rock weathering, of which two general types are recognised. *Physical* (or mechanical) weathering involves rock disintegration, without change in any of the constituent minerals. In *chemical* weathering, on the other hand, some or all of the rock-forming minerals suffer decay or alteration; some of these changes involve an increase in volume, thereby causing the rock to crumble or rupture; some entail loss of material and the formation of cavities, which promote further weathering; and some actually toughen the rock, as by the addition of silica or iron.

(b) FACTORS IN WEATHERING

Climate and mineral composition obviously have a great influence on the type and course of weathering. In the humid tropics, temperatures are consistently high, and moisture and humic acids are abundant everywhere. The rate of most chemical reactions increases with rise in temperature and increase in moisture. Silicate weathering, for instance, involving ionic exchange of cations from the crystal lattice and hydrogen ions from water, increases in humid tropical conditions, though it is very slow even there by any but geological standards. The subarctic lands are most prone to frost shattering, the hot deserts to the direct or indirect effects of temperature variation.

The effects of mineral composition are pronounced. Of the common rock-forming minerals, olivine is the least stable, followed in order by lime plagioclase, augite, lime soda plagioclase, hornblende and soda lime plagioclase, soda plagioclase, biotite, orthoclase, muscovite and quartz. Obviously, basic rocks such as basalt, containing much olivine, augite and the calcium rich plagioclase feldspars, weather more rapidly than, say, granite, which is rich in quartz and orthoclase. Structure and texture are also important influences, the first because the number of joints, for example, determines how many avenues are open to weathering agencies. The size of constituent fragments or crystals, and the perfection or otherwise of their interlocking has a bearing on the rate of weathering, particularly chemical alteration, for in fine grained rocks, the total surface area of the constituent crystals is greater. These surfaces possess high free energy and are on this account especially susceptible to chemical (though not necessarily to mechanical) attack. The rate of erosion, or evacuation of weathered debris is also significant for, if erosion is negligible, the weathered mantle may come to form a protective veneer on the land surface. Where, on the other hand, there is strong erosion, the products of weathering are rapidly evacuated and fresh rocks are brought within the range of weathering processes—there is said to be *renewal* of weathering.

(c) PHYSICAL WEATHERING

Processes responsible for physical weathering are thermal expansion, pressure release, crystal growth and the activities of living organisms.

Thermal expansion has long been cited as a cause of disintegration. Both granular disintegration and the formation of flakes, shells and massive sheets have been attributed to unequal expansion and contraction due to diurnal and annual changes in insolation. Rocks are poor conductors of heat and it is obvious that the surfaces exposed to the sun's rays are heated and should expand to a far greater extent than the rocks a few inches or feet below the surface. Due to its expansion, the outer mass becomes detached from the main body of the rock, forming a shell or thin sheet. This type of weathering was once referred to as *exfoliation*, but the term has now been applied to so many varieties of laminae, flakes, shells and sheets of different origins, that it is best avoided. But the types of weathering encompassed by the term are well represented in South Australia. Spheroidal and onion weathering of granitic rocks (Pls. 17, 22) have already been mentioned, as has sheeting (Pl. 20), but similar flaking has been found on quartzites in both the Flinders and the Mt Lofty Ranges.

Another argument, following roughly the same lines, is that as rock-forming minerals are of different colours, they therefore absorb heat at different rates, expand differentially in consequence, and therefore break up into the constituent mineral grains—*granular disintegration*.

Many travellers in the arid tropics, where diurnal temperatures are greatest, and where insolation should on this account be most effective, have reported hearing, in the evening or night, loud reports which they attribute to the cracking of rocks as they contract and rupture. In his account of the Burke and Wills expedition, Alan Moorehead reports that on 24 May 1861, Wills and King, wandering near Cooper's Creek, heard the 'noise of an explosion, as if of a gun'. The author dismisses this interpretation and suggests that what Wills and King heard 'was a piece of rock splitting off some distant cliff', implicitly as a result of temperature changes. Even this is unlikely, and what these two explorers heard was almost certainly the crash caused by dune sands and analagous with the 'singing sands', of some beaches. But this episode illustrates how readily temperature variations are first considered to explain otherwise inexplicable noises in the desert.

It is known that intense heat, such as is generated in bushfires, promotes flaking and splitting of rocks (Pl. 38). The nuclear explosions in Japan in 1945 caused rock disintegration. And for many years fires have been used as a quarrying tool in India and Egypt: the rock surface is cleared of soil and the intense local heat of fires built thereon causes the arching of a sheet, several inches thick which is easily broken into blocks with a hammer. But such heating is local and far beyond the range of normal diurnal temperature fluctuations, even in the deserts. Moreover, there is clear evidence that, even in conditions of extreme aridity and intense insolational heating, it is chemical, not physical weathering that is predominant. The Egyptian desert near Cairo experiences very low average rainfall and searing heat. Granite columns that have fallen on their sides are partly exposed to the full blast of the sun's rays, partly shaded and partly buried by the desert sands. Contrary to expectation, it is not the surfaces exposed to the sun that are weathered, but the shaded areas, and especially the areas that are or were buried in the sands. Even here there is some moisture in the surface sand, and it has effectively promoted decay and disintegration. Similarly, in northwestern Eyre Peninsula, in a 13-inch rainfall zone near Minnipa and Wudinna, many granite surfaces exposed to the powerful summer sun are quite smooth, but beneath even a thin veneer of soil and debris, the rock surface is intensely pitted due to the disintegration and chemical alteration of some of the rock-forming minerals (Pl. 39).

Experimental work has also indicated that heating and cooling do not directly produce detectable weathering. Such laboratory work is always open to the charge that the great periods of geological time cannot be simulated: if cycles of heating and cooling within the natural range were continued over a period of thousands of years, would they gradually cause fatigue and weakening of the bonds holding minerals together? The experimental evidence suggests not, but the question remains open because of the time problem.

However, it is equally clear that in many instances the insolation hypothesis has provided a too facile and ready explanation of weathering; it seems so logical and rings so true that in spite of difficulties and evidence to the contrary, it dies hard; because there are features difficult to explain in terms other than insolation, there are periodic and insistent revivals of the hypothesis. Recently, for instance, it has been persuasively argued that no other explanation is feasible for the boulders of the Olgas conglomerate (southern part of the Northern Territory), which are split off in the same plane as the hillslope in which they occur, and for certain

Weathering

Plate 38 Flaking induced by bushfire, Wilpena Pound. The intense localised and ephemeral heating of the outer skin of this (and many other) sandstone blocks on the slopes of Wilpena Pound caused expansion and rupture. Thin flakes of rock sprang away, and are now found scattered over the surface. The white scars are fresh, unweathered rock.

Plate 39 Pitting of the granite surface at Pildappa. On the left the granite is smooth; but on the right, near the gutter and where soil has been removed, the rock is rough and pitted by differential weathering of the minerals.

examples of blocky disintegration in the same region (Pl. 40).

It has been shown in the laboratory that temperature changes can cause minerals to fissure (crack microscopically) in the presence of moisture; and as there is occasional moisture in the soil surface, even in desert regions, this is significant. There is also some evidence that water can contribute to disintegration, without significant chemical alteration. In clays, which are most rapidly affected, there is dispersion, a phenomenon known to drillers as 'slacking': a solid core of clays will, after immersion in water, quickly disintegrate to a pile of clay particles. Presumably the ionic (electrostatic) bonding of juxtaposed minerals is weakened by water. Even in crystalline rocks such as granites the bonding of closely packed and interlocking minerals may be weakened by the accession of water. This may be an instance of slight physical activity, opening the way for chemical weathering. This process is probably significant, for the chemical changes involved in some spheroidally weathered rocks, for example, are very slight and appear unlikely to cause disintegration from volume change. The alternate wetting and drying of rocks is believed by some workers, particularly those engaged in coastal studies, to cause fatigue and eventual disintegration.

Many types of rock, but especially granites, are subdivided into a series of massive sheets or shells by arched fractures which transgress normal sedimentary, metamorphic and igneous structures. Such fractures are commonly attributed to offloading, or the *release of pressure* resulting from erosion of superincumbent strata. The hypothesis seems reasonable and is widely cited, but as discussed earlier (Chapter 4), it does not explain the field evidence and particularly the field relations of arched structures in some areas, and it has been suggested that they result from strong lateral pressures of tectonic origin. Whatever their origin, however, the arched fractures are yet another form of rock weathering.

As *crystals develop* or *grow*, they exert a pressure sufficient to shatter some rocks. The best known example is that of ice. In subarctic regions or at high elevations temperatures frequently oscillate about freezing point. Water in rock cracks and crevices suffers alternations of freezing and thawing, and in consequence oscillates between its solid and liquid forms. Changes in volume are involved, and the pressures exerted, though not as great as often assumed, because of incomplete confinement, are nevertheless sufficiently powerful to disrupt many rocks, and especially those that are *fissile* (finely bedded or well cleaved). Rapid disintegration of such rocks is achieved, and many shale and phyllite outcrops in the subarctic are covered by a chaotic mass of frost-shattered plates (Pl. 41).

The crystallisation of salt also causes disintegration of rocks under certain conditions, though there is doubt concerning its effectiveness on fresh crystalline rocks. Some authors have made great claims for the

Plate 40 Blocky disintegration of quartzite at Mt Conner, Northern Territory.

Plate 41 Frost shattered phyllites and shales near Knob Lake, Labrador. Note the chaotic mass of rock plates scattered on valley floor and lower slopes.

process in arid lands, but there is a dearth of basic knowledge concerning the pressures exerted by growing crystals. In weakly consolidated clays, in rocks that are already partly weathered, and in soft materials, salt crystallisation causes rocks to be shattered. In the suburbs of Melbourne situated close to the eastern shore of Port Phillip Bay, for instance, terracotta tiles are broken and weathered by salts blown in by onshore winds. Similarly, there is good evidence in Egypt and in some coastal regions, that salt crystallisation can at least contribute to the shattering of certain rocks, such as sandstones and shales. But there is no conclusive evidence that fresh, tough rocks can be disrupted by this means, though early workers, such as Jutson attributed much weathering and planation of hard granites at the margins of salt lakes to the process termed *exsudation* and involving the disintegration of rock through salt crystallisation.

As is the case with many other weathering processes it is difficult to differentiate between the possible influence of salt crystallisation and that of other mechanisms. In the early years of the century, for instance, it was claimed that igneous and other crystalline rocks in Manitoba had been 'chemically disintegrated', due to the action of salts in brine drawn over the rock surfaces by surface tension. Large boulders had been reduced to half their original size; but it was also acknowledged that hydration (see below) was important, so that the relative significance of each is hard to assess.

Tree roots and trunks can occasionally be shown to have forced apart adjacent joint blocks (Fig. 108), though it is necessary to realise that the roots merely grow in pre-existing cracks. Worms, rabbits and other burrowing creatures create avenues for other weathering agencies, and there is a suggestion that soil colloids may pluck off or loosen rock fragments, thus contributing to disintegration.

(d) CHEMICAL WEATHERING

The decomposition or chemical weathering of rocks is accomplished in a variety of ways. No rock forming mineral is absolutely inert chemically, but some minerals are far more readily altered than others. Even quartz (SiO_2), which is considered one of the most stable of minerals, is very slightly soluble in water.

A few minerals such as rock salt are significantly soluble in water. Others take up water (*hydration*); many more combine with hydroxyl (OH) radicles (undergo *hydrolysis*). Iron for instance readily unites with both water and oxygen to form various hydrated iron oxides, of which limonite and geothite are common examples and which are responsible for the yellowish or reddish brown colour of many weathered rocks. Both hydration and hydrolysis cause changes in the direction of volume increase and thus contribute to the general weakening of the rock.

Weathering

Many minerals, including calcite (of which limestone, a widely distributed sedimentary rock, is principally composed) are susceptible to solution in weakly acidulated waters (see Chapter 4 (c)). Weak carbonic acid is, for instance, produced by the combination of water with carbon dioxide in the atmosphere, and weak sulphuric by the interaction of rainwater with sulphur compounds in soot (hence the high corrosive activity, and the rapid weathering of building and monumental stones, in and adjacent to industrial zones). Waters containing humic acids also effect some solution. It is rather typical that the products of other chemical weathering processes are transported as carbonates, sulphates or chlorides in solution in groundwaters and rivers. The Mississippi, for instance, has been estimated to carry an average of 136 million tons of material to the sea each year in this way alone.

Fig 108   Widening of joint by tree trunk during growth near Palmer, S.A. The granite block has been moved to the right by 3 to 4 inches at A.

By reacting with water, oxygen, iron or carbon dioxide, minerals are wholly or partially altered. In some cases the structure of the rock is weakened; in others the volume is changed. Reactions are usually complex. For instance, the feldspar orthoclase subjected to both hydrolysis and carbonation produces a colloidal clay, soluble salt and silica:

$$2KAlSi_3O_8 + 2H_2 + CO_2 \quad\quad H_4Al_2Si_2O + K_2O_3 + 4SiO_2$$
Orthoclase   water carbon   clay   soluble   silica
                    dioxide   salt

Outside the humid tropics, the typical end products of chemical weathering are sand and clay, but in the humid tropics both tend to be unstable and compounds rich in Al, FeO and H_2O form the mantle of waste. Hence the development in such regions of laterite and bauxite, rocks rich in iron oxide and alumina respectively. Gravel is not formed as a product of weathering in the humid tropics; hence in these regions it does not appear in rivers, which are thereby deprived of one of their most effective tools of erosion. The course of weathering in these lands varies considerably but the sort of sequence of changes that is suffered in detail may be indicated by considering the weathering of a pervious volcanic ash. First, soluble salts of, for instance, Ca, K, Na and some SiO_2 are leached. FeO is oxidised to Fe_2O_3, and MnO to MnO_2. Where drainage is good, kaolinite is formed, but another type of clay, montmorillonite, is found where it is poor. The leaching of bases continues and the depth of weathering increases. Because of this leaching there is a relative concentration of Fe_2O_3 and Al_2O_3 in the near-surface horizons, while silica is precipitated in a layer close to the parent rock.

The iron and alumina-rich layer near the surface develops in nodular form and may form a thick carapace: this is laterite (ferricrete) or bauxite, depending on the relative predominance of Fe and Al in the crust. Fe and Al rich layers also form in 'monsoonal' lands. Laterite is widespread in northern Australia as well as in the central and southern parts of the continent, where it presumably originated under climatic conditions different from those which occur at present. At Weipa, in north Queensland, the commercial bauxite deposit was formed by the intense leaching of a sandstone. The ore was formed in the Tertiary, but formation is claimed to be continuing at present.

Massive pedogenic lime is called *calcrete* (*cf.* iron rich layers, laterite, or ferricrete), which forms massive beds or lenses and is common in many areas of South Australia, especially the Murray Mallee and Eyre and Yorke Peninsulas. Travertine is morphologically indistinguishable from calcrete but forms in stream beds and near springs, for instance in an intermontane basin of Gorge Creek (M.R. Mannum, 136844). Also in arid lands, and possibly also in certain lacustrine conditions, horizons rich in silica, and known as silcrete (in Australia, 'billy'), may form, while superficial silica in rocks is commonly mobilised to form siliceous crusts, susceptible to conchoidal fracturing. Such siliceous duricrusts are particularly common in the northeast of the State and the adjoining areas of N.S.W. where the silcrete has been shown to be of Oligocene–Miocene age (see Chapter 3, part (e), and Fig. 39) and it also occurs at the northern end of the Willochra Basin (in the southern Flinders Ranges) and in the Broughton valley, east of Port Pirie.

The role of organisms in chemical weathering is important. The effects of humic acids have already been mentioned and the extraction of soluble nutrients is also significant. On granite and other rock surfaces near Mannum and on the Eyre Peninsula, for example, lichens can be shown not only mechanically to disintegrate rocks with their hyphae, but also to extract iron from minerals and concentrate it at and immediately beneath the rock surface.

(e) EFFECTS OF WEATHERING

The primary significance of weathering is that it prepares rocks for transportation and erosion. Without preliminary weathering, rivers and wind—and probably glacier ice too—can accomplish little erosion.

Specific landforms also originate through weathering directly or indirectly. The development of resistant crusts, pans and horizons in soils renders a surface impenetrable, with significant consequences for run-off and erosion; after dissection, they form the resistant cappings of plateaux. Weathering is both selective and differential, and sometimes remarkable minor landforms, such as caverns or *tafoni*, weather pits or gnammas (see earlier) develop on this account. Some tors and inselbergs already described, are due to differential subsurface weathering and subsequent exposure. Also, certain 'boss and shield' forms (Pl. 42) well developed on

Plate 42 'Boss and shield' forms developed in sandstone, 18 to 20 miles north of Quorn, southern Flinders Ranges. Soil formerly covered the lower parts of the now exposed blocks, weathering was marked and consequently when, due to European settlement of the area, soil erosion occurred, these forms were exposed by differential weathering.

sandstone in the southern Flinders Ranges, and on granite on the Palmer and Caloote outcrops and northwestern Eyre Peninsula, are due to a concentration of moisture weathering at, or just below ground (soil) level. A similar process attains possibly its most spectacular effect quite

Plate 43 Overhanging slope at Ucontitchie Hill.

Fig 109 Development of flared or steepened and overhanging slopes on granite inselberg, Eyre Peninsula.

commonly on Eyre Peninsula, and at isolated sites at Ayers Rock, the Olgas, and in Western Australia. Here both structural and climatic circumstances are conducive to the development of differential weathering. The residual hills are massively jointed, compared to the surrounding plains (see earlier, Chapter 4), and the climate is arid or semi-arid so that with water being usually scarce, the concentration of moisture in the marginal zones is significant.[1] The result (Fig. 109) is the development of elegantly flared and steepened lower slopes like that shown in Pl. 43. In the humid tropics, the transportation of the products of weathering in solution may contribute significantly to the lowering of the land surface (see Chapter 11). But the most important work of weathering is in the preparation of rocks for transportation.

How this is accomplished varies from place to place and from time to time, according to climate and weather, though gravity everywhere and at all times provides the motivating force.

NOTE

[1] For further discussion of the evolution of these forms, see Chapter 14.

6. Rivers and Valleys

(a) INTRODUCTION

ALTHOUGH MUCH OF AUSTRALIA is either arid or semi-arid, rivers have been and still are dominant in moulding the landscape in many parts of the continent. Three different types of regions can be distinguished with respect to drainage. First, the *areic* regions, where the lack of surface streams is due either to lack of rainfall, local lithology, or, as is the case on the Nullarbor plain, a combination of both of these factors. Areas underlain by limestone and lacking surface drainage but with subsurface streams are said to have *cryptoreic* drainage. Secondly, very large areas of central Australia are drained by streams which lead to basins of interior drainage; an example of such an *endoreic* drainage basin is the Lake Eyre Basin which is the focus for streams serving over half a million square miles of South Australia, Queensland and the Northern Territory. *Exoreic* streams on the other hand drain to the sea (Fig. 7).

Because of the very marked seasonal distribution of rainfall, and high summer temperatures, most rivers outside the Eastern Uplands flow only *seasonally*. Those in the lower and more unreliable rainfall areas flow *intermittently*, and those in the most arid regions, where rainfall is extremely unpredictable, flow *episodically*.

The only major river in Australia is the Murray, which drains an area of more than 400,000 square miles and is 1,600 miles long from source to sea (Fig. 7). The combined Murray–Darling is, at 3282 miles, the fourth longest river system in the world, being exceeded only by the Nile, Amazon and Mississippi–Missouri systems. In catchment area, the Murray–Darling is also in world class, standing sixth to the Amazon, Congo, Mississippi, Yangtse Kiang and Ganges. But the average annual discharge of the Murray is far less than the other rivers cited. With an annual average discharge of 12 million acre feet, the river rates far below a stream like the Danube, which drains an area about 80 per cent of that of the Murray–Darling, yet has an annual discharge some 19 times greater than Australia's largest river: 228, as opposed to 12, million acre feet. The average run-off a square mile of catchment is 712 acre feet in the Danube basin, as opposed to 29 in the Murray–Darling basin. All this emphasises the arid and semi-arid nature of the catchment of the Murray: the average annual rainfall over the whole catchment is 17 inches. Only 5 per cent of the total catchment has a precipitation exceeding 30 inches a year, and none of this occurs in South Australia.

Most of the high rainfall zone is in the Kosciusko area, and it is primarily from this area, and the Victorian mountains, that the Murray derives its water. In South Australia only the Marne contributes discharge to the Murray, and this is negligible in comparison with the total.

The Murray is an *allogenic*, or *exotic*, stream, rising in high rainfall areas and having sufficient discharge to survive passage across a semi-desert region. In South Australia, and indeed in neighbouring parts of Victoria and N.S.W., the river loses more water by evaporation than it gains from precipitation, either directly or from neighbouring areas: at Lake Victoria, for instance, potential annual evaporation averages 60 inches, compared with an annual average precipitation of 10·35 inches, and at Milang, the figures are 41·17 and 15·01 inches respectively.

The Murray collects run-off from the tributaries which drain its broad basin, and flows westward until it approaches the barrier of the Mt Lofty–Olary upland. The Darling lies wholly outside South Australia, but is notable for its remarkably straight course, which is guided by a major fault in the underlying bedrock (see Chapter 3). At Morgan, the Murray makes a sharp turn southward in response to a series of low north-to-south fault escarpments located within the Murray plain (Fig. 110). Between Morgan and Blanchetown, at least, the Murray follows what appears to be a complex but well marked fault zone. And throughout its South Australian course the river pattern in plan is in detail clearly influenced by the northwest–southeast and northeast–southwest major jointing in the country rock (Fig. 111).

The river pursues a winding course in a relatively narrow trench which is in many places bounded by precipitous bluffs (Pl. 15, Fig. 112) made of the characteristic and widespread yellow-brown, richly fossiliferous Miocene calcarenite. There are many undercut bluffs and slip-off slopes with point bars (see below) on the inner side of the curves. The river is gradually widening its valley and developing a flood plain which is already important for agricultural and pastoral purposes, though some of the best water meadows are now permanently inundated following the 1½ to 2 feet general rise in river level after the completion of the Goolwa barrage at the mouth of the Murray in 1941.

The river is deepest close to the undercut bluffs, and it is here that the 'landings' of the old river steamers are situated. Large caverns or 'shelters' abound at the foot of the cliffs, and these were much favoured by the aboriginal population who lived in considerable numbers along the Murray—an oasis in the semi-desert—before and immediately following the arrival of Europeans. Excavations near Walkers Flat and Nildottie show that aboriginal occupation is of some antiquity and carbon-14 datings from hearths in the former locality reveal that the original Australians were on the Murray about 5000 years ago.

Fig 111 Joint control of the course of the Lower Murray river (*after* O'Driscoll).

Fig 110 Structural control of the course of the Murray in South Australia. The approximate limits of the postulated Pleistocene lake, Lake Bungonia, are also shown (*after* Firman).

Between Mannum and Morgan, the valley of the Murray displays a distinct 'valley-in-valley' form (see below and Fig. 113), and it is of interest that there are, scattered along the cliff top in the areas cited, small outcrops of a cross-bedded sandstone 20 to 25 feet thick with a massive oyster bed at its base, and of Pliocene age. The outcrops have not so far been located beyond the confines of the shallow wider valley, and it appears probable that the Pliocene sediments were laid down in a narrow estuary extending far inland up what is now the lower Murray Valley.

The flow of the Murray changes from time to time within very wide limits. In 80 years of instrumental recordings at Morgan, on the lower Murray, its flow has varied between a mere 4,000 cu. secs. (26–27 July 1902) to 139,500 cu. secs. during the 1956 floods (3–7 September 1956)[1] or roughly 35 times the recorded minimum. In its variability of flow the Murray is of course typical of all Australian rivers, for all experience periods of high and low flow, though the regularity and duration of each differs from region to region. The lack of surface waters in the rivers of inland Australia is notorious but from time to time, irregularly and unpredictably, these creeks and rivers burst into floods which are all the more devastating and damaging because the natural environment, as well as cultural features like bridges and crossings, are geared only to the

Fig 112   Morphological map of part of the Murray valley near Walkers Flat, S.A.

Fig 113   Valley-in-valley form in the Murray valley just upstream from Mannum.

usual arid state of the rivers. When seeing such outback rivers in their usual condition, it seems incredible that people should have drowned in them. On reading on a tombstone a few miles north of Quorn that Hugh Proby, 24 years of age, was drowned in 1852 whilst crossing the Willochra

Creek, a salt encrusted, innocuous looking, channel, one is initially led to think in terms of some dreadful folly, or even tiredness of this life on the part of Proby; but such tragedies are readily understandable to anyone who has witnessed these creeks in flow, and even more to those who have felt the tail of a heavily laden 4-wheel drive vehicle swing ominously when crossing even minor creeks which are in flood. These arid zone creeks can rise to flood levels with extraordinary rapidity; and they fall equally quickly, in the meantime having accomplished much erosion, transport and deposition. Such rivers are often fitted with major armaments. Growing in the creek beds are the well known and picturesque river gums, some of which are uprooted during the infrequent floods and

Table 3 Some River Catchments and Discharges

River and gauging station	Discharge (annual average—acre feet)	Catchment (sq. miles)
Burdekin (Home Hill)	6,190,000	50,400
Fitzroy (Yaamba)	4,120,000	53,500
Tully	4,081,000	1,210
Clarence (Gorge and Newbold)	2,269,200	6,674
Snowy (Jarrahmond)	1,678,000	5,100

Compare these figures with:

River and gauging station	Discharge (annual average—acre feet)	Catchment (sq. miles)
Murray drainage system	12,000,000	414,000
Flinders (Q'ld)	700,000	41,600
Collie (W.A.)	165,000	1,000

Source: *Bauer* and others.

are swept downstream to act as veritable battering rams. The impact of one trunk uproots another tree, and so the process tends to be cumulative. It is this weaponry that demolishes railway bridges (such as that at Hookina, a few miles northwest of Hawker) and does other major damage. But usually these rivers and creeks display dry beds, though an underflow is usually present.

Rivers in the better watered eastern areas flow permanently. They are still, however, subject to floods which despite a greater preparedness in the way of bridges, and so on, are even more damaging in flood than those of the arid lands since they occur in more intensively settled country. The floods on such rivers as the Hunter (February 1955), the Macleay, the Burdekin and other east coast rivers, are well known;

those headwaters of the Darling and other inland rivers which rise in the Eastern Uplands are not immune to similar heavy and disastrous flooding. None of these eastern rivers compares either in length or discharge with the Murray system, but several are impressive when their discharges are compared to their lengths and, even more so, when their catchments are compared. Several of the east coast streams rise quite close to the Pacific but, because of the geological complexity of the area, tend to follow circuitous paths to the sea: the Stanley, for instance, rises only 12 miles from the Pacific, but travels 180 miles to the Brisbane River, while the Burdekin, 425 miles in length, rises less than 40 miles inland. Thus, though they have long courses, they in fact drain only limited areas and their volumes are impressive compared to those of the inland rivers, including the Murray.

Whether streams are large or small, whether they flow to an interior basin or to the ocean margin, in desert or temperate regions, all behave in similar fashion from a hydrological point of view and achieve broadly similar geomorphological results, which are now considered.

(b) EROSION, TRANSPORT AND DEPOSITION BY STREAMS

Rivers, like soil and rock fragments, flow under the influence of gravity. The bed of a stream commonly displays irregularities, but the surface of the water always slopes downhill. Streams and rivers have a certain amount of energy, which varies with the volume or *discharge* of the river, the duration of flow (*time*), and the *velocity* of flow, which in turn depends upon the *stream gradient* and the *characteristics of the channel* through which the stream flows.

Each river tends to develop a smooth concave-upward profile from source to sea, known as the longitudinal profile or *thalweg*, and when all irregularities such as rapids, waterfalls and lakes have been eliminated from the longitudinal profile, the stream profile is said to be *graded*. It is commonly asserted that because the gradient of the longitudinal profile in general decreases downstream, the velocity of flow diminishes downstream in sympathy. Nothing could be further from the truth. Measurements of rate of flow at sites scattered along the same stream course have shown that there is, on the contrary, a general increase in velocity downstream. Irregularities are superimposed upon the general trend. Where there are constrictions, either lateral or vertical, in a stream channel (due to the occurrence of a resistant rock stratum for example), the stream flows more rapidly through the constriction than in wider sections of the stream (the Venturi effect). But in general, there is an overall increase in rate of flow downstream (Fig. 114).

The reason for this apparently curious state of affairs is partly as follows: whereas streams in mountainous regions flow through very irregular rocky channels, those of the plains have carved quite smooth

154   *Geomorphology*

Fig 114 Graph showing relationship between stream gradient and stream velocity (*after Dury*).

velocity distribution in prismatic channel (cm./sec.)

velocity distribution in river (m./sec.)

Fig 115 Distribution of velocity in stream in cross-section.

channels, due to their greater volume and flow through their own alluvium. Wherever the river is in contact with the channel walls or bed, a boundary condition develops and there is a loss of energy due to friction (Fig. 115). In mountainous streams, the *wetted perimeter* (the total length of channel section in contact with the water), where energy losses occur, is long compared with the cross-sectional area of the stream, and here frictional losses may amount to 96 or 97 per cent of the potential energy of a stream. In streams flowing on the plains, however, the ratio of wetted perimeter to cross-sectional area is low and frictional losses are relatively low. This contrast in frictional losses due to the nature of the channel, apparently counterbalances the effects of loss of gradient. Another factor causing plains streams to flow more rapidly than those of uplands is that the greater volume of the former gives a greater hydraulic head.

The river loses some of its potential energy in overcoming friction. Some energy is used for wearing away the channel walls and bed. The river thus acquires its *load*—the material carried in various ways by the moving water. Some debris is also brought to the river by tributaries, rainwash, soil and rock creep, gullying and landslides. Rivers, like the wind, effectively sort their load. The finer, lighter debris is carried more rapidly than the coarser, heavier material. The lighter debris *by-passes* the heavier, not only because the former travels faster, but also because the heavier material is moved less frequently. Rivers can carry or roll very much coarser material than can be transported by the wind, because water is more dense and viscous than air (a grain of quartz weighs only some $2\frac{1}{2}$ times as much as an equal volume of water but is some 2,000 times as much as an equal volume of air). Very coarse material, like cobbles and boulders, can be carried by rivers only by rolling them along the bottom of the channel. This part of the load is called the *bed load*, and it is carried by *traction*. Rivers, like the wind, also carry debris in *saltation* and in *suspension*. The load in suspension is carried along in the flow of water without touching the stream bed, whereas the load in saltation moves downstream in a series of jumps, bouncing along the river bed (Fig. 116).

The manner in which debris of a given density is carried by running water, varies from time to time. For example, many streams flowing to the Murray plains from the eastern Mount Lofty Ranges carry sand (derived from the weathering of granites and gneisses) in suspension or by saltation during periods of high flow, but during the decline of the streams after storms the velocity and volume of flow decrease and the sand is carried as the traction load. The river moulds the sand into dunes analagous with the transverse dunes of the deserts. These dunes exhibit peculiar features at certain velocities of stream flow, for the dunes appear to migrate upstream, against the current. Actually, sand from the slip faces of dunes is deposited on the upstream slopes of the next dunes downstream, so that although the sand is actually carried downstream, the dunes move upstream (Fig. 117).

Of the various parts of the load, that in suspension or saltation and that in solution are most important. The Mississippi carries 340 million tons of material to the sea annually in suspension and saltation, compared with 136 million tons in solution and 40 million tons in the traction load.

Clays are carried in suspension, and come to rest only if flow ceases, or if they are trapped between coarser debris. Clay particles are microscopically small, and their plate-like shape gives them a very low settling

Fig 116   Transportation of debris in a stream.

Fig 117   Upstream movement of dunes along a stream bed.

Fig 118   Erosion of platy-rock fragments by hydraulic pressure.

velocity, even in still water: whereas fine clay takes about a year to settle 100 feet, fine sand takes only about 2 hours. Much sand and fine gravel is carried by saltation. As in air, turbulent flow, consisting of irregular secondary movements and velocity fluctuations superimposed upon the average flow, is the most common type of flow in running water. Turbulent eddies, providing *hydraulic lift*, are important because they carry sand and gravel from the channel bed, where, because of the usual boundary condition there is frictional drag, and a zone of lower velocity, into an area of more rapid flow.

Coarse debris is rolled along the bottom (Fig. 116). The reason is that the lower parts of large fragments are located in the bottom zone of lower velocity whereas the upper part is subjected to a more powerful flow. Hence there is unequal pressure exerted, and the fragment is rolled along. Turbulent updrafts are again important in carrrying coarse debris over the peaks of adjacent coarse fragments.

Given material of the same density, the coarser the fragment the more difficult it is for the stream to carry. The reason for this is that the volume (and mass) of a particle varies with a cube function (the volume of a sphere is given by the formula $\frac{4}{3}\pi r^3$), while the cross-sectional area, upon which the flow of water exerts its force is proportional to a square function (the cross section area of the sphere, or the area of a circle, is πr^2). Thus, if there are in a stream two particles one with a diameter three times that of the other, it might be asserted that as the larger particle intercepts more water than the smaller, the amount being proportional to the cross-sectional areas of the particles, it should move along as quickly as the smaller one. But the weight to be moved is proportional to the volume of the spheres: the cross-sectional area of the larger sphere is 9 (3 × 3) times that of the smaller, but its volume is 27 (3 × 3 × 3) times that of the smaller, so that it is disproportionately heavy and difficult to move.

A distinction has to be made between the effort required to carry material and that necessary to overcome its inertia or pick up (erode) the same material. This applies particularly to fine material such as clays, which pack down to present a smooth surface to the water, wholly within the zone of low velocity and offering no projections to generate turbulence. Under such conditions the water may flow in thin sheets, one over the other (*laminar flow*), making erosion very difficult, especially as clays are highly cohesive due to their ionic bonding. Silt and clay are easily transported by rivers, but very difficult to erode.

The weight of debris a river can carry—its *capacity*—depends upon its volume or discharge, but the size of the largest particles it can transport—its *competence*—is a function of velocity at a given time. Hence small but swift flowing streams can carry quite large fragments. It should be noted, however, that a river can carry only what is available to it: no matter how swift the stream, it can carry material only as large as is available and as fragments are rather quickly disintegrated on a stream bed, large fast flowing streams may have only sand to carry.

In flood, rivers flow high and fast. Both capacity and competence are at a high level. With particles of the same shape, the competence of a stream varies with the sixth power of the velocity (V^6). With material of mixed calibre, the capacity varies with V^{3-4}. Thus floods are so important, that the form of rivers and features associated with them are imposed by floods, not by the 'normal' river.

Rivers erode their bed and banks in various ways. Some wearing is accomplished by solution (or *corrosion*). As mentioned in the previous chapter, all common rock-forming minerals are to some extent soluble in water, and even quartz (SiO_2), generally considered the most stable of minerals, is very slightly soluble in water. A few rock forming minerals are very readily dissolved in river water, and where rivers flow over outcrops rich in these minerals, solution is a significant erosional process. Beds of limestone, rock salt and gypsum, for instance, are readily affected.

The sheer force of running water, the *hydraulic action*, can cause fragments loosened by weathering to be removed. The fragments may be either individual crystals, aggregates of crystals, or, where the strata are fissile, or very well layered, plates of rock may be broken off, especially if the beds dip downstream (Fig. 118). Such plates of slaty rock detached by hydraulic action occur commonly in the Torrens valley near Hillcrest and Windsor Gardens (M.R. Adelaide, 650910).

Most erosion is accomplished by the scouring or abrasive action of sand and gravel carried by traction and in saltation and suspension. This *abrasion* or *corrasion* acts generally, though in some areas very marked localised scouring results from the whirling around of pebbles and cobbles in a limited area, forming pot-holes. Corrasion in running water is analagous with sand-blasting in wind. Again, storm or flood effects are important, for the erosional potential of a stream varies with the square of the velocity. Thus if the velocity of a stream is doubled in time of flood, erosion is increased four times, not twice. Not only is the impact of water increased, but more water and debris is hurled against the channel bed and banks in a given time.

The water of a river can also cause erosion by *wet-bank slumping*, which is particularly important where banks are clayey. When thoroughly wetted clays become unstable and collapse during flow, the debris or most of it, is immediately carried downstream. If, however, streams flow intermittently, the collapse may well take place after flow has ceased, providing clear evidence that it is collapse and not erosion due to stream flow that is responsible (Pl. 44). In the many gullies that front the Willunga scarp, as well as in gullies all over Australia, such evidence of bank collapse can be clearly seen. Also in clayey soils, *tunnels*, or under-

Plate 44 Slumping of gully banks, near Sellicks Hill, some 35 miles south of Adelaide.

Plate 45 Intensely gullied Tertiary sands and clays in a road cutting some 30 miles south of Adelaide (M.R. Echunga, S.A., 506462). In places water has penetrated into the subsoil, where tunnels have formed. Some of the friable rock particles have been washed out causing the dried surface crust to be undermined. The curious circular depressions are manifestations of this subsurface erosion, but their precise origin has not been investigated.

ground flows of water, often develop. Water seeps through the clays at the level of the water table, some clays being carried away in the process. A small aperture first forms, which is gradually enlarged, to form a tunnel (Pl. 45). The roof collapses, and a deep channel is formed.

The debris eroded and carried by streams is transported eventually to the ocean basins. But this is accomplished spasmodically, debris being dumped only to be picked up later, and very little material is carried directly from source to sea. In the case of interior drainage, such as that flowing to Lake Eyre, debris is deposited in the lower parts of the basin as broad alluvial spreads. It appears that several years' total load of debris is stored in each river valley, as alluvial veneers in flood plains, as valley fills, and as shoals and bars in the channels.

(c) BASELEVEL AND VALLEY DEEPENING

By eroding the channel bed, a river excavates its own valley. If only incision took place, a narrow, steep-sided chasm would result. This is sometimes found, though more commonly other agencies are active and cause the valley to be widened (see below). The river cannot, however, go on cutting down or lowering its bed. There is a lower limit, imposed by *baselevel*. For streams, baselevel is an imaginary line extending from sea level at the coast underneath the continents. It is *not* a horizontal plane, but is gently inclined at such a gradient that streams, when they attain baselevel, are still able to maintain a flow under the prevailing conditions of climate, vegetation and weathering (Fig. 119). Sea level is the *ultimate* baselevel of erosion. *Local* and *temporary* baselevels are also important. These are points which, though they differ from sea level, impose local and temporary lower limits of erosion upon particular streams or stream sectors. For instance, a hard rock stratum may provide a local baselevel for the stream upstream from it (Fig. 120a). Similarly Lake Eyre, which is below sea level, is the 'local' baselevel for half a million square miles of inland Australia (see Chapter 7). The rivers which flow to the lake can cut down as far as the level of the lake bed, which, at its deepest is about 46 feet below sea level. The local and temporary baselevel of erosion of all tributary streams is their point of junction with the trunk or main stream (Fig. 120b), a level which is constantly changing (see below). The tributaries cannot erode below the level of their junction with the main stream.

Assuming a very long period of time with no change in conditions, it may be imagined that eventually all local and temporary baselevels would be eliminated, and that everywhere streams would flow at or near, regional baselevel. Wind is not subject to the same controls, nor is moving ice affected so directly. The baselevel concept applies mostly to streams, though it should be noted that there is a lower limit to wind erosion imposed by the water table (see Chapter 7).

Rivers and Valleys

Fig 119 Regional baselevel.

Fig 120 (a) Local and temporary baselevel; (b) Local and temporary baselevel of a tributary stream at its junction with the main stream.

Fig 121 Earth flow and earth slip (*after Sharpe*).

(d) MASS MOVEMENTS OF MATERIALS

Concurrently with the incision of the river bed, various agencies are at work on the valley sides causing them to be worn back. Depending upon certain local conditions (slope budget), the valley sides may maintain a steep inclination, or they may be lowered. The agencies at work on the valley side slope include weathering, soil and rock creep; slumping, earthflows and landslides; rainwash, gullying, tunnel and tributary development; and lateral corrasion by the river itself. Weathering was dealt with in the previous chapter, and river work is considered below; here it is necessary only to comment on the various mechanisms of mass movement which play such an important part in the wasting and moulding of interfluvial areas.

Weathered material moves downslope under the influence of gravity. Such mass movements of material occur most readily where there is abundant ground water, where there are clays to provide lubrication, and where the heaving action of ice derived from groundwater provides a potent force for initiating such movements. In subarctic regions, the heaving action of ground ice, plus the presence in summer of thawed ground with much water overlying the permanently frozen and impermeable ground (*permafrost*), leads to mass movements of debris being possibly the most important single means of transport of weathered material in such regions. In the humid tropics, mass movements are similarly of great importance due to the rapid, intense and deep weathering of rocks, the common production of colloidal clays by weathering processes and the abundance of water. But in temperate regions, and even in arid and semi-arid lands, mass movements occur as a result of heavy rains. Mass movements take many forms, some obvious and spectacular, others imperceptible. It is the slower, more insidious, movements which are probably of most importance. Soil and rock *creep*, for instance, are noticeable only in very special circumstances, but by these means vast amounts of material are moved downhill and eventually to rivers and streams.

Mass movements include flows in which differential movement takes place, and slips and slides, in which a mass falls *en bloc* (Fig. 121). Slow flowage of debris includes soil and rock creep, in which tiny particles and fragments of soil and rock migrate downslope under gravity. In earthflows, mudflows and debris avalanches, rapid movements occur, and their results are easily detectable. A whole sector of a hill slope becomes unstable, probably as a result of accession of water and a flowage occurs in which different parts of the mass move at different rates (the centre of the unstable mass moves more rapidly than the base and sides because of frictional retardation of the latter). In similar circumstances, huge masses of rock waste may slide *en bloc* over the adjacent surface, while other masses may be rendered unstable by undermining: such *falls* and *slides* form yet another category of mass movement. If there is acute subsurface removal of material, perhaps due to transportation in solution, or perhaps due to tunnelling by man or other animals, *subsidence* can take place.

Attention has been drawn recently to earth flows which are lubricated, not by water and clays, but by air. After catastrophic rock falls, triggered possibly by earth tremors, debris flows under gravity downslope. In some very large flows in Iran, the U.S.A. and Canada, it has been noted that the debris is thin, but spread over a wide area, that there is no sorting and little abrasion of the constituent fragments in such flows which, in places, extend not only downslope but continue under their own momentum as far as 2,000 feet up gentle to moderate inclines. Eye witness accounts suggest very rapid speeds of movement (certainly more than 100 m.p.h. and, in one case, approaching 300 m.p.h. for a short time), and of blasts of air associated with these flows which can strip branches and twigs from trees. All this is interpreted as pointing to lubrication or fluidisation of the flow by air trapped within and beneath the falling and swiftly moving debris.

Plate 46 Small puffs of turf and soil in an intermittently flooded depression adjacent to the River Torrens at Birdwood, South Australia. These features are caused by the alternate wetting and drying, expansion and contraction, of the clay soils.

Several micro-landforms originate through the expansion and contraction of soils and other unconsolidated sediments. Such forms are perhaps best known from arctic and subarctic regions, where various forms of *patterned* ground (stone stripes, stone polygons, etc.) are common, and are due to the work of frost. In semi-arid regions, the alternate wetting and drying of certain clays cause expansion and contraction, resulting, in turn, in heaving of the surface on a small scale, and, in some instances, the establishment of a rudimentary circulation in cells in the soil. The well-known 'Bay of Biscay' soils have this character, and fence posts are commonly thrust from the ground due to the operation of this churning motion. Geomorphologically, small puffs and depressions (*gilgai*) are the usual indication of this form of mass movement, but, in some limited areas, upthrust masses give rise to curious pimples of soil and sod, as, for instance, in the Torrens alluvium near Birdwood (Pl. 46).

Mass movements are widespread in South Australia. Cracking and subsidence can be observed along the banks of almost any gully (Pl. 47), and slides and flows, though less common, are not rare. Both types of movement are well displayed on the Permian sands and clays of the Yankalilla area, south of Adelaide (Pls. 48, 49) where the clays have been washed down to form distinct horizons over which the overlying sands and clays readily slip and slide.

In the Flinders Ranges, debris avalanches are fairly common, and in the same region there is evidence of considerable soil creep. On many debris slopes for example that of The Bluff, 8 miles north of Quorn, fine material which has moved downslope is temporarily impounded behind obstacles such as large boulders, tree stumps and the like, to form small terracettes. In other localities, for instance 5–10 miles north of Wilpena, stream erosion has revealed that some of the lower slopes in this area are underlain by 2–3 feet of slope material (colluvium); moreover, the remarkable smoothness of the sub-debris slopes strongly suggests that during its downslope movement the coarse colluvium may accomplish a measure of smoothing of the underlying bedrock. That a few narrow valleys may contain even greater thicknesses of colluvium is suggested by an exposure (due to the excavation of a railway cutting) in the Pichi Richi Pass, southwest of Quorn, in which some 25 feet of fine and coarse colluvium occurs as a thick fill to the former valley floor (Fig. 122).

(e) VALLEY WIDENING

Where a stream is well above local baselevel, vertical incision may at first be most pronounced and valley widening may be relatively slow, so that valleys incised in a new surface tend to be relatively deep and steep-sided. Thus the gullies cut in the unconsolidated alluvial fans which front the Willunga scarp are deep and steep sided (Pl. 50), for the intermittently flowing streams have cut down as far as baselevel (local or ultimate) will

Fig 122 Field sketch of slope debris exposed in railway cutting in the Pichi Richi Pass, near Quorn.

Fig 123 Interlocking spurs.

permit, while the various processes at work on the gully sides, though active, have, as it were, been out-paced by the vertical downcutting. It is safe to predict, however, that with the passage of time, the valleys will be widened, and that eventually they will develop a narrow V-shaped cross section, the valley as a whole displaying *interlocking spurs* (Fig. 123).

It must be stressed that we tend to exaggerate vertical distances, and in reality, only where very special circumstances obtain are the gullies, and other features elsewhere termed gorges, deeper than they are wide. The Torrens Gorge, for example, is about 800 feet maximum depth,

Plate 47 Bank cracking near Sellicks Hill. These blocks become detached and eventually collapse into the gully.

Plate 48 Land slip in weathered Permian clays and sands, south of Normanville, S.A. Note the gap left behind by the slip and the mound where the mobile debris has come up against a stable slope.

Plate 49 Earthflows near Yankalilla, S.A.

Plate 50 Deep gully eroded in the unconsolidated clays and gravels of the alluvial fans which front the Willunga scarp. The gully is 10–12 feet deep.

Plate 51 Deep V-shaped gorge of the Onkaparinga above Noarlunga, S.A.

Fig 124 The Barron Gorge and Falls, near Cairns, Queensland.

but at this point is half-a-mile (roughly 2,600 feet) wide, while the gorge of the Onkaparinga just above Noarlunga is 300 feet deep, but almost half-a-mile wide (Pl. 51). The Grose valley, west of Windsor (N.S.W.) is in several places 1000 feet deep, but is between half and three quarters of a mile wide at these sites. The Barron Gorge, 9–10 miles northwest of Cairns, is between Red Peak (M.R. Cairns, Queensland, 617777) and Glacier Rock (M.R. 588756) over 1000 feet deep, but in this sector is $1\frac{1}{2}$ miles wide (Fig. 124). One of the narrowest gorges, Werribee Gorge is 600–700 feet deep but is 1500 feet wide (M.R. Ballan, Vic., 412535). Most valleys, even those that appear deep and narrow, are wider than they are deep.

The morphology and behaviour of valley side slopes depends upon their budget, which in turn varies with the effectiveness of erosional agencies on various parts of the slopes; this in turn varies with climate, lithology, vegetation and soil conditions, and the location of the river with respect to a particular slope sector.

Where erosion of the lower slope exceeds that of the upper, steep slopes are developed and maintained even during recession. Such conditions are found where for instance:

(1) A slope is capped by a resistant stratum.
(2) The base of a slope is attacked by a major river (as, for instance during meandering).
(3) The system of weathering and erosion is such that attack of high points in the relief is so slow as to be negligible, while the attack of lower slopes is comparatively rapid. Such tends to be the case in arid lands, and semi-arid lands.

Where, on the other hand, the upper slope suffers vigorous attack, relative to the lower, slopes decline or are worn down. Such conditions occur, for example, where:

(1) In the absence of an effective agent of evacuation, material either accumulates at the base of a slope, or is evacuated only slowly.
(2) The system of weathering and erosion is such that upper slopes are strongly attacked, as is the case in sub-arctic lands and in temperate lands where the soil and vegetation cover induces weathering, rounding and lowering of even the highest parts of the relief.

The first situation is illustrated in Fig. 4a, the second in Fig. 4b. Where structure is not a dominant factor, the distribution of weathering and erosion (controlled by climate and vegetation) assumes greatest significance, but most commonly the interplay between structure (including lithology) and process is delicate and complex. Some of the clearest illustrations of this slope budget principle are found in river and stream valleys. In the Murray river valley (Pl. 15, Fig. 112) steep slopes are maintained on the outside of valley windings because the river is located at the base of the cliffs and is not only actively eroding these areas, but is

Fig 125 Variation in slope form with intensity of river erosion at base.

Fig 126 Basin and defile forms in dipping strata of varied hardness.

Fig 127 Structural benches and valley forms in flat-lying strata of varied hardness.

also removing a very large part of the debris produced either directly by this erosion or by slumping from the cliff above. In areas where the river is distant from the base of the cliffs however, debris accumulates and an inclined bedrock slope is developed; moreover, as the pace of cliff recession is reduced the rounding of the top of the cliff through the evolution of the upper slope becomes apparent, and eventually this unit develops to such an extent that the cliff is consumed from above and below and is replaced by a smooth sigmoidal slope (Fig. 125). That it is an evolutionary or time sequence is suggested firstly by the constant relationship between slope form and distance from the river, and secondly by the definite evidence, in the shape of river sediments, that the river formerly was at the base of bluffs from which it is now distant, a feature which confirms the general theory of river winding and migration (see below). Similar slope—river relations can be observed in the Torrens Gorge, in Waterfall Gully and in many other river valleys near Adelaide, and are particularly well displayed in the gorges of the Blue Mountains, west of Sydney (Fig. 73a) and in Wittenoom Gorge, Western Australia (Fig. 74).

In many areas, structure exerts an important influence upon the form of valleys in cross-section. Where a river flows across strata of contrasted resistances to weathering and erosion, the width of the river valley varies directly with the hardness of the local bedrock. Gorges are eroded through resistant rock, and wider valleys, with extensive tributary development, in the softer rocks (Fig. 126): the river flows through a series of *narrow defiles* and *open basins* (Pl. 52). If the river flows through

Plate 52   North of Brachina Gorge—narrow V-shaped gorges eroded in resistant strata are separated by open valleys eroded in softer rocks.

horizontal strata of different hardnesses, *structural benches* are displayed (Fig. 127, see also Fig. 82b). Where the strata are tilted, *asymmetrical valleys* are developed (Fig. 128) due to uniclinal shifting, or preferred erosion along bedding planes.

Many east-west trending valleys in the Mt Lofty Ranges are asymmetrical, with the northern or south-facing slope steeper than the southern north-facing slope. The Torrens valley is a good example as is Pedlers Creek, south of Noarlunga. In almost every valley of course there are asymmetrical sections due to the river undercutting and steepening slopes during migration, but in the east-west trending valleys cited there is a general tendency to asymmetry. In the case of the Torrens between the Gorge mouth and Hillcrest, the river has been diverted northward by alluvial fans deposited at the base of the Eden fault scarp, which hereabouts runs northeast to southwest. Elsewhere, however, this type of explanation does not hold. It is possible that the asymmetry is related to aspect, that is to different microclimatic conditions prevailing on two slopes of contrasted aspects.

One argument along these lines, briefly summarised, suggests that rain runs directly off the northern slopes, and that the debris eroded is carried away by the river in flood. On the southern slope, however, the rainfall is more indirect in character, the water seeps slowly to the base, and the debris carried arrives after the river has fallen, so that the debris accumulates at the foot of the southern slope and diverts the river northward, thus causing the northern bank to be undercut.

Another similar possibility is that the rains, which come predominantly from the southwest, arrive not vertically but at an angle, so that the south-facing slopes receive more rain than the opposite slopes, and are thus degraded more rapidly.

In some regions, the processes causing the widening of valleys are retarded for various reasons, and in these areas, narrow gorges are found. The Colorado river, for instance, in one section of its course, flows through an arid region where rainwash gullying, creep and slip, as well as tributary development, are negligible. Moreover, the local rocks (mainly sandstones) are resistant. The result is the Grand Canyon. The Murray Valley in South Australia is a similar though less spectacular example of aridity and resistant rocks together inducing gorge development. The narrowness of the valleys in both cases and the consequent marked undercutting of bluffs is another important contributary factor.

(f) VALLEY EXTENSION

Rivers extend their valleys both headwards and seawards. The incision and lowering of stream beds in the headwater regions causes slopes there to become unstable through oversteepening. Slumping occurs, and the stream extends backwards into the divide. Typical examples occur on the Willunga scarp (Fig. 129). It is through headward extension that streams are able to *capture* others (Fig. 130) as has commonly occurred in the Flinders Ranges and elsewhere. (This process of capture is also known as stream *piracy*.)

Much of the debris eroded during the excavation of river valleys is transported by rivers to the margins of the oceans, where it is deposited. In tideless or near tideless seas, the bulk of the deposition takes place very close to the river mouth where *deltas*, which develop in various forms accumulate. The surfaces of deltas are gradually built up so that they are exposed at low tide, at least. Although the river lengthens itself seaward, and headwards, the most important way in which a river extends its length is through the development of river curves.

Fig 128 Development of asymmetrical valleys on inclined strata (uniclinal shifting).

Fig 129 Headward erosion or extension of stream on the Willunga Scarp.

(g) WINDING AND MEANDERING

All natural rivers have irregular courses. They do not flow in straight channels but wind about to a greater or lesser extent. If in a tank, water is allowed to flow down a prepared straight channel free from obstructions, a winding course is soon developed. The winding habit appears to be inherent in flowing water, for river curves, often perfectly regular and sinuous, are found both on the plains and in mountainous regions. Indeed, some of the most spectacularly sinuous valleys occur in upland regions: deep gorges describe smooth curved courses and are called *incised* (or ingrown) meanders (Fig. 131). Such meanders display close adaptation to structure, as is shown in Fig. 132 depicting sections of the Torrens Gorge. Like the meanders of alluvial valleys, ingrown meanders continue to develop until adjacent parts of the same curve cut through the intervening neck of land and truncate the loop, forming an *abandoned ingrown meander*, encircling a *meander core*. An example from the Torrens Gorge (before inundation resulting from the construction of the Kangaroo Creek reservoir) is shown in Fig. 133, and one from the Yarra showing an incipient breach of the narrow neck in Fig. 134 (M.R. Yan Yean, Vic., 231457). Good examples of incised meanders are commonplace; those in Australia have not generally been described in the literature, though some have, e.g. from the Colo River near Sydney, and from the basalt plateaux regions of north Queensland.

River curves form more readily and rapidly in alluvial plains than in upland regions, where very much more material has to be shifted, and where there is more likelihood of the river flowing across resistant strata which obstruct the development of river curves. However, even plugs of

Fig 130 Stages in river capture.

clay in alluvial plains have a similarly restricting effect. Many rivers like the Murrumbidgee (M.R. Wagga Wagga, N.S.W. sheet, Fig. 135), the Murray (Tocumwal and Albury, N.S.W. sheets, Figs. 136, 137) and the Yarra (M.R. Yan Yean, Vic., 425537 and area) exhibit innumerable sinuous river curves along their courses, though some of the curves exhibit a curious angular form, particularly in coastal districts (Fig. 138, Pl. 53).

In winding streams, the main current does not occur in the geometrical centre of the flow. It tends to be closer to the outside bank in each curve (Fig. 139), where the river is also deepest. Between the curves, about the *point of inflexion* (where the curves meet), shoals occur, according to some writers, because it is here that the flow is widest, being least parallel to the river banks, and the velocity also lowest. Because the channel is shallow it may be assumed that the velocity is greater there than in deeper sectors, but the cross-sectional area of the current, being oblique or non-parallel to the banks is actually rather greater here than elsewhere, so that the velocity is probably lower as is consistent with shoal development.

The river banks are eroded on the outside and downstream sides of each curve (Fig. 139). Concurrently, deposition takes place on the inside of each curve, at the point of each spur partially enclosed by the loop of the river. These are called *point bars* and the deposits, point bar deposits. Both are well displayed in the Torrens Gorge. The river gradually migrates laterally eroding *bluffs* and leaving behind a series of *slip-off slopes* (Fig. 131). The windings of the river develop until the curves reach a maximum radius, which is commonly fourteen to seventeen times the width of the river at any given point, when the intervening necks of land are cut through and the former river loops abandoned to become the well-known *ox-bow lakes* (Figs. 135–8, Pl. 54). The river also migrates along its valley, sweeping downstream in a series of curves, paring away the upstream sides of the interlocking spurs (Fig. 140), and eventually developing a flat floored *plain of lateral corrasion* which is floored with alluvial deposits (a complex of point bar deposits laid down during successive sweeps of the river) and which is bound by more-or-less steep river *bluffs* (Fig. 141). When the river has excavated a plain of lateral corrasion of such a width that the river curves can develop freely without further eroding the bluffs to achieve their maximum potential radius, the river curves are referred to as *meanders*. The belt within which they flow, and which is of the same width as the maximum radius of river meanders at that point, is the *meander belt*. The widening of the river valley does not cease with the development of meanders for the meander belt also migrates from side-to-side undermining the bounding bluffs and causing the lateral extension of the flat-floored plain.

The winding and meandering habit of rivers is obviously an important factor in landscape development. As yet, however, there is no comprehensive and reasoned explanation of their development. Many facts are known about meandering streams, but the basic cause of meandering is still not understood. It is known that there is a fairly constant relationship between stream discharge (Q) at bank-full stage and the width of the river, amplitude or radius of meanders and the wave length of the meanders. All are proportional to the square root of the discharge ($Q^{\frac{1}{2}}$). Laboratory work has shown that the size of meanders increases with increase in discharge, slope (to some extent) and angle of attack or degree of non-parallelism between current and banks. All other factors being equal, the more sinuous the stream the deeper it is.

Chance obstructions in a channel, the earth's rotation and excess of energy and load have all been cited as basic causes of stream meandering, but all have been found inadequate. Obstructions, such as trees and rocks, certainly divert flows unequally, but this is a subordinate effect, for streams of pure water display a meandering tendency. Other obstructions, such as rock bars, and even clay layers, actually restrict meandering by inhibiting lateral movement. If the Coriolis force has any effect on rivers, as has been suggested for more than a century, rivers in the Northern hemisphere should have a tendency to erode their right banks more than their left; and *vice versa* in the Southern hemisphere. There is no evidence that this consistently occurs. The load of a stream has little or nothing to do with meandering: its transfer appears to be an effect rather than a cause, for streams of meltwaters flowing on the surface of glaciers, and devoid of any sediment, exhibit the meandering habit, as do streams of distilled water flowing down sheets of glass (either on top or on the underside).

Fig 131 Form-line sketch of incised meander.

Fig 132 Incised meanders of the River Torrens and their relation to structures in the country rock (*reproduced by kind permission J. L. Talbot*).

Rivers and Valleys

Fig 133 Abandoned incised meander and meander core in the Torrens Gorge.

Fig 134 Incised meanders in the Dandenong Ranges, Vic.

Fig 135 Meanders on the Murrumbidgee, 10 miles west of Wagga Wagga, N.S.W.

Fig 136 Sinuous course of the Murray at Tocumwal, N.S.W.

There are strong suggestions that in rivers, helicoidal flows, spirals or vortices develop. This tendency may be initiated by the deposition of pools and shoals (or riffles) of highs and lows on the bed relief, which develop in any natural flow of water. Work in the U.S.A. has shown that even in relatively straight stream sectors, pools develop at regular intervals on the bed. The spacing of these is similar to that of the wave length of meanders that would be appropriate to the discharge of the stream considered. The moulding of the channel bed appears fundamental to the initiation of meanders, and the helicoidal type of flow to their development. The deposition of regularly spaced shoals appears to be analagous with wave development which occurs wherever one medium passes over another: air over water (see Chapter 8), air over sand

180 *Geomorphology*

Fig 137 Meandering course of the Murray near Albury.

Fig 138 The lower Onkaparinga river near Noarlunga showing meander loops and ox bow lake.

Rivers and Valleys

Fig 139 Path of the strongest current in stream and erosion of outside and downstream banks of a winding river.

Fig 140 Development of flat floored valley and truncation of spurs during gradual downstream sweep of meanders.

Fig 141 River bluffs and flood plain excavated by a winding river.

Fig 142 A misfit stream.

Plate 53 Arm Creek, west of Nicholson River, Northern Territory—a sinuous river course in the littoral zone of the Gulf of Carpentaria. Bentinck Island is in the distance. (*Dept. National Development*)

Plate 54 River meanders and ox bow lakes on the River Murray near Renmark. (*S.A. Lands Department*)

Plate 55 A braided and distributary stream, the Diamantina, in the northeast of South Australia. (*S.A. Lands Department*) (see Chapter 7), or water over sediment. In such boundary conditions, it seems that waves form, and in streams, the shoals initiate river curves and meanders.

Some of the established geometrical relationships of meandering streams are useful and important. The regular distribution of shoals and shallows, for example, is of importance in navigation. The consistent relationship between bankfull discharge, meander wave length and amplitude, and width of river has led to the strong suggestion (many would say demonstration) that in the recent past many rivers (for instance in Britain and north-eastern United States) had bigger discharges than at present. Many winding valleys were excavated by streams which, to judge by the geometry of the valleys, were much larger than those which now occupy them; the former river channels were not only wider but developed meanders of greater amplitude. The present streams are *misfit* streams for they do not match the geometry of their valleys (see Fig. 142). It is believed that the greater discharges date from wetter periods in the Pleistocene (see Chapter 10).

(h) BRAIDED STREAMS

Some streams consist of many channels separated by debris islands (Pl. 55). Others consist of a number of channels cut in the local bedrock, but interwoven and inter-connecting. In either case, the rivers are described as braided. Most braided streams in northern Australia are not winding —but these are exceptions. In other parts of the world, streams which are both braided and meandering (*anastomose*) are well known. Braided streams or stream sectors are wider and shallower than meandering streams. They are steeper and have higher bankfull discharges than meandering streams. As is shown in Fig. 143, for a given discharge, the braided stream has a steeper gradient than its meandering counterpart; and for a given gradient the braided stream has a greater discharge than a meandering stream.

Thus if a stream of meandering habit is tilted, say by an earth movement in the headwater region, it may change to a braided habit if the tilting is of a critical amount for a stream of the discharge considered. This appears to have occurred in northwest Queensland, where the Leichardt and Flinders rivers both show clear signs of being formerly meandering streams, but both now flow in incised braided channels. There is evidence of a slight uplift in their headwater regions during recent geological time (see Chapter 3(e)).

Thus discharge and gradient are primary controls of stream habit. An important contributory factor influencing the development of braided streams is the readiness with which shoals and alluvial accumulations generally are fixed or stabilised by vegetation. In arid and semi-arid regions, like central and northern Australia, where the majority of river

Fig 143 Relationship between stream gradient, discharge and habit (*after Leopold and Wolman*).

Fig 144 Chute on Kanyaka Creek, southern Flinders Ranges.

Rivers and Valleys 187

Fig 145 (a) and (b) Ria coast due to rise of sea level or subsidence of the land.

Fig 146 Deposition in river valley due to relative rise of sea level.

Fig 147 A truncated drainage system, Port Phillip Bay (*after Hills*).

courses are braided (Pl. 56) this is accomplished during the long dry periods between periods of flow. In the humid tropics where braided streams also are common (e.g. the Amazon), vegetation is also very readily established. Another contributary factor is the propensity to flooding which causes waters to spread beyond the confines of the channel and scour other, connecting, side channels; yet another is an abundant supply of debris.

(i) SHORTENING OF THE RIVER
Rivers lengthen themselves greatly. They also shorten themselves though not nearly to the same extent as they extend. They effect temporary shortening by cutting off their meanders. In flood too, the main current does not follow round the outside of curves but straightens so that the point bar is commonly eroded or separated from the main spur by a channel called a shute or *chute*. They occur very commonly in the Flinders Ranges where they are easily observed when the rivers are dry, as they mostly are (see Fig. 144).

(j) MOVEMENTS OF BASELEVEL
Changes in stream regime can be effected by several factors including climatic changes; alterations in the state of vegetation; and changes of baselevel, local or ultimate, caused by earth movements or by shifts of sea level. Possibly the simplest illustration of the effects of alterations in river regime on the landform assemblage is provided by shifts of sea level,

Fig 148 Port Jackson—a drowned river valley.

Rivers and Valleys

the ultimate baselevel of erosion. A rise of sea level relative to the land is called a *positive* movement of the sea, a relative lowering of sea level is termed a *negative* movement.

A positive movement converts the river mouth and the lower seaward part of the valley into either an *estuary*, a *fjord*, or a *ria* (Fig. 145) according to the nature of the relief. Islands and their irregularities are characteristic of such coasts. In the lower part of river valleys, there is deposition (Fig. 146). Rivers are shortened and the new drainage system truncated (Fig. 147). Sydney Harbour is one of the best-known drowned river valleys, but examples are common on the Australian east coast, in the Kimberleys and in the southwest of Tasmania (Figs. 148, 149, 150).

If sea level is lowered, a characteristic assemblage of forms is developed. Negative movements of the sea cause streams to be lengthened and drainage systems to be extended across the former coastal platforms and

Fig 149   Ria coast from the north Kimberleys, W.A.

the upper part of the Continental Shelf (Fig. 151). The coast tends to be smooth, regular and low lying. Rivers cut and lower their beds with renewed vigour, and are said to be *rejuvenated*. A new, deeper thalweg is developed. Where the new profile meets the older, more gentle thalweg, a sharp break of slope, called a *nick point*, and commonly represented by rapids and waterfalls is formed: the Barron above Cairns is an excellent example (Fig. 124). Concurrently, valley side slopes are steepened at their bases as they grade to the new river level, and a slope with distinct facets—*valley-side facets*—is formed (Fig. 152a) on either side of the river. The overall effect is of a small valley set into another, larger, but similar feature—a valley-in-valley form of which the Murray in the vicinity of Walkers Flat is an excellent example (Fig. 113). Tributary streams meet the main river in distinct breaks of slope: *discordant* junctions as opposed to the *accordant* junctions characteristic of graded stream systems.

Not all falls and rapids indicate nick points, for hard-rock strata crossing the river's path may well produce a break of slope; however, a true nick point and a hard stratum may be coincident. Nick points gradually migrate upstream, and the new valley grows at the expense of the old (which however, continues to extend in *its* headwater region). If a nick point encounters a resistant stratum (Fig. 152b) it may be delayed at that point. If it is a nick point, valley side facets will be associated with

Fig 150   Port Davey, southwestern Tasmania.

it and, moreover, there should be similar nick points in neighbouring valleys.

The incision of the main stream valley causes similar rejuvenation in all tributary valleys below the nick point, but it should be noted that similar effects result from stream meandering. As a winding river approaches the valley side, tributaries on that side are shortened and steepened and thus erode their beds with renewed vigour: they are rejuvenated and the former gradient or bed is left perched or hanging (see Figs. 153, 154). There are many examples in the gorges of the Mt Lofty Ranges. However, when the stream swings away from that tributary, it extends and builds up its bed. Thus in any given valley, all tributaries are rejuvenated where there has been a general lowering of base level, but where apparent rejuvenation is due to river migration, some valleys are incised, depending on their location with respect to the outside of river curves.

If rejuvenation proceeds to a stage where the former flattish valley floors are abandoned and left above the level of even the highest flood, *river terraces* are formed. A river terrace is an old flood plain now beyond the reach of the highest flood. *Erosional terraces* are formed through the lateral migration of a river during slow incision, and thus tend to be unpaired, i.e. at different elevations or opposite sides of the river (Fig. 155). Examples are common and are typically well developed in the Torrens Gorge and in the Torrens Valley between Hillcrest and Adelaide city (Fig. 156).

Fig 151 An extended drainage system. The streams flowed to the sea at shoreline (1), but after retreat of the sea extended to shoreline (2).

Fig 152 (a) Nick point and valley-side facets; (b) successive nick points accumulated at a resistant stratum; (c) valley in valley form at Mannum Falls.

Fig 153 Perched stream, a discordant tributary junction, Gorge Creek, eastern Mt Lofty Ranges.

Rivers and Valleys

Terraces due to *deposition* followed by incision are also common in the Adelaide area, for instance along the Torrens, Gawler and lower Onkaparinga rivers. They are easily distinguished from the erosional type, because they are built of alluvium[2] and, more important, are paired or matched, both being at the same elevation on either side of the river. (Fig. 157). Many of the gullies on the Willunga scarp display terraces of this type and on some, remnants of the former stream channel are preserved (Pl. 57). Deep narrow channels are excavated in the reddish-brown clays, sands and gravels of the alluvial fans fronting the scarp. In these, grey-black alluvium was deposited, causing the development of a flat alluvial floor over which wound shallow stream channels. Subsequently (probably following white settlement), the streams cut deeply into their own alluvium and into the fan deposits, leaving the former alluvial flats high and dry as paired constructional terraces.

River terraces are commonplace along some sectors of most river valleys. They are by no means restricted to the plain tracts but are widely,

Fig 154 Effect of stream winding on tributary valleys: (a) and (b) block diagrams; (c) and (d) in section.

Fig 155 Unpaired or unmatched river terraces.

Fig 156 (a) Morphological map of the Lower Torrens Valley; (b) Sketch block diagram of the terraces formed by lateral corrosion during slow incision: (1) Klemzig terrace; (2) Walkerville terrace; (3) Parklands terrace; (4) Hackney-Felixstowe terrace; (5) depositional terrace remnant of Walkerville Sand; (6) present channel of the River Torrens.

Fig 157 Paired terraces.

Plate 56 The Einasleigh River at Abingdon H.S., north Queensland. Parallel vegetated islands subdivide the channel—a braided river. (*C.S.I.R.O.*)

Plate 57 Shallow former stream channel preserved on terrace remnant, Willunga scarp if locally, developed in upland valleys, where they are found singly or in flights on slip-off slopes (Fig. 158). Many of the very fine river terraces of New Zealand have been well described, but there are few geomorphological accounts of Australian examples. They undoubtedly occur, having been mentioned incidentally in connection with other studies. One occurs 163 feet above river level along the Maribyrnong, at Keilor, Victoria; others on several of the Darling Downs Rivers, on the Nepean between Richmond and Emu Plains and on the Colo River, N.S.W., Terraces are well developed on the Swan and Helena rivers, Perth, where three distinct former river levels, represented in descending order by the Guildford, West Midland, and Helena terraces, stand higher than the present river bed. In several of the small topographical basins of the upper Murrumbidgee, e.g. at Yaouk, N.S.W. (M.R. Canberra, N.S.W., 1:253,440; 183,576) splendid, but strictly local terraces are displayed. Of particular interest are terraces described from the Hunter valley, and from southern N.S.W. and the A.C.T. (e.g. along the Molonglo) which are thought to be related to climatic fluctuations, to relatively dry (terrace building) and wet (terrace incision) phases.

(k) CLASSIFICATIONS OF STREAMS

Streams and their valleys may be classified in several ways, according to the criteria used.

(i) *Classification according to stage of development*

A cycle in the geomorphological sense is a sequence of events through which a stream, valley or landscape passes, the end result being similar to the original (see Chapter 11). It is conceived that a stream, for example, passes through recognisable phases of development which are described in human terms: youth, maturity, and old age or senility.

Youth sees the elimination of all irregularities in the longitudinal stream profile. At the end of youth a stream has a smooth profile or is graded, from source to sea. During youth the proportion of vertical to lateral erosion is at its greatest though incision in most cases is less than valley widening. Early maturity is occupied essentially with lateral corrasion and the development of a flood plain or plain of lateral corrasion. Middle maturity is reached when the valley width is equal to the width of the meander belt. The river passes into old age when the breadth of the valley is several times that of the meander belt.

Considering the development of valleys (Fig. 4b) in youth, remnants of the initial surface of low relief are preserved high in the landscape. Maturity is reached when the last remnant of the original surface is eliminated, and when there is as yet little or no flat land in the valley floors: this is the stage of *all-slopes*. Following maturity the slopes are lowered and the relief amplitude (or vertical distance between highest and

Rivers and Valleys

Fig 158 Terraces at Cudlee Creek, in the Torrens Gorge.

Fig 159 Classification of streams according to their relation to the underlying strata.

Fig 160 Streams named according to their relationship to underlying structures.

lowest points in the relief) which was at its maximum, henceforth decreases. Plains develop in the valley floors and, when these are several times as wide as the meander belt, old age is attained.

There may be slight anomalies between stream and valley development. This descriptive scheme is useful, but no absolute time connotation should be attached to the terms used. A stream eroding soft rocks and deceptively of old age type may, in absolute terms, be younger than a younger-looking stream which is excavating its valley in hard strata.

(ii) Classification according to origin

Streams may be considered in relation to the initial surface or slope upon which they flow (see Fig. 159). *Consequent* streams follow the initial slope of the land. *Subsequent* streams develop along zones of weakness, e.g. a soft stratum, zone of faulting. *Obsequent* streams evolve in relation to subsequent streams, as do *resequent* streams. Obsequent streams flow in a direction opposed to that of consequents and commonly are found on the downslope valley side of subsequents or on scarp faces. Resequent streams on the other hand flow in the same direction as consequents but are developed in relation to slopes formed later than those on which the consequents evolved. They are found on the upslope sides of subsequent valleys. Streams which fall into none of these categories are termed *insequent* streams.

(iii) Classification according to genetically related structures

Streams and valleys develop in geometric relation to certain structures in the underlying bedrock (see Chapter 2), and are labelled accordingly. Thus there are dip, strike, fault, anticlinal, synclinal and monoclinal streams and valleys (Fig. 160).

Fig 161 Superimposed drainage in the English Lake District: (a) folded Palaeozoic rocks; (b) Carboniferous limestone. The radial pattern developed on the limestone dome has been imposed upon the underlying contorted rocks.

Rivers and Valleys

(iv) Classification according to relations with foreign structures

In this category superimposed, inherited, antecedent and defeated streams are considered.

In *superimposed drainage*, the pattern of drainage is developed upon a higher stratum or sequence of rocks through which the streams erode to a lower mass of rocks with quite different structures from those of the higher. Thus the drainage pattern incised into the lower sequence bears no relation at all to its structures. The English Lake District provides a very good example (Fig. 161) but other examples are known, e.g. in the south Flinders Ranges (Fig. 162). *Inherited* drainage is similar to superimposed (or superposed as it is sometimes called), only here the original pattern derives not from a distinct and separate higher level rock sequence resting unconformably upon the other, but from a deep zone of weathering usually developed on a surface of low relief. Under such conditions a drainage pattern may gradually lose its relation to the structure of the underlying rocks.

In *antecedent* drainage it is assumed that an uplift occurs across established drainage lines, but so slowly that the streams can erode and maintain their courses. As a result, narrow deep gorges are excavated in the rising mass (Fig. 163). Antecedence is very difficult to prove and it is fair to comment that many instances of alleged antecedent drainage in fact involve river capture or superimposition; but Hills (*Physiography of Victoria*) has described the Dandenong Creek immediately east of Wheelers Hill (M.R. Ringwood, Vic., 233257) as of antecedent origin having maintained its course and cut a minor gorge during the differential

Fig 162 Development of superimposed drainage in the southern Flinders Ranges: (a) present pattern; (b) the superimposition in section; (c) and (d) the situations at levels 1 and 2 of (b).

uplift of the upland, and the Yarra 4 miles southwest of Yarra Glen (near M.R. Yan Yean, Vic., 347510) may be similar (Fig. 164) though other explanations are possible.

Defeated or thwarted streams are those which have been obstructed and diverted. The Murray near Echuca is an example related to earth movements (Chapter 3). Other defeated streams owe their obstruction and diversion to volcanic outpourings, as, for instance, to the north of Einasleigh, in north Queensland (Fig. 165). The Einasleigh river formerly flowed in a deeply intrenched loop (Inherited? Antecedent? Either is possible as both high level erosional surfaces and marked recent faulting are known in the area) excavated in porphyritic bedrock (A).

A late Tertiary lava flow however blocked the southern entrance at (B) causing the loop to be abandoned by the river, which found a new course to the east. In the same general area of north Queensland, major drainage modifications have been attributed to the late Cainozoic volcanicity; the headwaters of an ancestral Burdekin, for instance, having been defeated by lava flows and diverted westwards into the Gilbert catchment.

A rather special case of defeated drainage concerns disturbances due to glaciers.

If a mass of ice flows against or across the lines of regional drainage, lakes may be impounded between the slope of the land and the front of the obstruction. The lakes may overflow across a low pass and thus cause the erosion of a channel called a *glacial overflow channel* or *spillway* (see Chapter 9). Many examples are known in North America, Europe and Britain. The famous *urstromtäler* of northern Germany (Fig. 166) much used for canals, are channels eroded by glacial meltwaters flowing along the icefront. One of the most pronounced and obvious modifications of drainage caused by glacier ice is that of the Derwent in northern England (Fig. 167) which rises miles from the North Sea north of Flamborough Head yet flows directly away from the sea and reaches the ocean via the Humber estuary. The original outlet to the sea was blocked by ice and the diversion became a permanent feature.

Fig 163 Antecedent drainage: (a) initial profile; (b) stream maintains course across upfaulted block by eroding its bed as rapidly as uplift occurs.

Rivers and Valleys

Fig 164 Possible antecedent section of the Yarra; the loop of the river now flowing in the gorge may have maintained its course during the uplift of the Dandenongs.

Fig 165 Stream diversion by volcanism in north Queensland (*reproduced by courtesy of the Editor, Bulletin Volcanologique*).

Fig 166 *Urstromtäler* of the North European Plain (*after Shackleton*).

202 *Geomorphology*

Fig 167 The course of the River Derwent in Yorkshire, England.

(a) dendritic
(b) trellis
(c) rectangular
(d) radial
(e) centripetal
(f) annular
(g) parallel

Fig 168 Drainage patterns:
    (a) Dendritic drainage
    (b) Trellised drainage   e.g. Flinders Ranges, north of Quorn
    (c) Rectangular   e.g. Flinders Ranges, east of Wilpena
    (d) Radial drainage   e.g. Blinman area
    (e) Centripetal drainage   e.g. Lake Eyre basin
    (f) Annular drainage   e.g. Blinman area
    (g) Parallel drainage   e.g. Willunga scarp

In each of these examples, the present drainage system is not related to the structures of the rocks through which it flows but to past events and situations, although in most cases there is evidence of adjustment to the local structures.

(v) Classification according to relations to baselevel
Streams and their valleys may be *drowned* or *rejuvenated* (see pages 185–196).

(vi) Classification according to the pattern of drainage lines
Streams normally are closely related to the structures of the bedrock over which they flow. Their pattern is a result of structure and slope; and the pattern of streams can be used as a guide to the underlying structure. There are six principal types of pattern each with several subtypes which will not be described. Good examples of several of these major types occur in South Australia (Fig. 168) and in other States.

Dendritic drainage. Insequent streams indicating uniformly resistant strata, and usually horizontal unconsolidated rocks (Fig. 168a).

Trellis drainage. Structurally controlled, e.g. by alternate bands of hard and soft strata, more or less steeply dipping, or by recently deposited and aligned glacial deposits. Subsequent streams are long, and are joined by short consequent or obsequent or resequent streams (Fig. 168b).

Rectangular drainage. Strong structural control but less regular than trellis type. Streams follow joints or faults and are all subsequents. Typically developed in granite areas where joints exert strong control (Fig. 168c).

Radial drainage. Consequent streams flow out in all directions from an undissected dome (Fig. 168d). Where there is a basin structure all streams flow toward the centre and the pattern is described as centripetal (Figs 50, 168e).

Annular drainage. Developed on a dome or basin which has been dissected and in which concentrically arranged hard and soft strata are exposed. The principal streams develop in the soft strata and are joined by consequent, obsequent or resequent streams (Fig. 168f).

Parallel drainage. Where there is a pronounced regional slope, consequent streams flowing parallel to one another occur (Fig. 168g).

Irregular or complex patterns. These display no definite pattern.

These classifications are not mutually exclusive, and a stream can be labelled by a variety of names according to the criteria used. Thus a single stream could be considered, a strike, subsequent, rejuvenated stream forming part of a trellis pattern.

NOTES

[1] Archaeological excavations on the lower Murray have brought to light evidence of an even higher flood dating from *circa* 1100 B.C.
[2] However, erosional terraces can be excavated in alluvium.

7. The Arid Lands

(a) INTRODUCTION

HOT DESERTS NOW OCCUPY large areas of Australia (Fig. 169) and were even more extensive in the recent past. The landforms of the arid regions vary considerably from place to place (Fig. 8). In some parts of the Australian desert there are stark uplands, as in the northwest of South Australia, and in the MacDonnell, James and other ranges of the southern part of the Northern Territory. Much of the west and centre of the continent is occupied by fields of sand dunes. In South Australia, two sandy deserts—parts of the Simpson and Great Victoria deserts—are separated by a plateau of stony desert, or gibber plain, which is found also in the famous Sturt's Stony Desert and in many other parts of the northeast of South Australia as well as the adjacent areas in N.S.W. Clay deserts are common bordering the Flinders Ranges, and in the deserts of south Queensland, and central Australia. *Playas*, either *claypans* or saltpans (*salinas*), occur throughout the north and west, though the largest occur in association with upland regions. Lake Gairdner lies within its Gawler Ranges, while Lakes Torrens, Eyre and Frome, as well as several other major salinas are scattered around the western, northern and eastern margins of the Flinders Ranges. Lake Amadeus is a large salina in the Northern Territory and so common are salinas in the southern half of Western Australia that the area has been labelled 'Salinaland'. Elongate saltpans, isolated and desiccated remnants of a former drainage system, are numerous—Lakes Cowan, Seabrook, Monger and Carnegie are a few examples among thousands. Bordering the Australian Bight is another kind of desert, an area which would be desert by virtue of its climate alone, but the aridity is emphasised by its limestone lithology—the karst plain of the Nullarbor, the geomorphology of which has already been described.

In these desert areas, both wind and water are important agents moulding the land surface. Many common erosional features, such as hillslopes and plains, are similar to forms found in semi-arid and even temperate regions, and are due to the work of running water. Other forms, particularly some of depositional origin are essentially restricted to arid regions and are due to wind action.

(b) WATER IN THE DESERTS
(i) Importance of water
Although defined as an area of low average rainfall, no desert is

Fig 169   Map of the desert regions of Australia (*after Mabbutt*).

completely waterless. There are long periods when no precipitation is received but the rain that falls is sometimes in torrential proportions, and has more effect on the land surface than has similar rainfall in temperate regions. The reason for the effectiveness of rainfall as an agent of erosion and deposition in the arid lands is not that it is more intense than elsewhere: on the contrary, the evidence available suggests that there is a similar range and frequency of intense rainstorms in the hot deserts as in other climatic regions. Heavy and intense storms occur, but the effectiveness of the rain is related to other factors.

Vegetation is either sparse or absent from the desert land surface, which is therefore particularly susceptible to both the splash effect of falling raindrops (in a heavy rainstorm as much as 100 tons of soil an acre may be thrown into the air from a ploughed field) and the scouring effects of rills and streams.

The desiccated surface of the desert is relatively impermeable to water and little rain seeps into the ground; much of the water is held at the surface so that, although a very large proportion of the rain is returned to the atmosphere by evaporation, the run off remaining is rapid. Floods, which are especially effective in erosion and the transport of debris, are the rule rather than the exception in the deserts. The rapid runoff of rain in arid regions is also encouraged by the common presence of resistant cappings and pans of calcrete, ferricrete or silcrete (see Chapter 5). The intermittent nature of river flow means that large volumes of unconsolidated debris which is easily eroded, and which also provides the load, or tools of erosion for streams, are dumped on slopes and in valleys and are readily available during the next rains.

Finally, between rainstorms the land surface is but little changed, so that infrequent though these episodes are, the relative importance of running water is high.

Fig 170 Alluvial pans on the western margin of the Flinders Ranges, north of Port Augusta.

In addition to the effects of running water, chemical and physical weathering due to moisture is important. Its precise relative importance is difficult to assess owing to the possibility of past weathering under wetter conditions being inherited and displayed in the present landscape.

(ii) Desert streams
A few streams, such as the Nile, Indus and Murray, rise and derive their waters from beyond, but have sufficient volume to survive the passage across the arid lands (allogenic or exotic streams). Apart from these, desert rivers, or *wadis*, with steep sides and flat floors, flow only spasmodically. They rise and flood with remarkable rapidity following rains, and many a traveller has been caught in stream beds by such flash floods. A party of geologists camping in the dry bed of the Hay River, near the northern edge of the Simpson Desert, had the experience of seeing their camp float away on a flood in August 1962. The floods fall as quickly as they rise. Most rivers that rise in or enter deserts gradually fade and are lost in the desert sands. Some, such as the Hay, wind fantastically as they do so; others, such as the Diamantina (Pl. 55) divide into a number of distributaries, each losing itself in the desert.

The streams of desert uplands flow in rocky, steep sided valleys. Wash and rills and tributaries scour the bare hillsides of loose and weathered rock, and immense amounts of waste material are carried to the main river courses to be carried to the plains.

(iii) Alluvial fans
Where streams leave the uplands and debouch onto lowlands, they leave the narrow confines of the gorges they have excavated and spread, fan-like, over the plains. The area of contact between water and land surface (the wetted perimeter) increases, energy losses due to friction increase, and the stream deposits some of its load—the coarser fraction first. This, in turn, increases still further the wetted perimeter and energy loss, so that more deposition takes place and the shoals or debris islands formed still further retard stream flow. The result is that the stream deposits a large part of its load in the form of a low angle cone or alluvial fan, over which it flows in a large number of distributary channels. Commonly, alluvial fans built of layers of ill-sorted debris, coalesce to form a continuous apron fronting the uplands (Pl. 58; Fig. 170).

(iv) Pediments and slopes
Comparatively little water, carrying only fine material, survives to flow across the plains and then only in major floods. The channels of the plains are typically trough-shaped in cross section. They are either very winding or subdivided into many channels (braided) or both. They flow to the lowest part of the plain where ephemeral lakes form. These temporary lakes are called playas; when their floors are of clay or other

Plate 58 Alluvial fans deposited by streams emerging from an upland region, Zagros Mountains, Iran. (*Hunting Aerosurveys Ltd*) fine alluvium they are called claypans, but where there is an accumulation of salts, they are termed salinas.

Between the mountain border, which may or may not be fronted by alluvial fans, and the zone of thick accumulation in the centre of the basin, are relatively narrow zones of bedrock plains carrying only a veneer of debris, and called *pediments*.

The plains are only slightly dissected, with a smooth surface and gently sloping at angles between one and seven degrees. Lines of concentrated drainage are few. A veneer of detritus rests upon the bedrock, but this cover is thin and the plains are generally considered essentially to be erosional bedrock features. Such plains or pediments are commonly faintly concave in longitudinal section, though rectilinearity is common and convexity is not unknown. In arid, and especially in semi-arid lands, the transition between hill and plain tends generally to be more abrupt than in humid regions. This critical sharp transition between pediment and backing scarp is called the *piedmont angle*. Its origin is discussed in Chapter 11.

Pediments were first described from the American southwest but have since been reported from many parts of the world. It is generally agreed that pediments are forms typical of arid and semi-arid lands, but a few workers, principally the South African, L. C. King, consider that all plains moulded by running water are of this type. Many workers now consider that a complex of processes—weathering, rill wash, sheet wash and sheet flow are responsible for the moulding of pediments, which, it can be shown, erode regressively and gradually consume uplands.

One problem concerning the origin of pediments relates to the debris veneer or mantle which is such a common feature of these plains (Pl. 59). Indeed, the writer knows of no truly bedrock plains in South Australia which are quite devoid of debris; a mantle, usually of coarse quartzitic debris, is ubiquitous. Within and at the margins of the Flinders Ranges, around Brachina, Wilpena Pound, Italowie, for instance, this is so. Even where the mantle is of generally finer material, as in the Olary or Barrier Ranges near Broken Hill (Pl. 60), and in parts of the ranges of the north-west of South Australia, the effect is similar. These stone mantles are extremely important for they protect the sediments and weathered rocks beneath from surface erosion. However, bearing in mind the presence of the coarse mantle, what shapes the surface of the pediment? The surface is attacked by wind and water, and fine debris is removed, thus causing a concentration of the coarse fraction, and rendering the surface increasingly stable. The bedrock surface becomes more and more immune to surface agents, and it can be concluded that the bedrock pediment is moulded:

(1) At the scarp foot, by rills and wash, before the debris mantle is thick and immobile. As the scarp retreats, so this narrow zone of

Plate 59 Gibber plain near Wilpena. The upland is the Chace Range underlain by sandstone dipping to the left. Plateau remnants front the range and carry a mantle of coarse quartzitic debris similar to that which covers the valley floor.

Plate 60 Pediments and inselbergs at The Pinnacles, near Broken Hill, N.S.W. The mantle covering the pediments here is mostly of fine debris intermixed with fragments of gravel size.

active pedimentation migrates headwards (Fig. 171).

(2) After burial by the mantle by subsurface weathering and subsurface flushes of water. These activities do not necessarily reduce the relief of the bedrock surface; on the contrary, they may increase its amplitude.

The distinction between pediments and the valley side-slopes of humid temperate regions rests basically upon the nature of the junction between plain and backing upland. Other differences are of degree rather than type. The abruptness of transition between pediment and escarpment varies considerably from place to place. In some places the piedmont angle is so sharp that one can literally place a finger upon the angular contact, and some granite landscapes (Fig. 172), and semi-arid tropical karsts (Fig. 173) admirably display such junctions. Elsewhere, and more generally, the junction is not as sharp as it appears from some distance, for there is in reality a gradual change of slope, a smooth concavity or steep curve. This is restricted to a relatively narrow zone, and the transition from plain to upland in arid regions is commonly more abrupt than in, say, humid temperate regions.

An important feature of pediments, apart from the piedmont angle, is their quite remarkable smoothness (Pl. 14). This is rather misleading, for while the surface is certainly smooth, the bedrock beneath the debris mantle is broadly even, but irregular in detail. The surface smoothness is due to the evening effects of the debris blanket. Furthermore, the preservation of many old pediments in South Australia is due to concentrations of coarse debris in these mantles. Thus important features of pediments are caused by deposition, and not erosion.

(v) Playas

The water and fine sediment carried beyond the pediment fringe comes to rest in the centre of the local drainage basins. Here great thicknesses of sediment are deposited and many ephemeral lakes are formed, soon to become either claypans or salinas.

Many hundreds of playas, large and small, occur within the South Australian arid zone. Four salinas, Lakes Eyre, Torrens, Frome and Gairdner, are notable for their great size (Fig. 51); and Lake Callabonna is famous for its contained fossiliferous remains of giant marsupials.

Lake Eyre occupies an area of about 3,600 square miles in the driest part of Australia. It lies wholly within the 5 inch isohyet. The Lake was discovered by and named after E. J. Eyre, who did not realise what he had found: in 1840 he touched upon the shores of both Lake Torrens and Lake Eyre and saw Lake Frome from afar, from the top of Mt Serle in the northern Flinders Ranges, and he thought he had seen but one lake which he imagined encircled the northern Flinders on three sides.

Lake Eyre at its lowest point is about 46 feet below present sea level,

Fig 171　Pedimentation and scarp retreat (*reproduced by kind permission University of Chicago Press*).

Fig 172　Sketch of pediment and inselberg developed on granite in northwest Queensland. Note the sharp break of slope (piedmont angle) between hill and plain (*from photograph*).

which is the lowest point of land so far recorded in Australia. However, reconnaissance survey has suggested that an area near Poeppels Corner (Fig. 53), may be about 60 feet below sea level, but it awaits further investigation. For many millions of years, the Lake Eyre depression between the Eastern Uplands and the West Australian Shield has been an area of subsidence. The subsidence has been most marked on the western side of the basin. Hence the very marked asymmetry of structure and drainage (Fig. 50). The earth movements have not ceased and there is reason to believe that the Lake bed is still tilting to the south, for the Warburton 'groove' runs north to south (Fig. 53) strongly suggesting a southerly tilt.

A diagrammatic section of the sediments of the Lake bed and cliffs is shown in Fig. 174. The region clearly has a complex history. For most of the later geological time it has been a depressed area, and for the past 100 million years or so, there has been discontinuous deposition in lake basins. During the later part of the Cretaceous, an extensive sequence of lake deposits was laid down and deposition continued into the early Tertiary. The sediments of this ancient lake, called Lake Dieri, occur at depth below the present Lake Eyre. During early Tertiary times, many of the lake sediments were exposed and subjected to weathering, resulting in the formation of duricrust, in places rich in iron, but more commonly heavily indurated with silica.

Following this phase of weathering, shallow lagoon conditions prevailed, and the sands, clays and dolomites of the Etadunna Formation, with its rich fauna of mammalian, crocodilian, turtle and fish remains, were deposited. These also underlie Lake Eyre and occur in creek sections to the east of the lake.

In the stream channels to the east, alluvium was laid down and here a rich fauna of marsupial remains is found. In the lake itself there is evidence that some 40 or 45 feet of sediments were laid down above the Etadunna Formation. This phase of deposition was interrupted about 40,000 years ago, as indicated by small shells taken from the top of the

Fig 173 Abrupt piedmont angle at base of limestone cliffs, Napier Range, W.A. (*drawn from photograph taken by J. N. Jennings*).

cliffs that bound the modern lake and which have been dated by the radiocarbon method. By about 20,000 years ago the floor of the lake had been lowered to a level about 60 feet below present sea level, for the former lake bed is now about 15 feet below the present floor of the lake. Lastly, about 15 feet of sediments and salts have accumulated above the old lake floor. The sediments consist of silts rich in gypsum, though with sands and grit at the lake margin, and overlain by a crust of salt up to 17 inches thick. At a depth of 3 to 5 feet there is another stratum of salt in some areas.

Lake Eyre is the focus of a huge network of rivers. The Georgina, the Diamantina, the Warburton, the Thomson, Coopers Creek and the Barcoo all drain to Lake Eyre (Fig. 50). Nevertheless, particular circumstances must occur before water can reach the bed of Lake Eyre. Much of the huge catchment is extremely dry and it seems that one year of extraordinarily heavy rains serves only to soak the soil. Two consecutive years of heavy rains are necessary before the bed of the Lake can be covered completely, though more localised heavy rains (e.g. in the Macumba and Neales drainage during the winter of 1966) can carry water to the lake bed.

Lake Eyre was filled with water for the first time in human memory in the 1949–50 season. There were widespread rains throughout the Lake Eyre catchment in 1949 and 1950 and the whole of Lake Eyre North was filled, to an average depth of 7 feet, and a maximum, attained in the southeast corner, of 13 feet. Only a tongue of water extended through the Goyder Channel, connecting the northern and southern lakes. A study

Fig 174 Stratigraphic section of cliffs at the southeast margin of Lake Eyre Basin (*after King*).

of past weather records suggests that the Lake fills perhaps twice a century, though it may be partially filled in several years.

Like Lake Eyre, Lake Frome, Lake Torrens and many other of the larger salinas appear to be partly of tectonic origin. Lake Gairdner appears to be an infilled ancient valley system whose form in plan is strongly controlled by jointing in the Gawler Range porphyry. Lake Amadeus occupies the centre of a depression strongly down-faulted on its northern side and partly faulted on the south (Fig. 175).

Lake Frome is the least known of all the major salinas. It occasionally receives water from a wide area, including Wilpena Pound, but lies in the midst of a vast flat sand-ridge plain. On the salt surface there are mound springs about 100 yards in diameter and standing some 8 to 10 feet above the lake level. There are low cliffs at the lake edge in many places.

Lake Gairdner lies amidst the beautiful rounded red hills of the Gawler Ranges. A thin crust of salt is underlain by moist sands and silts, not more than a few dozen feet thick. Numerous 'islands' of the local bedrock, the Gawler Range porphyry, occur, and at the borders of the lake there are low cliffs and high, red sand dunes (Pl. 61).

Lake Torrens is underlain by a thick sequence of sediments, mostly freshwater and early Tertiary in age, and is bounded on the western side by a dissected fault scarp. A considerable body of water formerly occupied the Lake Torrens basin which is today a mass of red sand dunes of the longitudinal type. Most of the dunes are fixed, though there is considerable local wind erosion on the plains (Pl. 62). Two examples of small barchans have been found in this locality. As with Lake Frome, many major streams (such as the Hookina) which drain a large area of the Flinders Ranges occasionally flood and reach the lake.

The large quantities of salt found in the salinas may have been derived from three sources:

(1) It may have entered the various 'lake' basins at a time when the sea extended far inland. There is some evidence at Andamooka that the sea may have extended far inland during the Pleistocene, but the evidence is not unequivocal. Also, had there been marine flooding of the interior, there should be signs of it in the form of widespread sea shells, beaches, and so on. These have not, so far, been found.

(2) It may have been dissolved out of the rocks in the 500,000 square mile catchment area of Lake Eyre and the other major salinas: *connate* salts.

(3) It may have been blown in from the sea, or from coastal areas (*cyclic* salt). In the case of the far interior, it is difficult to visualise salt being carried so far.

Each of these possibilities has authoritative support. All three sources may have been partly responsible, but the second possibility—salts derived from the strata of the catchment—appears most feasible.

(c) THE WORK OF WIND

The material carried from claypans by the wind, and particularly the sediment of the river flood plains forms a modern source of material for the wind to shape into dunes. In the past, also, it seems that the vast areas of alluvium laid down in the great tectonic depression which underlies the Lake Eyre Basin were sifted by the wind, and the finer fractions carried away to be built into dunes or even further afield to form thin layers of wind blown dust.

(i) Transportation and deposition by the wind

Where the land surface is desiccated and little protected by vegetation, wind becomes a significant agent of transportation and deposition. The wind effectively sorts weathered debris into three main sizes: dust, sand and coarse sand, and gravel. Dust is easily carried in suspension by the wind: this is called *deflation*. Fine and medium sand can be blown about by wind; it is commonly between 0·15 and 0·30 mm. diameter and is well sorted. It is not carried in suspension, but is carried along in a series of leaps and bounds in a process called *saltation* (Lat. *saltare*—to jump).

Consider a single grain of sand. It is picked up by a turbulent eddy or updraught in the wind, thus carrying it out of the zone of lower air flow, due to the boundary layer condition which are present close to the ground, and where frictional drag or retardation occurs. Once out of this zone, it flies through the air. Eventually the pull of gravity causes the grain to fall to the ground. It hits the ground at an angle just under 15° to the horizontal and one of two things happens (Fig. 176). The grain, made of quartz, which is an elastic medium, may riccochet off a stone and bounce back into the air to begin another leap. Or it may splash into a mass of other sand grains, many being ejected into the air by the impact of the first grain. Each of these may then be carried by the wind, and each may therefore begin a leap. Some of the sand grains moved by the saltating grain may not be thrown into the air, or at least not far enough to reach the zone of higher velocity, but they may be moved a short distance—nudged, as it were, in the downward direction. This slow progress along the land surface is known as *creep*.

The wind is quite unable to move coarse debris such as gravel and this remains *in situ*. It may be broken down by weathering to a size suitable for wind transportation, but much coarse debris remains and, due to the removal of fines by both wind and wash, is gradually concentrated to form a resistant, protective mantle covering the land surface.

Plate 61 The salina of Lake Gairdner on its eastern side, bordered by sand dunes, 20 feet high.

Plate 62 Wind erosion on the Lake Torrens plain. The root system of this tree has been exposed, suggesting a local lowering of the land surface of 3 to 4 feet.

(ii) Deflation
Deflation is responsible for the evacuation of very large amounts of dust. Most of the so-called sandstorms of the desert regions are in reality duststorms—great billowing masses of thousands of tons of dust carried in suspension in the air several thousands of feet above the earth. Sand is rarely carried more than three feet above the ground, and most of it is restricted to a layer within eight inches of the surface. The dust is carried far beyond the confines of the deserts. It has been carried from the Gobi desert of central Asia to northern China, where great masses of wind-blown dust, called *loess*, blanket the landscape to depths of between 400 and 1,000 feet. Red dust from central Australia is occasionally carried as far south as Adelaide, Perth and Melbourne and, in the past, has been deposited in many parts of southern Australia to form thin sheets of wind blown silt, called *parna*.

(iii) Sand dunes
Sand in the deserts may form amorphous sheets, in which the only relief takes the form of rather vague swellings 10 to 20 feet high. Such sand seas, or sand sheets, cover large areas in the Kalahari desert of south-western Africa. But the most typical form of the desert lands is unquestionably the dune. It is not the only landform of the arid regions; it does not occur only in deserts, for sand dunes are commonplace in coastal areas; but it is in the deserts that dunes occur on a major scale. In the Sahara, for instance, there is an unbroken field of dunes covering a region larger than France. Several major dune types are known: some are fixed, but others are mobile and are moved by the wind.

Fig 175 Tectonic setting of Lake Amadeus depression (*after Tectonic Map of Australia, Geol. Soc. Austr.*).

The simplest kind of *fixed* dune is merely a drift of sand piled up against, behind, or within an obstacle. On the Willochra plain, between Quorn and Hawker, and on the Lake Torrens plains, for example, there are accumulations of fine sand up to six feet high amongst the roots and branches of the spiny Nitre bush (*Nitraria schoberi*). Others of fixed habit, though ordinarily changing in detail, occur on the Lake Torrens plains west of Wilpena, adjacent to creek beds, and there is an as yet unexplained ridge of sand up to 500 feet high bordering the Nullarbor on its northern side (Fig. 177).

Mobile dunes are of several types, but the most important are the barchan, the transverse dune, and the longitudinal, or seif dune. The *barchan*, perhaps the best known sand dune, is crescent shaped in plan,

Fig 176 Movement of material by wind.

Fig 177 Diagrammatic cross-section of northern margin of the Nullarbor plain (*after Ludbrook*).

with the projections, or horns, pointing down-wind. The side of the dune facing into the wind is gentler than the lee slope and the dune in section parallel to the wind is not symmetrical. Sand is swept up the gentle slope and over the crest, where it comes to rest (Fig. 178). Sand is continually removed from the windward slope to the lee side, and although the shape of the dune remains more-or-less constant, it in fact migrates down-wind. Barchans are common in the Sahara, Arabia, central Asia and the American deserts; they are not known in the Kalahari, and in Australia only in isolation and semi-fixed in habit. They form where strong winds blow consistently from one direction (the wind is said to be *unidirectional*), and where the supply of sand, though adequate, is not abundant.

Where the wind is unidirectional but the supply of sand is abundant, *transverse dunes* are built. They are aligned normal to the prevalent strong wind direction, attain considerable height, and, like the barchan, have a gentle windward slope and steeper lee face. They too move down-wind through the transference of sand, and are common in the north African and Soviet deserts. Where the sand supply decreases, transverse dunes break up into barchans.

Longitudinal dunes, also known as *seifs*, are possibly the most common of the mobile desert dunes, and occupy large areas in all but the American deserts. They apparently develop where there is plenty of sand, and where there is a *bidirectional* wind regime: the dunes are moulded by winds from two dominant directions (Fig. 179a, b, c). Longitudinal dunes attain considerable heights—more than 300 feet in the Sahara, 650 feet in Iran—and extend continuously over long distances. It is typical that in cross section, one slope is rather steeper than the other.

Why do dunes form in some desert regions? The accumulation of sand in masses of regular and streamlined form, is, once begun, a cumulative process. The problem is initiation. It is possible that in individual and probably rare instances dunes may have been initiated by obstacles, which having served their purpose are left behind as the dune moves downwind. The obstacle may take the form of a patch of especially coarse sand, sufficient to disturb the airflow and so cause the initial deposition. But this cannot be a general explanation, for it is quite inadequate to explain extensive and continuous forms like transverse dunes. It is likely that the dunes of the hot deserts are yet another manifestation of wave patterns developed under boundary conditions. As is the case on lakes, the oceans, and stream beds, friction between a moving medium, in this case air, and the underlying land surface causes turbulence. The turbulent eddies become regularised as a series of wave patterns in which there are certain areas of low velocity where deposition is favoured. It may be that in this way dune building is initiated.

Sandy deserts with dune ridges occupy an area of about 145,000 square miles within South Australia alone. The two major areas of active dunes

Fig 178   A barchan dune.

(a)

(b)

(c)

Fig 179   (a) and (b). Longitudinal dunes in the Simpson Desert, on 28 August 1963 and 19 September 1963 respectively. View to north—in (a) wind from southeast, in (b) from southwest (*from photographs supplied by H. Wopfner*); (c) The transformation of a barchan into a seif or longitudinal dune under a bidirectional wind regime.

are the Simpson Desert, which extends into the Northern Territory and Queensland, and the Great Victoria Desert, which extends into Western Australia. The Simpson Desert is far better known than the Great Victoria, but longitudinal dunes predominate in both (Pls. 63, 64), though small transverse and irregular forms are found near areas of deflation.

The Simpson Desert is underlain by sediments which, on weathering, provide an adequate supply of sand. Alluvial debris is also supplied to the area from far afield by the several major rivers which enter it and the deflation of river outwash plains is an important source of dune sediment.

The sand forms a thin blanket which attains a maximum thickness of about 120 feet in the centre of the Simpson, and thins toward the margins. The dunes are underlain by late Pleistocene fossiliferous fluvial and lacustrine clays, and the modern dune fields are of Recent age. However, there is evidence of earlier dune systems (see below).

The dunes stand between 20 and 100 feet above the interdune corridors, are about a quarter of a mile apart (within 100 yards either way) and, in some cases, continuous over great distances. Some have been traced over a distance of 200 miles. In many areas the dunes run parallel, but convergences and divergences are commonplace and over wide areas, a chain-like pattern is common (Pl. 63; Fig. 180). The dunes are asymmetrical in cross-section and the eastern face is the steeper. The ridges trend north-northwest–south-southeast in the Simpson desert proper, but there is a regular arcuate trend throughout the northeast of South Australia. North of Alice Springs, the dunes run more northwesterly and in Western Australia, west-northwest to east-west. To the south, in the Gibson and Great Victoria Deserts, the trend is generally east-west (Fig. 181).

The dunes are the most spectacular and characteristic form of the desert, but others are present. Between Andado Homestead and the Hale River, there are several low cuestas of duricrusted surface, similar to those found on the Diamantina–Cooper divide. Several major rivers enter the desert from the north and flow occasionally in the interdune corridors. And between Peoppels Corner (the location where the borders of South Australia, Queensland and the Northern Territory meet) and Lake Eyre, there are hundreds of salinas and claypans, large and small, between the longitudinal dunes.

Longitudinal dunes are generally considered to form under the influence of a strong prevalent wind, plus a cross wind of some strength. Madigan to whom we owe much of our knowledge of the Simpson Desert, considered that the dunes form as a result of strong southerlies, organised in vortices, moulding the sand accumulated in the depression, aided by strong side winds which cause the prevalent asymmetry of the dunes. More recent observations suggest that the dunes are blown by winds from

Plate 63 Convergent longitudinal sand dunes, Simpson Desert. View from south. (*Photograph: R. C. Sprigg*)

the southeast and southwest, the steeper face of the lee slope changing location according to wind direction (Fig. 179a, b) and the whole dune trending in a direction which is the resultant or vector of the two prevailing winds.

Most of the dunes are believed to consist wholly of sand which is spasmodically moved in a northerly or downwind direction. Near Lake Eyre, however, this is not so. Borings show that the sand which appears

Plate 64 Longitudinal sand dunes in the Great Victoria Desert (*Geological Survey S.A.*).

on the surface is only a veneer overlying a corrugated, eroded surface cut in soft sediments (Fig. 174). They are analogous with yardangs (see below), and were cut by the wind to which they are parallel, but have subsequently been covered by a thin sheet of sand. Such features are called *windrift dunes*, and one writer (D. King) urges that they, and not true longitudinal dunes, are typical of the Australian sandridge deserts. Such an hypothesis would explain several otherwise curious features, but roads have been bulldozed through the dunes in mid desert, exposing up to 20 to 25 feet of the dunes, and they are seen to be built wholly of sand, confirming that they are, in fact, of the depositional longitudinal type.

The Great Victoria Desert is less well known, but the dunes appear to be similar to those of the Simpson (Pl. 64).

The sand is only a veneer covering a surface of low relief eroded across rocks of various types, and of ages varying from Archaean over most of the area to early Palaeozoic, Permian and late Tertiary at the margins. What little evidence there is suggests that over much of the desert, apart from the eastern margin, the plain, which rises gently from south to north from about 600 to about 2,000 feet above sea level, could be

The Arid Lands

Fig 180 Pattern of longitudinal dunes in northeast South Australia (*taken from Poolowanna 1/250,000 map, Div. Nat. Mapping, Canberra*).

Fig 181 Pattern of longitudinal dunes in the Great Victoria Desert (*taken from Everard 1/250,000 map, Div. Nat. Mapping, Canberra*).

essentially that upon which the Mesozoic and Tertiary rocks, which occur toward the eastern and southern margins of the desert, were laid down. It is likely, therefore, that the plain upon which the longitudinal dunes have been formed by the wind is of very great antiquity.

Over most of the desert, which covers some 70,000 square miles in South Australia alone, longitudinal dunes prevail (Fig. 181). They trend east-west, and consist of red sand. They are up to 60 feet high and extend continuously for up to 100 miles. There are between two and four dunes to the mile in a transverse section. The dunes bear a cover of sparse vegetation. There are numerous claypans and salinas, of which Lake Maurice is the largest example.

The sands of the Great Victoria Desert are derived from the weathering of the rocks of the Shield and its several basins, and from alluvium derived from uplands and spread over the plains by a formerly extensive drainage system of which only a few discontinuous remnants, in the form of salinas, remain.

In the Canning, or Desert basin of Western Australia the dunes are also of longitudinal type, trending west-northwest to east-southeast except in the vicinity of uplands. The dunes, which display a remarkable parallelism, vary in elevation above the intervening corridors and depressions from a few feet to more than 100 feet; their width averages 15 feet. Because of similarities in some localities between the mineral composition of the sands and the underlying bedrock, it has been suggested that the dunes may be of windrift type, but the sand ridges are undoubtedly of the same origin as the Simpson Desert dunes and are part of a continental system (see Fig. 169). To the south of the Canning basin dunes of similar morphology occupy almost 400,000 square miles of central Western Australia and indeed extend into the adjacent parts of South Australia and the Northern Territory. The range of size is similar to that described, but in a few places even higher mounds have been noted. They are possibly comparable to those described at the northern margin of the Nullarbor in South Australia. For example, Streich Mound near the western margin of the Eucla basin (lat. 30° 30′ S; long. 123° 40′ E), is described as rising about 150 feet above the adjacent dunes and 330 feet above the depression three quarters of a mile to the west.

(iv) Stony desert[1] or gibber plain

The coarse debris left behind by the removal of sand and dust particles is called in Australia *gibber*, though other names are used in other places (*hamada*, *serir*, *reg*); in north America it is known as *desert armour*, on account of its protective function. The passage of sand across such gibber plains causes the gravel and stones to be polished and worn by the wind, forming *ventifacts*. Elsewhere, the sides of the stones are worn so that a roughly triangular cross-section is evolved; on this account, they are called *dreikanter* (Germ.—three sides). Many gibbers have acquired a veneer of iron and silica rich material—the *desert varnish* which colours them various shades of brown, ranging from yellow brown to deep, blackish brown.

In South Australia, gibber plains extend discontinuously from the Port Augusta region, northward to the Northern Territory border and beyond. They are best developed on a series of extensive plateaux which stand 100 feet or more higher than the level of the adjacent plains. Other extensive gibber plains occur to the north of the Flinders Ranges, between Lake Callabonna and Lake Eyre; and there are many large residual plateaux between Lake Eyre and the northeastern corner of the State which bear stony deserts on their upper surfaces. All along the interfluve between the Cooper and the Diamantina, for example, there are gibber plateaux. In addition to these occurrences, gibber plains and plateaux are known to a relatively minor extent from within the sandy deserts, and fringing the ranges and uplands, for example the northern Flinders Ranges.

The gibber is derived from the local bedrock, in some areas Precambrian, in others Cretaceous, but there are still quite extensive remnants of a formerly even more extensive duricrust of silcrete of mid-Tertiary age which is a rich source of resistant debris. When it is disintegrated by weathering it tends to form moderately coarse fragments. Any fine material is evacuated by wind and water from the locality and the coarse fragments remain *in situ*. Due to the removal of fine debris, the land surface is gradually lowered, and the coarse fragments of siliceous duricrusts are gradually lowered and concentrated. Many of the fragments possess a very thin veneer of desert varnish.

The central plateau area present on the western side of Lake Torrens and then, more or less continuously, between the northern tip of the lake and the State's northern border forms a relatively narrow upland divide between the sandy desert plains to the west and those to the east. The plateau is not featureless, for there is quite extensive dissection, especially toward the margins. There are also local basin depressions to which the intermittently flowing streams are graded, and, as a result, in the vicinity of such local basins several different levels of the gibber surface are commonly apparent. At the margins there are, in many places, spectacular bluffs, For instance, some 20 miles east of Coober Pedy the so-called 'breakaways' take the form of precipitous cliffs in which the underlying Cretaceous bedrock, weathered to many hues of white, red, brown and yellow, is exposed everywhere (Fig. 67b).

The gibber plains are not devoid of sand, for there are a few fixed dunes and some rather irregular mobile forms. Sturt, in his original account of the Stony Desert, stated there were on every side 'stupendous and almost insurmountable sandridges of a fiery red'. But most of the sand has been swept from these areas and has either accumulated in depressions between the gibber-strewn plateaux, as is the case in the northeast of South Australia, or has been carried windward (mainly northward) to lowland areas where the sand has been moulded into massive dune fields. But even here, in between the dunes and in the vicinity of residual rises and uplands, particularly those capped by silcrete, the ground, as Burke and Wills and their party found, is covered 'with sharp dark-brown stones that were' and are 'terrible to walk on'—the gibber plains.

(v) Erosion by wind

Wind is most important in the deserts for its work of carrying, depositing and moulding sand and finer material. It also achieves some erosion, largely by means of the sand-blast action: sand grains carried along by the wind close to the ground abrade or scour rocks and wear them away. The effects of wind erosion are, with one exception, minor, though often spectacular. *Mushroom rocks*, or *zeugen*, result from the wind etching away strata—especially soft strata—which occur close to ground level, where most sand is moved. Great whaleback-shaped ridges, elongated parallel to the wind and called *yardangs* occur, again eroded by the wind in soft sediments. They are up to 600 feet high in Iran.

The only major landform caused by wind erosion is the *deflation hollow*. These depressions, which are up to 60 miles across, are a common feature of many deserts. Some (Fig. 182a) are partly due to faulting, that is, to the subsidence of a part of the earth's crust; in others, the solution of the underlying (calcareous) rocks has influenced their formation (Fig. 182b); but deflation is either partly or wholly responsible for features like the Kharga depression, with its great oasis, in the Libyan desert. The depth to which the wind may excavate is effectively controlled by the level of the water table, for the wind cannot move moist sediments. When the water table is approached, erosion ceases (Fig. 182c). The proximity of water table and floor of deflation hollow also accounts for the frequency with which oases occur there.

Many hundreds of small, true deflation hollows occur in the sand ridge deserts of Australia, most of them elongated parallel to dune trend. Of the larger depressions, Lake Eyre, the only one studied in detail, has been interpreted in two ways. In coastal cliffs on the southeast shore of Lake Eyre, lacustrine silts have been dated as 40,000 years old from the C14 assay of contained shells. Beneath the adjacent lake bed, organic remains have been dated by the same method as being 20,000 years old. This evidence is taken by some workers to indicate a period of deflation between 40,000 and 20,000 years ago when, over an area of some 3,600 square miles, deflation removed at least 50 feet of silts and sands from the depression (the lacustrine sands in the coastal cliffs and dunes are 36 feet thick, and the old lake floor is about 15 feet below the present lake surface). Subsequently, some 15 feet of sands, silts, gypsum and salt have been deposited on the lake floor. In this view, Lake Eyre is a deflation hollow within a broader tectonic basin and the erosion of the lake bed provided materials for building dunes to the north.

There is an obvious discrepancy between the age of the dunes implied in this hypothesis, and that indicated from the stratigraphic evidence within the Simpson Desert: the deflation hypothesis requires the dunes to be between 40,000 and 20,000 years old, but the presence beneath the desert sands of fluvial and lacustrine sediments dating from as recently as 10,000 years (or possibly less), show them to be much younger. Of course it is possible that the suggested period of deflation provided material for generations of dunes older than those which now dominate the desert; and there is evidence of such an earlier dune field (see below). But even these older sands lie above, and are therefore younger than, the 10,000 year-old lake and river sediments. Alternative explanations should be considered.

The western margin of the salina appears to be coincident with a major fault which extends southward to delineate the western border of Lake Torrens (Fig. 51). This evidence takes several forms:

(a) Tectonic

(b) Solution and Collapse

(c) Deflation

Fig 182 Diagrammatic section across deflation hollows showing some suggested origins and limitation of deflation imposed by the water table.

(1) The essential rectilinearity of the escarpment on the western side of the salina.
(2) The linear zone is the focus of many earth tremors.
(3) On the salina nearby, the mound springs, formed by chemically rich waters emerging from deep in the underlying basin, display an aligned pattern in plan, suggesting that the artesian waters are rising along faults.
(4) The western escarpment is capped by gypsite which is underlain by a strongly gypsiferous clay. Bores put down in the bed of Lake Eyre reveal similar rocks in similar sequence beneath the superficial salts, silts and clays; the gypsite here cannot as yet be demonstrated to be of the same age as that capping the western scarp, but in light of the other evidence, probably is (Fig. 183a).

Thus it is suggested that marked faulting in the late Pleistocene has caused the lake bed to subside. The steep cliffs (Fig. 183) on both east and west sides of the Lake are due to either faulting and retouching by wave action, or wholly due to wave action, which may be very effective on unconsolidated silts and clays.

(d) DESERTS OF THE PAST

Both within the modern desert and in areas to the south, there is evidence that the sand ridge deserts were formerly more extensive. In a few places in both the Simpson and the adjacent Tirari[2] desert, remnants of older sand dunes occur beneath the modern ridges. The older sand contains many cavities now filled with calcium carbonate, but reminiscent of root systems of shrubs and trees which have rotted and been replaced. In other words, there is a suggestion that between the older and newer periods of dune deposition, there intervened a moister climatic phase during which some shrubby vegetation flourished. These older dunes were also moulded by winds coming from slightly different directions from those shaping the present sand ridges, for the older system is consistently aligned a few degrees anticlockwise in relation to the modern features.

In the Great Victoria Desert the dunes run west-northwest to south-southeast and east to west, in the northern areas, but swing to northwest-southeast in the southeast. South of a line drawn between Ceduna and the Gawler Ranges the dunes are now fixed, though obviously formerly active. Such fields of ancient dunes occupy much of Eyre and Yorke Peninsulas, and the Murray Basin (Fig. 8). They occur near Gawler, only 25 miles north of Adelaide and also in the western suburbs of Melbourne. Where the vegetation, which stabilises them, is removed, the sands are again susceptible to transportation and blowouts, or small deflation hollows occur.

The presence of such dunes clearly shows that truly arid conditions

Fig 183 (a) Diagrammatic geological section of western margin of Lake Eyre; (b) cliffs on western side Lake Eyre basin. The capping is of gypsite.

formerly extended over the greater part of South Australia, much of western Victoria, and large tracts of Queensland, N.S.W. and Western Australia.

(e) LUNETTES

The former extension of the deserts far to the south of their present limits and the general knowledge of climatic change in the recent past has been responsible for a mild controversy concerning the origin of a particular type of dune, the *lunette*. Lunettes are typical of semi-arid, rather than arid regions, and occur characteristically on the eastern side of lakes and playas (Fig. 184) though similar forms result from the deflation of sands and sills exposed in dry creek beds, as may be seen adjacent to Brachina

Fig 184 Lunettes (a) at Huttons Lagoon (*from air photograph*); (b) at Hynam Swamp (*permission Mrs E. M. Campbell*); (c) sketch of lunette at Bool Lagoon (*from photograph, supplied by Mrs E. M. Campbell*).

Creek a few miles downstream from the Gorge of the same name and adjacent to several streams in the Riverina. Superficially they resemble barchans, insofar as they are crescent-shaped in plan; but whereas the steeper side of barchans is the lee slope, in lunettes, it is on the upwind side, and the crest of the dune is close to the lake edge. Multiple lunettes are known (i.e. features in which several individual crescentic crests occur), and the composition of the features varies from silt to sand. Some sandy lunettes display cross bedding, indicative of wind deposition.

They are common in southern South Australian areas like Eyre Peninsula, the Mid-north (Lochiel, Peterborough) and particularly the Southeast; in Victoria, especially the Wimmera and the Murray valley; in southwestern N.S.W. and in the southern deserts of Western Australia; similar features have been noted on the eastern sides of lakes (e.g. Pelican Lake) in northern Queensland.

Hills, who first described these features, attributed them to phases when the lakes contained water. The lunettes he examined in north-western Victoria were of silt composition, and Hills argued that moisture laden air blown from the lake surface by the westerly winds would trap atmospheric dust and cause it to be deposited on the eastern shore of the lake. However, such an origin scarcely seems feasible for the sandy lunettes, which moreover display structures consistent with an aeolian origin. These considerations have led to other explanations for the origin of these features. Stephens and Crocker suggested that lunettes originate during periods when the lake beds are dry: westerly winds pick up clay aggregates or sand particles from the dry lake beds and carry them to the eastern margin, where they are trapped by vegetation to form dunes. Evidence from West Africa suggests that the crystallisation of salts in the lake sediments may loosen the cohesion between particles particularly those of the clays. This roughens the surface, increases turbulence in the wind near the surface and thus facilitates the erosion of the bed.

This hypothesis goes far toward explaining the field evidence, but certain problems remain. Salt crystallisation has to be invoked to render the physically compacted and chemically bonded clays of many lake beds susceptible to deflation, yet, while many lunettes are found in association with saline lakes, others, especially well developed, occur at the margins of claypans. If the lunettes are formed by wind erosion of lake beds when the latter are dry, i.e. during either summer or in long periods of aridity, surely the winds on these periods would come from the north or northwest, not the west? Some lunettes are located at the southeast corner of lakes, but many are not. And if wind erosion of lake beds is responsible for lunettes, why are they found in abundance only in semi-arid regions and not in the true deserts, where there are numerous playas which are mostly dry, but where lunettes, though known (e.g. in the north of South Australia between the Hamilton and Alberga rivers) are relatively rare, and these degraded?

Some of these difficulties can be resolved by suggesting that wind is not wholly responsible for the transportation of the debris which forms lunettes. In many present lakes, quite powerful waves are generated, despite the shallowness of the water and the smallness of the lakes. These waves are sufficient to erode platforms in resistant rocks (Pl. 65) and to move coarse gravel (up to 2 inches diameter on the shore of Lake Greenly, on southern Eyre Peninsula) and sand, which is carried to the eastern shores of the lakes during winter, when the lakes carry water. It may be suggested that this shoreline debris is picked up by winds during the summer months (northerlies and northwesterlies) and carried a short distance away from the lake margin to be trapped by vegetation and form features comparable with coastal dunes (see next Chapter) following the arcuate, wave-moulded shores and, thus, of crescentic shape.[3]

Plate 65 Shore platform cut in gneisses, southeastern shore of Lake Greenly, southern Eyre Peninsula.

This hypothesis seems better able to explain not only the distribution and shape of lunettes and their consistent association with lakes, but also their apparent scarcity in the deserts, where, it can be argued, the playas contain water too infrequently for waves to carry to the shorelines the large amount of debris necessary for lunettes to develop. On the other hand, it is possible that lack of available debris in very dry, encrusted lakes is the reason for the rarity of lunettes in truly arid regions.

Notes

[1] The Stony Desert was named by Charles Sturt in 1845, when, after reaching Strzelecki Creek and following it northward, he and his companion 'entered a region where the horses' hooves were cut by flint-like stones and left no track'.
[2] Located east of Lake Eyre and north of Lake Frome.
[3] As is often the case, invoking wind driven waves in explanation of lunettes is not new. In 1862, the Rev. J. E. T. Woods, describing the swamps of the northeast of South Australia, remarked that when these are isolated 'they possess ... a considerable mound or ridge of good black soil on the eastern side'. He attributed this, wrongly, to the accumulation of vegetation but conceived that the material was transported during winter, when the depressions contain water, and when the prevalent westerly winds drift debris over to the eastern side.

8. Coastal Processes and Forms

(a) INTRODUCTION

THE WORK OF WIND as an agent of transportation, deposition and erosion in arid lands was considered in the last chapter, and the transportation of debris in shallow lakes by wind-driven waves of water has also been mentioned as possibly contributing to the origin of lunettes. The wind is of greatest significance, however, in coastal geomorphology, for wind generated waves attain their maximum effect on sea coasts, and give rise to features which in broad view are azonal, being found throughout the world in a variety of climatic regimes, but which in detail display contrasts on account of climatic differences and which may vary in scale of development according to the exposure of the coast and the nature of the waves generated there.

(b) WAVES

In the open ocean, waves are merely shapes; very little lateral translation of water is involved. Waves originate with the frictional drag of moving air (wind) on a calm sea; ripples are created, the wind presses against the windward faces of such irregularities, and wavelets are formed. These in turn, coalesce to form waves. The wave length is the distance from crest to crest (or from trough to trough), the wave height the vertical distance from trough and crest, and the wave period, the time it takes for two successive crests to pass a given point (Fig. 185).

The effectiveness of wind in making waves depends upon its force (or velocity) the length of time it blows, and the extent of open water over which it blows unimpeded (a parameter known as the *fetch* of waves). Waves up to 100 feet high from trough to crest have been observed at sea in storms, but there is a limit beyond which the wind destroys, rather than increases the size of waves. In storms, the pressure applied by the wind to waves is very great, and when the wave crest becomes a wedge of water extending through less than 120° of arc, and the height of the wave is about a seventh of its length, the wave front is steepened, the wedge decreased still further, and eventually is blown off, forming a breaking wave in open water: the phenomenon known as 'white horses'.

Waves generated and maintained directly by the wind are known as *forced waves*. Waves formed by the impact of a stone on the surface of a pond are of this type, but just as these waves radiate from the point of impact, decreasing in amplitude and increasing in wave length as they progress, forced or wind-driven waves at sea spread beyond the area of origin as free waves or *swell*.

As waves approach the shore, they undergo critical changes in nature and morphology, both in section and in plan. When a wave reaches water shallower than half the wave length, the latter is reduced, as is velocity; the height of the wave increases; the wave base is retarded while the upper part continues at greater speed; finally the wave breaks. There is a translation of water up the beach known as the *swash*, some of which water (not all, because of percolation into the beach) returns to the sea as the *backwash* (Fig. 186).

Swell and forced waves driven by gentle winds tend to have a long wavelength. In such waves, particle motion is essentially orbital, and takes the form of a horizontal ellipse, even when breaking; the translation of water in such long waves remains essentially horizontal and, because they tend to build up beaches, are called *constructional waves*. On the other hand, waves generated by strong winds, and especially storm waves, on breaking develop a particle motion in the form of a vertical ellipse. Such short waves are called *destructional waves* because they dash into beaches which are combed down, or plunge into exposed rocks and quarry them.

Because waves break on entering shallow water they also suffer changes in plan as they approach the shore. Imagine a wave approaching the shore obliquely (Fig. 187a). One section of the wave enters shallow water before the other. This part therefore slows and breaks while the other continues at the more rapid pace. The orientation of the wave is thus changed, and the wave suffers *refraction*. The overall effect of this is to bring waves nearly parallel to the shore. A wave approaching an irregular or indented shoreline is similarly refracted (Fig. 187b), the waves being moulded more closely to the shape of the coast. There is, however, an important additional effect: wave energy is concentrated on headlands, and dispersed in bays (Fig. 187b) with the result that shorelines tend to be made smooth in plan. In addition to refraction, waves also undergo reflection and diffraction. *Reflection* occurs when a wave hits against a seawall or any obstruction, natural or man-made, rising out of deep water. The wave rebounds, suffering a reversal of movement, with the angle of reflection equal to the angle of incidence. *Diffraction* takes place when a wave passes beyond an obstacle, such as an island; the waves change direction and disperse, but even in the lee of obstacles, there is wave attack, albeit of reduced force. Thus at Victor Harbour, the northern side of Granite Island, facing the mainland, suffers attack by diffracted waves.

(c) MARINE EROSION

Waves pound against the shore with astounding force. There are many incredible yet well authenticated examples of the power of wind-driven waves and the damage they have wrought, especially storm waves. One of the best known concerns the harbour breakwater at Wick, in eastern Scotland. This structure was capped by an 800-ton block of concrete secured to the foundation by iron rods 3½ inches in diameter. The total weight is estimated to have been about 1,350 tons, yet, during a great storm in 1872, the whole mass was lifted bodily and dumped in the harbour. The breakwater was rebuilt and a larger capping, this time weighing 2,600 tons, was put in place but this too was removed *en bloc* during a later storm. It should be noted that Wick does not face the full fury of the open Atlantic. At Cherbourg, in France, individual rocks weighing up to 7,000 lbs were hurled over a wall 25 feet high by storm waves, and 65-ton blocks were shifted 60 feet. Waves break with tremendous force (at Wick, in the instances cited, it was estimated they exerted a force of about 6,340 lbs—almost 3 tons—a square foot) and the spray from breaking waves moves with great velocity, commonly at 70 m.p.h., while small jets have been observed to travel up to 170 m.p.h. The damage effected by such high velocity spray can well be imagined. A considerable amount of coastal erosion is accomplished by such *hydraulic* effects, with the sheer weight and velocity of water fracturing the rocks exposed at the shore.

The *abrasive* effect of boulders, pebbles and sand hurled against the shore by waves is also great, and the alternate expansion and contraction of air trapped in rock crevices also causes fracturing. Once fractured and fragmented, rocks are plucked away from the shore by waves to accumulate at the foot of the cliff, to undergo further attrition, and eventually to be evacuated along the coast (see below). *Solution* is also important on the coast, not only where limestones and other easily affected rocks are exposed, but fairly generally, for most rocks are in some measure soluble in sea water. Biological agencies, ranging from algae to boring animals also contribute to weathering and erosion, though their effects are commonly underestimated. The sea grape (*Hormosira*), which is found in abundance along many parts of the Australian coast, provides a common example. It forms a distinct matting on many coastal platforms, effectively protecting them from much of the force of wave attack. But

Fig 185   Some common wave parameters.

these colonies also ensure that, by and large, the platforms are never dry, even at low tide on the hottest days. Thus they contribute to the weathering of the bedrock.

The rate and nature of coastal erosion depends, in part, upon the aspect and configuration of the coastal sector in question. As has been men-

Fig 186 Features of a breaking wave.

(a)

AB=BC

(b)

Fig 187 (a) Wave refraction on a smooth coast; (b) Wave refraction on an indented coast.

tioned, headlands or irregular coasts attract more wave attack than embayments. If there are offshore islands to interrupt the free passage of waves, attack is less strong than where there is no such protective barrier. Parts of the east coast of Queensland are in some measure protected by the coral islands of the Great Barrier Reef, whereas the N.S.W. coast for example and the west coast of Eyre Peninsula are not. Hence the contrast between the boldly cliffed coast of the latter areas and the more subdued cliffs of the Pacific coast of Queensland. Off Victor Harbour, the southern, or outward, shores of Granite Island, as well as of the nearby Wright and Seal Islands, are exposed to the full force of the waves, and hence are steeper than the relatively protected landward slopes (Fig. 188).

The nature of rocks exposed on the shore is very important; indeed structure (including both disposition and nature of the rocks) may well be the most important factor determining the detailed morphology of the coast. Softer rocks are obviously eroded more rapidly than are harder strata, and some of the most spectacular cases of coastal erosion that have been recorded come from areas of unconsolidated strata. Toward the end of the last century the average annual loss from the coast of Holderness, in East Yorkshire, an area of unconsolidated glacial ground moraine, was nearly 6 feet. At Pakefield, near Lowestoft, also in eastern England, one point on the coast recorded a loss of 620 feet between 1883 and 1947, an average of nearly 10 feet a year. Almost one mile of volcanic ash was eroded from the Indonesian island of Krakatoa between 1883 and 1928, a rate of more than 100 feet a year.

Other processes besides waves contribute to the wearing back of land in coastal regions. Gullying and landslips contribute significantly to cliff recession; the chemical and physical action of water left behind at low tide, or thrown up as spray, though not thoroughly understood, is clearly responsible for the development of hollows similar to weather pits, or gnammas (see Chapter 4), and, through their extension and coalescence, form distinct benches. Water thrown up as spray collects in clefts and depressions in the exposed bedrock. There, the saline water weathers the rock with which it comes into contact, partly (and where made possible by the nature of the bedrock) by solution, partly by hydratation and similar processes. Some hollows develop a hemispherical shape (cf. pits), but more commonly, and possibly because of the general soaking and partial weathering of the upper layers of bedrock, broad, shallow, flat-floored depressions (cf. pans) evolve. Such depressions extend and join, and when the intervening walls are wholly consumed, a flattish bench or platform remains. Water left behind as the tide recedes behaves similarly, and contributes to the development of benches at inter-tide levels. This *water level weathering* is thus of considerable importance in shaping coastal forms.

Platforms formed by the coalescence of spray pools are not directly related to sea level, save insofar as the upper limit to which the spray is thrown is related to sea level; but this is a broad limitation, for during storms especially, spray may be flung scores of feet into the air.

(d) EROSIONAL FORMS

A simple assemblage of forms developed by marine erosion is shown in Fig. 189 and Pls. 66 and 67. It comprises a *cliff*, with *notch* at its base, and a *bench* or *platform* (also called an abrasion platform, a wave-cut bench, or *normal* platform). The cliff develops through strong attack by weathering, or erosion, or both, at and close to sea level; the rock above is undermined and collapses, forming a cliff. The form of the cliff is strongly influenced by structure (e.g. jointing—see for instance Pl. 16) and by the relative intensity of marine attack at the base and subaerial weathering and erosion on the face.

Boulder strewn cliffs are characteristic of granite exposures such as those at Wilson's Promontory, Victoria, and Granite Island, South Australia, and vertical cliffs of resistant strata (Pl. 37). Flat-lying strata of varied resistance to erosion give rise to structural benches, as at Cape Solander (between Sydney and Woollongong) and, for instance, near Palm Beach, Pittwater, N.S.W. Weak strata are rapidly weathered and eroded to give rounded forms, or where steeply dissected, sugar loafs, as for instance at Halletts Cove and Blanche Point (Fig. 134, M.R. Echunga, S.A., 477455, also Fig. 190). Convex cliffs may also result directly from the structure of the local bedrock, as for example at Halletts Cove (M.R. Echunga, S.A., 504664; see Pl. 67). An increase in relative significance of the subaerial forces over the marine agents causes a decrease in cliff inclination (Fig. 191). The notch in some areas is in part due to wave attack, but in limestone regions especially, is largely attributable to chemical weathering.

The *normal* platform is located between high and low tide levels. It is gently inclined close to the cliff foot, forming a ramp, but otherwise broadly horizontal. It is partly due to wave attack and abrasion, partly to weathering. The surface of the platform is in detail not smooth but irregular, even when the local structures are horizontal or sub-horizontal: numerous pittings, minor exploitation of joints and other fractures cause a considerable micro-relief to be developed. Nevertheless in broad view a distinction can be made between comparatively regular platforms developed on flat-lying bedrock, and *serrated* platforms formed on dipping strata. Numerous well-developed platforms occur along the N.S.W.

Fig 188 Field sketch showing the asymmetry of Wright Island due to contrasted wave attack —open sea to right of sketch.

coast. For instance where the country rock is the flat-lying Hawkesbury sandstone, regular platforms backed by benched cliffs are formed, as at Warden Head (M.R. Ulladulla, N.S.W., 1:252,440, 350634) Toalla Point (M.R. Bega, N.S.W., 1:253,440, 296442) and La Perouse; but at Barraga Point, near Bermagui (M.R. Bega, N.S.W., 1:253,440, 307497) on the South Coast, the bedrock is steeply inclined and a serrated platform has evolved. Similar contrasts are found south of Adelaide. The Halletts Cove platform cuts across steeply inclined, well-bedded strata, and in detail is serrated (Pl. 68), and displays several minor but closely related levels. It contrasts strongly with normal platforms developed on level-bedded strata a few miles to the south. At Blanche Point, for instance, the platforms are gently sloping and are structural benches coincident with particularly resistant early Tertiary strata. Other contrasted forms are found on granite exposures (e.g. the south side of Granite Island and the southwest tip of Yorke Peninsula) where the platforms are bouldery. Thus structural effects are clearly displayed on shore platforms. Resistant residuals which stand above the general level of the platforms, as at

Fig 189   Typical assemblage of coastal erosional landforms.

Fig 190   Field sketch of north side of Blanche Point, south of Adelaide, showing coastal cliffs, platform, notch, stack and convex forms on unresistant clays.

Toalla Point, N.S.W., and Blanche Point are called *stacks* (see Figs. 189, 190, 192).

This simple profile is common around the Australian (and other) coasts. For instance, the coasts south of Adelaide and north of Sydney consist of alternations of sandy beaches and cliffed headlands, where this cliff-notch-platform assemblage is well displayed. Note that the platforms terminate abruptly at their seaward end in a submarine cliff leading down to another, deeper platform: evidently the fluctuating surface we call sea level is not the lower limit of marine erosion, for another platform, permanently below even low tide level and called the *ultimate* platform is commonly developed seaward of the normal platform, as at La Perouse, Botany Bay, where the normal platform drops away abruptly on its seaward side.

In some areas in N.S.W., Victoria and South Australia, other platforms additional to the ultimate and normal platforms are present. They are particularly well represented on limestone coasts, but are by no means restricted to such a lithological environment. In the Sydney area, whence these forms were early described, these *higher* platforms are about 3 feet (though variable) above the normal platforms and are covered at high tide; a good example is seen at Wyargine Point, Middle Harbour, Port

Fig 191 Variation in form of cliff with variations in intensity of wave and subaerial attack.

Fig 192 Some of the Twelve Apostles, large sea stacks eroded in flat-lying sediments, Port Campbell, Vic.

Plate 66　Cliff, notch and platform eroded in aeolianite, Cape Northumberland. The cross bedding in the aeolianite is visible in the cliff, and it is clear that the platform consists of not one but several distinct though closely related levels.

Plate 67　Coastal cliffs and shore platform at Halletts Cove. The form of the cliff closely reflects the structure of the underlying bedrock, but the platform is eroded across the strata and is very rough and irregular in detail (see Plate 68).

Plate 68 Detail of serrated platform at Halletts Cove. Note pools of water left behind after the recession of the tide; these waters continue to weather the rocks.

Plate 69 Platform related to a higher sea level near Cape Northumberland.

Jackson, (M.R. Sydney, N.S.W., 256221), about 3 feet above the normal platform which, in turn, gives way to a lower bench. In Victoria these higher platforms are attributed to water-level weathering, and by weathering of cliffs above the level of saturation (groundwater) with the weathered debris removed by weak waves of translation. In support of this it has been noted on Phillip Island, Port Lonsdale and Sorrento, Victoria that shore platforms are widest (100 yards and up to 200 yards in favoured localities) at sheltered sites, where wave attack is weak. They are narrower on exposed coasts where they are reduced by wave attack.

The lowermost bench, located some 20 to 30 feet below low tide level and never exposed, is undoubtedly the result of quarrying by waves. Its level is at the generally accepted lower limit of significant wave activity. The bench, or series of benches, a few feet above normal high tide level (i.e. above non-storm high tide level) is undoubtedly due to solutional and other weathering effects in and at the margins of spray pools, for it is above the range of normal and in places even of storm wave activity. It is the so-called normal bench, located between high and low tide levels, which in some respects presents the greatest problem. It has been almost universally accepted as due to wave action, but in view of the fact that both weathering and wave quarrying are actively destroying it, this simple view is difficult to sustain. Why should waves erode significantly near the upper limit of their range? Waves achieve their maximum orbital motion or energy level at and near the sea surface, but it is also possible that the development of a platform is related to the location in the intertidal zone, where the emerging water table oscillates in response to tidal changes, where wetting and drying occur, and where rock disintegration is therefore quite pronounced. This normal platform (in reality a series of rough benches differing slightly in elevation one from another) may well be due to weathering to the lower limit of wetting and drying, the products of disintegration being readily eroded and evacuated by the waves as they break on the shore.

Workers like Fairbridge and Teichert in Western Australia have tended to interpret such multiple benches on coasts in terms of shifts of sea level: each bench is said to represent a normal platform developed in relation to a distinct and separate stand of the sea. Even platforms differing in elevation by only a very few feet (see also Chapter 10) are interpreted in this way. But a relief greater than the elevational differences between platforms has evolved and continues to develop on certain of our coastal benches. There is little doubt that several platforms are at present forming simultaneously on some parts of the Australian coast, as advocated by Jutson, Hills and others.

The question of interpretation is complicated by structural effects such as those described from the Sydney area. Also, the presence of multiple benches neither proves nor disproves movements of the sea relative to the land; the benches may be contemporaneous or they may be of different ages, but the evidence must come from other sources, not from difference in elevation. To this extent the question remains open and each area must be assessed on the available evidence. For example, at Cape Northumberland, in South Australia but close to the Victorian border there are both ultimate and normal platforms. There is also a distinct platform 20 to 25 feet above sea level (Pl. 69) with cliff-top dunes and calcrete accumulations indicative of a former, higher water table and land surface. This high platform is interpreted as of earlier age and as indicative of a shift of sea level, not only because it is so high, but because other evidence suggests a relative lowering of the sea.

(e) EFFECTIVENESS OF MARINE EROSION

Waves cannot erode platforms of unlimited width. Many years ago, plains of regional extent were attributed to wave erosion, but now it is acknowledged that waves are self-limiting in their action: the broader the platform cut, and over which the waves have to travel through shallow water to reach the margin of the land, the more energy is expended and the weaker are the waves which reach the foot of the cliffs. Thus there is a limit, generally thought to be about one mile, to the width of platform able to be developed by waves. As wave action at the base of a cliff becomes weaker, subaerial agencies such as gullying, wash and weathering assume dominance, and the cliff is degraded.[1]

The only circumstance in which broader platforms may be developed is where the sea level is gradually rising, or the land is slowly subsiding; then, ever deeper water covers the platform, thus reducing the amount of energy lost as the waves cross it.

(f) DEPOSITIONAL FORMS

Not only do waves and weathering produce much debris on the coast, but rivers also bring a large volume of material worn from the land to the margin of the sea and many coasts are emergent by virtue of aggradation or deposition of debris. Some debris is deposited at river mouths in the form of deltas, but much is moved along the coast, sometimes over considerable distances, by the process known as *longshore drifting*.

Although waves are refracted and for this reason tend to approach nearly parallel with the coast, only rarely, locally and ephemerally do they achieve perfect parallelism. Thus, the sand and other debris picked up by breaking waves is carried forward in the swash, obliquely up the beach. Some of the water soaks into the beach, but the remainder runs directly down the beach, following the steepest gradient, and taking some of the debris with it. But these particles are picked up by the next breaking wave and are taken further along the beach in a zig-zag motion known as longshore drifting. The overall direction is determined by the strength and duration of winds: thus debris travels along the shore in the direction of the prevailing winds (Fig. 193). Along the south coast of South Australia, along the Bight and in the Southeast, the drift is from west to east under the influence of the prevailing westerlies. Predominantly calcareous debris brought to the ocean margin by the Murray is carried to the southeast and according to some observations, there is a progressive decrease in carbonate content of beach sands along this coast from the Murray mouths towards the Victorian border. Along the north coast of N.S.W. and southern Queensland the dominant southeast or south-southeast winds cause a drift to the north.

Currents play a minor role in the transport of debris, particularly of fine material and in restricted passages, but sand and coarser debris can be moved only by longshore drifting under the influence of wind-driven waves. The evidence upon which this conclusion is based includes the following:

(1) Beaches and other coastal features built by deposition occur above high water mark, and thus beyond the reach of the currents.
(2) Only in very special circumstances can sand, for example, be moved by tidal currents and even then needs to be placed in suspension by waves so that currents may move it.
(3) All depositional forms found on sea coasts are found also on the shores of lakes, where there is no possibility of strong currents.
(4) In the laboratory, all known coastal depositional forms can be simulated by using wave action only.

Much of the debris carried by longshore drifting is thrown up by waves to form beaches, which are particularly well developed in embayments. Detritus derived from the erosion of headlands is carried into bays and there it accumulates, the composition of the beach material bearing a close relationship to the nature of the bedrock in the headlands. Many such 'capes and bays', alternations of promontories and bay-head beaches, occur in the lower Southeast, between Robe and the Victorian border and beyond, south of Adelaide and along the south coast from Cape Jervis to Goolwa, on Kangaroo Island, and on the Eyre Peninsula (Fig. 194).

The beaches change greatly in detail from day to day and from hour to hour (Fig. 195). They are built up during calm weather when constructional waves are active, and combed down—and even removed—during storms when short-period destructional waves are active. Several individual ridges or *berms* are built up, each representing a period of construction, and then wholly or partly destroyed. Cusps and ripple marks are common beach features. *Cusps* are crescent-shaped depressions ranging in length from a few feet to several hundred feet, and in depth from six feet or more to a few inches or parts of an inch. The 'horns' of

Fig 193 Longshore drift.

Fig 194 Examples of 'cape and bay' shorelines in South Australia. Refraction of dominant waves shown.

the crescents point seawards. Although they are clearly related to wave action the origin of cusps is little understood. *Ripple marks* too are formed by wave action: oscillatory wave motion creates horizontal vortices which cause differential deposition and erosion, and the development of ripple marks.

On every beach there are two simultaneous but opposed movements; water and debris are carried up the beach towards the land by the swash, while both are also carried to seaward by the backwash. Where the onshore wind is particularly strong, a hydraulic head may be created by the water of several waves being accumulated by successive waves. To escape seawards, the water tends to concentrate into a series of distinct currents, called rip currents, which flow away from the beach along the sea floor. These powerful local currents excavate *rip channels*. In the zone where waves break for a particular period of time, distinct ridges or bars form on the sea floor oriented parallel to the waves. The onrushing waves are carrying debris toward the shore; on the other hand, debris is being carried seaward by backwash, and on occasions, by rip currents. The encounter between retreating and advancing water not only makes the latter break, but also causes debris to be deposited, forming a *break-point bar*. There are often two or more such bars, one corresponding to high tide, one to low tide level. They are ephemeral features but seem prone to survive on protected coasts: at Christies Beach, (M.R. Echunga, S.A., 478585), there are often such bars formed near the beach, of shingled, coarse material and preserved for long periods because on this coast the really powerful waves break on the outer reef.

On coasts with gentle offshore gradients, larger scale features, called *offshore bars*, are formed by waves which break some distance from the coast. Some offshore bars are very extended. Off the east coast of the

Fig 195 Variations in beach form—beach profiles measured at Carmel, California (*after Bascom*).

Coastal Processes and Forms 251

U.S.A. some can be traced for dozens of miles. As with break-point bars, there may be more than one offshore bar trending roughly parallel with the coast, and related to varied conditions of the tide and wind. For instance, off the Queensland coast in the Gulf of Carpentaria three such bars are commonly visible on air photographs in any one section normal to the shore. However, all are gradually driven landward; their crests emerge above sea level and became *barrier bars* or *beaches* oriented normal to the dominant land direction. The coast of southern Queens-

Fig 196 Bar islands and wind resultant diagrams from the coast of southeast Queensland (*after Hails*). Note the orientation of the primary coastal elements which are of depositional origin, in relation to wind direction and the northerly longshore drift of material.

Fig 197 Beach and bar features in southeast Queensland (*after Hails*). Note the northward prolongation of the beach at Surfers Paradise (a result of northerly longshore drift) and the diversion of the Nerang River.

land, with Fraser and North and South Stradbroke Islands, provides fine examples of such emerged bars formed by waves which have been driven by dominant southeast winds and refracted (Fig. 196). The coast between Tweed Heads and Surfers Paradise is a good example of a beach ridge of similar alignment and origin (Fig. 197).

Dunes may accumulate on these emerged bars, as on Stradbroke Island, and lakes or lagoons are impounded by the barriers formed by the bars (see Fig. 198). They are gradually filled with sediment to become salt marshes, and eventually, low lying, but dry land.

Bars become spits when they become tied or attached to the coast. Once a bar is in shallow water, and particularly when it emerges, it is supplied with debris by longshore drifting, the material being thrown up by wave action from the sea floor and beach immediately in front of the spit. Some spits run parallel to the coast, others diverge from it. All major spits are aligned normal to the dominant wind (and, hence, wave) direction; though spits, like offshore bars, commonly display secondary spits or *laterals*. These have a different orientation from the parent spit and are built by waves from other less significant directions. Le Fevre Peninsula, for instance, appears to have been built up from the south by westerly waves, but there are laterals extending from the main ridges (Fig. 199). Several specific types of spit are developed but all are aligned normal to the dominant wind. *Tombolos* are spits which join an island to the mainland, for instance, that which connects Barranjoey (M.R. Broken Bay, N.S.W., 335505) to the mainland in Palm Beach, north Sydney. Some like Chesil Beach, in southern England, are aligned normal to the dominant wind and waves. An incipient tombolo is forming between Granite Island and Victor Harbour: the spit is being built gradually out from the mainland in the zone where refracted and diffracted waves meet after coming round both sides of the Island. Eventually, it may form a connection between the island and the mainland.

At low tide, a wide foreshore is exposed on many coasts. The material carried by longshore drift and waves to form beaches may, if of a suitable size, and when dry, be picked up by the wind and carried a short distance onshore, where it is trapped by vegetation and moister ground, colonised by special types of plant, and stabilised to form coastal dunes or *foredunes*. Several lines of such dunes may be present, as in the beach suburbs of Adelaide (Fig. 199). But where the source of supply is cut off, the inland dunes are lower than those closest to the sea. Coastal dunes up to 40 and 50 feet high are common in the southeast and on western Eyre Peninsula, and even larger ones are known from eastern Queensland, and the coast of Natal. Foredunes have been blown out to form U-shaped or *parabolic* dunes with the open end of the U facing upwind. These form where the lower ends of a dune are fixed by moisture and vegetation, while the upper part is susceptible to wind erosion. Such coastal dunes

Fig 198 Two examples of coastal lagoons from eastern Australia (*after Bird*).

Fig 199 Le Fevre Peninsula with main spits and laterals, and the Adelaide coastal area showing present and former coastal foredunes (*adapted from Adelaide 1-mile Geological map, Geol. Surv. S.A.*).

254   *Geomorphology*

attain gigantic size in eastern Queensland, often rising up to 700 feet and up to 924 feet on Moreton Island. However, not all parabolic dunes are of coastal origin. There are many parabolic dunes in the Murray mallee (Fig. 200) where they appear to have developed from pre-existing foredunes and seif dunes.

During the Pleistocene (see Chapter 9), great ice sheets developed in the Polar regions, taking water from the ocean basins and causing sea level to be lowered. As the ice masses waxed and waned, the sea level fluctuated. At times of low sea level, large areas of the sea floor were uncovered. Extensive areas of unconsolidated sands and other sediments, and the calcareous shells of marine organisms which lived there, were exposed. The latter were commonly broken into fragments by the pounding of waves. Onshore winds were able to pick up voluminous quantities of this calcareous sand and thus built large coastal dunes. The lime was spread through the dunes, and came to form a cement, or induration,

Fig 200   Parabolic dunes in the Murray Plains (*after Sprigg*).

which effectively preserved the otherwise fragile dunes. Calcareous sand blown from the exposed sea floor into coastal foredunes by the wind is called *aeolianite*. It forms extensive areas of dunes on the west coast of Eyre Peninsula, in the southeast of South Australia (see Chapter 10(d)), Victoria and the southwest of Western Australia.

NOTE

[1] Note the similarities between cliff and slope morphology—the slope budget concept applies here also.

PART D: HISTORICAL GEOMORPHOLOGY

9. The Quaternary: Direct Effects of Glaciation

(a) INTRODUCTION

THE NATURE AND DISTRIBUTION OF climates over the earth's surface has not been constant through geological time. Available evidence suggests that the 'normal' or typical climate during most of geological time was neither as varied nor as extreme as at present. Because of the inclination of the earth's axis to the plane of the ecliptic (the imaginary plane delineated by the earth's annual course round the sun), and because the earth makes its annual journey round the sun, there must at all times have been climatic zones or regimes varying systematically from equator to poles; but the contrast between the polar and equatorial regions has not generally been as great as it is at present. Ice sheets, and really arid hot deserts are not typical of the climate of geological time, which was apparently of savannah type, with moderately low annual rainfall and warm temperatures. But at least once during the Precambrian, perhaps again during the Siluro-Devonian, certainly in the Permian, and most recently during the Quaternary, the earth's climate underwent severe aberrations, resulting in the formation of deserts—cold deserts, with ice sheets on the one hand, and hot, truly arid deserts on the other. The reasons for these catastrophic changes are as yet far from clear, though the subject of many speculations. In the case of the Permian and Quaternary, the climatic extremes followed closely on the heels of widespread periods of orogenesis and the same is possibly true of the Siluro-Devonian and Precambrian period(s) of climatic aberration.

The climatic events of the Quaternary were important enough to distinguish it clearly from the preceding Tertiary period. If only because of their recency, they had widespread and significant geomorphological results which are the subject of this chapter.

One calamitous and far reaching effect of Quaternary climatic change was the refrigeration of high latitude and high altitude areas. Several other effects, some direct, others indirect, stem from this one event. Direct effects of refrigeration are the development and spread of ice sheets over vast areas of northern Europe, North America and Antarctica, as well as numerous smaller glaciers, some of them at high elevations on or very close to the equator. At the margins of these glaciers, frost action dominated and created a suite of characteristic landforms, while the drainage of such areas, as well as that of areas directly affected by ice, displays many peculiarities. Finally, the great weight of ice caused the areas it occupied to subside, and, after the melting of the ice, to rebound and rise again. Earth movements of this origin are still in progress in countries like Scandinavia, eastern Canada, and Scotland.

These direct effects are spectacular and overwhelmingly important in certain areas, such as Antarctica, including the Australian sector, but they are only local in their expression. The indirect effects of refrigeration and glaciation are far more widespread. In most of Australia these indirect effects are more important than are the direct influences.

As the ice sheets grew and extended, so were the other climatic zones pushed towards the equator. The desert borders migrated, and former areas of low rainfall became moister, with dramatic effects on plant and animal life. With the waning of the glaciers, climatic boundaries again shifted, and the desert boundaries changed again with important effects on the biota, including humans. During these climatic changes, climatically induced processes of weathering and erosion shaped the land surface into forms not typical of the present climatic regime. Because of climatic change, we find that some landforms and other features are, as it were, out of place,—are *relict* from a previous climatic regime and have been *inherited* from the past.

Secondly, with the growth of glaciers, water was taken out of the hydrological cycle, and precipitation, instead of being returned to the oceans, was trapped on the land in the form of ice. Thus during periods of glaciation, or glacier growth, the sea level was lowered; and conversely, when the glaciers melted, the level of the oceans rose. For this reason not only are coastal features found at levels different from the present limited zone of marine activity, but the baselevels of streams, for instance, varied, with important effects on the valley forms of exoreic streams. Variation in the average temperature of the ocean waters also caused slight fluctuations of volume and the level of the sea surface.

Finally, because of fluctuations in the gross amount of water in the ocean basins, the floor of the ocean is believed to have become unstable, causing variation in the capacity of the ocean basins, and consequently, shifts of sea level.

Clearly the *direct* effects of glaciation are of little importance in Australia, and are only briefly summarised here, but the indirect effects are of great significance. These aspects are considered in Chapter 10, but it must be stressed that other activities continued. They had nothing to do with climatic change, but were generated within the earth. In particular, volcanicity and earth movements of normal type, and not in any way related to Quaternary climatic change, affected various parts of the crust—including Australia—during this period.

(b) GLACIATION
(i) Modern ice masses
The two most extensive ice masses are the Antarctic and Greenland ice sheets. Together they contain 2·24 per cent of the world's total supply of water, compared with 97·1 per cent in the ocean basins; less than 0·02 per cent is contained in rivers and lakes, and 0·001 per cent in the atmosphere. The ice masses are important, not only because of their great volume and area, but also because similar ice sheets formerly extended over much of America and Europe, and thus, investigations of the behaviour of these two modern ice sheets provides important information which we can use to interpret and understand the effects of the former sheets.

The Quaternary: Direct Effects of Glaciation

(1) ANTARCTICA   With an area of some 3·5 million square miles, the Antarctic ice mass is the largest in the world. It is seven times as large as that in Greenland, exceeds 6,000 feet in thickness for more than 75 per cent of its area and, existing in an essentially ice-free world, exerts a significant influence now, as throughout the Quaternary, on sea level, climate and other aspects of the environment. Not all of Antarctica is ice, for at the coastal margins of the continent especially, mountain ranges (*nunataks*) protrude above the level of the glaciers, and form the rim of a broad basin within which the ice sheet is largely contained, escaping only through gaps in the rim. But these rock outcrops cover a relatively small proportion of the whole, for ice streams flow towards the ocean in all directions, and even extend scores of miles out over the ocean as the

Fig 201   Map and sections of Antarctica (*after Bentley, Cameron, Bull, Kojima and Gow*).

massive sheets of ice known as *ice shelves* (Fig. 201). On breaking up, they form (or *calve*) tabular icebergs.

Although some of the nunataks appear high, they are only the uppermost parts of huge mountains largely buried by the ice sheet. The ice is very thick (Fig. 201), rising to well over 12,000 feet above a bedrock floor which in places lies below sea level. The lowermost layers of the Antarctic ice sheet are thought to be at least 90,000 years old. The subglacial relief is irregular, particularly in west Antarctica, though more subdued in the east.

Although many details remain to be discovered, it is clear that a very large volume of ice covers the Antarctic continent, and that, if this mass were to melt, sea level all over the world would rise by about 150 feet. For this reason, the behaviour of the Antarctic sheet ice is generally considered to be the key to Pleistocene sea levels.

Studies of its budget, i.e. the gains and losses of snow and ice, have resulted in a rather different hypothesis. Although information on net gains and losses for the ice mass is sparse, it seems that the principal ice loss in Antarctica is by way of the ice shelves which spread northwards and calve icebergs, which eventually melt. However, it has been stated that if sea level were higher, more of the terrestrial glaciers of Antarctica would begin to float and thus ice shelves would become more numerous and extensive and more ice would be lost; and for this reason, it can be argued that sea level controls the Antarctic ice mass, and not *vice versa*.

(2) GREENLAND The Greenland ice mass is an elongate lens of frozen water (Fig. 202) extending over an area of 500,000 square miles. As is the case in Antarctica, the bedrock floor in places extends below present sea level; the topography of the floor is subdued, and similar to that in eastern Antarctica. Nunataks form a discontinuous coastal ring around the ice dome, which rises to more than 10,000 feet, the crest lying closer to the east than the west coast (Fig. 202). Some of the ice is relict in nature for tests have disclosed that basal ice from a depth of 4,500 feet below the surface is about 10,000 years old. On both east and west coasts there are small ice-free areas. A more extensive area, Pearyland in the far north of Greenland, is ice-free because of its very low precipitation.

The ice sheet flows outwards to the sea, where the glaciers calve icebergs, through gaps in the coastal ranges. In view of the vast area covered by the ice, and the known geological complexity, it might be expected that large volumes of far travelled (or exotic) rocks might be brought by the ice from the central to the marginal areas, and there dumped to form *moraines* (see below). In fact, in some areas are found only very small moraines built of local rocks, The suggestion has been made that a large part of the Greenland ice is stagnant, only the upper part being mobile, and causing erosion only near the coast.

(3) OTHER GLACIERS Modern ice masses other than these ice sheets

The Quaternary: Direct Effects of Glaciation 261

are insignificant, though of great interest. They include ice caps, valley glaciers, piedmont and cirque glaciers. Snow accumulates and suffers compression under the weight of the overlying snow, first to *névé* (also called *firn*) which is a mush of mixed snow and ice, and then to ice, a

Fig 202 Map and sections of Greenland (*after Greswell, and Baird*).

Fig 203 Cirque glacier.

Fig 204 Piedmont glacier, the Malaspine (*after Gilluly, Waters and Woodford*).

wholly crystalline material. Much snow and ice accumulates on high plateaux to form ice caps, whence it flows outwards to lower levels. Ice also accumulates in depressions on mountain sides; this also flows outwards, rounding out the depressions as it moves to form armchair shaped hollows, or *cirques* (Fig. 203). Such cirque glaciers commonly coalesce as they flow downstream to form *valley glaciers*, streams of ice flowing down constricted and confined courses in pre-existing valleys. In some places where such glaciers emerge from uplands, on to, say, a coastal plain, they emerge to form a *piedmont glacier* (Fig. 204). Many examples of ice caps, and cirque and valley glaciers are known, but piedmont glaciers are rare. The Frederikshaab glacier in Greenland and the Bering glacier of Alaska are examples, but the best known is the Malaspina glacier of southern Alaska.

The Malaspina is fed by several valley glaciers arising in the mountains and plateau of southeastern Alaska. The most important are the Seward, which is fed by scores of subsidiary valley glaciers, and which is up to 3 miles wide, the Tyndall, and the Agassiz glaciers. All unite on reaching the coastal plain to form the Malaspina piedmont glacier which has a length of 70 miles, an area of 1,500 square miles, and a maximum elevation of 1,500 feet above its margin. The surface is broadly undulating, but in detail rough and broken by thousands of crevasses and morainic ridges. Air photographs show that the ice of the Malaspina is fantastically contorted. At the edge of the glacier numerous small lakes are impounded by tongues of ice and by forest-covered moraines. There are short surface streams in summer, but they disappear through tunnels into the glacier, which is drained primarily by streams flowing within and below the ice mass (englacial and sub-glacial drainage). At the southern margin, hundreds of streams occur heavily laden with sediment. They flow under great pressure so that, in the immediate neighbourhood of the ice margin, they form powerful jets of water, emerge from the glacier and flow over the narrow coastal plains to the sea.

(ii) Glacier motion

Glacier ice moves outwards from the centre of accumulation and downslope at rates varying from a fraction of an inch to several feet a day. A small Greenland glacier has been observed to travel at 20 feet a day and Alaska's Yanert glacier moves at 25 to 30 feet a day. This flow is motivated by gravity, but the weight of ice pushing behind (the hydraulic head) can cause uphill movement over short sectors. Glaciers were first described in 1544 and only thirty years later it was known that they move. Glaciers exhibit differential movement, both in space and time.

(1) MOVEMENT ALONG THE LONGITUDINAL PROFILE Movement along the length of a valley glacier is governed in some measure, as in rivers, by the nature of the channel: flow is faster through narrow sectors than through broad basins. Apart from these local variations, velocity tends to increase

downstream from the head of the glacier to just below the névé limit (Fig. 205), from which point the velocity decreases to the snout. In the upper reaches it has long been observed that the ice tends to move downwards from the surface into the body of the glacier, and that conversely, there is an upward movement in the lower areas.

(2) MOVEMENT IN TRANSVERSE SECTION A consideration of boundary layer conditions (cf. rivers, Chapter 6) suggests that the centre of a valley glacier will move more rapidly than the margins which are in contact with the bedrock. Simple observations show that this is generally true but the increase in velocity from margin to centre is not gradual, as might be anticipated. Instead, the velocity gradient is restricted to a quite narrow marginal zone, with the bulk of the ice moving at a uniform rate as a stream within the glacier (Fig. 206). This type of flow is known as *block-schollen* flow. Because of the marked velocity gradient in the marginal zone, there is strong shearing which results in the development of numerous crevasses (Fig. 207).

(3) MOVEMENT IN VERTICAL SECTION Due to frictional drag, the basal area of ice is retarded. Thus, most commonly the upper area moves more rapidly than the lower (Fig. 208). A pipe placed vertically in a glacier will eventually lean forward. Such a pattern of flow is called *gravity flow* and observations on modern glaciers suggest that this is the most common type of behaviour. In some instances, however, it has been shown that, although basal retardation still occurs, the lower middle areas move faster than the upper ice. This type of flow implies a measure of plasticity in the crystalline ice, and is called *extrusion* flow. It is likely to develop in areas of irregular sub-glacial relief where rock bars give rise to restricted passage, and where more rapid flow is thus necessitated. Extrusion flow is of interest insofar as it goes some way to explain the otherwise puzzling scouring by glaciers of deep basins, and the eddy-type currents in ice commonly indicated by glacial scratches or *striae*.

(4) MOVEMENT IN TIME Terminal movement is at a maximum in summer, when meltwaters are most abundant. At the head, movement is greatest in winter, when most snow accumulation takes place. In addition to these normal variations, waves, or surges, sudden unaccountable phases of movement, several times more rapid than normal, are also known.

(iii) Pleistocene stratigraphy
Evidence in both Europe and North America has established a fourfold subdivision of the Pleistocene. In each continent, essentially simultaneously on both sides of the Atlantic, and probably simultaneously in both hemispheres, the ice sheets advanced and retreated four times, disregarding minor phases of advance and retreat.

This was first suspected following investigation in the valleys of rivers emerging from the Swiss Alps. Here four distinct gravel terraces (or

The Quaternary: Direct Effects of Glaciation   265

Fig 205 Movement of glacier in longitudinal profile.

Fig 206 Movement of glacier in transverse section.

Fig 207 Crevasses resulting in differential movement.

Glacier advances from
A-A' – B-B' in time t

Fig 208 Movement of glacier in vertical section.

O.D. — Older Deckenschotter
Y.D. Younger "
H. High Terrace gravel
L. Low " "

Fig 209 Section of the Inn valley (*after Wright*).

Deckenschotter), each traceable upvalley to glacial end moraines, and thus of valley train type, occur at different levels. The fact that they occur at different elevations, with phases of erosion intervening, implies a change of condition, a surmise supported by the presence of fresh loess overlying weathered gravels, and indicating different (interglacial) agencies (Fig. 209).

Table 4 Quaternary Stratigraphy

A Comparison of common terminologies (Glacial periods in capitals, interglacials in small lettering)

		North America	European Alps	North Germany	Traditional Mediterranean sea levels
Present					
	4	WISCONSIN	WURM	WEICHSEL	
		Sangamon	R/W		Monastirian
	3	ILLINOIAN	RISS	SAALE	
Pleistocene		Yarmouth	M/R		Tyrrhenian
	2	KANSAN	MINDEL	ELSTER	
		Aftonian	G/M		Milazzian
	1	NEBRASKAN	GUNZ	?PRE-ELSTER	
					Sicilian
					Calabrian
Pliocene					

Source: After *Flint*.

B Subdivision and absolute dating of late Pleistocene

	MANKATO Advance	11,400 years before Present
	Two Creeks Interval	
LATE WISCONSIN	CARY Advance	15,200 " " "
	TAZEWELL Advance	18,000 " " "
EARLY WISCONSIN (IOWAN)		60,000 " " "

Source: After *Stearns*.

In several parts of the world chronologically separate ground moraine material (called *drift*) can be distinguished by such features as the degree of weathering of the drift; the presence of non-glacial sediments (some including organic remains) between the drifts; the degree of erosion of the drifts; the provenance, or source area, of rocks in the drifts; and on direct dating of later drifts by the C14 method. Using such criteria, four separate major glaciations have been identified. They have been given different names in different parts of the world (see Table 4). Here the terminology used was established in North America where, although the total extent of each glaciation was comparable, the distribution of ice (and hence of drift) varied from glaciation to glaciation, each being either typically developed or initially identified in a particular place. Hence the allocation of State names to the glacial phases. The interglacials, too, are named after localities.

Thus, four times the ice sheets developed and spread, four times they withdrew and disintegrated. On each occasion they caused erosion and deposition, and had important indirect effects.

(iv) Glacial erosion
That ice erodes cannot be denied. It is testified by the numerous descriptions of surfaces scratched or striated by rocks carried along in the ice, surfaces plucked of loose fragments by moving ice, of grooves, of deep basins, many now occupied by lakes, and of debris of various grades carried far from its source. It can be visualized that masses of moving ice act as huge bulldozers which transport weathered and unconsolidated debris. However, in many areas, such as the Canadian Shield, the land surface has been modified, rather than radically altered, by the very large masses of ice that occupied the area. Also, in some areas soils have survived the passage of glacier ice (possibly through being frozen and hardened before the glacier arrived). It is widely acknowledged that in some areas ice eroded; in others, it deposited, and added to the land surface; elsewhere, the ice exerted a protective influence.

Late in the nineteenth century, a controversy developed between some scientists who considered that ice eroded more rapidly than streams and others who, although not denying that ice is capable of erosion, considered that streams work more effectively than moving ice. The arguments advanced by the glacial *erosionists* and the *protectionists*, as they are called, will be considered in the following section with reference to specific landforms resulting from the glaciation of mountain regions.

(A) CIRQUE Also known as a *cwm* or *corrie*, the cirque is one of the most common and striking of all glacial forms in upland regions and yet it has never been satisfactorily explained. A cirque is an armchair-shaped hollow consisting of steep head and side walls, a basin, and a threshold (or raised rim) separating the basin from the downhill slope. The headwall may be up to 3,000 feet high and, even where the cirque glacier is no longer present, there is little scree at its base. The basin may be occupied by a lake called a *tarn*. Where a glacier occupies the hollow, there is commonly a deep crevasse at, or near, the backwall and called a *bergschrund*.

For long it was held that the bergschrund played a critical role in the development of cirques. Early in the twentieth century, Willard Johnson, an American, descended a bergschrund and was impressed by the amount of shattered rock there. He argued that basal sapping or plucking at the base of the bergschrund was responsible for cirque development: he postulated that the rock fragments were carried in the base of the glacier and were instrumental in gouging out a basin in the underlying bedrock. Although this theory was virtually unquestioned for many years, serious objections can be levelled against it. Why, for instance, does the threshold survive erosion by the heavily laden basal ice? Temperature observations taken in bergschrunds have shown that there is very little variation there, indicating that the freeze-thaw action is not likely to be marked. Furthermore, the bergschrund is not deep (about 100 feet), making it difficult to understand how a backwall up to 3,000 feet high can be formed, unless it is argued that the wall was developed as the glacier waxed and waned, and the bergschrund migrated up and down the wall. Even so, one is faced with the problem of the base of the wall and the basin, indicative of strong erosion, being formed by a very small glacier.

It has been suggested that summer meltwaters soaking into the backwall and freezing there could effect some shattering, and meltwaters have been observed at some, though not all, cirque backwalls. How far such meltwaters penetrate down the backwall is unknown, and the lack of temperature fluctuation is also a problem. Subsequently it was advocated that the fracture of rocks which have been subjected to pressure release[1] was important in this context. The basin form of cirques (as well as of glacial troughs) is a major problem which may in part be explicable in terms of either an extrusion type of flow, or of a rotational movement in cirque glaciers (Fig. 210). There is some evidence for the latter, for dirt bands in cirque ice appear to dip down at the head and come up to the surface again near the threshold. However, the question then arises whether the rotational movement causes the basin form, or whether the latter induces the former.

(B) ARETES AND PYRAMIDAL PEAKS   Where cirques are 'eating back' into ridges and mountains, they tend to form knife-edged ridges which are called *arêtes*, or, where three or more are eroding back toward the same area, pyramidal peaks, of which the Matterhorn is a well-known example.

(C) GLACIAL TROUGHS (U-SHAPED VALLEYS) AND ASSOCIATED FEATURES
Valley glaciers are fed by cirque glaciers and flow as great streams of ice in valleys. Glaciated troughs differ from valleys excavated by rivers in several ways: they have steeper sides, and flatter floors, or display a catenary, or U-shaped, profile in cross-section, in contrast with the V-shaped river valleys of mountain regions. In glaciated valleys, spurs have been truncated and are therefore straighter than the river valleys of upland regions, which commonly display interlocking spurs. The floors of glaciated valleys are irregular, with many basins, and steps. Some of the basins are occupied by lakes which tend to be elongated and strung out like beads in a necklace, hence their name—*paternoster* lakes. Tributary valleys and streams are discordant with the main valley and stream—they are said to *hang*.

These features have been interpreted in several ways. Some authors consider the forms are due to marked glacial erosion, though the possibility that glaciers may have exploited deeply weathered areas underlying valley floors (such as is found in arid lands today) has not fully been examined. Others believe they are due to the protective action of ice, and preservation from erosion by rivers and streams. It is now generally agreed that ice erodes—it is a question of how rapidly, relative to running water.

The hanging valley, for instance, can be explained in two ways. The erosionists argue that larger glaciers flow down the main valleys than down the tributaries, which are thus eroded less, and so are left hanging after the withdrawal of the ice. The protectionists on the other hand claim that because the tributary valleys are higher than the main valleys, ice would persist longer in the former, thus protecting them from river work, which effectively lowers the main valley floors, thus causing the discordant junction to develop.

Similarly with valley steps, which are attributed by erosionists either to the ice picking out weaknesses and resistant areas of bedrock or to differential erosion, as at the junctions of glaciers. The protectionists, on the other hand, believe that the areas above the steps have been protected by ice, while those below have been exposed to river action and are therefore lower: each valley step marks a halt in the glacier retreat.

Although the protectionists have been able to marshall some evidence in support of their thesis, in general it does not provide a satisfactory explanation of the facts.

(D) FJORDS Fjords are long, narrow and deep glacial troughs that have been drowned by the sea. They commonly possess a lip, or threshold, where they join the sea. Many of them are very deep, due to the glacial deepening. Sogne Fjord, in western Norway, for instance, is 4,000 feet deep in places, but has a lip only 500 feet below sea level. Many fjords

Fig 210 Rotational movement of cirque glacier.

Fig 211 Bukken fjord (*after Gregory*).

are in west coast situations and are backed by precipitous ranges: the ice masses fed by abundant precipitation, must have flowed rapidly and caused much erosion. But where they entered the sea, the glaciers must have floated, and thus ceased to erode the bedrock—hence the lip. Many fjords are drowned glacial valleys which are developed from pre-glacial river valleys, the pattern of which in some areas was strongly guided by faults (Fig. 211).

(v) Glaciated lowlands
Erosion is typical of glaciated uplands and deposition of glaciated lowlands, though neither process is wholly localised in its activities. Thus depositional features are found in glaciated valleys, and minor erosional forms in glaciated lowlands. But, in broad view, the material eroded from the uplands is transported to the lowlands where it is deposited.

Landforms due to glacial deposition fall into two broad categories, according to the nature of the deposits. Some forms are developed wholly as a result of deposition by the glacier, while others are due to the deposition of debris by meltwaters derived from the glacier. The former are *glacial* deposits, the latter *fluvioglacial* (Fig. 212).

Glacial deposits, and the features formed by them, include moraines of various types. Any material deposited by a glacier is known as moraine, but it is laid down in various forms and positions. The most important is the *ground moraine* (till, or boulder clay) which is deposited as a sheet by the glacier. It covers wide areas of glaciated lowlands and, after the ice has melted, forms irregular hummocky plains pitted with depressions of various types. Some are chance hollows between moraine ridges, but others are kettle holes, where large blocks of ice embedded in the morainic material persisted after the main ice mass had melted; after the block melted, there was a depression which became a lake. *Drumlins* are in some places found in association with the ground moraine. Drumlins are smooth, oval hills consisting mainly of till, and with their long axes parallel to the direction of glacier motion. Drumlins occur in fields (in groups) located some distance from the ice limit and are due to particularly heavy ground moraine being moulded by the moving ice. The steeper slope (the stoss side) of the drumlin faces the direction from which the ice came, and the gentler, streamlined slope (tail), downstream. Some drumlins possess a core of bedrock, and these appear to be similar in origin to *crag and tail* features, wherein moraine is plastered both up and downstream of the obstacle.

Morainic ridges also form in relation to valley glaciers, for, as the ice moves forward and melts at the margins and in the terminal region, the debris it carried is piled up to form *lateral* and *terminal moraines*. If the ice front recedes a series of arcuate, roughly concentric terminal *recessional moraines* are left behind, each marking a pause in the retreat of the ice front. And if two or more valley glaciers unite, their lateral moraines merge to form *medial moraines*. Evaporation (or ablation) from the

Fig 212 Glacial and fluvoglacial features at the terminus of a glacier (*after Gilluly, Waters and Woodford*).

Fig 213 Maps of parts of Labrador, showing the profusion of lakes: (A) a granite area, showing strong joint control; (B) an area of folded sediments. Water bodies shown in white.

surface of the glacier also causes the concentration of debris to form an *ablation moraine*.

Just before final deposition, much glacially transported debris is, carried by glacial meltwaters and streams. Such debris is sorted and stratified, in contrast to the purely glacial material, and is moulded to rather different forms. Plains of such fluvioglacial material form distinct fans, or *outwash plains*, close to the ice front, where they are commonly found associated with terminal moraines, and where they display kettle lakes or ponds of similar origin to those of ground moraines; many extend long distances downvalley from the glacier snout, forming *valley trains*. As in constricted valleys, where the glacier flows close to bedrock walls, outwash deposits may be dumped in a narrow wedge, between ice and rock to form a *kame* which includes water-sorted material and much glacial debris. *Eskers* are sinuous ridges of sorted sand and gravel which generally display rudimentary stratification. They are best developed on lowlands glaciated by ice sheets, and form as valley trains in stream channels located upon, within, or beneath the ice. They bear little or no relation to the underlying geology and topography. Eskers are common in Finland, central Ireland and Labrador.

One of the commonest forms due to glacial erosion, especially common on lowlands, is the *roche moutonnée*, a low knob of rock, the lee side of which is plucked by ice action giving a distinct asymmetry.

Finally, the most typical form of glaciated lowland is the lake. Some areas, like Finland, and the lake plateau of central Labrador (Fig. 213) seem to consist more of water than of land, despite the fact that many of the former lakes have been infilled with debris and are now marshes. Lakes arise in such circumstances through either erosion or deposition. Any areas of weathered rock, any areas of weakness, are scoured out of the bedrock, glacial deposits block drainage lines, in both cases creating hollows or basins which are filled with water. Subsurface percolation is hindered or prevented by permanently frozen ground.

(c) PERIGLACIAL LANDFORMS

In subarctic and arctic conditions where precipitation is insufficient to permit glaciers to form, frost action is all-important. Soil moisture is frozen, forming a layer of permanently frozen ground (*permafrost*) at or close to the land surface. Permafrost is extremely tough (at the Knob Lake iron quarries in central Labrador, pockets of such frozen rock are so hard that the miners work around them rather than try to destroy them with explosives), and may partly account for the apparent resistance of certain areas to glacial erosion; it is impermeable, and hence is conducive to poor drainage and the formation of swamps; it is impenetrable to plant roots and, together with the intense cold, effectively inhibits plant growth.

The intense cold, and particularly the oscillation of the temperature about freezing point, causes many cycles of freeze-thaw activity. Vegetation is sparse and does little to protect the land surface against atmospheric temperature fluctuations. Many rocks, particularly those of fissile structure, are rapidly broken down by this freeze-thaw activity. Moreover, as water expands when frozen, formation of ground ice causes plant roots to be torn, and small areas to be raised. Such frost-heaving initiates much mass movement of material downslope, processes which are aided by the scarcity of vegetational binding and the common presence of permafrost. The frozen surface of the permafrost acts as a gliding or slipping surface and prevents the waters of the summer thaw from escaping into the soil. Thus a fluid mass of debris slides and slips downslope on the permafrost. Such soil flows (*solifluxion*) are instrumental in transporting relatively quickly, very large volumes of debris downslope, and small solifluxion terraces and lobes are typical of slopes in periglacial regions.

The removal of material from upper slopes leaves behind crude benches due to frost action and solifluxion; and the swift downslope flow of such debris is apparently capable of shaving smooth surfaces.

(d) ISOSTATIC MOVEMENTS

At present, Greenland and Antarctica both carry vast sheets of ice, and, in both, parts of the bedrock floor are beneath sea level. Moreover, the weight of ice has depressed the crust, causing a basin structure to form in Greenland. During the Pleistocene, when ice sheets spread equatorwards, extensive areas of Europe and North America, which are now ice-free, were covered with ice and depressed. The ice melt for the last time in these areas was so recent that their recovery, or uplift, still continues (Fig. 214).

Such earth movements, caused by the redistribution of load, are called *isostatic movements* because it is conceived that each unit area of the earth's crust should be underlain by an equal mass (volume × density) of rock and thus that high standing areas, like the Himalayas, are underlain by less dense rock, and the ocean deeps, underlain by a lesser thickness of crust, by denser material. Indeed, in terms of isostatic principle, the earth's crust is usually seen as consisting of a sphere of dense rock entirely covering the planet and, floating in this, rafts of lighter rock, which are the continents. The reality of the general concept cannot be doubted: not only are continents affected by loading and unloading, as a result of glaciation, but areas receiving large masses of debris also subside: thus the Mississippi delta has long been an area of subsidence and continues to sink, causing the downwarping of river terraces in the lower Mississippi valley (Fig. 215).

Such isostatic adjustments are generally considered to operate only on a regional scale (say 1° latitude square), the rigidity or strength of the earth's crust accommodating local redistributions of load. But it has been

Fig 214 Isostatic recovery of Scandinavia: (a) elevation of Scandinavia (in feet) during last 9,700 years; (b) present rate of rise per decade, in inches (*after Dury*); and (c) Britain, present rise and fall in mm-a-year (*after Valentin*).

reported recently that in the Andermatt region of Switzerland, local features may be attributed to such movements. Near Andermatt the valley sides are notable for a series of scarps, each facing upslope and each fault scarp coincident with the trace of a pre-existing fault (Fig. 216). Clearly the amount of uplift involved is greatest in the centre of the valley, and diminishes laterally. This has been interpreted as due to isostatic readjustment to deglaciation, with the greatest rebound occurring on the fault block where the ice was thickest.

Fig 215 Downwarping of the Mississippi delta, manifested in the distortion of the lower part of a terrace (*after Fisk*).

Fig 216 Small scale isostatic recovery along pre-existing faults in a U-shaped valley in the Swiss Alps.

(e) DRAINAGE MODIFICATIONS DUE TO GLACIATION

As explained previously (Chapter 6 (k,iv)), where ice flows across or against the regional slope, the natural drainage is blocked and meltwaters from ice and snow are impounded between the ice front and the acclivity of the land, forming lakes. Several such ice-dammed marginal lakes, or *proglacial lakes* occur at the border of the Malaspina glacier and the Marjelen See, blocked by the Aletsch glacier in Switzerland. The latter can usually be cited as a type example, but in 1965 it was drained presumably because of movements of the ice obstacle. During the Pleistocene, systems of such proglacial lakes developed in various places in North America and Europe. The Great Lakes are of this type, though isostatic warping was and is an important factor. Evidence for the former presence of such lakes includes shoreline features such as abrasion platforms and beaches, the type example being the famed 'Parallel Roads of Glenroy' in Scotland, where there are three horizontal shore benches located at 1149, 1068 and 857 feet above sea level. Lake sediments, including deltaic deposits and *varved clays* are also indicative of lacustrine conditions. Varved clays are characterised by well developed graded bedding, which is expressed as fine laminae or beds, each representing a year's accumulation. They are typical of lakes fed by glacier meltwaters and form in the following way: during the summer thaw meltwaters and sediment are carried to the lake; the coarser (sand) fraction of the sediment loads settles quickly to the lake bed, but the finer silts and clays remain in suspension. With the winter freeze, accession of water is greatly reduced and may cease altogether, and during this time, no coarse sediment is laid down, but the fines settle to the floor. In this way, a distinct layer is formed, comprising summer sands below and winter silts above. Next summer sands are again deposited, followed by fines, and so on. The sharp contrast between the fines of one year and the sands of the next cause a distinct and sharp lamination to develop. Overflow channels or spillways, through which lake waters escaped either to other proglacial lakes or to ice-free country, suggest the former presence of a lake. These spillways are characteristically trough shaped in cross section with a flat floor and steep sides. They lack tributaries and are independent of, or alien to, the regional drainage pattern. Whole systems of such spillways have been identified in some areas, classic examples being in the North York moors area, the North European plain, and south of the Great Lakes in North America, where the spillways from the lakes region to the Mississippi drainage system provided the waterways followed by the early French explorers of the continent.

Many spillways display curious humped and irregular profiles in longitudinal section, and many commence abruptly on hillsides. These features may indicate that the channels were scoured by subglacial waters flowing under high pressure. Such an interpretation may also explain why evidence for some of the postulated proglacial lakes which spillways allegedly connected, is scarce or absent; it should also be remembered, however, that much of the evidence is fragile and likely to remain fragmentary, particularly in areas long-settled by man.

Other drainage modifications occur where ice overrode the pre-existing terrain and blanketed it with drift: the postglacial drainage system need bear no relationship to the preglacial, though major elements commonly persist.

(f) DIRECT EFFECTS OF GLACIATION IN AUSTRALIA

Such direct effects of Quaternary glaciation are absent in South Australia, though in Tasmania, the Kosciusko area, and New Guinea there were small glaciers, and quite extensive areas of periglacial activity during the Wisconsin. These were altitudinal snow and ice fields, owing their development to their high elevation in low and middle latitude regions.

In the Mt Wilhelm region of New Guinea (Fig. 217) there are numerous cirques and associated forms and deposits including lateral and terminal moraines. Only one glaciation is evidenced, and this, from the state of preservation of the associated features, is of latest Wisconsin age. In the Kosciusko region of N.S.W. (Fig. 218) the glaciation is now considered to have extended over a maximum of 20 square miles, a much lower estimate than earlier interpretations. Some 13 cirques, were developed including Mawson (M.R. Kosciusko, N.S.W. & Vic., 243027), Tynham (278066) and Blue Lake (272054). Some have associated tarns and several have distinct moraines (228017). The Snowy valley (282026), northwest of Charlottes Pass, has a U-shaped profile. In general, the features at all but the highest elevations are attributed to intense frost action rather than glaciation. Moreover, the glaciation which is seen as involving a limited area of cirque and confluent valley glaciers, is regarded as of a single age (Wisconsin), though it is allowed that some of the larger cirques may have been initiated during an earlier glaciation.

In central and southwestern Tasmania (Fig. 219), the extent of Pleistocene glacial activity has similarly been severely reduced compared with earlier estimates, though the present limits are marginally more expansive than those of a decade ago. A small ice sheet affected the central uplands in the vicinity of Lake St Clair. Deep cirques, troughs, rock basins and valley steps are well developed, though U-shaped valleys are not. Typical hummocky ground moraine, end moraines and associated fluvioglacial deposits occur. Marginal to the ice sheets, small coalescent valley glaciers and piedmont glaciers shaped the landscape, while in the south and west, isolated small cirque and valley glaciers were formed. These landscape modifications took place in the latest Wisconsin, but in

Fig 217 Extent of Quaternary glaciation around Mt Wilhelm, New Guinea (*after Reiner*).

Tasmania there is evidence of multiglaciation. In the Forth River valley, an unconsolidated glacial till has been found resting upon glacial outwash and lake sediments which, in turn, rest upon almost 100 feet of cemented till. The age of the earlier glacial deposit is not known.

Quite apart from argument over details of the glaciations in each of these areas, an obvious anomaly is the virtual absence of evidence for any period of glaciation other than the most recent. Four periods are consistently recognised in the Northern Hemisphere, and multiglaciation is proved in New Zealand. It could be that glacial features and deposits were developed during earlier glacials, only to be destroyed or damaged beyond recognition during the Wisconsin. An intriguing alternative has been advanced with respect to New Guinea. New Guinea is tectonically unstable, and it is known that very large vertical movements have affected the island during the Quaternary: it has been reported that Pliocene coralline limestones, now occur at an elevation of 16,000 feet in the Carstenz Mts. Thus, as the New Guinea glaciation is of altitudinal origin,

Fig 218 Extent of Quaternary glaciation in the Kosciusko area (*after Galloway*).

it is possible that during the first three glaciations the island, though rising rapidly, had not attained a height sufficient for snow and ice fields to accumulate, a state reached only during the Wisconsin.

The only remnants of glaciation in Australia known to be earlier than the Wisconsin are of Permian and Precambrian age. In the Inman Valley, some 40 miles south of Adelaide, and at Halletts Cove (Fig. 220), Permian glaciated pavements, with striae are exposed, and glacial and fluvioglacial deposits (including varved clays) of the same age are widespread through southern Australia, for instance near Bacchus Marsh, Victoria, and in the Canberra district. In South Australia the provenance of some of the contained erratic boulders shows that the ice travelled from southeast to northwest. Victor Harbour granite occurs in the Inman Valley and Halletts Cove Permian deposits, and rocks similar to those exposed in small granite outcrops in the Southeast occur in several parts of the Gulf region, for instance, Yorke Peninsula.

Several features of the Inman Valley have been attributed to the Permian glacial episode, but care is necessary in interpretation. It is unlikely if not impossible that forms of such ancient origin could survive, unless the features were buried under sediments, thus preserved, and only recently re-exposed. Crozier Hill, for example, is often quoted as an example of *roche moutonnée* of Permian age; but in the field, it is clear that the undoubted asymmetry of the hill is equally explicable in terms of structure, for the gentler side is a dipslope, the steeper a scarp face.

Fig 219 Extent and types of glaciation in Tasmania (*after Derbyshire*). Key: 1. Eroded by ice sheet; 2. Reticular glacier systems and piedmont glaciers; 3. Discrete areas eroded by cirque and valley glaciers.

The Quaternary: Direct Effects of Glaciation

Fig 220 Map of the Halletts Cove area (*after Dept. Geol., Univ. Adelaide*).

Normal weathering can explain the scree and there is no sign of striations or undoubted plucking. Ice unquestionably passed northwestward up the Inman Valley, eroding a pavement and leaving behind deposits of various types; but the forms are overwhelmingly due to river erosion and mass movement; most of the glacial features are either buried or destroyed.

The Precambrian (Sturtian) glaciation is known only from its deposits, which are widely distributed in the Mt Lofty–Flinders Ranges. A unique instance of ancient multiglaciation is displayed at Halletts Cove, where an erratic block of Sturtian tillite (consolidated drift) now rests upon the Permian glaciated pavement.

NOTE

[1] The rocks have either crystallised at high pressures or been subjected to great stress, if only by the weight of overlying rocks or ice, and subsequently relieved of these stresses by erosion or melting of ice (see Chapter 4).

10. The Quaternary: Indirect Effects of Glaciation

(a) EUSTATIC MOVEMENTS

WORLD WIDE MOVEMENTS of sea level are called eustatic movements. In theory two types can be distinguished with respect to Quaternary sea level changes. During glacial periods, water was withheld from the ocean basins, with the results that:

(1) Sea level was lowered.
(2) Due to the unloading of the ocean floors and continental margins, the former are believed to have risen in readjustment, while the latter may have suffered broad scale warping or flexuring. In these ways the capacity of the ocean basins was reduced, thus compensating in some measure for the lowering (1).

When the ice sheets melted, sea level rose and the continental margins were depressed beneath the weight of water, causing an enlargement of the basins, but insufficiently to compensate for the rise in level brought about by the massive accession of water.

Thus two separate, unequal, and temporally distinct effects are involved. Those shifts of sea level which are a direct response to the withdrawal and release of water consequent upon the waxing and waning of the ice masses: these are *glacio-eustatic* changes of sea level. With very rare and trivial exceptions, modern glaciers, and the Antarctic and Greenland ice sheets in particular, are shrinking, and sea level is still rising. Statistical analyses of tide gauge data from all over the world show that the level of the oceans is rising by between 0·05 and 0·2 inches a year, and that it has risen by 1·77–3·7 inches since the middle of the nineteenth century.

Secondly, there are changes occasioned by tectonic movements of the sea floors and adjacent continental areas: these are the *tectono-eustatic* movements.

In theory, the two types can be distinguished by their relationship in time with dated glacier fluctuations, but in practice such correlations are complicated by several factors, including:

(1) Lags or delays in the response of the ocean floors to loading or unloading.
(2) Uncertainties as to the amount of marginal flexuring and of continental adjustment to loading under water and ice.
(3) Uncertainties as to the strength and rigidity of the crust.
(4) Varied estimates of the former mass of the ice sheets and other glaciers.

(5) Variations in the volume of ocean waters occasioned by the heating and cooling of those waters in sympathy with the same factors which caused the more dramatic development and disintegration of the ice sheets. If the temperature of all the water in the oceans were raised by 1°C., there would be an increase in volume which would cause sea level to rise by some 23·6 inches; but the circulation of the deep ocean basins is slow, the cycle being several thousand years, by which time atmospheric and surface temperature regions may have changed. Furthermore, an increase in atmospheric temperatures would result in greater melting of ice and calving of icebergs which would tend to lower oceanic temperatures. Thus the significance of this factor is uncertain.

Certainly the sort of changes envisaged by loading and unloading undoubtedly occur: Lake Mead, an artificial lake in Arizona is subsiding at a rate of 40 feet a thousand years as a result of loading its area of 232 square miles with 40 thousand million tons of water and 2 thousand million tons of sediment accumulated in the lake waters, a loading of 147 lbs a square inch. However, the subsidence will not continue for long, and is expected to total about 10 inches.

The infinitely more massive alternations of loading and unloading as a result of the decline and growth of glaciers must have had significant effects. Nevertheless, most abandoned sea levels are interpreted as of glacio-eustatic origin. The best known exception is the Daly level, named after a geologist, R. A. Daly who first recognised its world-wide significance. It stands some 16 to 20 feet above present sea level, and is considered to date from 3,000 to 3,500 years ago. On the southern shore of the Gulf of Carpentaria, for instance, shell beds standing a little more than 20 feet above sea level at Karumba have been dated as 3,300 years old and probably represent the Daly level.

(b) CRITERIA FOR THE RECOGNITION OF OLD SEA LEVELS
The features evolved on modern shorelines, and some mention of the types of deposits laid down there, have been described in Chapter 8. When any of these forms or deposits occurs out of reach (above or below) modern shore processes, a change in the relative positions of land and sea is indicated: the level of the sea has either risen or fallen (eustatism), or the land has moved (tectonism). The two cases are distinguished by the behaviour of the old shore features along the coast, for if sea level has changed they will be at similar (though not identical) elevations on all coasts, whereas deformation results in unequal dislocation, so that the coastal features dating from the same period in this instance occur at different levels along the coast.

Several types of evidence indicate the presence of old shorelines. 'Raised beach' is a conventional all-embracing and convenient term for indications of old shorelines now above sea level—though no beach need be in evidence and the area need not have suffered uplift!

Morphological evidence includes shore platforms, notches and cliffs, abandoned or deeply submerged beneath the sea, and the general configuration of the coast—rias, fjords and truncated drainage systems resulting from submergence (e.g. Port Phillip Bay, Fig. 102), while extended drainage (Fig. 103) and smooth flat coasts are in some areas indicative of emergence. The slope of river terraces may suggest their grading to a sea level (baselevel) different from present, but care is necessary in using these forms, and it is difficult to ascertain the level to which they were graded unless the then shoreline can be located (Fig. 221). Submerged forests, or man-made features such as harbours and buildings which have been wholly or partially drowned, may also be cited, though again care in application is necessary, in this case to avoid confusion between silting and submergence. Finally sediments or soils in alien environments are suggestive of elevational changes.

Fig 221 Extrapolation of former sea level from terrace remnants.

(c) THE TRADITIONAL GLACIO-EUSTATIC SCHEME

For obvious reasons, the interglacial high stands of the sea should be more easily recognised than the glacial low sea levels. Nevertheless Quaternary low sea levels are widely recognised. Off the east coast of North America, the Franklin shore, at between −240 and −330 feet can be traced for 180 miles. On the Sahul shelf, off northwest Australia, there is a consistent and well marked step at −350 to −390 feet which probably represents the lowest Pleistocene sea level. A number of submarine terraces have been recognised off the N.S.W. coast. The most obvious are grouped between 360 and 420 feet, and between 420 and 480 feet below present sea level. Their dating is rendered difficult by their situation and by the fact that they have suffered considerable warping during the Pleistocene. Remnants of an intricate major drainage system have been identified on the Sunda Shelf between Borneo and Sumatra, at a depth of 225 to 290 feet below sea level; again drainage to the sea level of the glacial maximum is indicated. A lowering of sea level during glacial maxima of at least 330 feet is widely accepted, and off the eastern and southern shores of North America there is evidence of a lowering of as much as 450 feet. Beneath the Adelaide beaches and in the Gulf area generally, there is widespread indication of a stand of the sea at about −30 or −35 feet.

Fig 222 Traditional scheme of high Pleistocene sea levels (*after Fairbridge*).

Fig 223 Detail for the past 20,000 years of traditional high Pleistocene sea levels (*after Fairbridge*).

The classic area for Pleistocene high sea levels is the central Mediterranean, where, it has been claimed, the ancient shorelines and intervening breaks of slope form a flight of terraces extending to several hundred feet above sea level. Since this thesis was first advanced (during the First World War) many such flights of shorelines have been recognised in many parts of the world. They apparently formed at successively lower levels, suggestive of a gradual lowering of sea level through the Pleistocene (Figs 222, 223), with the glacio-eustatic rises and falls superimposed, as it were, upon this long term decline. The several shorelines, the type areas for which are indicated by the names, stand at the elevations indicated below (Table 5), and are interpreted as being related to pre-glacial and interglacial phases of higher sea levels.

Table 5 The Traditional Scheme of Quaternary High Sea Levels

	Name	Average elevation m	ft	Age
Present				
	Monastirian (Main)	7·5	24	
	(Late)			Postglacial
	Tyrrhenian	18	58	Interglacial 3
	Milazzian	32	104	Interglacial 2
	Sicilian	60	195	Interglacial 1
	Calabrian	100	330	?Pre-glacial
Pliocene				

Source: After *Zeuner*.

If these are glacio-eustatic sea levels, it has correctly been reasoned that they should have affected the continental margins the world over. However, many remnants associated with such shorelines have been recognised not because of local evidence, but primarily because they should be there. Even where features which can be cited as indicating a former stand of the sea at that level (and much evidence susceptible to alternative interpretation has been used) there is no evidence of their age, either relative or absolute. Great care is necessary when suggesting that features are related to Quaternary high stands of the sea, firstly because it has been shown conclusively that the type sections in the central Mediterranean have been subjected to severe earth movements during the Quaternary, a fact which renders elevation itself quite undiagnostic of the age of the coastal features. The same is true of several other areas where the traditional scheme has been applied uncritically (see below).

Secondly, the whole scheme has been questioned by doubts concerning the behaviour of the Antarctic ice sheet. The Antarctic ice mass is so huge that its size has an important bearing on sea level. If it, and all the other ice in the world, melted then sea level would rise by about 170 feet. It has been tacitly assumed that during each interglacial, considerable melting took place returning sea level to elevations well above present. But in Western Australia, ancient strand lines standing only 10 feet above sea level have been dated as 35,000 and 37,000 years old. In other words (see Table 4B, page 266) these date from the minor interglacial between the Early and Late Wisconsin glaciations, and should therefore be well above sea level instead of only 10 feet above datum. Was the Antarctic ice mass essentially static during this interval? To what extent did it melt during the interglacials and to what extent, therefore, can high Pleistocene sea levels be anticipated?

Several late glacial and postglacial sea levels have been postulated quite close to modern datum, on the basis of platforms and other evidence; however, as suggested earlier (Chapter 8), several benches are forming simultaneously at present, close to modern sea level.

Doubts as to tectonic stability, the behaviour of the Antarctic ice mass, and the precise effects of present processes suggest that all possible Pleistocene shorelines should be carefully examined and judged on available evidence, and not identified and dated on the basis of a scheme which, though widely accepted, is surely illusory.

(d) PLEISTOCENE SEA LEVELS IN AUSTRALIA

Many scattered and mainly incidental observations of evidence indicative of relative changes in the level of land and sea have been made along the Australian coast. Examples of good evidence indicating former high stands of the sea come from N.S.W. where, in addition to a number of raised bars and stranded lagoons suggestive of a sea level higher by some 12 to 15 feet compared to the present and dated as between 3,500 and 4,000 years ago, there is apparently widespread evidence of a stand between 80 and 100 feet higher than present. Between Ballina and Forster, a distance of 200 miles, there is widespread evidence of a boulder beach, remnants occurring mainly at elevations between 80 and 100 feet, though scattered boulders occur up to 120 feet and up to 140 feet on Diamond Head (M.R. Hastings, N.S.W., 1,253440, 587074). Three miles south of Evans Head (M.R. Woodburn, N.S.W., 600890 and area) for example the beach remnants begin at about 60 feet and extend up to 80 feet with some boulders up to 120 feet on the Head itself. This sort of variation is consistent not only with the known vertical range of marine processes, but also allows for some slight dislocation since formation, a lack of which would almost be suspect.

In many cases it is difficult to know what significance to attach to field observations, for age determinations of features in most instances is not possible, and the tectonic setting is uncertain. The result is that adjacent areas can provide widely varied evidence.

On the coast of the Nullarbor plain, for example, evidence of both higher and lower sea levels has been recorded and it has also been shown that faulting at the northern margin of the Roe plain cannot be substantiated. Marine shelly limestone of Pleistocene age occurs at 80 to 102 feet above sea level in the Madura No. 1 bore; six miles south of Madura, limestone also of Pleistocene age occurs at 64 feet above sea level. At the eastern edge of the Eucla basin there is a calcareous marine limestone at 120 feet above sea level and a Recent marine calcareous sandstone occurs at 12 feet above sea level at the eastern end of the Roe plain, and at the head of the Bight there are shell beds of Recent age 6 feet above sea level. In several areas—Eucla, Merdagerrah and Head of Bight—aeolianite fronts the coastal cliffs and passes below present sea level, indicating formation at a time or times when sea level was lower.

On the adjacent coast of Eyre Peninsula, however, remarkably few Quaternary sea levels have been recognised. At several localities on the west coast (especially Cape Wiles, Streaky Bay) aeolianite rests on Archaean rock, the unconformity (or junction between the two rock types) approximating the present sea level. Emerged offshore bars and cliff-foot deposits now a few feet above sea level have been described near Whyalla, but the area is affected by faulting and the features probably have no eustatic significance. On Yorke Peninsula, on the other hand, numerous raised beaches have been recognised, all (with exceptions to be discussed later) within 20 feet of present datum. Several of the ancient strandlines are indurated with calcrete and thereby preserved. One of particular interest was described from Point Brown where there are shell beds located above a marine abrasion platform, and 14 to 16 feet thick: they were considered to indicate a sea level 10 to 12 feet higher than present. In the vicinity of West Cape (at the southwest extremity of Yorke Peninsula) there are several representatives of a platform eroded in gneisses, standing some 12 to 15 feet above present sea level, and partially buried beneath Quaternary aeolianite. On the east side of Spencer Gulf, north of Port Pirie, fossils from an emerged shell bed 10 feet above present sea level near the north of Baroota Creek have been dated (C14) as $2,615(\pm)75$ years.

On Kangaroo Island also, a stand of the sea 10 to 15 feet higher than present is well represented, with varied evidence, and shore features now at $+25$ feet, $+100$ feet, $+250$ to 400 feet are also indicated with a fair measure of certainty. Possible strand features occur at $+50$ to 75 feet and $+140$ to 175 feet, though the evidence is equivocal. In no case can these former stands be dated, except that they post-date the laterite of the main plateau of the island (i.e. latest Tertiary or Quaternary age). On the opposite side of Backstairs Passage, on Fleurieu Peninsula, shore features have been identified at $+26$ feet, $+135$ to 145 feet and 190 to 210 feet, again with no indication of age.

South of Kangaroo Island, a prominent and widespread bench feature at -300 to 350 feet on the Continental shelf has been mentioned by Sprigg and his associates and the course of the Murray (Fig. 224) can be traced across the shelf to the Continental slope just east of Kangaroo Island.

A submarine bench (or its equivalent) some 30–35 feet below present sea level is prevalent throughout the Gulfs region: it has been noted in St Vincent Gulf, and shallow water deposits with shells occur consistently beneath the Adelaide beaches from Largs to Brighton. The shells have been dated by C14 method as 6,350 ± 153 years old: the fact that this stratum with shells can be traced several miles beneath the coastal dunes, shows that no dislocation in a north-south direction has occurred since deposition, though the possibility of east-west distortion remains.

The nature of the old dunes of the Southeast was appreciated early and the area has long been recognised as a classic area for Pleistocene strand lines, but the area is likely to be known in the future not for the light it sheds on world wide Pleistocene sea level movements, but as an area of great complexity, inferences from which should not be extrapolated.

The facts are that from the Murray mouths southeastward to the Victorian border, upwards of 20 coastal sand dunes displaying typical aeolian structures, including shell fragments, and indurated and preserved by lime (hence the dunes are aeolianite dunes), occur in a zone extending from the coast to about 60 miles inland. To the northeast of this aeolianite zone there are many more parallel dune features, but they are built of red siliceous sands. The aeolianite dunes are all Pleistocene and the inland red dunes are younger than lower Pliocene in age.

The dunes run roughly northwest to southeast on a plain which slopes gently southwest to the coast (Fig. 225). In the interdune areas are broad swampy flats in which lagoons and associated lunettes are common. The

Fig 224 Former extended course of the Murray (*after Sprigg*).

Fig 225 Coastal foredunes in the southeast of South Australia (*after Blackburn, et al.*).

underlying bedrock is primarily calcareous and of Tertiary age; but in the Mount Gambier area, late Tertiary and Quaternary volcanic rocks occur (Chapter 3) and scattered throughout the area to the northwest are small granitic outcrops related to the underlying Padthaway horst or ridge. The smoothness of the ancient coastlines was interrupted by these outcrops which formed promontories and headlands, and the dune trends here are complex. Also, the general patterns are more distinct in the Lower than in the Upper Southeast, where a chaotic mass of dunes occurs.

Since the dunes are aeolian structures or foredunes comparable to those at present forming in several sectors of the South Australian coast, the elevation of the front toe of each dune should be an indication of the high water mark during the period of formation. Why are these old coastal features now far inland, and stranded far above present sea level? Some early workers regarded their present elevation as due wholly to tectonic uplift, but subsequently the location of stranded beaches was attributed primarily to glacio-eustatic effects. Many years before, a Jugoslav mathematician, Milankovich, had examined the consequences of the effects of periodic variations in the astronomical properties of the earth (e.g. the obliquity of the ecliptic, eccentricity of orbit) on the amount and distribution of solar radiation, received on the planet. He concluded that during the Pleistocene several major and minor peaks and depressions of the radiation curve would result, and related glacial and interglacial phases, and hence phases of low and high sea level, to his deduced curve[1]. This type of argument was vigorously expounded by Zeuner and adopted in the late 'forties and early 'fifties by Sprigg and others as a basis for dating the stranded dunes of the Southeast. But as Sprigg and Hossfeld stressed, and as Blackburn *et al* recently agreed, the whole area has been and continues to be tectonically active: the level of the toe of any dune is not constant, but falls to the northwest. Moreover, though topographic data is sparse, Hossfeld has shown that the amount of fall is greater in the inland than in the near coastal area, which is consistent with the idea of progressive tilting through the period of dune formation. The Murray mouths area is sinking or the Mt Gambier area is rising, or both events are occurring. A further difficulty, brought into prominence by Hossfeld, is that at least some of the dunes are complex, with more than one phase, and in some instances more than one type of coastal deposition represented within the single feature (Fig. 226).

The C14 dating of materials from within and between the dunes is, in a sense, a new start; for the information obtained by this technique, when sufficiently abundant, will provide a chronological framework into which the later environmental changes may be fitted. Although desirable, the time limitations of the C14 method of age determination are severe (see Chapter 2) and the complete unravelling of the late Tertiary and Quaternary history of the Southeast is a task which will not be accomplished easily or quickly.

The uncertainties introduced into the interpretation of the Pleistocene history of the Southeast by tectonic movements are characteristic of many parts of Australia. Faulting has been suspected along the Hampton Range, north of the Roe plain, and the whole of the Gulfs region forms part of the South Australian shatter belt. Yet recent studies on both sides of St Vincent Gulf have suggested that in both areas, flights of shore terraces extend up to 600 feet above present sea level and, that these shore features (the highest dating from pre-Pleistocene times) are undisturbed. The implication is that contrary to the current views of geologists, the faults which undoubtedly exist in these areas have been inactive over the past million years.

Fig 226 Section through the Woakwine dune (*after* Hossfeld).

In the area south of Adelaide, it has been claimed that there is evidence of former stands of the sea at 600, 540, 370, 105, 35, 26, 10 and 8 feet above present sea level. On Yorke Peninsula, old sea levels have been identified at the following elevations above present sea level: 695, 640, 560, 480, 420, 360, 255, 185, 130, 95, 60, 26, 12, 8·3, 4·3, and 2·9 feet. Both workers responsible for these findings date the levels according to present elevation, see Table 6.

In detail, the identification, nature and dating of these alleged former stands of the sea are dubious and cannot at present be accepted on both general and particular grounds. Not only are the Mediterranean-type sections affected by earth movements, but in both specific areas adjacent to St Vincent Gulf there is strong suggestion of Quaternary dislocation. Much of the detailed evidence on which are based identifications of ancient sea levels is fragmentary and of dubious validity. With respect to the 'postglacial' levels on Yorke Peninsula (and Gippsland), the concurrent development of multiple benches on present coasts makes their chronologic distinction unlikely.

Table 6 Postulated Pleistocene High Sea Levels in Southeastern Australia

Adelaide	Yorke Peninsula	Gippsland	Pleistocene stage
		1·8	
	2·9	2·2	
		3·0	
	4·3	4·5	Postglacial
8	8·3	7·5	
R			
10	12	11	Epimonastirian
R		R	
26	26	26	Late Monastirian
R			
35		R	Main Monastirian
R	60	R	
	95	R	
105		100	
	130	130	
		R	
		170	
	185	R	Sicilian
	255	260	
	360	360	
370			
R			
		R	
	420	420	
	480		Calabrian
540			
	560		
600			
	640		
	695		

R—regression of the sea to a level lower than present.
Source: After *Ward and Jessup*.

If sea level did attain levels 600 feet and more above present sea level, where did the huge volume of water involved come from, and whence did it go? If such elevations were attained, very extensive areas of southern Australia would have been flooded—in South Australia for instance much of Eyre Peninsula, the Lake Torrens depression and the Murray basin—where is the evidence for this? It has not been found despite an extended search.

It is clear however that tectonic displacement of significant but undetermined proportions and character renders difficult the reconstruction of past sea level changes. In the area south of Adelaide, on Fleurieu Peninsula and Kangaroo Island, in eastern Australia, as well as in Britain, there are benches and planate features which are readily interpreted as of marine origin even though they are now well above sea level. As in the majority of cases there is no direct evidence of the age of the features, there has been a very strong tendency to correlate these benches and the stands of the sea they are said to represent, on the basis of elevation and by comparison with the ages allegedly established in the Mediterranean type area.

This approach may eventually prove to be justified. But at present it is not. Quite apart from severe local and general problems the chronology of glacial development and melting in the two hemispheres has not been resolved, so that it is as yet far from clear what oscillations of sea level should theoretically be expected.

Surely the most reasonable approach at this stage is to collect the evidence for former stands of the sea and treat the evidence for their nature and age on its merits, rather than fit the facts to an overall scheme which though it may yet prove to be valid still awaits substantial corroboration.

(e) THE CONTINENTAL SHELF AND SLOPE

During periods of glaciation large areas of the present Continental Shelves were exposed. Rivers extended across them (see e.g. Fig. 224); benches were cut by waves during pauses in the advance or retreat of the ocean (see this chapter, section (c)). Also, it has been argued that during the Pleistocene glacials the exposure of large areas of unconsolidated sediment on the former sea bed caused submarine streams of water heavily laden with mud and silt—and called turbidity currents—to flow seawards across the continental shelves. These currents eroded the shelf and adjacent slope to form submarine canyons, of which examples have been cited off South Australia (Figs. 224, 227a and b), off the south coast of Western Australia and New Guinea (Figs. 227c, d and e) and many other parts of the world. Off South Australia the Murray trench, with a depth of $1\frac{1}{4}$ miles, is one of the deepest canyons in the world. However, in the case of the South and Western Australian canyons, their distribution with respect to basins of Tertiary deposition suggests that they may have originated before the Pleistocene, in the Tertiary or even earlier, an interpretation in some measure substantiated by the discovery, by geophysical means, of what are possibly similar trenches at the northern margin of the Eucla basin, and now buried beneath Tertiary marine sediments.

The Quaternary fluctuations of sea level also influenced the evolution of coral reefs. These take the form of *fringing reefs*, *barrier reefs* and *atolls*. The Great Barrier Reef, off Queensland and northern N.S.W., is a complex of atolls and reefs with a complicated history.

Many of these reefs are developed on subsiding foundations, but the changes of sea level were imposed on this gradual submergence. Coral

296   *Geomorphology*

Fig 227   Submarine canyons: (a) Distribution off southern and S.W. Australia; (b) Cross section of Bridgewater Canyons (38° 40′ S, 141° E) off southeastern Australia; (c) Cross section of Leeuwin Canyon (35° 10′ S, 115° 20′ E) off the southwest of Western Australia; (d) Plan of Perth Canyon off Fremantle; (e) Canyons off the north coast of New Guinea ((a)–(d) *after von der Borch*, (e) *after Sprigg*).

reefs are composed of myriads of coral polyps which have several requirements for growth and survival, notably:

(1) *Warm water* The water in which they live must be above 20°C and not more than 30°C. Thus coral is restricted first to the tropical areas (within 30° latitude of the equator), and particularly to the western sides of the oceans, where there are no upwellings of cold water. The reefs are confined to the surface layers of the tropical seas, for the water is cooler at depth than at the surface; corals grow to an absolute maximum of 300 feet depth and usually to a maximum of 150 or 180 feet from the surface.

(2) *Light* The algae which live symbiotically with the polyps require light for photosynthesis, so that the coral can for this reason also live only in the upper layers of the sea, where light can penetrate. Furthermore, dark silty waters prevent coral growth so that those oceanic areas close to river mouths are also devoid of corals.

If the earth were stable then coral should be found only to depths of 180 feet, or in exceptionally favourable circumstances, 300 feet. But it is argued that during the Quaternary low sea levels, coral reefs were eroded, and new reefs were established in relation to the new lower limit of growth and in a rather more restricted area. During the rises in sea level consequent upon glacial melting (interglacials) the corals grew upwards, because of the general cooling of the atmosphere and ocean, and these alternations were repeated several times, so that coral reefs are complex structures. In terms of these considerations coral reefs should extend to the maximum state of lowering of level, plus the maximum of environmental tolerance, i.e. 450 feet plus 300 feet = 750 feet, but no more. However several bores put down in reefs have penetrated through a few thousand feet of coral, showing that not only glacial sea level fluctuations are involved, but also that reefs are built on subsiding foundations (Fig. 228).

Fig 228   Evolution of coral reefs: (a) barrier reefs on a sinking foundation; (b) lowering of sea level and erosion of reef; (c) rise of sea level and growth of new reefs on foundations of old.

(f) EFFECTS OF MIGRATION OF CLIMATIC ZONES

Climatic factors largely determine the nature and effectiveness of the various processes of weathering, transportation and erosion, and deposition active in an area. They tend to develop characteristic suites of landforms. If the climate in an area undergoes drastic alteration, then the complex of processes (system of erosion or denudation) changes in sympathy and a different assemblage of the landforms is produced, so that one family is superimposed on the other. What is called a *palimpsest* surface is produced, the landscape displaying some forms which are in process of formation, others which are *inherited* from the past. The inherited nature of certain landforms is obvious, but in most instances interpretation poses many difficulties. One finds deep weathering in an arid region: is it developing slowly under present conditions or does it essentially derive from a former wetter period? There is evidence of stream erosion more powerful than is apparently possible now, but is this to be attributed to past periods of higher long-term discharge, and thus to a previous pluvial phase; or to, let us say, the flood of a millenium? This sort of difficulty is constantly being encountered by the geomorphologist and only rarely can some judgments be made; more often than not one can only suggest that one solution is more likely than another.

Quite apart from morphological and sedimentological features, several lines of evidence may be used to establish the fact of climatic change in areas untouched by or remote from ice masses.

(A) PALYNOLOGY (POLLEN ANALYSIS)   Pollen blown from trees and grasses settles on the land, on marshes or on lake surfaces, where it sinks and is incorporated in the bottom sediments. Though microscopic in size, pollen grains are exceedingly tough and resistant, but they oxidise easily; thus they are best preserved in reducing environments such as lakes and marshes, though some survive incorporated in terrestrial sediments and soils.

It is assumed that the environmental tolerance of vegetation has not changed drastically in the recent past, and furthermore, that the vegetation is in adjustment with, and therefore indicative of, the environment. Fossil pollens incorporated in successive sedimentary layers are taken as representative of the flora of the surrounding region. On identification of the pollen, the vegetation of the time period represented by a particular stratum can be reconstructed, and, by comparison with the present environmental range of the assemblage indicated, the climate of the past (late Cainozoic and especially Pleistocene) period can also be deduced. Though most readily applied in humid areas such as northern Europe and northern North America, where the late and post-glacial climatic sequences have been firmly established by this means, palynology has been successfully applied, albeit only by dint of much labour and tenacity, in such arid regions as the Sahara, where it has recently been possible to reconstruct climatic fluctuations of the recent past for this desert region. Thus far, however, the method has not proved rewarding with respect to the Australian arid and semi-arid regions in the Quaternary, but pollen and spores from much older sediments are proving valuable. Tertiary lacustrine sediments which occur in several basins within or adjacent to the upland backbone of the southern Flinders, mid-North and Mount Lofty Ranges, which display similar lithological characters and variations, and which lack macro-fossils, can be differentiated on the basis of their contained pollen and spores. In the Willochra basin (southern Flinders), the basal sediments are of Middle-Upper Eocene age; those of the Barossa Valley are Miocene; and those of the Golden Grove region, northeast of Adelaide, Eocene.

(B) FAUNAL CHANGES Fossils indicate that in the recent past certain animals lived in areas beyond their present or presumed range. For instance, the Lake Callabonna area is famous for its diprotodont remains, and similar fossils have been found in the Willochra basin (jawbone of *Nototherium*, dated as some 14,000 years old), near Orroroo (*Diprotodon* dated some 11,000 years old), and near the Balladonia Soak, on the Nullarbor plain. These creatures were herbivores and it seems unlikely that there would have been sufficient herbage to support them unless the climate was wetter and reliable, and vegetation more abundant than at present. In some areas depredation by aborigines could account for their extermination, for aborigines were present from at least the late Pleistocene onwards, and near Port Augusta diprotodont bones have been found in aborigine hearths, but this lacks conviction as a general explanation, and climatic change in the direction of desiccation is suggested.

(C) FOSSIL SOILS AND SEDIMENTS Soils and sediments which could not have formed under conditions now prevailing at the site are further evidence of climatic change. Dune sands in humid regions and lacustrine sediments in arid regions are obvious examples which will be considered further below, but the occurrence of frost-heaved soils in temperate lands, of *dreikanter* and relict calcrete (cornstones) in similar regions, and of laterites, typical of the humid tropics but now found in a variety of climatic regions, are other instances.

(D) DENDROCHRONOLOGY (TREE-RING ANALYSIS) Trees usually produce one growth ring a year. The thickness of the rings decreases with age, but superimposed on this normal variation are differences caused by climatic differences from year to year. In some areas, e.g. Labrador, it is summer temperature which is the critical factor governing the growth; in arid lands it is rainfall; but the thickness of the rings is a reflection of climate. Long climatic records have been constructed, particularly by using some of the very large trees of the American Southwest but there are difficulties and tree ring analysis provides a guide rather than an infallible record. An important feature however is that dating of the inferred climatic events is possible by simple count back.

(E) ARCHAEOLOGY AND ANTHROPOLOGY There is now clear and widespread evidence that considerable numbers of people once lived in areas which are now insupportable. Care is necessary in using this evidence for climatic change may not be involved; man may have ruined his own environment, as for instance in the case of the denuded, gullied limestone hills of Syria. Nevertheless the Tassili mountains were formerly inhabited by cattle herders who knew the giraffe and hippopotomus and wheat was formerly grown on the northern margin of the Sahara.

(F) OXYGEN ISOTOPES   There are three isotopes of oxygen, O16, O17 and O18. When water, which consists of hydrogen and oxygen, evaporates, the lighter isotope is lost slightly more rapidly than is the heavier. As the concentration of any one of the isotopes in part depends on temperature, the relative amounts of the various isotopes in any substance partly derived from water will also reflect the temperature of the time. Thus the carbonate shells of small animals contain oxygen isotopes in a ratio from which, by comparison with a known standard (modern shells), temperature at the time of formation can be deduced.

Thus by taking long cores of sediment from the sea floors and analysing the carbonate from the shells of contained fossils, the sea water temperature at the time of deposition of each layer can be inferred, and temperature curves established for the period of time represented by the cores. Since, in addition to oxygen, there is also carbon in the shells, there is the possibility of absolute dating within the range of the C14 method. Some very long cores have now been obtained from several of the world's ocean floors. They have been analysed and temperature graphs drawn. The major temperature fluctuations of the Quaternary are clearly shown.

Each of these methods can be used to demonstrate climatic change, an extremely significant factor in geomorphological interpretation. But the more direct morphological consequences of climatic change concern dunes, lakes and river patterns.

(1) *Ancient dune fields*   Former aridity is clearly demonstrated by the occurrence of dune fields, now established by vegetation, in areas where, apart from coastal types, dunes cannot now be supported. Such ancient fields of dunes occur in many parts of the world, including several parts of the western plainlands of the U.S.A., and the southern edge of the Sahara.

As mentioned earlier (Chapter 7(d)), Eyre and Yorke Peninsulas and the Murray Mallee display extensive fields of fixed longitudinal dunes, which are found also a few miles northwest of Gawler, and in the western suburbs of Melbourne. Dune remnants in the central Australian deserts of a trend slightly different from that of modern dunes have been mentioned in Chapter 7.

Though views differ as to whether deserts alternately expanded and contracted, or whether they maintained essentially a constant area but migrated north and south, their boundaries changed with the result that the climatic change responsible was clearly imprinted on the landscape.

(2) *Ancient lakes*   In modern desert and semi-desert regions, there are playas, both of salina and claypan type, which are dry save for infrequent and ephemeral floodings. But old shoreline features and lake sediments show that many of these were truly lakes, during the Pleistocene. There were hundreds of similar water bodies in the Great Basin of the western U.S.A. at times during the Pleistocene. The best known of these, Lake Bonneville, formerly extended over 20,000 square miles of Utah, but is now represented by the Great Salt Lake, a mere 1,500 to 2,200 square miles in area. In this and several other lakes of the region, several alternatives of aridity and lacustrine phases can be distinguished. Searles Lake in California is a good example.

In the Gobi desert of Mongolia, seven old beach lines which are nearly 30 feet higher than the 1920 level of the shrunken lake have been noted, and in central Africa, Lake Chad formerly stood at least 175 feet above its present level. Lake Woods, in the central part of the Northern Territory, now only 70 square miles in area, formerly extended over 1,100 square miles; and the history of Lake Eyre has been discussed previously (Chapter 7).

Either as a result of warping or climatic change, or both, a shallow lake developed in the Murray valley in South Australia during the Pleistocene. It is evidenced by up to 20 feet of lacustrine silts and its possible extent is indicated in Fig. 110.

Such evidence can only mean that the catchments of the drainage basins formerly enjoyed a heavier and/or a more effective rainfall and that subsequently the climate has deteriorated and become drier, though estimates of the amount of increased precipitation suggest that this is not as great as might be anticipated.

(3) *River terraces*   These have been widely used as indicators of climatic change, and they may well originate as a result of changes of discharge or regime consequent upon climatic change. But great care is necessary in the interpretation of terraces, for there are serious general difficulties.

River terraces (see Chapter 6) are either paired or unpaired, but in either case they form as a result of stream dissection. The latter may result from tectonic uplift, changes of sea level (baselevel) changes in land use (e.g. white settlement and land clearance—see Chapter 13)—or climatic change. Thus it is necessary to take a regional view and consider the distribution of the terraces with respect to the coast, evidence of sea level movements, known faults, and the dates of terrace cutting on the one hand and settlement on the other. Also, it must be remembered that even within a limited area, all terraces need not necessarily be of the same origin.

The Quaternary: Indirect Effects of Glaciation   303

Fig 229 Exposure of two alluvia on the Willunga scarp.

Fig 230 Present and prior streams in the Riverina (*after Pels*).

Even if the evidence suggests that terraces are of climatic origin, it is frequently difficult to judge the trend and degree of climatic change responsible, for the interplay of rainfall, temperature, vegetation and run-off is complex. Moreover, the precipitation and temperature commonly vary simultaneously.

Again, climatic changes in the headwater regions commonly have far-reaching effects downstream; and finally, terraces in tributary valleys may form wholly as a result of the lateral migrations of the mainstream, causing fluctuations of local baselevel within the minor valleys.

Many valleys, large and small, in the Mount Lofty Ranges and Mid-north of South Australia display dissected constructional paired terraces. These features have been described from Cape Jervis in the south to north of the Broughton valley; in all, two or three phases of erosion and two of deposition are represented. Red clays, sands and gravels were deposited either in pre-existing valleys or as alluvial fans fronting ranges; then narrow gullies were cut; these were filled with black-grey sediments, and were in turn dissected. The paired terraces occur on top of the black-grey alluvium (Fig. 229). Some of these valleys drain to the sea, others front known fault scarps or are downstream from them, some are near the coast, others near the divide between the Murray and Gulfs drainage. Some could therefore be interpreted as eustatic terraces, others equally well as due to tectonic dislocations. Some may have originated as a result of land clearance, though the relevant dissection in the Torrens valley occurred in mid-Recent times, well before European settlement, but after aboriginal occupation.

Because of their varied topographical situations it is reasonable to attribute many of the terraces to climatic change (not all, because individual examples may be of different origins, e.g. faulting, sea level change), but this can only be settled by dating widely scattered examples: they should have developed essentially simultaneously or in a progressive pattern of change from south to north or north to south.

(4) *Stream patterns*   Some streams are apparently too small for their valleys, while stream deposits and channels occur in profusion where today there are no or few streams (see Chapter 6). Both these situations may result from climatic change.

What is meant when it is stated that a stream is too small for its valley? It is not implied that a small stream cannot excavate a large valley for, it can, if given time. But the geometry of some valleys stands in strong contrast with that of the streams now flowing in them. Observations of modern rivers show that there is a direct relationship between discharge (or volume), stream width and the radius of meanders. Present rivers have a certain width of channel and meander, which is related to modern bankfull discharge; but the sides of the valleys in which they flow display meander bluffs of much greater radius, and indicative of higher discharges in the past. As in most instances there is no possibility of river capture, these decreases in discharge have been widely, and in all probability correctly, attributed to change of rainfall. However, the effects of short lived but effective floods have to be borne in mind, as has the possibility that the 'meander bluff' preserved in valleys and used as an index of former meander size, might be the imprint of the former meander belt. Such an interpretation may go some way to overcome the problem of enormous Pleistocene stream discharges postulated on the basis that the bluffs are related to meander size, discharges at variance with the rather small increases in Pleistocene glacial precipitation estimated, for example, for some of the lake basins of the American West. In any individual valley, it is necessary to ensure that the present river curves are the maximum possible development for modern discharges. In addition, the amplitude of river curves changes with gradient, and in tectonically active regions this may be a significant factor.

Another line of evidence of climatic change derives from fossil stream patterns. In the Riverina of western New South Wales, for example, a very large number of abandoned channels and associated levees, known as prior streams, lead down from the western slope of the Eastern Uplands to the Murray plains (Fig. 230). Several phases of deposition can be distinguished, but interpretations differ. Some, working from the amplitude of meanders, consider they originated in time of high discharge, i.e. glacial phases, of the Pleistocene. Others, on the contrary, believe they originated in arid periods, the phases of deposition (at least three in number) being separated by moister periods when soil development took place. It is clear in some areas that stream deposition was influenced by tectonic displacements—along the Cadell fault, for example; also, in view of known tectonic activity within and at the margins of the uplands, it is possible that tectonism has played some part in the evolution of this now abandoned ancestral system of streams.

All the evidence cited can be used and has been used to demonstrate Quaternary climatic changes, which had far-reaching effects on the landscape of Australia. But several important landform assemblages derive from Prequaternary times. These, and features resulting from prolonged weathering and erosion of the land surface, are considered in the next chapters.

NOTE

[1] Quite apart from local difficulties of interpretation in terms of the Milankovich-Zeuner hypothesis, there are certain general difficulties, though in fairness it must be added that those facing this particular are no greater than those facing other explanations of climatic change. But one which has come to the fore relatively recently is that according to the Milankovich-Zeuner hypothesis the events of the Pleistocene, including of course the oscillations of sea level, should be compressed into a period of about 600,000 years. Evidence from New Zealand, as well as North America strongly suggests that the Pleistocene glaciations began several millions of years ago.

11. Surfaces of Low Relief

(a) INTRODUCTION

IN PREVIOUS CHAPTERS, several significant and widespread features of Pleistocene origin were described. The Pleistocene glaciers had important effects on the landscape, but even in areas which are known to have been overwhelmed by vast ice sheets, pre-glacial features survive. In areas not directly affected by glaciation, and particularly in the tropics where the common development of duricrusts of one type or another renders surfaces highly resistant to erosion, plains of low relief form significant elements of the landscape.

(b) THE PENEPLAIN CONCEPT

The development in time of a single river valley was described in Chapter 6. It will be recalled that each valley extends in length, depth and width, the general tendency, though complicated by structural features, being for valleys to become broader and more open, with increasingly large flats occupying the valley floor. In the field, sequences of valley forms have been observed seemingly consistent with the hypothesis that many valleys pass through a series of stages and that each evolves through an orderly, predictable sequence of forms. Moreover, where such time sequences are not suggested by valley morphology, it is almost everywhere possible to cite reasons for this apparently anomalous state of affairs.

In many small valleys, as one walks upstream, the valley walls become steeper and closer; the flood plain becomes narrower, then discontinuous, and finally is lost; and the cross-section becomes more and more V-shaped. Structural effects are imposed on valley morphology, but they retard and modify, rather than fundamentally change valley development. Even where, for structural or climatic reasons, valley side slopes tend to maintain a constant form and inclination, and to retreat parallel to themselves, the progressive increase in valley width downstream, can be construed as an evolutionary sequence.

This type of interpretation—and it *is* inference, not demonstrated fact, for detailed observations have been made in only a few locations and over a short time period, so that the changes have not been observed—has proved very useful particularly from a descriptive viewpoint; so much so that the concept of evolutionary development has been extended to entire landscapes.

If it is conceived that many valleys develop in a given region, then the sequence of forms evolved will largely be a reflection of the individual valley development described earlier, though account must also be taken of the changing form of the areas between adjacent valleys—the divides or interfluves. If, for the sake of simplicity, it is assumed that there is instantaneous uplift of an area of low relief; that the uplifted mass is lithogically uniform or homogeneous; that there are no significant earth movements for a period of several millions of years; and that there are no catastrophic changes in climate or sea level for a similarly extended period, then the sequence of landscape change can be deduced.

Important stages in the idealised sequence of forms are shown in Fig. 231. At first the streams cut down rapidly, while several processes at work on the valley sides act relatively slowly. Comparatively deep valleys of V-shaped cross-section are excavated, and areas of low relief are at this stage found high in the landscape. As the streams approach baselevel, their rate of incision decreases, while valley widening continues.

Fig 231   Stages in the development of a peneplain.

Tributary development, gullying, landslips and earth flows, weathering and rillwash, cause the sides to recede until the slopes of adjacent valleys merge. At this stage, there are no flat areas of significant extent; the landscape consists of all slopes, and is considered to have reached maturity.

Henceforth, although the rivers continue to erode and lower their beds, weathering and rillwash cause the more rapid wasting of the interfluves, so that the *relief amplitude*, the height between ridge crest and stream bed, decreases. Eventually, a rolling or undulating surface of low relief comes into being. It is characterised by broad convex interfluves separating wide, open valleys, many displaying extensive flat flood plains. Such a surface of low relief, which has developed through river work and downwasting, is called a *peneplain* (almost a plain).

A peneplain is not flat, for relief amplitude may vary by as much as 150 to 200 feet within an area of a square mile, and remnants of circumdenudation called *monadnocks* (after Mt Monadnock in New Hampshire, U.S.A.), which survive either for structural reasons (more resistant rocks) or because they are located on major interfluves, rise above the general level of the peneplain. But slopes are gentle, even the monadnocks rising gradually from the level of the surrounding plains.

Once a peneplain condition is attained, weathering and erosion do not cease; but they proceed with increasing slowness as the streams approach closer to regional baselevel.

(c) PEDIMENTS

Surfaces of low relief develop also in arid and semi-arid lands. Some like the Carpentaria plains of northwest Queensland, developed on sedimentary sequences which offer little resistance to weathering and erosion, are morphologically similar to their temperate humid region counterparts. But many differ in certain respects and warrant a different name. They are called *pediplains* which are produced by the coalescence of a large number of pediments (see also Chapter 7). A pediment is generally defined as planate bedrock surface possessing few, if any, stream lines, sloping away from the adjacent hills at inclinations between $\frac{1}{2}°$ and $7°$, and displaying a concave upward profile in section normal to the nearby uplands (though some pediments are rectilinear in profile and others convex upwards). Pediments always have a veneer of debris though this thickness varies from place to place, affording a basis of classification used by French workers: *glacis de denudation*—a pediment with only a thin and discontinuous debris veneer; *glacis d'épandage*—a pediment with a thicker but still thin veneer, and with nubbins or knobs of rock protruding through; and *glacis d'ennoyage* with a blanket so thick that no rock remnants protrude. Pediments meet the adjacent uplands in an abrupt break of slope, the piedmont angle, a feature which in some few localities is truly angular, but more commonly belies its name and takes the form of a sharp concavity.

The origin of pediments was controversial, but now it is generally agreed that the features form through a combination of weathering, rill wash and sheet wash. In some localities lateral stream corrasion is significant. The presence of a detrital cover, however thin, poses problems, for such a veneer effectively protects the rock surface against surface agents such as rills and other flows of water. Some subsurface weathering and erosion undoubtedly takes place beneath the veneer, but the initial shaping of the pediment cut-rock surface seems to take place in the immediate scarp-foot zone and before a thick continuous debris veneer has accumulated. As the scarp recedes, so does the zone of primary pediment formation (Fig. 171). Thus those pediment surfaces which carry significant debris veneers (as is the case in South Australia) are developed over a period of time, with those parts of the pediment distant from the scarp-foot being older than those near it: they are *diachronic* surfaces.

Many pediments may coalesce to form pediplains, which like peneplains, are surfaces of low relief, but generally differ from the latter in a number of respects. They are smoother, and less dissected (have fewer stream-lines), they are mostly dominated by concave profiles, and meet the adjacent uplands in a piedmont angle. Such characteristics are clearly displayed in the Brachina, Wilpena and Italowie areas of the Flinders Ranges, in the Barrier (Pl. 60) and Cobar pediplains, for example, of western N.S.W. and in several others, particularly those underlain by crystalline rocks, in northwest Queensland (Fig. 172) and in areas marginal to the uplands of central Australia. But the smoothness, the undissected character, the concavities, can all be found in varying degrees in the peneplain in certain circumstances. Sparsity of streams, and hence smoothness of surface, may be related to soil and rock porosity or permeability. The form of the slope profiles is influenced by several factors, including stream texture, whether a stream is cutting down more rapidly than the valley side slopes are being downwasted. The abrupt break of slope between hill and plain, the piedmont angle, is therefore the critical, though not the only contrast between the plain types.

(d) ORIGIN OF PIEDMONT ANGLE

The piedmont angle has been explained in many ways. For instance, workers in the American Southwest, where faulting is common, considered the piedmont angle to be the result of tectonic dislocation, that is, to be the angular junction between adjacent fault blocks; the scarp retreated under weathering, the surface of low relief left behind at its base being the pediment. Against this hypothesis, as a general explanation of the piedmont angle, is the fact that the feature is found in many areas where no faulting has occurred.

Lateral corrasion has been cited as a significant factor in the development of the piedmont angle, for it has been suggested that rivers emerging from uplands to the arid plains meander along the mountain front, which is thereby undercut and steepened, thus causing an angular junction to form. But if this were the case, distinct scallops, the scars left by the meander loops, should be found along the upland margin, and these are notably absent. Moreover, it is a matter of observation that rivers debouching on to plains, though adopting a distributary habit, continue to flow away from the uplands toward the centre of the local drainage basin. Moreover, the piedmont angle occurs where there are no major streams and also around isolated uplands too small to generate any streams of concentrated drainage.

However, in areas such as the Wasatch Mountains of Utah, where many closely spaced rivers flow from the uplands, the mountain front is indented (Fig. 232), and the valleys are being extended, and the intervening ridges are being reduced considerably by lateral corrasion. In Utah, this process is predominant. In some Australian areas such as the Fitzroy Basin of Western Australia and near many major river outlets it is only of local significance, but in the Krichauff Ranges (N.T.) and other uplands underlain in whole or in part by impermeable rocks, lateral corrasion by closely spaced distributary streams is an important factor in steepening valley sides and the upland front.

Other workers, notably L. C. King working in South Africa, see the piedmont angle as resulting from contrasted processes. In his view turbulent flow causes the quarrying of the scarp face, but this same water adopts a laminar, or sheet, habit when it debouches on to the smooth pediments. The angular break of slope develops where the change of process occurs. However, it is very doubtful whether laminar flow in either water or air can develop under natural conditions, save very locally and ephemerally; observations on pediments during rains suggest that the detailed roughness caused by grains of sand and tufts of vegetation, disturbs any tendency to sheet flow and induces turbulence; and the different processes, if they occur, can be interpreted as the result of the pre-existing topographical situation, and not as the reason for that topography—in other words it is possible in this argument that cause and effect are confused.

Fig 232 Serrated scarp front dissected by closely spaced streams, which adopt a distributary habit, spread laterally and effectively wear back the valley sides and mountain front, for instance, Krichauff Ranges, N.T.

Structure is unquestionably a very important factor in the genesis of the piedmont angle, which is commonly located at lithogical or structural junctions. In the Flinders Ranges it is found at the base of sandstone or limestone escarpments; on Eyre Peninsula it occurs at the base of granite residuals (inselbergs) which are massively jointed, in contrast to the adjacent plains which are underlain by moderately jointed granite blocks. Resistant cappings—either primary (sandstone or limestone strata, basalt flows, dolorite sills) or secondary (pedogenic) accumulations, such as calcrete, silcrete, or gibber—also materially influence slope development and assist in the maintenance of steep slopes, which in turn are partially responsible for the abrupt break between hill and plain.

Superimposed on this structural control is the effect of differential weathering and erosion, both general and localised. At the general level, weathering and erosion are more pronounced on lower than on upper slopes in arid and semi-arid lands. On capped slopes, the reason is that the capping is tough and resistant; but even on lithogically homogeneous slopes, the concentration of moisture and the increased volume of flow on lower slopes causes the more rapid removal of these areas. As a result, slopes are steepened to an extent consistent with stability: if the slope is oversteepened, the upper area collapses, which causes the slope to recede, and the lower area to be masked temporarily with debris and to be built up to a more gentle inclination. Thus the slope budget in these dry lands is such as to induce sheet slopes and hence an abrupt junction between hill and plain.

In South Australia and the southern part of the Northern Territory there is evidence of a localised concentration of weathering, hence of erosion, of lower slopes over and above the general tendency for the excessive attack of lower slopes. Both on Eyre Peninsula (Fig. 109) and throughout the Flinders Ranges, evidence suggests that especially intense weathering affects lower slopes, and particularly the scarp-foot zone. In many places the local bedrock in the scarp floor is completely weathered to kaolin and similar products, while a relatively short distance away from the scarp, what are presumably similar strata are virtually unaltered. Such localisation of weathering in a narrow moat or gutter around uplands is particularly well demonstrated about the granite inselbergs of northwestern Eyre Peninsula (Pl. 70), where the bedrock is mineralogically identical, but where the granite beneath the plains is more closely jointed than that which underlies the residuals (Fig. 96). Steepened or flared slopes, as described earlier, are the result.

This results from a number of circumstances. Broadly, rainfall on uplands is always significantly heavier than on the adjacent plains, and streams tend to flood out on to the latter, only to fade and die on the arid lowlands; their wetted perimeter therefore increases, and their velocity decreases, thus allowing more time for percolation. A concentration of moisture may thus be expected in a zone marginal to uplands, whether local or regional. Finally, many ridges and ranges are formed by sandstone and limestone, or by massively jointed rocks, the former acting as aquifers and giving rise to spring-line effects downslope. The latter are comparatively impermeable and again cause an excess of water in the adjacent area downslope; in both cases local hydrological conditions give rise to a concentration of water in a zone immediately downslope from an especially resistant area.

This zone of intense weathering is etched out by streams; hence the development of strike (scarp-foot) valleys, of linear depressions, of isolated pediment surfaces, and most important, of very steep slopes (Fig. 233). Where there has been concentrated scarp-foot weathering,

Plate 70   Overhanging slope and weathering front exposed in man-made reservoir at Yarwondutta Rocks, near Minnipa.

Plate 71   Unconformity between tilted Precambrian rocks below and a Quaternary conglomerate above at Boolcunda Creek 13 miles northeast of Quorn.

Surfaces of Low Relief

steep scarps are developed and maintained; scarp retreat takes place; an abrupt break of slope in most areas separates hill and plain. In humid temperate regions, for example, where the vegetation cover is widespread, where soil cover is well developed, where moisture and hence weathering are more evenly distributed over the landscape, no such marked concentration of weathering and erosion occur. In certain structural and lithogical (and hence hydrological) situations there is a strong tendency for similar processes and forms to develop, but this is not as general as in the arid and semi-arid lands. Alternately, even in arid regions, where the bedrock is uniformly weak, downwasting prevails.

Fig 233 Development of piedmont angle by a scarp foot weathering and regrading of slopes.

(e) PENEPLAIN, PEDIPLAIN AND OLDLAND

The distinction of pediplains and peneplains rests upon the nature of their junction with adjacent uplands. Since this depends not only on climatic but also in considerable measure on structural factors, it follows that pediments are not exclusively restricted to any one climatic region: given the right structural circumstances, a sharp break of slope may develop in any climatic region. Hence the occurrence of inselbergs in many climatically contrasted parts of the world (see Chapter 4(b)). Similarly, slopes may be wasted and lowered where rocks are uniformly unresistant and so, given the right structural environment peneplains are found in some semi-arid and even arid conditions. However, although there are many exceptions, pediments are most commonly developed in desert and semi-desert lands and peneplains in humid temperate regions.

A further problem is that in certain areas of extensive plains, there are no residuals by which to judge the nature of the junction of hill and plain. Furthermore, what we see now is, almost certainly, a retouching and modification of the surface and may not be diagnostic of past evolution. Although the time scale is obscure it can be shown in the Flinders Ranges and elsewhere, that the sharpening of the scarp floor angle is a recent geological event; although not really extensive, remnants of much more gently inclined slope assemblages are widespread: the dissection of these has given rise to the present much steeper scarps. On the morphological evidence, peneplains have become pediplains only during the last few moments of geological time.

Mention must also be made of surfaces of erosion which are due largely to subsurface evacuation of material, primarily, though not wholly, in solution. The significance of solution in landscape evolution and in the development of peneplains has long been appreciated, but the theory was not given quantitative expression and specific elaboration until 1962, when Trendall emphasized that during deep Tertiary weathering (lateritisation) in East Africa, such a significant volume of the parent rock was evacuated in solution, that lowering of the land surface by several score feet could be effected without any surface erosion at all. This type of surface of low relief is termed by Trendall an *apparent peneplain* because although resembling a peneplain morphologically it differs genetically from the latter.

There is therefore a case for suggesting that some ancient land surfaces should be given a label with non-genetic implications, such as *old land*, referring to the fact that surfaces of low relief have been developed over considerable periods of time, but without reference to the mode of reduction.

(f) OTHER TYPES OF EROSIONAL LAND SURFACES

Several other genetic types of land surface which may form part of peneplains or pediplains may now be mentioned.

Many major rivers have, in their lower reaches and close to baselevel, carved broad flood plains, which are called *panplains* and which are an inherent part of many peneplains and pediplains. In all cases, however, Quaternary sea level fluctuations have undoubtedly given rise to aggradation in the lower reaches of such valleys, thus emphasising their broad, flat-floored character. The lower Mississippi valley is an example, though here the situation is further complicated by the subsidence of the delta and adjacent regions.

Deep and intense weathering beneath a peneplain or pediplain can give rise to another type of surface, called the *etch plain*. The mantle of weathered material (the *saprolith* or *regolith*), overlies intrinsically fresh bedrock, the two meeting at the *weathering front*, which is the limit of effective weathering. Either following rejuvenation or because streams can more readily erode the weathered material, the whole, or certain horizons, of the weathered profile are stripped away, and a new plain surface is etched out. The new level, which is not related to regional baselevel, is virtually coincident with the weathering front, and is called the etch plain (Fig. 234). The Maranboy erosion surface, in the Daly River basin, was produced over wide areas by the removal of the less resistant, less silicified parts of a weathering profile produced below the older and higher Bradshaw surface. A weathering profile in turn evolved on the Maranboy surface so that it is not merely an etch plain, though it displays some characteristics of one. In the Kimberleys, Mt Hann, underlain by a lateritised weathering profile, stands prominently above the general level of the dissected Kimberley plateau, which is not greatly weathered, suggesting that the latter may be a dissected etch plain. In central Western Australia, most of the so-called new plateau may be an etch plain, for, in the Wiluna–Meekatharra area, the mesa residuals of the old plateau are underlain by weathered granitic bedrock, with the level and attitude of the weathering front coincident with that of the newer lower level.

In the Mount Lofty Ranges immediately west of Palmer, the local granites and gneisses have been worn to a surface of low relief, surmounted only by a very few tor clusters and low mesa-like residuals. These last are of considerable interest, for they are capped by ferricrete overlying deeply weathered bedrock and surfaced by a spread of angular quartzitic debris. They are part of a formerly continuous surface, and clearly are remnants of an old surface of low relief; the deep weathering, lateritisation, and quartzitic gravel all point to an old landscape of low relief. The weathering front beneath the remnants is at the same elevation as the general plateau surface, which can thus be interpreted reasonably as an old etch plain (Fig. 235), now dissected.

A surface of low relief may be buried beneath more recent sediments, and thus be protected and preserved. In this buried state, it is called an *unconformity* (Pl. 71), and is clearest when marked by a clear angular

Fig 234 Development of an etch plain.

Fig 235 An etch plain in the eastern Mt Lofty Ranges.

Fig 236 Evolution of an exhumed erosional surface.

Surfaces of Low Relief

discordance between the beds above and those beneath. Also it can be evidenced in more subtle ways, for an unconformity represents a break in deposition, a time break, an erosional interval. If the unconformity or old erosional surface is re-exposed and is again expressed as part of the land surface through the removal of the overlying and later strata, the exposed unconformity is called an *exhumed* (stripped or resurrected) surface (Fig. 236). In most areas these surfaces are well expressed on the landscape because of the lithological contrast between strata on either side of the unconformity, the older generally being tougher. The exhumed pre middle Mesozoic (late Jurassic or early Cretaceous) land surface is well represented on the western margin of the Great Artesian basin, as well as in adjacent uplands; and in northwest Queensland, a pre middle Cambrian exhumed surface is locally important. In the north Flinders Ranges, the upfaulted highlands in some places carry remnants of marine Cretaceous bedrock similar in every respect to that beneath the adjacent Frome plains. These Mesozoic outliers, like Mt Babbage, stand in isolation above the general high plain level, and the elevation and attitude of the unconformity between the Cretaceous and underlying Precambrian suggest that the high plain is essentially the surface on which the Cretaceous sediments were laid down, and is an exhumed surface of pre Cretaceous age (Fig. 237).

At the northern extremity of the Willochra basin, a surface of pre middle or upper Eocene age is exposed. In middle-upper Eocene times the basin was occupied by a lake in which sediments were deposited. At the margins of the basin, these sediments have been and are being removed by erosion, and the underlying surface eroded in Precambrian and Cambrian rocks exposed (Fig. 238).

An exhumed surface of similar pre Eocene age occupies much of the Para fault block, north of Adelaide. The block is tilted down to the south and east, and in the depression formed by the gentle dip slope of the Para block and the steep west-facing escarpment of the Eden block (Fig. 239) are preserved sands and clays which are of Eocene age, and which were deposited in a lake. With one exception, at Crouchs Hill (near Golden Grove), no indication, in the form of beach deposits, has been found to suggest the former limits of the lake; but the occurrence of isolated Eocene deposits to the west of the main outcrop shows that it was formerly more extensive (Fig. 240). The Precambrian which is exposed over most of the Para block has been revealed through the erosion of the higher parts of the Eocene outcrop; the general slope of this surface is continued without appreciable break into the Precambrian Eocene unconformity detected in borelogs, so that the rolling surface cut in Precambrian rocks may be interpreted as an exhumed surface of pre Eocene age.

In the instances cited, an earlier surface of low relief due to fluvial erosion has been buried by marine or lacustrine sediments. As the lake or ocean waters spread over the surface, some modification due to wave action may be expected. But it is only modification in detail, for all extensive erosional surfaces are caused by stream action, not waves, which as an agent of planation is self-defeating and limited (see Chapter 8).

Fig 237 Section through the Mt Babbage region (*after Woodard*).

Fig 238 An exhumed surface near Probys Grave, southern Flinders Ranges. The Precambrian and Cambrian rocks are steeply dipping; the level bedded sandstone is of Middle or Upper Eocene Age.

Fig 239 Section through the Para Block.

(g) DEPOSITIONAL PLAINS

Plains due not to erosion but to deposition by rivers are important elements of most landscapes, but are especially significant in arid lowlands. Not only are there the normal, rather restricted, flood plains and terraces, but aggradation on a regional scale can give rise to extensive plains of constructional origin. These have been called *sediplains* but *aggradational* or *depositional* plain is as good.

Fig 240 Map of the Para Block (*after Adelaide 1-mile Geological map, Geol. Surv. S.A.*).

In central Australia, large areas are of this nature, for the basins of internal drainage have received sediments for long periods of geological time, and widespread aggradational surfaces have been built up in this way. The plains of northern Victoria and of the Riverina of western N.S.W. are of this nature; the intermontane Willochra plain is primarily a depositional surface of Quaternary age; the Lake Torrens and Pirie and Adelaide plains are of similar origin and age; and the surface of the Nullarbor plain is almost coincident with the limit of Miocene deposition and thus is of similar character.

Even surfaces which are broadly erosional carry a mantle of coarse debris which smooths out erosional irregularities, and effectively preserves the underlying bedrock.

Thus depositional elements are a significant element of the morphology of plains.

12. Cyclic and Non-cyclic Landscape Development

(a) GEOMORPHIC CYCLES

SURFACES OF THE TYPES DESCRIBED may be developed in the same area not once but several times, so that elements of various surfaces, exist in the same area possibly of different character, but of different age ranges. Thus, time is an important factor in landscape analysis and interpretation.

The time factor was formally integrated in geomorphological analysis late in the last century primarily by the efforts of the great American geomorphologist W. M. Davis who evolved the concept of the geomorphic cycle, which is also known as the cycle of erosion; but as weathering and deposition, as well as erosion are involved, the term *geomorphic cycle* is preferable. The gist of the cyclic concept is that, commencing with an initial landscape generally assumed to be one of low relief, the land surface passes through an orderly sequence of forms but eventually returns to a surface of low relief, to an assemblage of forms apparently identical with the original: hence the use of the term cycle. Landscapes in which there is preserved evidence of more than one geomorphic cycle are called *multicyclic*. In a real sense the cyclic concept is a product of its age, for it is evolutionary in character, and was conceived in an age when the scientific climate was dominated by the Darwinian Theory.

The first elaborate exposition of the geomorphic cycle concerned landscapes developed under humid temperate conditions. Davis's presentation of the scheme was both vigorous and vivid, and his colourful analogy of human life and landscapes, both developing the stages of youth, maturity and old age, captured the imagination of the scientific world. As described in Chapter 11, it is generally assumed that uplift of the land is relatively rapid, and under humid temperate conditions the stream valleys which are initially cut into the mass are deep and narrow. Subsequently, the valleys are incised and gradually widen. The rivers approach close to baselevel so that the rate of incision decreases, and thus relief amplitude gradually diminishes. The downwasting of divides continues until there is a plain of low relief dominated by broad convex swells —a peneplain (Fig. 4b). Thus the landscape passes through an orderly, evolutionary and predictable sequence of forms in which, theoretically, the end product is similar to the initial surface. If a cycle is interrupted by major uplift of the land, causing rivers to be rejuvenated and the landscape to be revived on a large scale, it is postulated that a similar sequence of developments will ensue.

Workers in arid and semi-arid lands especially were able to observe landform assemblages at variance with those of the Davisian or 'normal' cycle. In such areas and especially where resistant rocks occur, the downwasting of interfluves is not apparently important, and instead of suffering decline slopes tend to maintain a constantly steep inclination during recession. The reasons for this contrasted behaviour of steep slope elements is probably related to the particular system of weathering and erosion in arid lands, where there is a tendency for crusts, horizons and pans, all resistant, to form at and near the land surfaces. After dissection they tend to form hard protective cappings to plateaux, thus causing the reduction to be slow of the upper surfaces and of the upper parts of steep slopes; and the effects of water, the most important agent of weathering and erosion in such areas, are most apparent on lower slopes—rills and streams for instance are more effective on lower than on upper slopes if only because of their greater volume on the lower slopes. Thus the morphology of escarpments tends to be constant. For a particular lithology and a given set of climatic conditions, slopes are steepened to a maximum compatible with stability. But they nevertheless retreat and, in course of time, the ratio of plateau and plain varies in an orderly manner. Again the cyclic concept can be applied in the interpretation of the arid and semi-arid landscapes.

Although it does not provide answers to all problems of landform analysis, the cyclic concept is one of the most fruitful ever formulated in geomorphology. There are, however, many difficulties. Even now, there is little knowledge of the physical and chemical details of the processes which Davis invoked to bring about his sequence of changes, but it can be asserted that cyclic interpretations of landscape offer a guide to what happened and when, though not how it happened. At times, the cyclic concept has been applied uncritically and erosion surfaces have been identified on the basis of uncertain evidence. But this is the fault of the workers concerned and is not an adverse criticism to be levelled at either the concept or its author. A common misconception concerns the initial form of the land surface: even assuming that cyclic development occurs, the cycle need not run its course and the starting condition for the next cycle could be a landscape of considerable relief.

A major difficulty with the cyclic concept as generally considered concerns erosion during uplift of the land, which clearly must occur. More significant, however, is the causal interplay or connection between uplift and erosion.

(b) ISOSTATIC RESPONSES TO EROSION

In peneplanation, the wasting of divides is a dominant feature of development. In pediplanation, bluffs are maintained at a constant (usually steep) inclination and recede. But in both, it is conceived that landscapes evolve through a cycle. Only by a major alteration in or interruption of conditions can the inevitable be deferred. In the cyclic interpretations, a measure of stability of the earth's crust is assumed: it is conceived as essentially analagous with what physical scientists term a closed system.

As a simple example of a closed system an absolutely insulated cylinder of gas may be considered. The gas at one end is hotter than that at the other. There is a maximum energy potential at the initial stage, but in a certain time that energy is fixed and conditions are uniform, because diffusion ensures that temperature conditions in the gas will attain parity. In a geomorphological context an upraised land mass is endowed with a certain amount of energy which is dissipated during evolution until a form of least available energy—the peneplain, pediplain or other surface of low relief, is reached.

Such a concept of isolation and rigidity is unrealistic. Modern earthquakes and volcanicity are reminders that the earth is alive and mobile. In North America, Britain and Scandinavia, there is abundant evidence that isostasy is a valid concept. The hypothesis of isostasy, states that there is equal mass in each major unit area of the earth's crust, and that any change in mass meets with a response in adjustment (see Chapter 9). Scandinavia, for example, was buried beneath a great mass of ice during the Pleistocene: the earth's crust bowed under its weight, just as the rock floor beneath the Greenland ice mass has subsided under the weight of the ice sheet (Chapter 9). When the ice melted, a great weight was removed from Scandinavia and the crust rose, and is still rising at a maximum rate of 0·4 inches a year.

In peneplanation, a great mass of rocks is gradually removed from one part of the earth's crust, transferred, and deposited elsewhere. When landscape development has reached the stage of all slopes maximum relief amplitude is attained. A great volume and weight of rocks has been evacuated. Thus, high peaks are raised even higher due to the crust rising in response to the reduction of the load. The high mountains of the Himalayas typify this and it is a fact that mountains attain their greatest elevations some time *after* the sediments of which they are largely composed have suffered folding and faulting. By the same precepts, areas which receive the bulk of material derived from the mountains and continents subside—areas typified by the Indo–Gangetic plain in northern India, and the Mississippi Delta region (Fig. 215).

From this type of evidence it has been realised that to reduce a land mass to baselevel, either by peneplanation or pediplanation, a far greater mass of rock than originally stood above baselevel has to be removed. It has been estimated that to reduce a high land mass to peneplain condition, a mass of rock about five times the original volume of the mountain mass would have to be removed. A further estimate is that with erosion of about 3 feet a millenium, an area with 5,000 feet of relief could be reduced in about 10 million years.

Arising in part from the fact of isostatic response to erosion, but based essentially on the principle of dynamic equilibrium, non-cyclic interpretations of landscapes have recently been revived and elaborated.

(c) NON-CYCLIC LANDSCAPE DEVELOPMENT

The alternative to considering the limitations of an isolated or closed system, is the more realistic attitude which considers the earth's crust analogous to an *open system*, in which there is a constant exchange of energy and material. A change in one part of the system induces an equal and opposite reaction in another (Le Chatelier's Principle): remove x million tons of rock from an area and, slowly, after a period of maladjustment, an equal mass will rise to take its place from below, and the x million tons distributed elsewhere will cause equal subsidence. Complications are introduced by such factors as the strength of the earth's crust, which can accommodate some changes; but as a general rule, the open system type of interpretation is valid.

Open systems have two important attributes. Firstly it is possible to attain a *steady state* when, although there is constant exchange, the situation remains in equilibrium. Secondly a closed system, with cyclic development, may be regarded as a special case of an open system, in which energy exchange is at zero and where there can only be loss of free energy.

In geomorphological terms rocks may be eroded and replaced from below, but the form of the surface remains the same: it may be regarded as static, but is really in *dynamic equilibrium*. Dynamic equilibrium can perhaps be illustrated by the example of a bath being filled with water by a tap. The rate of inflow can be controlled. The outlet of the bath, however, is not a plug, but a slit, say $\frac{1}{2}$ inch wide, extending from top to bottom of one side of the bath. When water is fed into the bath at x gallons a minute, some will be lost through the slit but the water level will rise until the area of slit available to the water allows water to flow out at x gallons a minute. If then the rate of inflow is kept constant, water is constantly fed into and lost from the bath, but the water level will remain static. If the rate of inflow is increased, the water level will rise until more of the slit is available for water to leave by, when a static level will again be maintained. If rate of inflow is decreased, water will flow out of the bath more rapidly than it is fed in, and the level will be lowered until an area of the slit used is such that outflow equals inflow, and again a static level is maintained.

If the bath is filled by heavy inflow and then the supply cut off, the water level will fall until the bath is empty.

This is a special case of the open system, and is in fact analogous with the closed system described earlier.

In terms of landscape development, it can be understood if a rising block is subjected to river erosion, the rivers will cut down their beds as fast as baselevel will permit. On the initially steep-sided slope, gullying, landslip, etc. will be rapid and the slopes will be degraded. River bed and slopes will be degraded to a point where the rising rocks can be eroded (by wasting and rivers) at a rate equal to the rate of regeneration from below (Fig. 241): the landscape is in dynamic equilibrium. The rocks are constantly changing through erosion and replacement from below but the form of the surface remains static. If there is a change in rate of uplift or in rate of weathering and erosion (say through climatic change) then the slopes and so the whole land surface go through a short period of maladjustment or change. They are steepened or lowered, to a gradient at which the rate of downwearing again is equal to the rate of uplift of material.

Fig 241 A land surface in dynamic equilibrium. Uplift is equalled by the uniform erosion which takes place at the surface. The three surfaces shown should be visualised as maintaining the same elevation.

Considering a single river valley, it may be that the form of the valley in cross-section depends upon stage, process and structure, as outlined above. On the other hand the form may be interpreted in terms of dynamic equilibrium. The slope of the valley side is everywhere of such an inclination that as much debris is transported to the base as can be evacuated by the stream. If it cannot be evacuated it accumulates and deposition spreads up the slope. The upper part continues to be reduced however, thus decreasing the inclination and mantling the bed-rock with a veneer of protective debris. If the debris can readily be evacuated, basal steepening occurs and the slope provides more debris. On this basis the valley cross-section depends upon rock type, microclimate, climate, vegetation and the velocity and volume of the river, as well as river behaviour (e.g. winding, meandering). Thus the form of individual valleys may be interpreted in terms of self-adjusting mechanisms such as are typical of open systems, as entire landscapes may also be interpreted.

This idea has aroused much interest. Such equilibrium can only be attained where the wasting of divides (i.e. peneplanation) is significant, where rainfall is heavy, and the texture (or spacing) of the drainage elements close. Such conditions occur in several of the known and active orogenic belts (Fig. 2), and here the possibility of dynamic equilibrium as a tool in landscape interpretation and understanding has to be considered.

In New Guinea, for instance, conditions are favourable. Rainfall is notoriously heavy over much of the island. Rivers and streams are numerous and closely spaced. The island is tectonically active: the reported occurrence of Pliocene corals at very high elevations has already been mentioned. Further suggestion of rapid uplift comes from Aitape, on the north coast. Wood, shell and other organic materials, including mangrove from a littoral situation associated with a human skull and about 5,000 years old (C14 dates of the materials varied between 4,400 and 5,700 years B.P.) are now 170 feet above sea level. Thus optimum conditions occur for the development of a land surface in dynamic equilibrium and the first quantified work on slopes in New Guinea strongly suggests that erosion is uniform on all parts of the slopes studied, a finding consistent with dynamic equilibrium.

However, what applies in such tectonically unstable areas need not necessarily occur in less active regions, and in areas which are arid, or where streams are widely spaced. In the Ozarks of central U.S.A., for instance, the landscape has been analysed specifically with the cyclic/non-cyclic contrasts in mind, and it has been firmly concluded that the former offers the more reasonable interpretation.

It is difficult to conceive dynamic equilibrium being important where the wasting of divides is apparently insignificant, as in many arid regions. The effects of baselevel control are also important for, regardless of the rate of uplift of, say, a fault block, streams cannot erode their beds, and the intervening divides cannot be lowered, below the local baselevel. As in certain areas maximum uplift is several times the rate of maximum erosion, baselevel control is all-important. Local climatically controlled variations in weathering and erosion will guide slope (thence landscape) development; and time-independent forms (i.e. forms in dynamic equilibrium) are unlikely to develop. Even in areas suffering marked uplift, variations in the sort of rock emerging at the land surface must cause variations in the form of the land surface.

Another relevant piece of evidence derives from studies of relative rates of erosion, for in some regions at least, and as mentioned in Chapter 1 (c), uplands are being worn down more rapidly than are the adjacent plains. The mountains are indeed being made low and the form of the landscape is not constant.

Finally, the concept of dynamic equilibrium does not take adequate account of inherited forms. Frost-riven cliffs may persist as prominent features of a land surface, remaining relatively untouched by modern processes, for many thousands of years. Resistant weathering carapaces like ferricrete and silcrete dominate landscape development literally millions of years after they have developed. High energy storm effects, whether evolved in a few hours or in the space of a few thousands of years (as with the meander bluffs and valleys of misfit streams), remain impressed on the landscape long after they originated.

Nevertheless, an examination of the geological concept of dynamic equilibrium occasioned by the challenge of the realities has brought out strongly several significant weaknesses in and difficulties inherent in the cyclic theories. These can be met by taking a more realistic view of the complexities of the environment. The cyclic concept, in its simplified form, rests on what are surely unreasonable assumptions; such stability of environment as demanded in the review presented above cannot be attained; all the evidence points to a constantly changing tectonic and climatic background. Yet such surfaces of low relief exist. As will be described shortly, the rolling plains of northwest Queensland (cut across Cretaceous sediments) and the Eyre Peninsula (before the onset of aridity and the formation of longitudinal sand dunes), eroded across crystalline rocks and are examples related to essentially present baselevel. Remnants of other surfaces, apparently dominated by convex interfluves, occur in the present landscape. Peneplains or pediplains should be regarded as composite features related not to a single stable baselevel, nor developed in an absolutely stable area of the earth's crust, not evolved during a period of climatic uniformity, but in an environment in which no *major* disruptions or disturbances occurred. Thus while the two cited examples of peneplains evolved, there were climatic changes, shifts of baselevel (sea level) and, in the case of northwest Queensland, earth movements (warping); each caused new facets to be developed in the land surface but all of these have become part of an overall surface of low relief dominated by convex interfluves. They include features related to different climates and are thus not only *multiphase*, but also *polygenetic* in character.

It is only when a major disruption occurs, particularly in respect of tectonism, that the surface is disturbed drastically and a new geomorphic cycle initiated.

(d) STABLE FORMS

Various considerations have led to the conclusion that erosional rates can differ by very large orders of magnitude within short lateral distances and that various landscape elements may persist for many millions of years. This stability of the land surface may relate to structural (lithological) factors, as is the case with ferricrete, silcrete and gibber-protected surfaces, or it may be due to climatic factors, for example persistant aridity, in which environment geomorphic processes seemingly act slowly. Elsewhere, however, they have been attributed directly to huge variations in

Cyclic and Non-cyclic Landscape Development

Fig 242 Stabilisation of land surface and development of stepped topography as a result, first of the differential weathering of granite, and second, of the resistance of granite to weathering and erosion when exposed to the air. The two knobs or ridges come to the surface as a result of erosion, and once exposed, act as local stable baselevels for the areas upstream and upslope (*after Wahrhaftig*).

Fig 243 Interplay of uplift erosion and wasting (*after Kennedy*).

the concentrations of erosional activity.

Of particular importance is the suggestion that a rock may change its geomorphological attributes according to its topographical location. Implicit in the interpretation of overhanging slopes on granite (see Chapters 4 and 14) is greater, or more rapid, weathering of that rock in subsurface situations, as compared with granite exposed to atmospheric agencies. This type of argument has been elaborated into an explanation for the very marked stepped topography found in the granitic Sierra Nevada of California. It is urged that wherever there is a granite outcrop it is weathered only very slowly, and acts as a local baselevel for the streams (and hence the slopes) upstream from it. The subsurface granite continues to be weathered rapidly but the resistant exposed mass is stable and thus affords a protective rim against erosion for the bedrock upstream from it (Fig. 242). The granite surface is weathered and eroded only slowly as a result of baselevel control. It is not in dynamic equilibrium and is not changing very rapidly. The exposed bedrock forms ridges which tend to become more and more pronounced and stand higher and higher in the relief, because of the concentration of weathering in the valley floors.

A similar situation has evidently occurred in the southern Flinders Ranges through the Cainozoic. The framework of the present relief was established by the Eocene and subsequently relief amplitude seems to have increased rather than diminished because of structural contrasts initially, but subsequently because of the concentration of weathering and erosion in valley floors. As mentioned earlier, the Canberra landscape is on one interpretation a stable one, having changed but little since the Palaeozoic; it should be mentioned, however, that other workers would attribute the forms to processes active much more recently.

Such slowly changing forms may be said to be *stable*.

(e) INTERRELATION OF BASELEVEL, STREAMS AND WASTING

The occurrence of surfaces of low relief in the landscape may suggest that erosion and wasting have outpaced uplift, but it is important to appreciate that surfaces of low relief need not necessarily develop close to regional baselevel.

In theory, landscapes may be analysed in terms of three factors—uplift, river incision and wasting (by which is meant the complex of processes responsible for the reduction of interfluves). Uplift and river incision are related through their effect upon and contact with baselevel. Wasting and incision also are related because wasting cannot proceed beyond the level of river incision, which thus provides a local baselevel of wasting. But there is no connection between uplift and wasting. Thus, in combination there are nine possible ways in which landform assemblages may develop,

Table 7   Interplay of Uplift, Incision and Wasting

Uplift > Incision	Incision > Wasting	1 Increasing relief
	” = ”	2 Static relief
	” < ”	3 Decreasing relief—P
Uplift = Incision	” > ”	4 Increasing relief
	” = ”	5 Static relief
	” < ”	6 Decreasing relief—P
Uplift < Incision	” > ”	7 Increasing relief
	” = ”	8 Static relief
	” < ”	9 Decreasing relief—P

P—peneplain or other surface of low relief.
Source: Adapted from *Kennedy*.

according to the relative rates of uplift, incision and wasting (see Table 7).

Typical profiles for the nine cases are shown in Fig. 243. Cases 1 to 3 result in various types of 'perched' relief, well above baselevel; cases 7 to 9 in relief at regional baselevel; and 4 to 6 in relief located at an intermediate level. An important conclusion resulting from this theoretical analysis is that surfaces of low relief can develop, in theory at least, high in the landscape as well as close to baselevel.

The effects of such an interplay of factors may be illustrated by reference to the Mt Lofty Ranges. This upland is dominated by a well developed and deeply weathered (lateritised) surface of low relief, located high in the landscape. It occurs at elevations of 1,400 to 1,500 feet in the vicinity of Adelaide and about 1,000 feet on the Fleurieu Peninsula to the south. In some localities, this surface has been so strongly dissected that the surface has been eliminated; but it occurs throughout the Ranges and its former continuity cannot be doubted. The deep weathering occurred late in the Tertiary and may even have continued into the early part of the Pleistocene.

The conventional interpretation (Fig. 244) of this situation is that the deeply weathered surface of low relief developed close to regional baselevel (sea level) essentially during the late Tertiary. This surface was then elevated to its present situation by faulting during the late Tertiary or early Quaternary. Dissection has subsequently reduced the area of the old surface.

This interpretation may be valid. Remnants of the deeply weathered surface attest to its former widespread occurrence and neither can the faulting be doubted. But if this hypothesis is correct then the deeply weathered former land surface should be found on the depressed, as well as on the raised, fault blocks (Fig. 244); such evidence has not so far been found.

It may be that the ferricrete has suffered marked solution by groundwaters, and that though present, it has not yet been discovered. An

330   *Geomorphology*

(a) — laterised land surface

(b) — Eocene sediments

Fig 244   Traditional interpretation of the evolution of the Mt Lofty Ranges.

zone under influence of rejuvenated stream | zone still graded to former base level at ✗

Fig 245   Perched relief in the Mt Lofty Ranges.

Fig 246   Imprint of three cycles on a land surface.

alternative interpretation is that the surface of low relief did not form at a near regional baselevel and was not disrupted by faulting. It may be argued that regional uplift by faulting outpaced stream incision, and that local wasting of divides outpaced incision (Case 3 of Table 7). That this was so is suggested by the fact that although dissection of the Mt Lofty Ranges is pronounced in certain localities, such erosion is most marked in the marginal zones; and over wide areas of the central Ranges stream gradients are exceedingly gentle. If we consider the area east of Adelaide, the River Torrens and other streams have excavated deep gorges in the uplands but the Torrens is deeply incised only as far as Gumeracha; beyond that the Torrens has not been rejuvenated and pursues a gentle gradient. The main local baselevel here is provided by the limit of the nick point or rejuvenation head on the Torrens. Subsidiary local baselevels are provided by the low gradient Torrens itself. Thus, although in the area drained by the Torrens in its Gorge section there is a large relief amplitude and active dissection of the old land surface, in that central area served by the non-rejuventated river, incision is very slow and could well be outpaced by the wasting of divides. Thus, although the situation is changing as the nick point of the Torrens (and other rivers) advances into the upland, it may be argued that during rapid uplift, a surface of low relief may have developed in a perched situation high in the Ranges (Fig. 245). The fact that it was perched would increase the through-drainage of ground waters and possibly enhance the development of deep weathering profiles. Such a mode of development is consistent with the present situation in the Mt Lofty Ranges and would explain why deeply weathered (lateritised) profiles have not been found on the depressed fault blocks.

Such concepts emphasising baselevel control, the preservation effects of weathering accumulations, and the slowness of change of some landscapes, go some way at least in overcoming difficulties inherent in the cyclic schemes of landscape development. The accumulation of gibber, or silcrete, for instance, could help to explain why surfaces *a* and *b* in Fig. 246 can persist well into another cycle (or in the case of *a*, into two further cycles). All this is not to suggest that all landscapes evolved cyclically at all times: the cyclic concept is but one of several geomorphological models, and the field evidence should be examined to see which model most closely matches the observed facts—non-cyclic and cyclic, peneplain and pediplain, and so on.

(f) EXAMPLES OF COMPLEX LANDSCAPES

Many landscapes of regional extent appear not only to be multicyclic but polygenetic. They not only display evidence of more than one geomorphic cycle, but also of having been moulded by more than one set of processes.

Classic areas of multicyclic origin include southern Africa, the Central

Plateau of France and southeastern England; but landscapes of similar type have been described from many parts of Australia. Very broadly, three major cycles and surfaces have been detected, the oldest of Mesozoic age, the second (which is commonly duricrusted) of early-mid Tertiary age, and the youngest initiated in the late Tertiary or Quaternary. There are others locally developed and preserved, but these three appear to have been continental in their effect and extent.

In northwestern Queensland, for example, three major cycles of erosion are recorded in the landscape, being evidenced by surfaces of low relief (or remnants thereof), two of which have suffered warping, and each clearly distinguishable in time. The earliest surface was eroded during the early Mesozoic (pre late Jurassic), and warped during the Jurassic so that it remains preserved as a basin structure beneath the Carpentaria Basin (Fig. 247). The basin was inundated by the late Mesozoic (principally Cretaceous) marine transgression, which followed in consequence of the tectonism and was buried and preserved beneath the thick sedimentary sequences laid down in that sea. The sea receded in the late Cretaceous, and the sediments exposed, plus the remnants of older rocks which had

Fig 247 Erosion surfaces in northwest Queensland.

1 pre-"Mesozoic" (Jurassic?) surface
2 Tertiary surface — duricrusted
3 modern plain surface

Fig 248 Diagrammatic section through Peake and Denison Ranges showing erosional surfaces.

stood as islands above the Cretaceous seas, were subjected to prolonged subaerial weathering and erosion; the land surface was deeply weathered, resulting in the widespread formation of ferricrete, and of bauxite in a few localities of which Weipa is an example; it was reduced to one of low relief, and then in the late Tertiary (Miocene or Pliocene) was warped in the same sense as before. The present Isa highlands, and Einasleigh uplands rose, and the Carpentaria basin again subsided. The northern part of the latter was drowned by the sea, the southern part deeply dissected by rivers. Wasting and river erosion have reduced most of the Carpentaria basin to a peneplain; in the adjacent uplands extensive, and in places deep, valleys have been excavated. In these upland regions, remnants of the Mesozoic cover have been removed, and the pre middle Mesozoic surface re-exposed—an exhumed surface. The duricrusted (lateritised) early-middle Tertiary surface is resistant to erosion and persists as plateau and mesa forms throughout the region (Pl. 72).

In a broad area astride the Queensland–Northern Territory border west of Mount Isa, a yet older surface is well preserved and exposed. This was formed before the middle of the Cambrian, buried by upper Cambrian sediments and subsequently resurrected. However, its expression is only local. The pre middle Mesozoic surface, which is displayed at both margins of the Carpentaria Basin, is also represented to the south and particularly on the western edge of the Great Artesian Basin. It is represented in the summit crests of the MacDonnell and other Ranges of central Australia where Tertiary duricrusted surfaces (the earlier with silcrete, the later with laterite) have also been developed, and in Victoria, upwards relative to the adjacent plains, which are still underlain by Cretaceous and younger strata. Most of the relatively weak Cretaceous beds have been removed by weathering and erosion, but remnants like Mt Babbage, perched on fault blocks of varied elevation, bear witness to the true nature and antiquity of the present high plain surface—an exhumed land surface of low relief and of pre Cretaceous age (see earlier).

The Flinders Ranges have been deeply dissected, and only in a few localities, where resistant sandstones occur, is this ancient surface extensively preserved. It is fairly commonly represented in the northern Flinders but in the south only in limited localities such as in the core of the anticline between Dutchmans Stern and The Bluff, near Quorn (Fig. 249, Pl. 73), and around the Edeowie Gorge at the northwestern extremity of Wilpena Pound (Fig. 250) where the sandstone is weathered to a depth of several dozen feet.

Weathering and erosion have been closely guided by the structure of the underlying bedrock: streams exploited the comparatively weak outcrop to form the major valleys where the sandstones, particularly, have remained upstanding. In the major valleys especially, there is further evidence of the multicyclic character of the Ranges, for standing above the present valley floor at elevations which may vary from place to place, between 30 and 100 feet, are mesa remnants so numerous that they must once have formed a whole, higher, surface. Thus, three distinct levels of erosional character are commonly displayed in the Flinders Ranges. The higher surface is of pre Cretaceous age, and in the southern Flinders the lower levels have been determined as of late Tertiary and Quaternary ages. In the case of the two younger surfaces, the whole region was not reduced to low relief (on the contrary the relief amplitude can reasonably be argued to have increased, rather than the reverse), only the valleys and plains being markedly affected by stream rejuvenation. The three surfaces nevertheless can be considered cyclic in origin.

In the Adelaide region, a very prominent deeply weathered surface surmounts the Mt Lofty Ranges (Fig. 251). As discussed previously, the origin of the surface is controversial but whatever the answer, the evolution of the Adelaide landscape is more complex than it at first appears to be.

To the west of the Gulfs region, on Eyre Peninsula, there is evidence not only of the multicyclic, but also of a polygenetic landsurface, i.e. a landsurface which has developed under the influence of contrasted climatic conditions. Much of the Peninsula is occupied by a broadly rolling plain of low relief traversed by northwest and southeast trending fixed sand dunes and underlain in many places by calcrete. Adjacent to the east coast subdued but distinct uplands rise to 1,300 feet above sea level, and in the north the Gawler Ranges stand even higher. A few ridges, ranges and residuals, some of bornhardt type, stand in isolation above the general plain level. Remnants of a lateritised or otherwise deeply weathered surface stand high, but lower than the summit peaks, in both the eastern and Gawler Ranges. It is particularly well preserved in the south, near Port Lincoln (Fig. 252). It was probably beneath this surface, which extended over the whole region, that the domed inselbergs of the northwest of the Peninsula, were differentially weathered.

The dislocation of the surface and interruption of the cycle by faulting occurred in the Pliocene; the plains related to present baselevels developed as a result of a renewal of dissection and erosion which clearly post dates the Pliocene, i.e. is of Quaternary age. Equally clearly, the broadly-rolling topography of the present plain, with a co-ordinated valley system, results from the work of rivers; but none exist now. Any rain percolates back through the calcareous and arenaceous subsoil. Furthermore the dunes which traverse the area are now fixed, with further evidence of environmental change.

Several erosion surfaces are known from the Eastern Uplands. In some areas they can be separated and approximately dated in relation to the basalt flows or to the lake sediments which in many places underlie these extrusive rocks. In New England, for instance, the Tertiary basalt

Fig 249 Erosion surfaces north of Quorn.

rests on lacustrine beds of Eocene–Oligocene age. It has suffered deep weathering (including lateritisation) and erosion, and here the basalt-capped plateau represents an old erosional surface of post-basalt age (Fig. 253), generally regarded as Miocene. Subsequently, two further cycles have left their imprint on the region; the first is represented by broad, rolling interfluves between the river valleys, but below the basalt; the second, by the deep river gorges themselves.

In southern N.S.W., erosional surfaces have long been recognised, for instance, in the Shoalhaven region. In the Kiandra area, the old peneplain surface has been dated by lacustrine sediments which rest on it: it is of Eocene or older age. Elsewhere, however, the age of the erosional levels is controversial. Generally speaking, some workers tend to relate the upland plains and summit crests of southeastern N.S.W., between 4,000 and 5,000 feet above sea level, to a master surface of Miocene age: all subsequent erosion is thus attributed to the late Cainozoic. Alternately, other workers regard this high surface as of much greater antiquity

Fig 250   High level erosion surface in the Edeowie Gorge area.

and even of Palaeozoic age. This ancient landscape is considered to have changed slowly and slightly: a stable assemblage of forms.

In Tasmania five distinct erosional surfaces have been identified. The lowest standing between 300 and 900 feet may be of marine origin; the others are regarded as fluvial in origin, and above the highest stand residual monadnocks attaining elevations between 4,400 feet and 5,300 feet, in Cradle Mountain, Barn Bluff and Frenchmans Cap, all in central Tasmania.

Fig 251   The deeply weathered (lateritised) land surface in the Mt Lofty Ranges (*adapted from Barker 1-mile*, and *Adelaide and Gawler 1-mile Geological map, Geol. Surv. S.A.*).

Fig 252 The lateritised land surface near Port Lincoln (*after Lincoln 4-mile Geological map*, Geol. Surv. S.A.).

Fig 253 Erosion surfaces in the Armidale district (*after Voisey*).

Plate 72 Mesa and butte remnants of a lateritised early-middle Tertiary erosional surface in northwestern Queensland, south of Cloncurry. (*C.S.I.R.O.*)

Plate 73 Erosion surface near Dutchmans Stern, north of Quorn.

13. The Work of Man—Anthropogenic Influences

IT MUST NOT BE IMAGINED that during each geomorphic cycle, processes act at a steady or even rate; as suggested earlier, within each cycle, there are several minor phases or *epicycles* during which, processes are accelerated or retarded. The complications of landscape evolution and the minor cycles forming an inherent part of each major cycle, may be illustrated by the changes wrought by intensive human settlement of the earth.

Since man spread over the earth's surface he has extensively modified his environment. Some of the changes effected have caused new landforms to develop, so much so that, late in the last century a Russian geographer wrote that he 'could not conceive a physiography from which man had been excluded'. Deforestation, introduction of exotic plants and animals, the use of agricultural machinery, the building and use of tracks and roads, and overgrazing of pastures have all, singly and in combination, altered the pre-existing quasi-equilibrium of the environment and caused accelerated erosion and deposition to occur. So significant is this physiographic activity initiated by man that many workers consider a new anthropogenic epicycle of erosion to be occurring.

The clearance of woodland or forest for agricultural purposes has various and complex repercussions, and bushfires may achieve similar results. Of greatest importance is the exposure of the land surface to erosive agencies, especially raindrop and wind. The removal of timber can cause a rise in the water table, and with it salts, causing destruction of vegetation at the surface and hence exposure of the land surface to erosion. Removal of plant litter causes loss of soil structure and particularly of porosity: hence run-off is increased. Run-off from a bare soil surface is many times that from a sward or woodland area. Vegetation has a binding influence upon the surface soil and its loss promotes erosion. Overgrazing has similar effects and the introduction of animal pests, such as the rabbit, also has a deleterious influence. Even the clearing of stones from the fields—and the great heaps of rocks in many fields in the Murray mallee, for instance, are witness to thousands of hours of backbreaking work—induces erosion through the removal of a natural protective capping.

The removal or reduction of vegetation also renders the land surface susceptible to wind action. The voracious nibbling of the goats of nomadic herdsmen in several areas on the margins of the Sahara has intensified and extended the desert. It has been said that in some areas the nomad is not so much the son of the desert, but its father. Similarly on the southern edge of the Kalahari and in the Australian deserts and semi-desert areas, overgrazing has caused dunes which were fixed by vegetation to be re-activated.

These changes wrought by man are widespread and well-known, and require no elaboration here, but it is less commonly realised that the introduction of new species of plants (either deliberately or accidentally) may also change the environmental equilibrium. Exotic species may not withstand climatic extremes of a new environment as well as the natives. For example, in the southern Flinders Ranges, introduced annual herbs and grass quickly replaced the native perennial ground cover following white settlement in the area in the mid-nineteenth century. The annuals do not withstand the summer heat and drought as well as the natives and consequently, at the end of the dry season, the soil surface is usually quite bare and thus susceptible to wash and to gullying.

Tracks and roads are ready made channels for run-off (Pl. 74), and are moreover devoid of vegetation and impermeable because of compaction: hence they are readily washed away. No water permeates through the surface of sealed roads but the precipitation that falls upon them, drains the road margins, which are usually bare, and which are (where there are no gutters and drains) vulnerable to erosion.

Such anthropogenic works render the soil surface susceptible to erosion by run-off and particularly by heavy and rapid run-off associated with

Plate 74   An eroded road near Nonning, Gawler Ranges.

torrential downpours. Many of the gullies in South Australia can be dated to a particular storm and the recency of the erosion is evidenced by buried fenceposts and other anthropogenic or anthropogenically introduced features such as the bones of the horse. Man's activities may not cause serious erosion and deposition, but they render the land surface vulnerable to climatic accidents. The relative roles of man and climate have long been argued in relation to the arroyas of the American High Plains and Southwest, but it now seems generally considered that man has played a decisive part in their initiation.

Gullies are perhaps the best known and most obvious manifestation of the new epicycle of erosion and deposition. They are known from many parts of the world and there is evidence that in some long-settled areas, like western Europe where gullies are not now a prominent feature of the landscape, they were more prevalent in past times. Gullies are prominent in many parts of South Australia, but particularly where the country rock is either unconsolidated or easily weathered: where there are alluvial fills, as for instance on the Willunga scarp (Pls. 50, 75), and in valleys in the Flinders, or where disaggregated Permian clays crop-out south of Adelaide (Pls. 76, 77, 78, 79). But even in these optimum areas, ploughing has disguised some incipient gullying; and in some valleys near Yankalilla for instance (e.g. M.R. Yankalilla 1/50,000 sheet 307183) one side of a valley is gullied, the other, under the plough, is not, though observations during and after rains show that both slopes are suffering marked erosion.

Though not so obvious as gullies, sheet erosion is perhaps quantitatively more significant, and has influenced extensive areas of the land surface. Its importance is suggested by accumulations of detritus at fences, at the foot of slopes and by the exposure of tree roots and former areas of subsurface weathering, resulting in the revelation of minor caverns and pedestal forms at the surface.

On a very much more limited scale, man has influenced the morphology of bedrock slopes. At one archaeological site near Walkers Flat in the Murray Valley in South Australia, it can be shown that periods of occupation and desertion of the site have caused changes in the relative rates of erosion and burial of the back-wall and have caused the formation of a stepped bedrock surface. Man's mining activities have also caused local subsidence of the earth's surface and waste heaps are also prominent in some localities. On a larger scale, man has drained swamps and arms of the sea (as for instance in the Dutch Polderlands, the English Fens and the swamps of the Southeast) and has also created the shallow lakes known as the Norfolk Broads.

Through tapping underground water and oil supplies, man has caused local subsidence. Perhaps the best example of this is Mexico City, which is built on old lake sediments. The city water supply is derived from

Plate 75 Deep gully in unconsolidated clays and gravels of the Willunga scarp.

The Work of Man—Anthropogenic Influences 345

Plate 76 Old plough furrows in pasture are deep enough to channel run-off and cause a concentration of drainage and hence erosion in the Permian clays and sands of the Yankalilla area.

Plate 77 Further stages in the exploitation of furrows to form gullies in the Yankalilla area.

Plate 78 Deep gully in Permian shale, Yankalilla area.

these beds, but with the extraction of water, the volume of the rock is decreased, causing contraction and subsidence which in some areas amounts to more than 20 feet in the last century. This naturally has disastrous effects on buildings in the area. In his attempts to overcome this difficulty, man has introduced a nice distinction. Some of the tall modern buildings have been placed on stilt foundations which penetrate through the shrinking sediments into a solid bedrock; some of the earlier modern buildings lack these foundations and, because of their greater weight, sink more rapidly and cause old buildings to collapse *toward* them (Fig. 254). The buildings on stilt foundations are stable, but subsidence continues around them causing the older houses to collapse *away* from them.

Fig 254 Effects of subsidence due to withdrawal of water.

Principally, human occupation of the land surface has resulted in an acceleration of erosion, the loss of valuable soil, and the initiation of a new epicycle of erosion and deposition, within the broader, major geomorphic cycle.

14. Conclusion

THE PRECEDING CHAPTERS PROVIDE an account of some, though by no means all, important factors involved in the evolution and understanding of Australian landscapes. The numerous examples cited demonstrate the ready application of general geomorphological concepts to the interpretation of those landscapes. Though the emphasis changes from one area to another, structure, process and time are three general headings in terms of which the development of Australian landforms may usefully be analysed, and readily understood.

It is necessary to emphasise that these principles cannot be regarded as general laws, and that they cannot be applied in a mechanical, stereotyped fashion. Similar forms can evolve in different ways (homeomorphs, or *convergent landforms*)—U-shaped and hanging valleys, shore platforms, and lakes are examples. Each area, each landform, is in some measure unique and is a law unto itself. Only facts derived from field observations can provide a key to the acceptance or rejection of a given interpretation; and in most instances, generalizations must be qualified in order to meet the field evidence as closely as possible.

The geomorphologist works by the method of *multiple working hypotheses*, which consists of the following stages:

(1) Field observation.
(2) Interpretation of field evidence through the formulation of as many generalizations or hypotheses as can possibly explain the field results.
(3) Testing of the deducible consequences of each hypotheses derived in (2), and comparing these consequences with the field evidence. Some or all will be thus eliminated.

In practice these stages are not clearly and distinctly separated; for example, hypothecation follows swiftly on almost any isolated observation. But the testing of hypotheses, and the conscious attempt to eliminate them, lends rigour to the geomorphological method and goes some way to overcoming the inherent difficulties of the subject which render interpretations so varied and problematic—they include lack of a satisfactory body of physical theory, the immensity of geological time, the widespread inheritance of forms, and the rarity and difficulty of accurate first-hand observations of processes in action.

This working method may be illustrated with reference to the steepened, flared or overhanging slopes which are found so commonly on the inselbergs of northwest Eyre Peninsula, and elsewhere, and which have been described and illustrated (Chapters 4, 5; Figs. 96, 109; Pls. 29, 43). These forms have been attributed to subsurface differential weathering and subsequent exposure by erosion; but behind this assertion is the following reasoning.

The significant characteristics of these forms are that they occur both on lower slopes and in clefts and valleys within the uplands; that they are most commonly and best developed (highest, greatest overhang) on the southern and eastern aspects of these hills; that the steepening is not necessarily horizontal, but in several places occurs in sloping zones; that the overhang is at a maximum on the points of spurs; that they occur beneath the present land surface as well as above it; and local geological and geomorphological evidence shows that they must have evolved in the latest Tertiary or the Quaternary era.

When these facts had been noted, the question 'How did they form?' had to be answered. What possibilities are there?

(1) Could they be old sea cliffs? Wind-driven waves could cause a steepening, or a trimming, of the lower slopes of inselbergs, and high stands of the sea allegedly occurred during the late Cainozoic.
(2) Could they be due to wind erosion (sand blasting)? The localization of steepening close to plain level is consistent with this theory, and the surrounding terrain bears witness to Quaternary aridity, for fixed longitudinal dunes traverse the plains.
(3) Could the steepening be due to running water? Downslope increase in volume could cause increased erosion in the same direction, and this, combined with splash and cavitation effects, could conceivably shape the features under discussion.
(4) Could they be due to weathering of some description?

These possible hypotheses will be considered and tested in turn.

(A) MARINE ORIGIN

If the features are abandoned late Cainozoic sea cliffs, then it follows that the sea must have extended over much of northwestern Eyre Peninsula. Yet no evidence of its former presence has been found—no marine fossils or sediments, no beaches, no caves—away from the immediate environs of the present coast. Moreover, the aeolianite on the west coast of Eyre Peninsula shows that during the Pleistocene the westerlies were dominant then, as they are today. Therefore, the highest cliffs should face the direction of maximum wave-attack, namely, the west. In fact it is the south and east slopes which are most steepened.

(B) AEOLIAN ORIGIN

Aspect also counts against the aeolian theory. The Australian sand ridge deserts are generally agreed to have developed in relation to a vast anticlockwise wind circulation; in northwestern Eyre Peninsula, the local evidence points irrefutably to the dune sand being blown in from the northwest, and therefore the maximum wind erosion should be found on the northwest sides of the hills. But the steeper slopes face the opposite direction. Moreover, it is difficult to see how the wind could erode solid granite (if it is capable of this) beneath the land surface. It may be argued that the erosion was accomplished, and then the slopes buried, but the detritus which naturally overlies the subsurface flares (demonstrated in excavations, as well as by augering) is weathered granite *in situ*.

(C) RUNNING WATER

Certain theoretical difficulties face the hypothesis which attributes to running water the power to erode these elegant slopes. But hydrological theory is in places equivocal or general, so that this is not a conclusive argument. What is damaging is the occurrence of the flares buried beneath weathered granite. Minor points of argument are that if the westerlies were dominant as rain bearing winds in the Pleistocene, as they are today, then, as with the marine hypothesis, the westerly slopes should be the steeper; but they are not. Furthermore, if running water was responsible, maximum overhang should have developed at the heads of valleys, where water flow is concentrated, not at the points of spurs, where it is diffused.

(D) WEATHERING

The two stage theory of tor formation has already been described, and it may equally apply to these overhanging and steepened slopes. In the semi-arid environment in which they occur, run-off from the bare rock surfaces of the inselbergs is high, but spreads only a short distance around the bases of the hills. There it soaks into the soil and rock, which are weathered. The weathering front spreads not only downwards but laterally and particularly beneath the edge of the exposed granite of the hill (see Fig. 109). When subsequently baselevel is lowered, the front is exposed (cf. etch plain) as are the flares.

This hypothesis accounts for the shape of the lower slopes; for their distribution not only around the bases of the uplands, but also in valleys and clefts, where in some places moisture-retaining soil and rock debris can still be seen; for their occurrence in sloping zones, where the steepening rises or falls in sympathy with the plain-hill junction; for their distribution in plan, for moisture will be longer retained on the shadier southern and eastern aspects; for the maximum development of overhang on the points of spurs, where two zones of subsurface weathering intersect, causing an even greater concentration of moisture and weathering; and, of course, the hypothesis is consistent with the known age and subsurface occurrence of the forms.

This does not eliminate all problems. Typical questions remaining unanswered include:

What was the erosional agency causing the etching out of the flares? If streams, when were they active? There are no surface streams in the area now.

What is the relation, if any, between the subsurface weathering, and the erosion which exposed the flares, to arid and moist periods of the Pleistocene?

To what extent, if any, are the linear depressions found at the base of steepened slopes in central Australia, western Africa and the Sahara, and clearly related to the same sort of processes as cause the development of flared slopes, due to subsurface evacuation of weathered bedrock?

But this analysis provides an example of how the method of multiple working hypotheses is applied.

In applying this method, the geomorphologist has to balance two interests which can be opposed. His theoretical armament is important. It increases the range of hypotheses he can consider. The more profound his knowledge of theoretical concepts, the wider his field experience (comparative method) the higher the quality and the greater the range of his field observations. But his theoretical knowledge must be critically applied. The only authority is not the text book or teacher but field evidence: as Gautama Buddha said almost 1,500 years ago:

> Believe nothing on the faith of sages of
> the past
> Or on the sole authority of your masters
> or priests;
> After examination believe only what you
> have tested and found reasonable.

Theory should not become dogma and inhibit imagination—'that quality so necessary in life, art, and science'. Without this quality, derived largely through reflection, little real progress is possible.

Finally, it must be recognized that it is not always possible to achieve a definitive interpretation of landforms: 'Truth in geomorphology, indeed, is seldom more than increasing probability.' Some problems are so difficult that one can cynically agree with Mark Twain that 'The researches of many commentators have already thrown much darkness on this subject, and it is probable that, if they continue, we shall soon know nothing at all about it.' Repeated researches on the same problem or area can certainly confuse the issue, but even if the results are negative or if no new difficulties are discovered, a reasonable answer should eventually emerge. Given theoretical advances, not only in geomorphology but in other sciences also, given new information (especially good topographical maps), and given an unfettered but controlled imagination, then an hypothesis will surely sooner or later be evolved, which satisfies the field evidence derived from the landscape—which is, after all, the final court of appeal.

REFERENCES AND SUGGESTED FURTHER READING

This bibliography is not intended to be comprehensive. Certain basic and relevant works are cited, but others of the review type are mentioned because of the leads they give to the literature, as much as for their inherent value. These notes should be regarded only as an introduction and a starting point.

GENERAL
Good general textbooks on geomorphology include:
> DURY, G. H., *The Face of the Earth*, 225 p. Pelican (1959)—particularly good for its account of rivers.
> HOLMES, Arthur, *Principles of Physical Geology*, 1288 p. Nelson (1965).
> SHELTON, J. S., *Geology Illustrated*, 434 p. Freeman (1966)—demonstrates exceptionally well many geological features and their geomorphological implications.
> SPARKS, B. W., *Geomorphology*, 371 p. Longmans (1960)—recommended for its critical and honest approach to geomorphological problems.
> STRAHLER, A. N., *Physical Geography*, 534 p. Wiley (1965).
> THORNBURY, W. D., *Principles of Geomorphology*, 618 p. Wiley (1954)—a full description, beautifully illustrated.

Australian examples are not illustrated in the above books. The only examples in book form are to be found in:
> ANON., *Land Research Series*, C.S.I.R.O.—contain results of contemporary and thorough investigations on many aspects of the environment (including geomorphological maps of large areas of Australia and New Guinea).
> HILLS, E. S., *Physiography of Victoria*, 292 p. Whitcombe and Tombs (1940).
> JENNINGS, J. N. and MABBUTT, J. A. (Eds), *Landform Studies from Australia and New Guinea*, 434 p. A.N.U. Press (1967)—recently published and contains several essays of general interest.
> JUTSON, J. T., 'The Physiography of Western Australia', 336 p. *Geol. Surv. W. Austr. Bull.* 95 (2nd ed., 1950).
> TAYLOR, Griffith, 'Physiography of Eastern Australia', 17 p. *Comm. Bur. Met. Bull.* 8 (1911)—a remarkably perspicacious work.

French language publications include:
> de MARTONNE, E., *Traité de Géographie Physique*, (Vol. 2) 1057 p. Colin (9th ed. 1951)—still contains much of value.
> DERRUAU, M., *Précis de Géomorphologie*, 415 p. Masson (2nd ed. 1965)—a good concise account.

This and the various volumes of TRICART, J., and CAILLEUX, A., *Cours de Géomorphologie* possibly provide the best coverage of the fields in any language.

German language

MACHATSCHEK, F., *Geomorphologie*, 164 p. Teubner (1949)—a brief but sound treatment.

Journals

Many geographical and geological journals carry geomorphological research papers, but two journals are now devoted exclusively to work in this specialist field. They are:

Revue de Géomorphologie Dynamique—publishes mainly in French. Although appearing irregularly, is lively and rewarding.

Zeitschrift für Geomorphologie—papers in English, French or German and summaries in the two other languages.

CHAPTER 1

Basic works pertaining to this chapter are:

DAVIS, W. M., *Geographical Essays*, 777 p. Dover (2nd ed., 1954) —first published in 1909 this is a full and elegant summary of many important geomorphological concepts; includes a discussion of the erosion cycle in humid, temperate and glacial regions. Some parts of this book, though more than 50 years old, are required reading for serious students of the subject.

PELTIER, L. C., 'The geographic cycle in periglacial regions as it is related to climatic geomorphology', 1950 *Assoc. Amer. Geogr. Ann.* 40: 214–236—contains a theoretical and systematic review of the concept of morphogenetic regions.

TRICART, J., 'Application du concept de zonalité à la géomorphologie', 1957 *Tijdschr. Kon. Ned. Aar. Genootsch.* 74: 422–434 —includes map (Fig. 2 herein) showing world distribution of the various regional zones.

Rates of erosion are summarized in the following works but there is very little information available on rates of geomorphological activity.

CORBEL, J.,'Vitesse de l'érosion', 1959 *Zeitschr. f. Geomorph.* 3:1–28.

JUDSON, S. and RITTER, D. F., 'Rates of regional denudation in the United States', 1964 *Jour. Geophys. Res.* 69: 3395–3401.

MENARD, H. W., 'Some rates of regional erosion', 1961 *Jour. Geol.* 69: 154–161.

SCHUMM, S. A., 'Disparity between present rates of denudation and orogeny', 1963 *U.S. Geol. Surv. Pro. Paper* 454: 13 p.

Significance of storms is stressed by several authors including:

WOLMAN, M. G. and MILLER, J. P., 'Magnitude and frequency of forces in geomorphic processes', 1960 *Jour. Geol.* 68: 54–74.

Slope budget is considered by:
> TRICART, J., 'L'évolution des versants', 1957 *L'inf. Geogr.*: 108–115.
> TWIDALE, C. R., 'Some problems of slope development', 1960 *Jour. Geol. Soc. Austr.* 6: 131–148.

The Davisian concept of cyclic landscape development is criticized by:
> HACK, J. T., 'Interpretation of erosional topography in humid temperate regions', 1960 *Amer. Jour. Sci.* 258(A): 80–97.
> KING, L. C., 'Canons of landscape evolution', 1962 *Geol. Soc. Amer. Bull.* 64: 721–752.
> ——, *Morphology of the Earth*, 699 p. Oliver and Boyd (1962)—a massive work.
> PENCK, W. (Trans. H. Czech and K. C. Boswell), *Morphological Analysis of Landforms*, 429 p. Macmillan (1953).

CHAPTER 2
Most elementary geological texts provide an elaboration of the ground covered in this chapter. Typical examples which have not already been cited include:
> GILLULY, J., WATERS, A. C. and WOODFORD, A. O., *Principles of Geology*, 534 p. Freeman (2nd ed., 1959).
> HILLS, E. S., *Outlines of Structural Geology*, 182 p. Methuen (3rd ed., 1953)—an excellent text at more advanced level.
> ——, *Elements of Structural Geology*, 483 p. Methuen (1963)—a more sophisticated work.
> READ, H. H. and WATSON, J., *Introduction to Geology*, Vol. 1 'Principles', 693 p. Macmillan (1963).

Geology of Australian States are reviewed in certain issues of the *Journal of the Geological Society of Australia*:
> 1958 *The Stratigraphy of Western Australia*
> 1958 *Geology of South Australia*
> 1960 *Geology of Queensland*
> 1962 *Geology of Tasmania*

In press: A similar volume on New South Wales.

Papers cited in the text include:
> de KEYSER, F., 'The Palmerville fault—a "fundamental" structure in North Queensland', 1963 *Jour. Geol. Soc. Austr.* 10: 273–278.
> GILLULY, J., 'Distribution of mountain building in geological time', 1949 *Geol. Soc. Amer. Bull.* 60: 561–590.
> GRANT, C. KERR, 'The Adelaide earthquake of 1 March 1954', 1956 *Trans. Roy. Soc. S. Austr.* 79: 177–185.
> HARRIS, W. J., 'Physiography of the Echuca district', 1939 *Proc. Roy. Soc. Vic.* 51: 45–60—an important and most fascinating report.

LAMBERT, I. B. and WHITE, A. J. R., 'The Berridale wrench fault: a major structure in the Snowy Mountains of New South Wales', 1965 *Jour. Geol. Soc. Austr.* 12: 25–33.

STAUFFER, M. R. and RICKARD, M. J., 'The establishment of recumbent folds in the lower Palaeozoic near Queanbeyan, New South Wales', 1966 *Jour. Geol. Soc. Austr.* 13: 419–438.

CHAPTER 3

Tectonic and structural landforms are differentiated in:

COTTON, C. A., 'A note on tectonic and structural landforms', 1948 *N.Z. Jour. Sci. and Tech.* (Sec. B) 29: 96.

Lineaments are discussed by:

HILLS, E. S., 'A contribution to the morphotectonics of Australia', 1955 *Jour. Geol. Soc. Austr.* 3: 1–15.

——, 'Morphotectonics and the geomorphological sciences with special reference to Australia', 1961 *Quart. Jour. Geol. Soc. London* 117: 77–89—and other papers which thoroughly discuss lineaments with reference to Australia and their effects on drainage patterns.

STEERS, J. A., *The Unstable Earth*, 345 p. Methuen (5th ed., 1950)—a concise and readable, if now rather out-of-date review of those theories which endeavour to explain major features of the earth's relief (and other controversial topics).

TWIDALE, C. R., 'Physiography of northwest Queensland', 1956 *Geogr. Studies* 3: 1–11—mentions effects of lineaments on drainage patterns.

VENING-MEINESZ, F., 'Shear patterns in the earth's crust', 1947 *Trans. Amer. Geophys. Union* 28: 1–61—mentions the global pattern of lineaments.

Tectonic patterns in South Australia are considered in:

ANON., *Geological Atlas of South Australia*, Geol. Surv. S. Austr.

GLAESSNER, M. F. and PARKIN, L. W. (Eds), *The Geology of South Australia* (see Ch. 9, Webb, B. P. 'Summary of tectonics'), 163 p. Melbourne University Press for Geol. Soc. Austr. (1958).

SPRIGG, R. C., *Geology of South and Eastern Australia* (see pp. 37–56, 'On the structural evolution of the Great Artesian Basin', and pp. 71–88, 'Oil and gas possibilities of the St. Vincent Gulf graben', Austr. Petrol. Expl. Assoc. Conference (1961).

Tectonic patterns of the Adelaide region may be further studied in:

BENSON, W. N., 'Note descriptive of a stereogram of the Mt Lofty Ranges, South Australia', 1911 *Trans. Roy. Soc. S. Austr.* 35: 108–111.

FENNER, C., 'The major structural and physiographic features of South Australia', 1930 *Ibid.* 54: 1–36.

GLAESSNER, M. F., 'Some problems of Tertiary geology in southern Australia', 1953 *Roy. Soc. N.S.W. Jour.* 87: 31–45.

STEEL, T. M., 'Subsurface stratigraphy in the western suburbs of Adelaide', 1962 *Quart. Geol. Notes* (Geol. Surv. S. Austr.) 2.

WARD, T., 'Eustatic and climatic history of the Adelaide area, South Australia', 1965 *Jour. Geol.* 73: 592–602—this paper is discussed (*Ibid.* 1967) in a paper by C. R. Twidale, B. Daily and J. B. Firman, and further in Ward (*Ibid.*, 1967).

Other areas in South Australia:

CRAWFORD, A. R., 'Geology of Yorke Peninsula', 1965 *Geol. Surv. S. Austr. Bull.* 39: 96 p.

HORWITZ, R. C., 'The geology of the Wakefield Military Sheet', (Rept. Investigation), 1961 *Geol. Surv. S. Austr.* 18: 32 p.

MILES, K. R., 'Tertiary faulting in northeastern Eyre Peninsula, South Australia', 1952 *Trans. Roy. Soc. S. Austr.* 75: 89–96.

WARD, W. T. and JESSUP, R. W., 'Changes of sea level in southern Australia', 1965 *Nature* 205 (4973): 791–792.

WOPFNER, H., 'On some structural development in the central part of the Great Australian Artesian Basin', 1960 *Trans. Roy. Soc. S. Austr.* 83: 179–194.

Volcanic features and regions in Australia:

GILL, E. D. and SHARP, K. R., 'The Tertiary rocks of the Snowy Mountains, Eastern Australia', 1957 *Jour. Geol. Soc. Austr.* 5: 21–40—volcanic areas in eastern Australia.

JENNINGS and MABBUTT, *op. cit.* (Galloway, R. W.—Hunter Valley; Ollier, C. D.—Western Victoria).

SPRIGG, R. C., 'Geology of the South-East Province, South Australia', 1952 *Geol. Surv. S. Austr. Bull.* 29: 120 p.

TWIDALE, C. R., 'Physiographic reconnaissance of some volcanic provinces in north Queensland', 1956 *Bull. Volc.* II (18): 3–23.

Landscapes in northwest Queensland and Canberra:

ÖPIK, A. A., 'Geology of Canberra City district', 1958 *Bur. Min. Res., Geol. and Geophys. Bull.* 32: 99 p.—discusses origin of Canberra landscape.

TAYLOR, G., *op. cit.*—first suggests the warping of the land surface in northwest Queensland.

TWIDALE, C. R., 'Late Cainozoic activity of the Selwyn upwarp', 1966 *Jour. Geol. Soc. Austr.* 13: 491–494.

WHITE, H. L. (Ed.), *Canberra. A Nation's Capital* (see Ch. 6, pp. 115–152,—Noakes, L. C. and Öpik, A. A., 'Geology and geomorphology'), 243 p. Angus and Robertson (1954).

CHAPTER 4

GLAESSNER and PARKIN, *op. cit.* (in Ch. 1 and 2 Campana, B. considers tectonic development of the Flinders Ranges, and the Mt. Lofty Ranges).

JACK, R. Lockhart, 'Geology and prospects of the region to the south of the Musgrave Ranges . . .', 1915 *Geol. Surv. S. Austr. Bull.* 5: 72 p.

JOHNS, R. K., 'Stratigraphic correlations in the Lake Torrens Region', 1963 *Quart. Geol. Notes* (Geol. Surv. S. Austr.) 6.

——briefly considers the nature of the sandstone in the Lincoln Gap and adjacent areas.

KING, L. C., 'Canons of landscape evolution', 1953 *Geol. Soc. Amer. Bull.* 64: 721–752—useful reference on slope form and development.

SAVIGEAR, R. A. G., 'Some observations on slope development in South Wales', 1952 *Trans. and Papers Inst. Brit. Geogr.* 18: 31–51.

——, 'Technique and terminology in the investigation of slope forms', 1956 *Prem. Rapport Com. par l'Etude des Versants, Amsterdam*: 155 p.

Granite weathering:

WILHELMY, H., *Klimamorphologie der Massengestein*, 238 p. Westermann (1958)—a good general text on granite weathering and forms.

Tors:

JONES, T. R., 'Notes on some granite tors', 1859 *Geologist* 2: 301–312—an early reference to the two-stage theory of tor formation.

LINTON, D. L., 'The problem of tors', 1955 *Geogr. Jour.* 121: 470–487—see also King, L. C. who discusses this paper (1958 *Ibid.* 124: 289–291).

Inselbergs:

BREMER, H., 'Ayers Rock, ein Beispiel für klimatische Morphologie', 1965 *Zeitschr. f. Geomorph.* 9: 249–284.

BUDEL, J., 'Die "Doppelten Einebnungsflächen" in den feuchten Tropen', 1957 *Zeitschr. f. Geomorph.* 1: 201–228—discusses possible origin of inselbergs.

KING, L. C., 'A theory of bornhardts', 1949 *Geogr. Jour.* 112: 83–87—an important paper.

OLLIER, C. D., 'The inselbergs of Uganda', 1960 *Zeitschr. f. Geomorph.* 4: 43–52.

—— and TUDDENHAM, W. G., 'Inselbergs of central Australia', 1962 *Zeitschr. f. Geomorph.* 5: 257–276.

SPARROW, G. W. A., 'The granitic relief of southern New England', 1961 *Austr. Geogr.* 8: 132-137.

TWIDALE, C. R., 'Contribution to the general theory of domed inselbergs', 1964 *Trans. and Papers Inst. Brit. Geogr.* 34: 91-113.

Karst landform evolution is discussed in most general textbooks on geomorphology. Specific accounts are:

JENNINGS and MABBUTT, *op. cit.* (see Jennings, J. N., 'Karst in Australia').

JENNINGS, J. N., 'Some geomorphological problems of the Nullarbor plain', 1963 *Trans. Roy. Soc. S. Austr.* 87: 41-62—description of the karst of the Nullarbor.

Helictite is a journal devoted entirely to the Australian karst; accounts of specific karst features are given in 'Australian Landform' series, *Australian Geographer*, 1963 *et seq.*

CHAPTER 5

Weathering is considered in most textbooks and many papers are concerned with it incidentally. A very useful summary is:

REICHE, P., 'Survey of weathering processes and products', 1950 *Univ. N. Mexico. Publ. in Geology* (3): 134 p.

Specific aspects of weathering are to be found in the following noteworthy papers:

BARTON, D. C., 'Notes on the disintegration of granite in Egypt', 1916 *Jour. Geol.* 24: 382-393.

BLACKWELDER, E., 'The insolation hypothesis of rock weathering', 1933 *Amer. Jour. Sci.* 26: 97-113.

GRIGGS, D. T., 'The factor of fatigue in rock exfoliation', 1936 *Jour. Geol.* 44: 625-635.

MOHR, E. C. J. and von BAREN, H., *Tropical Soils*, 498 p. van Hoewe (1959)—a useful review of weathering in the humid tropics.

OLLIER, C. D., 'Insolation weathering: examples from Central Australia', 1963 *Amer. Jour. Sci.* 261: 376-381.

WATANABE, T. *et al.*, 'Geological study of damages caused by atomic bombs in Hiroshima and Nagasaki', 1954 *Jap. Jour. Geol. and Geogr.* 24: 161-170.

CHAPTER 6
Rivers and their activities:

BAUER, A. F. T., *Availability of Stream Gauging Information in Australia*, 82 p. Dept. Nat. Dev. (1954)—contains facts and figures about Australian rivers.

DURY, G. H., *The Face of the Earth* (*loc. cit.*)—contains concise review of recent researches on rivers and their activities.

JOHNSON, D. W., 'Streams and their significance', 1932 *Jour. Geol.* 40: 481–497—old but worthwhile reading.

LEOPOLD, L. B., WOLMAN, M. G. and MILLER, J. P., *Fluvial Processes in Geomorphology*, 522 p. Freeman (1964)—most comprehensive account produced to date and refers to work by officers of the U.S. Geological Survey, published as Professional Papers.

PARDÉ, M., *Fleuves et Rivières*, 233 p. Colin (1955).

ZERNITZ, Emilie R., 'Drainage patterns and their significance', 1932 *Jour. Geol.* 40: 498–521.

Volcanic disturbances of drainage in northern Queensland are mentioned in Taylor (1911) and Twidale (1956) already cited.

Aboriginal remains near the River Murray:

HALE, H. M. and TINDALE, N. B., 'Notes on some human remains on the lower Murray valley', 1930 *Rec. S. Austr. Mus.* 4: 145–218.

MULVANEY, D. J., 'Archaeological excavations at Fromm's Landing on the Lower Murray Valley, South Australia', 1960 *Proc. Roy. Soc. Vict.* 72: 53–85.

——LAWTON, G. H. and TWIDALE, C. R., 'Archaeological excavation of rock shelter no. 6, Fromm's Landing, South Australia', 1964 *Proc. Roy. Soc. Vict.* 77: 479–516.

Landslides and related topics:

KENT, P. E., 'The transport mechanism of catastrophic rock falls', 1966 *Jour. Geol.* 74: 79–83—details some spectacular landslides.

SHARPE, C. F. S., *Landslides and Related Phenomena*, 137 p. Cooper Square Publishers (2nd ed., 1960)—an excellent summary of the processes and results of mass movement.

WASHBURN, A. L., 'Classification of patterned ground and review of suggested origins', 1965 *Geol. Soc. Amer. Bull.* 67: 823–866 —balanced and comprehensive review of a difficult and complex field.

Terraces:

AUROUSSEAU, M. and BUDGE, E. A., 'Terraces of the Swan and Helena districts . . .', 1921 *Jour. Roy. Soc. W. Austr.* 7: 24–43.

BUTLER, B. E., 'Periodic phenomena in landscapes as a basis for soil studies', 1959 *C.S.I.R.O. Soil. Publ.* 14—see also other works by this author and van Dijk, D. C., in other *C.S.I.R.O. Soils Publs.*

COTTON, C. A., 'Classification and correlation of river terraces', 1940 *Jour. Geomorph.* 3: 27–37.

GARBETT, M. S., 'Geomorphology of the Gawler River Valley', 32 p. 1963, B.A. Hons. thesis, University of Adelaide.

TWIDALE, C. R. and DAILY, B., 'Cainozoic history of the Adelaide region', *Trans. Roy. Soc. S. Austr.*: in press.

WALKER, G. T., 'Physiography of the Torrens Gorge', 60 p. 1962 B.A. Hons thesis, University of Adelaide.

CHAPTER 7
Arid regions of central Australia:

KING, D., 'The sand ridge deserts of South Australia and related aeolian landforms of the Quaternary arid cycles', 1960 *Trans. Roy. Soc. S. Austr.* 83: 99–108—a recent review.

MADIGAN, C. T., *Central Australia*, 258 p. Oxford (1936).

——, 'The Australian sand-ridge deserts', 1936 *Geogr. Rev.* 26: 205–227.

——, 'The Simpson Desert Expedition, 1939', 1945–46 *Trans. Roy. Soc. S. Austr.* 69: 188–239; 70: 45–63—this author was the first to describe systematically the arid regions of central Australia.

MOOREHEAD, Alan, *Cooper's Creek*, 223 p. Reprint Soc. edn (1965)—gives an excellent impression of the arid interior.

Desert landforms:

BAGNOLD, R. A., *The Physics of Blown Sand and Desert Dunes*, 265 p. Methuen (1941)—indispensible to any serious student.

BLISSENBACH, E., 'Geology of alluvial fans in semi-arid regions', 1954 *Geol. Soc. Amer. Bull.* 65: 175–190.

KING, L. C., 'The pediment landform—some current problems', 1949 *Geol. Mag.* 86: 245–250.

PEEL, R. F., 'Denudational landforms of the central Libyan desert', 1941 *Jour. Geomorph.* 4: 3–23.

——, 'Some aspects of desert morphology', 1960 *Geography* 45: 241–262.

——, 'The landscape in aridity', 1966 *Trans. Inst. Brit. Geogr.* 38: 1–23.

TATOR, B. A., 'Pediment characteristics and terminology', 1952 *Amer. Assoc. Geogr. Ann.* 42: 294–317; 43: 47–53.

TRICART, J. and CAILLEUX, A., *Le Modelé des Regions Sèches* (Pt 2), 179 p. C.D.U. Paris (1961)—a fine review of desert landforms.

Lake Eyre and the Nullarbor Plain:

BONYTHON, C. W. and MASON, B., 'The filling and drying of Lake Eyre', 1953 *Geogr. Jour.* 119: 321–330.

JENNINGS and MABBUTT, *op. cit.* (see Wopfner, H. and Twidale, C. R., Ch. 7, 'Geomorphological history of the Lake Eyre basin').

JOHNS, R. K. and LUDBROOK, N. H., 'Investigations of Lake Eyre', (1963) Rept. Investigation *Geol. Surv. S. Austr.* 24: 104 p.

KING, D., 'The Quaternary stratigraphic record on Lake Eyre North and the evolution of the existing topographic forms', 1956 *Trans. Roy. Soc. S. Austr.* 79: 93–103.

LUDBROOK, N. H., 'Subsurface stratigraphy of the Maralinga area', 1961 *Trans. Roy. Soc. S. Austr.* 84: 51–59—brief description of massive dune bordering northern edge of the Nullarbor Plain.

Lunettes:
BOWLER, J. M. and HARFORD, L. B., 'Quaternary tectonics and the evolution of the riverine plain near Echuca, Victoria', 1966 *Jour. Geol. Soc. Austr.* 13: 339–354—mentions age of lunettes in western Victoria.

HILLS, E. S., 'The lunette, a new landform of aeolian origin', 1940 *Austr. Geogr.* 3: 15–21.

JENNINGS, J. N., 'Le complexe de sebkhas', 1955 *Rev. Géomorph. Dynam.* 6: 69–72.

STEPHENS, C. G. and CROCKER, R. L., 'Composition and genesis of lunettes', 1946 *Trans. Roy. Soc. S. Austr.* 70: 302–312.

WOODS, J. E. T., *Geological Observations in South Australia: principally in the district southeast of Adelaide*, 404 p. Longmans Green (1862)—see pp. 27–29 for early reference to swamps and lunettes.

CHAPTER 8

Coastal geomorphology students have many fine texts of which the following are most pertinent to this book:

BASCOM, W., 'Beaches', 1960 *Sci. Amer.* 203(1)(Aug.): 80–94.

BIRD, E. C. F., *Coastal Landforms—An Introduction to Coastal Geomorphology with Australian Examples*, 193 p. A.N.U. Press (1964)—a good systematic treatment of Australian coastal forms.

—— and DENT, O. F., 'Shore platforms on the south coast of New South Wales', 1966 *Austr. Geogr.* 9: 207–217—includes description of those south of Sydney.

DAVIES, J. L., 'Wave refraction and the evolution of shoreline curves', 1958 *Geogr. Studies* 5: 1–4.

——, 'Beach alignment in southern Australia', 1960 *Austr. Geogr.* 8: 42–44.

——, 'A morphogenic approach to world shorelines', 1964 *Zeitschr. f. Geomorph.* 8: 127–142.

FAIRBRIDGE, R. W., 'Geology and geomorphology of Point Peron, Western Australia', 1947–8 *Jour. Roy. Soc. S. Austr.* 34: 35–72.

——and GILL, E. D., 'The study of eustatic changes of sea-level', 1947 *Austr. Jour. Sci.* 10: 62–67.

GUILCHER, A., *Coastal and Submarine Morphology*, 274 p. Methuen (1958)—a particularly fine text.

HAILS, J. R., 'The coastal depositional features of southeastern Queensland', 1964 *Aust. Geogr.* 9: 207–217.

HILLS, E. S., 'Shore platforms', 1949 *Geol. Mag.* 86: 137–152.
JENNINGS, J. N., 'The influence of wave action on coastal outline in plan', 1955 *Austr. Geogr.* 6: 36–44.
JUTSON, J. T., 'Shore platforms near Sydney, New South Wales', 1939 *Jour. Geomorph.* 2: 237–250.
KUENEN, P. H., *Marine Geology*, 567 p. Wiley (1950)—many chapters valuable to geomorphologists.
TEICHERT, C., 'Late Quaternary changes of sea-level at Rottnest Island, Western Australia', 1950 *Proc. Roy. Soc. Vict.* 59: 63–79.

CHAPTER 9
Evidence for the nature and distribution of climate through geological times is scattered widely through extremely diverse literature which includes:
BROOKS, C. E. P., *Climate through the Ages*, 439 p. Yale Univ. Press (1928).
CHARLESWORTH, J. T., *The Quaternary Era*, 1700 p. (2 vols) Arnold (1957)—represents a lifetime's work and is an encyclopaedic summary of the literature on the latest geological period.
SCHWARTZBACH, M., *Das Klimat der Vorzeit*, 211 p. Enke (1950).

Glacial geology and the ice age are covered in the following works:
ANON, 1954 *Arctic* 7—useful reviews of several aspects of polar geomorphology.
BELLAIR, P., 'L'antarctique, réfrigérateur du globe', 1962 *Rev. Gen. Sci.* 69: 271–276.
BOYÉ, M., *Glaciaire et Périglaciaire de l'Ata Sund, Nord-Oriental Greenland*, 176 p. Expéd. Polaires Paul-Émile Victor, Hermann (1950).
FLINT, R. F., *Glacial Geology and the Pleistocene Epoch*, 589 p. Wiley (1947).
——, *Glacial and Pleistocene Geology*, 553 p. Wiley (1957).
HOLLIN, J. T., 'On the glacial history of Antarctica', 1962 *Jour. Glac.* 4: 173–195—a study on the budget of the area.
WRIGHT, W. B., *The Quaternary Ice Age*, 464 p. Macmillan (1914).

The Journal of Glaciology is devoted exclusively to matters on glacial geomorphology, and many of the most recent results of research in Antarctica and Greenland are recorded in its various issues.

Pleistocene sea levels:
STEARNS, H. T., 'Eustatic shorelines on Pacific islands', 1961 *Zeitschr. f. Geomorph.* Suppl. 3: 3–16—a useful review.

Cirque erosion:
 BATTLE, W. R. B. and LEWIS, W. V., 'Temperature observations in bergschrunds and their relationship to cirque erosion', 1951 *Jour. Geol.* 59: 537–545.
 JOHNSON, W. D., 'The profile of maturity in Alpine glacial erosion', 1904 *Jour. Geol.* 2: 569–578.
 LEWIS, W. D., 'A meltwater hypothesis of cirque formation', 1938 *Geol. Mag.* 75: 249–265.
 ——, 'Pressure release and glacial erosion', 1954 *J. Glac.* 2: 417–422.
 —— (Ed.), *Norwegian Cirque Glaciers*, Royal. Geogr. Soc. Res. Series 4 (1960).
 RUSSELL, I. C., 'Malaspina glacier', 1893 *Jour. Geol.* 1: 219–245 —the original account of this glacier.

Reviews of the erosionist and protectionist viewpoints and references to the original literature are included in Holmes (see Bibl. 'General') and:
 WOOLDRIDGE, S. W. and MORGAN, R. S., *The Physical Basis of Geography*, 445 p. Longmans Green (1937).

Drainage diversions following glaciation are referred to in many texts citing examples in Britain, Europe and North America:
 KENDALL, P. F., 'A system of glacier-lakes in the Cleveland hills', 1902 *Quart. Jour. Geol. Soc. London* 58: 471–571—the area is in northeast England.
 SISSONS, J. B., 'Some aspects of glacial drainage channels in Britain', 1960 *Scot. Geogr. Mag.* 76: 131–146—contains important criticism of their nature and of the channels relating to the diversions.

Glaciation in Australia and adjoining areas:
 CAMPANA, B. and WILSON, R. B., 'Tillites and related glacial topography of South Australia', 1955 *Ecolog. Geol. Helv.* 48: 1–30 —cites work of earlier geologists e.g. Howchin and David.
 COTTON, C. A., 'Growing mountains and infantile islands on the western Pacific rim', 1961 *Geogr. Jour.* 127: 209–211.
 DERBYSHIRE, E. *et al.*, 'A glacial map of Tasmania', 1965 *Spec. Publ. Roy. Soc. Tas.* 2: 1–10.
 ——, 'Discussion on the glacial map of Tasmania', 1966 *Austr. Jour. Sci.* 29: 102–104.
 GAGE, M., 'New Zealand glaciations and the duration of the Pleistocene', 1961 *Jour. Glac.* 3: 940–943—discusses multi-glaciation in New Zealand.
 —— and SUGGATE, R. P., 'Glacial chronology of the New Zealand Pleistocene', 1958 *Geol. Soc. Amer. Bull.* 69: 589–598.
 GALLOWAY, R. W., 'Glaciation in the Snowy Mountains—a reappraisal', 1963 *Proc. Linn. Soc. N.S.W.* 88: 180–198.
 GLAESSNER and PARKIN, *op. cit.* (Campana, B. in Ch. 1 reviews Permian glaciation in South Australia.)

REINER, E., 'The glaciation of Mount Wilhelm, Australian New Guinea', 1960 *Geogr. Rev.* 50: 491–503.

CHAPTER 10
Changes of sea level at different periods are covered in the works listed:
General:
    DALY, R. A., *The Changing World of the Ice Age*, 271 p. Yale U.P. (1934)—worthwhile particularly on Quaternary changes in sea level.

This topic is also reviewed in KUENEN, *op .cit.* (see Bibl. Ch. 8).

High Pleistocene sea levels in the central Mediterranean:
    DEPÉRET, C., 'Essai de co-ordination chronologique général de temps quaternaires', 1918 *Acad. Sci. (Paris) Comptes rendus* 167: 418–422—original description of this classic area.
    ZEUNER, F. E., *Dating the Past*, 474 p. Methuen (2nd ed., 1949)—typical of wide support in favour of Depéret.

However, the validity of this traditional interpretation in the type area has been questioned and numerous studies have confirmed the original findings of:
    CASTANY, G. and OTTMANN, F., 'Le quaternaire marin de la Méditerranée occidentale', 1957 *Rev. Géogr. phys. et Géol. dynam.* Sér. 2, 1: 46–55.

Pleistocene and Recent sea levels in Australia:
    BAUER, F. H., *A Regional Geography of Kangaroo Island*, 712 p. Ph.D. thesis, A.N.U. (1959—copy in S. Austr. Public Library).
    BLACKBURN, G. *et al*, 'Soil development associated with stranded beach ridges in southeast South Australia', 1965 *C.S.I.R.O. Soil Publ.* 22: 66 p.
    BROCK, E. J., *The denudation chronology of the Fleurieu Peninsula*, 176 p. M.A. thesis, University of Adelaide (1964).
    GILL, E. D., 'Reports of the ANZAAS Quaternary Strandlines Committee', *Aust. Jour. Sci.*—several issues.
    HOSSFELD, P. S., 'Late Cainozoic history of the southeast of South Australia', 1950 *Trans. Roy. Soc. S. Austr.* 73: 232–279.
    JENNINGS, *loc. cit.* (1963).
    LANGFORD-SMITH, T. and HAILES, J. R., 'New evidence of Quaternary sea levels from the north coast of N.S.W.', 1966 *Aust. Jour. Sci.* 28: 325–353.
    PHIPPS, C. V. G., 'Evidence of Pleistocene warping of the New South Wales Continental Shelf', 1966 *Geological Survey Canada Paper* 66-15: 280–93 (*in* Continental Margins and Island Arcs, Rept. Symposium, Ottawa, Canada, 1965).
    SPRIGG, *op. cit.*

TWIDALE and DAILY, *loc. cit.*
WARD, *loc. cit.*
WARD, W. T. and JESSUP, R. W. *loc. cit.*

Submarine canyons and coral reef problems:
HEEZEN, B. C., 'The origin of submarine canyons', 1956 *Sci. Amer.* vol. 195 Aug: 36–41.
KUENEN, *op. cit.*
SPRIGG, R. C., 'Submarine canyons of the New Guinea and Australian coasts', 1947 *Trans. Roy. Soc. S. Austr.* 71: 296–310.
von der BORCH, C. C., 'Distribution and origin of submarine canyons off southern Australia', *Marine Geology*: in press.
——, 'South Australian submarine canyons', 1967 *Austr. Jour. Sci.* 30: 66–67.

Evidence for deducing climatic change—summary and assessment:
BUTZER, K. W., *Environment and Archaeology*, 524 p. Methuen (1965).
ZEUNER, *op. cit.*

Specific examples include:
BOWLER and HARFORD, *loc. cit.*
BUTLER, B. E., 'Theory of prior streams a causal factor in soil occurrence in the Riverine Plain of southeastern Australia', 1950 *Austr. Jour. Agric. Res.* 1: 231–252.
DURY, G. H., 'Misfit streams: problems in interpretation, discharge and distribution', 1960 *Geogr. Rev.* 50: 230–233.
——, 'Incised valley meanders on the lower Colo River, New South Wales', 1966 *Austr. Geogr.* 10: 17–25.
EMILIANI, C., 'Ancient temperatures', 1958 *Sci. Amer.* vol. 198 Feb.: 54–63.
FIRMAN, J., 'Late Cainozoic lacustrine deposits in the Murray Basin, South Australia', 1965 *Quart. Geol. Notes* (Geol. Surv. S. Austr.) 16.
FLINT, R. F. and GALE, W. A., 'Stratigraphy and radiocarbon dates at Searles Lake, California', 1958 *Amer. Jour. Sci.* 256: 689–714.
GROVE, A. T., 'The ancient erg of Hausland . . .', 1958 *Geogr. Jour.* 124: 528–533.
HOWELL, C. and BOURLIERE, F., *African Ecology and Human Evolution*, 666 p. (see pp. 230–245, Grove, A. T. and Pullam, R. A., 'Some aspects of Pleistocene palaeogeography of the Chad basin') Methuen (1964).
LANGFORD-SMITH, T., 'The dead river systems of the Murrumbidgee', 1960 *Geogr. Rev.* 50: 368–389.
LHOTE, H., *The Search for the Tassili Frescoes*, 236 p. Hutchinson (1959).
PELS, S., 'Late Quaternary chronology of the Riverine Plain of southeastern Australia', 1966 *Jour. Geol. Soc. Austr.* 13: 27–40.

References and Suggested Further Reading 365

CHAPTER 11
Peneplains, pediplains and associated features:
    BAULIG, H., 'Peneplains and pediplains' (Trans. Cotton, C. A.), 1957 *Geol. Soc. Amer. Bull.* 68: 913–930.
    CRICKMAY, C. H., 'The later stages of the cycle of erosion', 1933 *Geol. Mag.* 70: 337–347.
    DAVIS, W. M., *op. cit.*
    DURY, G. H., 'Duricrusted residuals on the Barrier and Cobar pediplains of New South Wales', 1966 *Geol. Soc. Austr. Jour.* 13: 299–307.
    —— and LANGFORD-SMITH, T., 'The use of the term *peneplain* in descriptions of Australian landscapes', 1964 *Austr. Jour. Sci.* 27: 171–175.
    HILLS, E. S., 'Die landoberflache Australiens', 1955 *Erde* 86: 197–295.
    JENNINGS and MABBUTT, *op. cit.* (Ch. 6, Twidale, C. R., 'Hillslopes and pediments in the southern Flinders Ranges'.)
    KING, L. C., *loc. cit.* (1953).
    MABBUTT, J. A., 'A stripped land surface in Western Australia', 1961 *Trans. and Papers Inst. Brit. Geogr.* 29: 101–114.
    OPIK, A. A., 'Geology and palaeontology of the headwaters of the Burke River, Queensland', 1961 *Bur. Min. Res. Geol. and Geophys. Bull.* 53: 249 p.
    TRENDALL, A. F., 'The formation of "apparent peneplains" by a process of combined lateritisation and surface wash', 1962 *Zeitschr. f. Geomorph.* 6: 183–197.
    TWIDALE, C. R., 'Origin of the piedmont angle', 1967 *Jour. Geol.* 75: 393-411.

CHAPTER 12
General references for this chapter include:
    DAVIS, *op. cit.*
    KING, *op. cit.*
    PENCK, *op. cit.*
Steady state theory and the relative rates of tectonism and denudation:
    BRETZ, J. H., 'Dynamic equilibrium and the Ozark landforms', 1962 *Amer. Jour. Sci.* 260: 427–438.
    CRICKMAY, C. H., *A preliminary inquiry into the formulation and applicability of the geological principle of uniformity*, 50 p. Private Publ., Calgary (1959). But see also JUNGERIUS, P. D., 'Age and origin of the Cypress Hills plateau surface in Alberta', 1966 *Geogr. Bull.* 8: 307–318.

GILLULY, J., 'Distribution of mountain building in geological time', 1949 *Geol. Soc. Amer. Bull.* 60: 561–590.
——, 'Geologic contrasts between continents and ocean basins', 1955 *Geol. Soc. Amer. Spec. Paper* 62: 7-18.
HACK, J. T., *loc. cit.*: 80–97.
KENNEDY, W. Q., 'Some theoretical factors in geomorphological analysis', 1962 *Geol. Mag.* 99: 304–312.
MENARD, H. W., *loc. cit.*: 154–161.
SCHUMM, S. A., *op. cit.*
WAHRHAFTIG, C., 'Stepped topography of the southern Sierra Nevada, California', 1965 *Geol. Soc. Amer. Bull.* 76: 1165–1190.

Multicyclic landscapes:
ALLEY, N. F., 'Cainozoic history of the middle Broughton drainage basin', 119 p. 1967, B.A. Hons. thesis, University of Adelaide.
BAULIG, H., *Le plateau central et sa bordure méditerranéenne*, 590 p., Colin (1928).
CRAFT, F. A., 'The coastal tablelands and streams of New South Wales', 1933 *Proc. Linn. Soc. N.S.W.* 58: 437–460.
DAVIES, J. L., 'High level erosion surfaces and landscape development in Tasmania', 1959 *Austr. Geogr.* 7: 193–204.
FENNER, C., *South Australia, a Geographical Study*, 325 p. Whitcombe and Tombs (1931).
KING, L. C., *op. cit.*
LANGFORD-SMITH, T., DURY, G. and McDOUGALL, I., 'Dating of the Duricrust in southern Queensland', 1966 *Austr. Jour. Sci.* 29: 79–80 (but see also EXON, N. F., MILLIGAN, E. N. and DAY, R. W., 'Dating the duricrust in southern Queensland', 1967 *Austr. Jour. Sci.* 30, p. 110).
—— and DURY, G., 'Distribution, character and attitude of the duricrust in the northwest of New South Wales and the adjacent areas of Queensland', 1965 *Amer. Jour. Sci.* 263: 179–190.
MABBUTT, J. A., 'The weathered land surface in central Australia', 1965 *Zeitschr. f. Geomorph.* 9: 82–114.
TWIDALE, C. R., 'Chronology of denudation in northwest Queensland', 1956 *Geol. Soc. Amer. Bull.* 67: 867–882.
——, 'Chronology of denudation in the Southern Flinders Ranges', 1966 *Trans. Roy. Soc. S. Austr.* 90: 3–28.
VOISEY, A. H., 'Erosion surfaces around Armidale, N.S.W.', 1957 *Jour. Roy. Soc. N.S.W.* 90: 128–133.
WOOLDRIDGE, S. W. and LINTON, D. L., *Structure surface and drainage in southeast England*, 176 p. Phillip (2nd ed., 1955).

WRIGHT, R. L., 'Deep weathering and erosion surfaces in the Daly River basin, Northern Territory', 1963 *Jour. Geol. Soc. Austr.* 10: 151–164.

Other surfaces of low relief in Australia are described in the *Land Research Series*, Div. Land. Research, C.S.I.R.O., Melbourne.

CHAPTER 13

Key references on the effect of man on the physiographic landscape are:

DARBY, H. C., *Draining of the Fens*, 312 p. C.U.P. (1940)—man's elimination of swamps and shallow lakes.

JACKS, G. V. and WHYTE, R. O., *The Rape of the Earth*, 313 p. Faber (1939).

LAMBERT, J. *et al.*, 'The making of the Broads', 1960 *Roy. Geogr. Soc.* (London), *Res. Series.* (3): 153 p.—a classic instance of a major example of man made features, until recently unsuspected.

SHARPE, C. E. S., 'Geomorphic aspects of normal and accelerated erosion', 1941 *Trans. Amer. Geophys. Union:* 236–240.

THOMAS, W. L. Jr (Ed.), *Man's Role in Changing the Face of the Earth*, 1193 p. Chicago U.P. (1956).

Others of interest for the Australian reader include:

JENNINGS, J. N., 'Man as a geological agent', 1965 *Austr. Jour. Sci.* 28: 150–156.

WILLIAMS, M., 'Historical geography of an artificial drainage system: the lower southeast of South Australia', 1964 *Austr. Geogr. Stud.* 2: 87–102.

APPENDIX

A. Regional Subdivision of South Australia

South Australia occupies an area of 380,000 square miles or some 12·8 per cent of the total area of the Australian continent. For purposes of description the State has been divided into 17 physiographic regions (Fig. 8):

(a) Arid uplands
    (i) Ranges of the Northwest
    (ii) Peake and Denison Ranges
    (iii) Arcoona plateau
    (iv) Gawler Ranges
    (v) Flinders Ranges
    (vi) Olary upland
(b) Arid plains
    (i) Great Victoria Desert
    (ii) Lake plains
    (iii) Nullarbor plain
(c) Semi-arid uplands
    (i) The Mid-north
    (ii) Mt Lofty Ranges
    (iii) Kangaroo Island
(d) Semi-arid plains
    (i) Eyre Peninsula
    (ii) Yorke Peninsula
    (iii) Murray plains
    (iv) The Southeast
    (v) Gulf plains

Each of these will be described. The detail included in each account varies, partly because of our relative ignorance of some areas, but in some measure to avoid repetition, certain regions having been considered in whole or in part and in various contexts, in previous chapters.

(a) ARID UPLANDS
(i) Ranges of the Northwest
In Precambrian times a complex series of igneous intrusions were emplaced in what are now the Musgrave, Everard, Mann and Birksgate ranges—the Ranges of the Northwest. These and other rocks were compressed from east and west so that ancient structural trends run north-south. The ancient uplands were eroded and the sediments so derived

were laid down in the ancient ocean and became part of the great Adelaide geosyncline. The rocks of this trough were disturbed and contorted during a period of mountain building which occurred in the early Palaeozoic. The compression dating from this phase came primarily from north and south so that the principal structures of this period have a strong east-west trend which is imposed upon the ranges themselves. It seems likely that the ranges have been uplands more-or-less throughout geological time. They have been worn down and thrust up again several times. What we see today are the remnants of a once much higher and extensive mountain range.

The ranges run discontinuously from near the main north-south highway westward to the Western Australian border and beyond. The Musgrave, Everard, Mann and Tomkinson ranges are all part of the same geological unit, as are the numerous isolated nubbins and hills both to the south and north of the main ranges. The ranges are surrounded on all sides by flat plains which stand at an elevation of 1,700 to 2,000 feet above present sea level. Longitudinal sand dunes traverse many of these plains from which the ranges protrude abruptly. They quite commonly rise to elevations of three and four thousand feet, and occasionally higher. The highest point in South Australia, the peak of Mount Woodroffe (4,970 feet) is in the Musgrave Range.

In the east, the ranges are drained by intermittently flowing streams such as the Alberga and its tributaries which carry waters towards and sometimes into Lake Eyre. The Officer is the largest of several rivers which occasionally flow southwards from the ranges into the Great Victoria Desert. Its channel is lined by river gums because there is a good underflow (or underground flow of water) in the river sands, but surface flows are rare. Indeed, the Officer has not flowed beyond the upper 30 to 40 miles during recorded history. Most of the streams flowing either to the deserts or into inter-range valleys die soon after reaching the plains. These streams have laid down low-angle alluvial fans which are of limited area, probably because the upland areas drained by the streams are so comparatively small. The fans are not as conspicuous, as those found in other desert regions nor as those which front the southern Flinders and Mt Lofty Ranges. However, the streams have contributed, together with the wind, to the considerable thicknesses of unconsolidated debris which is found in the valleys: in the Musgraves, for instance, the flat valley floors are in places underlain by up to 150 feet of red alluvium which masks an undulating rock floor.

The forms displayed by the various ranges differ according to their construction. Many of the ranges are built of granite or granitic rocks. Some, such as the Everard and Birksgate ranges are made of massive blocks of granite, each major block being about half a mile in diameter. Each block has been weathered and eroded to the form of a great dome, and the east-west trending ranges comprise a series of such rounded domes. Weathering has evidently proceeded most rapidly along major joints and these domes must thus be seen as massive tors. The domes display thick sheets of granite, those at the surface having broken into a series of subrounded joint blocks, some of which display caverns on the undersides. On the surface of the domes there is development of arid crust, and abundant scaling of the rock. There are also many flat-floored gnammas or pans. There are spectacular domes also at Mitchells Nob, in the northern Musgrave Range.

Throughout most of the Musgrave Range, however, there are pointed straight-sloped ridges, shaped rather like the ridge of a roof, which rise from the alluviated valleys. These too are of granite but the rock here is broken into numerous small joint blocks. Only bare rock is exposed in the steep ridge sides. Similar forms occur in the Tomkinson Range where, in addition to the granitic rocks there are considerable exposures of basic[1] crystalline rocks. They too form roof-like hills and are remarkable for the angular blocks of rock which are strewn over their slopes. There are a few minor bluffs coincident with the outcrop of especially tough bands of rock.

In the Indulkana Range, east of the Everards, sedimentary rocks give rise to plateau and cuesta forms according to their disposition.

Scattered over a wide area to the south and north of the principal uplands, isolated islands of rock stand starkly above the sandy plains. Mount Conner (a mesa of quartzite), and Ayers Rock and the Olgas (domes of arkosic sandstone and conglomerate respectively), are well known examples to the north, in the Northern Territory. Also beyond the border are the Kulgera Hills, a scattering of isolated low-rounded granite hills, with well developed gnammas. Between the main ranges and Great Victoria Desert proper are numerous inselbergs, such as Mt Tietkins, Mt Harcus and Bowden Hill, to name but a few, taking several forms according to the nature of the local rock, but all rising steeply from the plain. The plain is mostly a sea of sand, but in some areas remnants persist of a once widespread duricrusted plain. This, plus the presence of Tertiary lake limestones beneath the Officer Basin plains, shows that the Ranges of the northwest were developed during, and are residual from early Tertiary times or even earlier.

(ii) Peake and Denison Ranges

Between 30 and 100 miles south of Oodnadatta, on the western margin of the Lake Eyre basin (Figs. 9, 248) occur several ridges which though small in area and low in elevation, nevertheless contrast strongly with the flatness and monotony of the surrounding plains. These are the Peake and Denison Ranges which are built of Archaean and Proterozoic rocks. They were involved in the Adelaide geosyncline and are similar to the ranges of greater extent to the northwest. The Ranges stand up to 1,000 feet above than the surrounding plains which are at an elevation of 200 to 400 feet above sea level. The surrounding plains consist of the flood plains of the Neales and Peake rivers which flow to Lake Eyre, and sand dunes which trend northwest to southeast. The uplands consist essentially of a series of cuestas with a gentle western slope and a steep eastern face. The height of many of the crests is similar. The eastern face of the Ranges as a whole is straight and steep and is a fault scarp.

On the western side of the Ranges, there are many flat-topped hills of sandstones, probably Jurassic, which have a ferruginous capping. The surrounding mesas and plains have a mantle of gibber on which desert varnish is well developed.

The ancient Precambrian rocks were involved in folding with marked north-northwest to south-southeast axes. Subsequently the north and south pressures which so strongly influenced the Ranges of the northwest also affected the Peake and Denison Ranges, causing some faulting. During the later Mesozoic it is possible that the uplands were buried by sediments. After the Jurassic and Cretaceous, the Ranges were exhumed. It seems likely that the possible old erosion surface indicated by the evenness of the Peake and Denison skyline is of pre(?) Jurassic age (Fig. 248). Since the Cretaceous, there has been duricrusting, regional doming (the Cretaceous rocks dip outwards in all directions) and faulting. The eastern face of the Ranges is so little dissected that some of this faulting must have occurred recently.

Thus, in the Peake and Denison Ranges, there is evidence of three stages of erosion, each separated by a phase of earth movements and of:

(1) The pre Cretaceous or Jurassic plain surface which is present atop the Ranges, and which is found also beneath the sediments around the Ranges.

(2) The Tertiary duricrusted surface which is present on the Jurassic and Cretaceous rocks and above which stood the Ranges.

(3) The present plains which are extending along rivers roughly east to west, and growing at the expense of the other two surfaces, particularly the Tertiary.

(iii) Arcoona plateau

This is a dissected plateau located on the western or Shield side of the Lake Torrens salina. Isolated remnants of the plateau extend as far south as Lincoln Gap and Whyalla. It is developed on flat-lying flaggy sandstones and quartzites of Precambrian age. The landform assemblages displayed consist of repetitions of the plateau, mesa and butte forms bounded by steep slopes like those described from the Lincoln Gap region (Chapter 4 (a), Figs. 67, 69–72). The pronounced linear escarpment which delimits the plateau on its eastern side is probably a dissected fault scarp.

The plateau surface generally lies below 1000 feet above sea level and almost everywhere is much lower (400–600 feet), though north of Whyalla it attains 1200 feet. Although the underlying strata are flat-lying, the plateau surface in detail cuts across individual beds and is therefore of erosional origin. Evidence from the southern extremity of Lake Torrens suggests that the surface of low relief is of considerable antiquity. A well-developed silcrete profile is preserved on remnants of a lowland surface situated some 700–750 feet below the plateau and some 50 feet above the bed of Lake Torrens (which in turn lies 112 feet above sea level). If the silcrete is of similar age to the duricrust of the northeast of South Australia and adjacent parts of Queensland and New South Wales then this lower surface is of mid Tertiary age and the much higher plateau even older.

(iv) Gawler Ranges

The Gawler Range porphyry outcrops extensively in an area to the north of Eyre Peninsula. The rock, which is of volcanic origin, is some 1,535 million years old. It is called a porphyry because larger feldspar and quartz crystals are set in a groundmass or matrix, the details of which are not discernible to the naked eye. Though variable, the rock has a reddish hue, which is imposed on the bare hills of the Ranges.

The principal ranges and valleys within the upland trend east to west, though Lake Gairdner, which is probably an alluviated valley system, runs meridionally. As is the case in the Everard Ranges, it may be that strong east-west fractures cause these dispositions, but the major joints run northwest-southeast and northeast-southwest, a trend imposed on minor valleys. The western border of the Ranges is a pronounced topographical feature running northwest to southeast parallel to one of the prominent joint directions; projected to the southeast, it is seen to be part of a possible lineament trend.

The uplands rise to more than 1,500 feet in such hills as Nuckey Bluff and Mt Yardea, where the relief amplitude is about 1,000 feet. Most of the hills are lower, and are broadly rounded. However, in detail the slopes are rough and rocky, and many remnants of polygonal columns (which presumably mark the sites of ancient vents), crop out on the hill slopes. Some scarps are distinctly faceted, with high bluffs, and here polygonal joint columns are commonly displayed. In a small area 7 to 8 miles east of Yardea Homestead sheeting has been observed in the porphyry. Most of the hills are of similar elevation, and several are flat-topped. These high plains are remarkably smooth, being surmounted only by occasional isolated joint blocks; they display no sign of deep chemical weathering, the rock at the surface being essentially fresh. These are remnants of a former erosional surface, but it cannot as yet be determined whether they are of pediplain or peneplain type, or of etch plain character. By correlation with the adjacent Arcoona plateau it appears likely that the surface is of at least early Tertiary age.

No permanent streams now flow in the Ranges. The valleys of the hills, in their detailed morphology, are profoundly influenced by structure—the side walls are composed of angular joint blocks. The rivers, which excavated and are eroding these valleys, flow only intermittently. They debouch on to the main valleys and adjacent plains, where they flow for a short distance before disappearing. They carry coarse debris to the upland borders, and sand and clay (derived from the weathering of the porphyry) to the main valleys which are thereby filled, in some instances to depths of more than 200 feet. This is one reason for the abrupt junction between hill and plain. It is possible that in former times, permanently flowing streams moulded the surface of the Ranges but there is no evidence on this point.

Lake Gairdner is only the largest of several salinas located within or at the margins of the Gawler Ranges. The salt surface displays several minor forms related to expansion and contraction of the salt crust, and there are red dunes up to 50 feet high at the margins of the Lake bed. The outline of Gairdner is influenced by jointing, and the same is true of several other of the salinas, e.g. Lake Gillies.

(v) Flinders Ranges

The Flinders Ranges form an upland finger of semi-aridity surrounded to east, west and north by truly arid plains. The Ranges rise abruptly from these desert lowlands, to elevations almost 4,000 feet above sea level in St Mary Peak in the central part of the upland. The highest peaks occur in this central area around Wilpena. To the south, the upland is greatly dissected, and there are considerable areas of intermontane plain. To the north, plains are less extensive, and the general elevation of the land is therefore much higher. The uplands are drained by rivers which flow to four distinct baselevels. In the south, a small area of the Flinders Ranges is drained by tributaries of the Broughton which flows to Spencer Gulf. In the north, a number of small streams, including the Frome and the Mundy, flow to Lake Eyre; by far the greater part of the Ranges is drained by rivers which flow either to Lake Torrens or to Lake Frome. Generally speaking, the southern part of the upland drains to Lake Torrens, via rivers such as the Willochra and the Hookina, while the northern part drains to Lake Frome by way of such waterways as Big John Creek, the Hamilton and the Siccus-Wilpena system which, it should be noted, rises less than 2 miles from the Lake Torrens plains.

The upland originated in Precambrian times, when a great thickness of sediments was laid down in a great trough, the Adelaide geosyncline, extending from Kangaroo Island in the south to the far north of the State and beyond. The great wedge of sediments deposited in this trough, was, in early Palaeozoic times, compressed, with the result that the strata suffered gentle folding and considerable faulting. The landscape we see today is the result of differential weathering and erosion of the lithologically varied folded strata. In large measure, therefore, the landscape of the Flinders Ranges is a structural landscape, though in some areas, as in the Paralana fault scarp, the underlying structures are directly expressed in the relief and must therefore be identified as of tectonic origin.

Streams are, and apparently always have been, the principal agents of erosion, and moisture the principal agent of weathering. It is due to water exploiting the weaknesses of the exposed bedrock that the pattern of relief we see today has developed. However, wind plays a considerable part in evacuating the finer products of weathering from the upland, and the occurrence of fixed longitudinal dunes suggests that in the recent geologic past, aeolian activities were even more important.

The etching out of the landscape has not proceeded at an even pace, for there is evidence in the form of old erosional surfaces of low relief, and of dissected valley floors, of periods of relative landscape stability separated by phases of renewed and intense dissection. The general chronology of denudation in the Ranges involves three major cycles or phases of erosion. The first is of Mesozoic age and is best represented by the plateau surface of the northern Flinders Ranges, though remnants of what appears to be the same surface occur in the central and southern Flinders Ranges—in the Wilpena Pound (Edeowie Gorge area) and to the north of Dutchmans Stern (near Quorn). Prolonged erosion during the early Tertiary resulted in the development of extensive valley floors only a little higher than the present valleys and plains; and then, during the Quaternary, renewed dissection resulted in the development of the modern landscape. Several thousand feet of sediment have been removed during this prolonged erosion and in some areas inversion of relief has taken place.

(vi) Olary Upland

This region comprises a broad low ridge standing between the Murray plains to the south and the Lake Frome plains to the north. It is underlain by folded crystalline and sedimentary rocks of Precambrian age, and drained by intermittently flowing streams running south-southeast and north-northwest.

Relief is not great. The upland falls from about 1,750 feet in the vicinity of Peterborough, to just under 700 feet near the N.S.W. border. Within the upland, the highest hills (cuestas on gently dipping strata), domes associated with crystalline granitic rocks, and isolated remnants of circumdenudation, stand no more than 600 feet above the general level of the high plains which form the greater part of this region.

The presence of intensely weathered strata on the high plain suggests that it is an erosional surface (possible of etch plain character) developed possibly during the Tertiary and subsequently uplifted by regional arching, and dissected particularly at the northern and southern margins.

(b) ARID PLAINS
(i) Great Victoria Desert
The Great Victoria Desert is not well known, but the principal features appear to be similar to those of the Simpson Desert in the Lake plains region. In addition to the other landforms mentioned in connection with the Simpson, there are, particularly toward the northern and south-eastern margins of this desert, many low outcrops of granite and porphyry, usually taking the form of low whalebacks or clusters of tors. Mobing Rock and Mulgathing Rocks are large granite whalebacks. That crystalline rocks are not far beneath the sand surface is shown by their frequent occurrence in the floors of playas. Toward the eastern margin of the desert appear numerous residual mesas and plateaux, essentially built of granite but capped by Mesozoic strata similar to those that outcrop more extensively to the east.

There is only a veneer of sand covering a surface of low relief eroded across rocks of various types and of ages. They vary from Archaean over most of the area, to early Palaeozoic and Permian at the southern margin, and Tertiary in the Officer basin in the north. There is little evidence on the point, but what there is suggests that over much of the desert, apart from the eastern margin (the plain which rises gently from south to north from about 600 to about 2,000 feet above sea level) could well be essentially that upon which were deposited the Mesozoic and Tertiary rocks, which occur toward the eastern and southern margins of the desert. On the south margin the Tertiary sediments of the Eucla basin thin quite gradually and sections show that there is very little difference between the slope of the surface and that of the bedrock surface upon which the sediments were laid down. It is likely that the plain, upon which longitudinal dunes have been formed by the wind, is of very great antiquity.

Longitudinal dunes prevail over most of the desert. They trend east-west and consist of red sand. They are up to 60 feet high and extend continuously for up to 100 miles. There are between two and four dunes to the mile in a transverse section. At the southern margin of the desert, which covers some 70,000 square miles in South Australia alone, where the desert meets the Nullarbor plain, there are great accumulations of sand up to 500 feet high. The dunes bear a cover of sparse vegetation. There are numerous claypans and salinas, of which Lake Maurice is the largest.

The sands of the Great Victoria Desert are derived from the weathering of the rocks of the Shield and its several basins, and from alluvium derived from uplands and spread over the plains by a formerly extensive drainage system of which only a few discontinuous remnants remain, in the form of salinas.

(ii) Lake plains

The Lake plains consist of lowlands draining to Lakes Eyre, Torrens and Frome. Each of these drainage basins is a broad tectonic feature, each being an area of subsidence. All three have certain elements in common. Each focuses upon a dry lake bed or salina. All three of the major salinas appear to be of tectonic origin, being delineated, in part at least, by known and active faults. In each, sandy deserts of long parallel dunes form a prominent part of the landform assemblage. In the Simpson Desert to the north of Lake Eyre, the dunes are actively developing, and the same is true of the Tirari Desert at the northern extremity of the Lake Frome basin; but in many parts of the Lake Frome and Lake Torrens lowland, the longitudinal dunes are now fixed. In each of these plains, stony desert or gibber plain is an important component. In each case, the desert landscape is of Recent age, the best evidence for this coming from the Simpson Desert region where the sands rest upon fossiliferous lake clays which are probably of late Pleistocene or early Recent Age. In all three regions, however, there are remains of older landscapes: in the Torrens and Frome basins, outliers of the Flinders Ranges, and in the northeast, extensive remains of the folded Miocene duricrust.

(iii) Nullarbor plain (see Chapter 4)

This is a covered karst owing its desert character partly to the dominant limestone lithology and partly to climatic aridity. The surface is virtually featureless, but beneath the plain are extensive cave systems. The most spectacular feature of the plain is the rugged cliffed coast.

(c) SEMI-ARID UPLANDS
(i) The Mid-north

The Mid-north region extends from south of Melrose, where the Flinders Ranges may be said to terminate, as far as Gawler and the Barossa Valley. It forms a broad upland, intervening between the Murray plains on the east and the Gulf plains and Yorke Peninsula to the west. The border with the plains is everywhere distinct, taking the form of abrupt escarpments. The southern boundary with the Mount Lofty Ranges is sharp, for there is a high, steep escarpment; but in the north, the border between the Flinders and the Mid-north is gradational. The region forms part of the Adelaide geosyncline which suffered general folding and faulting in the early or middle Palaeozoic. The various structures have been differentially weathered and eroded, with the result that the topography at present consists of narrow north-south trending ridges underlain by quartzite and separating broad, open and shallow valleys underlain for the most part by argillaceous bedrock. This meridional trend is only regional, and in detail there are departures from it according to the disposition of the underlying beds. The region is drained by the Burra, the Broughton and the North Para systems, all of which flow only intermittently. In each case the major stream sectors are of strike character with the connecting consequent or obsequent sectors developed through capture.

Although the topography of the Mid-north is superficially simple and straightforward, detailed examination has revealed considerable complexity. In the Broughton and Barossa Valleys are preserved extensive deposits of Tertiary lacustrine sediments analagous with those of the Willochra basin to the north and with the Golden Grove-Highbury region to the south. Both in the Broughton and in the Barossa, the lake sediments are of Miocene age (in contrast with the two other areas mentioned where the lacustrine sediments are Eocene). But in and around these Tertiary depositional areas, the landscape history is complex. There are remnants of pre Miocene surface, of a Miocene duricrusted surface, and of a late Tertiary-Quaternary plain of erosion. The Miocene duricrusted surface tends to be silicified at lower topographic levels, though lateritic remnants occur high on some of the ridges, e.g. near Kapunda. Thus one must visualise the present topography pattern as persisting through long geological periods. In the middle Tertiary, earth movements caused the impounding of quite extensive lakes, and during the Miocene the area was baselevelled and extensively weathered; at this stage, the ridges stood only a few feet above the general plain level. Subsequently renewed dissection has caused the development of a greater relief amplitude, the dissection of a large part of the Miocene surface, and the development of a new plain of erosion and, at the same time, the re-exposure of small areas which represent the pre Miocene landscape.

(ii) Mt Lofty Ranges

The Mt Lofty Ranges are part of the Adelaide geosyncline, but the predominant features of the region are due to block faulting (see Fig. 56). The whole of the horst block comprises a number of faulted blocks, but only at the margins has there been late Cainozoic dislocation which is expressed directly in the landscape. During the late Tertiary an extensive lateritised surface of erosion developed in the Ranges (see Fig. 251.) Considered with the evidence of faulting the general interpretation is that this plain of erosion developed close to regional baselevel, and was subsequently up-thrust along ancient fault lines; and it is now suffering marginal dissection. The difficulty with this interpretation is that no down-faulted lateritised remnants have so far been discovered, either exposed or in bores, and the possibility must be considered of the laterite developing in relation to lower rather than regional baselevel. In other words, the deep weathering may have been aided by the uplift of the land, thus providing an easier passage for the ground waters and thus enabling a much greater depth of weathering to develop. But whatever its origin, this lateritised peneplain is a predominant feature of the ranges. The smooth skyline behind Adelaide is due to this peneplain and even more extensive remnants are to be found in the south in the Fleurieu Peninsula. The peneplain is surmounted by only a few residual remnants (monadnocks) such as Mt Lofty, Mt Gawler and Mt Gould.

The other important events which determine the present topography are both related to glaciation. In the south, and particularly in the Inman Valley, small remnants of the Permian glaciated landscape have been exhumed and from extensive parts of the southern Mt Lofty Ranges, prominent glacial and fluvial glacial deposits can rise to characteristic landforms (in particular they are especially susceptible to gullying and to land slips and landslides). During the Pleistocene glaciation, as mentioned in Chapter 9, there were considerable variations of sea level. These ancient stands of the sea are alleged to have left their imprint on the present borders of the Mt Lofty upland. In particular, various flights of marine plains and benches are claimed from the Fleurieu Peninsula, and from an area south of Adelaide. But as indicated previously (Chapter 10), the evidence for the age and origin of some of these undoubtedly planate features is dubious and some at least may be of pre Pliocene age. In other words these marine features, if they are such, owe their present elevation not so much to Quaternary sea level movements, but to uplift.

(iii) Kangaroo Island
Kangaroo Island is very similar to many parts of the Mt Lofty Ranges. It consists of a lateritised plateau developed on Precambrian and Cambrian rocks; the plateau is known to be bordered, in part at least, by faults and the plateau has been extensively dissected at the margins. As is the case with the Mt Lofty Ranges, various planate features in these marginal zones have been interpreted as due to Quaternary high sea levels. In the north of the Island there is evidence of later Tertiary volcanism.

(d) SEMI-ARID PLAINS
(i) Eyre Peninsula
Surface occurrences of ancient rocks which underlie the whole of Eyre Peninsula are widespread only in the east of the area. The Peninsula is a resistant block and part of the great West Australian Shield, and very old rocks outcrop extensively in the kite-shaped area between Sleaford Bay, Buckleboo, Pandurra Homestead and Whyalla. The Archaean rocks consist of folded sediments, including quartzites, and metamorphic rocks

such as gneisses and schists. They have been strongly folded and faulted with the fold axes and fault strikes trending predominantly north-south, though there are also major northeast to southwest trends. After this phase of earth movements, Proterozoic rocks were laid down on a broad and extensive coastal shelf. It is believed that these sediments, consisting of very thick beds of sandstones, are related to the quartzites and other rocks laid down in the Adelaide geosyncline to the east of Eyre Peninsula. These shelf deposits have not been disturbed to any great extent. They rest horizontally or nearly so, and occur in the Lincoln Gap region in the far northeast of the Peninsula, though they persist to the north and remain little dissected in the Arcoona plateau.

During the early Precambrian (1,960 to 1,800 million years ago) granites were intruded over wide areas of the west and northwest of Eyre Peninsula, and volcanic flows (or shallow intrusions in the form of horizontal sheets or sills) were extruded in the north of the Peninsula about 1,500 million years ago—the Gawler Range porphyry.

The only rocks of an age later than lower Palaeozoic are small deposits of early Tertiary sediments in the shallow Cummins basin and in coastal areas; and the extensive but thin superficial deposits of siliceous sand and limestone which blanket most of the centre and west of the Peninsula. Though thin, they are of considerable geomorphological importance.

To a very large extent the topography of Eyre Peninsula is a direct reflection of the nature and structure of the underlying bedrock. The Archaean rocks of the east and south project abruptly and high above the level of the adjacent plains to elevations of up to 1,200 feet. The quartzites form the high points of the relief and give rise to cuesta and hogback forms; but high rather steeply inclined slopes leading up to only slightly rounded ridge crests and peaks are characteristic of the Archaean rocks. Many of the ridges and peaks in the Archaean are underlain by synclinal structures. Where there are gneisses, slightly rounded joint blocks occur. The subhorizontally disposed Proterozoic sandstones form plateaux and mesas (or tent hills) according to the degree of dissection. They form some of the highest areas on the Peninsula, rising to well over 1,200 feet at Corunna and commonly achieving levels of 600 or 700 feet close to the Spencer Gulf shore. These table-top hills display steep sides with precipitous high bluffs, and there are typical examples near Lincoln Gap (Fig. 67a).

The Archaean rocks are greatly faulted. Many of the faults, which run north-south, are still active. Differential movement along them has caused the development of many fault scarps, ranging in height between 5 and 50 feet, in unconsolidated rocks which have been laid down on top of the old Archaean strata but which have been affected by the displacement of the ancient rocks. Most of the uplands of eastern and southern Eyre Peninsula are associated with the outcrop of the Archaean. For instance the Marble Range, a synclinal structure, in the far south of the Peninsula, rises abruptly from the plains to a height of more than 1,000 feet.

There are only a few outcrops of solid rock in the centre and west of the Peninsula. These are predominantly of granite, which give rise to low whalebacks or steep sided inselbergs. In detail, they display many typical granitic landforms which were formerly important on account of the opportunity they offered for water conservation schemes. Many of the bare hills have been enclosed by low stone walls which prevent water from running into the sands of the surrounding plains and divert it into tanks or excavated reservoirs. Before the Tod River water was piped to the northwestern area, such water supplies (e.g. in Wudinna, Ucontitchie, and Pildappa hills, Yarwondutta Rocks) were very important, and the granite formed local early foci of settlement.

For the most part, central and western Eyre Peninsula consists of an undulating plain. It is not to be explained in terms of the nature and structure of the underlying granite, porphyry and Archaean rocks which, borings show, underly the plain at only shallow depths. The plain, rising from the coastal beaches, dunes and cliffs up to 700 feet above sea level, and rising to the north and centre of the Peninsula from the coast, has to be explained in other ways.

The plain of western and central Eyre Peninsula is underlain by a variety of bedrock. The presence of quite high hills scattered over the surface of the plain shows that considerable thicknesses of rock has been eroded from the west and centre. The plain that has been left is the result of long-continued erosion. It formed before the great system of dunes which now traverse its surface developed. A plain of its extent must have been excavated by a system of streams of which little sign now remains. Above the level of the plain there stand isolated ridges and domes of granite and other rocks, called inselbergs.

There are signs that long before this plain of low relief developed there was another plain formed on the Peninsula, for remnants of it, deeply and intensely weathered in places, remain as prominent features of the landscape. In the south for example there is a dissected plateau capped by laterite on the western side of and lower than the higher parts of the Archaean Ranges (Fig. 252). The dissected plateau which now stands between 500 and 750 feet above sea level, slopes gently down to the west and is part of what was formerly an extensive plain of low relief. It is noteworthy that in the Cummins basin there are some 450 feet of sediments of early Tertiary age which were deposited apparently in a marine lagoon close to the shoreline. Some of the sediments may have been derived from the early stages of cutting this former plain.

Many of the granite inselbergs of the northwest of Eyre Peninsula have flattish tops, and they lend support to the theory that there was formerly a higher plain of low relief extending over much of the area.

Moreover, very close to the centre of the Peninsula is Central Mount Wedge, a flat-topped remnant of folded Archaean quartzites and probably yet another remnant of the high plain. This former plain has since been greatly dissected and the deeply weathered bedrock beneath the then surface, eroded. The present erosional plain has grown and extended at its expense.

The weathered, lateritic high plain developed during Tertiary times for it was apparently disrupted by faulting and in the northeast marine sediments of Pliocene age are deposited at the foot of the fault scarps, so that the plain that was faulted must be older. The planation of the centre and west must therefore have been accomplished during the Pliocene and Quaternary. In addition, during this same period, the plain was blanketed with siliceous sand, in the northwest and centre, and with calcarous sand in a 30-mile wide belt on the west coast between Streaky Bay and Coffin Bay.

The siliceous sand dunes are continuous with those of the Great Victoria Desert. They trend northwest to southeast except in the vicinity of uplands where local winds determine the dune trend. They are now fixed, and obviously formed during an earlier period when, because there was less rainfall, there was less vegetation and the land surface was prone to wind action. There is therefore evidence of climatic change in this region: the borders of the true desert were formerly far south of their present position.

Coastwards of these dunes, there is a broad region of dunes of similar trend but the sand is here heavily indurated with lime. The siliceous dunes have a pan of calcrete, but the calcareous dunes of the coastal belt are permeated throughout by lime (the rock is called aeolianite). Aeolianite is found throughout southern South Australia and attains great thicknesses in some places, e.g. 600 feet on Wedge Island.

(ii) Yorke Peninsula

Geomorphologically, Yorke Peninsula is in many respects similar to Eyre Peninsula, as might be expected in view of their proximity. Faulting is important in determining the major outlines of both (Figs. 51, 59, 60). In eastern Yorke Peninsula, as in eastern Eyre Peninsula, there are many faults, many manifested in fault scarps, many of which run parallel to the shores of the Gulfs. Yorke Peninsula is about 100 miles long and 50 wide, and its boot-like plan is determined by structure, and particularly by faults. Of these the Kulpara fault is most clearly expressed topographically.

Although underlain by similar Precambrian rocks, Yorke Peninsula is not as high as its western neighbour, nor is there as great a relief amplitude. The highest point on the Peninsula, little more than 700 feet above present sea level, occurs to the northeast of Arthurton, and the average elevation of the northern part of the Peninsula is about 300 feet. To the south the land is lower, averaging about 100 feet but rising to more than 200 feet over considerable areas. In general, the topography is broadly rolling, partly due to the nature of the bedrock relief, but also caused by the presence of northwest to southeast trending longitudinal sand dunes similar to those of Eyre Peninsula and like them, now stabilised by vegetation. Thin occurrences of marine Tertiary rocks occur in eastern and southern Yorke Peninsula, especially close to the fault zones. Calcrete is common all over Yorke Peninsula, and in the south there is up to 50 feet of aeolianite blanketing the landscape. Cliffed shorelines are common and on them there is evidence of former, higher, stands of the sea; for instance at Point Brown stranded shell beds indicate a sea level 10 to 12 feet above the present.

The great contrast between Yorke and Eyre peninsulas, apart from the lack of relief in the former, is the occurrence of Permian rocks of glacial origin throughout Yorke Peninsula, and particularly south of the line drawn between Port Victoria and Port Vincent. Here the Permian glacial rocks blanket the landscape eroded across Archaean, Proterozoic and Cambrian strata to depths up to 1,000 feet. Some of the rocks contained in the glacial sequences are similar to rocks found in the Southeast and probably were carved by ice some 200 to 300 miles across the State about 200 million years ago. Reference to the Permian glacial period is made in connection with the southern Mt Lofty Ranges in Section C (ii) of this Appendix; but in Yorke Peninsula, the effects of Permian glaciation cannot be observed at the surface, save indirectly insofar as glacial deposits fill what would otherwise be broad depressions.

The broadly rolling surface of Yorke Peninsula is obviously an erosional surface cut across strata of different ages and resistances. In view of the presence of shallow basins of early Tertiary rocks in the south of the Peninsula, it seems clear that these were derived from erosion of the adjacent land, and the surface must therefore be of Tertiary age. There is no direct evidence of this in the form of, say, laterite. The surface of low relief has since been blanketed by aeolian sand and calcrete, and disrupted by faulting, probably on more than one occasion, but certainly in Recent times—the Kulpara fault scarp is so fresh and little dissected it cannot have been long in existence.

(iii) Murray plains

The Murray plains occupy a very large area of southeastern South Australia. The area is bounded on the north by the upland of the Olary, to the west by the ridges and ranges of the Mt Lofty and Mid-north uplands, and to the south by the Southeast region. For the purpose of this Appendix, the Victorian border forms the eastern limit, but in reality of course the State border is not discernible in the form of the land, and the same features are found on both sides of the artificial boundary.

The area is one of low to moderate rainfall. To the south, Mt Gambier receives about 30 inches of rain a year, but to the north rainfall decreases in amount and reliability: Renmark averages 10 inches, Blanchetown 10½ inches and Pinnaroo 13½ inches each year. The area is broadly a rolling plain, most of which lies less than 300 feet above sea level. The plain is developed upon sub-horizontally disposed sedimentary rocks, principally limestones, of early and mid Tertiary age. These sediments rest upon a floor of crystalline rocks, which reach the surface in the lower Murray Valley in the areas of Mannum, Tailem Bend and Caloote. They occur also in a broad zone—the Padthaway ridge or horst—bounding the Murray plains and the underlying basin on the south-western side. To the north of the Padthaway ridge and eastward from the Mount Lofty Ranges, the sub-Tertiary floor slopes down gently and the overlying sediments thicken. In South Australia, the basin is deepest in the vicinity of Loxton and Renmark where the Tertiary passes into Cretaceous rocks almost 1,500 feet below sea level, though the depth of the crystalline basement here is unknown.

There are other crystalline rocks in the lower Southeast where there are late Tertiary and Quaternary volcanic outcrops. Masking these Tertiary and igneous rocks over the greater part of the area are superficial deposits consisting of siliceous sands and kunkar (a limestone formed as a soil horizon) in the Murray plains; and calcareous and siliceous sands, as well as aeolianite and clay in the Southeast.

The topography of the Murray plains is broadly rolling. Very large areas consist of sand ridges, generally aligned east to west, but in detail commonly irregular or displaying parabolic or U-dune form. Close to the dunes the intervening plains are underlain by sand, but there are broad shallow depressions essentially devoid of sand where calcareous soils, which are common throughout the basin, are developed. Some of the dunes, probably an older generation, have had their upper parts removed by the wind.

Notwithstanding their apparent simplicity of form, the Murray plains have a complex origin and history. The Tertiary strata which outcrop over the greater part of the plains (disregarding the veneer of superficial deposits) are subhorizontally disposed viewed regionally but in detail there are shallow folds and warps, and there are some faults. The surface of the plain cuts across various strata; the surface is not coincident with the outcrop of a single resistant bed, so that it cannot be interpreted as either a structural surface or a sediplain, i.e. an original surface of deposition, but must be attributed to erosion of the exposed emergent Tertiary sea bed. As there was deposition continuously throughout the later part of the Mesozoic and early and middle Tertiary the modification of the sea floor must have taken place after the Miocene, when the last evidenced widespread deposition took place. It may be that the Pliocene sands were deposited in a long narrow estuary coincident with the present course of the River Murray as far upstream as Morgan, and were derived from the erosion of the adjacent plains.

During the Quaternary, a massive sheet of calcrete began to develop as a soil horizon. It has been added to since, is still forming and is found throughout the region. Also, during this period, a lake developed in the northwest of the plains, leaving behind a few feet of sediments as evidence. The River Murray cut down below the plain surface and through the floor of the first shadow valley, and has since developed a narrow, flat-floored valley. Had the plains been built of rocks other than limestone there would have been more tributary development and thus a great deal more dissection. The old erosional surface has been preserved by virtue of the permeable nature of the bedrock, and by the climatic aridity.

The incision and rejuvenation of the Murray was probably initiated by the first of four Pleistocene glacio-eustatic lowerings of sea level (see above). The river is unusually deep in its lower reaches. It is more than 100 feet deep at Murray Bridge, which is probably a reflection of the glacial low sea levels to which the river was able to cut down in its lower reaches. During the interglacial high sea levels, the valley was drowned. Sediments were deposited in the valley and the sea penetrated inland. The higher stands of the river are evidenced by muds and clays containing abundant shells in many places, and near Mannum, located 10 feet above normal river level. The alternations of rise and fall of river level by cut and fill in the riverine alluvia of the valley floor ensures the continued widening of the valley.

One feature uncovered by the excavation of the narrow Murray trench near Mannum is a remnant of the pre Tertiary landscape, a granite dome upon which surface the Tertiary sediments were laid down. Bores show that the crystalline basement beneath the plains is very irregular. There are hills and valleys of considerable amplitude, and in some of the depressions there are considerable thicknesses of Permian glacial deposits. Mesozoic sediments were laid down in the lower areas of the old landscape, and as the Tertiary progressed, higher and higher parts of the relief were inundated by the sediments deposited at first in a lake but later in a huge embayment of the sea. In many places there are small exposures of pre Tertiary rocks but they are more-or-less weathered and eroded.

(iv) The Southeast

The Southeast province is underlain by the Padthaway ridge or horst, which is bordered both to northeast and to southwest by deep sedimentary basins containing Palaeozoic, Mesozoic and Tertiary rocks. The sedimentary cover on the Padthaway horst is thin, and the crystalline basement is exposed in numerous small outcrops of granite. These give rise to typical tor-strewn hills, particularly in the Upper Southeast.

Close to the Victorian border, in the Mt Gambier area, several small but prominent volcanic extrusions of late Tertiary and Quaternary age occur. The landforms associated with these volcanic outcrops include characteristic craters and calderas.

Apart from these two types of crystalline rock outcrop, the exposures in the Southeast are all unconsolidated Quaternary sediments. The region consists of a plain which slopes gently from the northeast to the coast in the southwest, but in detail, great complexity is introduced by the presence of sand ridges associated with ancient Quaternary and possibly even earlier shorelines (Fig. 225). In the Upper Southeast, the sand ridges have a very complex pattern, considerably due to the occurrence of the granite outcrops previously mentioned, and which profoundly affected shoreline development. But in the Lower Southeast, the dunes take the form of numerous parallel or sub-parallel regions of aeolianite, the result of lime induration of sand dunes. These parallel foredunes separate ill-drained inter-dune flats, in which small lakes are common. Lunettes are associated with some of these lake beds.

Although several attempts have been made to ascertain the Quaternary history of this region, and to assign specific dates to various of the dunes, none so far offered is satisfactory. Several of the dunes are complex features and have themselves been inundated by the Quaternary sea. Until far more absolute dates are available no history of the region can be reconstructed.

(v) Gulf plains
These lowlands border the Gulf of St Vincent and Spencer Gulf on their eastern sides. They do not form a single lowland but consist of a series of discontinuous plains, the most important of which are the Pirie plains, the Adelaide plains (which extend from Port Wakefield to Brighton) and the Willunga plain. Each is underlain by a considerable thickness of Cainozoic marine and terrestrial sediments, and though each varies in its detailed morphology, each displays similar assemblages.

Most of the streams which debouch from the backing hills die out shortly after reaching the lowlands, but a few, such as the Broughton, Light, Gawler and Torrens survive to reach the coast. All, however, deposit material on the plains, particularly in the piedmont zone where coalesced alluvial fans are well developed. The general plain surface slopes gently to the coast, where foredunes are commonly developed, though in some regions the coast is low, and fringed by mangroves. North of Adelaide, relict longitudinal dunes, inherited from an earlier period of more arid climate run northwest to southwest across the plains.

Many of the valleys, and notably the Broughton and the Gawler immediately downstream from the town of the same name, display fine examples of constructional river terraces but this aspect is more appropriately considered with respect to the terraces of the Torrens.

B. The Adelaide District

(a) INTRODUCTION

The city of Adelaide is bisected by the Torrens Valley and is overlooked and dominated by the Mt Lofty Ranges. The latter rise from the plains upon which the City is built by the much dissected yet still precipitous Eden fault scarp. The escarpment, which varies in height between 600 and 800 feet, is arcuate in plan, trending north-south near the Torrens Gorge, but swinging round to the southwest in Adelaide's eastern and southern suburbs before reaching the coast at Seacliff. Although they are considerably dissected by the Torrens, Sturt and South Para rivers, by their tributaries and by numerous smaller streams, the Ranges possess a remarkably even skyline, which is particularly noticeable when viewed from the City. Over wide areas, the uplands are gently rolling at elevations between 1,300 and 2,000 feet. As explained in an earlier chapter, this is due to the presence of an old surface of erosion located high in the present relief. Standing above the general level of the plateau, or ancient peneplain, are several isolated residual hills or monadnocks such as Mt Lofty itself (2,384 feet above sea level), Mt Torrens (1,913 feet), Mt Gawler (1,779 feet) and Mt Gould (1,739 feet).

To the west of the Eden scarp is an assemblage of landforms which has developed over a period of at least 70 million years and probably rather more. They are shown in Fig. 156a. The feature that dominates the northern half of the Adelaide district is the Para fault block, which is similar to those of the main ranges but is exposed only to the north of the City because it has a distinct tilt down to the south. The block is present beneath and to the south of the City, as is shown in bores, but, like other fault blocks still further to the west, it is buried beneath unconsolidated sediments and the waters of the St Vincent Gulf. In the vicinity of the Little Para River, the surface of the block is similar to that of the main ranges to the east, but whereas the latter maintain their elevation and rise southward, the Para block falls away from just over 700 feet in Para Hill to 150 feet in North Adelaide. In effect, there is a hinge line to the south of which the Para block has sagged and twisted (for besides tilting down to the south the block is also tilted down to the east). As a result of these factors, there is an escarpment between the Para and Eden blocks being first apparent below Crouchs Hill and increasing in height southward. It is the very obvious Eden Scarp.

Thus, the major features of the relief of the Adelaide district are a direct reflection of faulting in the ancient rocks which underlie it. The relief is tectonic in origin. Nevertheless there are significant features of the Adelaide landscape due to weathering, erosion and deposition during the past 70 million years. For instance, the strata of which the Para block is built are greatly contorted; yet the surface of the long, gentle eastern slope of the block is rolling and must have been planed off by erosion. A similar explanation must be invoked for the plateau developed on the southern exposed extremity of the Para block, between Hillcrest and North Adelaide, and called the Hampstead plateau, and in the City itself. Along the floor of the Torrens valley between Hillcrest and the City there are several terraces separated by low but distinct breaks of slope. These and many other features can be understood only by reference to the events of geological history.

(b) EARLY TERTIARY CONDITIONS

About 70 million years ago, in early Tertiary times, the main outlines of the present relief were already in existence. The Precambrian rocks had long before been broken up into a series of fault blocks, and these blocks had been moved differentially, relative to one another. The ranges have been raised and worn down several times, and there is some evidence that during the early Tertiary there were hills a little east of Adelaide, though their elevation and extent are unknown. The seas flooded round the fault blocks and submerged the lower lying parts. Thus south of the River Torrens (west of the Eden fault) and west of the Para fault, early and middle Tertiary marine rocks are located in bores. In low lying areas above sea level, sediments worn from the surrounding higher land were deposited in river valleys, and especially in swamps and freshwater lakes.

The Para fault block slopes gently down both southward and eastward and in the depression between the gently rolling eastern slope of the block and the Eden escarpment are sands and clays deposited in a freshwater lake. The Hope Valley area was marshy. Fossils preserved in lignitic clays there show that they, and probably the lake sediments to the north also, are of early Tertiary (Eocene) age. The limits of the old lake are not known. It is clear that the lake was more extensive than the outcrop of lake or lacustrine sediments in the Highbury–Golden Grove area. To the west of the main outcrop there are a few small isolated occurrences of the sands overlying Precambrian rocks, indicating that the lacustrine beds formerly extended farther to the west and that they have since been extensively eroded. With the exception of some large well rounded quartz boulders found below Crouchs Hill, no signs of a former lake shore have been discovered; the lake beds terminate on the eastern side of the depression against the Eden fault, close to which there are no signs of a former beach, suggesting that the eastern limit of the Highbury lake lay still further to the east. This eastern limit of the old lake beds is well seen at Duhnes Quarry (M.R. Adelaide 723940) where the Eocene beds, displaying cross bedding, have been dragged up by vertical movements along the fault (Fig. 26b), and where there are no coarse cobbles such as one might reasonably expect to find on a beach close to hilly terrain.

The sands and clays deposited in the Highbury lake are extensively quarried for use in the building industry. The lake and the sediments laid down in it also provide evidence as to the age of two important geomorphological features.

The first is the gently sloping and rolling eastern slope of the Para block. Eocene sands and clays were deposited on a surface cut in Precambrian strata. This old surface is in many places deeply and intensely weathered, so much so that the Precambrian rocks, as well as the Eocene, are worked for kaolin, a mineral that results from the weathering, by water of clays, and which is used for the making of cream bricks. It is likely that the Eocene clays were derived from the erosion of the weathered Precambrian bedrock. Now the surface of the Precambrian bedrock is essentially the surface upon which the lake beds were laid down: admittedly some rock will have been eroded away since it was exposed to the elements, but essentially, and especially along ridge and spur crests, the surface of the higher parts of the Para block is that upon which the Eocene beds were deposited. The surface is not and was not flat, for quite deep narrow valleys, as well as gently rolling hills in the surface of the Precambrian rocks have been exposed in quarries. There is no abrupt topographical break between the outcrop of Precambrian and Tertiary. Instead, the latter thin out and disappear imperceptibly on the western side of the outcrop. Moreover, sections drawn across the Para block using known topographical and borelog information indicate that the pre Eocene surface continues without interruption beneath the younger rocks. It will also be recalled that thin outcrops of the lacustrine sediments occur to the west of the main outcrop and fairly high on the block. All of these facts suggest that the relatively soft Eocene strata have been eroded from the backslope of the Para block, re-exposing the surface cut in Precambrian rocks upon which they were originally deposited (Fig. 239). Such a surface which has been buried and then re-exposed is called an exhumed surface. It is suggested that the eastern slope of the Para block is of this type, subsequently somewhat eroded, but intrinsically developed rather more than 70 million years ago. Remnants of a surface of similar age are exposed in several small isolated areas immediately to the north of the River Torrens between Beefacres and the Eden scarp, where early Tertiary sediments have been stripped from Precambrian rocks.

(c) THE ANTIQUITY OF THE RIVER TORRENS

The second feature which on one interpretation can be dated by a consideration of the Highbury lake, is the River Torrens in the sector between Athelstone and Hillcrest. In one view it is a very ancient stream, for there is strong suggestion that an ancestor of the present river flowed into the Highbury lake and dumped its load in the still waters:

(1) Close to the present course of the river between Athelstone and Beefacres there are isolated exposures of what was once a continuous train of boulders, cobbles and gravels set in a matrix of sand and clay.

(2) The coarse debris consists predominantly of well rounded quartz or quartzite fragments, though other rock types—cherts, slates, jasper, schists—occur and are known either in the Mt Lofty Ranges or in the Precambrian sequence exposed in the river bed below the Gorge mouth. The shape of the cobbles is fluviatile rather than marine.

(3) The calibre or average size of the coarse debris diminishes westwards from up to three feet maximum diameter at Athelstone to one or two inches at Beefacres.

(4) In the quarry and roadside exposures at Beefacres there is clear and typical, if rudimentary, cross bedding indicating deposition in running water.

(5) The level of the base of the gravels falls progressively westwards: from some 300 feet at Athelstone, to 250 feet at Paradise and 225 feet at Beefacres.

(6) At Beefacres there are mixed with the gravels, lenses of yellow, white and brown mottled sands and clays identical with the Eocene lacustrine sediments that outcrop extensively only a short distance to the northeast; the two exposures are related by discontinuous patches of the early Tertiary sediments.

Fig 255 Section through Gun Emplacement, Anstey Hill.

This evidence is interpreted in the following manner. The gravels and other coarse debris are part of an old river bed deposit which was deposited in the Highbury lake during the Eocene. The river drained part of the Mt Lofty Ranges, from which it eroded its coarse and fine sediments, but which were carried some distance, were worn and smoothed and thus became rounded. When the river entered the lake it deposited its coarse load first, hence the progressive decrease in size of coarse fragments to the west. The prevalence of quartz and quartzite in the coarse fragments suggests that the predecessor of the Torrens drained a quite old land surface, though the provenance of the rocks must also be taken into account. The fine fraction of the load carried by the river was more widely distributed.

However, the evidence is not unequivocal and it is possible to argue that the Torrens is much younger, dating from Pliocene times. The sea penetrated into the area immediately south of the gravel remnants for long periods during the middle and late Tertiary, and it may be considered that since gravels are unlikely to have survived such prolonged attack they must postdate the marine incursions.

(d) LATE CAINOZOIC EVENTS

What occurred after the draining of the ancient lake is not clear. The early Tertiary beds were certainly exposed to weathering, for in some places the weathered horizons can be observed above the unchanged Eocene sands and clays. At the Gun Emplacement, at the base of Anstey Hill for instance, the section shown in Fig. 255 can be seen. The flat top of the Emplacement was once a plain surface. A cone of angular scree material was deposited on the plain and was perhaps related by faulting to the uplift of the ranges behind the plain. It will be recalled that the Eocene beds of Duhnes Quarry have been affected by faulting, so that the lake may have dried up and the surface sediments weathered before the faulting occurred. Once the lake beds were exposed they were eroded as well as weathered, and the process of exhumation of the pre Eocene plain commenced.

Also belonging to this period are two platforms or plateaux, the first extending over the southern part of the Para block, and called here the Hampstead plateau. It ranges in elevation between 225 and 150 feet, is very broadly rolling, and gives way to the northeast to much more distinctly rolling topography along a line which runs northwest from Hillcrest and is a continuation of a ridge of Precambrian rocks which lies beneath Campbelltown Hill and is exposed at the western end of the Hillcrest defile. The plateau truncates middle Tertiary marine strata and therefore must be younger than this. The surface of the plateau is heavily indurated with calcrete; this is seen in the quarry and road cutting at Beefacres, but can also be demonstrated by boring, or trying to bore, in any garden on the plateau.

The City plateau is underlain by Pliocene rocks, is remarkably flat and smooth, and is situated at an elevation of 125 feet. It extends to the north side of the river, where St Peters Cathedral is built on a small platform at the same elevation. The origin of both it and the Hampstead plateau are unknown. The Hampstead plateau has the appearance of a subaerial plain worn down by rivers, rills and weathering, but the City platform could be a wave cut platform. The ages of the two, both relative and absolute, are also not certain, though both could be early Pleistocene.

Finally in this rather uncertain phase of local geological history, alluvial fans were deposited at the base of the Eden and Para fault escarpments. Following uplift, both the ranges and their escarpments were subjected to intense erosion by rivers and streams. Much of the rock worn away from the ranges and escarpments was deposited at the base of the escarpments. Streams were quickly choked and diverted by their own alluvium, which was spread in great cones or fans, which are called alluvial fans. Each stream deposited its fan, and adjacent ones met and merged so that a continuous apron of alluvium fronted the ranges. Thus along the front of the Para and Eden scarps there are such coalesced alluvial fans. The eastern and southern suburbs of Adelaide, the eastern parts of Elizabeth and Para Hills, are located on such fans, which are underlain by beds and lenses of both coarse and fine material, the coarse debris representing former stream courses. Their surfaces slope gently down from the base of the backing scarps.

These alluvial fans have been built up over a long period of time, sometimes subject locally to erosion, but with deposition prevailing. Their development began with the most recent uplift of the Ranges.

(e) THE TORRENS VALLEY

The River Torrens excavated a valley below the level of both Hampstead and City Plateau. This part of the river valley is therefore more recent than both of these features. As Pliocene beds are exposed in the plateau to the south and in the old valley bluffs that are present in the University campus, this section of the Torrens valley is essentially a Quaternary feature, and has developed during the last million years or so. Since it cut its valley, which is both deeper and wider than the present narrow shallow channel, the Torrens has alternated between filling and eroding its valley.

(i) Klemzig Sand

Initially the Torrens excavated a valley which is at its deepest some 70 to 90 feet below the present valley floor. It is not known whether the river choked its own valley with its own debris and then scoured it out, and if so how many times. But toward the end of the Pleistocene it deposited a thick stratum of red clayey sandy alluvium, called the Klemzig Sand, which is now encountered in all bores sunk in the valley below Hillcrest, and is commonly exposed in the present river banks. The Sand is up to 90 feet thick though commonly about 40 to 60 feet. The maximum exposed thickness is about 25 feet. The Sand contains numerous coarse grains of quartz, occasional lenses and thin beds or rounded gravel, which indicate former stream beds, quite numerous lime nodules, and is massively but very poorly jointed. In the Hillcrest defile and immediately downstream, the Sand has a basal boulder bed the materials of which are probably derived from the erosion of the gravels and cobbles deposited by a much older Torrens upstream from the defile. The boulder bed rests directly upon the Precambrian slates in the defile and merges upwards into the red coloured Klemzig Sand.

The Sand is considered to have been deposited by the river for the following reasons:
(1) It occurs only within the river valley.
(2) It contains some thin beds and lenses of well rounded gravels and cobbles.
(3) In the Hillcrest defile the boulders of the basal bed are inclined with their long axes at an angle of about 30° to the horizontal, whereas on beaches the angle of inclination is generally flatter.
(4) The shape of the boulders is predominantly fluviatile rather than marine or lacustrine.
(5) Fossils are rare in the beds but late in the last century mammalian remains, including *Diprotodon*, an extinct giant marsupial, were found at Croydon, and the late H. M. Hale found *Diprotodon* at shallow depth in the Sands near the Torrens Weir in the early nineteen thirties. *Diprotodon* favoured marshy riverine environments.

These fossils also provide a clue as to the age of the Klemzig Sand for *Diprotodon* in southern South Australia at present ranges in age between late Pleistocene and mid Recent. However a more precise dating of the beds is possible. A borehole sunk at Largs showed that at a depth of just more than 30 feet below sea level the red-brown clays, which are either the equivalent of or are derived from the Klemzig Sand, are directly overlain by sands containing shells. These shells have been dated by the C14 method which shows that they are about 6,350 years old. The red-brown clays may be the equivalent of the Sand, but it is possible that they are sediments which have been eroded and re-deposited; they arise from the erosion of the Sand which occurred between Hillcrest and the City (see below). Nevertheless the shells provide a minimum age for the Sand: if the red-brown clay is the equivalent of the Sand, then the latter is just more than 6,350 years old. If the clays are the re-worked Sand, then the latter are older. In either case the Sand must be more than 6,350 years old.

Following the deposition of the Klemzig Sand, thereby raising the level of its own bed and almost filling its own valley, the River Torrens proceeded slowly to cut down in its own alluvium, swinging from side to side as it did so, and thereby creating a series of river terraces in the valley between Hillcrest and the City. The development of these terraces and their significance, is considered in the next section. Similar terraces, though of more limited extent, occur in minor topographical basins, which are separated by spurs of harder rock, between Hillcrest and the Gorge mouth (see Fig. 156a).

(ii) Walkerville Sand

During one of its cross valley migrations, the Torrens suddenly and rapidly incised its channel, carving a very narrow valley to a depth of 25 to 30 feet, and abandoning its old valley floor. The river was able to enlarge and widen this new valley to only a very limited extent before it again started to build up its own bed, and deposit alluvium. This alluvium is grey-black rather than red-brown in colour. It has a silty feel though it contains abundant fine sand and is therefore called the Walkerville Sand. Unlike the Klemzig Sand it contains no lime nodules. It forms a distinct fill confined to the narrow channel excavated in the red alluvium; as it rests upon the Klemzig Sand it must have been deposited later than it. The Walkerville Sand, which is preserved only in limited areas adjacent to the present channel in the Vale Park and

Fig 256 Break of slope at junction of Klemzig and Walkerville Sands.

Felixstowe areas, did not quite fill the narrow channel for there is commonly a low but distinct scarp where the Klemzig and Walkerville sands meet (Fig. 256). The deposition of the Walkerville Sand caused the death and burial of old river red gums, whose trunks and roots are preserved in the alluvium (see for example at M.R. Adelaide 634889). The wood has been dated by the C14 method at 4,860 years old, so that the deposition of the younger sands must have commenced about that time.

After the narrow valley cut by the Torrens had been almost filled with the grey alluvium, the river changed yet again, and cut down its bed, causing the present narrow steep sided trench to be excavated 20 to 25 feet deep. Most of the Walkerville Sand was eroded, so that the reddish Klemzig Sand is exposed in most places along the present valley. The river pursues a winding course, and in flood is actively undercutting its bank in many places on the outside of river curves. This lateral erosion, as well as the levels of the floods are indicated by markedly horizontal cuts in the alluvium. Another potent cause of bank collapse and retreat is wet-bank slumping which occurs when the clays and sands of the alluvium become wet and unstable.

There is clear evidence that the River Torrens has on several occasions during the past few thousands of years alternately excavated and filled its valley; it has alternately aggraded and degraded its bed. Such shifts of baselevel, in theory, can be caused by one or more of several factors. The local evidence must be examined and interpreted on its merits. We will first examine the general case, then the local situation, and then endeavour to interpret the evidence.

(iii) Terrace development

If a river which has developed a flat valley floor, cuts down and excavates a relatively narrow valley to such a depth that even in the highest flood the river does not reach the level of the former valley floor, the old abandoned floor is called a river terrace.

Although they are built of alluvial fill, the terraces of the Torrens have resulted from lateral corrasion during progressive down-cutting and are therefore of erosional type. They are not paired and there is a clear suggestion that they are in fact unpaired. The only possible exception is the Klemzig terrace which may, or may not, represent the upper level of the Klemzig Sand; if it does it is a fill or constructional terrace, but the others are certainly of the unpaired erosional type. They developed in the following manner.

After the deposition of the Klemzig Sand, the Torrens began slowly to cut down, migrating from one side of its valley to the other as it did so. It first swung to the south side of the valley and then moved to the north, regrading the valley floor at a slightly lower level, and destroying all but one remant of the old floor. This is the Klemzig terrace which escaped destruction probably because the Torrens crosses the Precambrian ridge in the Hillcrest defile with a southerly tendency. The main force of the flow was thus directed away from the northern bank, where the terrace remnant is preserved; but on the southern side, where, between the Glynde Hotel and Campbelltown Hill there is an old meander bluff, erosion was pronounced.

This process of migration and regrading of the valley floor occurred at least twice, in both cases leaving behind a terrace on the northern side—the Walkerville and Parklands terraces—but leaving no corresponding features on the southern side. The river once more migrated southward, leaving the Parklands valley floor behind it; then commenced its return journey northward, cutting a valley floor very slightly lower than the Parklands surface—a matter of 2 to 3 feet lower—and had reached roughly its present position when it began cutting down much more rapidly. A narrow channel was cut, beginning about 4,860 years ago; then it was almost wholly refilled with alluvium, and since then the river has yet again excavated a deep and narrow channel.

It may be argued that the terraces described are paired terraces, but that the southern counterparts of the Klemzig, Walkerville and Parklands terraces have been eliminated by erosion. It may be so. But there is only negative evidence to support the claim, whereas the Felixstowe-Hackney terrace is consistently lower than the valley floor on the northern bank of the river: an examination of an accurate contour map shows this possibly better than field observation, and for this reason the terraces are regarded here as unpaired. It is clear that in spite of this, the river was cutting down so slowly that a former local baselevel can be reconstructed from the profile of the lowest terraces.

(f) THE COASTAL ZONE

A series of long dune ridges extends between Largs and Seacliff, running parallel to the present coast. There are usually three dunes of whitish sand behind the shore, but discontinuously between Somerton and Seaton there is a series of reddish dunes; the latter are older than the three white sand dunes. Each results from westerly winds carrying sand from the exposed beaches and depositing it a little way inland. To the north of Largs the evenness of the shore continues on the western side of the Le Fevre Peninsula but on the eastern side there are visible a series of hooks or spits with a strong east-west component. Here the configuration of the coastline has been influenced by the Port River.

It will be recalled that the River Torrens during the mid Recent excavated a series of terraces in its middle valley. The terraces were eroded from the reddish Klemzig Sand and the eroded material was deposited to the west of the City as a large alluvial fan, which is plainly directed toward the present Port River. There, the former Torrens must have had its outlet to the sea, thus allowing the uninterrupted development of the coastal dunes. The Torrens probably divided into a number of distributaries, each of which choked and diverted itself until eventually a major diversion to the south side of the fan occurred causing the river to empty its waters on to the plains behind the dunes in a swampy area from which waters filtered rather than flowed to the sea.

Beneath the coastal zone there are various sediments which show that:

(1) All the coastal forms are of very recent geological age, not more than a few thousand years old.

(2) There have been several changes in the relative level of land and sea in the past few thousand years.
(3) There is no evidence of a southerly tilt of the land in the past few thousand years.

Shells from the sands beneath Largs have been dated at 6,350 years old, so that the third and fourth beds in the sequence and the modern dune and coastal forms are younger than that. They are now located 30–35 feet below sea level, whereas originally they were deposited very close to sea level. Sections constructed on the basis of borings along the Adelaide coast show that there is no appreciable southward tilting of the land since the beds were laid down as one might expect from a consideration of the Para block. In light of this, it appears more likely that the 30 feet relative fall in land level is due not to tectonic movements but to a rise in sea level.

On the basis of evidence from the Adelaide area and elsewhere in South Australia, some workers have postulated a complex sequence of sea level changes (Fig. 257). Some of the evidence invoked (horizons

Fig 257 Postulated late-Quaternary changes of sea level in the Adelaide district (*after Sprigg*).

of calcrete, mangrove swamp deposits located below sea level, beach sands high above sea level) is not easy to interpret with certainty. For instance, what is the relationship of calcrete to the land surface. Could geological changes, e.g. sand deposition, kill mangroves? In light of these and other difficulties, it seems wise not to press the evidence too far at this stage.

Both in the Torrens valley and in the coastal zone there is abundant evidence of changes from erosion to deposition, and changes in type of deposition. Four factors could, acting either singly or in combination, have caused these changes. Each has been mentioned in earlier chapters, and the *modus operandi* explained. They are:

(1) Faulting;
(2) Climatic changes;
(3) Human activities;
(4) Sea level changes.

There is indisputable evidence that each has had some effect in the Adelaide area. The evidence for sea level changes has been outlined above. Beneath Croydon and Kent Town rocks, of Pliocene age occur at widely different elevations, indicating either faulting or strong warping (flexuring or gentle folding) since the Pliocene rocks were laid down. The earth tremors which occasionally shake Adelaide suggest continued slight movements along faults in the area.

There is some evidence that the Torrens was formerly a much bigger stream, that it is now too small for its valley—a misfit stream. Along the northern side of the valley there are preserved old meander bluffs, for instance at Vale Park and in the parklands immediately south of Robe Terrace. These old meander loops were obviously very much larger than those developed by the present river. It is a matter of observation that the radius of these loops is some 40 times the width of the present river, whereas generally the maximum radius of a loop is of the order of 14 to 17 times the width of the river. This indicates that at the time the last of the Klemzig Sand was deposited, the river Torrens had a much greater discharge than it has now.

Man has triggered erosion (and therefore deposition) in several ways. He has caused deforestation, accidentally by firing, and deliberately by clearing land for agricultural purposes. This causes increased and more rapid run-off, and brings a tendency to flooding; thus the effect is similar to that of a climatic change. The use of agricultural machinery, and even the building of roads induces increased erosion and accelerated erosion. The introduction of new plant and animal species can also cause erosion.

However, not all activities of mankind have been detrimental. There is some evidence that the use of top dressing has improved pasture in the Adelaide Hills, stabilised the land surface and decreased the rate of run-off and the frequency of floods. Whereas it used to be a profitable sideline in the Birdwood and Gumeracha districts to collect sand and gravel deposited by the Torrens during its flood periods, the amount of debris now shifted is so small that it is not worthwhile.

Thus each of these factors *could* have influenced erosion and deposition in the area discussed. It is not sufficient to let the matter rest there: they *could* have an effect, but did they? In evaluating the importance of evidence we must compare what should have happened in certain circumstances with what has happened, judged on the available evidence.

To take a simple example, the works of man cannot be invoked in explanation of any but the most recent and slightest modifications of the landscape. The white man has been here only 130 years, the aborigine for a longer but still geologically insignificant period (up to 25,000 years ago appears a reasonable 'guestimate' of the time of the aborigines' arrival in the State). Study of early maps suggests that white men have had relatively little influence on the land surface; in all probability the aborigines had even less.

Faulting is another possibility to be considered. Earth movements affecting Pliocene and younger rocks are clearly evidenced in borelogs along the Para fault complex to the west of the City of Adelaide. Thus, some of the baselevel changes manifested in the landforms and sediments of the Torrens valley between the City and Hillcrest are almost certainly due to this cause. But not all; and in any case faulting provides no general explanation, for, if earth movements were entirely responsible for cut and fill in the Torrens valley and elsewhere, such features should be restricted to the vicinity of fault lines. Cut and fill involving forms and materials similar to these described for the Adelaide district are known from many parts of the Mt Lofty Ranges, and even further afield: in some places the features are close to known faults, but in others they are not. Therefore faulting is not a necessary condition causing cut and fill.

The evidence for high and low stands of the sea during the Quaternary is restricted to the coastal zone. Elsewhere there are serious doubts. For instance it is quite possible that the phase of near stable baselevel evidenced in the Parklands and Hackney Felixstowe terraces could have been related to a sea level which stood some 80 to 100 feet above the present, which would bring the sea up to the Torrens Weir, and inundate all the plains west of the City. In this case there should be sea shells and other signs of the former presence of the sea in the Hindmarsh, Thebarton and Croydon areas and elsewhere, but despite extensive boring, and considerable exposures in brickpits, none has been found. If the great fan of outwash material in this area had been deposited in water, i.e. as a delta, there should be evidence of it in the form of typical deltaic structures but there are none. Instead, the sediments are remarkable for the absence of any structures. The presence of *Diprotodon* at Croydon is indicative of riverine rather than marine conditions. The sea did invade the area in the late Pliocene, and left behind sediments and possibly eroded the City plateau, but there is no incontrovertible evidence of Pleistocene or Recent marine incursions in the area.

We turn finally to the possibility of climatic change. The direct evidence for this is slight: the enlarged meander loops on the Torrens, the former presence of *Diprotodon*, the changes in colour of the sediments, the development of calcrete and ferricrete in the same general area. None of these is diagnostic on its own and is susceptible to explanation in other terms. Yet the indirect evidence points firmly to climatic change as the principal cause of the cut and fill described for the Adelaide area. It has been stated that cut and fill, and in particular the twin sequences of black or grey alluvium resting in channels cut in red-brown alluvium, is found in widely scattered areas. It is known from as far south as Cape Jervis to the Spalding district in the north. It is known adjacent to the coast and on the high plains many miles from the sea. It is known from fault scarps and from areas devoid of such structures. Surely the most reasonable explanation of this distribution is that climatic changes during the recent past have caused similar changes in run-off and river regimes which are manifested in the terraces, valleys and deposits that have been described?

Faulting probably initiated the original excavation of the middle Torrens valley, but many of the late Pleistocene and Recent events certainly seem most reasonably explained by climatic changes. Whether wetter or drier, warmer or cooler, is debatable, but climatic changes have almost certainly occured.

NOTE

[1] Rocks rich in iron and magnesium.

Index

Abandoned ingrown meander, 176
Abrasion (corrasion) in rivers, 158
  on shorelines, 238
Accordant tributary junction, 190
Adelaide District (S.A.), structure of, 57–59
Adelaide Geosyncline (S.A.), 53, 78
Aeolianite, 252, 255
Allogenic stream, 124
Alluvial fan, 207, 208
Anastomose stream, 185
Ancient dune fields, 301, 302
Antarctica, 259, 260
Antecedent stream, 200
Anticline, 11
Apparent peneplain, 314
Areic drainage, 148
Arête, 268
Armchair-shaped hollows, 116
Arnhem Land (N.T.), 86
Asymmetrical valleys, 174, 175
Australia, structure of, 49–51
Ayers Rock (N.T.), 107, 166
Azonal landforms, 5

Backwash, 237
Barchan, 219, 220
Barrier bar (barrier beach), 251, 252
Barron River (Queensland), 190
Base level, 160
  changes of, and influences on valleys, 188–196
  local base level, 160
  temporary base level, 160
  ultimate base level, 160
Basin (structural), 13, 14
Beach, 248
Bergschrund, 268
Berm, 248
Berridale Fault (N.S.W.), 27
Black Mountain Horst (A.C.T.), 31, 32
Blue Mountains (N.S.W.), 83, 85
Bornhardt see Domed inselberg
Boss-and-shield forms, 145
Boulders of disintegration *see* Tors
Braided stream, 185, 188
Breakpoint bar, 250
By-passing, in streams, 155

Calcrete, 134, 144
Caldera, 67
Canberra area, structure of, 64
Canning Desert (W.A.), 226

Carbon-14, 43, 44
Cave, 128
Cavernous weathering, 80
Chemical weathering, 142
  hydration, 142
  hydrolysis, 142
  solution, 143
Chute (shute), 188
Cirque, 263, 267, 268
Classification of streams, 196–203
  antecedent, 200
  consequent, 198
  defeated, 200
  inherited, 199
  insequent, 198
  obsequent, 198
  resequent, 198
  subsequent, 198
  superimposed, 199
Cliff, 241
Cliff notch, 241
Climatic change, evidence of, 299 et seq.
  ancient dune fields, 301, 302
  faunal changes, 300
  fossil soils, 300
  oxygen isotopes, 301
  palynology, 299, 300
  tree-ring analysis, 300
Climatic change, geomorphological effects of, 298 et seq.
Clint, 127
Close jointing in granites, 104, 105
Coastal processes and forms, 236–255
Compartment weathering, 112
Consequent streams, 196–203
Constructional landforms, 49
Constructional waves, 237
Convergent landforms, 347
Cooleman Plain (N.S.W.), karst topography of, 127
Coral reefs, 295–298
Corestones, 96, 99, 102
Corrasion, *see* Abrasion
Corrosion, 158
Cotter Horst (A.C.T.), 32
Covered karst, 128
Crag-and-tail form, 271
Craton, 49
Creep: of sand in deserts, 216
  of soil and rock, 162
Cross folding, 14

400

Index

Cryptoreic drainage, 124, 148
Crystal growth, effect of in weathering, 140
Cuesta, 87, 92
Cullarin Horst (A.C.T. and N.S.W.), 31, 32
Currents, role of, in coastal transport, 248
Cusp, 248
Cycle of erosion *see* Geomorphic cycle

Dating of rocks, 36–45
  by carbon-14, 43, 44
  by fossils, 36, 42
  by radioactivity, 42–44
Defeated stream, 200
Defile-and-basin topography, 172, 173
Deflation, 216, 218
Deflation hollow, 228
Deforestation, as a geomorphological agent, 341, 342
Delta, 175
Depositional plain, 318, 319
Deposition on coast, 247–254
  barrier bar (barrier beach), 251, 252
  beach, 248
  berm, 248
  breakpoint bar, 250
  by wind, 216–228
  cusp, 248
  foredunes, 252, 254
  offshore bar, 250, 251
  parabolic dunes, 252, 254
  spit, 252
  tombolo, 252
Desert armor *see* Gibber
Deserts of the past, 230, 231
Deserts, morphological types, 204
Desert streams, 207
  varnish, 227
Destructional landforms, 48, 49
Destructional waves, 237
Differential weathering, 81
Dip, 10, 11, 15
Dip fault, 22
Discordant tributary junction, 190
Disposition of strata, effect of, 78–93
Doline, 127
Domed inselberg, 105 et seq.
Dome, structural, 13, 14
Dreikanter, 227
Drip curtain, 128
Drumlin, 271
Dune *see* Sand dune
Duricrust, 134
  calcrete, 134, 144

ferricrete, 134, 144
laterite, *see* ferricrete
silcrete, 134
Dynamic equilibrium, 323

Earth flow, 162, 163
Endoreic drainage, 148
En echelon folding, 14
Epicycle, 341
Erosion: coastal, 237–241
  glacial, 267 et seq
  rates of, 4, 5
  river, 153–160
  system of, 3
  wind, 228–230
Erosional coastal forms, 241–247
  cliff, 241
  cliff notch, 241
  high platform, 243, 246
  normal platform, 241
  platform, 241
  serrated platform, 241
  stack, 242, 243
  ultimate platform, 243
Esker, 273
Estuary, 189
Etch plain, 315
  in Central W. Australia, 315
  near Palmer (S.A.), 315
Eustatic movements of the sea, 283
Everard Ranges (S.A.), 109, 110
Exfoliation, 137
Exhumed forms, 121, 123
Exhumed surface, —
  Adelaide District (S.A.), 317
  Flinders Ranges (S.A.), 317
  N.W. Queensland, 317
Exoreic drainage, 148
Exmouth Gulf (W.A.), 65
Exotic stream, 124
Eyre Peninsula (S.A.):
  granite landforms of, 110–115
  polygenetic erosion surface of, 334

Fault, 22
  breccia, 28
  definition of, 22
  dip, 22
  drag, 28
  gouge, 28
  hinge, 24, 27
  normal, 22
  oblique, 22
  recurrent, 28

reverse, 22
step, 28
strike, 22
tear, 27
thrust, 22
Fault control of streams, 33
Faulting, 10
  drainage disturbance by, 33–35, 40, 42
  field evidence for, 28–35
  fault breccia, 28
  fault drag, 28
  fault gouge, 28
  fault step, 28
  mullion structure, 28
  slickensides, 28
Fault-line scarp, 28
Faults, geometry of, 22
Fault scarp, 28
Faunal changes, 300
Ferricrete, 134, 144
Fetch, 236
Fiord, 189, 269–271
Fires, effect of in weathering, 138, 139
Fixed dunes, 219
Flares see Overhanging slopes
Flatiron, 87, 92
Flat-lying strata, effect of, 80–86
Flinders Ranges, Southern, (S.A.),
  cross section of, 19
  morphological map of, 18
Fluvio-glacial deposits, 271
Fold, 10
  cross, 14
  en echelon, 14
  isoclinal, 13
  modern, 21, 22
  overturned, 13
  pitching, 11
  plunging, 11
  recumbent, 13
Forced wave, 236
Foredunes, 252, 254
Former stands of the sea, 285 et seq.
  evidence for, 284, 285
Fossils, 36, 42
Fossil soils, 300
Futter's Range (Vic.), 46, 47

Gawler Block (S.A.), 53
Gawler Ranges (S.A.), 110
Geological time scale, 43
Geomorphic cycle, 320–323
  alternatives to, 328–331
  and isostasy, 321–323

Geosyncline, 49
Gibber, 226, 227
Gibber plain, 226–228
Glacial:
  depositional forms:
    drumlin, 271
    kame, 273
    moraine, 271
  deposits, 271
  erosion, 267 et seq.
  erosional forms:
    arête, 268
    cirque, 263, 267, 268
    hanging valley, 269
    paternoster lake, 269
    pyramidal peak, 268
    roche moutonnée, 273
    u-shaped valley, 269
  erosionist interpretation, 267 et seq.
  overflow channel, 200
  protectionist interpretation, 267 et seq.
Glaciation:
  direct effects of, 257
  drainage modifications due to, 276, 277
  in Australia, 277–280
  indirect effects of, 257
  in New Guinea, 277–280
  in Tasmania, 277–280
  in the Kosciusko Region, 277–280
  pre-Quaternary, 256, 280–282
  Quaternary, 256 et seq.
Glacier, Malaspina, 262, 263
  motion, 263, 264
  piedmont, 263
  valley, 263
Glasshouse Mountains (Queensland), 67
Gnamma, 116, 117, 118, 119
  armchair-shaped hollows, 116
  pan, 116, 120
  pit, 116, 120
Graben see Rift valley
Graded stream profile, 153
Grampians (Vic.), 46–48
Granite landforms, 95 et seq.
Granular disintegration, 97, 137
Greenland, 260
Grike, 127
Gulfs Region (S.A.), 57–63

Hade, 11
Hamada see Gibber
Hamersley Plateau (W.A.), 86
Hanging valley, 269
Headward erosion, 174, 175

Index

High platform, coastal 243, 246
Hillslopes, 5–7
 faceted, 6, 80
 graded, 6
Hogback, 88
Horst, 28, 31, 32
Hot deserts, 204–235
Hum, 128
Hydration, 142
Hydraulic action, 158
 lift, 157
Hydrolysis, 142

Imbricate zone, 22, 24
Incised meander, 176
Inheritance of landforms, 5
Inherited forms, 299
Inherited streams, 199
Inlier, 11
Inselbergs, 105 et seq.
 joint control of, 112, 114
 sheet structure in, 107, 111, 113, 125
Insequent stream, 198
Interlocking spurs, 165
Inversion of relief, 86, 87
Insoclinal folding, 13
Isostatic movements and glaciation, 274–276
 recovery in Britain, 275
 recovery in Scandinavia, 275

Joints, definition of, 22
 significance of, 95 et seq.
Kame, 273
Karren, 127
Karst topography, 124–134
 optimum conditions for, 126
 window, 128
Kimberley Plateau (W.A.), 86, 315
Knick point *see* Nick point
Krichauff Range (N.T.), 13, 18

Lake Bonneville (U.S.A.), 302
Lake Chad (Central Africa), 302
Lake Dieri, 213
Lake Eyre (S.A.), 211–215
 origin of, 228–230
 origin of salts in, 215, 216
Lake Frome (S.A.), 215
Lake Gairdner (S.A.), 215
Lake Greeny (S.A.), 234
Lake Torrens (S.A.), 215
Lake Woods (N.T.), 302
Landform assemblages, 1

Landforms:
 azonal, 5
 coastal, 241–254
 constructional, 49
 convergent, 347
 destructional, 48, 49
 granite, 95 et seq.
 inherited, 299
 on folded sediments, 86–93
 stable, 326–328
 structural, 46
 tectonic, 46
 zonal, 5
Landforms on folded sediments, 86–93
 cuesta, 87, 92
 flatirons, 87, 92
 hogback, 88
 in Flinder's Ranges (S.A.), 87
Landslide, 162, 163
Lapiés, 127
Laterite *see* Ferricrete
Law of superposition, 36
Leeuwin Horst (W.A.), 32, 34
Limestone pavement, 127
Lineament, 49, 51, 52
 in South Australia, 51–56
Local baselevel, 160
Loess, 218
Longitudinal dunes, 220
Longshore drifting, 247
Lunette, 231–234

Malaspina glacier, 262, 263
Man as a geomorphological agent, 341–346
Marine depositional form *see* Deposition on coast
Marine erosion, 237–241
 abrasion on shoreline, 238
 effectiveness of, 247
 erosional forms, 241–247
 rates of, 240
 solution on shoreline, 238
Mass movement of materials, 162–164
Meander, 177
 abandoned ingrown, 176
 belt, 177
 core, 176
 incised, 176
 origins of, 177–185
Misfit stream, 185, 304, 305
Mobile dunes, 219, 220
Modern folding, 21, 22
Modern ice masses, 258–264

Monadnock, 307
Monocline, 11, 16
Moraine, 271
Morphogenetic regions, 2–5
Morphogenetic system, 3
Mt. Babbage (S.A.), 11, 12
Mt. Clear Range (N.S.W.), 32
Mt. Lofty Ranges (S.A.), structure of, 57–63
Mueller Plateau (N.T.), 86
Mullion structure, 28
Multicycle landscapes, 320
  examples of, 331–340;
    Flinders Ranges (S.A.), 333, 334
    Gulfs Region (S.A.), 334, 337, 338
    New England (N.S.W.), 334, 336, 339
    N.W. Queensland, 332, 333
    Southern N.S.W., 336, 337
    Tasmania, 337
Multiphase cycle, 326
Multiple working hypotheses, method of, 347
Murray River, 95, 98
  data on drainage basin of, 148–150
Mushroom rock, 228

Nick (knick) point, 190
Non-cyclic landscape development, 323–326
Normal platform, coastal, 241
North-West Queensland, recent warping in, 65, 66
Nullabor Plain, karst topography of, 128–133
Nullagine Plateau (W.A.), 86
Nunatak, 259

Obsequent stream, 198
Offloading (pressure release), 116, 140
Offshore bar, 250
Oldland, 314
Olgas (N.T.), 106, 108
Onion weathering, 97, 103
Orogenesis, 49
Outlier, 11
Outwash plain, 273
Overhanging slopes, 145, 147, 347–350
  in granite landforms, 145, 147
Overturned fold, 13
Oxbow lake, 177
Oxygen isotopes, 301
Palimpsest surface, 5, 299
Palynology, 299, 300
Pan, 116, 120
Panplain, 315

Parabolic dune, 252, 254
Parallel retreat of slopes, 7
Parna, 218
Paternoster lake, 269
Patterned ground, 164
Peake and Denison Ranges (S.A.), 11
Pediments, 81, 94, 207–211, 308, 309
  morphology of, 209
  origin of, 209, 211
  piedmont angle, 209
Pediplain, 308
Peneplain concept, 306, 307, 320
Permafrost, 162, 273
Permian glaciation in South Australia, 280–282
Phreatic waters, 132
Physical weathering, 137–142
  crystal growth, 140
  effect of fires, 138, 139
  exfoliation, 137
  granular disintegration, 137
  pressure release, 140
  salt crystallization, 140
  thermal expansion, 137–140
Piedmont angle, 308, 309–313
  origin of, 209, 211, 309–313
Piedmont glacier, 263
Pit, 116, 120
Pitching fold, 11
Plain of lateral corrasion, 177
Plateau landscapes, 80
Platform, structural, 49
  coastal, 241
Playa, 211–216
Pleistocene stratigraphy, 264, 266, 267
Plunging fold, 11
Point bar, 177
Polje, 128
Polygenetic surface, 326
Port Phillip Bay (Vic.), Fault, fracture pattern of, 26
  structure of, 64
  truncated drainage system of, 187
Pressure release *see* Offloading
Proglacial lake, 276
Pyramidal peak, 268

Quaquaversal dip, 15
Quaternary high sea levels, 287, 288
  low sea levels, 285, 286
  sea levels in Australia, 288 et seq.
  sea levels, Gulfs Region (S.A.), 289, 290, 293–295
  sea levels, N.S.W. coast, 288

Index

sea levels, South East of South Australia, 290–292
   stratigraphy *see* Pleistocene stratigraphy
Radioactivity, 42–44
Raised beach, 284, 285
Rates of erosion, 4, 5
Recumbent fold, 13
Reg see Gibber
Regolith, 315
Relief inversion *see* Inversion of relief
Resequent stream, 198
Ria, 189
Rift valley (graben), 32
   East African, 37
   Fitzroy River (W.A.) 32, 38, 39
Rillen, 117
Rip channel, 250
River erosion, 153–160
   gorges, ratio of depth to width, 165–171
   terraces, 191, 196, 302–304
   depositional, 193, 196
   erosional, 191
   transport, 153–160
Roche moutonnée, 273
Rock types, 9, 10
Rowsley Scarp (Vic.), 46

Salina, 211
Saltation in deserts, 216
   in rivers, 155, 156
Salt crystallization, 140
San Andreas Fault (Calif.), 27
Sand dunes, 218–226
   barchan, 219, 220
   fixed, 219
   foredunes, 252, 254
   longitudinal, 220
   lunette, 231–234
   mobile, 219, 220
   parabolic, 252
   sief, 220
   transverse, 220
Sand dune deserts in Australia, 220–226
   Great Victoria Desert (S.A., W.A.), 224–226
   Simpson Desert (N.T., S.A.), 222–224
Sandstone weathering forms, 85, 86, 93
Saprolith, 315
Scarp retreat, 321
Sea level:
   deposition at, 247–254
   erosion at, 237–241
   Quaternary high sea level, 287, 288
   Quaternary low sea levels, 285, 286

Aradional glacio-eustatic scheme of high sea levels, 285–288
Sediplain, 131
Selective weathering, 81
Serir see Gibber
Serrated platform, 241
Shield, 49
Shore platforms, origin of, 246, 247
Shute, *see* Chute
Sief dune, 220
Silcrete, 134
Slickensides, 28
Slipoff slope, 177
Slope *see* Hillslope
   budget, 6, 81
   decline *see* slope lowering
   lowering, 7, 81
   retreat, 81
Solifluxion, 274
Solution, 143
   on shoreline, 238
   pan, 128
South Australia, location of epicentres in, 54
   North East, structure of, 64, 65
   structure of, 51–56
Spheroidal weathering, 96, 99
Spillway, 200
Spit, 252
Stable landforms, 326–328
Stack, 242, 243
Stalactite, 128
Stalagmite, 128
Step fault, 28
Stony desert, 226–228
Storm effects, 8
Stratum contours, 11, 15, 16
Stream capacity, 157
   capture, 175, 176
   competence, 157
   load, 155
   patterns, 203, 304, 305
   piracy *see* stream capture
   profile, graded, 153
   rejuvenation, 190
   thalweg, 153
   velocity, distribution along river, 153–155
   velocity in cross section, 154
Streams, bed load of, 155
   bypassing in, 155
   energy of, 153
   traction load of, 155
   wetted perimeter of, 155

Strike, 10, 11, 15
  fault, 22
Structural bench, 80, 81, 92, 172, 174
  landform, definition of, 46
Structure:
  effect of disposition on strata on, 78–93
  effect of flat-lying strata on, 80–86
  geomorphological significance of, 1, 78
Submarine canyons, 295
Subsequent streams, 198
Superimposed streams, 199
Suspension (in rivers), 155, 156
Swallow holes, 127
Swash, 237
Swell, 236, 237
Sydney Harbour, 189
Syncline, 11
System of erosion, 3

Tafoni, 117, 121, 145
Tarn, 268
Tear fault, 27
Tectonic landform, definition of, 46
Temporary base level, 160
Tent hill, 79
Terra rossa, 128
Thermal expansion, 137–140
Thrust fault, 22
Time and stage in geomorphology, 7, 8
Tombolo, 252
Tors, 95–104
  Armidale District (N.S.W.), 96
  Devils Marbles (N.T.), 100
  Kosciusko Region (N.S.W.), 96
  North Queensland, 96, 103
  Palmer (S.A.), 95, 96, 99, 100
  two stage development of, 100, 101
Tortoiseshell rock, 121
Traditional glacio-eustatic scheme of high sea levels, 285–288
Transportation by wind, 216–228
Transverse dunes, 220
Tree ring analysis, 300

Ultimate base level, 160
  platform, coastal, 243
Unconformity, 315, 317
Uniclinal shifting, 174, 175
Urstromtäler, 200, 201
U-shaped valley, 269
Uvula, 128

Vadose waters, 132
Valley glacier, 263
Valley-in-valley form, 150, 151
Valley side facets, 190
  slopes, morphology and behaviour of, 171–173
Varved clays, 277
Ventifact, 226, 227
Volcanic forms, distribution of, 66
Volcanic forms, examples of, 68–75
  Hunter Valley (N.S.W.), 73–75
  North Queensland, 75
  South East of South Australia, 68–71
  Western Victoria, 73
Volcanic landscapes, 66–77
Volcanoes, composition and morphology of, 67

Wadi, 207
Water in deserts, 204–216
Water in deserts, reasons for effectiveness of rain, 205, 206
Water level weathering, 240
Wave fetch *see* Fetch
Wave refraction, 237
Waves, 236, 237
  constructional, 237
  destructional, 237
  forced, 236
Weathering, 135–147
  cavernous, 80
  chemical, 142
  compartment, 112
  definition of, 135
  differential, 81
  effects of, 145, 147
  factors in, 136
  front, 315
  onion, 97, 103
  physical, 137–142
  role of organisms in, 142, 144
  selective, 81
  spheroidal, 96, 99
  water level, 240
Weather pit *see* Gnamma
Western Australia, South West Portion, structure of, 64
Wet-bank slumping, 158
Wilpena Pound (S.A.), 25
  geological map of, 20
Wind erosion, 228–230
  wind in deserts, 216–230

Yardang, 228
Yorke Peninsula, structure of, 61, 63

Zeugen, 228
Zonal landforms, 5

CRADLE OF CONQUERORS: SIBERIA

BY ERWIN LESSNER

    CRADLE OF CONQUERORS: SIBERIA

    AT THE DEVIL'S BOOTH

    PHANTOM VICTORY: THE FOURTH REICH

    BLITZKRIEG AND BLUFF: THE LEGEND OF NAZI INVINCIBILITY

CRADLE OF CONQUERORS:

SIBERIA

by Erwin Lessner

DOUBLEDAY & COMPANY, INC., GARDEN CITY, NEW YORK, 1955

Library of Congress Catalog Card Number 55-8407

Copyright ©, 1955, by Erwin Lessner
All Rights Reserved
Printed in the United States at The Country Life Press, Garden City, N.Y.
First Edition

Grateful acknowledgment is made to the New York Public Library, whose sheer inexhaustible treasures enabled me to complete the research for this book.

CRADLE OF CONQUERORS: SIBERIA

CHAPTER ONE This is the story of a land whose very name spells terror and invokes images of arid, icy wasteland dominated by howling, demonic elements that bestir man's worst passions and unite with them to make Siberia a terrestrial inferno, an anteroom to Satan's own torture chamber of affliction and eternal remorse. And yet Siberia is one of the most beautiful countries in the world, whose sight should stimulate the devout admiration of any receptive human and whose procreative munificence could give a happy life of plenty to five times as many people as have ever vegetated there in fear, hatred, and want.

Kamchatka Peninsula, with its glaciated volcanoes up to 15,666 feet high, has no equal in scenic grandeur anywhere; the alpine majesty of the Altai Mountains, almost equally high, is second only to the Himalayas. Lake Baikal, deepest fresh-water lake in the world and the most abundant in fish, with its fantastic mirages and breath-taking settings, is one of the world's sublime wonders. Amur River sweeps miraculous fertility eastward, along almost 3000 miles of savagely splendid land. The valleys of great streams running north toward the Arctic Ocean are wide and serene as the Creator's moods. Even the arctic belt of tundra, rimmed by a vault of eternal ice, reflects the glory of a quaint sunset rather than the terror of destructive storms. Hundreds of thousands of square miles of black earth produce luxuriant crops. On boundless steppes grass grows higher than a man on horseback. The texture of blossoming Siberian meadows defies description. Forests larger than European empires are domes of awe-inspiring splendor. The glittering surface of Siberia, permeated with nature's magic sounds and scents, is a glorious cover of a treasure chest, for, hidden beneath the surface lies inexhaustible wealth of infinite variety—gold, platinum, silver, copper, iron, coal, graphite, jasper, porphyry, kaolin, and rock salt.

Eons ago large sections of Siberia were submerged under the waters of a tropical ocean and rhinoceros-like beasts roamed its shores. Later, diluvian glaciation was kind to the land. Only north of the sixtieth parallel was Siberia buried under a harness of ice, while in Europe glacial masses choked Southern countries as Italy and Spain down to the fortieth parallel and more than half of North America was a wilderness of crevassed ice.

After glaciation came to an end, most of Central and Eastern Siberia emerged as an alpine land interspersed with great lakes. Eventually most of the lakes vanished, leaving succulent bottoms of black earth. Mountains leveled off into wooded hills, abodes for fur animals from bears to ermines, and innumerable kinds of game.

In a land the size of Siberia—roughly five million square miles—climates are necessarily varied. Modern Russians have claimed that both the world's highest and lowest temperatures can be found in Siberia, yet the heat on the scorched shores of the Aral Sea has not yet equaled the world's all-time high of 136.4°, registered in 1923, twenty-five miles south of Tripoli, North Africa. However, Siberia's title to include within its boundaries the cold pole of the world has remained unchallenged since 1869, when Baron Maydell, a distinguished explorer, recorded minus 82° at Verckojansk, a small township of 400, on the Yana River, in Yakut Province, not quite 100 miles north of the Arctic Circle. Until Maydell came, no one in the wilderness settlement had ever seen a thermometer and, for a long time to come, no native learned to read one. Maydell's visits, however, fell in a comparatively mild winter, for on November 21, 1892, a deportee metrologist reported a low of 93.5°.

Verckojansk, however, is not a place of desolation. The average July temperature is a pleasant 59°, with maximums ranging in the eighties. During the brief, hectic summer, vegetables grow and hardy corn ripens on sundrenched patches. Horses and cattle find plenty of fodder on pastures along the river, sheltered by mountain ranges from high winds. In December and January men and beasts stay indoors. For the two-legged creatures this is the season of *sapoi*, the most absolute and lasting intoxicant known to man. Homedistilled concoctions of terrific potency which the males gulp down by the pint, usually on the first day of hibernation, reduce them to a state of primitive functioning for a number of weeks during which they are faithfully attended by their sober wives.

But lately the palm of being the coldest spot on earth has passed to Omyakon, another settlement in Yakut Province, some 500 miles to the southeast, on the latitude of 64°, where Soviet meteorologists began to make observations in 1927 and recorded a fantastic low of 108°, with a January average of minus 60°. The six or seven semi-savage families of reindeer herdsmen and hunters who live in Omyakon stay indoors for three months. Some edibles are grown there and reindeer have all the moss they need for subsistence. Low humidity upsets otherwise lethal effects of the temperature.

Extreme as Siberia's phenomena are, Siberian nature is not a killer. On June 30, 1908, a thunderous roar was heard from the Yenisei to the Angara rivers, about 300 miles apart. Hunters told of flashes of fire far up north, and in the city of Krasnojarsk people gossiped about a bomb explosion on the rail yards. Investigations produced no results until 1927, when it was discovered that a meteorite had hit the ground in the Tunguska region, almost 400 miles from Krasnojarsk. The mass of cosmic matter, believed to have consisted of 500,000 tons of iron, nickel and other ores, had kindled a forest fire that burned down a track 105 miles long; there would hardly have been survivors had the cosmic missile hit a populated area. In 1947 another meteor, estimated at several thousand tons, exploded high above the forests of Kodar, showering a large area with a hail of hot iron fragments. Neither meteorite caused a single casualty.

Earthquakes are largely unknown in Siberia, and droughts are rare, much rarer than devastating conflagrations of the steppes set by pyromaniacs.

Man would have had ample reason to give the hospitable vastness a friendly name. Man's callous indifference to nature, however, left the land unbaptized for thousands of years. Only in the sixteenth century of our time was the name of "Sibir" first recorded. Tribute collectors from Muscovy, sent out to gather sable furs from a Siberian prince who lived in the bourg of Isker about ten miles from the present site of Omsk, considered their assignment strenuous and unrewarding. The trip was long and precarious, the prince unenthusiastic about paying dues and stingy with handouts. His residence was a glum place, and even weather was poor when they arrived there in the early spring. They probably called weather and mood *siwerko*—meaning cold, windy, and cloudy. In due course Muscovite scribes perverted the word into *sibir* and substituted it for Isker. Natives did not use that name, but when Russian conquistadores subsequently invaded the space beyond the Urals, they applied the name *sibir* to all the land they trod under their feet, unaware of its immensity and variety.

There have been other interpretations of the name's origin. Some say that Siberia stands for "threshold," which, however, has no linguistic foundation. Others claim that it stands for "north" (*sever* in Russian); yet Siberia is east of ancient Russia, not north. So it seems most likely that the name was born out of disgruntled morosity of men who did not appreciate the gracious munificence of the country they held under their sway.

History is essentially an account of men's doings. The history of Siberia is that of its peoples, but many of them left no conclusive trace of their actual achievements. And even though in a distant past settlers from the Yenisei Valley and migrants from the south who went to the western steppes represented well-developed cultures, and even though some of the world's most successful conquerors were of Siberian origin, the fact remains that no important cultural or artistic feats, no accomplishment in the field of law and in the advancement toward a better state of human affairs originated in Siberia. And yet Siberia made a contribution to mankind, the most tragic, fateful, and consequential that imagination could conceive. For indications are that in Siberia originated the cross.

Ancient Siberians used to pin their dead on poles and put the bodies in upright positions in the graves. Possibly they also executed culprits in such postures. Traveling Chinese merchants observed the custom; Chinese executioners, in quest of new and more spectacular methods of putting their victims to death, seem to have perfected the sordid pole. From China knowledge of the cross spread west, and eventually reached Rome.

CHAPTER TWO Early Nestorian Christians from Western Asia and early Christians from Northern Russia believed that the vastness yonder was the land Magog. These people lived more than 2000 miles apart, and it is doubtful that there was any intercourse between them. When St. Cyril, converter of the Russians, was born in 827, the Nestorian creed was already four centuries old. There are no indications that the two groups knew of the land they considered Gog's patrimony, and their dogmas differed in essential points. Yet both were convinced that, "in the latter years," Gog's mighty host would descend upon them like a devastating storm and chastise them for their transgressions, but that the Lord, after inflicting untold misery, would redeem the survivors, destroy the instrument of His wrath, and then the millenium would dawn upon purified mankind.

Christendom didn't settle in Siberia until the turn of the seventeenth century; but long before that Siberian horsemen and many auxiliaries in their service had covered faraway lands like thunderclouds. Three times they had established their rule in areas much larger than that of ancient Rome, and the prophecy of Ezekiel remained unfulfilled. The later Siberians, stubborn in their heathenism and wary of the cross raised by their Russian conquerors, paid little, if any, attention to the Scriptures, and the invaders were no true converters; they even sympathized with aboriginal shamanism and adopted some of its superstitions. The natives never knew of Gog and Magog.

The Book of the Prophet Ezekiel, Chapters 38 and 39.

And the word of the Lord came unto me, saying, *Son of man, set thy face against Gog, the land Magog, the chief prince of Meshech and Tubal, and prophesy against him,*

And say, Thus saith the Lord GOD: Behold, I am against thee, O Gog, the chief prince of Meshech and Tubal:

And I will turn thee back and put hooks into thy jaws, and I will bring thee forth, and all thine army, horses and horsemen, all of them clothed with all sorts of armour, even a great company with bucklers and shields, all of them handling swords:

Persia, Ethiopia, and Libya with them, all of them with shield and helmet:

Gomer and all his bands: the house of Togarmah of the north quarters, and all his bands, and many people with thee.

Be thou prepared, and prepare for thyself, thou, and all thy company that are assembled unto thee, and be thou a guard unto them.

After many days thou shalt be visited: in the latter years thou shalt come into the land that is brought back from the sword, and is gathered out of many people against the mountains of Israel, which have been always waste: but it is brought forth out of the nations, and they shall dwell safely all of them.

Thou shalt ascend and come like a storm, thou shalt be like a cloud to cover the land, thou, and all thy hands, and many people with thee.

Thus saith the Lord GOD; it shall also come to pass, that at the same time shall things come into thy mind, and thou shalt think an evil thought:

And thou shalt say, *I will go up to the land of unwalled villages; I will go to them that are at rest, that dwell safely, all of them dwelling without walls, and having neither bars nor gates,*

To take a spoil and to take a prey; to turn thine hand upon the desolate places that are now inhabited, and upon the people that are gathered out of the nations, which have gotten cattle and goods, that dwell in the midst of the land.

Sheba, and Dedan, and the merchants of Tarshish, with all the young lions thereof, shall say unto thee, Art thou come to take a spoil? hast thou gathered thy company to take a prey? to take away silver and gold, to take away cattle and goods, to take a great spoil?

Therefore, son of man, prophesy and say unto Gog, Thus saith the Lord GOD: In that day when my people of Israel dwelleth safely, shalt thou not know it?

And thou shalt come from thy place out of the north parts, thou, and many people with thee, all of them riding upon horses, a great company, and a mighty army:

And thou shalt come up against my people of Israel, as a cloud to cover the land; it shall be in the latter days, and I will bring thee against my land, that the heathen may know me, when I shall be sanctified in thee O Gog, before their eyes.

Thus saith the Lord GOD; Art thou he whom I have spoken in old time by my servants the prophets of Israel, which prophesied in those days many years that I would bring thee against them?

And it shall come to pass at the same time when Gog shall come against the land of Israel, saith the Lord GOD, that my fury shall come up in my face.

For in my jealousy and in the fire of my wrath have I spoken, *Surely in that day there shall be a great shaking in the land of Israel;*

So that the fishes of the sea, and the fowls of the heaven, and the beasts of the field, and all creeping things that creep upon the earth, and all the men that are upon the face of the earth, shall shake at my presence, and the mountains shall be thrown down, and the steep places shall fall, and every wall shall fall to the ground.

And I will call for a sword against him throughout all my mountains, saith the Lord GOD: every man's sword shall be against his brother.

And I will plead against him with pestilence and with blood; and I will rain upon him, and upon his bands, and upon the many people that are with him, and overflowing rain, and great hailstones, fire, and brimstone.

Thus will I magnify myself, and sanctify myself; and I will be known in the eyes of many nations, and they shall know that I am the LORD.

Therefore, thou son of man, prophesy against Gog, and say, Thus saith the Lord GOD; *Behold, I am against thee, O Gog, the chief prince of Meshech and Tubal:*

And I will turn thee back, and leave but the sixth part of thee, and will cause thee to come up from the north parts, and will bring thee upon the mountains of Israel:

And I will smite thy bow out of thy left hand, and will cause thine arrows to fall out of thy right hand.

Thou shalt fall upon the mountains of Israel, thou, and all thy hands, and the people that is with thee: I will give thee unto the ravenous birds of every sort, and to the beasts of the field to be devoured.

Thou shalt fall upon the open field: for I have spoken it, saith the Lord GOD.

And I will send a fire on Magog, and among them that dwell carelessly in the isles: and they shall know that I am the LORD.

So will I make my holy name known in the midst of my people Israel; and I will not let them pollute my holy name any more: and the heathen shall know that I am the LORD, the Holy One in Israel.

Behold, it is come, and it is done, saith the Lord GOD; this is the day whereof I have spoken.

And they that dwell in the cities of Israel shall go forth, and shall set on fire and burn the weapons, both the shields and the bucklers, the bows and the arrows, and the handstaves and the spears, *and they shall burn them with fire seven years:*

So that they shall take no wood out of the field, neither cut down any out of the forests; for they shall burn the weapons with fire: *and they shall spoil those that spoiled them, and rob those that robbed them, saith the Lord GOD.*

And it shall come to pass in that day, that I will give unto Gog a place there of graves in Israel, the valley of the passengers on the east of the sea; and it shall stop the noses of the passengers; *and there shall they bury Gog and all his multitude: and they shall call it the valley of Hamon-gog.*

And seven months shall the house of Israel be burying of them, that they may cleanse the land.

Yea, all the people of the land shall bury them, and it shall be to them a renown the day that I shall be glorified, saith the Lord GOD.

And they shall sever out men of continual employment, passing through the land to bury with the passengers those that remain upon the face of the earth, to cleanse it: after the end of seven months shall they search.

And the passengers that pass through the land, when any seeth a man's bone, then shall he set up a sign by it, till the buriers have buried it in the valley of Hamon-gog.

And also the name of the city shall be Hamonäh. Thus shall they cleanse the land.

And, thou son of man, thus saith the Lord GOD; Speak unto every feathered fowl, and to every beast of the field, Assemble yourselves, and come; gather yourselves on every side to my sacrifice that I do sacrifice for you, even a great sacrifice upon the mountains of Israel, that ye may eat flesh, and drink blood.

Ye shall eat the flesh of the mighty, and drink the blood of the princes of the earth, of rams, of lambs, and of goats, of bullocks, and all of them fatlings of Bashan.

And ye shall eat fat till ye be full, and drink blood till ye be drunken, of my sacrifice which I have sacrificed for you.

Thus ye shall be filled at my table with horses and chariots, with mighty men, and with all men of war, saith the Lord GOD.

And I will set my glory among the heathen, and all the heathen shall see my judgment that I have executed, and my hand that I have laid upon them.

So the house of Israel shall know that I am the Lord their GOD from that day and forward.

And the heathen shall know that the house of Israel went into captivity for their iniquity; because they trespassed against me, therefore hid I my face from them, and gave them into the hands of their enemies; so fell they all by the sword.

According to their uncleanliness and according to their transgressions have I done unto them, and hid my face from them.

Therefore thus saith the Lord GOD; *Now will I bring again the captivity of Jacob, and have mercy upon the whole house of Israel, and will be jealous for my holy name;*

After that they have borne their shame, and all their trespasses whereby they have trespassed against me, when they dwelt safely in their land, and none made them afraid.

When I have brought them again from the people, and gathered them out of their enemies' land, and am sanctified in them in the sight of many nations;

Then shall they know that I am the LORD their God, which caused them to be led into captivity among the heathen; but I have gathered them unto their own land, and have left none of them any more there.

Neither will I hide my face any more from them; for I have poured out my spirit upon the house of Israel, saith the Lord GOD.

The cradle of mankind is sometimes believed to have been the Middle East, between the Nile and Mesopotamia. Yet it is not simple to visualize how men could have spread from there to all the populated parts of the globe, or to explain the infinite racial varieties of the *homo sapiens,* had they all originated in one and the same area. In fact there must have been several cradles, far apart, and one of them seems to have been in Siberia between Lake Baikal and the Orkhon River, where mountains offer protection against storms, where forests give shelter to creatures, where steppes produce edible plants, and where there was no want of either milk or honey. In gloriously serene regions astride what is now the Siberian-Mongolian border roamed scattered clans of dark-haired, flat-nosed, stocky men, long before their Chinese neighbors had completed their legendary migration to establish the oldest consolidated empire on earth.

The dark-haired clansmen claimed descendancy from a giant wolf who was blue, like the sky. They were hunters and fishermen, ignorant of soil cultivation, and unaware of its usefulness. There were more fish in rivers, lakes, and streams than they could consume, and there was game in the forests to last them forever. Man's principal provider was an enormous elephantine creature with a rough, brownish coat, a short, high, pointed skull, smallish ears, and long, curved ivory tusks. The giant herbivore was an easy prey to man, the smallish carnivore who attacked it with crude axes of stone and trained his wit to watch the animal's habits for better tracking methods and more effective killing devices. Hunting the mammoth gave the descendants of the wolf—the Mongols—their first primitive cultural impulses. It shaped their habits and determined their wanderings. In the beginning Mongols did not wander far from their main camping grounds, and the various clans lived so widely apart that frictions should have been infrequent. But then the mammoths began to migrate. Maybe that instinct urged them to get beyond the killer's range, or the climate, gradually warming up, made them feel uncomfortable in their ancient habitat; in fact herds of mammoths started on a long trek. They advanced north toward the rim of the arctic tundra, and from there spread east and west. The most daring hunters followed their prey; less venturesome men stayed behind. Eventually they lost contact with each other. The migration of game and trackers lasted an infinite period and covered enormous distances. Those who turned west eventually crossed the Ural Mountains and ranged as far as Scandinavia; the eastern group reached the narrows between the Asiatic and American continents. The pursuing hunters met other people of uncertain origin. They battled strangers with the fierceness, cunning, and voracity they had developed chasing the mammoth. Chase had taught them the art of ambushing their prey and co-operating in the kill, tactics which other tribes ignored even though they had skills the descendants of the blue wolf still lacked. The victorious hunters utilized the abilities of the defeated by putting them to work producing weapons and building shelters of bark and reindeer skin; and they mated with their women, adding Mongol features to those of indigenous races. The comfort of being served made them stay for lengthy periods, and they took entire families along when they left. Wandering, they lost their national identity and obscured that of people they subdued. Bullet-headed Yakuts, tall sinewy Chutski, and many more tribes came to resemble the Mongols. A few Mongol characteristics can still be found as far west as Finland and the northernmost provinces of Sweden and Norway, and in the opposite direction well beyond the Asiatic mainland.

The narrow strip of water, now called the Bering Strait, in which the Diomede Islands form a chain of steppingstones, did not stop the mammoths. Long before the dawn of our era, thousands of years before Eric the Red set course for Northwestern America, Asiatic mammoths made a bid for survival by migrating to Northwestern America. On their trail hordes of black-haired, weather-beaten men with high cheekbones, clad in furs, and greased with oil for protection against the cold, trickled across the narrows. Perhaps they walked over the ice in a winter rougher than any on our records, or they used primitive canoes as were known in these regions from times immemorial. Ethnological qualities of American Eskimos and Indians indicate distant kinship with the Siberian hunters; totem poles discovered in Alaska bear close resemblance to objects of worship found in Siberia; and the primitive armament and fighting methods of the Indians were similar to those of early Siberians. Traffic across the Bering Strait continued through the ages. To the people of Northeastern Siberia, America was not a new world, but "Alashak," the "big land," as ancient as their own.

The name "Alashak" was in use on both sides of the Bering Strait when the first Western explorers reached the barren area. But modern linguistic experts found no similarities in Siberian idioms with those of the American Eskimos or Indians. The vocabulary of the migrating hunters, like that of the people with whom they mixed, must have been narrowly limited. These men did not converse; they used their undeveloped gift of speech only to name objects and express primitive wishes. They altered their terminology as they met new people, and in the course of events they forgot their origin and even the purpose of their migration.

The mammoth died out before man began to record history, but, even extinguished, it benefited the distant offspring of its extinguishers. It is said that elephants retire to hidden grounds when they feel their end approaching and that a fabulous wealth of ivory is supposed to exist there; yet no elephants' burial grounds have been discovered. The mammoth did have burial grounds on the lower Lena River and they were known to Siberian tribes who lived in the neighborhood. They used the tusks as material for tackle and implements, and they sold them to Chinese and Arab merchants who sold the ivory abroad with fabulous profit.

Actually the name "mammoth" originated with the Arabs, who learned that the tusks came from a colossal beast, and thought that this might have been the behemoth of their saga. Siberians perverted *behemoth* into *memot*, and the Russians eventually pronounced it *mamut*.

The Russian conquerors of Siberia first scoffed at the natives' tales of a giant animal, but took all the ivory they could find, and when they were shown huge bones found in marshes and dug out of the ground, they insisted that these were plants rather than fossils, and did not believe that the curved pieces of ivory, up to fifteen feet long, could be tusks. But the material being a salable commodity, they put the native slave labor digging the frozen ground for more of the kind. In 1799, one and a half centuries after the Russians began to exploit Siberian ivory, the first mammoth carcass was excavated. It was so perfectly conserved that dogs who ate some of the flesh suffered no evil effects. The mammoth was approximately fourteen feet high, and, but for its fur, small ears, and corkscrew-shaped tusks, it very closely resembled the Indian elephant. Two more carcasses were found in 1901 and 1908 respectively. By now the stores of mammoth ivory are about exhausted without ever having enriched the Russian treasury. Corrupt Russian overseers embezzled large quantities before the precious matter could reach official storehouses; storehouse guards stole some more before the goods went to the market; market commissars snatched part of the remainder. The thieves dealt with receivers of stolen goods, who paid but a fraction of the regular price and, in turn, undersold legitimate traders.

The tribes and clans who stayed behind when the mammoth hunters left encountered another beast that was to shape the course of their history, and that of many nations which would be visited by the men from Lake Baikal and from the Orkhon Valley and by their eastern neighbors and kin. For the tarpan turned pedestrians into horsemen. It existed since the end of the ice age, a shaggy, uncouth, grayish creature with a long, dark tail, a bristly mane, and a thin goat's-beard. Tarpans lived in the steppes of Dzungaria, south of the Altai Mountains and at the fringe of the Gobi Desert. They were the fastest runners the men had ever seen, and their stamina was practically unlimited. The hunters realized that by using these creatures as mounts they would outrace every game, and they succeeded in domesticating this smallish ancestor of the horse. The domesticated tarpan grew slightly larger and developed bushy manes and hoofs as hard as steel and greatly increased the range of action of the mounted hunters. It stimulated their combative inventiveness, the only remarkable ingenuity these men possessed. Gradually Mongolian clans learned to operate in fast-moving formation and, looking for weapons less clumsy than their crude axes, and of better range and accuracy, they found the bow. Bows and arrows were used in Siberia even before the aborigines learned the craft of pottery, and saddles and stirrups were known to Siberians who used only furs and fishskins as garments. The mounted men ranged the steppes as far east as Manchuria and as far west as the foothills of the Altais. They collided with other peoples, and the archers on horseback were victorious over men of higher and peaceful cultures. The motive of the forays was not only hunting; to feed their horses, the men needed access to even larger grass steppes. And as they used, ate, and milked horses, they discovered other animals which could be domesticated—sheep and bison-like yaks. Along with their herds grew an increased need for yet more grassland; and as they discovered that people less militant than they, but rich in desirable objects, lived along their path, they extended their raids to conquer more men and women who would provide them with what they coveted at first sight. In Central Siberia, just as in the north, the vanquished were made to serve the victors. The belligerent herdsmen profited by the achievements of the bronze and iron ages. They began to live in felt tents, to wear finer garments and footwear, and to use wheeled carts without having to acquire peaceful skills. Conquest stimulated the merger of clans into larger tribal units, and of bands into small armies.

Earliest tribal fusions may not have outlasted the particular purpose for which they were made, and they probably never survived the domineering individuals who brought them about. But the rudimentary pattern of Asiatic military nations was established, as primitive horses carried savage riders toward attractive spoils. Contours of an Asiatic version of leadership emerged as imperious men assumed command of armed bodies, perhaps one hundred strong, with their raw will the one and only authority.

What made the lawless horsemen accept one individual's leadership? Outstanding hunting and fighting skills alone would not quite explain the phenomenon. There is reason, however, to believe that their superstitions were legion, and that black magic played a major part in establishing the first tribal leaders. These men made no distinctions between alien races and kin. Internecine struggles were frequent, in particular when the carts were loaded with spoils. Slaves were forced to participate in battle. Formidable as they were, the warriors of the steppes shunned prolonged engagements in which their high-speed tactics could not have been sustained. Tradition indicates that it was not considered humiliating to flee when the opening assault failed to carry its objective.

Still, in prehistoric times new peoples penetrated into Siberia. Mankind was in foment from the Western Mediterranean to the Pacific. The grandiose migration of the most highly civilized people of antiquity took place eastward through Mesopotamia, toward the Indus River, Pamir, along the southern rim of the Gobi Desert, and south of the Himalaya Mountains, through Burma and Thailand, into China. It established the earliest provinces organized by law, which formed the framework of the world's oldest and mightiest empires: Persia, India, China. The flood of traveling mankind spilled over natural barriers; peoples less numerous than the principal nations poured into the steppes between the Caspian and Aral seas, and through the Pamir gap into Siberia, where they found land, attractive even to the dwellers of warmer zones. Wave after wave of men hit Siberia: some fair-haired, light-skinned; others with Oriental features, all on higher levels of civilization than the aboriginal horsemen and mysterious tribes they encountered on their long track to the basins of the Irtysh and the Yenisei, the regions around Lake Balkhash, the Ural Mountains, and the rim of the barren land that bordered the frozen marshes south of the Kara Sea.

This migration did not go east beyond the Yenisei basin; in view of the immense distances between the Middle East and that region, it would have been logical if the wanderers had stopped, partly out of weariness, partly because the wooded lands farther east appeared less fertile. When the sources of migration ran dry, Western Siberia had a comparatively large population, much larger than the east of the country. It cannot be determined when the nomad horsemen first became aware of the presence of Yenisei men, Ugrians, Samojeds, Uigurs, Tunguses, and many more nationalities in the western confines of their roaming grounds; their names can usually be traced to sources other than the peoples themselves. The Yenisei men, for instance, seem to have called themselves "Den" or "Din." They were skilled artisans whose fine ornaments and objects of bronze have delighted modern archaeologists; and they were also advanced agriculturists who knew how to irrigate land. The Siberian Ostjaks, remainders of the Yenisei men, have retained their ancestors' fair complexions, fine hair, and oval faces, while the descendants of Ugrians and Samojeds have black hair, sallow complexions, flat faces, and broad noses, indicating that they were all but absorbed by the nomads from the Far East. The Ugrians were well versed in bronze casting, artistic pottery, and even ironwork. Ugrians discovered and worked the iron mines of the Ural Mountains, trading in turn the metal and its produce, and delivering it as a tribute to conquerors who probably were of Mongolian origin. The nation of metalworkers knew how to make the implements of war, but not how to fight wars. In this they differ from the Finns, frequently presumed to be of Ugrian stock, and this divergency would indicate that the Finns were not descendants, but had been temporary masters, of the peaceable ironmongers.

To the Yenisei people came men of similar character and skills who had wandered north over the Altai passes, apparently under pressure by warlike tribes from the south or east. Pressures may never have ceased inside Siberia, even though it may have come from sources other than the violent Mongols and their kin. The Yeniseis were in contact with the Skolotes, or Scythians, warlike horsemen armed with bows and arrows. The Scythians were apparently inferior to the Mongols in tactics even though their mounts were of far better breed; but they were stronger than the Dins, and trade between the two peoples seems to have been profitable only to the stronger party. The Scythians eventually settled and established an empire of their own in Southern Russia and Western Siberia. They exchanged goods with the Greeks and formed one link between Europe, Siberia, and China.

Remains of Scythian culture exist in the extreme southwest of Siberia:

kurganes, tombs seventy feet high, dating back to the period between the seventh and eighth centuries B.C. They are built over vaults in which chieftains were laid to rest in arms and armor and with many treasures. The armor resembled the Greek mail. Weapons consisted of short, double-edged swords, and lances and javelins. In galleries leading to the vaults, excavators found carts, presumably used as hearses, and the skeletons of horses, oxen, and beheaded servants. Among the buried treasures were pieces of Chinese silk.

Those tombs, apparently dating back to the period that followed Scythian settlements, were also found in Mongolian areas. They were not as neatly built as the originals, but there can be little doubt that they were built after the western model by slaves who had been dragged into captivity by savage raiders and massacred after their work was completed. Early Siberians, even those of comparatively high culture, erected permanent structures only for their dead. No ruins of mansions, palaces, and temples have been found, no friezes and tabulary, which could have told the story of magnificence and misery. Yet there is evidence, infinitely more conclusive than ruins and fragments could have been, that life in Siberia was not always auspicious for the races who had reached the land that seemed so full of promise. Areas densely populated in antiquity turned into wasteland in which a few scattered and debris nations led a life of fear and superstition. Not nature's cataclysms but man-made catastrophies reduced the immigrants to their pitiful status; spoliation, and rape devastated Siberia long before the Russian seizure of this one third of Asia.

The remnant populations have almost no folklore, no sagas, and no traditions except a crude demon cult. They believe that demons are, and always were, the driving power of events—vicious and corrupt spirits, amenable only to exorcism by greedy, perverted men and women, and that nothing but calamity could result from their domination. But even the most hapless of men had hope. After a giant wielding an iron club had marched him from the realm of the living to that of the dead, he might be resurrected as a petty demon, capable of subjecting the living to vicious chicanery and blackmail.

Only untold perennial misery could have generated so misanthrophic a creed.

Mongolian raiders caused many, but by no means all, of the calamities that visited those who dwelled between the Yenisei Valley and the Urals. The nations of Central and Western Siberia also fought among themselves for a variety of reasons, one of which probably was trade rivalry. Trade started in antiquity, when merchants from the mellower south of Asia and their purchasing agents ranged far and wide through the northern continent in quest of precious furs for which they paid with glittering trinkets and fabrics; and it continued intermittently well into the Middle Ages, when bold and cunning traders from Northern Europe gathered riches from the Ural and the plains beyond and paid even less than their competitors.

For a long period, which may have started in 3000 B.C. or even earlier, only lesser Mongolian hordes crossed the Yenisei. The formidable horsemen found another, infinitely more rewarding, goal of their endeavors, some 700 miles southeast of the Orkhon River valley, beyond the Gobi Desert.

The ancient horsemen did not usually ride in that direction. The terrain was rough. There were few large tracts of grassland. High-velocity windstorms, carrying sand in the summer and needle-sharp particles of ice in wintertime, rendered the journey trying even for the hardiest races of men and mounts. It will never be established to what particular tribe they belonged, what caused them to trudge so far off the beaten track, or exactly when they turned in the fateful direction. One day, however, a party of weary, wayward horsemen, ragged and spreading obscene odors of rancid fat which was used as a protection against biting winds, reached a land the like of which they had never seen, and which was inhabited by people even more puzzling than the land in which they lived. The Mongols must have stared with dull, astounded eyes, at the sight of gardens and houses, of men and women in fancy attire who conversed and strutted leisurely, who did not smell, and whose appearance indicated opulence beyond the savages' imagination. The Siberians were in China.

The savages' natural reaction would have been attack, the shooting of arrows, a violent dash toward wealth untold, followed by orgies of rapaciousness. It would have been strange, indeed, had they acted differently. The Chinese, who make no specific mention of this first encounter with the horsemen, later used terms such as the "Malodorous" and the "Mendicants," to describe the intruders. The former is self-explanatory; the latter implied that the savages begged for alms. Nothing would be more alien to the Mongols than supplication; but maybe the Chinese did not care to acknowledge that they had been ravaged by high-smelling, brutish creatures, compared to whom, domestic bandits looked and acted like gentlemen.

The horsemen did not leave empty-handed. The mysterious encounter on the fringe of China probably was one of the most fateful events in human history.

Apparently the sight of the first spoils taken from China stirred other clans of horsemen into a frenzy. It gave their erratic raids a new direction. More and larger groups went southeast; Chinese border guards repelled several assaults, which stimulated the merger of tribes into larger groups of attackers, held together by the permanency of their objective. It taught indurate men to invoke supernatural help by cultic means. It accomplished what the taming of the tarpan and the introduction of the bow had started: the building of conqueror nations. The Chinese, in turn, had to concentrate on defense. They had to build new fortifications and to adopt a kind of militarism, which was distasteful to the diligent people, and became detrimental to its unity. For Chinese armies often would be used by provincial rulers for individual bids for power, and internecine struggles often overshadowed the fight against foreign aggressors. Weak emperors were constrained to hire barbarians, settle them along the border and supply them with new and better weapons to keep other barbarians away. They paid wages which barbarian chieftains came to consider as tributes that were their due. There were battles about tributes, defenders turning aggressors or abandoning their assigned areas of defense. Even powerful emperors, who quelled mutiny and chased transgressors away, could not quite remove the threat, although they occasionally imagined they had done so. The Siberian vastness provided an unassailable refuge to fleeing horsemen and an area of concentration for renewed attack. The danger, lingering on for centuries, interfered with Chinese relations with other cultured nations and had its effects on China's silk trade. With the horsemen ranging as far as Tibet ties between China and India loosened.

Silk traders had told the Chinese emperors a great deal about the Western world. But with the Siberians raiding communication lines and intercepting trade the monarchs were reluctant to chance soldiers and goods on a precarious venture.

Had China joined hands with Greece, and later with Rome, the world might have been unified at the beginning of our era. There might have been no prophecy of Gog and Magog; and the world might have been spared the Dark Ages had not the greedy, ignorant, crude archers conglomerated into invincible armies which eventually swept west, unleasing the avalanche of migrating nations that eventually burst into Europe.

The effects continued into the later Middle Ages, and even into our time. Without the military might of the Mongols there would have been no unified Russia and Siberia would not have come under the sway of tsars and Bolsheviks.

CHAPTER THREE China's legendary wealth, its mercantile expansionism, and its dangerous attraction for marauders date back to 2640 B.C. In that year, as Chinese chroniclers record, Si-ling, one of Emperor Huang-ti's wives, invented the silk loom, and her august husband decreed that henceforth his subjects should devote much of their time growing mulberry trees and breeding silkworms. Export of silk was encouraged, but extreme penalties faced those who would take silkworms or looms out of the realm. The tale goes that an imperial concubine, jealous of Si-ling, hid a few silkworms under her elaborate coiffure and smuggled them into India, where she gave so exact a description of the loom that eventually the Indians were able to weave their own silk. Otherwise, however, the secret was well kept, much better than that of any other production process any time anywhere.

Early invaders of Chinese territory seized neither worms nor looms. But the savage horsemen raved about silk. Their greasy, unkempt women wrapped their high-smelling bodies in the luscious fabric, soiling it as it touched their skins, but perceiving new, prickling emotions as they wore silk. Sluggish females were stirred into fierce sensuality and the effect on their males was tremendous. They would stake their own lives and those of their horses for a piece of silk, and silk even changed some of their traditional habits: for, if they could not obtain all they wanted by robbery, they would pay for it with whatever goods or services were demanded. Chinese merchants established the basic bartering value of silk at par with that of sable: one patch of silk for sable furs of equal size. But if the silk-hungry savages had had a particularly prosperous hunting season, silk might go up to twice the price of sable. The horsemen did not feel cheated, however. No amount of fur could do to their women what a small piece of silk did. Chinese emperors, anxious to placate or to hire unruly neighbors, offered bales of silk to clans and tribes who struggled among themselves for the coveted prize. Silk may have temporarily cushioned the impact of the horsemen's rush, but it attracted an ever-growing number of militant hordes to its source. They came from Dzungaria, and the approaches of Pamir, from Lake Baikal and the valley of the Amur, from the forests of Manchuria, and the confines of the Korean Peninsula, where a proud nation lived in the self-imposed seclusion of a peculiar culture. They roamed the fringe of the country of silk, like rapacious wolf packs, irritated by the lack of vast grazing grounds for their mounts and the inaccessibility of Chinese walled towns. They came to hate the cities and gardens and well-tended fields that did not yield the right kind of fodder for their horses.

Ki-tai (or Cathay), the horsemen called China. Ki-tai, the Siberians call it to the present day. The people of Ki-tai spoke of the savages as Tatas (Tatars), which, like the term "barbarians," originally used by the Greeks, stands for foreigners. The disparaging meaning of "barbarians" was established in the course of historic events, as the people to whom it applied proved to be crude and violent.

The Chinese also spoke of Türküts or Turcs, a race akin to the Mongols, and, by implication, to the Tatars. Tshino, a legendary Mongolian chieftain, was said to have first encountered the Türküt somewhere along the northern shores of Lake Baikal, but the time of that event and its immediate consequences remain veiled in mystery. The Türküt—they seemed to have originally called themselves Bite (or Beetae)—were not a homogeneous ethnological group. Their social organization was no less primitive than that of the Mongols who "discovered" them; Kirghizes, Huns (or Hiung-nu), and a great number of smaller Siberian ethnic groups were Turcs. The Huns were next in line for the designation of "the Malodorous." The term "Mendicants" applied to many tribes who came to gather silk, and to test the strength of Ki-tai, groping, fumbling, attacking and recoiling, and being hammered into aggressive shape on the anvil that the long Chinese border became for the foreigners from the steppes.

Chinese merchants visited the roaming grounds of the horsemen. They ranged as far north as the lands where the reindeer supplanted the horse and where natives would give any number of furs for silk and iron arrow points. But traffic was precarious and attracted only the boldest men. No Chinese emperor, however powerful, would provide armed escort for traders going to regions in which cannibalism was said to be rampant, and patricide a filial duty because only the spirit of a murdered man would be privileged to haunt the living.

The main highway of Chinese trade led west toward high civilizations. Persian kings, Egyptian priestesses, glorified Greek hetaerae, Roman great ladies, princesses and courtesans whose beauty shaped history wore the smooth fabric that acted as a universal aphrodisiac. And there is reason to believe that Helen of Troy's transparent garment was made of silk gauzes rewoven from closely textured Chinese material.

Silk was the East's glittering envoy to the Mediterranean, the pioneer of international trade which included spices, woolens, rugs, jewels, crystals, glass, and fine horses from the West, jade and rhubarb from China, and furs of Siberian origin. Silk trade provided warlike people along its road with peaceful occupations. Its proceeds created extravagant desires for luxury. Silk stimulated the dispatch of diplomatic missions to distant lands and accounted for fleeting visions of a civilized world united by trade. The lure of silk provided tremendous incentive to early seafarers. The seaway to China and India was known to the ancient Egyptians and Ethiopians. Ships manned by galley slaves traveled from Red Sea ports, past the Gulf of Aden, to the Arabian Sea, and to the mouth of the Indus River; they went to Ceylon, Burma, the Straits of Malacca, Sumatra, and to Hanoi, then a Chinese port. Pirates roamed the route, pillaging cargoes or blackmailing owners to hire them as protectors. Local governors charged arbitrary port and transit dues—actually heavy taxes. For lengthy periods conditions must have been chaotic, interrupting sea traffic. Alexander of Macedonia in all likelihood knew about the seaway to India, but he did not consider it a potential route of invasion.

One man, however, who had served as a general in the phalanxes of Alexander revived the naval traffic between the Middle and the Far East. He was Ptolemy Soter (367–283 B.C.), who ascended the throne of Egypt as an elderly man and founded a dynasty which was extinguished by the suicide of Cleopatra some 300 years later. Ptolemy, who longed for the treasures of the East and possessed a highly scientific mind (he was the founder of the Library of Alexandria), seems to have studied old charts which convinced him that the sea route was the safest communication between his realm and that of Eastern emperors. Under his sponsorship naval traffic to the East was resumed on an unprecedented scale. Egyptian ships left the expanded Red Sea ports of Hormos and Berenice, for the long voyage to Palibothra (Patna) on the Ganges River. Egyptian craft stopped at Eudaemon (Aden) to load Arab perfumes and incense; a multitude of exotic goods sold on Egyptian markets indicates that the vessels also touched many other lands and islands between the Arabian and the China seas. Roman merchants, who did a thriving business with Egypt, joined Egyptian skippers from the Red Sea carrying treasures from west to east, from east to west. When the Romans gained control of Egypt, Egyptian and Roman merchant fleets co-operated. Rome built warships to protect the trade against the threat of both pirates and of the Himyarites, an Arab nation that had established itself in Eudaemon.

The Himyarites, seafarers who aimed at a transit monopoly between Africa and Asia, viewed the expansion of Roman-Egyptian shipping with dismay. But Rome defended its mercantile interests with energy and cunning. Not only did Roman warships outfight Himyarite raiders; Roman punitive land expeditions hit Eudaemon territory from the north and imposed prohibitive duties on perfumes when the Himyarites did not give in. The Himyarites, who depended on Roman and Egyptian markets, meekly tried for a compromise that would keep them on the naval map. But Rome was unyielding; and, faced with the choice of seeing their commerce destroyed or their shipping at a standstill, the Himyarites chose the latter. Yet, as Rome's prestige waned in the third century of our time, Arabs, Nubians, and Ethiopians intercepted Roman shipping in the Red Sea. Some 600 years after the first Ptolemy restored sea traffic between the ancient empires of the East and West, the route vanished into oblivion. A millennium of dark ages would go by until the search for the forgotten route would be carried to a climax by Christopher Columbus' voyages.

The greatest part of the East-West traffic was carried over a land route later referred to as the "silk road." It cannot be established with reasonable accuracy exactly when the first caravans left China to trade with people who lived in the direction of the setting sun or in what ways trade expanded to span half the globe. Sections of the silk road led through Southern Siberia to the west of the Altai Mountains, and from the Ob to the Irtysh rivers. Excavations of tombs produced pieces of Chinese silk dating back to an early period. Well north of Urga, holy Mongolian city, not far from Lake Baikal, graves of chieftains contained textiles of Western origin, indicating that caravans returning to China with Greek goods touched Mongolian home grounds. Other Siberian finds include Chinese silk lined with sable and adorned with gold plates, and garments of ermine dyed green and red more artistically than either aborigines or slaves could have made them.

Trade caravans should have been anxious to avoid the roaming grounds of the rapacious foreigners. Yet the incentive of high profits lured merchants all the way north, to the land of the savage reindeer breeders, and to the wolf-man's perilous haunt, where survival was uncertain but remunerative. What Chinese silk traders told of their ventures is not conclusive. They mentioned names of peoples they met, but corrupted them into Chinese. Their reports do not indicate what these peoples' customs were, and what eventually became of them. West of the Hiung-nu, the records say, roamed the Hu-te, the Chien-k'un, and the Ting-ling. The Chien-k'un were also referred to as Uigurs, and they had their homestead in the steppes now inhabited by the Kirghizes. And there were also the You-ts'ai, the You, the Lin, Wu-i, and Hu-chich, who at the time of their discovery by the Chinese were no nations in the true meaning of the word, for they had no ethnical characteristics, no laws, no central leadership, no established territory. They seem to have traded with the caravans, exchanging horses, cattle, sheep, and furs for industrial products of which silk should have been the principal item. The Chinese were generally uncommunicative about their customers, and they regarded detailed information as trade secrets, no less restricted than military ones. For 2000 years following the invention of the silk loom, the Western partners of the Chinese trade did not record anything pertaining to business.

Not before the turn of the sixth century B.C. did Aristas of Preconnensus mention the nations Greek travelers had encountered in the distant northeast. Only fragments survive of Aristas' opus, the Arimaspea, parts of which were used by Herodotus (484–25 B.C.), the dean of history, in his study of the Scythians. He describes them as nomads who dwelled in covered wagons, drank mare's milk, and bartered with Greeks. The Scythians had migrated west to the Don River valley to escape harassment by the Massagetae, a belligerent nation of Asiatic, obviously Siberian, origin. Portions of the Arimaspea tell of a journey made by a man from Preconnesus from the Sea of Azov to the land of the Issedones, far to the distant northeast.

According to him, nine peoples lived along the road of trade and migration: the Sauromatae, the Budini, the Thyssagatae, the Iurcea, remnants of the Scythians, also the Agrippaei, the Issedones, and beyond the Issedones, the traveler learned, were the Arimaspi, a one-eyed people, separated by gold-guarding griffins from the Hyperboreans, who dwelled on the sea. All these nations but the Hyperboreans encroached on their neighbors, and the range of their struggles extended as far as the "southern sea," where the Cimmerians lived.

The journey undertaken by the man from Preconnesus, however, was not an isolated venture. Scythian traders, we are told, regularly traveled along that road of trade and migration; they used seven interpreters, one for every idiom they did not speak. They started north, from a region "destitute of trees," meaning steppes, and they took fifteen days to reach the wooded country of the Budini, "who sell furs." Beyond the Budini country toward the north extended "a desert of seven days' journey"; after crossing the desert, and turning northeast, the travelers reached the homesteads of the Thyssagatae and the Iurcea, who hunted in a lightly wooded country. In wandering east, through level land, deep-soiled first and rocky later, the roaming grounds of the scattered Scythian tribes were reached. The distant Scythians were constantly battling the Agrippaei, bald, flat-nosed men with prominent cheekbones, who lived in the foothills of lofty mountains. The Agrippaei could not climb mountains, but the Issedones had goat's-feet that carried them over rocks and snow fields to the distant side of the heights, where men slept six months a year, had no merchandise to trade with, but lived on gold stolen from the griffins.

Herodotus too used this story, but made no comment. Scrutiny indicates that it contained a fundamental error as to the direction of the route, which, according to Aristas, should have led in a north-northeasterly direction toward the Arctic Sea. But the existence of treeless steppe and a wooded zone fifteen days away would indicate that the road starting near Taganrog did not lead north, but east-northeast, and that the Budini lived somewhere in the southern Ural Mountains, where an abundance of fur animals roamed the woods. No desert existed, either in the southern Urals or straight north of the Sea of Azov, and trade routes would certainly have avoided regions of utter desolation. Indications are that the general direction continued easterly, through lightly wooded territory, "deep-soiled" level land—obviously regions of black earth —and rocky grounds. The Mongoloid features of the Agrippaei leave little doubt about their origin, which indicates that the trade route continued in the direction of upper Irtysh River, toward the northwestern gateway of China. It would be inexplicable why a trade route should lead to the homesteads of a people who had no merchandise to sell or barter. And had Aristas' traveler gone as far north as the chronicle implies, he would have reached no higher mountains than the Urals, with a top elevation of 5535 feet, and crossed by several low passes, which to tread required no "goat's-feet." The Altai Mountains, however, ranging up to about 15,000 feet, are rough and lofty. Plainsmen were hardly able to climb the forbidding slopes, and they may well have considered mountaineers who could do it as crossbreeds between goats and men. *"Altai"* stands for gold. Gold mines are still operated there, and they must have been known in antiquity. The Scythians possessed much gold, which seems to have come from the Altai Mountains, and the mysterious, peaceable Hyperboreans were obviously the Chinese.

Aristas' traveler did not meet the "Hyperboreans," and at the time of his voyage no direct contact existed between the peoples of the East and West. Otherwise the traders would not have needed seven interpreters to deal with the people along the road. In fact the Chinese transferred their silk road farther to the south, through Sinkiang via the Pamir gap, toward Persia, where customers were more civilized and goods for barter more attractive and plentiful. They did, however, continue trade with the Siberians through intermediaries, business-minded people, who grew prosperous and soft in the course of events. Alexander of Macedonia settled Greek colonists on the confines of India, where they remained after the phalanxes left. These Greeks engaged in trade with the "Seres," the silk people: main distributors of the beautiful fabric. The Seres were tall, with light eyes, reddish hair, and oval faces. They might have been related to the Scythians. The saga of the Nordic type of Asiatic man survived in several variations, one of which is that of the Aryans. The reddish-haired silk traders on horseback were eventually overthrown by belligerent archers from the east, who also swept over the Greek colony and restored the bow-law to all parts of Siberia.

In the third century before Christ the savages came very close to imposing their rule on Ki-tai, after that country had been split into separate provinces by internecine strife. Two thousand four hundred years after the invention of the loom the Tatas, Mongols, and Turcs were still brutal and primitive, but they had acquired two sources of might that their distant ancestors did not possess: a creed that lent itself to the promotion of tribal merger into large and coherent national bodies; and wealth that, stimulating the urge for even greater riches, provided the means to raise more horses, and to acquire additional equipment for the armies whose aggression the new creed sanctified.

CHAPTER FOUR The creed that engulfed all of Siberia in an infinitude of variations, spread to parts of Northern China and Korea, and left traces on the American Indians, Eskimos, Lapps, and ancient Finns may not actually have originated in Siberia, but in India. Its name, "shamanism," is a Tunguse inflection of the Indian *shramana*—ascetic. Scholarly definitions of shamanism call it a protracted form of natural religion, which invokes natural powers through spectral and ghostlike mediation; others call it a cult based on the belief in demons, spirits of deceased men and beasts, which communicate with wizards who have the faculty of dispatching their own souls yonder or luring the spirits thither, of inducing them to heal sickness, to charm hunting, and to make weather to turn tides of battle and personal fortunes, all with the approval of higher deities.

Clemens of Alexandria, Egyptian scholar, said that "sarmans" were hermits not dwelling in houses, covering their bodies with bark, eating wild fruits, and drinking only water. Those "sarmans" had feeding habits quite different from those of the Siberian wizards. Thomas Hyde and Kämpfer, turn-of-the-eighteenth-century scientists, differ in their interpretation of the term "shaman." Hyde thinks that it meant "those who sigh," or "those who belch," while Kämpfer insists that "men without passions" would be the fitting definition. The shamans undoubtedly belched a great deal; passions, however, were part and parcel of their performances.

Actually the multitude of aspects of shamanism defies interpretation in terms of religious science. The creed may be considered a codification of fears and superstitions, astutely administered by magicians for their own benefit and for that of any ambitious individual who might pay for it.

Counterparts of the Siberian shamans were the anegkok of the Eskimos, and the medicine men of the American Indians. The medicine men's divination dances, their outbursts of ecstasy, trance, and autohypnosis were similar to the antics which Siberian shamans performed well into the twentieth century.

A Siberian legend recorded in 1892, by Professor V. M. Mikhailowsky, tells the story of the first shaman: At the dawn of humanity, so Buryaet tribesmen claimed, celestial spirits were divided into two groups: the good, who dwelled in the west, who had created man and wanted him to live happily forever; and the evil, who dwelled in the east and plotted against humanity. When their wicked power caused people to fall ill, to suffer, to die, the good spirits created an eagle to come to the rescue of the imperiled; but men did not understand the eagle's cry. They would not have believed that a mere bird had the power to help them. The eagle besought the western spirits to bestow upon him the gift of human speech. The kindly creators could not grant the request, but they made a woman fall in love with the bird, and from their union, Khara Gyrgan, the first shaman, was born. This magician's powers were so great that God, supreme good spirit, decided to challenge him. God made a rich maiden fall ill, and her parents called Khara Gyrgan, who realized that the girl was ill because God held her soul in bondage. Undaunted, he swung his tambourine and flew on it, toward heaven, right to God's banquet table, where he saw the maiden's soul floating in an open bottle of wine. Before he could free her, however, God corked up the bottle and covered it with His right hand. The shaman transformed himself into a yellow spider and bit God on His right cheek, so that the supreme good spirit clapped His hand to the aching spot, releasing the bottle. Khara Gyrgan opened it, grabbed the soul, and thus healed the girl. Angrily God reduced Khara Gyrgan's cunning, and decreed that henceforth the powers of no shaman would ever match His own.

Other Siberians have different legends.

The Yakuts say that the first shaman was a giant of immense strength who challenged the power of God, who transformed the blasphemer's body into a heap of reptiles and sent a fire to scorch the crawling mass. One lizard escaped destruction, and, together with a frog, the lizard begot demons who have provided Yakuts with shamans of both sexes ever since.

The Tunguses credit the devil, master of evil spirits, with the creation of the original shaman; and among the people of the Altai Mountains, Erlik, ruler of the underworld, is considered the highest deity to whom a shaman can apply in matters concerning private individuals.

Old Finnish and Karelian heathenism, closely akin to Siberian idolatry, says that the spirits who determine the fate of men were dwellers of the waters; and that the supreme spirit—Ukko, the Old One—resided at the bottom of the deepest lake. Ukko listened to the entreaties of wizards, whom the Karelian Lopars (Lapps) called moials.

A shaman's marks of distinction varied among different tribes. The Tunguses requested that a candidate for shamanism make it credible that a deceased wizard had chosen him for his successor, and that he was on intimate terms with ranking evil spirits.

Yakutian usage required that Emeket, the guardian spirit of dead shamans, select new wizards. Usually Emeket would choose a relative of the late shaman, make him rage, gabble, pass out, recover, and run about like mad. The possessed would throw himself into fire and water, stab and cut his own limbs, feed on bark, and keep acting like a demon until appointed. The consecration took place in an open field or on a hilltop, with an aged shaman performing the rites. The candidate, clad in a shaman's garb, was invested with a tambourine and drumsticks. Nine chaste youths stood to his right, nine virgins to his left, as he recited a magic formula after the aged wizard. The end of the ceremony was marked by the offering of an animal whose flesh was distributed among members of the community.

Among Samojeds and Ostjaks, the office of shaman was hereditary. Both men and women were eligible. Buryaets of Southern Siberia preferred offspring of people who had been killed by lightning.

Ceremonial costumes of shamans, as described by modern explorers, consisted of the *orgoi*—a cloak of silk or cotton, blue for a wizard who dealt with evil spirits, white for one whose sponsoring demon was good—a hat of lynx fur with a tuft of ribbons, and soft leather boots. The cloak was adorned with metal horses, birds, and drinking cups. High-ranking shamans, once they had received five ablutions, had their garments lined with fur, and their cap exchanged for an iron hat with two edges turned up like horns and trimmed with small iron gadgets like rings and spoons.

Female shamans sported fancy accessories. Buryaet sorceresses wore three antlers on their iron hats and up to thirty ribbons of black and white fur suspended from shoulders to ground. Yakut women shamans adorned their cloaks with gaily embroidered strips of silk hung with tassels. It appears, however, that neither tradition nor decorative attire made common people trust women shamans as firmly as they trusted men.

The shamans' cultic implements—sticks adorned with horses' heads, bells, and fur ribbons, a tambourine, and several lesser charms—were kept in a painted wooden box standing on legs almost two feet high; the paintings represented the sun, the moon, one female, and two male figures.

Shamans of both sexes performed fakir tricks. They swallowed burning coal. They stabbed themselves, without apparent injury, in the head, liver, and stomach. They made objects disappear and turn up again at the most unlikely places. Most of these tricks were obvious fakery, carried out by amazingly primitive means, but occasionally the shaman really seemed to possess extraordinary powers. Shaman ecstasies and convulsions frequently were either simulated, or were produced by dangerous potions; yet enthralled audiences raved, shouted, and swayed no less violently than the wizard. They would blindly follow his signs, convinced that the shaman's convulsions were the demon's own manifestations of supernatural powers that would wane as the spasms abated. The body of an entranced shaman was believed to radiate healing powers. People brought their sick to witness a wizard's ecstasies. The suggestive effects of shaman juggling has survived into our time. Russian invaders of Siberia, Christians at least in name, also fell for the tricks. In eighteenth-century Irkutsk a Russian horde seized a young shaman, crucified him, and cut his body into pieces to boil medicine from his "curative flesh."

A nineteenth-century Russian account of shaman rites describes an invocation of Erlik by a *kam,* as people from the Altai Mountains called their wizards:

The *yurta* (felt hut), in which the ceremony took place, was crowded with villagers watching the kam, who, at a low voice, told of having started on a journey to Erlik's abode. He was on his way through the mountains, flying toward the "Red Land Ki-tai," and from there he turned in the direction of a yellow steppe over which "no magpie could fly." But "with songs we shall traverse it," he exclaimed, and in a soft, monotonous singsong in which the audience joined the wizard announced that the steppe had been crossed, but that he was now facing Temir Shaikha, the iron mountain, whose peak pierced heaven. Nobody could fly as high as the lofty slopes; only by ascending step by step would he make his way. The shaman breathed hard, staggered, stopped, moved on again. The audience, too, breathed hard; they made encouraging motions, but nobody tried to support the kam, who, panting, spoke of bleaching bones lining his way, remnants of weaker shamans who had fallen by the wayside. . . . The gasping kam reached the mountaintop. "Men's bones are heaped up in rows, there are scattered bones of horses, too . . ."; the wizard was now riding on horseback downhill toward the jaws of the earth, a hole leading to the underworld. He dismounted as he reached the shore of a lake. A hair was spanned over the huge surface of water: the bridge that visitors of the underworld had to cross. No sinful creatures could cross the hair. They would fall, and while their bodies rotted at the bottom of the transparent waters, their souls would suffer punishment ashore. There were sinners also among kams: one soul's ear was nailed to a pillar; he had been an eavesdropper. But the kam who told the story was free of blame. He got safely across, and after beating off a fierce pack of watchdogs, he stood in front of the jaws of the earth. Virtue, however, had no effect on the keeper of the gates; he wanted presents, or else the kam would not pass. The audience put big slices of meat, skunk skins, and small pails of home-brewed beer before the kam. The keeper seemed satisfied, for the kam disclosed that he was being admitted to Erlik's yurta. From then on the wizard acted and spoke two parts, his own and that of the ruler of the underworld. He bowed, held his tambourine against his forehead, pronounced the greeting formula *"mergu, mergu,"* and tried to explain the purpose of his intrusion. Erlik emitted a rough shout of anger that sent the wizard reeling back. The audience was dismayed, but the shaman advanced again, only to be repulsed by another outburst of wrath. At last Erlik chose to speak. "Those that have feathers fly not hither, those who have bones walk not thither; Thou black, ill-smelling beetle, whence cometh thou . . . ?" Thus encouraged, the kam introduced himself, and offered "Prince Erlik" a drink of beer that had been poured into his tambourine. Erlik drank—the wizard enacting the procedure with sonorous hiccups—and asked for more. More beer was poured into the tambourine, and presents were offered to the prince of the underworld: a freshly killed ox, garments, furs. "May these gifts, which no horse could lift, clothe thy neck and body." Erlik was mollified, and the beer he kept drinking produced a happy mood. The kam mocked and heckled the tipsy prince, who, between thunderous hiccups, promised to multiply the petitioner's cattle, "and his mare shall have a fine colt . . ." The shaman turned around and crouched. He now rode back to earth on a wild goose. They landed. The kam made a few steps on tiptoe and sat down. A man took his tambourine, another reached for the sticks. The kam rubbed his eyes, as if awakening from a deep slumber: "My journey has been successful, and I was well received." After some haggling with the crowd he kept part of the goods presented to Erlik and to the keeper of the gate.

In other parts of the Altai Mountains more elaborate rites were held by top ranking shamans, to mediate between tribes and Bai-Yulgen, the mighty god who dwelled in the sixteenth heaven. The shaman selected a birch grove close to a meadow, and an elaborate yurta was built around a young tree. Nine steps were hewn into the lower trunk; a branch was rammed into the ground and a noose of horsehair fastened to it. On the first evening of the ceremony the soul of a horse was offered to Bai-Yulgen. The shaman waved a twig of birches over the back of the live animal (where, according to the creed, the souls of all creatures were located) to drive the soul into his tambourine. Eventually he completed the procedure, and the soul with the shaman's voice reported, "Here I am, Kam." Next the shaman sat down outside the yurta, on a low stool shaped like a goose. Waving his arms, he chanted at the top of his lungs: "Below the white sky, above the white cloud, below the blue sky, above the blue cloud, mount, O bird, to the sky."

"*Ungai gak, kaigai gak, gak, gak,*" the shaman's lowered voice responded. This was alarming. It meant that the horse's soul had escaped from the tambourine and that the bird was pursuing it. Silent spectators gesticulated wildly, trying to join the chase. At last the soul was back in the tambourine pinfold, but the shaman kicked and neighed, indicating that the captive was fighting back. The horse had not yet been touched, but now the shaman turned against it with an angry outcry. Everybody got frantic. Raving, howling, foaming men tore the animal into bits with knives and axes. They devoured the raw, bleeding flesh, with the shaman getting the choicest parts and the skin being sacrificed to Bai-Yulgen. The sanguinary orgy ended the first part of the ritual.

On the following day, after sunset, the shaman made his pilgrimage to the god. As he sang an incantation, a fire was kindled inside the yurta, meat was fed to the spirits of the tambourine. "Come to me O Kaira-Khan, Master of the Tambourine, with six bosses, come to me, amidst tinkling. If I shout, '*Chokk,*' bow thyself, if I cry, '*Mé,*' accept my gift." After a similar invocation to the master of the fire, the kam raised a cup, gulped, and handed morsels of horseflesh to onlookers who swallowed them eagerly, as symbols of the spirits.

Nine garments, fumigated with juniper and adorned with colored ribbons, were brought in. "A-A-A," the kam exclaimed, "garments with triple collars, look at them thrice, turn them over thrice, gifts they are—let them be thy cover, Prince Yulgen, full of gladness." The shaman donned his ceremonial helmet, fumigated the tambourine, and summoned the birds of heaven whose appearance he announced with the customary: "Here I am, Kam."

"Celestial birds," he replied, "five Merykuts, with mighty, brazen claws—the moon's claws are of copper, the beak of the moon is of ice, mighty is the flapping of the broad wings, the long tail is like a fan, the left wing hides the moon, the right wing covers the sun. Thou art the mother of nine eagles, soaring, approach my right eye and sit on my right shoulder."

"Gak—Kagak—Kak."

The shaman bent his right shoulder, as if crushed by the weight of the celestial bird. He beat the tambourine that seemed to have become extremely heavy. He rose with great effort, stumbled around the birch tree, fell on his knees, implored the "porter spirit" to help him up, rallied, beat his tambourine, and moved the drumsticks to scrape uncleanliness away and to liberate the souls of those present from wicked Erlik. The crowd turned their backs to the shaman, so that their souls could be easily reached. The wizard muttered unintelligible sounds, trembled, tripped, swung into a dance; the audience, too, began to dance, slowly first, then faster and ever faster. They shouted, raved, embraced each other in lewd, often perverse, postures. The kam patted the women's breasts with his tambourine, touched the men's extremities with drumsticks, then indicated with gestures that everybody was being invested with ceremonial garments and hats, to be ready for the prophecies that would follow. The shaman now combined in himself the powers of his wizard forefathers. He paused, the audience's passions abated; but then the kam had another spell of ecstasy, circling the birch tree at a dizzy pace, raising his tambourine. "Gok, Gok, Gok." Onlookers kindled a small fire near the roots of the tree. The wizard, oblivious of the glow, prepared to climb the steps in the trunk, but turned away and, roaring, made for the sacrificial horse skin spread at the entrance of the yurta. Crouching on the skin, he pretended to ride heavenward. "Aikhai! I have reached one zone, Shagarbata! I have climbed to the top steps! Shagarbata! I shall rise to the full moon!" As he kept riding, he indicated that the horse's soul had gotten tired and that he had changed to a goose. After passing three more zones he told in a tearful tone of the bird's and his own exhaustion. Fortunately, however, the wizard had already reached a region where information on weather could be obtained from spirits. The spirits forecast rain, which the shaman communicated to the audience in singsong: "Kara Shurlu, with six staves, drips on the low ground. Nothing with hoofs can protect itself, nothing with claws can uphold itself." The upward journey was resumed. Higher heavens were symbolized by mysterious animals, whose parts the shaman enacted: The Karakush, a black bird who helped the wizard, was treated to a pipe of tobacco, which the shaman smoked with gusto. A cuckoo interfered, but was shot by the Karakush. An elusive hare was difficult to catch, but eventually the shaman reached the zone where the creator Yayuchi, acting on Bai-Yulgen's orders, revealed the future. The shaman's voice was a confusing mutter, but nobody asked questions. Leaving Yayuchi's heaven, the shaman rose to the moon, then to the sun, and kept indicating that he was rising even higher. Only famous wizards could safely claim to be passing the ninth zone, beyond the steps in the tree, and to penetrate celestial regions above the twelfth. At last the shaman dropped his tambourine, moved his drumsticks in a strange rhythm, and, as complete silence settled over the crowd, pronounced an address to the god of the sixteenth heaven, the top of the Golden Mountain; "Lord, to whom three ladders lead, Bai-Yulgen, owner of three flocks; the blue slope that has appeared, the blue sky that shows itself, the blue cloud that whirls along, inaccessible blue sky, inaccessible white sky, placed a year's journey away from the nearest waters, Father Yulgen, thrice exalted, whom the edge of the moon's ax avoids, who uses the hoof of the horse, thou, Yulgen, who hast created men swarming around us, thou, Yulgen, who hast endowed us with all cattle, let us not fall into sorrow; grant that we may resist the great evil spirit, do not hand us over to him, Thou, who hast turned the starry sky thousands and thousands of times, do not forsake us because of our sin."

The speaker closed his eyes. His muscles slackened as he finished the invocation, yet his voice remained clear, as he recited Bai-Yulgen's reply. The god made another weather forecast, elaborated on future harvests, and explained what further offerings he expected. The shaman's bearing indicated a state of trance as he elaborated on the god's demands. Bai-Yulgen designated the individuals who should supply the animals intended for sacrifice. At last the shaman fell silent and slid to the ground. Nobody was allowed to utter a sound until he recovered. After a few minutes he rubbed his eyes, stretched his limbs, wrung his sweat-drenched coat, and greeted the assembly as if he had returned after a long absence.

Bai-Yulgen's wishes were met without delay. Not even the greediest men dared ignore the god's command, but contributors would try to recover at least parts of the meat, as it was distributed among the members of the community. The shaman got the lion's share.

The third and final part of the ritual did not include religious ceremonies. It was a social gathering in honor of the god, a drinking bout in which immense quantities of kumiss, the traditional Siberian beverage brewed of mare's milk, were consumed. Beer was strong enough for Erlik, but the people's urge for intoxication asked for something more powerful—and kumiss had provided Siberians with inebriations from time immemorial.

Southern Siberian faithfuls ordained their wizards with flagellant rites; old shamans scourged the novices' bared backs with birch twigs, soaked in a hot concoction of bark, thyme, juniper, hoofs, horns, hair, and animal's blood. While hitting the novices, they pronounced instruction formulas, such as: "If a rich man calls thee, ride to him on a bullock, and do not charge much for thy services." "If a poor man calls thee, accept whatever he offers you." "Should a rich man and a poor man call for thee at the same time, go to the poor man first." The flagellation was occasionally inflicted by persons of the opposite sex. Whips were also used to chase evil spirits from sick persons; if the whip did not produce the desired effect, the shaman applied boiling water, and made dangerously deep incisions in delicate parts of the sick body. Milder treatment included sucking of boils and sores, ritual dances, and the offering of young animals.

In the nineteenth century the decaying remnants of mighty Siberian hordes, once the terror of emperors, kings, popes, and patriarchs, and now at the mercy of arbitrary Russian tyrants, had no vision of greatness. Their ambitions did not go beyond satiation, petty vengeance, and survival; yet they would invoke the same spirits their distant ancestors had called to promote ventures that shook the foundations of the world. And those wizards who faked and cheated for a slice of horse meat and a cup of kumiss applied essentially the same tricks their predecessors had used to help merge rival bands into the host of Huns, Awars, Magyars, Mongols, Tatars, and to convince dull warriors that the entire world and all its peoples were their property.

The ancient horsemen of the steppes were not afraid of humans. But they were haunted by fears of the elements, of apparitions and phantoms—of everything they could not outride or slay. They dreaded darkness. Wind threw them into terror. Rustling leaves frightened them more than the clink of arms, and every corpse or carcass was an unassailable spirit with evil designs. All the objects of their fears had to be placated, or at least bribed into turning against other men.

The earliest form of worship in Siberia was probably Satanism, with every clan, every family, having its own ritual. Shamanism brought scattered idolatries into a system with regional variations. There are no indications of a central religious organization in Siberia at any time. However, Siberian idols, dating back to a very early period, have two characteristics in common: they face east, and they stand either on the ground or on poles—never on pedestals. The totem poles of North American aborigines also face the rising sun.

Early Siberian conquerors were no converters to the shamanite faith and the shamans were no warriors. They would not stake their prestige on an action the outcome of which profane clansmen could see. The wizard's power should remain clouded in awesome mystery. Yet spiritual and mundane powers did not clash. They collaborated. As Siberian chieftains and princes merged their tribes and peoples, or conquered hordes akin to their own, all shamans stayed in office and invariably acclaimed the victor as the chosen of their demons. Co-operation between shamans and military leaders produced nations on horseback, a hundred thousand and more archers strong. Ever-growing bodies of Siberian raiders burst over Chinese land; new hordes exploited experiences gathered by their predecessors. To booty in goods was added the ransom, which the Chinese would pay for the release of kinsfolk driven into captivity. The raiders' prosperity grew. Their princes gathered riches that enabled them to satisfy the demands of their own shamans, and also to corrupt other wizards into urging their leaders to accept the suzerainty of some rich nobleman.

The Siberians' nomadic urge was not affected by numerical growth; their instincts rebelled against restriction by boundaries. But with China remaining the goal of their raids, and their vast number of animals requiring huge pastures, they concentrated on the grasslands beyond Lake Baikal as a suitable springboard, with several Siberian tribes aiming for that same target. Their internecine feuds gave the Chinese a series of breathing spells without which the empire might not have survived.

CHAPTER FIVE Ancient China was too large a realm to be safely governed by any single man, unless his name carried hypnotic power. In the fifth century before Christ, imperial might waned. First, governors of the five main provinces exceeded their vast delegated powers, and gradually princes and princelings, district administrators and magistrates defied their sovereign and their superiors. China's rulers turned into figureheads, and eventually lost even their symbolic authority. Two hundred years after the decline had started, the monarchs were debilitated, ostentatious seigniors whose authority and mental horizon were limited by the gates of their elaborate palaces, and whose policies concentrated on the cabals, perversions, and intricate abominations that pervaded their residences.

Provincial governors and district heads used executive forces to consolidate their arbitrary rule. Even though they were highly cultured men, their procedures did not essentially differ from the methods applied by the "malodorous," the "beggars," and other barbarians expanding their domain. The silk-clad, jewel-studded, perfumed dignitaries used trickery and violence to seize neighboring provinces and to gather sufficient territory and subjects to proclaim themselves emperors in their domains and aspirants to the throne of all China. Provincial armies, all of which called themselves imperial, were locked in a war of pretenders. Up to thirty petty supreme war lords, who styled themselves emperors, drained China's resources to ravage China. Temporarily the northern frontier was almost bared; professional soldiers and chariots were diverted to battlegrounds in the interior and only local levies of inadequately trained men garrisoned the long line and the fortifications far apart from one another. The line was frequently pierced by raiders; defenders were dispersed, or captured and held for ransom. One single big push—no stronger in fact than several attacks in the past—would have cut clear through China, and some greasy leader of horsemen would have ascended the imperial throne.

The big push, however, did not materialize during the decades of extremity. The chaos subsided; pretenders aged and died; military stalemates developed; armies wearied; mass desertions increased in frequency; corrupt officers led their men over to the camp of anybody who would pay wages or promise to do so, and mercenaries had no desire to do more than collect their pay.

A ruthless and determined man, with the material and suggestive strength to make the leaderless, demoralized masses of China believe in his omnipotence, would be able to seize the reins of the central government and restore it to a degree of power it had never had before.

Ch'in Shih Huang-ti fitted the pattern and became the man of destiny.

The year was 240 B.C. "Thanks to his wisdom, energy, and saintliness," a court historian recorded, "Ch'in Shih Huang-ti has pacified and united under a single sceptre, all countries within the four seas, chased away the barbarians of the South, forced into obedience all the lands under the sun and the moon. He has reduced ancient Princedoms and Kingdoms to the status of counties, and he made the most humble of his subjects live in happiness; for henceforth no wars will be possible during the lifetime of at least ten thousand generations to come."

The "barbarians of the South" may have been the Tibetans who had joined the intruders during the period of China's worst wretchedness. The Emperor's pacification of "all countries within the four seas" could also refer to Siberia, and possibly even to countries in Southwestern Asia. But there is little evidence that Ch'in Shih Huang-ti held his scepter over domains beyond the historical boundaries of China, and it appears as if China had maintained no contact with the subcontinent of India while under his rule. The slogan of "peace for ten thousand generations" has since been adopted with variations by many statesmen and dictators. The original prophecy was as vain as the exultations of the imitators. The generation that witnessed the rise of Ch'in Shih Huang-ti was not spared the horror of war, and their children had no reason to believe in a multiple millennium.

Not even during the climactic decades of the pretenders' struggle did Chinese caravans discontinue traffic with foreign lands. The merchants paid whatever dues local rulers would collect and still managed to make profits. They were not only efficient in economics, but were also interested in science and politics. Their observations of events along the silk road, and of the displacements and disappearance of nations beyond the highway of trade, were duly recorded in geographical tablets and tables of history. The feuding pretenders, however, did not care to study the documents.

The new Emperor, who liked to be extolled as the first real Emperor China ever had, was interested in writings; so greatly interested, in fact, that he ordered all books that did not conform with his views to be burned. Geographic tablets and merchants' accounts were not burned, however; from them he learned that some of the nations west of Pamir, with whom the silk traders used to deal, had been pushed away or destroyed by horsemen sweeping the distant parts of Siberia; that large and ominous concentrations of riders had been forming on and off in the Baikal region and in the boundless forests beyond the lake; that bloody wars had been fought among primitive tribes; and that, as China had been decaying, new nations had formed at its northern and western doorsteps. The overweening Emperor would not consider these barbarian groups to be nations in the sense the word applied to his own subjects, but he was determined to force them into obedience. Besides pacification of the perennial rapacious raiders was a sound goal. As long as China's northern boundary was unsafe, the country's economy would be slow to recover and the ruler's global designs could not be carried out.

The new nations said to have formed on the threshold of China were, in fact, not new in the ethnical sense of the word. Mongols and Turcs (the latter then referred to as Tu-küeh by Chinese chronicles) were still roaming their historic grounds, but their organizational structure had changed as the rule of individual leaders expanded. The battles between the horsemen, of which vast burial grounds are the only records, temporarily made the Hiung-nu the strongest contenders for hegemony in Siberia.

The Hiung-nu ranged from the Ordos to the borders of Persia. Their actual numbers were incredibly small compared to the vastness of their roaming grounds; yet they could quickly assemble hard-hitting forces in any area of resistance. Battering the doors of the weak, they forged themselves into greater coherence. They made no organized attempt at seizing Persia, however, disrupted in the aftermath of subjugation by Alexander of Macedonia, in the years 334–31 B.C. Later they also missed their opportunity to seize China.

The Hiung-nu staged nuisance raids on China after Ch'in Shih Huang-ti came to power. But the Emperor's ruthless energy restored discipline in his army, turned marauding mercenaries into soldiers, and corrupt bandit chieftains into officers. In forced marches his troops reached the border regions in the early spring of Ch'in's first year of rule just as the raiders, emerging from winter camps, opened the harassing season. As summer approached, the Emperor decreed that an army of unprecedented size be drawn up to mete out punishment upon the barbarians. Five hundred thousand men were mobilized, according to the Emperor's historians. They were equipped with the finest weapons engineers could devise: chariots with scythe-like accessories to mow down enemy ranks, catapults, high-power bows, and improved javelins. The figure 500,000 probably included camp followers who usually outnumbered combatants. Ch'in Shih Huang-ti rode in pomp at the head of his host through the major cities of the empire, but he did not actually take the field; and because he did not quite trust his generals, who still might use their forces for a domestic *putsch* rather than for a foreign war, he assigned Li-sé, a ranking member of his cabinet, as something intermediate between commander-in-chief and political commissar. Li-sé's powers awed the generals, but they involved a terrific responsibility: The Emperor's orders were to chasten the Hiung-nu so thoroughly that they would never again disturb the peace. Failure to carry out the order would stir the Emperor's anger—wrath gruesome beyond words.

The first year of Ch'in Shih Huang-ti's rule was not yet over when couriers arrived, reporting the complete destruction of all enemy forces and the glorious advance of the Chinese troops through all the lands under the sun and the moon. The Emperor ordered elaborate festivals to celebrate "victory and peace for 10,000 generations," but frolicking crowds near the Ordos border were suddenly attacked by Hiung-nu hordes who gathered immense spoils and dragged a great number of young men and pretty girls into slavery. Li-sé, no less panicky than the few survivors, tried to placate his raging sovereign by explaining that the raiders belonged to a splinter tribe which had been absent from the scene of battle of annihilation and was now being hotly pursued; its destruction, and that of any other tribe that might have been overlooked, was only a matter of short time. The Emperor accepted the explanation.

The "short time" lasted ten years, during which many hostile raids hit China, while bulletins from the field told of several victories, every one decisive.

The Hiung-nu did not issue battle reports, but it would not be surprising if the Chinese had remained masters of the battlefield in most, if not all, major engagements. Holding a battlefield had little meaning to horsemen; they did not think in terms of ground, but of spoils, and would not stay on at the scene of battle even if the enemy were shattered.

In 229 B.C. the unfortunate Li-sé prostrated himself before his emperor and submitted his final report. The enemies were a band of mendicants, he claimed wearily, not worthy of imperial attention. They had neither cities nor supply centers that could be occupied; they were nomads, wandering around, hard to catch up with, almost impossible to keep under control. "You may send light troops against them; mobile units will penetrate deep into enemy territory, but they will eventually starve there. You may use forces, heavily supplied with food and weapons, but they won't be able to follow the Hiung-nu through their wastelands. And even if you were to conquer all the lands which they now roam, they would evade you and move to even more distant regions; and if you could round them up you could never make them settle down and till the soil. You would have to kill them all. . . . Continuation of the campaign would sap your army's strength to the delight of the savages. I have therefore withdrawn the bulk of your forces into areas where no supply trouble exists." These areas were parts of China. Only patrols remained beyond the border, and they did not venture far inside the "wastelands."

Li-sé paid the price for failure, for which he had to assume responsibility, for the Emperor was infallible. And because peace for ten thousand generations remained the cornerstone of imperial policy, it had to be assured by means other than military victory.

The Emperor decreed that fortifications be built, so strong that they would forever bar invaders from the soil of China. This was a far cry from the aim of ruling "all countries under the sun and the moon," but court historiographers did not amend earlier assertions on the extent of the imperial sway.

Ch'in Shih Huang-ti did not permit the name of his engineers who drafted the blueprints for the Great Wall to be recorded for posterity; there should be no other builder than the Emperor, and no other genius deserving to have his name associated with the most fabulous construction of all times. The Great Wall made Egyptian pyramids appear like toys, and would have dwarfed modern fortifications like the Maginot, the Siegfried, and the Mannerheim lines. The Chinese stronghold was considered impregnable when it was constructed and it was further strengthened and repaired for almost 1700 years. And though later it did not permanently halt enemy attacks, it prevented several invasions, impeded many more, and diverted drives of Siberian horsemen in a westerly direction. Without the wall the Migration of People might have taken a different course; for China was a more alluring goal than the distant west, of which the migrating hordes knew nothing except that it was not protected by a bulwark so strong.

Thirty-four old border fortresses were rebuilt as anchors and key points of a wall 1000 li—roughly 1500 miles—long; small watchtowers were established at distances of 100 yards; catapult emplacements and archery covers controlled the entire forefield. The wall was between fifteen and thirty feet high. Its facings of brick and stone were an average of thirteen feet apart and filled in with earth so firmly compressed that it could carry practically any load of men and materials. The wall was so wide that three cavalry men could ride on it abreast. Moats and ditches barred its northern approaches; storehouses inside the fortification contained everything that defending soldiers might need in a long battle. An ingenious signal system permitted concentration of adequate forces in any sector within a short time. A garrison of 300,000 was to be billeted in quarters more comfortable than city barracks. The fortified line ran over mountains and plateaux up to 7000 feet high, through winding valleys, deep gorges, across rivers and streams, through wastelands and rocky grounds, across territory in which not even hardened herdsmen had ever set up their huts. About 2,000,000 workers labored on the wall, which took eighteen years to complete—an amazingly short time in view of the unparalleled magnitude of the project, and the primitive means of construction.

Work was begun in 228 B.C. The Emperor had all men under criminal sentence conscripted; murderers and robbers worked side by side with unsuccessful generals and authors of burned books. The military draft was suspended to enlist young men into the labor force. Hundreds of thousands perished from accidents, overwork, and exposure, but no rebellion occurred. People hardly ever rebel against a strong tyrant; they seem to save their vindictiveness for his feeble epigoni. Ch'in Shih Huang-ti's prestige was not affected by the futility of the ten-year war against the Hiung-nu. He had proud achievements to his credit: he gave China uniform laws that safeguarded justice; he reformed the administration, dividing the country into thirty-six provinces and clearly defining the governors' powers; he introduced free trade throughout the realm, and a system of weights, measures, and currency, from which everybody profited except crooks. And it seems that the Chinese people trusted that the Great Wall, erected at a terrific expense in life and property, would eventually achieve its purpose.

The Emperor died the year it was completed. His last decrees dealt with the building of the defense armies. His son was a weakling, neither administrator nor soldier, effeminated by the delights of palace life and inhibited by his father's imperiousness. Ch'in Shih Huang-ti had no delusions about his successor, and worried about the future of his realm. Reliable reports told of strong barbarian hordes gathering beyond the border, inexorably, menacingly. Officers asserted that the hordes were not yet a real threat, and that there was a strong possibility that they would start fighting among themselves and vanish into the vastness. But merchants, better acquainted with horsemen's affairs, said that a strong leader had arisen in the Ordos who was rallying tribes that had previously shunned mergers and fought subjection; and that the camps of his followers already spread beyond a man's view, and kept expanding. According to the traders, these barbarians were wealthy; they owned countless bales of silk, splendid furs, gold, jewels, and even fine horses of foreign breed. Barbarians liked glitter, but after being saturated with its spectacle they would trade gold for arms and use the arms to devastating effect. Indications were that the barbarians were already bartering objects of value against Chinese-made bows and arrows of improved range and penetrating power. There was no legal ban on arms traffic. The Emperor himself was a champion of free trade. Despite his innate scorn of barbarians the aging monarch might have felt a certain affinity with the man from Ordos, who was doing what he himself had done in China, and it might have given him a weird comfort to think that the barbarian too might raise a successor who could not uphold his father's achievements.

Ch'in Shih Huang-ti's son was never put to the test. He was murdered three years after he ascended the throne and with him a short-lived dynasty came to an end. By the sheer law of momentum the central government apparatus continued in existence with thirty-six governors, countless princes and generals, feuding for its control. So concerned were the pretenders with their own objectives that they did not watch the portentous developments right across the Great Wall.

They did not even know that the mysterious leader of the barbarians was a Mongol, that his name was Modo, that his wizards had proclaimed him the chosen of celestial spirits to rule the earth, and that his title was Khaghan or Khan-Emperor. They knew nothing of Modo Khan's efforts to create a novel type of military organization co-ordinating the operations of huge bodies of horsemen. Modo divided his host into divisions 10,000 strong, to operate under a united command. The organization had been tried in victorious engagements with princes and chieftains who opposed his rule. Losses were covered by enlistment of prisoners of war, but no more prisoners were enrolled than required for the purpose; for the Khan did not want too many alien elements in his army which already consisted of three times as many men from annexed tribes as of Modo's own people. Ten divisions from the Ordos—hardened, fierce fighters—were the Khan's elite troops. The army was his nation; its regulations were his empire's only law. Trade was the Khan's monopoly, but he permitted his subjects to share in the profits, according to their merits and his moods. Division commanders were his aristocracy, lower-ranking officers formed a privileged caste, and soldiers were superior to slaves not admitted to the ranks.

Had it not been for the Chinese campaign against the Hiung-nu, Modo might never have become Khan. Probably he would have gathered a horde of several 10,000 men, roamed around hitting the Chinese border every now and then, only to be swept away, like other barbarian princes, by Siberia's human tides.

But, fighting the armies of the unifier of China, the Hiung-nu lost their grip on the Ordos, and the bulk of their hordes migrated in a westerly direction, possibly even as far as the Volga River. Ravages along the silk road indicate that the Hiung-nu destroyed trading nationalities and gathered huge spoils. They probably paid but scant attention to the Chinese retreat in 230 B.C. and returned to their eastern roaming grounds only much later, after Modo Khan had made his bid for domination of the world.

His world was China. The Ordos, the Baikal, and all the grass steppes were its hinterland. When he struck in 202 B.C. he had forty divisions, according to a Chinese count.

Four hundred thousand horsemen rode against the wall, echeloned in depth, spearheads discharging arrows from Chinese-made bows, and making way for the next ranks of mounted archery. The hail of arrows swept parts of the rim clear of defenders; the signal system was poorly operated, defense concentrations were delayed; and several catapult emplacements remained unmanned. Mongol attackers had little trouble scaling the front wall after slaves filled out ditches and moats. Ramps were built to lead horses across; yet the Mongol array in depth produced endless delays. It took several days to lead a single division across an undefended sector of the fortress; and Modo's unfamiliarity with the Chinese supply system led his men to search the empty countryside for food, while big stores were right within their grasp. With five or ten elite divisions Modo could have breached the Great Wall and turned the flanks of its defending armies before they could regroup, but with 400,000 horsemen waiting in endless file, the Khan cooled his heels at the border, while the Chinese generals, united in the emergency, organized a stand.

The Chinese were best trained to fight in close formations or to hold a fortified line. To break formation and swarm out in small groups usually created confusion and entanglement. The Mongols were most formidable in small, hard-riding units; had Modo Khan ordered his army to disperse as the Chinese heavy troops appeared, the Mongols would still have encircled and annihilated the enemy with little loss to themselves. But the horsemen's leader was determined to use his host in solid formation, and this was his undoing. The Chinese held their ground against numerical superiority. After inflicting and in turn suffering heavy losses Modo recrossed the wall to lick his wounds. He never returned. Did his generals liquidate the Khan? Did vassal princes rebel after the spell of invincibility was broken? Did wizards forsake the chosen of the spirits in the spirit's name? Nothing is known of Modo Khan's death, but it hardly was non-violent. His makeshift empire dissolved into princedoms, leaving behind the germs of a crude Mongolian nationalism that had yet to run its cataclysmic course. Soon after Modo's retreat the Hiung-nu were back in strength on the threshold of China. They had no trouble in reestablishing themselves as the strongest nation of horsemen, but they did not immediately attack the wall. A new era in Chinese-Siberian relations opened around 200 B.C.

Victory over the Mongols consolidated the Chinese Empire. Emperors of the Han dynasty, not as omnipotent as Ch'in Shih Huang-ti, but strong and resourceful, reorganized their country's policy toward the horsemen from Siberia. They undertook to domesticate the savages, to settle those who, according to Li-sé's report, could not be settled—not to make them till the soil to which they had little affinity, but to defend the approaches to the Great Wall for a regular fee.

It was a bold experiment, strangely similar to the Roman Empire's later attempt to turn barbaric neighbors into loyal lansquenets, and equally portentous. But while decadent Rome succumbed to the barbarians' treacherous violence, China, blackmailed and invaded by its mercenaries, developed a mysterious faculty of absorbing her subduers. China could shape Siberians into conquerors and also into Chinese. China paid ransom, tribute, fees, and pensions, according to the turns of the tide; and this strange corelationship between China and her neighbors continued well into the nineteenth century when Mongolian princes, then a backward, primitive lot, accepted Chinese suzerainty in return for yearly pensions. Those pensions ranged from 2000 ounces of silver and 25 pieces of silk for nobles of the first class, to 200 ounces of silver and 7 pieces of silk for members of the sixth. The sovereigns who granted those pensions were members of the Manchu dynasty, descendants of militant tribesmen who once had roamed the northeastern approaches to China and whose earliest assaults had been repelled by Hiung-nu guards.

CHAPTER SIX Chinese piety did not permit the supreme design of a great ruler to fade away; and the etiquette of court chroniclers required recording of such designs as having been gloriously achieved—no matter what actually had happened. The tables told that Ch'in Shih Huang-ti had united all countries within the four seas under his scepter, and that no wars would be possible for ten thousand generations to come. Later emperors, who might have found countries within the four seas yet unconquered and who were involved in wars, would have to reverse this situation, lest they lose face as squanderers of their grandiose heritage.

A hundred years had passed since Ch'in Shih Huang-ti unified China. The Han emperors had not yet acquired new territories, and raiders from Tibet had made several violent incursions. The relationship between China and its Siberian mercenaries had passed through tumultuous stages and there had been serious internal strife. The rulers chose to ignore the sovereign existence of other nations within the four seas. They considered as satellites the lands to which their trading subjects traveled, because they were supposedly policed by horsemen in Chinese pay and viewed latent conflicts with Tibetans and Siberians as domestic affairs. Emperor Wu-ti, however, who ruled from 140 to 86 B.C., abandoned his predecessor's ostrich policy and boldly conceived his own version of universal rule and permanent peace. It was a grandiose concept of a coalition of trading, manufacturing, and seafaring nations, under Chinese sponsorship, and protected by Chinese and Siberian mercenary armies. The armies of other members of the coalition were not taken into consideration and control of the seas was not elaborated upon. Siberians who refused to serve as mercenaries or rebelled against the authority of the sponsor were to be driven off to distant wastelands outside the civilized world.

In 128 B.C. an imperial ambassador left China to view the places that should form part of the realm. Chang Ch'ien was an erudite, dignified, and persuasive gentleman. Interpreters, couriers, and picturesque guards accompanied him. One courier reported that the mission had safely reached the regions where a silk-trading people lived, and was continuing west. For almost ten years nothing more was heard of the embassy. Then Hiung-nu officers handed a letter to a Chinese section commander on the wall. The document, in elaborate diction, and with artfully painted characters, came from Chang Ch'ien, who notified his sovereign that he was being held for ransom by marauding Hiung-nu tribesmen whose indigent intellect did not permit them to value the meaning of his credentials.

The place of detention seemed to be somewhere in the mountains of Southwestern Siberia. The letter had been written nine years before, and the prisoner might be dead. The officers insisted that he was still alive, but could not explain the delay of the message and did not seem to realize the gravity of the offense committed by arresting an imperial ambassador. Abducting Chinese nationals was routine for Hiung-nu soldiers, who used to trade them for a piece of silk; in this case, however, the captors charged ten pieces of silk for every member of Chang Ch'ien's party. The irate Emperor vowed fearful revenge, but meantime the ransom was paid.

Chang Ch'ien was released, unhurt, and so were all his companions. But instead of returning to China the staunch dignitary continued his voyage. He went on to Fergana, where people had heard about China and where princes expressed gratitude for the visit by an ambassador from the famous land. From Fergana he proceeded to Bokhara, where he found that its people, called Yue-tshi, looked exactly like the Hiung-nu, and that their limited vocabulary was practically identical with that of the horsemen. Their king, a squarely built, ridiculously overdressed man, whose elaborate court ceremonial was a travesty of refined procedures, bragged about his exploits. He boasted to have recently conquered the remnants of Alexander's Greek-Bactrian phantom state and consolidated it into a mighty land that would eventually expand toward the setting sun and the great sea beyond. (This seemed to have been the Caspian.) He knew about China and its silk; he might accept Chinese protection against attacks from the east, and was ready to trade horses and products manufactured by his new subjects for Chinese goods.

The Ambassador listened, but did not try to dissuade the King from his expansionist plans. Scientifically minded as he was, he spent some time in Bokhara tracing the origin of the Yue-tshi.

In fact the Yue-tshi were a Hiung-nu tribe, and had seen service along the Great Wall. There they had feuded with their kinsmen, had been defeated and chased away. In long years of migration through the steppes and mountains of Southern Siberia, they had shed their pursuers, skirmished with weaker tribes, lived on spoils, and eventually reached northern Persia. The land was wealthy, its population industrious and pacific, and even though it had too many cities to please the horsemen, there were still enough pastures for their mounts. The Yue-tshi moved in, with no more intention to stay than a swarm of locusts. They massacred myriads and destroyed buildings, but there were still people and half-ruined cities left when they got weary of extirpation. Men were put to work for their captors, and Yue-tshi nobles, wanton and curious, moved into palaces in quest of strange, extravagant delights. Trembling Greeks catered to their whims, perverting and coarsening their own refinement to please the uncouth conquerors. The Yue-tshi found that city houses had their merits and that workshops could produce luxuries. The King, who had stayed in his big tent while his nobility explored the cities, moved into the biggest palace of Bokhara, had it crowded with rugs, horses, and female entertainers, until the royal residence had become a combination of storehouse, stable, and brothel. He noticed that people in his new domain had lived under a law he did not care to study, but he permitted its application to the natives. His own people remained under his uncodified command, but gradually some details of the natives' law were adopted as customs.

For the first time in recorded history a Siberian people acquired outward appearances of statehood: settlement and elements of law. But savage nomad instincts were still rampant, and Chang Ch'ien's report to the Emperor predicted that the Yue-tshi would not survive as a nation. His prophecy was borne out in 76 B.C., when a Yue-tshi king who led his army westward met annihilating defeat at the hands of Mithridates VI, King of Pontus, who, in turn, was routed 13 years later by Pompey's Roman legions.

Chang Ch'ien went on to Syria. He visited the Parthians, and he may even have been to India, even though his account does not elaborate on that country's size and wealth.

"There are large and prosperous countries in the West and Southwest," he reported to his emperor after an absence of more than fifteen years. "These countries are full of rare objects. They have populations living in fixed abodes and given to occupations not unlike those of the Chinese. They are greatly interested in trade with China, but they lack strength." Only in the region of Samarkand, where the Parthians lived, did the Ambassador find formidable warriors. The Parthians were proud and would not accept protection, but Chang Ch'ien opined that they could be bribed into collaboration.

Wu-ti had not yet chastened the Hiung-nu for the indignity inflicted upon his ambassador. Several 10,000 horsemen were stationed along the Wall. They chased other tribes away and terrorized the Chinese border population they were paid to protect. The violent mercenaries had long forgotten about Chang Ch'ien and the ten-pieces-of-silk ransom. To take them to answer now would require elaborate explanations; also a punitive expedition would not necessarily be a walkover; the horsemen might even turn the tables and invade China. The Emperor's vow being irrevocable, however, cringing Chinese generals suggested that a punitive blow be inflicted upon local tribesmen dwelling at the scene of the outrage.

Soon Chinese army bulletins announced smashing victories; annihilation of malefactors, permanent pacification of the trade route, and hot pursuit of fleeing barbarians through the valley of a big river, probably the Irtysh. As usual the barbarians had nothing to say.

Around 100 B.C. formidable Hiung-nu tribes massed on the extreme ends of their immense roaming grounds, pushing weaker groups out of their way, overrunning other Siberian nomads from the Urals to the Altais and possibly even far up in the north. If these shifts were caused by the Chinese campaign, this would have been a most unfortunate result of alleged victory. It strengthened the barbarians opposite the Chinese border and threatened Western Asia, distant anchor of the prospective trading coalition. However, it cannot be ruled out that these movements heralding the Migration of People were part of the violent Siberian drive for concentration and hegemony; that Wu-ti's armies had not really crossed the border; and that the victory bulletins were face-saving tricks.

The Emperor himself may have known more about the punitive expedition than his subjects learned. For when he resumed work on his plan, he no longer included Siberian mercenaries in the security pattern, but decided that China's own soldiers should defend its trade partners against incursion from all quarters, including the savage Siberian north. A military-geographical expedition was sent to India to reconnoiter a new silk road which would eliminate the hazards of the ancient route.

The expedition was ambushed by mountaineers from the eastern Himalayas; and together with its members perished the project of a southern silk road that might have become a strong link between China and India.

Wu-ti dispatched embassies to every country visited by Chang Ch'ien to impress foreigners with the might and glory of the Han court, with the fabulous generosity of the ruling Emperor, with the unparalleled abundance and security that Wu-ti's favor would bring to nations who cast their lots with China. The cleverest diplomats of the empire led the missions: the shrewdest merchants, and the most impressive-looking officers of the imperial guards formed its staffs. Hundreds of professional soldiers, uncomfortably garbed in elaborate costumes and equipped with useless loads of heavy weapons, escorted the pompous parties. Each mission carried gifts from sovereign to sovereign; the finest embroidered silk, and the most artful golden ornaments Chinese craftsmanship could produce. The men's mounts and even the draft horses were of pure breed, magnificent for parade, but ill-fitted for long voyages. The aging Wu-ti saw every embassy off and was pleased with its appearance. Expensive as these embassies were, they could bring handsome financial return. Four decades of directing China's intricate economic affairs had turned the Emperor into a business-minded man.

The ambassadorial parties were not molested by roaming savages. The savages themselves were getting increasingly business-minded. Since the guardians of the wall collected immense quantities of silk, they engaged in a trade of their own, frequently underselling old, established merchants. Yet their competitive practices did not involve violence. Trade was inviolable; and in the eyes of Siberians ambassadors were glorified merchants.

Most nations visited by Wu-ti's missions had the unfailing business acumen of cultured Orientals. Their princes were ready to discuss future commercial relations in great detail. The offer of Chinese protection was often enthusiastically received; but it soon turned out that the parties had different notions of protection. Almost every Western Asiatic ruler was involved in feuds with his neighbors. Innumerable old scores were to be settled and claims to be enforced. Everybody interpreted the Chinese offer to mean that Emperor Wu-ti's armies would carry out the Western Asiatics' aggressive and resentful designs. When the ambassadors explained that the Emperor's objective was concord through prosperity, the princes' enthusiasm lessened markedly. They showed little understanding of the dangers threatening the civilized world from the north.

Some rulers claimed not to have heard of the hard-riding, aggressive barbarians from Siberia. Others said that the steppes in which these horsemen roamed were far away and that their countries were safe against attack. Yet others, like the King of Fergana, insisted that appeasement was the only way to deal with the invincible Hiung-nu and their redoubtable kin and that the presence of Chinese soldiers would provoke attacks which could be avoided by payment of tributes. Nobody wanted Chinese garrisons on his territory, even though their design was protection.

The Parthians had military suggestions of their own: Wu-ti should not bother about the small states between India and the Roman outposts, but join Parthia in its war against Rome. Together they would conquer the arrogant empire and establish a condominion of the world. The Parthians had effectively fought Roman ballistae with bows and arrows. With Chinese war machines they would destroy the legions. Wu-ti's ambassador, though careful not to hurt the Parthians' martial feelings, insisted that mutual business was better even than co-belligerency.

Rome was on the march. Small Arab and Seleucid peoples, squeezed between expanding Roman dominions, Parthia, and Syria, were doomed to lose their independence or be destroyed. A new invasion route of what is now the Middle East had been thrown open by shifts in Southwestern Siberia, and in areas as far west as the Black Sea. Nomad nations disappeared and through the vacuum advanced, inexorably, the warriors of Rome. They had not yet met the Hiung-nu, but they were descending upon Armenia and stretching out mailed fists in the direction of Wu-ti's projected realm of trade. Ambassadors did not meet legion commanders—this was a delicate matter to be dealt with at the highest level. Roman officers, too, were reluctant to meet the Chinese.

Wu-ti's diplomats decided that it would be futile to sign long-term commercial treaties with people who might soon be overrun. Yet they did thriving business with imperiled Arabs and Seleucids, buying at low prices whatever treasures the potential fugitives still owned and reselling them at huge profit through other ambassadors in apparently secure areas.

Embassies also collected priceless presents for their emperor. The time was not auspicious for international pacts, but import-export trade might never again be so profitable. Since proceeds from missions were legally the Emperor's, the ambassadors did their business in Wu-ti's name while pocketing the profit as agents' fees.

The first ambassadors returned after four years; stragglers arrived but five years later. Wu-ti checked the presents and smiled. Wealth was power. Wealth would be the safest foundation of his universal empire.

Business arrangements, however, were not as profitable as they had appeared. The King of Fergana received deliveries of silk, but failed to send breeding mares as had been agreed upon. Wu-ti was not a simple mortal who could take such matters to the courts. Defaulting on an obligation toward the Emperor of China was *lèse-majesté* to be washed off in blood. All of China's cavalry, nearly 60,000 strong, was mustered for a drive on Fergana. Thousands of carts carried provisions for three years; immense herds of cattle trudged in the wake of the cavalry, slowing its advance to a crawl. Chinese garrisons along the Great Wall were immobilized by a complete absence of mounted soldiers, which gave Siberian mercenaries ample opportunity to pillage and to blackmail. Campaign expenses were higher than the total profits from trade agreements, but the Emperor, who felt his end approaching, was convinced that a realization of his design depended upon the forcible collection of Fergana's debt. Wu-ti did not live to see the horses from Fergana arrive in his residence, but he was still alive when express riders announced Fergana's defeat.

Emperor Wu-ti's successors burned incense before his ancestral tablets; worshipers paraded before his shrine. For centuries he was praised as the achiever of another exalted aim, centuries during which China's foreign trade shrank, its universal policies were superseded by isolationism, and internal strife was resumed at a dangerous scale.

The late Wu-ti's design produced an endless sequence of petty vexation. Swindlers plagued the Court, telling about alleged travels to distant lands with wonderful business opportunities; they requested, and obtained, assignments as imperial brokers, received valuable merchandise on credit, and disappeared for good. Trade caravans sent out to acquire new customers disposed of their wares at nominal prices; men in charge gave confusing accounts of their dealings with obscure potentates, probably dummies of the Siberian horsemen. Even trade with respectable and old, established clients was no longer prosperous. Prices fell, fees skyrocketed, transportation costs kept mounting. The Chinese Court withdrew from its burdensome commitments, deciding to leave trade to private merchants and to collect small taxes rather than to continue the operation. Traders were advised to travel only on routes regularly patrolled by the army. The Court would not grant convoys for protection in remote areas.

This implied virtual abandonment of any attempts to establish official relations with Ta Ts'in, the great land from which the glass came, to which went, through intermediaries, most of China's silk; the realm whose coins circulated throughout most of Asia—the Roman Empire.

China cared less for Roman goods since Chinese manufacturers had learned the art of glassmaking and produced it at much cheaper prices than its weight in jade, as the Romans had charged it. Textiles like those made in Rome were also produced in Egypt and Syria; and none of the precious jewels coveted by the Chinese emperors originated within the confines of the Roman Empire.

As time went by, Rome no longer promoted eastern commerce either. In the declining empire politicians looked for spectacular issues and found them in the silk trade. Senate orators stormed against the drain upon the treasury by an annual outlay of ten billion sesterces—roughly the equivalent of $400,000,000—in bullion for an unnecessary, nay, immoral and absurd luxury. Silk was immoral, for Roman matrons, even senators' wives, draped themselves into rewoven transparent silk gauzes that made them look provocatively nude—nuder even than if they had been naked. Silk absurdly disturbed social peace. Poorer women envied and hated those who could afford the luxury of indecent exposure; and textile workers were idle because of silk imports. Those passionate harangues did not result in anti-silk legislation, but they did have temporary averse effects on foreign trade.

However, female demand being stronger than man-coined political slogans; silk imports soon increased in quantity.

Empires of the steppes formed and vanished. Chinese dynasties came and went. Centers of transit trade shifted from Persia and Arabia to Ceylon and Abyssinia. An upstart emperor from the Siberian grasslands became known as God's Scourge to a terrorized Christian world. The Roman Empire split, Western Rome went down, Ostrogoths invaded the Eternal City; but silk kept traveling west, giving a consoling taste of voluptuous luxury to people of ancient culture threatened by the maelstrom of barbarism.

After Rome had been sacked, Byzantium, the heir and mainstay of Roman refinement, considered the import of silk a major affair of state. As long as Persian and Abyssinian brokers competed for the Eastern Roman market, prices of the precious fabric were low, but they trebled when those rivals signed an agreement that gave the Persians a monopoly on silk imports to Byzantium.

In A.D. 540 Emperor Justinian summoned the best legal minds of the realm to deal with the price problem. Their deliberations produced a ceiling order, no less wordy than its modern counterparts, and no better enforceable. Contemptuous Persian dealers withheld regular deliveries, preferring to deal with Siberian nomads, who, in turn, supplied Byzantium's black marketeers.

In a countermove Emperor Justinian sent secret agents to Kashgar to meet Tibetan highwaymen who served as agents of Chinese manufacturers.

In an operation, details of which were never disclosed but should have included audacious ventures, hairbreadth escapes, and dime-novel conspiracies, a few silkworm eggs, none larger than a pin's head, traveled 5000 miles from China to Eastern Rome. According to Chinese law, the smuggling of silkworm eggs was still a crime worse than matricide, but the culprits apparently escaped punishment. The eggs were hatched on the Mediterranean island of Cos and after A.D. 550 Byzantium had its own silk industry.

Links of trade loosened. Civilizations drifted apart. Fast-traveling, ruthless barbarians struck east and west, forming a bridge of destruction, where meditating, diffident, cultured men had failed to establish a constructive span.

The history of Chinese-Roman relationship is one of frustration.

In the days of Wu-ti, and throughout the Parthian wars, Roman emperors did not want to establish contact with Chinese embassies; the Chinese war potential was said to be colossal, and the Chinese emperors easy to offend. With the struggle in the Middle East putting a heavy strain upon Rome's military establishment the emperors wanted to avoid additional risks. The Chinese emperors, in turn, took a dim view on admitting foreign diplomatic missions into the interior of their land. Foreigners, whatever they pretended to be, were always considered spies. Foreign merchants were not admitted beyond checking points.

When the Romans eventually reached their farthest line of expansion and borders became stabilized, military governors of boundary provinces advised against sending missions to China, contending that it was safer to trade by sea or through intermediaries, and to refrain from ticklish diplomatic relations. Rome hesitated; governments passed the topic on to their successors, experts wrote opinions which were, in turn, amended by later generations of experts. Only in A.D. 50 was the first practical action undertaken: A man whose name is unrecorded but who is said to have been a Roman citizen of Greek or Jewish origin was sent to deliver a personal letter from the Roman to the Chinese emperor. The content of the letter is veiled in mystery. The messenger traveled on a trade galley scheduled to call at an Indus River port before proceeding to China. He did arrive in India, but it is not established what happened to him and the letter afterward.

In A.D. 166 the Chinese Court was notified of the arrival of ambassadors from Rome. His Majesty was so thrilled to see men from Ta Ts'in that he ordered them admitted without screening procedures. The Romans did not look quite as distinguished as the Emperor had expected. They did offer presents, as etiquette required, but the presents were products of India, not of Rome, which was a serious infraction of the rules. And instead of elaborating on their sovereign's high concern for the Chinese emperor's health, on Rome's greatness, and her admiration for China, the visitors talked about nothing but purchase plans, which was a grievous lack of courtesy. Mortified Chinese courtiers contended that the men from Rome were impostors and, of course, spies. The Emperor, however, assigned a high dignitary to escort them back to Rome, convey his personal compliments to the ruler, and to present him with a gift of choice dwarfs. One year later the capital learned of the demise of this dignitary on the high seas. The Roman Emperor received neither the compliments nor the dwarfs, but Roman circus crowds watched three slit-eyed Lilliputians in hopeless fights against women gladiators, as that was a favorite entertainment for connoisseurs. The ambassadors had been crooks, and their trick paid off well: dwarfs to be thrown before powerful women commanded a high price.

Sixty years later, and again in 284, Roman merchants applied for admission to the Court of China; their requests were curtly denied.

CHAPTER SEVEN The three-lane bridle path, the watchtowers, and artillery emplacements atop the Great Wall afforded a view of the camps of the mercenaries. When the horsemen had arrived, they had dwelled under bare, felt covers, crowded into incredibly small space to keep one another warm. Even chieftains, elders, and wizards had been crudely lodged. One century later chieftain-princes resided in large tents grotesquely overloaded with adornments, with patches of silk, and metal carvings stuck on totem poles. Officers and wizards vied to make their own accommodations look colorful and glittering, and even the simple soldiers' tents had collections of savage ornaments. Grazing horses of the rough aboriginal kind now mingled with breed animals, mostly white mares. The men added ill-fitting pieces of finery to their crude garb, and the women, who rarely left their wagons, looked like a dauber's daydream. From ugly Spartan quarters camps had changed into even uglier exhibits of their inhabitants' rapaciousness and barbaric taste.

Relations between the Chinese soldiery and the mercenaries, however, had remained unchanged. There was no trace of the camaraderie that almost invariably develops among servicemen. Chinese soldiers never visited the tent camps, and they were more concerned about keeping the foreigners out of their own quarters than to hold the wall. Officers confined themselves to rudimentary communications with their opposite numbers. When the mercenary horsemen patrolled the wall, Chinese signal- and artillerymen looked the other way, grimaced to dramatize their disgust with the foreigners' smell. The foreigners had no use as yet for Chinese hygiene, and they made it a point to annoy their employers by their exudations.

Chinese and barbarians took entirely different views of the profession of soldiery. To the Chinese draftees it was a bothersome duty, to the mercenaries a natural habit. Both parties disdained the other's viewpoint. Chinese officers studied barbarian tactics and found the hit-and-run evolutions primitive. The leaders of the horsemen watched Chinese war machines and thought that they were built to make up for the shortcomings of Chinese individual soldiership. Even though paid in the name of a Chinese emperor they had never seen, the barbarians did not feel that they owed allegiance or loyalty to China. The horsemen's ethics, exemplified by their wizards' oracles, approved of raids on Chinese territory, the more profitable the better. It was easy to cross the wall in sectors their own men patrolled. It seemed more important to them to hold these sally ports than to defend other sectors of the wall.

Around 70 B.C. mounted Tibetans who had learned some of the Mongol and Hiung-nu (later called Huns by Westerners) military methods, staged an attack on China. Hiung-nu horsemen, called upon to repel the Tibetans, did not budge. A Hiung-nu prince who had established control of a great number of groups proclaimed himself Great Khan and trained an army of 100,000 for a mass raid on China. The Tibetans were no match for well-equipped Chinese troops who finally caught up with the invaders. The Hiung-nu waited too long, and in 63 B.C., when they forced the wall, China's army was ready to compress the horsemen in so narrow an area that they were unable to stage their outflanking, fast-moving attacks.

The enlightened ruler of China wanted to pacify the mercenaries forever. China had spent fortunes for these men's dubious services, but had never tried psychology. The Emperor's advisers were as skeptical as the ceremonial permitted: swordsmen insisted that the Siberian rabble, even if clad in silk and riding on white chargers, had no flair for subtleties. Trade experts sighed that one piece of silk meant more to the barbarians than persuasion and treasury officials warned against ever higher fees, the only argument the mercenaries understood. The Emperor, however, assigned old hands in the frontier trade to visit princes, court their favor with special bargains, and suggest that miraculous opportunities were waiting for the customer, but that the Great Khan stood in their way.

The result of the delicate missions delighted Emperor Heüan-ti. The Great Khan was disposed of.

His successor had anti-Chinese chieftains summarily executed. The Emperor bestowed upon him the hereditary title of a Chinese general and granted permanent commissions to his ranking officers. Commissions carried high salaries and entitled their holders to enter certain parts of China. The officers visited Chinese cities where they were lavishly entertained and acquired a new outlook on the merits of cleanliness, in particular that of young women. The new policy did not reflect upon the relationship between Chinese and mercenary enlisted men, who still kept apart, but the security of China was greatly improved. In the year 9 B.C., however, another emperor, Wang Mau, reduced the rank of another Great Khan and the number of Hiung-nu commissions, declaring that the horsemen did not deserve high distinction.

The demoted Hiung-nu were furious. Just when they had come to understand the importance of saving face, their Chinese tutors made them lose it. For eighty years the Hiung-nu kept avenging the insult by savage incursions; China's armies suffered heavy losses, and governors from border provinces kowtowed before cabinet ministers, imploring them that the wise imperial order be amended to meet the barbarian's inferior intelligence. For the better part of eighty years China's keenest minds pondered over ways and means to save the face of a Chinese emperor even after nothing was left of him but an ancestral tablet. Various attempts at substituting intrigue for distinction failed; and meantime thousands of Chinese were killed, fair cities reduced to rubble.

Time—always China's faithful ally—worked against the Hiung-nu, however. The horsemen split. One group migrated to the far west, 2000 miles beyond the Chinese border. Another pushed on to the western end of the Great Wall, leaving only a small force on the crucial Ordos region. The Ordo group was under the command of the Great Khan, who demanded that the tribes on the western end of the wall take his orders. Yet tribal princes claimed independence. The Great Khan threatened to use coercion. Chinese agents managed to lock the Hiung-nu in a fratricidal war. Over grasslands, through sandy plains and hillsides, along river valleys and lake shores galloped archers on horseback, death personified, charging wildly in the fastest actions ever fought. They raged against men and beasts, destroyed the vestiges of parvenu splendor. They were killers as uninhibited as their most primitive ancestors. In every camp Chinese agents stirred the chieftain's frenzy by claiming that the Emperor wanted him to become Great Khan, that after just one more victory in the internecine strife he would be granted armed support. After several years of carnage the Emperor of China had a powerful army assist the western Hiung-nu against the Ordos group. Chinese political analysts who had learned of Hiung-nu tribes pressing toward the threshold of Europe expected the western group to join them eventually, which, after destruction of the Ordos forces, would leave China in full control of the forefield of the wall.

In the ensuing battle 200,000 prisoners were taken. The Chinese claimed the prisoners, and left the other spoils to their co-belligerents. The captives were enlisted in the Chinese armies to serve under the exclusive command of Chinese officers. This was an experiment, quite successful when it was made, but difficult to repeat, because China hardly ever again made so many prisoners of war. The political analysts were borne out by the facts. Their Hiung-nu allies did not stay to enjoy the fruits of conquest—news reached them, probably expedited by Chinese couriers, that far away, where the sun set, gains waited for them, richer than any they could achieve on the spot, and to be gathered without hazard or exertion. From the battlefields on the Chinese border weary horsemen rode off—toward the setting sun.

The Hiung-nu's sense of time and co-ordination in action and hunt was infallible, but it was absent in migration. Tribes lost touch with long-time neighbors, established contact with foreigners, fought them, or united with them, stayed together as long as horse pastures were abundant, split or battled as fodder became short. The scarce effects of Chinese culture vanished completely. The only remaining souvenirs were shreds of silk and a few white horses.

Most migrating tribes stayed off the silk road, but merchants, death-defying in quest for prosperous barter, visited roaming horsemen on distant grounds and bartered weapons for furs. Hunting furs became the wanderers' main occupation. It occupied them for many seasons, induced them to make detours. Again they would meet and fight foreign people, prevail through fast-moving tactics, hold skilled craftsmen in bondage, and enroll able-bodied youngsters.

In vast grasslands migrating tribes would stay for long periods, even for the lifetime of one generation, which, in those days, lasted hardly twoscore years. Bodies of horsemen would unite, and occasionally engage in major campaigns against people of whose existence they had learned by accident. The traces of those campaigns against other Siberian people are confined to burial grounds. But the invasion of India through the mysterious "Hunas," coinciding with the advance of the Huns through the Russian plains, indicates that errant ex-guardians of the Great Wall descended upon the wealthy subcontinent.

A group of horsemen who had reached an area 2000 miles west of the Chinese border when civil war broke out there received influx from the east in the latter part of the second century. Kinship did not necessarily imply friendship. There was a good deal of feud among chieftains, and skirmishing for pastures, but gradually the western Hiung-nu grew in number and hardened in military organization. In the Ural Mountains, on the northern Caspian shores, at the gateway to Persia, horsemen empires formed again without law and determined boundaries, but they were very aggressive.

Roman generals whose legions consisted mostly of foreign warriors reported that savages from the east were attacking their outposts. What seemed to be an audacious onslaught on Rome's bastions was, in fact, a dismal flight of small nations hit by the impact of the Hiung-nu's advance. Their advance was slow and unmethodical when it began, in the third century of our time, with horsemen debouching from the Ural Mountains and tapping their murderous way to better pastures. Waves of fugitives burst against Roman garrisons in the confines of the decaying Dacian Empire, which had once stretched from Western Russia to Moravia. They swept over "Trajan's Wall," which the Roman emperor had built against incursions from the northeast. Roman garrisons folded up as fugitives bounced against their armed camps.

The legionaries in the northeastern frontier were no-land's-men, and patriotism was to them an alien notion. The violent tide from the east perplexed them; and when they learned eventually that the people who had forced their way into the legions' camps were being pursued by a superior foe, their pagan superstitions pictured him as the embodiment of all the evil spirits of their creed. Only with great difficulty and after evacuating some territory could the Roman officers prevent mass panic and restore their lines. A number of fugitives remained in front of the new positions.

The Hiung-nu stalled again. They were not aware of the effect of their earlier advance upon the Roman positions. They probably knew little, if anything, about the Roman Empire, and had no idea of the exact location of its borders. They were reasonably comfortable in Central Russia, and their scouts rarely went beyond the present site of Moscow, then an uninhabited grove.

Scores of years went by. Beset by many troubles, Rome no longer considered the northeast a sensitive spot. Well-trained Ostrogoth and Visigoth soldiers had moved into the plains north of the Black Sea and it was good to know them at a safe distance from civilized centers.

A Hiung-nu center of gravity formed on the Caspian Sea. A new ruler had arisen; a strong-willed man; a favorite of the celestial spirits, according to the wizards; a great soldier; and a conqueror. Some said that his name was Balamir, others called him Balamber. Some claimed that he was a giant, others said that he hovered over his people like a storm cloud, and yet others whispered that he was a one-eyed gnome.

In the year 372 "Balamir-Balamber's" host broke camp and moved toward the Volga River. The Hiung-nu were well mounted, abundantly supplied with bows, arrows, knives, and axes. They were divided in squadrons of 100 horsemen each, 10 squadrons formed a group and 10 groups a major unit of 10,000.

The Huns, as the Hiung-nu were now generally called, engulfed small nations in their path and crushed them to dust. Beyond the Volga, in the fertile valley of the Don, and in the northern foothills of the Caucasus Mountains, dwelled the Alanis, who had been tilling the soil and resisting Roman attempts at subjugation for a long time. The Alanis fought bravely, but were helpless against the hail of well-aimed arrows and the speed of the shaggy horses. The Huns prevailed practically without loss to themselves. The visitors had no use for the vanquished's agricultural skills; their diet was strictly non-vegetarian. They fed on meat—preferably the flesh of worthless horses, after tenderizing it by putting it under the saddle and riding on it for several days.

As Hun patrols crossed the Don, a handful of terror-stricken Alanis fled to the headquarters of Hermanaric, aged Duke of the Ostrogoths, to tell that myriads of fierce warriors were descending upon the lands bordering on the Sea of Azov; soon they would overrun the Ostrogoths and the rest of the world. Duke Hermanaric pledged himself to root out the plague with his own sword. The fall of 372 went by; winter came, but there was no trace of the fierce host—only rumors carried by scattered fugitives. When nothing happened in the warm season of 373, Hermanaric boasted that the warriors who had crushed the Alanis were afraid of attacking him. And as 373 came to an uneventful end, the Duke invited his nobles to a drinking bout during which he issued a challenge to the ghost enemy. The Huns ignored the challenge, continued to scout the land and to feed their horses; but then, in the spring of 374, they invaded the Ostrogoth realm. Hermanaric committed suicide on the scene of his army's disaster; his son prostrated himself before the King of the Huns and accepted humiliating vassalage.

The Visigoths learned of their neighbors' debacle and, hopeful that the Huns would again bid for time, organized a nationwide retreat. This constituted a remarkable logistic feat. Old people, women, children, and household goods were loaded on carts; cattle were driven by mounted shepherds; the armed forces deployed to guard the migrant nation's flank and rear, a strong mobile group stood by to engage enemy scouts, and allow noncombatants to get away before the flood of aggressors could burst upon them. A long column moved toward the Dniester in perfect order and discipline. The crossing of the river proceeded methodically when clouds of dust arising from the stone-dry steppes to the east indicated that the Huns were approaching.

The Huns closed in with nerve-racking speed. Visigoth rear guards were unable to delay the attack. Waves of fleeing soldiers broke over hapless civilians. A frantic mob struggled for river crossings as Hun archers poured missiles into the affray, and then used knives and axes in an orgy of slaughter and loot. Pillaging the belongings of the Visigoth nation, the horsemen permitted survivors to escape from the scene of disaster.

The Visigoths fled in the direction of Trajan's Wall, crossed it, found Roman camps manned by small bands of demoralized loafers, and frantically went to work to strengthen the fortifications. The Huns, however, cleared the wall without difficulty. The Visigoths fled beyond the Balkan Mountains into Thrace and applied for asylum in that Roman province. Emperor Valens granted the request, hoping that the chastened Visigoths, together with other frontier troops would form a secure line of defense across the Balkan peninsula. A Hun invasion was considered imminent. In Rome generals and statesmen studied reports on the Huns drafted by fugitives. The horsemen were ill-smelling killers, unpredictable and rapacious. Their number was legion, they said. They did not give reliable figures or suggest how to deal with the Huns.

Huns roamed the territory, which was to become Hungary. They later invested Moravia and made incursions into Austria, sacking, massacring, enslaving local populations. Their ruler collected tribute from princes whose realms he did not care to explore. Central Europe trembled. Christians and pagans alike considered the Huns the instrument of divine wrath, but the Huns themselves lived happily—in their fashion.

Roman champions of peaceful coexistence with barbarians, who had been unusually taciturn when the storm broke, recovered their eloquence. They predicted that the high tide of Hun advance was receding, that the Huns were settling down and soon would be ready for negotiations with Rome. With the Roman citizenry, increasingly oblivious of military glory and contemptuous of the paraphernalia of militarism, reformed barbarians would rejuvenate the Roman Army. Just like the Goths who had been settled in Thrace, these Huns should be invited to move closer to the Roman Empire, and eventually join its armed forces.

High-placed Romans were skeptical about the effects of dealings with the barbarians, but since they had no constructive suggestions to offer, their sophisticated arguments were overruled. Meantime the Goths were equipped with the best that Roman arsenals could offer, and moved to the Balkan border where Roman garrisons were under heavy pressure.

And while Gothic troops marched into the Middle East, Roman emissaries went to Pannonia to meet the Huns. They carried presents: silk, gold, and spices. The Hun ruler accepted it all; interpreters said that he was pleased and ready to show his appreciation. The Romans needed additional soldiers to castigate an old foe, Tyrant Maximus. The Huns offered a few thousand of their own horsemen and a big batch of captured auxiliaries for a fee that amounted to a stiff tribute. A treaty was signed, Maximus defeated, and Hun troops returned to Pannonia loaded with booty in addition to their fee.

The Goths had not been quite as successful in Asia, and they did not return to their erstwhile asylum in the Balkans, but went dangerously close to the heart of the empire, to Italy proper. Gothic princes asked for a share in the civilian government; and Roman authorities had no means to deny their claims, which started with the inclusion of Gothic representatives in provincial administrations, and developed into Gothic influence in the affairs of the court and the nation. In 408 Alaric, King of the Visigoths, who as a young prince had had a narrow escape at the Dniester, collected 3000 pounds of pepper, 4000 tunics of silk, and big quantities of gold in return for a promise not to sack Rome, which he broke two years later. Other foreigners, emboldened by Rome's efforts to turn them into soldiers, roamed the outskirts of the crumbling empire. Vandals and Suebi ranged along the Rhine and entered Gaul and Spain. Vandals under King Gaiseric moved into Africa to establish a Mediterranean realm of their own; and, in 429 Roman garrisons evacuated the British Isles through pirate-infested waters.

The Huns were still stronger than the unchained nations combined. King Rugulas, ruler of the Huns at the time of Western Rome's collapse, held court in his sumptuous tent camp in the Hungarian plains in an atmosphere of splendor which borrowed and overdid the regalia of exaltation from Eastern and Western Roman courts. Rugulas's throne was higher than that of civilized emperors, his bodyguards wore more spectacular garments than their occidental counterparts, his courtiers followed a ceremonial of burlesque intricacy, court banquets turned into barbarian bacchanalia. Ambassadors were required to present gifts of savage splendor and to render homage to the King in a clownish fashion. Rugulas's imperial concept centered on adulation of his person, and his princes, in turn, cringing before their sovereign, were anxious to be wooed and showered with gifts by subordinates and foreigners.

Emperor Theodosius II of Eastern Rome tried to humor Rugulas by making him an honorary general, with an annual salary of 350 pounds of gold. Rugulas accepted the salary, but ignored the commission. Any Hun squadron leader wielded more power than Theodosius's top military men.

The Huns now controlled the lands between Central Siberia and the Danube as far upstream as Carnuntum, near Vienna, yet theirs was not an organized empire. Control of the lower Danube Valley was strategically vital. Theodosius, hoping that the Hun was not aware of this, urged its inhabitants to be loyal to Rome, and to migrate to Roman territory if they were threatened. Rugulas, however, considered himself lord and master of all lands and peoples along the Danube. He called his scribes and dictated a note of protest, one of the most insulting documents in Western history, asking for penitence and redress. Even though not all of the Hun's invectives lent themselves to translation, those they understood made the Emperor and his counselors shudder. A delegation was dispatched to sign a compact, anything Rugulas would deign to accept, multiplying the abusive King's salary, offering all the gems of the imperial treasury, and all the beverages of the imperial cellar, for the shadow of a condescending smile.

But Rugulas was a plethoric man, and violent emotions affected his health. When the jittery delegates arrived at the Hun outposts, they learned without grief of the King's demise. Yet the incident was not closed. The delegates were directed to proceed to Margus, near the present site of Belgrade, to receive the demands of Rugulas's successors. The Eastern Romans, however, were not admitted into the presence of the royal princes, Bleda and Attila; they only learned that their terms were unconditional recognition of the Huns' sovereignty on the left bank of the Danube and on a strip of land along the right bank; forcible return of emigrants; and an annual tribute of 1900 pounds of gold.

The delegates signed at once, paid the first installment of the tribute, and had the emigrants marched to the banks of the Danube where Hun officers took them over. This was capitulation. Yet it was a contract, the first to be signed with the Huns, hailed as the beginning of an era of normal relations with the formidable horsemen. From Western Rome soldiers of fortune, political wizards, schemers, and quacks journeyed to Pannonia, now the Promised Land of adventurers. The two rulers, it was said, were hostile toward each other, and joining the winning party at the proper time would mean tapping inexhaustible gold mines. Even from Byzantium distinguished-looking dodgers went to the Hun's camp, and stayed there, allegedly as advisers.

In the following twelve years the Huns turned their attention to Media and Persia. Europe breathed with relief. Hun garrisons stayed in occupied territory, but there was no further expansion. The Middle East became the scene of harrowing atrocities and of strange battles between rival horsemen. Did the Huns split among themselves? Had other Siberian tribes moved into these regions? Had Eastern Roman intriguers a share in the diversion eastward and the ensuing strife? The archives of Byzantium shed no light upon the matter, yet it would not be surprising had the distinguished-looking strangers been agents of the Eastern Roman government.

In 445 Bleda died of undisclosed causes; and in the same year Attila, now sole ruler of the Huns, marched straight on to Byzantium. Terror struck the city, gates were closed, but everybody inside was convinced that the first assault would carry the place and that no living creature would survive. The "Scourge of God" (as Attila was called) was lifted for a doomsday lashing.

In front of the outer walls the Huns set up siege machines: battering rams on wheels, with arrow-proof leather armament, and huge ballistae of Chinese make. Obviously trade with China had continued throughout the Huns' devastating migration, and Chinese emperors had gladly supplied the Hiung-nu with potent weapons against faraway people and places.

A few stone balls were thrown against the walls, but they were not well aimed. However, the defenders were awed by the display of Hun might and number. The besieger's camps covered an area much larger than that of the big city; it formed an arc of shelters, stores, and compounds, dominated by a glittering tent bigger than the Emperor's palace and the largest church of the city combined; this was the residence of Antichrist, who scorned the faithful. Solid formations of foot soldiers trained in assault tactics near the wall. Swarms of horsemen skirted the bastions, discharging arrows in mischievous pleasure. The monster that was the Hun army played cat and mouse with its victim.

The Emperor had not left his town; nor had his officers or clergy abandoned the staggering citadel. There was no security anywhere as long as Attila's host was not conquered.

In the Emperor's residence prelates, statesmen, and officers deliberated, argued, and prayed. In the streets crowds held silent vigils, waiting for the sign of a miracle that might yet save them from destruction.

One morning they saw an embassy, headed by the empire's most renowned diplomat, leaving town for the camp. From battlements sentinels watched every move of the embassy which entered the tent of Antichrist after much delay, and while throngs knelt in Byzantine Constantinople's narrow streets, the Emperor's ambassadors knelt before Attila.

No Eastern Roman dignitary had seen the legendary Scourge of God before. He was a short man, bowlegged, barrel-chested, with a big, ball-shaped head and small, deep-set, vicious eyes, a flat nose, a dark complexion, and a sparse beard. Attila stood on the top of a staircase leading up to his throne. He met the embassy with an outburst of rage, roaring, gesticulating, brandishing a dagger. Hundreds of colorful guardsmen, armed to their teeth, huddled together in the throne hall like sheep in a storm. They were familiar with their overlord's violent passions, which usually broke off as suddenly as they had started.

The ambassadors prostrated themselves. Their Greek interpreter lay flat on the ground and made a few attempts to translate the King's roar, but eventually abandoned his efforts.

After a few, seemingly endless, minutes Attila fell silent, descended the stairs, and paced the floor in a strange gait—a rhythmic display of boundless arrogance and contempt. The King knew that, when he sat on the throne, his short, curved legs made him look droll rather than dangerous, and that he was no imposing sight even when standing; so he adopted the marching habit, developed it into an impressive show, and took to outbursts of rage after he noticed that they shocked audiences into submission.

The Eastern Romans' abjection boosted his self-exaltation. Wasn't he the greatest power on earth, the absolute inexorable law? Byzantium's very existence was an offense to him. Couldn't he sack the city, turn it into a pasture for his horses? But he would decide otherwise.

Did Attila, the soldier, surmise that his army, in which slaves outnumbered Siberian horsemen, might not be invincible? The prancing Hun abused the ambassadors, berated them for deceit and cabals, for disloyalty to him whom their wretched country owed tribute and allegiance. He did not elaborate on his charges. In fact Eastern Rome had carefully refrained from action that could arouse the tyrant's ire. But the ambassadors did not dare to inquire or object. They had to face the Hun as he spoke, but they were not allowed to stand higher than he was, and so, crouching on their knees, they effected crawling turns which made them look more ridiculous than Attila would have appeared on his throne. The chief interpreter resumed his translation. The King was displeased, he stated; the King was vexed, the King resented . . . The Greek had to keep right behind the King not to miss a single of his words. He hobbled after Attila, in a posture that was a caricature of obeisance. He had to use his hands to support himself. The ambassadors watched these hands with morbid fascination. They hardly listened to the monotonous translation; the outcome of their mission, the fate of their city and empire, the fate of Christianity depended on the translator's free use of his hands.

Attila circled the embassy . . . he heard a tinkling sound, turned, and saw a knife on the floor, obviously fallen from the folds of the interpreter's coat. Attila kicked the weapon with his foot. It hit the knee of a cringing diplomat. The diplomat paled. The interpreter kept crawling. Attila pranced on. He would levy a fine in gold, he said, 2100 pounds. . . .

The ambassadors were delighted. They had not achieved their real objective, but if the Hun would lift the siege for a mere 2100 pounds of gold, this was an unbelievably lucky chance. Attila motioned the party to leave. The ambassadors hastened to comply. The interpreter stayed.

He had been hired to stab the King. He had charged fifty pounds of gold and collected in advance. Now that the plot had failed, the Greek had no desire to refund. He had the gold safely hidden away outside the walls. Attila had the interpreter assigned to his own staff.

The bulk of the Hun forces marched off to the Danube Valley. More than five years passed without new invasions. Then, in 451, the storm broke. Attila's hordes raced through the lower and upper Austrian plains, into Bavaria, and toward the Rhine. They spread south to the foothills of the Alps, and north beyond the Main. Wherever they went, settlements went up in flames and bodies of men, women, and children littered the ground. Enlisted chattel-slaves were even more savage than the Siberian horsemen themselves.

None of the horsemen had ever seen Siberia. There was no Siberian folklore telling of ancient Hiung-nu exploits. Yet the hordes sweeping Austria and Germany acted exactly like their own ancestors and other roaming conquerors. They did ascend and come like a storm, they were like a cloud to cover the land—they destroyed what human skill had built, enslaved those who possessed useful skills, slaughtered many more, and enlisted the survivors to serve in their ranks and help inflict upon other nations the same sufferings that had decimated and debased their own. Siberia invaded the lands that Roman civilization had reclaimed from wilderness, and destroyed the last vestiges of a culture that had resisted decadence and the onslaught of European barbarians.

Siberia spread across the Rhine, poured into Gaul on a route that would forever remain the classical road of invasion of France. Attila raced on, elated by lust of conquest, exalted by his own power. The Hun armies, swollen by draftees, were a colorful agglomeration of subdued tribes, adventurers, and highwaymen of various nations, who flocked to Attila's host. Germans, Franks, Vandals mingled with Celts, and Carniolians—under totem poles that had once been raised along the Chinese Great Wall.

Theodoric, King of the Visigoths, and Aëtius, a distinguished Roman soldier, maintained armies of pagan mercenaries in Southern France. King and general joined to fight the Huns.

And while Attila pushed to the banks of the Loire and laid siege to the city of Orleans, Aëtius and Theodoric marched north. On June 24, 451, the two armies clashed on the Catalaunian fields. Attila's men were superior in number and equipment, but the satellite forces were not closely integrated into the Hun army. Confusion of languages interfered with transmission of orders and attacks failed because of misunderstanding and lack of co-ordination. The Roman-Visigoth forces could not fully exploit the enemy's disadvantage, however. They reeled back whenever hit by the hail of arrows from the horsemen's bows. It was a confusing, kaleidoscopic battle which claimed heavy casualties on both sides. King Theodoric was among the killed. Three times the fighting was broken up in darkness and resumed at dawn. One of the many legends about the battle tells of the spirits of the killed fighting on in the clouds that gathered above the blood-drenched fields. On the morning of the fourth day weary Visigoths and Romans saw the enemy gather in formation, but instead of charging, Huns and satellites marched off. Aëtius did not even attempt pursuit.

Attila recrossed the Rhine. The Huns licked their wounds, but did not consider themselves defeated, and the setback in France did not affect their ability to invest any European country. In the spring of 452 the savage cohorts broke into Italy. The Alpine barrier did not stop their advance. Again settlements went up in flames, people down in misery. There was no army on the peninsula to oppose the intruders. Aëtius prudently stayed in France.

No sovereign had yet dared to call on Attila since the Scourge of God started his march of destruction; and after his experience with the embassy from Constantinople the King of the Huns refused to receive any embassy, even if it carried cartloads of treasures.

Pope Leo I went to meet the conqueror. He carried no gold or jewels, but he carried the Cross. Cross in hand, he presented himself at the Huns' outposts, who sneered at the odd character and let him pass. He pointed at the Cross when insolent Hun officers questioned him about his designs; and he raised the Cross when Attila, intrigued by stories of the stubborn visitor, had the Pope admitted. The modestly garbed Pontiff neither knelt nor bowed. Through Attila's interpreter, the same who had collected the fifty pounds of gold, the Pope told the King about Christ, who had suffered to redeem mankind, who was the King of Kings, and whose law was justice and mercy; no mundane ruler was above the law of Christ. The exact wording of the address is unknown, but its effect was miraculous. Attila did not work himself into synthetic rage; he neither pranced nor blustered, but explained almost meekly that he had been wronged and that the purpose of his invasion was to right, not to inflict, injury.

Honoria, granddaughter of Emperor Theodosius, he contended, was his lawful bride. She was held in captivity by some wretched intriguer in Rome, and she had written to Attila, protector of the weak, imploring him to save her and make her his wedded wife. She had sent him a ring as a pledge of her love. And Attila had come to Italy to free the girl, to marry her, and to punish the offender.

The Pope had never heard of a granddaughter of Theodosius held in captivity. The story sounded fantastic. Maybe it had been concocted by some fool or knave, but there was also a possibility that Attila had a gift of storytelling not previously recognized by his chroniclers. It might take some time to establish the truth, and it was doubtful that Attila would accept facts contrary to his version. Already Northern Italy was in ruins; if the Huns continued their advance, Rome faced another sacking—one from which the Holy City might never recover.

The Pope besought the King to refrain from further violence; should Honoria still want to marry him, she would be brought to his court with all the distinction due to her rank; and if she had been unrightfully detained, the guilty would be punished.

Attila was amenable. If Jesus had died to make justice prevail, he, the King, would wait to see wrong righted. But he would not wait forever, he said. If he would not get, in due time, what was due to him, woe to Rome, woe to the Pope, woe to Christianity.

The authenticity of Honoria's story could not be reliably ascertained, and Attila himself did not seem to care too much for the lovelorn princess. But he spared Rome and, in the following year, married Damsel Ildico, an unromantic girl of non-imperial blood but most unusual charms. These charms were, in fact, too powerful for the forty-eight-year-old King's vitality. After a drinking bout he succumbed to Ildico's intense caresses.
And with Attila succumbed his empire.

Ellac, Attila's eldest son, led the army back to Hungary. Already on the march there were indications of satellite mutiny, and as soon as the Pannonian camp was reached, Visigoths and Gepids seized supply dumps and attacked dismounted horsemen. In vain did Ellac muster the elite of his cavalry to quell the uprising. In a furious melee 30,000 horsemen—about two thirds of the total number—were killed. Ellac was literally cut to pieces by Gepid knifemen. The victors gathered the spoils and marched off, leaving the remnants of their former masters perplexed and bewildered by their sudden impotence and poverty.

Dengizieh, another son of Attila, proclaimed himself King and, having inherited his father's cockiness, he dispatched a messenger to Constantinople, requesting the annual tribute. The Byzantine emperor did not deign to reply, whereupon Dengizieh issued a declaration of war and led his small horde into the Balkan Peninsula.

The Hun princes rebelled against Dengizieh, and when the vanguard of the Byzantine forces reached the Danube, they were greeted by Hun officers who handed them the head of Dengizieh as a token of their peaceful intentions, and offered to enlist in the Byzantine army for frontier guard duty or any other service the empire might request.

The ruler of the empire, however, mindful of the past discouraging experience with mass enlistment of barbarian mercenaries, had no desire to hire the horsemen and thus give them an opportunity to rally for another drive. The severed head of the last King of the Huns was graciously accepted, and officers were told that their application for enlistment would be considered later. The Eastern Romans resorted to the same expedient that China had used to deal with troublesome neighbors. Byzantine agents visited chieftains, and soon Hun tribes along the lower Danube were engaged in fratricidal strife. As a result, Byzantium, whose intrigues fostered the struggle, enjoyed a period of peace.

A few Hun clans did not stay in the Danube River valley. They trudged east, toward the big steppes whence their ancestors had come and to which instinct urged them to return. It was no safe retreat, however. Victims of the invaders and their descendants who watched their onetime conquerors trek away like a downtrodden lot of cattle thieves rose in a disorganized but savage drive of revenge. All the way from the Wallachian plains to the Volga they followed the Huns like wolf packs, taking a heavy toll of the fugitives. From the forests emerged Slav tribes to join in the pursuit of the men who, a few short years before, had been the instruments of the Scourge of God, and who were now a disheartened band of sneakers who did not even dare to use their arrows against weak, but implacable, foes.

CHAPTER EIGHT

Slowly Europe recovered. Historic molds had been shattered, but what remained of their content was cast in new shapes; from the ruins of Western Roman military might rose the spiritual authority of the Church. In Central and Western Europe a new generation was struggling for new national organizations. Byzantine emperors, sole heirs of ancient European conceptions of universal power, pondered about ways and means to control the world's resources. Even Byzantium's economic strength was reduced by payment of tributes, maintenance of an expensive army, and unsatisfactory trade. The rest of Europe was destitute. The Huns had sucked the countries dry and they themselves were now mendicants without having made restitution. A long period of peace and construction would have been required to reform and ramify.

Early in the sixth century, when Europe was still in dire need of repose, another human wave from Siberia burst into the steppes west of the Ural Mountains, and swept on toward the Volga and Dniester rivers. The newcomers were horsemen on shaggy mounts, armed with bows and arrows, axes and knives; they were fearful to look at, with their flat, ugly features and their two thin pigtails. Byzantine scouts reported that these were Awars, a people no less bloodthirsty than the Huns, and equally determined to subjugate the continent. Byzantium prepared for war, while meditating about possibilities to avoid a clash, at the expense of other nations.

The Awars established themselves in the Russian plains; they spread to the shores of the Black Sea and to the mouth of the Danube. Slavs retreated into forests; other nations in Central Russia were submerged by the violent tide or pushed to the arid north. The conquerors' pace slowed down as they advanced; they might stall for years while new Awar groups came up from the rear. When the bulk of the Awars reached the Black Sea, their number was as large as Attila's host had been. Remnants of feuding Hun tribes were absorbed by them; they did not gain much strength by the addition of the stragglers, but received a great deal of information about countries that lay ahead of them.

Thus the Awars learned that Byzantium had gold and silk, and that despite its strongly fortified capital it was vulnerable to extortion. The mere presence of a big Awar army on the border would make the Byzantines ready for payment of tribute. The Awars established a huge camp of carts on the left bank of the Danube, and waited. Their Khan held court in a tent, not as roomy as

Attila's silken palace had been, and raided neighboring regions, destroying peaceful settlers and seizing their meager belongings. The campaigns were meant to intimidate the Emperor, but Byzantium did not react.

In 557, at last, an impatient Khan dispatched Kandikh, a trusted soldier, across the border to present demands to the Eastern Roman emperor. The Awars wanted an annual tribute and cession of territory. The Emperor was ready to pay, but suggested that they look for territory elsewhere. Lands, immeasurable in size, and of inexhaustible wealth, he told the twin-pigtailed envoy, were within their grasp; they were inhabited by wicked people, cunning schemers, but impotent to deal with courageous warriors. Already the Emperor had considered waging war upon the villains, and now he was ready to ally with the Awars to crush the common enemy. He offered military advice and expert guides. Kandikh objected that this would put the brunt of the fighting upon the Awars; the soft-spoken Emperor told of the propitiousness of Byzantine blessings, the Awar replied gruffly that he wanted more than good wishes. The meeting became deadlocked. When at last Kandikh took leave to report to his Khan, the Emperor assigned Valentinos, his top expert on dealing with barbarians, to accompany the delegate as a matter of courtesy.

Valentinos went straight to the ranking Awar shaman, who resided in a massive cart drawn by a team of four oxen. There he stayed overnight; and on the following morning the shaman entered his Khan's tent, a few steps ahead of Kandikh. Before the delegate had an opportunity to report on his unsatisfactory talks, the Khan learned from his wizard that, by the favor of the heavenly spirits, a man had arrived who could show the way to prosperity. Valentinos, enacting the part of a seer in best shaman tradition, revealed his miraculous forebodings; and whatever Kandikh thought of the act, no man, however reputable, could denounce the chief shaman as a cheat.

The Awars turned against Slav tribes who had rather recently settled in the Danube Valley. The Antes, the Wendes, and the Slovenes were, in turn, massacred, looted, and their homesteads destroyed. Their small herds of cattle did not satisfy the Awars' greed, and their simple farming implements were of no value to conquerors who did not till the soil. But the shaman found that the course of events was as auspicious as the spirits wanted it to be, and they were now on the threshold of even larger and wealthier lands farther upstream. A clumsy column of oxcarts drove up the Danube Valley: drove Lombard (Langobard) settlers of Pannonia, usually aggressive people, to seek shelter in the rough mountains of the northern Balkan Peninsula. The Awars continued into Austria. Again settlements went up in flames, again people were slaughtered.

Yet nobody was impressed into the army, the Khan did not believe in foreign mercenaries. Advancing at a snail's pace, the army reached the Thuringian hills five years after Valentinos' oracle. They had yet to find the wealth it had forecast.

The horsemen were in a grim mood. They felt ill at ease in the densely wooded narrow valleys of that part of Germany, where they could not even find enough fodder for their mounts.

In Thuringia, Emperor Siegbert had assembled his troops and those of his vassals; foot soldiers familiar with rough terrain, and well trained in hand-to-hand fighting in the woods. Siegbert's men caught the Awars by surprise and inflicted staggering defeat upon the horsemen, who fled in disorder, abandoning their carts and baggage.

They did not rally until they had reached Western Hungary. Their situation seemed hopeless. The German army could crush the demoralized hordes; the Lombards, who no longer had reason to hide, were strong enough to deal with them. The Awars themselves were at the verge of disintegration into small, feuding groups, as had been the case with most routed Siberian nations.

But Emperor Siegbert did not press the pursuit, and the Lombards happened to be at odds with Gepids who now lived in the Transylvanian mountains, and were reluctant to engage in hostilities that could lead to a two-front war. Three years after the battle of Thuringia a new Awar khan took the reins, a clever, energetic ruler who knew how to prevent further disintegration of his people. Khan Bayan, who had learned Byzantium's tricks, sent an ambassador to the Lombards and offered an alliance under the terms of which they would retain control of Pannonia, while the Awars would establish themselves in Wallachia, after the certain defeat of the Gepids.

The Lombards accepted with alacrity; and several months later the Gepids were annihilated. But the Lombards had good reason to regret their association with the Awars. Not only did the Awars claim all the spoils, they also refused to confine themselves to settling in the preassigned areas. Backed by his shamans, Khan Bayan proclaimed that the Awar realm should extend as far west as the Austrian border, including Pannonia. The Lombards, unable to wage battle, eventually accepted the establishment of Awar bases in Pannonia, with the understanding that garrisons would collect no tribute and not interfere with local administration. The Awar commanders in Pannonia turned out to be exacting, arrogant tyrants who treated the Lombards as inferiors and requisitioned their property without compensation. When a Lombard delegation wanted to cross into Western Hungary to present grievances to Khan Bayan, they were told to fight or to leave.

The Lombards chose the latter. They migrated into Northern Italy to join their kin in the Po Valley. Bayan's might was not challenged from Central Russia to the German border. The horsemen settled down. Slaves they had captured did their farming, building, and housework. For the first time aborigines of Siberia lived in permanent buildings. Villages covered circular areas, reminding one of cart camps; houses were fairly large, but never had more than one room, as a soldier's tent should have. In winter beasts and men lived together. It was a comfortable life for the ex-nomads, but it made the Khan worry, lest his men would become effeminate and an easy prey to enemies at large. Bayan considered every neighbor an enemy, even Byzantium, which had been proclaimed an ally on the eve of the Awar's first drive to the west. He expected attacks from west and east by the Germans, who had yet to exploit the fruits of the victory in Thuringia, and by Asiatic nations, which had overpowered what remained of Awar tribes in the distant steppes north of the Caspian Sea. The Awars, like other Siberian militant nations, could not adapt themselves to defensive warfare; they had to attack or to flee. The Khan wanted to attack. The closest objective was the Balkans. This was Byzantine territory, but the Bulgars lived there too and they were said to be wealthy. Bayan could attack the Bulgars, seize whatever they owned, and still profess amity toward the Byzantines, should a strong Eastern Roman army turn up at the spot. As he was making plans, he did not know that the Emperor of Byzantium no longer considered the Awars a predominant Eastern power.

Eastern Rome had the best intelligence service in Europe; in fact the only one deserving that name.

While the Awars were in Germany, missionaries and trade caravan leaders returning from Asia reported that big changes were taking place along the trade route. Twenty years before the great steppes had been controlled by three nations: the Mongol Chou-Chou, who spread from Manchuria to the vicinity of Lake Balkhash; the Hephatites, an unstable people who roamed the territory between Lake Balkhash and the Aral Sea, and, from there, westward by descendants of Hiung-nu stragglers who had stayed behind when their kin's horses trampled Europe asunder. Then suddenly a new great power had emerged from the Altai Mountains: the Tou-kine, former vassals of the Chou-Chou, who had rebelled against their masters and had become the dominating power in Asia beyond the Chinese wall. The Tou-kine were also called Türküt, which in the Mongol idiom meant "the strong ones"; they were in fact stronger than any other nation. They would soon invest the approaches to Byzantium, and it would be wise to make a deal with them before they attacked the empire. The Türküt were not averse to dealings, and, even though their manners were somewhat rough, they were not as bloodthirsty as other savages from the steppes. They enjoyed trade and barter, and never injured missionaries, whom they considered merchants in a peculiar way. Intelligence services recommended that a diplomatic mission meet the Türküt, make arrangements to put East-West trade under their protection, and even grant them certain monopolies.

Byzantium would not grant long-term privileges to upstart Asiatics, who might be gone tomorrow, swept away by the tide of some other nation. However, the empire had trade posts on the Crimean coasts, and imperial counselors liked the idea of enlisting the Türküt as defenders of the land approaches to the peninsula in return for trading concessions.

The Emperor chose Valentinos to make the deal. The clever ambassador, however, made a grievous mistake. At the Khan's headquarters, on the Asiatic-European border near the Caspian Sea, he went straight to the Khan's tent, instead of first consulting shamans, and opened his address by saying that his sovereign did not really need anybody's good will or protection; for Byzantium was the strongest empire in the world, and allied with the next strongest nation: the Awars. He could not proceed; for the long-haired Khan blushed with rage and exploded in a furious harangue. The Awars, he thundered, had been defeated, crushed, annihilated in Asia; only runaways could have reached the western lands, and he considered it an insult to mention the Awars in his presence. "At the mere sight of my horsemen's whips," the Khan roared, "they will crawl for cover into the intestines of the earth. But we shall use our swords to destroy what remains of that breed of slaves, we shall exterminate them like vermin, crush them under the hoofs of our horses. And next, we shall chastise Byzantium for its insolence, and treacherous relations with vermin."

In vain did Valentinos attempt to explain that the alliance with the Awars was not really a close association; that it could be superseded by a lasting and intimate pact with the Türküt; his words and those of the interpreter were drowned in the Khan's roar; and the ambassador withdrew in a less than dignified attitude.

A dejected Valentinos hurriedly returned to his Emperor's distant court, convinced that the Türküt would soon invade the West.

Türküt light units traveled fast. When Valentinos rode into Byzantium, news had just arrived that cavalrymen carrying wolves' heads on poles as field badges had wiped out the empire's Crimean trade posts and emptied the storehouses.

The expected invasion of the Balkans, however, did not materialize. The Türküt were interested in the Middle East rather than Europe.

The Türküt's aggressive interest in Persia became Byzantium's great concern. Persia, under changing domination, remained the hereditary enemy, without which, even in those days, a self-respecting nation could not do. Should the Türküt throw their might behind Persia, the Eastern Roman Empire would be caught in pincers—Sassanide Persia in the east, the unreliable Awars in the north. Byzantine emperors were students of history; they felt that a civilized empire could easily recover from defeat suffered from another civilized nation, but that it had only a slim chance of survival after being overrun by barbarians. Valentinos was in disfavor. The imperial counselors, however, were at a loss how to contact the Khan again.

And while the issue was under uncomfortable consideration in the East Roman capital, Türküt Khan Boumin, who had freed his people from Chou-Chou suzerainty and defeated the Awars in Asia, now displaced the Hephatites, and annihilated Siberian stragglers along the ancient silk route, unifying the eastern and western branches of the nation. He was their Khagan now, and his Empress, Istämi, of Chou-Chou descent, was the brain that directed Khagan Boumin's statesmanship. Istämi was fond of beautiful things, and of people who produced them; she wanted the Türküt to associate with refined nations. Maniakh, a merchant who supplied her with luxuries from the East and West, told her of Byzantine splendor and of Valentinos' unsuccessful mission, and she requested that the blunder be remedied at once. Boumin was ready for a deal with Byzantium, and, early in 568, Maniakh journeyed to Europe to suggest that the Emperor send another embassy to Asia to arrange for political, military, and economic agreements between Türküt and Eastern Rome.

Persian agents are said to have offered the merchant-diplomat fantastic bribes to keep him from carrying out his assignment, but Maniakh was incorruptible; and he had reason to expect colossal benefits should his mission succeed.

He was extremely well received at the Emperor's court, and Zemarchos, another Byzantine diplomat, was selected to visit Boumin, to present him with Byzantium's cordial greetings, its most precious presents, and assurances of friendship.

Byzantine archives contain Zemarchos' report about the Türküt people: "They live in felt tents, let their hair fall, wander from one region to the other in quest of pasture lands and springs; their main occupations are the breeding of herds, and hunting; they have little regard for old people, but hold men at the peak of their strength in high esteem; they ignore the administration of justice, but they have an intricate system of local and military administration. Their top ranking officers are the Ye-pou, the Che, the Te-k'in, the Sou-li-pat, and the To-Tu-pat; they have twenty-nine classes of minor officers. Offices are hereditary. The soldiers are armed with bows, arrows, whistling arrows, javelins, sabers, and pieces of armor, they wear ornamented belts and have wolves' heads on the tops of their banners; the Emperor's satraps call themselves the 'Wolves.' When a man dies, his next of kin kill a lamb and a horse, and put the carcasses in front of the deceased person's tent as an offering; then, they circle the tent on horseback seven times, uttering lugubrious outcries, and each time they pass the entrance of the tent, they cut their faces with knives, crying so that blood and tears mingle. The procedure is repeated on the day of the funeral. A heap of stones is erected on the burial grounds, one stone for every man the defunct has killed in his own lifetime. After the death of a father, an elder brother, or an uncle, the son, the next-eldest brother, or nephew, in that order, marries the widow, or, in case there is no widow, her sister.

"The Khagan is clad in green silk, a garb not worn by his subjects. His tent opens in the direction of the rising sun.

"The Türküt consider it glorious to die in combat, and are ashamed to admit that any of their male relatives died of a disease or, worse even, of old age.

"They venerate demons and ghosts, and have their religious rites performed by magicians who claim that the universe is divided into layers, the upper 17 of which constitute the heavens, the lower 7 or 9 the underworld, the realm of eternal darkness; the surface of the earth lies between heavens and the underworld. Ruler of the heavens is Tängri, whom all men shall obey. The souls of virtuous men go to heaven, those of vicious people are banished to the underworld. The highest goddess is Oumai, protectress of children; innumerable genii dwell on earth in the waters, on holy places and high mountains."

The ambassadorial papers are not explicit about actual results of the parleys. But Zemarchos undoubtedly signed some contracts.

Once the threat of invasion was averted, Byzantium was in no hurry to co-operate. The East Roman Empire was certain to outlast the fluctuating realms of the steppes. And actually Boumin's empire soon crumbled. But hardly could the Byzantine emperors have conceived that one splinter tribe of the Türküt nation would conquer their capital almost nine centuries after the meeting in the tent camp, and establish the Osman-Turkish state on the ruins of Eastern Rome.

Contemptible as the Awars had become in the eyes of sixth-century Byzantium, the fact remained that they were a power to be reckoned with. General Priscus, one of Eastern Rome's keenest military minds, advocated preventive war, but the Emperor was old and did not want to take to the field and most of his advisers also were aged men who preferred precarious stability to adventure. Priscus's plans were shelved, and while the second Byzantine embassy studied Türküt habits, Bayan invaded Bulgar territory and began to lay it waste.

On an inscrutable spur of a moment, however, Bayan's hordes evacuated the Balkan peninsula and headed for Germany. The Awars evened their score with Emperor Siegbert; they met the German army in terrain better suited for their type of warfare, and put it to disorderly flight. But they did not proceed farther to the west; they returned to Hungary, moved back into their circular villages, and put their slaves to hard work. In 587 their ruler called them for another campaign into the Balkans. The horsemen crossed the peninsula in west-easterly direction, sacked cities at the sites of Adrianople and Burgas, and rode toward the chain of hills that protected Byzantium's northern approaches, where they were checked by hastily concentrated Byzantine forces. Leisure had had averse effects upon the horsemen's martial spirits. Bayan withdrew, but five years later he attacked once more. This time Byzantium had made good use of the respite. Priscus, who had taken charge, had formed cavalry units whose speed of maneuver made the Awars appear slow and he devised new tactics for simultaneous assaults on enemy troops and communications. The Awars suffered staggering defeat and Bayan had great trouble to extricate his hordes from encirclement.

Priscus was under orders to battle the intruder only south of the Danube but not to cross that river. This saved the Awars from destruction. The general argued with his Emperor and imperial advisers, asking that restrictive orders be rescinded, and the Awars be disposed of for good. Statesmen objected that a campaign into Central Europe would expose the empire's vital defense lines to other Asiatic barbarians that might turn up.

After nine years of Byzantine haggling and Awar consolidation an aging General Priscus was authorized to cross into Hungary, but he was supposed neither to go west of that country nor to stay away for more than one year. Fast as the Byzantine cavalry was in action, the army's marching speed was determined by heavy supply columns. More than half of the allotted time had passed when Priscus forced Bayan to give battle. Four of Bayan's sons were killed, the horsemen lost almost two thirds of their effectives, panicky hordes fled across the Austrian border. Priscus did not cross the line. Another opportunity to destroy the terrorists from Siberia had been missed.

Bayan died in 602, a wealthy man. His treasures had been well hidden. But Awar chieftains and soldiers had lost most of their belongings. Their villages were flattened, their stores seized, and, worse even, the greater part of their slaves had run away. Only a successful marauding campaign could restore the Awars' prosperity; yet it took seven lean years of training, drain upon the new Khan's property and work to rebuild an Awar army. The new force was not deemed adequate to challenge Byzantium's power, so the Khan chose the route once taken by the defeated Lombards. In 610 his men turned up in Northern Italy. The stench of death and smoldering fires pervaded the province of Friuli, whose soothing beauty had domesticated the Lombards but did not temper the Siberians.

In Friuli a Byzantine ambassador visited the Khan, expressing his Emperor's friendly feelings and reminding him of a never-denounced alliance between their nations.

Emperor Heraclius of Byzantium had no friendly feelings for the Khan, but his realm was threatened by Sassanide Persians who raided Minor Asia, and by the Bulgars who after the Awar invasion had moved into Wallachia, Moldavia, and Bessarabia, and were becoming aggressive.

The Khan's self-complacency was tremendously boosted by the Emperor's message, but in the same measure his respect for Byzantium's strength declined. He replied haughtily that he was prepared to meet Heraclius after suitable arrangements had been made and his own designs in Italy had been achieved.

It took eight years to complete the arrangements. The Awars' designs in Italy were achieved as soon as all their carts were loaded with spoils, and every soldier had his slaves.

In 619, at last, the Byzantine-Awar meeting took place in Thrace on Byzantine territory. The Khan had agreed to leave his own army behind, on the left bank of the Danube, while the Emperor was accompanied by several hundred bodyguards.

But as Khan and Emperor exchanged greetings, the sound of battle was heard. A Byzantine officer dashed into the conference tent and almost dragged his sovereign outside to waiting horses. Heraclius galloped away, escorted by a few officers, as the rest of the guards sacrificed themselves to hold off masses of Awars who had swarmed across the river.

Heraclius had a narrow escape. And while light units joined action to delay Awar advance, the capital prepared for a siege. One Awar attempt to seize the place by a coup was beaten off; the Khan eventually abandoned the assault.

While the Byzantine embassy had cooled its heels in Italy, Persian agents had visited the Khan. A plot had been hatched to abduct the Emperor and take his city by surprise. Should Byzantium resist, a Persian army en route from the east would join the Awars within a few days. Caught in a vise, Byzantium could but capitulate. Awars and Persians would divide the empire among themselves.

The Persians, however, had not penetrated far into Asia Minor when the meeting in Thrace opened, and they discontinued their advance when they learned that Heraclius was safely back in his city.

Byzantium kept its ruler and its capital, but it lost whatever prestige it had retained from Priscus's day. The Awars expected immediate retaliation for the outrage. As it did not come, they concluded that Byzantium was tottering and that their next invasion would be a pushover. The Khan did not intend to share easy and gigantic spoils with the unreliable Persians. But he needed reinforcements to carry out the campaign at such speed that his forces would control all of the empire before Persia, under the pretext of collaboration, could stage an invasion of its own; mobilization of Bulgar manpower would be the answer to his problem. The Bulgars, however, defied Awar conscription officers. Their chieftains were outright insulting, and the ruler of the Bulgars, who called himself King, insinuated that he should be proclaimed Khan of both nations. An irate Awar Khan thereupon began to negotiate with Persia. The Persians enjoyed the game of intrigue and double dealings, in which the barbarians were hopelessly outclassed.

Not until 626 was another Persian-Awar agreement signed. Under its terms the Persians would receive most of Byzantium's territory, including all strategically important areas and trade posts. Again the Khan's soldiers appeared under the walls of Byzantium; this time a Persian army reached the opposite shore of the narrow Bosporus, but could not cross the strait, in face of a superior Byzantine navy. The Persians maneuvered cautiously; the commanding general was directed to avoid high casualties and let the Awars spend their power in mass assault so that his army could deal with Awar attempts at treachery after the fall of the capital.

But Byzantium did not fall, as the fence-sitting Persians realized after three years of siege. In 629 they marched off without ado. The abandoned Khan threw every man who could carry a knife or shoot an arrow against the battlements, but the Awar army melted away. The walls were neither breached nor surmounted.

One year after the Persians had left, the Awars sneaked away to Hungary, a battered, demoralized, shrunken lot. They saved themselves from Bulgar conquest by promptly recognizing their former subject's independence; appeased the Croats, a southern Slavic group, by grants of land in southern Hungary; and refrained from raids into neighboring territory. The Khan's treasure was still intact: the proceeds of more than one century of marauding. The Khan established his rather modest court in sight of his riches. A new city, circular shaped, like all Awar settlements, developed on the site of Győr, sixty-five miles west of present Budapest. Construction work proceeded slowly. The Awars could no longer keep slaves. They were awkward in handiwork and untaught in planning. They tried to imitate the crafts they had seen in their violent contact with Western culture, but whatever they built or manufactured retained a travestying touch of barbarism.

No ambassadors visited the Khan's residence, and had it not been for Charlemagne the Awars might well have become the first Siberian nomads to turn into a settled, sovereign Central European nation.

Charlemagne, King of the Franks, and founder of the Holy Roman Empire, was illiterate but an eager listener to scholars' and learned jesters' accounts of foreign people. Learning of the Awars' past invasions of Germany, and their continued existence close to the eastern borders of the empire he was about to build, he decided to uproot that source of trouble forever. Charlemagne's host took the Awars' capital almost without a struggle and, without the shamans, neither the Khan nor any of his men would have survived. The wizards, however, offered to abjure their deities, and to accept Christendom; the Awar people, trembling for their lives, and convinced that their celestial spirits were just as impotent as they themselves, prostrated themselves before the Cross.

Charlemagne invariably spared converts. But he had the Awars moved to a narrow reservation near the Austrian border. There the onetime refugee-conquerors lived, as undistinguished breeders of cattle and horses.

Their shamans erected crosses just as they had set up totem poles. They beseeched Jesus Christ, as the Lord of the everlasting sky, to fatten their herds. And because Frankish padres assigned to supervise the neophyte's rituals objected to sacrifices, the wizards kept their parishioners' offerings, without which, the Awar Christians trusted, no prayer would be granted. Nothing was heard of the Khan's treasure, and of the fate of the Khan, who joined his people's conversion. It could be that the riches disappeared on the transfer to the reservation, but it cannot be ruled out that the Khan disappeared, together with his gold, to become the first ex-potentate to go into a wealth-cushioned exile.

The Awars never trespassed the boundaries of their reservation. Nearly one hundred years after their transfer Western Hungary was swept by human drifts in the wake of eruptive migrations from the East. And when the storm abated, the Awars had disappeared.

CHAPTER NINE Nationalism, proud consciousness of collective ethnical characteristics, had not been noticeable among earlier Siberians, whose conception of kinship did not go beyond common camps and commanders. The Türküt became the first nomads to develop a national pride, one as aggressive and ferocious as the barbarian character. The Türküt were convinced of their pre-eminence, and of their design to rule the world.

This conviction kept them from ruin and disintegration while they were held in bondage by the Mongolian Chou-Chou. The Chou-Chou had once defeated the Türküt, killed most fathers, and put the sons to work in the iron mines and forges in the Altai Mountains. Bondsmen were not permitted to own arms, but not even the most gruesome punishment could deter the Türküt from hiding away some of the weapons they made for their masters.

Sometime around 500 an armed insurrection of the Türküt not only freed them from bondage but made them the dominant power in Southern Siberia. They set out to unite their kin into one nation.

They had but vague ideas of the whereabouts of their relatives. Chinese traders, the only sources of information in Siberia, spoke of groups of long-haired, swarthy men they had encountered on the borders of Manchuria, on the upper Yenisei and near Lake Balkhash; others were said to roam sections of the ancient silk road. They referred to these people as T'ou-kine, but they were not sure that they actually were members of one and the same family.

The Türküt divided their forces, drove east and west and crushed tribes that were not their kin, and imposed their rule upon those to whom they believed themselves related. They wanted the Türküt nation to be under centralized leadership by one master tribe and incorporation was tantamount to subjugation.

Violent tides of migration were unleashed by Türküt expansion. Siberian people, even if they were not directly hit, had a strange faculty of registering pushes by strong nations. All over the wide land people moved away from the danger zone, sometimes colliding as they went, the weaker succumbing to the stronger, and the stronger gaining momentum by their victory. The breakers of migration continued to hit Eastern Europe long after the Türküt drive had come to a halt.

The Türküt were the first Siberian nation to record history. On a boulder an inscription in runic characters was found, reading: "When the Blue Sky above and the dark earth below were created, the son of men came into existence between heaven and earth. Above men ranged our ancestors Boumin Khagan and Istämi Khagan. They organized and administered the Empire and the institutions of the Türküt people. They had many enemies, but in various campaigns they subdued and pacified numerous peoples from the four corners of the world. They made them bend their knees and lower their heads. They established our rule in front (the East) as far as the forest of Quardikhan [Khingan Mountains], and to the rear (the West) as far as the Iron Gates (in the Altais). The Blue Türküt's khagans were wise and gallant, their officers were bold and sage, all their nobles and all the people were righteous."

Another inscription, deciphered at Kocho Tsaidam, tells of the Türküt east of the Altai Mountains: "The sons of Türküt nobles became slaves. Their pure daughters turned serfs. Türküt forsook their ranks and accepted Chinese commissions. They submitted to the Chinese Emperor, devoted their labor and their strength to him, fought for him, and to him surrendered their Empire and its institutions."

Emperor Wen-ti defeated the Western Türküt and, according to the ancient Chinese custom, had them enlisted as mercenaries. In 589 he solemnly proclaimed eternal peace and permanent disarmament; he reformed taxation, reorganized courts of justice and provincial administrations, and passed the task of disarmament on to his successors, who, in the old tradition, forgot to carry it out.

Emperor T'ai-tsong subjugated roaming horsemen in the high mountain regions of Outer Mongolia and the approaches to India in the first part of the seventh century, and had this feat glorified in a proclamation: "Those who, before me, have claimed to have subjugated the barbarians, did, in fact, vanquish but the Ts'in-che, the Houang-ti, and Han Wou-ti. But, by drawing my three-feet-long sword, I have forced into submission the Two Hundred Kingdoms, imposed silence upon the Four Seas; and the most distant barbarians came, one after the other, to swear allegiance."

The designation of the peoples that were previously vanquished is not conclusive. Chinese chroniclers used terms none of the respective tribes would have understood. The number of kingdoms said to have been subdued is a fantastic overstatement.

T'ai-tsong did not draw his three-foot-long sword against the Eastern Türküt, but dispatched a mission to the camp of the ruling Khagan, T'ong Che-hou, to offer peace and good will.

"These barbarians have extremely numerous horses," returning diplomats told their Emperor. "The Khan wore a coat of green silk, his hair hung down, but on his forehead he wore a twisted ribbon of silk, ten feet long. He was surrounded by 200 officers, clad in brocade, their hair braided. Lesser members of his military entourage were mounted on horses and camels, they wore furs and fine linen, and carried long lances, banners, and bows. There were so many of them that you could not see the end of the array. The Khan bid us to sit down and treated us to wine and music. The barbarian music is extremely loud and the tunes are savage, yet they charm the ear and gladden the heart. The Khan drank the first cup with us and then his officers joined the party.

Food was served: quarters of broiled lamb and veal. Everybody was happy, and peace and friendship are now secure."

Türküt garments, beasts, and entertainment summarized a century of roving conquest. The fine linens were souvenirs from Europe and so, probably, was the wine. The camels came from Persia, the brocades could have been taken from trading as well as manufacturing nations, and the music could have been picked up anywhere along the southern rim of Asia. Even the broiling of meat was great progress as compared to Siberian eating habits. The Chinese report demoted their ruler by calling him Khan instead of Khagan. The title of Khagan implied sovereign rule over an entire nation, and T'ong Che-hou ruled only the Eastern Türküt. Soon his realm would shrink even further. Such a reduction had been the supreme objective of the Chinese mission. Peace and good will were only means to that end.

In a gesture disguised as an act of supreme courtesy he bestowed ranks and commissions upon Türküt officers and nobles, and invited them to move to China.

The Türküt came, were fascinated, and stayed. China's courtesans, its theaters, and palaces were delights that no amount of warring and carousing in tents could offer. Service in the Chinese Army was infinitely more comfortable than riding through the vastness hunting for kinfolk. China offered generalcies, and the title of Khan, to noble officers who recruited their former units into the Chinese service. A Chinese general was far better off than a Türküt officer of the Khagan's guard. Superficially Sinofied Türküt nobles enlisted their former subordinates into the Chinese Emperor's service; the "Marching Men," as these auxiliaries were called, policed the fringe of the Gobi Desert, drew Chinese army pay and food, but remained barred from Chinese cities.

Li-tai-po, Chinese poet laureate, writes about the Marching Man: "He never opens a book, but he knows how to rush out to hunt; he is skillful, strong, and bold. In the fall, his horse is fat, magnificently nourished by the grass of the steppes. How superbly disdainful he looks, galloping through the plains, his whip clinking in its gilted sheet, or lashing the powdery snow. Spirited by generous wine, he calls his falcon, and sets out for the wide open lands. His bow, bent vigorously, is never unbent in vain. Often, several birds fall, hit by his whistling arrow. Men retreat to give way to him, for his valor and his belligerent spirit are well known throughout the Gobi."

Less than one decade after the Chinese peace-and-good-will mission had come to T'ong Che-hou's camp, tribes deserted their khagan and became Marching Men, and few officers remained in their sovereign's service.

T'ong Che-hou died, a hapless, bewildered man, and his successor vanished, never to be heard of again. It was a low point in Türküt history, but it was a new beginning rather than a dismal end.

It appears as if China had not wanted to hire remnants of an apparently doomed nation. The last Türküt trudged away to the Orkhon River near Lake

Baikal, where many Siberians grew to conquering strength and again raided China. The Emperor ordered his Marching Men to repel the intruders; the generals, incensed at the thought of "losing face" through the action of their barbaric kin, staged a terrific slaughter. One of these men bragged of having had 11,000 prisoners decapitated, and their skulls piled up on the battlefield. Türküt raged against Türküt and, despite the superiority of Chinese-manufactured weapons the renegades did not quite destroy their kin.

Another khagan, Khoutlouk, is credited with having restored the Türküt Empire. An inscription says:

"The common Türküt people have been lamenting: 'Once, we were a nation, and we had an Empire. Where is our Empire now? We were a people, and we had a Khagan. Where now is our Khagan?' Thus they spoke, and so speaking they became enemies of the Chinese Khagan; and fighting they found the strength to hope that they could reconstitute and reorganize themselves. Thereupon, the Chinese swore: 'We shall annihilate the Türküt, we shall make them a people without posterity'; and they set out to destroy us. But the God of the Türküt, who dwells in Heaven high above, and the holy spirits of the Türküt on earth and in the waters, did not want this to happen. And to keep our people from being destroyed, and to restore it into a nation, they lifted my father Khoutlouk to the peak of Heavens, and bestowed supernatural power upon him. Returned to earth, he set out to conquer with only 25 faithful, and soon, their number rose to 70, and Heaven's endowment made my father's men be as wolves, and its enemies like sheep. After its number had grown to 700, my father's host dispossessed unruly Khans and prevailed upon independent people, reducing them to slavery. They imposed upon their slaves the institutions of our ancestors. In the south, the Chinese were our enemies; in the north, the Nine Oughouze were our enemies, the Kirghizes, the Ouriquans, the Thirty Tatars, the Ki-tai, all were our enemies. My father, the Khagan, took to the field 47 times, and fought 20 battles. And because Heaven favored him, he took Empires away from those who had owned Empires; he pacified his foes and made them bend their knees and bow their heads."

Heaven's favor, however, did not protect Khoutlouk's empire from remaining in a state of foment. The subdued people did not meekly accept imposition of the Türküt's ancestral institutions, and Khoutlouk's son had no successor who could have commemorated his father's exploits. He was deposed by a rebellion of unpacified chieftains, and Khagan Mo-tsh'o became the most prominent Siberian potentate.

Mo-tsh'o would not be satisfied with precariously ruling over refractory nomads and their unmanageable leaders. He would not content himself with another empire of the steppes.

Mo-tsh'o wanted to rule China. Again Türküt hordes attacked China. They crossed the wall and in 691 invested the outskirts of Peking. Only a supreme effort by Chinese regulars saved the capital. Türküt generals in China's service gave a poor account of themselves.

Several Sinofied Türküt acted as Mo-tsh'o's clandestine advisers in the intricate game of intrigue that developed between the Khagan and the Empress of China.

Wou Tsö-tien, widow of Emperor Koa-tsou, had snatched the throne from the rightful heir, and held it for twenty-one years with all means, fair or foul —principally the latter. She was completely unscrupulous, a ruthless despot, and a maniacal sadist, but she possessed perfect cunning and a sharp intellect. Wou Tsö-tien was ready to use all her guile and a substantial part of her country's treasures to turn Mo-tsh'o into an ally of whom she might rid herself after his assistance would no longer be needed. While fires still smoldered in the outskirts of Peking, she sent a message to the Khagan; sweet words of friendship, assurances of peaceful intentions, and extravagant promises.

Advisers warned Mo-tsh'o not to let the Empress hold the initiative. They helped draft a strange document: a Türküt protest against her unlawful seizure of the Chinese throne in which Mo-tsh'o styled himself protector of the legitimate heir and pledged himself to fight until this prince would be restored to his right.

The Empress, who had already disposed of the pretender, engaged in complicated argumentation about Chinese laws, and eventually she came out with a surprising proposition: in return for Mo-tsh'o's recognition of her sovereign rule she would assure future legitimacy by designating her nephew as her successor and making him marry the Khagan's daughter. A picture showed the Empress's nephew as a very handsome youth, and Mo-tsh'o's daughter was plain, even by Türküt standards, but it required considerable persuasion on the part of the advisers to keep the Khagan from accepting the offer. They insisted that, by stalling, Mo-tsh'o could extort even more.

The K'i-tan, powerful vassals of China, were in rebellion. The Empress was afraid of engaging the greater part of her armies in the struggle, lest her residence would be bared of loyal defenders and she herself exposed to attack by domestic foes. Mo-tsh'o offered assistance, but in a manner that left no doubt that he would join the K'i-tan if the Empress refused his terms: a stiff fee in silk, rice, armor, and new weapons from Chinese arsenals, experts to teach the Türküt operation of complicated machines, Türküt participation in mapping the campaign. The Empress did not dare reject the terms; and, after the K'i-tan were crushed by joint Türküt-Chinese action, she did not refuse Mo-tsh'o's insulting demand that all spoils be handed over to him as the sole victor. But when the Khagan requested that China pay him an annual tribute, Wou Tsö-tien refused to comply. She would rather go down fighting than accept such humiliation by a barbarian.

The Türküt slashed through Chinese defenses. Prosperous cities were laid waste, its inhabitants massacred wholesale. The capital, however, was not attacked. Mo-tsh'o wanted the Empress to stay so that after each raid he could send her messages restating his demand for tribute and raising its amount. The sums he demanded at last lost every aspect of reasonableness, and were well beyond the limits of what even the richest land on earth could bear. The irate Empress ordered that a census be taken of the population of her country.

This was the first census in China's history. It gave a figure of 37,140,000 in the year 703, while the Türküt, according to reliable information, numbered only a few hundred thousand. The discrepancy encouraged Wou Tsö-tien to stake everything on one decisive battle. She did not take into account, however, that every able-bodied Türküt was a soldier, while only a small fraction of her own subjects had ever served in the army.

In 706 a Türküt army under Mo-tsh'o's personal command was camped near Ming-cha-chan when the bulk of the Chinese forces arrived on the scene. A Chinese general of pure national stock was in command, but several of his aides were of Türküt descent, picked men who were expected to perform their duty. But the descendants of the Türküt supplied Mo-tsh'o with invaluable information while the Chinese army was on the march, and when the battle opened they ran over. The Chinese disaster was complete. Only very few men escaped to tell the story of enemy cavalry ripping their lines apart. Thousands of captives were butchered, others led away to serve the Türküt. "The onetime slaves," an inscription tells, "became owners of slaves; they conquered and organized those who had once held them in servitude."

But again Mo-tsh'o did not march on to Peking to seize the throne. A number of Siberian tribes, possibly remnants of the short-lived Türküt western empire, or other "gathered" kin, displayed an independence that the Khagan would not tolerate, and even boasted of their freedom.

It is said that the aging Khagan, instead of being assuaged by glory, became ever more vindicative, cruel, and tyrannical; that he was given to insane outbursts of rage. Perhaps, maddened by the impudence of the distant kin, Mo-tsh'o was impatient to make an example of them that would forever discourage disobedience.

The roving hordes were no match for the Khagan's army. "We crossed the wooded slopes of the Altai Mountains, and marched up the Irtysh River. We killed the Khan and enslaved his people," an army historian engraved on a rock in the Irtysh Valley.

The Khagan did not want to return to China before having disposed of all antagonists. The aging man's haunted imagination pictured traitors everywhere. The generals who had deserted the Chinese became the object of his maniacal suspicion. Would not these men desert him, too? Didn't they plot with a new Chinese Emperor, successor to Wou Tsö-tien, who had been reported dead? He had the generals put under surveillance; he ordered that all persons with whom they had contact be checked and watched; he planted stool pigeons among loyal officers, and had many executed without investigation.

Combating imaginary conspiracy, the tyrant and his henchmen begot real plots involving China. Mo-tsh'o's punitive squads drowned the insurgents in seas of blood; he visited scenes of vengeance accompanied by his favorite nephew, Kul-tégin, a taciturn giant, whom the Khagan had selected as chief adviser to his son and successor. Mo-tsh'o eventually dealt with his henchmen only through the offices of his nephew; nobody but Kul-tégin had access to him at all times; nobody but Kul-tégin knew where the next blow would fall. And one balmy morning in July 716 Kul-tégin emerged from Mo-tsh'o's tent holding in his hand the Khagan's severed head.

Kul-tégin had joined the conspirators. He had Mo-tsh'o's only son and most other relatives put to death, and all his henchmen liquidated. He did not bid for the khaganate, however, but with the blessings of China he had it pass upon his elder brother Mo-kin-liu.

Khagan Mo-kin-liu thought that only a large-scale foreign war could close all internal rifts. Annoyed by Peking's constant interference in Türküt affairs, he prepared another campaign against China.

But then a strange figure emerged in his camp on the banks of the Orkhon River: Ton-you-cook, a Türküt-Mongol of whom the saying went that he was 1000 years old and embodied the wisdom of thirty generations. Ton-you-cook advised his ruler against war; with the people exhausted by fratricidal strife, and famished, with their herds dispersed and their horses ill-kept, he predicted that they would face annihilation in battle. But when the Khagan suggested that he might deal with the Chinese rather than fight, to adopt the Chinese way of life, to build walled cities, and embrace Buddhism and Taoism, the wise man objected: only nomadic life befitted the Türküt, only as nomads could they strike at the enemies and make booty when the moment was auspicious; only as nomads could they extricate themselves if aggression failed. The Türküt, he said, ought to be like their symbol, the wolf, leaping at their prey when they felt strong, fleeing and hiding when they were weak. In a walled city they would be trapped. Buddha and Lao-tse were no good for them: these gods wanted men to be mild and enlightened, which did not befit warriors. "Don't go to the open plains now," he exclaimed. "If you go there, you shall perish. But if you stay in the forests of the Orkhon, where there is neither wealth nor worry, you shall preserve an eternal empire."

Mo-kin-liu did not march against Peking. His people called him The Wise.

Wisdom, however, offered no protection against violent death. Mo-kin-liu was assassinated by his own palace guard, whose commander also stabbed the Emperor's widow to death and usurped the throne.

Three Türküt tribes battled for control of the unstable empire, and the Chinese dealt with all of them. Around 744, when the northern tribe of the Uigurs emerged victorious, they pledged loyalty to Peking.

The Uigurs built a new capital on the Orkhon River. Quara Balgassoun, City of the Court, was a camp of lavish tents, and it had no walls. The beginnings of Uigur hegemony were auspicious. The Chinese T'ang dynasty struggled for survival against internal foes; Emperor Mo-yen-tsho implored the Uigur Khagan to come to his rescue and offered an annual tribute of 20,000 pieces of silk; when the Khagan was in no great hurry to carry out his pledge of loyalty, the Emperor augmented his bid by marrying off one of his daughters to the barbaric sovereign. Twice the Uigur armies saved the Emperor. Twice they pitched their tents on the palace grounds of Peking, and the Khagan, oblivious of Ton-you-cook's axiom, moved into the state rooms of his father-in-law. In 757 he met Manichaen missionaries who initiated him in their creed outlawed in most Western countries.

Manes Manichaeus, a Persian, had begun to preach in A.D. 240; he pretended to be an Apostle of Christ, but his creed, even though it contained some essentials of Christendom, was incongruous with the teachings of the Church. The Khagan was dissatisfied with his shamans, who had not shown much enthusiasm for his marriage to the Chinese princess, and did not proclaim the Blue Sky's approval of his policies. Unwilling to alter them, and to part with his noble and attractive spouse, the Khagan adopted Manichaenism and proclaimed it the official religion of the Uigurs, and ordered his subjects to settle down and cultivate the soil. "This country of barbaric customs, permeated with the fumes of blood, has been transformed into a land in which vegetables are grown, and people urge one another to do good." Thus the event was recorded for posterity.

The urge for doing good, however, did not prevent the converted Khagan from plotting for control of China. The self-styled protector of Manichaenism requested that a great number of Manichaen clergymen be admitted to China and be granted unlimited access anywhere. With Uigur guards camping on his palace grounds, the Chinese Emperor could but comply. The Manichaens founded religious communities in every part of the empire, and acted as Uigur agents and informers, with whose support China could be undermined. To this, no Uigur officer would object and not even the shamans would oppose a program aiming at conquest. But the wizards were appalled at the clergymen's desire to spread their creed among the common Uigur people, and to initiate the superstitious illiterates into culture and, worse even, literacy. The Manichaens translated writings from the Iranian, Sanskrit, and Chinese originals for the benefit of Uigur advancement and their own permanent establishment within a strong nation.

The common man, however, had no use for literacy, and was not fond of the new art of tilling the soil, which was harder work than hunting, and less remunerative. The shamans exploited their discontent and missed no opportunity to insist that disasters like poor crops, cattle diseases, or floods could not strike if the Blue Sky and the celestial spirits would receive their due. Secret shamanist societies formed right under the Khagan's eyes, and in distant regions entire Uigur tribes returned to the old faith. The Khagan's authority waned; Uigur princes were split in two camps, some supporting the shamans, others strictly adhering to the Khagan's creed.

In China, utopian land reforms had produced near chaos; dangerous hit-and-run invasions by Tibetans, strife, banditry, misrule, plagues, and catastrophies took a high toll; while the census of 754 revealed a population figure of 52,880,000, the figure was down to 16,900,000 ten years later; and even though it rose again, China still had fewer inhabitants in 840 than in 703.

The year 840 was a crucial year for China and for the Uigurs. The Chinese had offered clandestine encouragement to Uigur traditionalists. They had hired Uigur shamans to spy upon the Manichaens; they had promoted local Uigur rebellions and with the help of their merchants they had maintained relations with the Kirghizes, whose strength kept growing while that of the Uigurs declined.

The Kirghizes who roamed the Siberian Yenisei Valley had practically no culture and no inhibitions, but a great deal of prowess as archers and cavalrymen. Lured by the traders' accounts of fabulous treasures stored in the Uigur capital, they descended upon the Uigur heart lands like an avalanche—savage Siberia sweeping away semi-civilized Siberians. Uigur shamans sided with the invaders, proclaimed them the chosen of the Blue Sky, and turned against their Manichaen rivals in an orgy of murder to restore the ancient cult.

Wise Ton-you-cook's views had been corroborated by events. Abandoning their nomadic life, and accepting a creed of mildness and sagacity, the Uigurs had fallen an easy prey to those who were like wolves and who had struck at the auspicious moment. Now the Kirghizes ruled the forests of the Orkhon and all the lands within a circumference of more than 1000 miles. The Kirghizes' notions of an empire were not too different from a wolf pack's conceptions of its hunting grounds, and they had no notions whatever of nationalism. Being strong, they struck in every direction, wherever the going was good and quick. China was a tempting objective—according to what they knew from Chinese traders, and possibly from subjugated Siberians—but was no easy prey. Turning toward lesser goals, the Kirghizes lost their opportunity to become a major factor in China's policy. Instead the Cha-t'o, an obscure Siberian people, became the Türküts' and the Uigurs' heirs to power on the border of China.

The Cha-t'o had fled the nation-gathering campaign of the khagans and had roamed the southwestern border of China until the Tibetans seized their cattle and chased the herdsmen into the barrenness of the northern wastelands, where they were found by Chinese patrols and saved from starvation by an assignment as border guards. The Cha-t'o became good soldiers, and reasonably disciplined; so disciplined, in fact, that the Chinese picked the best officers and men for their own army. Outside the Great Wall crude Cha-t'o became a mainstay of China's defense; inside refined Cha-t'o became a major element of national security—which was tantamount to getting involved in intrigue and conspiracies.

In 907, when the last emperor of the T'ang dynasty was overthrown by the bandit leader Tshou Wen, Cha-t'o generals in charge of protecting the Emperor did not lift a finger in his defense.

In 936 the Cha-t'o made the bid for the throne of China; their general Che-kin-t'an became Emperor. After thousands of years of raiding and blackmail, of service and intrigues, a Siberian ruled the oldest and most highly civilized empire of the world. Che-kin-t'an was partly Sinofied; he no longer met the standards set by Ton-you-cook; and it took other Siberians to depose his house.

The K'i-tan were riding again. Five hundred years before the Cha-t'o generals forsook the last T'ang Emperor, the K'i-tan roamed the steppes around Jehol, preying on Chinese caravans and galloping away whenever they encountered strong resistance.

Centuries of hit-and-run banditry hammered the K'i-tan into a body solid enough to stage a large-scale campaign.

Chinese merchants did but little business with the K'i-tan, who were slow to learn the art of trading and thus received less information about events and conjectures in the East than the more trade-minded tribes. But the vacuum of power that developed in China and in parts of Siberia was eventually felt by the K'i-tan, who struck blindly and hit the Kirghizes, already softened by well-being. Again the cruder barbarians overran the less primitive; Kirghiz remnants returned into the distant vastness, leaving the K'i-tan in control of the Orkhon. But A-pao-ki, leader of the K'i-tan, guided his hordes to the plains around the present site of Chita, into the Amur River valley; to Manchuria, to the present Maritime Province, and across the Yalu River into North Korea. A vast, loosely knit Tunguse empire folded up. Its soldiers deserted to the invaders. Clan and tribal leaders prostrated themselves and a stunned population submitted without resistance. A-pao-ki could have invaded China from the east, through sectors not covered by the Great Wall. Yet he died suddenly, in terrible convulsions. Murder was rampant among the K'i-tans, but the K'i-tans used knives, arrows, or ropes to dispatch their victims; poison was not applied—not even by women.

A-pao-ki's widow attended her husband's funeral, surrounded by Chinese dignitaries in ornate gala. Nobody remembered having seen those men before. And yet they had been with the dowager for a long time, disguised as slaves, but actually working as her eyes, ears, and brain, and, through her, as A-pao-ki's guiding spirits, architects of his policy and of his death. The Chinese did use poison, and probably they decided to have the lady administer it to her husband when she was unable to dissuade him from some design inimical to China.

Had it not been for the restraint required by the ritual, K'i-tan chieftains would have massacred the Empress and her outlandish retinue on the spot. With obsequies lasting for several weeks, however, the first destructive fury subsided and the next move was up to the widow. Had she claimed the throne, the chieftains would have made short work of her; but she suggested that the nobles and ranking soldiers convene in a diet and select as their ruler one of

A-pao-ki's two sons. The assembly's choice fell upon Tö-kuang, who assumed the title of Khan; yet, for several years all matters of importance were handled by Chinese counselors, and the ultimate decision rested with the overpowering widow. The old woman wanted to organize the K'i-tan state after the pattern of China. Chinese civil-service experts came to the K'i-tan camp, directing K'i-tan chieftains how to administer their tribes; the chieftains were stripped of independent prerogatives, such as recruitment and taxation. Refractory nobles were executed at the site of A-pao-ki's tomb: "sent to report to their exalted ruler," as the saying went.

Once a dignitary about to be sent to report to A-pao-ki shouted that the dowager herself ought to communicate with her husband. The widow never missed an execution. Coldly she declared that, her life being most important for the K'i-tan, she could not yet go, but that, as a token of her faithfulness, she would give the doomed dignitary a gift for the late ruler: and she cut off her left hand and threw it at the culprit.

She did not die from the injury, but her strength waned, and when, in 936, the army proclaimed Tö-kuang Emperor, the dowager was dead.

Fifty thousand K'i-tan cavalry, reinforced by Tunguse auxiliaries, were ready to march. Had the wicked dowager lived, she probably would have told her son to intervene in China and seize the throne rather than abandon it to a Cha-t'o general. However, Tö-kuang did not possess the energy of his mother, and her Chinese advisers, whom he had taken over, were split among themselves. K'i-tan chieftains clamored for raids into China, or sale of K'i-tan protection to the Chinese, or both. Tö-kuang had his forces loot Chinese territory, and in turn hired them out to support the Court of Peking against interior revolt. It was a most lucrative policy, and the chieftains were well satisfied with extra profits they did not have to account for.

Tö-kuang wore Chinese silk robes and slept with perfumed Chinese courtesans who were experts in "twenty-seven love-making postures." The chieftains considered him to be completely Sinofied and were convinced that, should their khan ever become Emperor of China, he would depose all K'i-tan nobles in favor of Chinese.

Within six years China had three emperors, the last of whom refused to hire Tö-kuang's soldiers, and declined payment of tributes. This forced Tö-kuang's hand, and he decided that China must be subdued. To this the chieftains could not object, but they were determined to prevent their khan from becoming Emperor. The K'i-tans seized Peking, captured Emperor Tschon-kau-ai and his court, and advanced through the wealthiest provinces of China like bloodthirsty wolves.

Chieftains were perplexed by what they found in China. Vastness could not amaze a Siberian, but organization, intercommunication, and economic co-operation in large areas puzzled the men whose sole conception of rule was military power. Tö-kuang died in 947. His successors felt that, rather than moving ever deeper into the strange empire, they should seize one rich slice of it, satisfy their urge for luxury from its proceeds, and otherwise consolidate their realm of the steppes.

In China, meantime, families of ancient nobility contended for the throne. In 975 the Song (or Sung) family emerged victorious. The K'i-tan tacitly acknowledged the Song dynasty, but retained their grasp on Peking and Ta-t'ong Province as voluptuary and source of wealth. The Songs made no bid for return of the capital, and twenty-nine years later even signed a treaty of peace with the K'i-tans, formally ceding Peking and Ta-t'ong to the Siberians.

K'i-tan khans and princes, K'i-tan soldiers and officials preferred Peking to their people's tent cities, and they would rather live in Ta-t'ong Province than on the Orkhon, where there were no worries, but no riches and pleasure, either. Already Chinese pleasures mollified the barbarians.

The Song emperors moved their capital to K'ai-fong, and from there watched the expansion of other barbarian hordes, the Djürchäts and the Tangouts.

The Djürchäts were of Tunguse stock. After the K'i-tans established themselves in China, they moved into the plains of the Amur, and advanced toward the Yalu River.

The Tangouts roamed the Tibetan border. Chinese intelligence still referred to the northern barbarians only as neighbors; "Tatars." The Tatars were barred from the approaches of the empire by a *cordon sanitaire* of Djürchäts, K'i-tans, and Tangouts. Djürchäts, K'i-tans, Tangouts would start fighting among themselves, drawing the Tatars into the caldron of steppe warfare. Barbarian would destroy barbarian, and China would emerge as the sole beneficiary of destruction to enjoy the often promised millennium.

The eleventh century went by; developments along the borders of China were slow. Emperor Housi-tsong, who ascended the Chinese throne in 1101, would not have forced the issue, had it not been for his artistic inclinations. Housi-tsong was a brilliant sponsor of the fine arts and a painter of unusual merit. The noblest works of Chinese art had been left behind in Peking, the shrine of Chinese cultural accomplishments.

The Emperor became obsessed with the idea of recovering his country's treasures by liberating Peking. If Djürchäts or Tangouts still hesitated to attack the K'i-tans, they should be roused to action by well-tried means. Peking, Housi-tsong told his uneasy advisers, had to be recovered by "calling barbarians against barbarians, those who are remote against those who are nearby." The K'i-tans were near; the Djürchäts were their neighbors.

A Chinese ambassador traveled from K'ai-fong to the Ussuri Valley to negotiate with the ruler of the Djürchäts. "The Khan lives amidst flocks and pastures in an encampment where there are neither roads nor ramparts," he reported. "He received me, sitting on a throne covered with twelve tiger skins, and invited me to a barbaric feast, with inebriate drinking, noisy music, savage dances, pantomimes of hunt and combat and painted women juggling mirrors to reflect beams of light."

A pact was concluded. China would supply the Djürchäts with loads of the latest military equipment; Chinese experts would train Djürchät crews to operate new weapons, and teach Djürchät cavalrymen new tactics to counteract K'i-tan maneuvers. Chinese intelligence services, which had informers throughout K'i-tan-occupied territory, would provide the Djürchäts with constant reports on enemy movements. The Djürchäts would go to war against their neighbors within one year. China granted advance recognition to Djürchät claims to all lands held by the K'i-tans outside of the ancient Chinese and Korean borders. Peking and Ta-t'ong Province should be restored to China, and the occupied parts of North Korea returned to independence.

The Djürchät Khan opened his campaign less than one year after the compact had been signed. In nine years he wrested Manchuria, the rest of Maritime Province, and the lands on the Amur from the tottering K'i-tans; he penetrated into the Orkhon region, shattered the hold of the defeated on the land around Lake Baikal, and crushed K'i-tan garrisons on the Yalu River. He did not march to Peking, and did not occupy Northern Korea.

Emperor Housi-tsong moved cautiously. He did not want to antagonize the victorious Khan by rash moves that could arouse the barbarian's suspicion. He dispatched only small military detachments to Peking, just enough to police the city, and he did not move the seat of his government to an area close to the theater of mopping-up operations.

But the Djürchäts interpreted the Emperor's caution as an indication of weakness. They turned against China, engulfed Peking, crossed the Yellow River, and headed for K'ai-fong before the Chinese Army could block the advance. K'ai-fong fell; Housi-tsong, and one of his sons were captured and led away to the encampment of the Djürchät Khan in Central Manchuria, near the present site of Harbin. In vain did the unfortunate Emperor plead with the Khan to honor his pledges; in vain did he appeal to him to spare China, if he refused to spare its ruler. The Khan, seated on his tiger-skin-covered throne, surrounded by drunken officers, had the captives strangled, and ordered continuation of the drive to seize Nanking, where the second of Housi-tsong's sons was trying to organize defenses.

The Djürchät cavalry, superbly trained by Chinese experts, advanced like a tropical hurricane. The country supplied all their needs, including mounts. The hardened riders crossed the Yellow River and established a broad, Djürchät-controlled belt between the Tangout area and China. This, however, became their undoing.

The Tangouts were alarmed by Djürchät progress; they had no intention of leaving the immense spoils of China to their neighbors. While Djürchät cavalry rode into Nanking, hordes of mounted Tangouts dashed into China.

Now barbarians were fighting barbarians, not in the distant regions of Siberia, but in Central China. The suffering Chinese people could not distinguish between the invaders, who all looked and behaved alike. They called them Kin. The Kin could not be stopped by scattered Chinese troops, but other circumstances provided relief to the hard-pressed empire. The barbarians refused to part with their loot, and gradually their mounts turned into pack animals carrying immense loads of spoils, invaluable treasures mixing with ridiculous trifles. Even requisition of additional horses could not restore the barbarians' mobility. The men, who usually responded to their leaders' every word and gesture, could no longer be made to ride in formation, for every soldier insisted on staying with his loot. A lightning advance slowed to a snail's pace. The invaders suffered from the subtropical heat in Southern China, thirty to forty degrees above summer temperatures in their homelands. And the terrain offered increasing difficulties. In the north whence they came big rivers were few and far between. But the invaded land was crisscrossed by watercourses, some of them canals; and the horsemen felt as if caught in a puzzling system of water traps. The Chinese added to the invaders' troubles by opening locks and dams and inundating large areas. Density of population posed yet another problem. In the barbarians' native land there were five square miles to one person. In the parts of China in which they were now operating, more than a hundred people dotted every square mile. To the invaders this seemed a human sea, almost as difficult to cross as flooded areas. They massacred thousands, demolished whatever buildings they encountered, and yet were unable to clear the land of people whom they considered obstacles to warfare. And as they spent their time and energy killing and destroying, the Emperor was building up an army beyond the Yangtse which was ready to strike when the invaders crossed the river. The Chinese array was highly scientific—a vise to choke the attackers. Had it not been for a Chinese peasant who led the Kin through the only remaining gap in the encirclement, none of the invaders would have escaped. But even so, the Kin had to withdraw far up to the North. Yet the Kin were not decisively beaten.

Under the terms of a settlement between China and the Kin, who adopted that name, the Chinese recovered but part of their empire. Peking remained in enemy hands.

In 1153, fifteen years after the settlement, Khan Tikou-nai established his residence in Peking. The Kin became addicts to Chinese luxuries and to the Chinese way of life as they saw it. Clan leaders, Kin officers and officials abandoned their camps and moved into Chinese cities; Peking was a superlupanar, a glorified drinking place, a showboat on solid ground, where Kin wearing Chinese garb and Chinese hair-do reveled day and night. Nothing but violent tempers that often led to bloodshed remained of former soldierliness. The revelers saw no need to take to the field against more distant barbarians who occasionally raided outlying regions of Kin China.

In this attitude they were supported by the Khan's favorite shaman, named Goshi. Other shamans had grudgingly accepted a decline of their influence when the debauched Khan surrounded himself with Chinese counselors who told the barbarian that enjoyment of the empire's boons was an emperor's noble duty. Goshi approved of the Khan's sensual ministrations, and asserted that the Blue Sky had selected the Kin to rule, not only over part of China, but over the entire empire.

The Khan made Goshi his top adviser, and the shaman held this position by mere flattery and bluster. But once when he could not answer Tikou-nai's inquiry how the rest of China could be conquered within one year or less, his master had a flare of anger, which proved fatal to the shaman.

Some Kin nobles resented the murder of Goshi. Chinese imperial agents, cleverly working through entertainers, professional gamblers, and procurers, exploited their irritation to stir disaffection. The Kin army was thoroughly undermined when in 1161 Tikou-nai, tired of waiting inactively for control of all China, ordered his men to conquer the Songs' realm. Near the mouth of the Yangtse River, Kin cavalry engaged in mutiny in face of a reasonably well-disciplined Chinese army. The Khan, who tried to restore order, was torn to pieces by his horsemen, and while Kin generals argued whether or not to retreat, the Chinese crossed the big river and put the Kin to flight.

Defeat, however, unified the Kin, who dreaded nothing as much as the loss of their Chinese voluptuary. Tikou-nai's successor, Wou-lo, who called himself Emperor of the Kin, reorganized his forces and repulsed Chinese vanguards. In protracted parleys lasting until 1165 the Kin retained their slice of China in addition to an annual tribute payable in silk and silver.

Wou-lo enjoyed the empire's boons; Kin officers and officials enjoyed their privileges and sinecures; Kin soldiers garrisoned in China were torn between fornication and boredom; but nobody wanted to return to Siberia and frugality. The Kin no longered considered themselves Siberians. They were Chinese in their own rights, and what went on beyond the Great Wall was none of their concern. Many tribes were said to be on the move. May hungry wolf packs roam the fringes of the Kin Empire, they would never establish themselves on its territory.

The Song emperors knew of migrations of Tatars—Mongol clans—but they were reluctant to have their diplomats interfere. Nature should take its course. Tatars and Kin would eventually come to grips and bleed each other white. China's road back to Peking would be paved with barbarians' bleaching bones.

CHAPTER TEN In Central and Eastern Russia small groups of Slavonic origin survived the Hun and Awar floods by taking refuge in woods, marshes, and hills away from the barbarians' road of invasion. They cleared forests, tilled the soil, and were frightened into peaceful obedience. Yet they were reluctant to settle permanently in regions still threatened by the murderous east. A constant trickle of violent migrants poured through the Ural passes, the sally ports of Siberia, flotsam from the storms that hit the vastness yonder, but still strong enough to oppress or destroy the scattered peasantry. Chroniclers give no details of the little tragedies that occurred in the wake of the great migrations, repetitious in pattern, heartrending to the afflicted. The melancholy Slavonic folklore which originated long after those calamities had run their course reflects only the general mood. Yet some characteristic features of the modern Russian peasant—his endurance and submission, his slyness that helps him to survive the worst tribulations, and his pent-up emotions that may burst into destructive holocausts —were shaped by the trying experiences of his ancestors.

In brief lulls between invasion imaginative and daring chieftains led tribes away to better safety. Among those who went west were the Slavonic people under Tshech and Lech. They settled in Bohemia, in areas assigned to clans by those two chieftains, and meekly accepted the suzerainty of neighboring Moravian princes who had narrowly survived the onslaught of the Awars. And when missionaries from Byzantium converted the princes to Christendom, the Czechs, as the people of Tshech and Lech were called, accepted the new creed. Frontiers in Central Europe hardened after the Czechs settled and Charlemagne forged his empire. Farther to the southeast, however, all of Europe except Byzantium remained in flux.

The Bulgars were the only European nation strengthened by eastern aggression. Had it not been for Awar onslaught the Bulgars may have vegetated in the forefield of the Byzantine citadel, an obscure also-runner among small nations. Yet the Awars kindled the fire of Bulgar combativeness, and Bulgar hordes moved into the power vacuum that developed in Eastern Europe and in the extreme southeastern parts of Siberia, around the Aral Sea. This was the first time Europeans invaded that region, even though Bulgarian nationalism tends to disclaim the invasion, and the bards of Bulgarian historic greatness tell of their people's Turco-Caucasian origin and its legal title to a phantom empire reaching from the sources of the Volga to the Aral Sea, and from the Armenian border to the Aegean Sea. Unfounded as such tales are, the Bulgars temporarily controlled large areas, and they probably mixed with various other peoples, including splinter tribes of Hiung-nu stock and possibly Türküt stragglers. They extorted substantial payments from Byzantine emperors, raided the empire, and ambushed its trade caravans. In 811, Bulgar Khan Kroom, whom nationalists posthumously dubbed The Terrible, defeated Emperor Niciphorus and had a drinking cup made of the vanquished man's skull, a feat that eulogists claim was in the finest Bulgar tradition. Actually the procedure was of Hun origin. But the exploit did not net Niciphorus's empire for Kroom; his army was routed under the very walls of the capital, and three decades later Christianization put an end to the aggressive ventures of the medieval Bulgarians.

At the high tide of expansion the Bulgar-controlled lands remained bisected by the realm of a proud and powerful ancient nation that grimly held on to its territory through many recurrent invasions. The Khazars had lived on the northern foothills of the Caucasus Mountains at least since the second century of our time, but possibly even much longer, for it is said that Khazar warriors forced Alexander of Macedonia to make a detour on his way to India. Maybe the Khazars were of Türküt extraction, even though the prevalence of red hair among them would contradict this assumption. In antiquity Khazar tribes roamed the great route of trade, occasionally acting as intermediaries between Eastern and Western merchants. They did not often engage in aggressive warfare, but fought savagely against any intruder and, if victorious, harassed the beaten foe on his retreat. The Huns could not destroy the Khazars, although some of their hordes forced their way through Khazar territory, and Awar migration left no deep scars there. They built cities, did business with Byzantium and Persia, and repelled belligerent Arabs who interfered with their commerce.

Khazar khagans had Byzantine architects construct a grandiose trade center at the Don bend: the city of Sarkel, a strong fortress and ideally located market place. To Sarkel went merchants from Byzantium, from the Middle East, and from Africa, among them a number of Jews. The Khagan was his people's mundane and religious sovereign. The Khazar's creed was of a shamanist variety. Like the Siberians, they had no codified law, yet they did have elaborate business regulations. The khagans were tolerant and inquisitive rulers who encouraged Christian missionaries and were interested in Mohammedanism. The Jews did not propagate their religion, but Jewish traders at Sarkel observed the ritual, and in the eighth century Khagan Bulan adopted the Jewish religion. The circumstances of this extraordinary conversion remain controversial. It has been said that a learned Jew, Isaak Sangari, explained the essentials of Judaism to the Khagan, who was so impressed by the identity of Jewish law and religion that he adopted the faith as foundation of national laws. It was also claimed that in search for an official religion Bulan invited a learned disputation between ranking clergymen and chose the creed whose representative sounded most convincing. The Khazar nation, however, was not forcibly converted, and only a fraction of the people followed the Khagan's example. Jewish merchants who made their home in Sarkel became partners of converted Khazars; more Jews arrived as refugees as the plight of the Jews worsened elsewhere. Jewish-Khazar traders carried oriental goods far into Russia and Poland; they met coreligionists from Germany. Some of the features of modern Polish and Russian Jews, quite different from those of their Mediterranean counterparts, point at Khazar origin.

The Khazar aristocracy repudiated Judaism as a mercantile rather than a heroic creed. But they enthusiastically embraced Mohammedanism, when Harun-al-Rashid, Khalif of Bagdad (765–809), of *Arabian Nights* fame, sent missionaries to Sarkel.

In 851, St. Cyril and his brother, St. Methodius, visited the Khazars, with the blessings of the Byzantine Emperor, who was worried by the growing influence of non-Christian monotheism. The nobility was not responsive, but small people, jealous of growing Jewish prosperity, acclaimed the mighty missionaries. Cyril later became Apostle to the Slavs, translator of the Scriptures, and deviser of the Slavonic alphabet and, quite unwittingly, laid the foundation for eventual domination of the Greek Orthodox Church by the rulers of Russia.

Yet a considerable number of Khazars remained pagans—and the religious babel stimulated bigotry. When religious riots broke out, Byzantium interfered. Christianized Slav princes, more anxious to grab Khazar territory than to promote religion, joined the action. Khazar strength was declining when the continent was shaken by another eruption of the Siberian steppes.

Deep in Central Asia, men-mills, driven by the tides of migration, kept grinding people, pulverizing the softer, casting aside the harder, and putting them on long treks. The Petchenegs, apparently distant kin of the Türküts, were driven from their roaming grounds. They did not follow a straight course, though, but drifted west along the edge of steppes, controlled by more powerful tribes, and went zigzag to avoid dangerous clashes and yet to feed their herds. For a short time they stayed in the forests of the southern Urals, but shortage of pastures forced them out into the plains across the mountain range. Rapaciousness guided the Petchenegs' advance which, strangely enough, did not immediately hit Sarkel, but reached the Sea of Azov west of the mouth of the Don.

There they encountered the Magyars, horsemen like themselves and typically Siberian in their way of life. The Magyars, too, had been pushed aside by Asiatic upheavals. Magyar-Petcheneg collision produced a ricocheting effect; the Petchenegs' motion was slowed down, while the Magyars, who had been static, rolled west, fighting rear-guard actions against the Petchenegs' scouts and Khazar patrols.

The Magyars' exact origin is no more precisely established than that of most Asiatic nomads. Having survived as a nation, however, the Magyar-Hungarians spared no effort to have their historians prove that they actually were of much nobler descent than other Easterners. Enthusiastic chroniclers assert that their ancestors were an itinerant master race—ruling, raiding, and eventually releasing other nations all the way from Korea to the western terminal of Magyar migration. They dispute claims to Magyar-Mongol affinity as exemplified by high cheekbones and slightly slit eyes of modern Hungarian herdsmen, and insist that the ancient Magyars were the hard core of an agglomeration of Turco-Finnish-Ugrian aristocrats, with particular emphasis upon the Turcs, as a conquering elite. The Magyars' ancestors must have been tenacious to escape destruction inside Siberia, but the fact that they are not known to have participated in any invasion of China, and that their migration remained unnoticed by either Chinese or Persians, indicates that they were less than outstanding conquerors.

By 880 the Magyars reached the mouth of the Danube. Stopped by Byzantine border guards, and harassed by Khazar forces, they agreed to pay tribute to Byzantium and Sarkel. And because their herds were depleted, they accepted a Byzantine offer to serve as mercenaries against the Bulgars. Byzantium, however, did not want the Magyars to get out of hand; so it appointed Arpad, a friendly prince of Khazar blood, to rule the Magyars, and Byzantine officers to reorganize their army. In their first action in the service of Byzantium the Magyars crossed the Danube, devastated Bulgarian territory, but had to retreat into the rugged mountains of Transylvania when Petchenegs invaded the Danube Valley.

In this emergency Arpad had a strange visitor: a German nobleman from Emperor Arnulf's court, who suggested a German-Magyar alliance against Prince Sviatopolk of Moravia, who had incorporated Western Austria and parts of Hungary into his empire. The German offered a generous share in the spoils. Officers from Byzantium encouraged Arpad to side with the Germans.

In 895 the Magyars rode out of the Transylvanian wilderness into the Hungarian plains, an army as brutal and vicious as any Siberian horde. Contemporary chroniclers relate that they behaved no better than Attila's Huns. Terror spread through Greater Moravia, paralyzing its troops, who surrendered in bulk, only to be massacred by their captors. The horsemen burned, looted, raped, and killed, and neither their Khazar prince nor their Byzantine generals curbed their frenzy. Greater Moravia was destroyed. For five years the Magyars camped in the Hungarian plain, with the Transylvanian mountains forming a natural obstacle for the dreaded Petchenegs. In 900 they followed one of Attila's courses into Italy, where they sacked cities as far inland as Pavia.

The invasion of Italy was a flagrant violation of the agreement with Emperor Arnulf. After pillaging Northern Italy the aggressors switched north, penetrated into Austria, and along another Hun route of invasion into Bavaria. Louis, the Child, last emperor of the house of Charlemagne, with his tiny army, was crushed by the Magyar onslaught. For forty-five years the overweening Magyars became the plague of Central and Western Europe. Their record of destruction includes Lorraine, Burgundy, the Provence, the Champagne, and revisited Italian cities. The Magyars seemed bent on destroying whatever was left of Western civilization and their triumphant paganism threatened Christianity. Yet their strength was great only in comparison with the weakness of their victims.

Otto I, ruler of a new German Empire, was the first to put a substantial army in the field to stop the Magyars. On August 10, 955, the opponents met in the Lech Valley, in Bavaria, close to the site of the disaster of Louis the Child. The Magyars were routed and fled to Hungary three hundred miles away, where they rallied not sufficiently to resume aggression, but strongly enough to survive. They might have been overwhelmed by Christian nations had it not been for Prince Vaik, who, in 997, offered to embrace Christianity and to lead his people into the fold of the Church. Pope Sylvester II, and his brother-in-law, German Emperor Henry II, were enthusiastic at the prospect of a Christianized buffer state to deal with the Eastern barbarians. Vaik became Stephen, first King of Hungary, later canonized, wearer of the legendary crown which was presented to him in the year 1000 by Pope Sylvester II.

Khazar troubles, the Magyar migration, and the Petchenegs' still-threatening presence in crucial areas of Russia had been vital factors in the first drive for unity among the Eastern European Slavs, which had culminated in their historic message to Rurik, Scandinavian chieftain-prince: "Our land is great and fertile, but there is no order in it; come and rule over us."

Rurik came in 862, and founded the first Russian monarchy. But he did not bring much order to the great and fertile land. The Petchenegs, unaware of their part in the momentous event that was the foundation of Russia, lived on the shores of the Black Sea, on the right bank of the Danube, and in the border regions of the Khazars' empire. Their leaders were unimaginative men who could not make up their minds in what direction to strike. Bulgar khans hired Petcheneg horsemen, and after the Bulgars' power waned, princes of the house of Rurik enlisted Petcheneg hordes. With their help Rurik's son Igor—who thus initiated the now-one-thousand-year-old, and never-successful, Russian drive for control of the Dardanelles and the Bosporus—made his first attempt to capture Byzantium in 944. But the horsemen were riding for a bloody nose, and their descendants who first repeated the attack eighty-two years later on their own fared no better.

The Petchenegs went empty-handed when the Khazar Empire succumbed to Russian and Byzantine attacks. Sviatoslav, Prince of Kiev, seized Sarkel in 965. Sixty-five years later the last vestiges of the Khazars' colorful realm were wiped off the map, split among Russians and Byzantines, whom enmity did not keep from sharing other nations' spoils.

Another Siberian wave hit the Russian plains. From the shores of the Irtysh River, two hordes moved through the gap between the Ural Mountains and the Caspian Sea: the Kiptchaks (whom Europeans called Komani or Kumans), and the Oughouzes. The Kiptchaks caught up with the Oughouzes, decimated them, and leisurely established themselves in the grasslands between the Volga and the Don. The newly converted Russian rulers tried to pacify the horde through missionaries; the Byzantine Emperor sent recruiters with cash, and promises of more. The Kiptchaks proved unsusceptible to the teachings of Christ, but impressionable by money.

On April 29, 1091, joint Byzantine-Kiptchak forces beat the Petchenegs decisively and drove them into Wallachia. There they vegetated for almost three decades, until a Byzantine army inflicted the coup de grâce on the unsuccessful invaders.

European civilization, compressed into narrow areas during the aggressive migrations, expanded well beyond the regions that had once been the sphere of Rome's mitigating domination. Christianization, the alpha and omega of Western enlightenment and progress, moved forward, secured by the consolidation of Christian states. Hungary was safe, Poland spread its wings, and Russia was no longer a defenseless feeding ground and rallying center for nomads.

The realm of Rurik's dynasty encompassed only a fraction of Russia's present territory, and even this limited area was split into autonomous territories. City governments and princes were expected to hold out against foreign aggression. Kiev was the oldest Russian city and center of gravity of Christian Russia. Its powerful rival was the city of Novgorod, some six hundred miles to the north, a budding trade center jealous of its independence and proud of its achievements. Novgorod's original Slavic character was overshadowed by the influx of German artisans, merchants, and teachers; the city's laws were Westernized, and its people shared in the government to an extent that Russian nobles considered dangerously extravagant. Novgorodians looked for expansion of trade rather than for territorial acquisitions; their city, however, had strong walls and well-stocked arsenals. Novgorod merchants did business with the Baltic regions and Scandinavia, and with seafaring nations of the northwestern parts of the continent, whom they supplied with furs of finest quality. Many of these precious skins came from Siberia, and to keep competitors away from places where they purchased them, they invented gruesome stories about the inhabitants.

In the fifteenth century some of the scare-tales were recorded in the Novgorodian Script *About the Unknown Peoples of the Eastern Regions:* "If the Samojeds have a visitor, they kill their children to treat him to their flesh, and if the visitor dies he too is eaten. In the country of the Mongonsees, people cast their skins, and for one month every year they live in the water; for, would they stay on land, their bodies would burst asunder. Other Samojeds who trade with sable and arctic fox have shaggy animals' legs, and still others have their mouths at the crown of their heads, and they cannot talk. When eating, they crumble meat or fish, put it beneath their fur caps, and as they chew, their shoulders move up and down. There are still more Samojeds, who look like other people but, during the winter, they stay dead for two months, and this is how this comes to pass: The affected sits down, a flow of water pours from his nose and freezes to the ground, the icicle fastens him to the ground, and holds him there, dead, until the sun revives him. Should the icicle break prematurely, however, he will not revive."

Cannibals, people casting their skins like snakes, mute misfits, and the temporarily dead could frighten the competition away from purchasing areas. Novgorod profited from the effect, even though occasionally other foreigners would visit the land of ghosts and sables. Poles and Englishmen are known to have been to Northern Siberia at the time, or soon after, the Novgorodian Script was drafted.

From Kiev, Byzantium, Poland, and Germany missionaries went to temperate zones of Siberia, and found the inhabitants not frightening. "They are short, with massive, thick-set bodies and curved legs," one eyewitness tells. "Their faces are large, their noses look bruised, their Adam's apple protrudes almost ridiculously; they have slit eyes, puffed up lips, thin beards, stiff black hair, and a swarthy skin scorched by wind, sun and frost." The visitors agreed that the people were quite formidable but not really aggressive. There seemed to be no reason for them to go to war. They had everything they wanted—cattle and horses, clothes, accommodations, and carts. To their dismay the missionaries found that Nestorian Christian heresy had had a head start among the Naimans, who lived on the Irtysh; but Nestorianism was said to have no effect on the weather and shamans were still in charge of rain. Missionaries were busy reclaiming Naiman souls from paganism and false doctrine.

There was good news from the Mongolian Keraits. A chieftain had been lost in the steppes and guided back by an apparition which introduced itself as a Christian saint. Also the Khan of the Keraits had asked for a mission to his people, and missionaries were wanted by the Kirghizes from the Upper Yenisei.

The outlook was bright in Siberia—the land that still had no name. But deep shadows of dissent had fallen over the citadel of Christendom, and the cradle of the faith was in the hands of arrogant infidels.

The specter of schism between Western and Eastern Churches, long rampant, became real in 1054, when Pope Leo IX pronounced excommunication of the Patriarch of Constantinople, and the defiant Patriarch continued in office. The heads of the two churches were sovereign in name only; the German emperors usurped the right to nominate popes. The patriarchs of Constantinople depended upon the support of the Byzantine emperors. When, in 1094 Pope Urban II freed the Roman Church from mundane interference, the Greek Church was sufficiently organized to resist any attempt at forcible reincorporation into the Roman Catholic realm. Only if it had controlled the Holy Places of Christianity, might Rome have been able to put the Patriarch under irresistible pressure.

But Jerusalem was in Seljuk hands, and pilgrims recently returned from the city were said to have told of Christian sufferings and humiliations. The Seljuks had turned into a magnificent nation that dominated the Middle East and held people of ancient culture under its sway. They were Mohammedans and, as such, religiously fairly tolerant. The authenticity of the pilgrims' accounts was not thoroughly checked and it would not be surprising had they been purposefully exaggerated for the record. The Pope thought that an appeal to Christian princes to unite and capture Jerusalem would result in pious protestations of noble intention but produce no results. The princes did not want the power of the Roman Church to rise even further. Pope Urban decided to appeal to the people. He convoked a council to Clermont-Ferrand, France, in which the minor clergy was seated in numbers. The Pope himself took the floor; his magnificent oratory on the sufferings of pious Christians, the desecration of Holy Places, the insolence of the infidels, and the forbearance of the mighty swept the council. The call for a popular crusade resounded through the assembly hall. With well-organized spontaneity crusade preachers rose all over France to urge devout, able-bodied men to gather and free the Holy Land. A few months after the appeal was launched Peter of Amiens, Fulcher of Orleans, and Walter Sans Avoir (Walter Havenot) led throngs of devout burghers and ardent peasants, intermingled with riotous adventurers, toward the sacred goal. The men were untrained, poorly armed, and inadequately supplied; none of them ever saw the Holy Land. The adventurers deserted en route, the zealous succumbed to hardship and starvation. One year after the ill-fated expedition an army of knights from France, Normandy, and Lorraine, joined by small contingents from Germany, started out for the Orient. Bishop Adhemar of Le Puy accompanied the host as a papal legate, but he could not control the riotous warriors. Their main concern was personal emolument and they quarreled about future spoils long before they even reached Byzantium. Emperor Alexios of Byzantium, a former soldier of fortune who had, in turn, collaborated with and fought against the Seljuks before seizing the ancient throne, notified Bishop Adhemar that he would not let the crusaders trespass on Byzantine territory unless they pledged allegiance to Byzantium. This was about the last thing the Roman Church would tolerate, but the mutinous knights accepted the request. Joined by Byzantine regulars, they invaded the Holy Land, and captured Jerusalem on July 15, 1098. The capture of Jerusalem, however, made the holy sites an apple of discord between mundane rivals rather than a rallying center of the Church. The crusaders fought among themselves, right under the eyes of watchful Mohammedans. After almost half a century of struggle the enemies of King Ludovic (Louis VII) of France, who took the Cross in 1147 with no more saintly intentions than his rival monarch crusaders, disintegrated because of lack of supplies and internal feuds.

Families of the first Christian conquerors of Jerusalem engaged in cultural and commercial activities and championed an exchange of scientific and artistic ideas between East and West, which largely benefited the latter. This led to further deterioration of relations between Venice and Byzantium, which had been struggling for the lion's share in Oriental trade.

Meantime Sultan Saladin of Egypt and Syria seized Jerusalem. A Third Crusade, in 1189, did not recover the Holy Sepulcher, but strained relations between France, England, and Germany to a point that seemed to make war inevitable. But then Enrico Dandolo, Doge of Venice, directed the gathering storm against Byzantium.

Byzantium proclaimed a general boycott of all Venetian trade. With its government's connivance a Byzantine mob massacred Latin inhabitants of the capital. Venice's effective reprisals against Byzantine shipping could not be followed up by adequate land action. Yet with another crusader's force gathered at the approaches of Byzantium, the vindictive, wirepulling Doge argued, and because Jerusalem was a place difficult to capture and even more difficult to hold, Byzantium could be partitioned.

So the crusaders invaded Byzantium; Venice grabbed important bases in the Mediterranean and Aegean seas, French knights seized coastal sections. Soldier-merchants from Genoa, always jealous of Venice, seized the opportunity to establish themselves in the Crimean Peninsula; in 1204 a Latin government replaced the Greek rulers of the ancient land, and when, sixty-seven years later, another Greek dynasty seized the throne, it could not restore Byzantium's strength. What remained of the former Eastern Roman Empire kept vegetating, impotent at sea, weak on land, no longer a serious obstacle in the way of Asiatic conquerors.

Pope Innocent III, who occupied the papal throne when the Patriarch of Constantinople was left without powerful support, could proclaim himself God's Vicar on Earth and Overlord over all mundane Lords, he could invest kings with their realms as his fiefs, but he still lacked control of the Holy Places to guarantee permanent unity of the Church. He ordered mundane lords to organize another crusade, but did not live to see it materialize. The only Christian host to set out for the East in Innocent's lifetime was that of boys and a few girls, members of the Children's Crusade, which wound up in despair and ruin.

The Fifth Crusade eventually led to the capture of Damiette, prosperous port city on the mouth of the Nile, in which all but five thousand of a population of seventy thousand perished. But as usual the leaders of the hodgepodge army quarreled among themselves and soon were, in turn, besieged by Mohammedan forces.

Christian unity remained a distant goal. Devout Christians worried if it would ever be achieved, when a message of hope and faith came from Jacques de Vitry, Bishop of Ptolemaïs. World domination of the Cross was miraculously assured, the bishop wrote to the Pontiff, to the King of England, the Duke of Austria, and the University of Paris. A Christian king had arisen in India. His name was David. He had taken to the field at the head of an army of unparalleled strength, to punish the infidels. David was the grandson of Prester John, and legitimate King of Jerusalem. Already he had seized the lands of many Mohammedan princes, and collected indemnities which would be used to rebuild the walls of Jerusalem in pure gold.

The exuberant message should have aroused considerable scepticism in Rome, and professors in Paris might have wondered about Prester John whose very existence was a matter of doubt; but the peoples of Europe were eager to witness a miracle, and neither the Church nor a learned institution wanted to quell popular expectations. Even the Jews, persecuted by the crusaders, hated and harassed in European countries in which they lived in dispersion, were gladdened by the tidings. To the Jews, King David of India was their own ancient King, whose return would free the Jewish people from bondage and perennial wanderings.

The modern world held its breath, waiting for King David.

CHAPTER ELEVEN The crusaders were apprehensive. Their own record, and that of their predecessors, was permeated with atrocities. A King of Jerusalem might avenge the crimes committed against his people.

In European capitals the letters of the Bishop of Ptolemaïs were at last closely studied; it turned out that the wording was not completely identical. One copy called David King of the Jews—*Rex Judeorum*—which seemed improper, if not blasphemous. A stern inquiry produced the prelate's assertion that this was a scribe's mistake, a misspelling; the title should have read: *Rex Indeorum*—King of India.

The peoples of Europe were not interested in subtleties of spellings. They kept waiting for the promised triumph of the Cross. And, as time went by, and nobody had laid eyes upon David and his host, the pious remembered that to the Lord a thousand years were like a single day. David would come.

Oriental nations, however—Christian, Mohammedan, and pagan alike—showed signs of apprehension. The Saracens, instead of being heartened by the crusaders' recent setback in Egypt, were almost apathetic. The Seljuks and Egyptians showed no aggressive designs. And in the Russian steppes Kuman tribes broke camp and drove their herds to Western countries, applying for asylum in almost frightened terms.

No new conclusive report on King David and his army had reached the West, but constant rumors told of their exploits. They had crushed the Afghans, overwhelmed the Persians, entered Armenia and Georgia, where many Christian settlers lived. David was invincible, and both ubiquitous and elusive.

In Germany, Emperor Friedrich II attributed David's elusiveness to fear of the West's superior fighting prowess, and staged another crusade to give the Reich control of Jerusalem before the Indians arrived. The German knights found the city practically undefended, the people anxiously waiting for the King from the East, and reports on his progress coming in like gusts of wind heralding a tempest. And yet, not even the people of the Holy Land had seen Indian vanguards. But then a small vessel arrived from the Genoese trading outpost of Sudak, on the Crimean Peninsula, carrying fugitives—ragged, hollow-cheeked, their eyes reflecting extreme, nightmarish horror—destitute remnants from a large, prosperous community, who were almost incapable of giving a sensible account of their ordeal.

They had seen King David's men.

Gradually their story was put together from fragments: Hordes of mounted men had invaded the peninsula. They rode as fast as lightning, and their arrows had darkened the skies. They carried siege machines such as the world had never known before. The walls of Sudak had crumbled under their impact. Men who fought back were instantly killed. The place was sacked and pillaged, its inhabitants massacred but for the very few who could get aboard ship ahead of the whistling arrows. The horsemen had short legs, swarthy complexions, and were obviously cannibals. The fugitives had noticed no crosses, but standards on high poles.

At first the account was considered the hallucinations of fear-ridden minds. But then it was learned that Christian settlers in Armenia and Georgia had fared no better than the Genoese of Sudak, and that there too the murderers had been savage, swarthy horsemen carrying poles but no crosses. Almost immediately thereafter traders reported that some of the mightiest princes of Russia had met disastrous defeat at the hands of wild mounted archers and that Southern Russia was devastated.

The fearful news spread over Europe. It was felt that King David's host could not have committed such outrages, but the people's predilection for miracles produced another version of legend: Not David was on his way west, but descendants of the Three Kings of the East, who, to recover the relics of their holy ancestors, had set out for Cologne, where the relics were preserved, with men and horses and chariots. And even though the men had committed acts of violence, Europe ought to welcome the Three Kings' progeny in a manner worthy of their descent and design.

Rome discouraged further tales. Authorities from the Holy See stated that another roaming horde from the East had ravaged certain regions on the fringe of Europe, but that indications were that its strength was exhausted, that it would vanish soon, and that the damage it had done was trifling if compared to the past ravages by Huns, Awars, Magyars, and Petchenegs.

The learned men in Rome seemed to be borne out by the facts; for several years no new reports on the horsemen's misdeeds came in. A complete lack of information from distant Asia, however, was alarming. For many years no missionaries had returned from there.

Rome could not know that India, torn by strife, was rapidly succumbing to a Mohammedan *gori* of Afghan nationality, who disdainfully ruled most of the rich subcontinent through his favorite slave Kutd-ud-din, founder of the slave dynasty; the Pope's intelligence services had no clear picture of the state of affairs in parts of Asia west of India, where Mohammedan sultans and khalifs had brought a colorful variety of nations under their sway, remnants of cultures older than those of Greece and Rome. They were now rapidly losing their realms to uninhibited and powerful invaders. Nobody outside the

Far East realized that China's fifty millions were being trampled asunder by mounted hordes of little more than 100,000, whose leaders made small, if any, distinction between the Siberian Kin and the Chinese Song dynasties. And had the experts at Rome, the most enlightened and educated men of their time, known all these facts and conditions, they could not possibly have realized that the invaders of Western Asia, the ravishers of China, the raiders of Sudak, Armenia, and Georgia, and the victors over the Russians were men of one and the same sovereign.

King David was none other than Temudshin, the Djenghis Khan whose name would forever become the symbol of worldwide destruction.

The earlier life of Temudshin is veiled behind a screen of anecdotes concocted to flatter and to glorify the conqueror, to show him as the chosen of destiny, or, at least, to explain his monstrously phenomenal career, which started when he was close to fifty—a rather advanced age in those days. The year of his birth, around 1155, is not established beyond doubt, yet one thing seems certain: Had it not been for his father's premature death, when the boy was only twelve years old, Temudshin would have spent his life serving in the Kin army, one of hundreds of Mongol nobles who hurried to enlist in the armed forces of Peking. But Father Yesogai died shortly after obtaining a commission for himself, and his widow Oelun-Eke vainly tried to have young Temudshin enrolled in the forces, in any assignment they might give a child. And because Yesogai had left but small funds his widow with her four sons and two stepsons left the expensive capital for the primitive pastures on the Onon River where Temudshin had been born and where they had left a number of horses and a flock of sheep with cattle breeders from their clan.

However, the guardians refused to return the animals, claiming that the boy was not fit to manage his property. Resentment and frustration, and a domineering mother's fierce vindictiveness, were Temudshin's strongest impressions during his formative years, and those are the strongest impetus to tyranny.

Young Temudshin hated China, all of China—Kin, Song, and even the Kara Ki-tais, who dwelt in the land of Issyk-Kul and Kashgar under the supervision of Chinese-appointed governors, and who aped the Chinese in every way. He had never been to the Song Empire or to the Kara Ki-tai provinces, but frustration and his mother's rantings made him loathe everything and everybody Chinese or Sinofied.

The hopes of the Song that Kin and barbarians would destroy each other seemed to have been in vain. The nomads who had in turn served and fought Peking, who had both protected and looted the empire while it still included the venerable capital, showed increasing signs of accommodating to the Chinese way of life. They had not yet settled, but already their migrations covered limited areas. Naimans roamed west, along the fringe of what is now Outer Mongolia, where the Altai range extends to the rim of the Gobi; the

Keraits held the lands on the upper Orkhon River and adjoining them lived the Merkits, in the mountains extending to the picturesque southern shore of Lake Baikal. Mongols kept their herds in the Onon and Kerulen river valleys, and farther up north lived Oirats and Taidjuts; small Tatar tribes inhabited the woodlands of Manchuria and the approaches to Jehol. Already they could be seen tilling the soil, but in most instances attempts at agriculture were quickly abandoned. Chinese and Kin emissaries, traders, informers, missionaries, and quacks visited the Siberians, who, after having been infatuated with silk from time immemorial, became addicts of sweets, and would barter sable furs for half their weight in gaudily colored bits of sugar.

They traded horses for candy; and, chagrined by the Chinese's disdain for their shaggy beasts, acquired Arab stallions at fancy prices, to improve the breed. Chinese buyers still paid small prices for Mongolian ponies, but the hybrid animals were faster and sturdier than earlier Mongol mounts and of greater value in combat. Combat remained an essential element in Mongolian considerations, but combat against rival tribes rather than against Kin and China.

Chinese traders also supplied weapons, which, however, did not command as high a price as candy or silk.

The military was still in high esteem among the Siberians, but already prosperous cattle breeders and merchants claimed social distinction for their respective castes. Hereditary titles of nobility increased in numbers. "The Valiant" was a title reasonably well-to-do civilians could easily acquire; "The Chief" was one step up the aristocratic ladder and still within grasp of non-warriors; next came "The Sage," usually reserved to ranking military men; but only a descendant of chieftains could be dubbed "Prince." Non-commissioned cavalrymen and simple little people were excluded from nobility, but they were called "Soldier" and "The Honest," respectively, to distinguish them from slaves and laborers from conquered tribes.

The aristocrats held slaves, lived in *yurtas* (felt tents), set up in groups, or mounted on chariots; they hunted on horseback and used trained falcons. Manual work was considered degrading. Service with the Kin army was the most coveted goal of young Mongol nobles.

The shamans were a privileged caste quite apart from other groups. They stayed in the woods where fur hunters and trappers lived in primitive bark huts, or officiated in the plains, in tents set up apart from the nobles' camps.

Temudshin's father is said to have been a prince. This sounds unlikely in view of the clan's disrespectful attitude toward the family. But Yesogai must have been a member of the aristocracy, or else the Kin would not have granted him a commission.

His mother did not want Temudshin to engage in Sinofied activities such as trade, or, rather, the family did not have the means to start a business, so Temudshin turned hunter and fisherman, and used the proceeds of his profession to acquire horses. He owned nine mares; brigands stole eight of them, but, as chroniclers claimed much later, the gallant youth recovered all of them in brisk action, assisted by Bogortshu, a chance acquaintance, who eventually became a member of the family. This is the first exploit with which Temudshin is credited. At twenty he married Börté, a chieftain's daughter. Polygamy was customary among the Mongols, but, being in very modest circumstances and still responsible for his mother and younger brothers, he could not afford more than one wife. Börté's dowry consisted of a sable coat less valuable than a big box of candy, but good enough to offer as a good-will present to the recruiters of Togrul, ruler of the Keraits. Temudshin had, at last, decided to engage in a military career, and he enlisted in the Kerait army. Anecdote recorders who worked on the topic of Temudshin with no less zeal than modern magazine writers toil on their profile stories insist that Temudshin immediately won the favor of his new sovereign, who treated him as a son and not as a subaltern officer. And they go on to tell that once, when Temudshin and his wife were ambushed by bandits who kidnaped Börté while Temudshin narrowly escaped, Togrul himself helped to recover the young woman. The chroniclers did not seem to think that readers could take a dim view of the courage and chivalry of a husband coming out of an ambush whole and healthy while leaving his hapless wife behind. One contemporary tells of Temudshin wrestling with problems the exact nature of which is not revealed. Everybody agrees that he was a very religious man, an ardent believer in the Eternal Blue Sky's omnipotence, and in the miraculous capacities of other celestial spirits. Temudshin himself is quoted as having said time and again that the supreme deity became the source of his power and the spur of his deeds.

But Temudshin quotations, like Temudshin anecdotes, should be taken with more than one grain of salt. The primitivity of Mongolian idioms and the innate taciturnity of the people contradict chroniclers who picture the sinister Mongol as a wisecracking talker. Yet one quotation deserves recording. Shortly before his death, after spilling the blood of countless millions and destroying the monuments of age-old cultures, the ailing tyrant growled to his Chinese adviser: "I don't know if men really approve of what I did, but I don't care."

He must have cared a great deal for social advance, however. It seems that he was constantly involved in squabbles about personal promotion, and in this respect he was just like most Mongols of the period. "Valiants" used every means at their disposal to become "Chiefs," "Sages" posed as "Princes," "Soldiers" and "Honests" plotted and cringed to have their status raised to nobility. Temudshin seems to have been on good terms with the shamans, and to have had shaman support in his struggle for promotion. A Kerait officer's salary was not too high; his money could not have attracted the wizards, but with Buddhism, Taoism, and even Christendom and Islam making headway in Siberia it would not be surprising had ranking shamans supported the ambitious nobleman, expecting good returns should he ever establish himself in a prominent position.

At forty, however, the age in which military men usually had reached, if not already passed, the peak of their careers, Temudshin was still a minor figure among Togrul's generals. He had led cavalry in many successful small encounters with marauding tribes and rebel clans, but there had been no major battles. His record was just good enough to secure him a humble place in the retinue of his sovereign, when Togrul went to Peking in 1198, to pay his respects to the Kin Emperor.

Roaming Tatars and nondescript horsemen lately had conducted raids beyond the Great Wall, and, like a Chinese, the Kin ruler set Siberian against Siberian. He invited Togrul to instigate war among the neighbors, entertained the Keraits lavishly, and showered them with titles and honors. Togrul was named Wang (King) of his own people, and of all other Mongolian and Tatar nations to be gathered under his rule. Peking would not contribute armed forces to establish Mongolian national unity—it is doubtful whether Peking wanted the goal actually achieved—but Togrul was flattered by the distinction, annoyed by recent intrusions into his own territory and hopeful of receiving Chinese war material at low cost. Like every member of the Wang's suite, Temudshin received a title which his hatred of China and particularly Peking did not keep him from accepting; his title, however, was of the lowest rank.

The Kerait campaign to unify the Mongols started immediately after the Peking visit. Wang Togrul's better-equipped, better-led, and better-mounted forces wrought havoc among the enemy. At this point, Temudshin's historians tell, the Wang's unfaithful brother staged a coup, deposed Togrul, and would have put him to death had it not been for Temudshin's loyalty. Temudshin came to the King's rescue with his own troops. Somehow Togrul assembled a new army, regained power, and conquered the insurgents as well as marauding tribes and many more people. But he did not deal with his loyal general as he had promised and he did not give him the proper share in the loot, which mostly consisted of slaves.

This account is controversial. The Wang's unfaithful brother is not mentioned elsewhere and it is questionable whether he actually existed. Temudshin's troops numbered no more than 10,000 in an army at least five times that number, and it is hard to see how they could have rescued Togrul. And it is equally hard to understand how the deposed Wang could have assembled and equipped a new army in no more than two years—for the campaign ended early in 1201.

Temudshin's biographers were obviously determined to discredit the "ungrateful" Togrul in order to exonerate the general for seizing power.

In the summer of 1201 a *kuriltai* of all Mongolian princes convened. Even Tatar and Türküt grandees were invited to attend the Diet, in which existing feuds between kinfolk and neighbors were to be settled and allegiance be sworn to a supreme ruler of all Mongols. A huge city of felt tents and carts sprang up in the Orkhon River Valley. The greatest soldiers and the most famous wizards gathered. There were solemn religious ceremonies in which the shamans outdid each other in claims of having reached the highest of heavens, talked to the most exalted of spirits, and received momentous inspirations. The members of the Diet consumed prodigious quantities of meat and of *kumiss,* made from the milk of the finest white mares, and deliberated in between. The ruler of all Mongols and Tatars was foreordained; Togrul was still King, and swearing the oath of allegiance to anybody else would have been rebellion. Yet the Kuriltai turned toward selecting a man to rule the world. Shamans insisted that the Eternal Blue Sky wanted his chosen to become Goor Khan—King of the Universe. A King of the Universe was above and beyond the King of Mongolia. This was rebellion by implication, a trick devised by shamans and connived in by speculating princes and the military, who saw a better chance if they joined an outsider than if they served the Wang.

Many Mongolian chieftains and all Tatar and Türküt voted—by acclamation—for Temudshin, whom the wizards had revealed as "Tängri's chosen" in a kumiss-drinking bout. Only one prince of doubtful repute, we are told, rose to argue against the choice. Togrul, who was probably stone-drunk, hardly understood the meaning of the procedure. Except for the members of the conspiracy the whole assembly seems to have been intoxicated, but when the proud princes recovered sufficiently to comprehend that they were now subjects of a general, pandemonium broke out. The wizards held out for Temudshin; he was the Goor Khan, the ruler of all men in the name of Tängri. Some of the conniving princes ran for cover with the sobering Togrul, who appealed to all loyal men to rally around his throne; others, however, stood by the Goor Khan.

Civil war was in the making, and civil war broke out after the Kuriltai dissolved. The princes mobilized their armies to a test of strength. Officers from non-Kerait Mongol forces had hardly heard of Temudshin before, but when they learned of his selection by Tängri, devout men deserted to his camp. They were joined by fortune hunters who, even among semi-barbarians more than seven hundred years before modern totalitarianism, realized that nonentities who had sided with a potential dictator before he was in power could rise to exalted rank. Everything depended on the outcome of the first battle. If Temudshin were defeated in the opening round, he would be abandoned by his followers and doomed to oblivion.

The first battle did not take place between Temudshin and Togrul, however. Through shaman cunning, or by an act of betrayal, Togrul's return to the Keraits was delayed until he found himself practically in Temudshin's custody. This had telling effects upon the morale of the Naimans, first Mongolian people to battle the Goor Khan. Many Naiman officers deserted the ranks on the eve of the clash.

The Naimans suffered a setback, but it was not a shattering defeat, and Temudshin's stock rose even though he had not yet won. He could not afford to dispose of Togrul, who, in turn, tried to come to terms with him. Temudshin stalled, then, insisting that first things should come first, turned against the Tatars. The Tatars had been instrumental in the travesty of the Kuriltai, and the Goor Khan should have been grateful; but he presented a surprising explanation for the attack, claiming that his father had been assassinated by Tatar agents. Nobody had ever heard that Yesogai had been murdered, and it was hardly credible that foreign agents would have bothered to kill so unimportant a person, but nobody dared contradict.

When the thaws came to the plains and hills of Transbaikalia, Temudshin's mounted army, organized in units of 10, 100, 1000, and 10,000, descended upon the Tatar tribes. The massacre that occurred in May 1202 assumed proportions unprecedented even in these regions where human blood was much cheaper than the blood of sheep. Usually Siberian victors allowed their soldiers to kill survivors, rape women, and loot individually. The Goor Kahn, however, ordered how captives should be slain. He decreed spoils, including human beings, to be gathered, and allotted to soldiers in accordance with their rank and their conduct in battle, with himself, the supreme commander, to have first choice of objects and slaves. Transgressions were punishable by death, and extreme sentences were never commuted.

The Kin Emperor sent good-will messengers, with presents and protestations of admiration, to the camp of the victor, who greedily collected the precious objects and curtly acknowledged flatteries. The envoys from Peking, all Chinese of the old diplomatic school, took the Goor Khan's brusqueness for soldierly simplicity, and volunteered advice. Many treacherous and aggressive tribes were still at large, led by envious, plotting chieftains, and they said that the Goor Khan would not be secure until he would have conquered and pacified them all. They acted as if security of the Khan and his realm were their emperor's foremost concern, talked about the threat to the flank and rear of Temudshin's armies by lawless hordes, north, east, and west—from every direction but Peking; they produced maps, showing to the Khan of the Universe how far the lands extended from where he might be threatened— and they transmitted Peking's offer to send geographical specialists to his headquarters. And while the Kin envoys stayed in the tent city, Song ambassadors arrived with more presents, good wishes, and advice. Temudshin grabbed presents and listened glumly to the men from the far side of China who expressed their sovereign's delight about the Goor Khan's successes and warned against the enemies of the new Mongolian Empire which seemed to include the unpredictable Kin.

Temudshin's early victories had not soothed his old frustrations. His hatred for China and all things Chinese was as vivid as ever, and much more acute as the day of revenge seemed to dawn. He wanted to know his victims as thoroughly as possible before attacking. Chinese advice aimed at keeping him away from the two empires, but talk about security was not unfounded. He had to secure his flank and rear, thereby making more prisoners, auxiliaries for the great drive south into the two Chinas.

There was no time to lose; not even shaman witchcraft could make him into a young man again.

The summer of 1202 went by with mopping-up operations; many more people died, more booty was gathered. Winter came early that year. Temudshin's troops were still dispersed in pursuit of Tatar remnants when the first snowstorms raked the land around Lake Baikal. The armies were ill-equipped for a winter campaign, and it was not Mongolian custom to be in the open air during the roughest season. The Goor Khan ordered his shamans to break the cold spell so the army could assemble in winter quarters; the wizards beseeched Tängri, but the snows came in drifting even more violently, and the frost encased unprotected men in deadly crusts of ice. Temudshin's army suffered more casualties through the cold than it had suffered in action. The Kin and the Song envoys had left when the first snowflakes drifted down, and did not witness the hardships which reduced the Goor Khan's fighting power and the unrest that spread through his makeshift camp. The men huddled together in light tents, freezing, hungry, grumbling. Not even their fear of Temudshin's informers and of his ruthlessness against infringers of discipline kept them from voicing discontent. Ranking officers cautiously encouraged the soldiers' mulishness. They regretted having accepted tutorship by a person who was their inferior by origin and actual rank; secret threads were spun to the almost forgotten Wang, who lived among the shivering army.

The army's sufferings were no less grievous than those of Napoleon's Grande Armée on its retreat from Moscow 610 years later; for even though not all of the Goor Khan's men had to march, temperatures near Lake Baikal were at least thirty degrees lower than in Western Russia. Temudshin did not stir his soldiers' wrath by Draconian measures. He pretended not to know that cavalrymen in their wind-swept tents charged that the Goor Khan had cheated them by letting his greedy family pick the most valuable spoils before an inventory was made. Instead he had shamans prophesy more victories and greater spoils—soon, very soon, after Tängri would have granted their request for fair weather. And he called on Togrul and offered to marry his daughter, so that the Universal Empire be a family entail.

The Wang was in no hurry to make Temudshin his son-in-law. He pleaded for time and asked for more personal freedom. Temudshin, anxious to humor the aging Wang, had the guards withdrawn from his tent. Togrul escaped and joined the anti-Temudshin forces, who, led by Kerait loyalist princes, began to gather in the Siberian forests near the site of present Nerchinsk.

The thaw season of 1203 lasted longer than usual. Temudshin reorganized his army and restored its morale. Many officers and men deserted him, but he did not mind losing mutinous elements. He knew how to infiltrate the enemy ranks, however. One of Togrul's sons was at odds with his father. Temudshin offered to let him share the throne should he collaborate, and sent shamans to the forests to convince the simple soldiers that the Goor Khan was the true and only chosen of the Sky; and, most important, Temudshin dispatched a peace mission to Togrul. The Wang listened to their vague proposals, to the dismay of the Kerait princes who wanted to attack Temudshin before he was ready.

Togrul hesitated to take the offensive as long as there was a chance of peace. His reluctance, so unusual for a Mongolian sovereign, irritated princes who kept their own troops in a permanent state of alert. When Temudshin's band launched a surprise assault, the Goor Khan experienced the only reverse of his career; his troops suffered substantial losses, including a few of Temudshin's most trusted associates, and fell back to the shores of faraway Lake Bar Nor.

Disengagement and withdrawal were carried out under cover of darkness, undisturbed by the victors. This was, in fact, not Temudshin's accomplishment. The Goor Khan was in tears—mourning dead friends, as his historians explain —more likely, out of self-pity and inability to cope with the perplexing problem of defeat. The commanding officer in those trying days was a former Naiman general who had deserted his people to cast his lot with Temudshin, and whose mere name, Subotai (Subugatai) would later become the nightmare of European peoples and rulers.

A glum-looking, curb-legged, warrior of square build, Subotai was one of the world's outstanding military geniuses, but otherwise a simple, if not dull person—a Prussian-type brass-head long before the introduction of the term and the foundation of the Kingdom of Prussia. To him the universe was an agglomeration of battlegrounds, some of which were temporarily out of operation, and mankind consisted of chessmen of battle. Subotai's thoughts centered on moves in the game of war, the faster the better, and on blows as concentrated as they could be administered. Never in the heyday of the German Blitzkrieg in 1939 and 1940 did the speed of motorized Wehrmacht equal that of Subotai's cavalry in the first half of the thirteenth century. Subotai's conception of concentration of missile-throwing power in running action was more revolutionary than Napoleon's shattering concentration of artillery. His pattern for mobile warfare included only three designs of outmaneuvering and encircling the enemy, but it was sufficient to paralyze every foe with whom the curb-legged warrior ever crossed swords. Subotai's desertion to Temudshin was the one and only act of disloyalty in his long life. He was never again interested in cabals, and he blindly followed instructions and rules, even if this meant to break up a campaign at the peak of success.

Had it not been for these characteristics Subotai might have become the one and only military leader to conquer all of Europe. But at the time that he led the remnants of Temudshin's army toward the Manchurian lake he hardly thought that he would ever be on the verge of conquering a distant continent.

After his recovery the Goor Khan took council with his shamans and with a Chinese adventurer whom he happened to meet near the Manchurian border. It was decided to appeal to Togrul's sentimentality. The Chinese was a man of literary talent. He drafted a poem in which Temudshin tenderly called the Wang his admired patriarch, assured him of his everlasting devotion and gratitude, and asserted bluntly that he never had intended to infringe on his obligations toward him. "I was no less bewildered than anybody else," the rhymes explained, "when the shamans revealed my vocation. It must have been the will of the spirits of deceased Khans, who watched the Kuriltai."

Togrul showed the poem to his princes, who sneered and asked that Temudshin be liquidated, and he showed it to his shamans, who were against radical action, allegedly in order not to antagonize the deceased Khans, but actually because they all had been personally involved in the deceptive magic at the Kuriltai. The aging Wang waited. He was getting ever more irresolute and depressed.

Temudshin reassumed charge of his horde, and led it to the region of present Chita, where they camped near Baldjouna, a pond that supplied people and horses with muddy waters. His men called themselves Baldjounists; they were the hard core of Temudshin's followers. The summer of 1203 was lean and precarious for the Baldjounists, but it was also disappointing to Togrul's paladins. The Wang was no leader, and without a leader their hopes would come to naught. It would be better to enlist with the Kin Emperor, or, rather, to find another king or prince who did have energy and design profitable to all who sided with him while the going was good.

As the leaves turned red and golden, officers on horseback came to the muddy pond, to offer Temudshin leadership of all tribes, hordes, and troops who were dissatisfied with Togrul.

And when the first night frosts hit the land, a rejuvenated army assaulted Togrul's ill-guarded, half-deserted camp. The Keraits did not even fight. Togrul was killed when he took to horse.

Within a matter of weeks lightning tactics brought all of Eastern Mongolia, the Baikal region, the lands near the Great Wall, and the approaches to the Gobi under Temudshin's iron militaristic rule.

CHAPTER TWELVE Unlike Siberian rulers of the past, the Goor Khan was not content gathering the spoils of conquered realms. Reared on conspiracy, deceit, and rebellion, and aware of the immense recuperative powers of the nomads of the steppes, he was determined to keep every corner of his land under ironclad control and every inhabitant in a status of abject submission. Temudshin had not yet a clear concept of civil law, but he ordered his officers who patrolled the wide regions to impose rules of military discipline upon all people they encountered, and he would not permit persons of rank to stay with their decimated clans. Chieftains and elders were detained in Temudshin's retinue. Disobedience and dubious intentions were capital offenses, and no time was wasted with investigations or trials. Accusations by officers or professional informers were accepted as evidence.

The Baldjounists reaped the fruits of their desperado steadfastness. Temudshin, distrustful of newly enlisted tribes and of officers of vacillating loyalties, established the Käshik, a guard, the army's elite and its center of gravity, its eyes and ears, and, under the command of trusted officers, a body to which the Baldjounists were collectively admitted. The Käshik enjoyed preferred treatment and the members preyed upon the common soldiers with the ardency of vicious supermen.

Temudshin's shamans organized spy nets among their counterparts in areas not yet conquered, promising traitors high rewards after their community was subdued. Strongest among the free people were still the Naimans, and treacherous Naiman wizards warned that their Tayan (King) was assembling a substantial, well-mounted army in the Altai Mountains. Nestorian missionaries were said to advise the Naiman ruler and to engage in illicit deals with minor demons who might do some harm. The Nestorians learned of the reports; knowing enough about Temudshin to realize that they would not be spared should he conquer the Tayan, they sneaked out of the Tayan's camp, joined Temudshin, and provided him with crucial information.

The Mongolian horses were in poor shape; they would need a good deal of grazing on succulent pasture lands, but there was no time to lose. The Naiman army was growing stronger. Temudshin ordered an immediate offensive. The Naimans' camp was several hundred miles away, but the hard-driven ponies covered the distance in an amazingly short time. When Temudshin's army came into sight, an experienced Naiman officer suggested that they fall back behind the Altai range to lure Temudshin into following them until his weary horses would be completely exhausted and his army fall an easy prey to fast-moving Naiman cavalry. Most princes and generals agreed, but one ranking shaman objected: "No good man should ever show the enemy his back, or the crupper of his horse."

The Tayan wanted to be a good man, which decided the issue; the battle was joined. The day was Temudshin's. By nightfall the Tayan was dead, and his army dispersed.

Subotai was ordered to destroy every remaining unit and to kill every ranking noble and officer, even if he had to ride to the end of the world. To hunt down the defeated enemy leaders to the remotest part of the earth became a cornerstone of Temudshin's military policy. The Goor Khan himself set out with the bulk of his army, visiting the tribes who had not partaken in the campaign, giving them the choice between death and enlistment as auxiliaries with the status of slaves. Most tribes surrendered; those who did not were exterminated with painstaking efficiency. Two years after the battle of the Altai the returning Subotai reported that all fugitives had been tracked down. His conscription list was exhausted. He had been in many distant lands, and the

Mongol military signs had spelled terror in the hearts of many strange peoples.

It was Subotai's cavalry, equipped with some Chinese-made war machines, whom the believers in King David and his zealous host had encountered!

The ancient empire of the steppes was now Temudshin's; but the most vital scores, the reasons for the Goor Khan's never alleviated frustrations, remained to be settled. Among the captives was the Tayan's Guardian of the Seal, a man of keen intellect, whom Temudshin occasionally consulted. The Guardian of the Seal made suggestions for even tighter control of Temudshin's territory, but he was of no great help when the Goor Khan asked for a detailed plan to conquer the Kin and the Song empires within a short time. Temudshin's generals claimed that many years would be required to make the army ready for the great battles ahead. For the most part the generals were younger than their commander in chief, and more patient than he could afford to be. The Goor Khan would have preferred to find a solution of his problems without shaman help; too often already had he relied upon the wizards and he did not want them to become all too strong. But where the military and the wise men had failed the shamans would have to fill the gap.

The most powerful of all shamans was Kötchü, who had recently succeeded his father in office. This father had lived with Oelun-Eke for a great number of years; the old woman was still extremely lively, imperious, and meddlesome. Kötchü was not her son, but her tool, and, as such, her favorite, whom she was anxious to establish as a power—her power—second to none, not even to Temudshin, her first-born. She insisted that Kötchü could ride up to the highest heaven on his gray horse, that she had heard him talk with Tängri, and with all the spirits close to the supreme divinity.

No shaman or prince dared to contradict the formidable and violent dowager, who occupied the largest cart tent of the court and of whom the saying went that at the age of seventy she still slept with career-minded guardsmen.

Calling upon the shamans meant putting Oelun-Eke in charge. Temudshin did not relish the thought, but he was at a loss what else to do.

Kötchü promised to obtain advice from Tängri and asked that another Kuriltai be convoked so that peers of the realm would witness the Eternal Blue Sky's revelations. Temudshin called princes and generals to assemble in a Diet.

Another tent city sprang up at the sources of the Onon River, but the dwellers of the Diet tents were no longer free agents to be intoxicated, intrigued, or coaxed into compliance. Many participants had been virtual prisoners, and the rest were puppets or, at best, bewildered petty chieftains who had been overlooked in the general round-up after the defeat of the Naimans. A few Kirghiz princes from the Yenisei Valley took the oath of allegiance before procedures started.

In a weird ceremony in a clearing of the dark forests Kötchü called upon Tängri, and amid spasms and convulsions shouted that that divinity consecrated the Very Mighty Khan, the Khagan ruler of all rulers and overlord of the universe; and that all emperors, kings, princes, and all peoples of the world were ordered to submit to the rule of the Very Mighty Khan, whose own people comprised all those who lived in felt tents, regardless of tribal distinctions.

The Mongolian word for Very Mighty Khan was Djenghis Khan.

The shaman boasted to have solved all of Temudshin's conquering problems. Had not Tängri ordered the peoples of the world to accept his rule? Could any ruler or nation defy this command? Temudshin and his generals may have thought otherwise, but with celebrations of his selection resounding through the tent city scepticism seemed out of place.

Kötchü was triumphant. Oelun-Eke was pleased. The shaman made a bold bid to rid himself of Temudshin's younger brothers, who viewed his influence with angry concern. After he denounced the princes as plotters against the Djenghis Khan's life, pandemonium broke out at court. Temudshin seized the opportunity to rid himself of the shaman. He sentenced him to death for false accusations. Picked executioners broke Kötchü's neck, careful not to spill one drop of blood: blood, in the Mongol's belief, is the carrier of the soul. A man who lost one drop of blood as he died could not bring his soul intact into the realm of death.

Almost everybody was pleased to know Kötchü transferred to the next world more or less intact. The irate dowager, however, told Temudshin that the executed shaman would complain to Tängri and that the Eternal Blue Sky would hear favorably what a man of high standing with divinity had to say. Tängri might demote the Djenghis Khan and withdraw his support.

The Djenghis Khan was already preparing his next military venture. His generals said that even with Tängri's blessings and orders a minimum of four years' preparation was required to ready the army for an invasion of China. The year being 1207, he would not be able to attack before 1211, aged fifty-six. Oelun-Eke was a spiteful woman, but extremely clever and considered a sorceress. Temudshin wanted to make up with Tängri before his mother or her dead favorite could intrigue against him, and delay, if not frustrate, the crucial operation.

Usun, a shaman of considerable inventiveness and undoubtedly also of superior showmanship, was appointed Kötchü's successor. He had to walk the tightrope arranging for heavenly blessings of Temudshin. Neither prince nor privates, nor, least of all, slaves, should doubt the validity of the Djenghis Khan's previous consecration, but yet the act had to be confirmed. Usun staged a ceremony in which the celestial spirits were implored to bless a particular venture of their chosen, the righting of a wrong committed by villainous foes—the Kin. The most eminent spirits dwelled in the skies above Mt. Kenteï. The Djenghis Khan, with Usun as intercessor and interpreter, should plead his case before the celestial forum. As a sign of his subjection to the one and only authority higher than his own, he should appear before the spirits in the attire of a man surrendering to a victor, bareheaded, his belt suspended over his shoulders.

If Temudshin was shocked at the idea of people watching him in so humble a position, Usun allayed his misgivings: the men would admire their ruler's shrewdness in courting the good will of the spirits, and they would see that the Djenghis Khan not only preached, but also practiced, obedience in the one and only instance it was required.

The Khan and the shaman went to Mt. Kenteï, with thousands of bystanders looking on. There, on the top of the mountain, Temudshin bent his knee nine times, made a ritual offering of kumiss, and addressed Tängri: "O Eternal Blue Sky, I am about to take up arms to avenge the blood of my ancestors, whom the Kin have ignominiously slain. Approve of my undertaking, and lend me your support."

Next Usun performed his ceremonial of riding up to the abode of the exalted; then he proclaimed with clear enunciation that the spirits were particularly well disposed toward Temudshin and that they would always support him. Tängri acknowledged the entreaty, and approved of it.

People were awed, and Temudshin himself must have been encouraged. Beneath the hard core of cynical exploitation of his subjects' credulity he preserved a great deal of traditional superstition; enough to make him believe that an angry Tängri would have given a sign of his displeasure. But the spirits did not seem to mind the Djenghis Khan's corruption and the duplicity of his plea.

Preparations for all-out war were stepped up after the pilgrimage. Chattels, horses, and objects collected in the process of tribal submissions had to be allotted to the beneficiaries. This was not booty gathered in battle, and Temudshin decreed that only the ruler and his princes were eligible as recipients. A Tatar prisoner of war who had learned the art of writing in Uigur characters put down the rules.

This was the first written law of the Mongolians, immediately followed by another decree establishing their duties and those of all other people under the sky.

Certain rules of behavior are said to have been traditionally observed in Temudshin's family; they became the foundation of the Yassak, a rudimentary code of law.

The Great Khan imposed upon the military and civilians the duty of absolute obedience to his orders. Disobedience was a crime punishable by ignominious death. The death penalty was also mandatory for murder, thievery, dealing with stolen goods, premeditated lies, adultery, and sodomy—the last rampant among the cavalrymen. Foreign rulers who did not heed Mongol surrender requests were termed guilty of disobedience, and so were all men who had individually or as a community resisted Mongol attackers. Temudshin's family would forever top the edifice of Mongol feudal society. It would be called Altan Oorook, the Golden Family; its head would automatically be Khagan, and his legitimate sons ranking princes of the Universal Empire. The Yassak also called the realm Nootook, standing for Pasture Land, on which the conquerors' beasts would forever graze. The pastures would be divided among the princes, who would remain under the suzerainty of the Khagan, but free to allot shares to the lesser Mongol nobility, their liege men. Only non-Mongolian peoples would be serfs.

During Temudshin's lifetime, the Yassak was supplemented by many *biliks* (decrees), ranging from military regulations to funeral standards, and imposing the death penalty for bathing in running waters or belching in other people's tents. Only Temudshin was entitled to amend the Yassak. After his death the law would remain petrified.

Forty years after its promulgation a Franciscan friar, Plan Carpin, visited the Mongols, and described some effects of the Yassak: "The Mongolians are the most obedient people of the world. They venerate their chiefs even higher than friars venerate their superiors; they would never tell him an untruth. There are few litigations and arguments among them, and no slayings. Only few minor thefts are recorded. Nobody appropriates stray animals, and if a man finds stray stock, he will try to locate its owner and shepherd the herd back to him. The women are usually chaste."

News of the Yassak must have reached China soon enough—there were still Chinese traders on Mongol-held territory—and some of its stipulations must have sounded ominous to Chinese ears. The denunciation of resisters to Mongolian domination as "disobedients," doomed the Emperor and his soldiers, and the designation of conquered territory as "pastures," augured evil for built-up areas and farmlands. But whether the Kin and Chinese considered it a boast that should not be taken literally, or whether the civilized Far East was frightened into inertia, Temudshin's preparations for the great onslaught went on undisturbed.

Civilian advancement came to an abrupt end and titles were reserved to the military; all opportunities the conquering state had to bestow went to the army. The army owned the land, and whatever the land could produce served the army's needs and the soldiers' comfort. Even ostracized auxiliaries had something to look for under the Yassak. After enough non-Mongolian prisoners were made, the Great Khan would admit proscribed kin into the army as regulars, giving them an opportunity to acquire slaves themselves and to avenge all their previous sufferings on these wretches.

The rank and file were promised unlimited promotion; every private could raise to generalcy provided he distinguished himself accordingly.

Temudshin's Baldjounists were growing sluggish and saturated by a privileged way of life. The Djenghis Khan would not deprive his faithful of their privilege, but he enlarged the cadre of the Käshik, and had hand-picked scions of meritorious families admitted into the Guards. A non-commissioned guardsman could issue orders to the commander of one thousand regulars.

The traditional division of the army into sections of 10 (*arban*), 100 (*djagoon*), 1000 (*minggan*), and 10,000 (*tümen*) remained unchanged; but larger units were organized: the corps composed of three tümen, and the field army of three corps. Co-operation among various units was improved to a degree in which they worked together like parts of a clockwork, and could be switched around at a moment's notice. Not even at the peak of the Roman Empire's military strength had its cohorts achieved the precision of the Mongol units. Every man was superlatively trained for individual action. To the architects of Temudshin's host combat was hunting, with the enemy the game. Men were tracked down with the skill and ruthlessness acquired chasing beasts of prey. Group hunting tactics applied in patrol action preceding full-scale attacks. Mongolian squadrons were taught to charge enemy marching units in full gallop; the squadron swarmed out as it approached the marchers, dispersed them, pursuing any single men and gathering again before other enemy forces could come to the relief of the attacked. If the surprise element did not work, the Mongols would vanish out of sight with bewildering speed. Mongolian scouts were superior archers; they could shoot while riding hard, they hit the mark almost unfailingly at ranges up to two hundred yards, and were still dangerous at four hundred. The men were well trained in the use of swords, axes, javelins, hooks, and lassos, but close-quarter fighting was to be delayed as long as possible. Just as hunters would not close in on big game as long as it was strong and alert, the Mongols would harass the foe until he was no longer able to defend himself properly.

Mongolian generals, probably advised by experts from cultured lands, developed a pattern of psychological warfare. Potential enemies were shaken by artfully planted rumors of Mongolian invincibility and enormous numbers; they were told that nothing but surrender could save their lives and property; reports would be spread about wholesale destruction of recalcitrant nations.

The Mongolian army had a training ground, the small Kingdom of Si-Hia, on the northwesternmost border of China, formerly a part of the empire. Temudshin chose Si-Hia as the experimental theater of war. Tactics were tried on Si-Hia people—highly civilized men of remarkable industrial skill, and a military organization similar to that of Song China. The King, believing that Mongolian intrusions were just old-fashioned raids with some modern tactics added, hastened to pay a stiff tribute; the Djenghis Khan collected and kept attacking. The King offered the aggressor his attractive daughter in marriage. Temudshin had her sent to his camp, and continued the raids. Mongolian military analysts came to the conclusion that the Mongol army could always defeat an enemy three to four times its own number in pitched battle, but that Mongolian siege equipment and heavy weapons had to be improved to take fortifications without high losses.

Chinese merchants delivered all the weapons they could get hold of, but it was learned that Chinese engineers were working on new war machines of enormous destructive power. Without such arms, the analysts contended, conquest of Kin and China would be a slow and difficult operation. However, should the Great Wall be crossed swiftly and without major casualties, it would be possible to seize centers of Chinese arms production in time to grab the coveted equipment.

The Kin had entrusted defense of a key sector of the wall to Öngüt-Turcs, who had narrowly escaped Temudshin's man hunt. Psychological-warfare specialists learned of a malcontent Öngüt chieftain and hired him as their agent. He was advised to indoctrinate the soldiers with the belief that, in case of Mongolian attack, their choice lay between joining the victor or perishing from his blows. The chieftain voiced optimism, but indicated that it would take time to do the job.

Training and equipment of the Mongolian army continued. Every soldier received two bows and quivers, one set of bows and arrows for rapid shooting in swift motion, the other for high-precision discharge in slow movement; a curved saber, an ax, an iron club, a hooked pike to unseat enemy horsemen, and a lasso. Camp uniforms included fur caps with ear muffs, felt stockings, solid boots, and knee-length fur coats. Battle dress comprised a leather helmet covering the nape, and a leather vest that offered reasonably good protection against arrows at long range. No provisions were made for campaigns in warm climates; the men's hardiness was expected to overcome the handicap of high temperatures.

Mongolian generals experimented with preserved food and a method was devised to preserve milk by a process that was the equivalent of modern dehydration. Horsemen on the move received supplies of dried milk every morning; they would put their rations into leather bottles filled with water; the motion of riding produced enough porridge to feed the man, who would then not have to stop for requisitioning and cooking.

Patrol tactics were revised to include, not only scouting, but also to set the stage for entrapment of enemy forces. Plan Carpin gave an account of these tactics: "As soon as the vanguards sight the enemy, they charge, every man shooting 3 or 4 arrows; if the foe's ranks are not shaken, the Mongols retreat in the direction of their main forces, which, quickly alerted, will set a trap for the pursuers. Should a cautious enemy refuse to pursue retreating vanguards, these men will turn around, and keep harassing him at long range, inflicting casualties without loss to thcmselves. The Mongols will learn a great deal about enemy deployment, number, and equipment, while their opponents will know nothing about the army they are about to face. Mongolian generals are careful to keep their losses to a minimum; they shun battle against all too heavy odds. Heavily outnumbered, they will wait for reinforcements, and in the meantime ravage the countryside, one or two days' ride away from the enemy and in the direction from which reinforcements would arrive. The enemy could but come to the assistance of the afflicted. He would change from battle array to marching order, becoming vulnerable to harassing attacks by patrols, and eventually face lightning attack by regrouped and reinforced horsemen."

So stunned were the military of other nations by Mongolian operations that for a considerable period of time they did not even study enemy strategy and tactics, but accepted defeat as something inevitable.

Actually, when facing aggressive cavalry supported by foot soldiers, the Mongols opposed the opening charge only by a screen of their own horsemen who, after discharging a volley of well-aimed arrows, retreated behind a solid formation of archers on foot; saber- and spearmen. Infantrymen were usually Siberian auxiliaries impressed into the service. By fighting hard they had a chance to become freemen-soldiers, and so they held out tenaciously, forming hedgehogs of spear points. More often than not the hedgehog stopped the onrushing attacker, but even if the infantry had to fall back, it would do so slowly and in good order. Meantime the main Mongol cavalry forces would deploy on both sides of the foe, charge in gallop, and annihilate him. Generals who took care to cover their flanks found no remedy against a Mongolian trick called "flourishing standards." Onrushing cavalry would suddenly bare one wing and concentrate on the other, starting an enveloping drive that was completed before the enemy realized that it was on. Foes who waited for the Mongols to assemble on the battlefield, to accommodate their own deployment to that of the enemy, found themselves caught in a noose of mounted archers who leisurely shot the army up as if this were target practice.

The vast training, equipment, and psychological-warfare program was completed on schedule. In 1211 thirteen *tümen* were ready to strike, 130,000 men, who, according to estimates, would be superior to between 400,000 and 500,000 soldiers of any other nation known to the Mongols. None of these nations, not even the two Chinas combined, had a standing army of a larger size, to the best of the Mongol general's knowledge.

The men liked their profession; they were nurtured on accounts of fabulous riches, and even more fabulous wenches, who waited for them abroad. Their innate cruelty was stimulated by training, and their ambition reached fever pitch as they were lectured on the award and promotion system. Every private pictured himself at least as a noble *minggan* commander, with tents full of silk, candy, slaves, and whores; and armed slaves nursed sweet dreams of holding slaves of their own, and treating them much worse than they had been treated themselves. Frustrations exploded into ferocious fighting ardor.

Temudshin, Djenghis Khan, Khagan, Goor Khan, Supreme War Lord, looked back on long years of frustration and resentments of his own, sharpened by impatience and repression. He would repay the boyhood humiliation and all disappointments of his younger years with a usurer's interest—to a nation who knew nothing about them and to an emperor who had not yet ruled when he was refused enlistment in the Kin army. So immense were his accumulated grievances that no Kin hecatombs would satisfy his thirst of revenge. The land of the Kin would be turned into pastures of Mongol cavalry horses, and so would the land of the Song—and still this would be but a drop in the bucket of his flaming wrath. All lands of the earth would be laid waste, and their people decimated. He did not really want kings and countries to surrender. He had no use for so many slaves. And yet the Djenghis Khan, relishing murderous designs more than any other soldier in his instrument of destruction, was perhaps the only person in the huge camp who hesitated to strike. Did Oelun-Eke, still not reconciled to the death of "her" shaman, foster her son's most secret misgivings? Did Temudshin himself distrust his vocation? Did the unifier of so many tribes and peoples, the champion of total obedience, doubt the firmness of enforced unity and the obedience of the subjected after the army left for distant goals? Temudshin stayed in his elaborate tent, guarded by the tallest Käshik soldiers, and did not issue marching orders.

CHAPTER THIRTEEN The mounts were fed on superbly succulent spring grass. Soldiers greased their bows and submitted to camp routine. Generals, having completed their prewar tasks, waited to be called before the Djenghis Khan for the final briefing. Army shamans performed listless wizardries, produced favorable weather forecasts and generally auspicious augury, and wondered how they would be remunerated until the men could plunder at their heart's desire. Chief Wizard Usun was glum and noncommittal.

From China arrived merchants, as usual, and also a growing flood of opportunists, professional informers, and traitors who had learned of Mongolian military preparations and expected permanent fat assignments with the future conquerors. The Kin Emperors, they said, were effeminate; they had lost all of their ancestors' rigor and courage; their nobles were Sinofied debauchers rather than soldiers; mercenaries were undisciplined and ready to run over; Chinese generals and officials still despised the ruling usurpers and would not obey their orders in an emergency; and the common people were an apathetic lot. Absconders from the Song Empire, less numerous than their counterparts from the Kin, told of South China's weakness and its expected disintegration under powerful blows.

All this was duly reported to Temudshin; and yet he issued no orders. Had it not been for the Yassak and its credo of discipline the men would not have withstood the strain of waiting; but not even soldiers indoctrinated with obedience could be expected to wait forever. The army was like an avalanche that had gathered on the edge of a steep slope: it was bound to break loose, either sweeping Temudshin away in a savage riot or descending upon the world beyond the Siberian steppes. The fate of this world, of scores of millions on two continents, hung in the balance.

Then a trivial incident, inconsequential under normal circumstances, decided the issue.

The old Kin Emperor died in Peking, and, as customary, special ambassadors notified foreign princes who held Kin titles of nobility of the new Emperor's ascendancy. The ceremonial required that princes receive the message on their knees; every man titled by the Emperor was supposed to be his vassal. Thirteen years before, in Peking, Temudshin had received a title. As a matter of routine, an ambassador went to the Djenghis Khan's headquarters, a smooth, courteous gentleman who was not to arouse the belligerent Khan's sensitivities. Yet to bend his knee before the ambassador of a sovereign he was pledged to destroy would ruin the Djenghis Khan's prestige among his own men. This forced Temudshin's hand. He received the ambassador outside of his tent, before thousands of cavalrymen gathered for the occasion. They saw their supreme commander stand upright, they heard him shout at the top of his lungs that the Kin Emperor was a contemptible imbecile not worthy of a salute, least of all of prostration; and as the hapless ambassador stood thunderstruck, Temudshin spat in the direction of Peking. This was an insult no emperor could take without losing face forever, and it amounted to a declaration of war.

Temudshin had a final ceremony staged to please Tängri and remind the Eternal Blue Sky of its promises.

"O Eternal Sky, I have armed myself to avenge the blood of my uncles whom the Kin have slain ignominiously. Lend me your support," the Djenghis Khan's voice rang out in the presence of as many soldiers as the field outside the camp could accommodate. The shamans, led on by Usun, shouted that Tängri approved of the vengeance, and would lend support. It did not matter that the slaying of Temudshin's uncles was a very new charge; Tängri apparently was no hairsplitter.

The invasion forces consisted of one army of three corps; four tümen were left behind to act as reserves and to police the realm. The Käshik joined the field army.

Crossing the Great Wall required no struggle; the Öngüt chieftain had done good work. Right and left of the section over which the Mongols marched and rode mercenaries fell back, sweeping regulars along.

As if on parade, the three corps rolled into the land of promise. Again, before the dull eyes of the rank-and-file killers from the steppes spread a land such as they had not been able to visualize, even in wishful dreams. It was like a display of treasures free for the taking. In the profusion of prosperous settlements single villages contained more desirable objects than the Mongolian army had gathered throughout the unification campaigns. Of the swarming population of skilled men and attractive women almost every person was valuable as a slave. At first no resistance was encountered, but Temudshin and his generals spent a few uneasy days. This was the acid test of discipline. Would the soldiers keep in tight formation, as were the orders, and wait for a distribution of booty that would come later, or would they maraud, rebel against the discipline which was the army's source of strength? The Käshik was alerted to deal with the slightest symptom of insubordination; the guards spied on the cavalrymen, but there were no signs of disorder.

The Kin were not as effeminate as informers had claimed. The Sinofied descendants of the Djürchäts threw whatever forces they could muster into the northwestern gap and most Chinese generals remained loyal to the Emperor.

However, the Kin armies arrived piecemeal and were immediately chewed up by lightning operations. The invaders laid the land waste, section after section. Thousands were butchered, tens of thousands herded into slavery. Herding slaves to the hinterland required escorts, and even though Mongol casualties were insignificant, effectives were shrinking, and major battles were still ahead. The Djenghis Khan did not want too many prisoners. The guards reported that villagers went into hiding at the Mongols' approach, and returned to their places after the invaders had left. Orders were issued to level every building and to stop gathering booty and slaves until the big cities were taken.

Only a few cities had been seized in the initial drive, some by surprise, others through treason. Mongolian arrows were impotent against fortifications, and neither speed nor boldness made walls crumble. Chinese defensive tools of war were even more effective than expected, and no arms production center had yet been captured. Temudshin and his generals devised a new ruse. The Mongols would turn up as far as a hundred miles away from a city, head in a different direction, and have informers convey the news to city magistrates. The gates would be opened while the Mongols, covering upward of sixty miles a day, would swing back toward the place, and enter it before the defenders could take action.

More medium-sized cities were taken, razed, and depopulated, but Peking was not yet solidly surrounded; and Temudshin, who personally led the assault against the city, was unable to force its walls.

The year 1211 went by, and 1212; 1213 found Temudshin still not in control of the empire he had hoped to overrun.

The Djenghis Khan diverted two corps to rural sections to devastate what was still intact; the third corps circled Peking. Inside the battered capital, generals argued that Peking, its population doubled by the influx of refugees, could not withstand a protracted siege. Already stores were running low and disease spread rapidly. They urged the Emperor either to order an all-out sortie or to make peace at any price—short of surrender. The Emperor hesitated, the officers pressed for a decision and eventually had their ruler assassinated just as the vanguards of the two detached Mongol corps arrived in the vicinity of Peking.

Woo Too-po, the new Kin Emperor, was a mediocre man whose strongest impulse was fear. He offered to negotiate peace and Temudshin agreed to talk. His acceptance was couched in insulting terms, but nobody in Peking seemed to mind abuse. The Djenghis Khan asked for a fantastic war indemnity. The Emperor scraped together whatever he could lay hands upon; caravans carried gold, silk, a variety of precious goods, and sugar to the Mongolian camp; 3000 Arab horses of finest breed were delivered; and Temudshin also collected a large number of selected young men and women, including Djürchät princes of the blood for his personal use.

In 1214 the terrible army marched back at a leisurely pace, leaving behind the most dreadful memories—and the first pictures of Temudshin. Prior to the Djenghis Khan's meteoric raise nobody had cared to immortalize his features, and afterward no artists had seen him until he rode on his white horse near the walls of Peking.

Chinese painters made no caricature of the despot, but they seemed to have been loath to draw him as he wanted to be shown: as a man of impressive, ageless handsomeness. Their pictures show a man who could pass as a typical Mongol for textbook use. Only the eyes reveal individuality: eyes of a cat about to leap at its prey. Official descriptions of Temudshin call him unusually tall, and they say that his chin, barren until the age of fifty, suddenly released a profuse growth of long hair. The tale of the beard reveals the tyrant as a man of petty vanity. It is likely that he was no taller than his average subjects, whose massive upper bodies stood on short, crooked legs, and that he never grew a big beard.

Mongolian rear guards remained uncomfortably close to Peking, and the uneasy Emperor transferred his residence to K'ai-fong-foo. Temudshin called this a breach of faith. Woo Too-po, the Djenghis Khan charged, had aggressive intentions or else he would not have gone into hiding. The Mongolian army turned in its tracks and raced back toward Peking. A Kin relief army carrying supplies to the city was scattered by Mongolian roving cavalry.

Strangely enough Temudshin had not requested surrender of Chinese war material. Powerful weapons were still available to the defenders, who used them with telling effect. Catapults threw containers filled with high explosives, generators produced smoke screens and asphyxiating gas, and thundering iron barrels hurled balls against the besiegers. As early as 1214, China could produce artillery barrages and practically all phases of gas warfare; but weapons alone could not decide the issue. Peking was taken by storm. In a mass assault of gruesome ferociousness, shock troops crawling over ramps of corpses, the Mongols broke into the city.

Peking's very size baffled the soldiers. It seemed absurd to build up an area on which the horses of one tümen could find abundant pastures; and there seemed to be too many people for selection—the horsemen would have to butcher them all. The supreme commander's nod was required to start the work of destruction, but the nod did not immediately come. Temudshin needed engineers to build his own artillery, gas generators, and siege machines; he wanted a supply of shrewd Chinese statesmen, geographers, linguists, and other useful persons; he needed more beautiful wenches for his own entertainment and that of his favorites; and he did not want his soldiery to loot the Imperial Palace until he had picked the most tempting objects himself.

When at last the soldiers were turned loose, it took them one month of unbridled savagism, of frantic rape, pillage, and arson to reduce Peking to scorched ruins littered with corpses—a hollow, rat-infested shell from which, as it seemed, no city could ever rise again.

The Chinese selected for service were all impressive-looking; Mongols did not believe in great capacities hidden behind undistinguished appearances. One man stood out even among those prisoners: he was tall and bearded and while the others knelt when their new master passed them in review, he did not budge; he did not falter under the victor's fixed, piercing, cat-eyed glance, and when the Djenghis Khan asked him for his name he answered with a commanding voice: "Yeliu-tch'ou-t'sai."

He was a prince of Chinese imperial ancestry, a scholar of history, philosophy, and of the fine arts. Temudshin, stirred by curiosity about the workings of that bold man's mind, had him called in for consultation on efficient methods of turning the universe into a horse pasture. The captive objected to the design, which not even a ranking general or shaman would have dared to do. To criticize the ruler of the universe was a manifestation of disrespect and warranted the death penalty. Yeliu indicated that he was aware of the possible consequences, but explained that all destruction would be futile, for it would be ephemeral altogether and would deprive the demolisher of emoluments, for nature was constructive and stronger than any man. And "stronger than any man" included Temudshin.

But Temudshin did not punish the challenge to his omnipotence. Yeliu became his secret counselor, the only man to whom the tyrant would talk without witnesses, the mirror of Temudshin's actions, the voice of a conscience that was not fundamentally Temudshin's own, but that he adopted occasionally and which eventually enabled ancient lands to survive the tribulations inflicted by the Mongol ruler's unscrupulously rapacious self.

The Song emperors gleefully watched the downfall of the Kin. The capture of Peking was greeted with mischievous enthusiasm. Siberian conqueror wiping out Siberian impostor.

The Songs hoped to placate Temudshin and keep him out of their own realm. A Song prince was assigned to convey the Emperor's respects to the Djenghis Khan, to congratulate him on his victories, to praise the legitimacy of his venture, and to warn him against a letup in his drive that would give the Kin an opportunity to restore their sinister power. The Songs had paid an annual tribute to the Kin; now they offered to pay it to Temudshin: 250,000 ounces of gold and 250,000 pieces of silk, augmented by good-will presents, of which the Song Emperor sent the Djenghis Khan a load of stunning samples.

Outside of Peking, where Temudshin had set up headquarters, the prince was subjected to humiliating procedures. He was made to walk between two pyres, so close that his elaborate ceremonial robe was singed and his perseverance put to a severe test. This was said to purge him from evil spirits. The gifts too were purged in the gantlet of fire. But worse was yet to come. Tängri wanted a close glimpse of the prince and his cargo. For a full week, the hapless aristocrat cowered under open sky outside the Djenghis Khan's tent, in scorching heat and drenching rain, the precious objects cluttering the ground. When at last admitted, the prince's attire and the presents, which included delicate varicolored tissues, were in an embarrassing condition. However, he delivered his prepared address in reasonably good attitude. A Käshik officer assigned the prince a place among the girl entertainers, and ordered him to attend all the banquets that would follow. The banquets started with orgies of *kumiss* drinking, and the eating of boiled meat, and culminated in houris' performances. The Song prince mutely sat through banquet after banquet, but this did not prevent his tormentors from charging that he had dodged one party, for which neglect he had to atone by drinking Chinese rice wine until he lost consciousness. When he recovered, he was notified that the Song tribute was accepted, but that his unsolicited advice on future dealings with the Kin had been rejected. Peace would reign henceforth between Mongols and Kin.

Actually Temudshin had lied and there would be no peace between Mongols and Kin. A lie was a capital crime! But Temudshin's word was considered stronger than the law.

Several districts of the Kin Empire had escaped disaster. Refugees roamed the outlying provinces, trying to cross into Song China. The Song Emperor, desperately pondering what to do to protect his country, had border guards reinforced to prevent illegal entries. Mongolian administration of conquered wastelands and survivors did not function. Chinese experts offered counsel, but Temudshin was not yet ready to have foreigners run their own country's affairs, even on a low level, and the Mongols had no officials capable of dealing with the complex problems of a strange, ruined land.

Yeliu had noticed his master's preoccupation with the security of Mongol flanks, and his detestation of the Kara Ki-tai. The learned Chinese showed Temudshin detailed maps revealing the strategic importance of the regions of the upper Irtysh in the southern part of Central Siberia, where the Kara Ki-tais lived; to the west of that river were other nations, alien to the Mongols by race, culture, and creed, who might join the Kara Ki-tais in a sneak attack on Mongol supply lines.

Temudshin agreed that the Kara Ki-tais had to be reduced at once, and that the nations farther to the west, some of whom might still remember Subotai's man hunts, would have to perish unless they acknowledged his rule of the universe. But, to the disappointment of Yeliu, who had hoped to give China a breathing spell, the Djenghis Khan decided that the Kin Empire's enslavement, and the organization of its war production for the Mongolian benefit, should proceed.

General Mookooli, a Baldjounist ruffian risen from the ranks, was put in charge of Kin affairs. He received one under-strength army corps of 23,000, an equal number of auxiliaries, and authorization to enlist as many former Kin mercenaries as he could find.

Mookooli gathered 62,000 mercenaries of Siberian stock, but progress of his operations was slow. The homeless masses were too elusive to be rounded up wholesale and, having nothing to lose, groups of refugees engaged in guerrilla warfare. The desperadoes never defeated the pursuers, but their resistance permitted the aimless refugees to evade the murderous horsemen. The flood of the persecuted surged back and forth, in accordance with mysterious laws of human gravity, always one step ahead of destruction. They found temporary refuge behind the walls of repopulated cities. Mookooli ordered captive engineers to build more powerful siege machines. Chinese-built walls crumbled under the blows of Chinese-built armored battering rams. The Mongols entered towns and killed every living creature, but yet the human sea kept heaving. In 1223, at last, informers whose sole reward was a precarious lease on their own lives reported that the bulk of refugees was heading for Hot'shong on the Yellow River. There the Mongolian hordes caught up with their victims. Mookooli and his most trusted henchmen halted at the bank of the river to watch corpses of the massacred float downstream; they sat on their horses and drank kumiss, a goblet full for every big batch of bodies. Cheers to the living victors! Mookooli reached for yet another goblet, slipped from the saddle, and was as dead as a battered and drowned Chinese. His lieutenants said that exhaustion had accounted for the demise of the meritorious officer.

The carnage on the Yellow River claimed several hundred thousand lives; yet nature's constructive powers prevailed over the ravagers; the decimated people was not destroyed.

The Kara Ki-tais were invaded in 1218. Another Guards general, named Djébé, was put in charge of two tümen, apparently a trifling force for the purpose. But the cavalrymen met no resistance and more often than not were cheered as liberators. The soldiers were startled; glum and morose, they received the ovations, wondering whether this was not a novel form of expressing fear or defiance, and determined to justify the former and to castigate the latter.

The Mongolian high command had permanently adopted psychological warfare, but it is hardly credible that the generals from the steppes were sufficiently well informed and inventive to make the Kara Ki-tai people acclaim the invaders. Yeliu, who was both, seems to have had a hand in psychological preparations. At the time Temudshin first crossed the Great Wall, Kütchlüg, a maniacal nomad hunter from the Altai Mountains, usurped the throne of the Kara Ki-tais. Religious persecution, man-made famine, and instigation of sanguinary feuds among princelings marked his rule. Being a shamanist, King Kütchlüg made the Moslems the main target of his deadly intolerance. His people loathed him, but were unable to cast off the yoke. Then, shortly before the Mongolian invasion, strange men turned up in Mohammedan settlements.

of Kara Ki-tais, who called themselves seers and announced that an avenger was coming to chastise Kütchlüg and to bring justice and freedom to the oppressed. When the tyrant's police were unable to arrest a single seer, he decreed cruel retaliations against villages in which seers had been reported talking to the people; and when even his own followers dodged his orders, he frantically adopted Nestorian Christendom to gain divine support. But then news came that Mongol vanguards were crossing the border. Kütchlüg fled to the wilderness of Pamir, where he was found by avengers, and killed.

The seers vanished. Mongol horsemen were not turned loose on the Kara Ki-tais. It must have required a major effort on Yeliu's part to persuade Temudshin to spare the people; nobody but the secret counselor could have dared suggest such restraint. But to leave the Kara Ki-tais unscathed turned out to have been good policy: it was to serve as an advance base for a continued campaign in the direction of the setting sun.

Mohammedanism was building new empires between Southwestern Siberia, the Mediterranean, and the Arabian Sea. Most recent among the new realms was that of Khwarezm, which expanded from the Aral Sea to the Caspian, to Samarkand, the Hindu Kush Mountains, and to the Persian Gulf. It was ruled by a clique of officers who had formerly served the Seljuks, and whose ambition was second only to Temudshin's. They wanted to be overlords of all Mohammedans, heirs to Persia at the peak of her expansion, emperors of India, and kings of Egypt. King Mohammed, who ruled Khwarezm in 1218, was a boisterous braggart who had but vague notions of administration, but who relied on his army to hold his realm together and to enlarge it at his will. The army was large; no other career was as promising as that of soldier; and Khwarezm made no distinctions among different races, provided they were Mohammedans. The braggart King was preparing to invade Bagdad when he learned of the Mongols' conquest of Kara Ki-tai. The number of cavalrymen engaged in the invasion made him sneer: twenty thousand were less than one tenth of his own effectives poised to strike; a handful of hard-riding savages not warranting precautionary measures.

But the hard-riding savages swarmed along the borders of his empire; and they were reported at so many places simultaneously that King Mohammed, beginning to doubt the authenticity of the figure 20,000, delayed his campaign to get a better picture of the situation.

The Khalif of Bagdad, who knew more about Mongolian strength than his aggressive neighbor, applied for Temudshin's assistance against Mohammed. His request was courteously received, but the answer was noncommittal. Mongolian diplomacy had certainly improved. Next a trade caravan came to a northern Khwarezm border province; the leader identified himself as a subject of the Djenghis Khan, and asked that trade relations between Mongolia and Khwarezm be opened formally. His wares were tempting enough; but the provincial governor, who had heard that all Mongols were spies, had the caravan leader executed without a trial, and the goods confiscated. Temudshin asked for amends, but received no reply. Mohammed was not yet certain whether the Mongols were bluffing or really intent upon attack, but he believed that his governor's action, and his own disregard of the Djenghis Khan's note, would be taken as an indication of strength and discourage the horsemen. Provocations, however, never intimidated the Mongols. Temudshin actually enjoyed being provoked: this would make Tängri even better inclined to help his chosen.

The Djenghis Khan journeyed to the Irtysh River to direct the preparations for a grandiose campaign. With him came all the reserves from Mongolia, and the elite of the auxiliaries. All in all Temudshin had nearly 150,000 men available, still less than Mohammed, who, now aware of Mongolian aggressive intentions, ordered mass levies of recruits.

The Khwarezm generals discounted rumors about the enemy's superior generalship, contending that there could be no finer generals than they themselves. Mohammed, who presided over the war council in his capital of Goorgandj, agreed vociferously. The Mongols, the war council decided, were basically hit-and-run raiders, as their ancestors had been; and whatever new tricks they had devised, they would be helpless against a strategy that concentrated on the defense of essential border strongholds and road hubs, letting the attackers spend their strength in local assaults until a large operational army would finish them off in one big, well-aimed blow.

In the summer of 1219, Mongolian cavalry advanced along the right bank of the river Syr Darja. This seemed a poor road of invasion; supply lines ran through the notorious hunger steppes. There was optimism in Khwarezm headquarters, where the Mongolian system of feeding the men on dry milk was unknown. It took the Mongols until early winter to reach the first major fortress town. One tümen, under the joint command of Temudshin's younger sons Djagatai and Ogödai, attacked Otvar, but could not take it by storm, and settled down to a protracted siege. Another tümen, led by Djoetchi, the Djenghis Khan's eldest son, crossed the border east of the Aral Sea, sacked open settlements, but did not penetrate far enough to be more than a nuisance. Only one minor fortress on the upper Syr Darja gave up to a Mongolian troop of 5000 after gallant resistance and with the small garrison evacuated by river barges.

It really looked like raiding warfare, old steppe style. The Khwarezm soldiers who had seen action were in high spirits; all the talk about Mongolian invincibility seemed nonsense spread by cowards who did not want to fight. It seemed no longer necessary to gather a huge operational army; reinforcement of outlying garrisons would secure easy victory. Parts of the main forces were diverted to border zones, recruiting was discontinued, and general vigilance relaxed.

This was precisely what Temudshin had been waiting for and what he had been aiming at by his deceptive strategy. In February 1220 his main forces, superior now to anything Mohammed could put in his way, dashed into the enemy country and, gathering momentum as they rolled on, reached Bokhara before the Khwarezms even realized that this important city was threatened. The place was garrisoned by the finest troops Mohammed could muster, religious fanatics, daredevils, veterans of many campaigns. But Chinese-built war machines shattered the walls and caused conflagrations in the city. The defenders tried a mass sortie to break the deadly siege ring. From atop walls and high buildings civilians watched as the garrison was engulfed by a hail of well-aimed arrows, and killed to the last man by charging cavalry. The massacre was not yet completed when a citizens' deputation prostrated itself before Temudshin, surrendered the city, and asserted that they had had no part in its resistance to the legitimate overlord of the universe. Mongolian agents in disguise had spread word that the lives of those who did not fight the ruler of the universe would be spared. Bokhara was pillaged with bloodcurdling efficiency. The population was looted, raped, insulted, tormented, but not butchered wholesale. However, those who, even if by one gesture, protested against mistreatment were immediately put to death. Mohammedan clergymen who attempted to prevent the desecration of the grand mosque were literally hewn to pieces. Temudshin studied the rape of Bokhara as a pattern for future dealings with surrendering cities, and he found that panicky crowds at large slowed the routine of destruction.

Samarkand was next. Its turn came only one month later. The famous ancient town with its partly Iranian population resisted five days, the time it required to bring the siege machines into action. Then the garrison laid down its arms and applied for admission into the Mongolian army. But the soldiers were put to death; running over could not exonerate previous resistance. The law of Siberia knew of no attenuating circumstances. In accordance with the experience of Bokhara the population was evacuated and driven into enclosures before Samarkand was destroyed. The detained people were screened: artisans and generally useful persons were drafted for forced labor; about three quarters of the rest were put to death, the others driven back into the smoldering ruins and abandoned to their fate.

Creeping, paralyzing fear pervaded Khwarezm. Nobody believed that the conquerors could be stopped. Mohammed's favorites, the members of his officers' clique and civilian appointees, thought only of their own security. The braggart ruler turned into a nervous wreck, a tottering wretch who implored his own governors to give him asylum, and begged the Khalif of Bagdad for assistance, but was forsaken by friend and foe.

Mohammed fled his capital before the Mongols arrived. Chinese engineers in Temudshin's service built dikes and dams on the Amu Darja, which caused high flood waters to engulf the doomed city. Only a few artisans were allowed to escape the deluge.

The former ruler of Khwarezm had become an outlaw fugitive. According to the Yassak, he had to be brought to bay as a criminal, guilty of disobedience and armed resistance to the ruler of the universe. The fastest Mongolian units, headed by Djébé and Subotai, took up pursuit, leaving desolation in their wake. Hundreds of thousands of corpses littered their tracks. Only in December 1220 did the pursuers reach their goal. A raft drifted near the shores of the Caspian on which lay the body of Mohammed, who had died from exhaustion and exposure.

Like Kin China in its distress, Khwarezm turned into a land of nomads. Streams of fugitives wandered around with no other objective than evading the murderous horsemen. But the fast-moving pursuers seemed omnipresent; wherever the victims turned, fellow-sufferers told them that the killers were nearby; fear-haunted minds pictured the dreaded riders as numerous as the sand of the sea. There was no mercy from the hunters, and no compassion among fellow-men; unconquered towns closed their gates to the fugitives, citizens did not want to share quarters and supplies with wanderers. The potential victims outnumbered the Mongolian armies 100 to 1, but there was no resistance. Lone Mongolian riders encountered large groups of able-bodied men who went down on their knees, and waited, with downcast eyes, to be either ignored or killed. The horsemen mostly did the latter, without haste or emotion. Mongolian junior officers were swamped with pleas for mercy, offers for ransom, and frantic assurances that, come what may, the citizen would not resist. The officers brushed the pleas aside, and tümen commanders, besought by deputations who prostrated themselves before their horses, rode on, over bent backs.

Temudshin stayed with his fastest-moving units; the strain of riding fifty and more miles a day did not tell upon the sexagenarian who witnessed the Khwarezms' demoralization and coolly pondered about the implications of terror. Terror seemed the most powerful of all weapons. Terror crushed the thought of resistance. Terror could not be stopped by walls and borders. Terror's language was understood by men anywhere. He would make an example of Khwarezm that would make the rest of the world lie prone before his tümen. He would not be diverted from his aims by philosophers—not even by Yeliu, whose stock was rather low in those days.

The Djenghis Khan ordered that cities who had not surrendered to Mongolian vanguards in an earlier stage be subject to spectacular punishment presided over by Mongol dignitaries. Nishapur was the object of his particular wrath; under its walls, a Mongolian tümen commander had been killed by an arrow. The tümen commander's widow, sitting on a vantage point, presided over the sinister spectacle. Nishapur had since capitulated; its magistrates protested that the fatal arrow was a stray shot and that the poor marksman had been punished, but it was to no avail. The woman ordered that all citizens be put to death. One regiment of a thousand was assigned to the task: the children first, then the women, finally the men. Each soldier dispatched eighteen human beings. The presiding avenger was not satisfied: she suspected that some of the victims "simulated" being dead, and ordered that the corpses be beheaded and the heads neatly piled up in pyramids, a procedure which was to become part of Mongolian routine. Still the woman craved for more blood. And because no more humans could be found she had the regiment dispatch all cats and dogs of Nishapur.

But the effects were not as expected. Utter despair carried the germs of recklessness. A few cities resisted. It was frantic, disorganized resistance, carried out by a handful of men and women who were almost as perilously threatened by capitulation-minded neighbors as by Mongolians; and it was always in vain. Temudshin did not even use his machines to reduce the places. Despite his butcheries he had too many prisoners already, and he used the surplus to form bridges of corpses, heaped up in front of the walls, over which his men marched into the city.

Apprehension that some of the conquered might "simulate" death gave rise to other misgivings. Would not victims be overlooked by the executioners, thoroughly as they searched houses and cellars? The Mongols did not want to take chances. Several hours after the massacre came to an end, prisoners toured the desolate places shouting that the Mongols had left and that everybody should come out of hiding. The trick produced bloody gleanings.

The territories of Armenia and Georgia, on the opposite ends of the battue, were constantly violated by Mongolian incursions, but the rulers of these countries, mindful of Subotai's campaign early in the century, ducked and hoped that this would prevent worse to come.

One of Mohammed's sons, a youth who had given no remarkable account of himself the day of Khwarezm's splendor, turned up in the rugged regions of the Afghan border, where he established a mountain stronghold and assembled hardy men to descend upon Mongol flying-destruction squads. The Mongols suffered losses and an incensed Djenghis Khan ordered one army corps to smoke out the presumptuous band. The stronghold was located high above a valley, beyond range of arrows and Chinese throwing machines; a path not large enough to let two men pass abreast led up to the fortress. The Mongols attacked single file, and were repulsed. Temudshin rallied more than two thirds of his effectives to deal with the foes, who, short of supplies, evacuated their shelter, and fled in the direction of India, with the horsemen in pursuit. Only scattered remnants got safely across the Indus River, among them their leader, whom the autonomous Sultan of Delhi granted asylum at his court.

Mongolian patrols forded the Indus and penetrated into the lowlands. The horsemen wore fur caps, heavy coats, and thick boots and the heat was suffocating. Not even hard training, unquestioning discipline, and savage determination could overcome the summer of India. Temudshin never got a glimpse at this part of his universal realm, and the Prince of Khwarezm was temporarily safe.

CHAPTER FOURTEEN The closing months of 1222 saw Temudshin in a pensive mood. He had conquered neither Song China nor India, and the maps that Yeliu had taught him to study with a keen mind revealed many more unconquered lands far beyond his grasp. And Temudshin was feeling quite old. Nearly all the companions of his youth were dead. A new generation worshiped him as an idol, on a throne instead of a totem pole. They abided by his law, but could not understand his sentiments. The Djenghis Khan lived in an immense tent of felt and silk, adorned with the finest treasures of various civilizations. His generals' tents, set up around his own, were not quite as large, but almost equally pompous, and even the soldiers' quarters were more comfortable than his family dwellings had been in the lean days of his youth. His army was not only the most powerful, but also the wealthiest of the world; it owned enormous territories, immense herds of beasts and slaves, and many other riches. The soldiers were satiated; only discipline kept them from becoming debauched. But their Djenghis Khan was dissatisfied, even worried. So much remained undone. A little more than two years before, when he used to consult Yeliu almost daily, he had confided to him his craving for eternal life. The Chinese had told him that more than 1600 years before, another aspirant for universal rule, Darius, King of Persia, had wanted to live forever, or at least until the entire world would be at his feet. But Darius had died like any other mortal, his design unfulfilled. Only wisdom was eternal, Yeliu told the Djenghis Khan.

Temudshin was not a wise man, but he had unlimited imagination—a Siberian imagination, reared in the immensity of that land and the worship of the limitless sky above it. He would have wanted to be wise in the true, exalted meaning of the word. Skills were not wisdom. These Chinese, Iranian, and Indian craftsmen who produced machines, silk, sweets, and knickknacks such as playing cards, to which the average Mongols took a fancy, or even books, which the Chinese had been printing for some 250 years already—they were smart, but you could commandeer their produce. You could not commandeer balanced wisdom. Religious wisdom might even bring fulfillment of his cravings. Yeliu said that the Taoists were paragons of erudition. Temudshin requested the most learned Taoists to be brought to his camp. This had been at the time that Samarkand went down in ruins. And still Yeliu had not brought the Taoists before him.

Did Yeliu think that the Djenghis Khan's temporary neglect exempted him from discharging his obligations? Nobody ever ceased to be Temudshin's servant.

He needed servants. Kin China and Khwarezm were part of the universal empire, but reports indicated that Kin China was in its death throes and no longer useful, and that Khwarezm, with its cities raped, its population reduced to barely one fifth of its original number, was an empty shell. Even useful slaves ceased to be helpful as their tools and working places were destroyed. Chaos ruled in countries that should serve as springboards for continued drives. Terror, annihilation for annihilation's sake were not a panacea; maybe Yeliu's ideas about administration were sound. The Mongolian generals would not see the point unless Temudshin issued such orders, but he could not issue comprehensive orders without Yeliu.

Yeliu-tch'ou-t'sai stayed in a small, barren tent slightly apart from the ranking officers' quarters, waiting for Temudshin's call, which, at last, came around New Year's, 1223.

The secret counselor, guessing his master's innermost thoughts, explained that continued persecution of conquered nations was wasteful. The people should be ruled to the advantage of the conqueror; they should be taxed and conscripted, made to produce and transport goods. Temudshin acted promptly. He assigned district civilian commissars (*darougatchi*) to administer conquered territory; and because Mongols were not qualified for the jobs, he chose his experts from among Chinese, Persians, and highly educated Uigurs.

Conquered people were allowed to settle. Services were established. But Temudshin would not permit construction of big cities, and farm areas were curtailed to allot more space to grasslands.

When the first darougatchi were being selected, Yeliu's Taoists arrived at Temudshin's headquarters, then on Afghan territory, south of the Hindu Kush. The Djenghis Khan received the men, seated on a throne of massive gold, surrounded by his bodyguards. He asked at once that they produce the means to live forever. The Taoists did not deny the existence of such means, but they used cryptic words to circumscribe their mystic nature—terms that not even the most interpretative minds could have understood. And when the impatient Djenghis Khan requested that they concoct a drug for him, they claimed wearily that this would take a very long time and would require the collaboration of many other Taoists. They asked to be allowed to return to Kin China, and for special protection of Taoist convents there.

Temudshin granted the requests, and never got a drug. Actually he hardly expected the men to produce it, for after they had gone he turned his interest in religious wisdom to Mohammedanism, whose fundamentals were explained to him by a mullah, in the ruins of the great mosque of Bokhara. The Djenghis Khan approved of many Mohammedan principles, but he objected to the compulsory pilgrimage to Mecca; he called it superfluous, because all places on earth were alike; they were all under the common roof of the Eternal Blue Sky.

Temudshin's headquarters moved frequently, not always according to the changing military situation, but in order to maintain the essentials of nomadism, the traditional Mongolian way of life and source of Mongol strength. The Djenghis Khan's renewed appreciation of Yeliu was not diminished by the Taoists' unsatisfactory performance. He consulted his secret counselor about amendments to the Yassak, to cover all the phases of conquest, administration, organization that would be incumbent upon his successors.

In the summer of 1223 tents were set up in the steppe not far from Lake Balkhash. Temudshin held a Kuriltai with his sons. Eighty thousand Mongolian cavalrymen camped nearby. The Kuriltai was a formality. With disobedience a capital crime there could be no dissent to Temudshin's dictum, and the members of the ruling family spent most of their time hunting.

The Mongolian war machine, however, was a *perpetuum mobile* that knew no neutral gear. While eight tümen added martial splendor to the Djenghis Khan's hunting, three tümen under Subotai and Djébé were dispatched to secure the Mongol right flank. Securing the flank sounded the knell to Afghanistan, Georgia, and Bagdad, and to small nations, remnants of former conquering and trading tribes who had found deceptive tranquility along the historic highway of migration and exchange of goods. Subotai and Djébé knew that the Abbasside Khalif of Bagdad, after much soul searching and consultation with his experts, had decided to save himself, his people, and his country by passive obedience to the conqueror's law. They had also learned that the Georgians, weary of their previous passive policy, planned to make a major defensive effort. The Georgian cavalrymen's mounts were believed to be faster than the Mongol ponies, and they intended to give battle in the plains where speed would decide the issue. Subotai led the Georgians into a trap where they had no operational space, and destroyed the defenders of the Christian country to the last men. Afghanistan, already ravaged by previous incursions, was turned waste with a thoroughness the traces of which remain to the present day. The two generals had no orders to mend their conquering ways, and they were not concerned with what happened to devastated territory afterwards.

The southern flank was now secure, and Siberian tribes who roamed up north could never constitute a threat. The Mongols left small occupation forces in conquered lands and in the territory of Bagdad. The bulk of the horsemen crossed the passes of the Caucasus Mountains, into the steppes between the Caspian and the Sea of Azov. Christian Alans, descendants of Sarmats, Tsherkess tribes, and Lesghiens, fled at their approach. So had their distant ancestors of whom they had no records, but whose distress had left its marks on their minds, sought safety from ancient Siberian invaders. But not even the Huns had been as skilled in tracking down peoples as the Mongolians were. The ax fell upon the victims. Kuman remnants greeted the army from the East as friends and brethren. The Mongols' baggage carts were still overloaded with booty even though some of the heavy siege machines had been left behind. Djébé revealed his peculiar sense of humor by freely distributing gifts to the Kiptchaks, and having them massacred as they danced around the pile of goods.

Subotai dashed into the Crimean Peninsula, razed trade posts, unaware of the psychological effects of the attack on Sudak, and then the army continued westward to the Dniester River.

Hard-riding estafettes communicated with the Djenghis Khan's headquarters, informing Temudshin about the fantastic progress of the small army. It was sheer boldness to push on into space, but Byzantium, as Mongolian intelligence undoubtedly knew, was no longer the road block it once had been, and information about Central Europe did not convey the impression that a Mongolian army of only twenty thousand was seriously threatened from these quarters. The Djenghis Khan had not yet made up his mind, however, whether to consider Subotai's and Djébé's advance a grandiose reconnaissance, or the great campaign, which would join with his main forces.

Mongols rode through grassy flatlands. The men fed their horses, greased bows, mended their uniforms with regulation sewing equipment, and occasionally disposed of fugitives. But despite their intelligence services neither Subotai nor Djébé, nor Mongolian general headquarters, was aware of the recent rise of Russian power and unity. On the banks of the Dniester a reconnoitering Mongolian *minggan* ran into an army of 80,000 and was decimated by the joint forces of the Princes of Kiev, Tchernigov, Smolensk, and Halicz. The princes celebrated this outcome as a decisive victory. Their boisterousness grew as a Mongol truce officer presented himself at their headquarters to negotiate an armistice. The Mongol explained that his countrymen had no hostile intentions toward the Russians and would withdraw after settling an old score with the Kumans.

Prince Mistislav of Halicz, who was married to a beautiful Kuman princess, had the Mongolian truce officer put to death for insulting his wife's people.

Thereupon the Mongolian generals issued a declaration of war. But instead of attacking, they pulled back—for safety, as the Russians believed, but actually to get their booty beyond the enemy's reach. The Russian military organization was clumsy; their army could not maintain order as it advanced, while the Mongols leisurely regrouped and concentrated as they retreated. Near Mariupol on the Sea of Azov, the Mongols turned. Less than one third of the Russian forces under the Prince of Halicz were in line. They were routed by hails of arrows from three sides, and, fleeing, they engulfed the second array, from Smolensk. Mongolian sharpshooters circled the straggling masses, using their bows with devastating effect. The Prince of Kiev gathered his own and Tchernigov's rear-guard troops and remnants from the rest of the army in a hastily fortified camp, but after a brief stand he surrendered on condition that his own life and that of his soldiers be spared. Subotai accepted the surrender, and ordered the execution of prince and army.

The Mongolian army did not exploit this triumph, however. The

Djenghis Khan ordered his victorious generals back to headquarters, on the Orkhon River 4000 miles to the east. On their way Djébé and Subotai defeated Bulgar troops near the present site of Stalingrad, and, being in too great a hurry to follow up their victory the usual way, they accepted a pledge of fealty and tribute by Bulgar merchants who were engaged in prosperous hide, wax, and honey business.

Subotai was careful not to abandon the territory he left behind. He had few men to spare—about one soldier for every two miles of the long track. Yet he stationed units of ten in regular intervals, trusting that local people would not dare challenge the Mongols. In fact the Mongols retained strategic control of the long road.

On the Orkhon River the victorious generals found the Djenghis Khan strangely changed. Temudshin, usually averse to wordy reports, requested that they tell him every detail of their campaign; and when even Subotai, the more articulate of the two, failed to satisfy his curiosity, he ordered him to repeat his story over and over again. He would gloat over the number of people killed in massacres, and zealously recapitulate the disastrous figures. Previously, when military issues were under discussion, the ruler had shunned female company. Now Temudshin always kept girl entertainers in his tent, at least twenty, picked for slenderness, grace, and twittering voices. Subotai and Djébé were not squeamish (the law against adultery actually applied only to women); but it was bewildering to see the aging Djenghis Khan dallying between campaign reports with exotic beauties. Bewilderment turned into irritation when they realized that Yeliu, the civilian, the philosopher, the scholar, was Temudshin's chief mentor in military and geographical affairs. The secret counselor had a map of all lands invested by Mongolian cavalry, painted in colors: red for the south, black for the north, blue for the east, oyster white for the west; purple, the center, and the Mongol's symbol, a white falcon, displayed in every corner. Temudshin enjoyed explanations on hand of the colored maps, even though they were, in the general's opinion, lacking in strategic soundness.

Only their awe for his exalted authority kept the generals from considering the Djenghis Khan a befuddled oldster. Yeliu, however, who catered to his master's fancies, knew that Temudshin had not really changed; only that he was now resigned to mortality and wanted to have fun before the hour would strike. His insistence that Subotai tell him the same story over and over again had a purpose: Temudshin wanted to remember every detail for his posthumous report to Tängri.

He had also recapitulated the army's report on China; eighteen million Chinese were dead; put to the sword, starved, killed by disease and exposure. The Djenghis Khan had asked Yeliu to show him the exact limits of Mongolian control of China: he did not want either exaggeration or palliation, Tängri would accept nothing but the truth.

The old Djenghis Khan would not tolerate infractions of his Yassak, the law that was stronger than any one man. His son Djoetchi was on an inspection tour in Central Siberia when Subotai and Djébé arrived at the Djenghis Khan's headquarters. When Temudshin ordered him to return to listen to the generals' report, the prince excused himself because of illness, but a member of Temudshin's household just returned from Djoetchi's camp insisted that the prince was in fine health. He even insinuated slyly that the heir to the throne was jealous of Subotai, whose conquering record paled his own. The Djenghis Khan flew into a wild rage; in vain did Yeliu use all his persuasiveness to keep the ruler from extreme retaliation before he had found out the truth. Temudshin ordered executioners to his disobedient son's camp, and to inflict the extreme penalty upon Djoetchi. But when the party arrived the prince had died—succumbed to a virulent disease.

The Djenghis Khan retired to his tent and stayed there all alone, for forty-eight hours. Terror-stricken guards heard shouts and roars inside. The master of the earth argued with the spirits of heaven, apologized to the soul of his wronged son, and swore vengeance upon all trespassers of the Yassak.

Butchering the calumnious member of Temudshin's household would not satisfy the guiltless soul and, less even, the raging father. Only mass sacrifices could assuage the dead and the living. An entire tribe would have to perish.

The Si-Hias, who survived on the Yellow River, had once been charged with failure to produce their quota of auxiliaries. At the time Temudshin had ignored the matter, probably because the facts had not been fully established; but after the death of his son in the fall of 1226 he ordered the offenders annihilated.

At the head of ten tümen the Djenghis Khan raced to the Yellow River. His retinue included all the members of his family, including Yesoui, his wife Number One, and all his princes and generals. But Temudshin would not allow any other military man, not even Subotai, to assist him in the conduct of operations; and he would not permit Yeliu, who counseled moderation, to interfere. This campaign should show the ranking officers that they were no peers in soldierly genius to their supreme commander.

Temudshin wanted to fight. He assigned informers to warn the King of Si-Hia and to urge him to mobilize all his able-bodied men. Three hundred thousand Si-Hia assembled on the banks of the Yellow River to meet a Mongolian army one third that number. Temudshin's family gathered on a hill overlooking the frozen river, the frozen lakes and ponds, over which charged the Si-Hia cavalry. Mongolian horsemen kept off the ice; from adjoining banks and shores they discharged their bows on the enemy, whose mounts slipped and fell in the commotion. Si-Hia infantry was stopped by heaps of dead horses and riders; it was ambushed by Mongolian sharpshooters, decimated, and turned into a frantic mob into which Mongols penetrated with devastating effect. No Si-Hia survived the carnage. The victor surveyed the counting of the dead. The number of his victims from Manchuria to Russia now exceeded thirty millions.

From neighboring Chinese territory a messenger brought a huge golden bowl filled to the rim with exquisite pearls, gifts of a citizenry imploring Temudshin's mercy. The Djenghis Khan did not deign to touch the treasure, but had the pearls thrown out in the snow so that everybody who cared for the jewels could pick them up.

The Si-Hia capital resisted the Mongolian siege for many months. But when it was laid, Temudshin had already turned over command to his generals, and had gone to the vicinity of the Great Wall for meditation. It was there that he is said to have told Yeliu about his indifference to men's judgment of his actions. Before leaving he ordered that no creature be left alive in the doomed capital, but that the remainder of the Si-Hias outside the city be turned over to Yesoui as her personal slaves.

On August 18, 1227, a dispatch rider arrived at the camp with the report that the capital and its people had been destroyed. A lance stuck in the ground, point down, in front of Temudshin's tent, indicated that the occupant was sick. The approaches to the residence were guarded by a tight array of soldiers; not even the Djenghis Khan's family, or Yeliu, were entering the tent, and the guardsmen whispered that the ruler of the universe was dying.

In fact Temudshin was dead. His sons feared that the announcement of their father's passing might loosen ties of allegiance and destroy the realm before they could seize the reins. But Yeliu, who had a better judgment of the coherence of the empire than the princes, insisted that the army would remain loyal to the Yassak even after its promulgator's demise. Only should the princes forsake the law would the realm disintegrate. Late in August, 139,000 Mongolian soldiers assembled on the approaches of the Great Wall were informed that their Djenghis Khan was dead and that his sons had inherited the army and the realm—all the lands under the Eternal Blue Sky, conquered or yet to be conquered.

The army took the announcement as a call to obedience and conquest. The empire was secure—the first Siberian state to survive its founder, unshaken.

Temudshin's body was carried to the region of Mt. Kaldoun and put into a small wooden replica of his tent; the elaborate funeral would take place after the question of succession had been settled. No non-Mongol should know the location of the casket and the burial grounds. Unfortunate Chinese who saw the procession on its march were put to death.

Temudshin's will provided that each of his legitimate sons be provided for with a number of Mongolian tribes and adequate grassland to support them, and an annual revenue from the treasury of the empire. Conquered lands should remain indivisible parts of the universal realm; but their governorships were assigned to princes of the blood, called henceforth the Djenghiskhanides. One Djenghiskhanide would be Great Khan, Emperor of the Universe, with all of Temudshin's prerogatives but one: the right to amend the Yassak. Great khans could issue decrees and regulations, but they were subject to changes and repeal. The Yassak was unalterable.

Djoetchi's fief passed upon his son Batu. It included governorship of all steppes between the Irtysh and the Volga rivers. Djoetchi, it was rumored, was not Temudshin's legitimate son, and court gossip called Batu a bastard's bastard. But so strong was the respect for the Djenghis Khan's will that nobody challenged Batu's title to the bequest. Batu himself—mild and wise according to his court chroniclers, an ogre according to the tradition of Russia, where he spent most of his later life—was clever enough to keep apart from his uncles, to play deaf to gossip, and to build up a position of individual power.

Djagatai, Temudshin's second son, was awarded the governorship of Kara Ki-tai and Uigur and guardianship of the Yassak. He was a disciplinarian, a fanatic to whom the letter of the law meant more than his own life.

Ogödai, the third, received only small territories east and northeast of Lake Balkhash. He was the most intelligent of the brothers, but Temudshin had always disapproved of his laziness and his inclination to debauchery.

Toului, the youngest, was appointed to govern the land on the Onon River, and, as keeper of this, the original patrimony, he became titular head of the family, pending the nomination of a Great Khan by a Kuriltai. He was given Temudshin's tent, which carried colossal prestige, and, most important, he received personal control of 101,000 elite soldiers, while command of the remaining 28,000 was shared by all other brothers.

Yesoui received all income from Khwarezm and the title to a governorship if she chose to administer the territory.

Temudshin, the polygamist who should have had a great number of illegitimate offspring, did not provide for them in the manner he did for Batu, Djagatai, Ogödai, and Toului, but he left numerous bequests for princes, soldiers, and less prominent individuals who led a luxurious life as state pensionaries.

No known provisions were made for Yeliu, who continued to draw a salary inferior to that of a *minggan* commander. But Yeliu was the most important person of the realm. Only Yeliu could deal with administrative problems; only Yeliu knew all the intentions of the late Djenghis Khan; only Yeliu was able to organize the governors' provinces.

The crucial Kuriltai was expected to take place no later than 1228, but Yeliu, in a patient game of intrigues, managed to delay the convocation of the prince's Diet until 1229, when he was certain that their choice would fall on Ogödai, and not on Djagatai, whom the Mongolian generals would have preferred to succeed his father.

After Ogödai's installment as ruler of the universe the funeral rites for his father were held at the site of his provisional burial place. They lasted three days. The Djenghis Khan's remains were placed on a throne. Immense offerings of choice food and drink were made. A hecatomb of splendid white horses was made, and, finally, forty beautiful girls of noble birth, adorned with the most gorgeous finery, were dispatched to serve Temudshin in the other world.

Temudshin's tomb was never found, but the saying goes that its location remains known among Mongolian herdsmen to the present day.

CHAPTER FIFTEEN "You can conquer an empire on horseback," Yeliu had once told Temudshin, "but you cannot govern it from the saddle."

The Djenghis Khan had never explicitly acknowledged the validity of this thesis, which would have disqualified nomads as rulers of conquered empires, but he let Yeliu, who had taken an instinctive dislike to horseback riding, draft basic rules of government. Now that the empire builder was dead, Yeliu wanted to establish a dualism of administration, a permanent division into a military and a civilian branch of government. This was, in fact, a revolutionary pattern, restricting the soldier's traditional omnipotence. Of all the legitimate heirs only Ogödai had been prepared to accept Yeliu's plan. The new Great Khan was fundamentally lazy, anxious to delegate his duties, and clever enough to have them split among rival agencies. He wanted Yeliu to head the civilian branch of the administration, but the secret counselor, careful not to violate the law of obedience, suggested that the office be entrusted to a non-Chinese. As long as peace with China was not secure, other dignitaries might distrust a Chinese-born administrator.

Upon Yeliu's recommendation Ogödai appointed Tshinkai, a Kerait of Nestorian faith, as civilian administrator and prothonotary of the realm. No decree could be promulgated unless it carried Tshinkai's signature. The shamans were outraged at the prothonotary's creed. They took it for a deliberate insult, which it was. Yeliu wanted to eliminate the wizards' influence upon empire policies, and Ogödai distrusted the shamans sufficiently to make the controversial appointment.

Yeliu continued to dwell in his simple tent way apart from the generals' dwellings. After Tshinkai's nomination he relinquished his title of secret counselor because he felt that no assignment with the present ruler could carry the prestige of his past association. He was now called upon to interpret the Djenghis Khan's most intimate thoughts and to quote his confidential remarks. Yeliu was not responsible for fallacies committed by the Djenghis Khan's successor; he was the voice of the infallible Temudshin.

Tshinkai would not sign a decree unless Yeliu approved of it—in the name of his defunct master; and between hangovers Ogödai was anxious to consult with the wise Chinese. Ogödai's inclination to debauchery was even greater than Temudshin had suspected, and it would occasionally worry Yeliu, who did not want the Great Khan to lose face. The tent in which Temudshin had spent his years of greatness became the scene of uninhibited and violent drinking bouts. From hundreds of golden goblets kumiss spilled over the great hall, in which the founder of the Golden Family had sat on his golden throne. Guards officers, courtesans, and entertainers were lying on the floor, the men belching, snoring, or semi-consciously groping for women's flesh, the girls obscenely stirring the drunkards' lasciviousness. On the throne reeled the Great Khan, dropping goblets, gulping, and fumbling for female limbs. Such orgies lasted several days and were invariably followed by glum hangovers. Tshinkai did not join his master's parties, and Subotai, in charge of the empire's military affairs, attended only when he could not avoid it. The general, an aging man himself, took a dim view of conquering prospects unless the Great Khan devoted more time to his soldiers.

Subotai wanted war. Yeliu wanted peace. Both men wanted to divert the carousing Great Khan's attention to their objectives.

Yeliu had a Mongolian budget introduced. Taxes were payable in silk, silver, grain, or livestock—10 per cent of all horses, oxen, and sheep, 10 per cent of personal incomes. Most of the revenue should come from Kin China. Estimates figured that a Kin population of 10,000,000 could produce an annual income of 500,000 ounces of silver, 80,000 pieces of silk, and 400,000 sacks of grain for the treasury. But the primary condition was that the people be left in peace. Much of the revenue should be used to build a system of transportation and communication spanning all parts of the huge empire: relay stations, well supplied with fine horses, reliable personnel selected among ex-cavalrymen, and solid conveyances to carry travelers and goods at great speed over vast distances.

Subotai clamored for the lion's share in the state expenses; the army needed more stores, better weapons, and an independent transportation system. Without a strong army, he claimed, there soon would be no areas left to be administered, and only fear of armed reprisals could make vassals pay their dues.

Ogödai approved of taxation as well as of a large military budget. Newly trained Mongolian administrators received assignments vacated by the retirement of previous appointees. But the Mongols had been educated in Chinese schools, and they were almost completely Sinofied. Sinofied meant not only cultivated, it also meant corrupted. Yeliu championed a decree making corruption in office a criminal offense. But Ogödai, a spendthrift himself, saw no reason why officeholders should not enrich themselves.

The conquered nations watched the change in government with elation. They did not believe that Temudshin's empire would last much longer than its founder and they prepared for liberation by reconstruction and active resistance.

The Kin made a remarkable comeback. Subotai's intelligence reports indicated that the Kin recovery was by no means limited to economic matters.

Kin generals were secretly building up a new army, trained to deal with Mongolian strategy and tactics, and equipped with weapons which Kin engineers brazenly withheld from their Mongolian overlords. And from the distant West came news that Khwarezm had all but restored its independence.

The general asked for a two-front war: now it would be a walkover, but it might require a major effort later. The empire was based upon dynamic nomadism; it had to strike and to expand, lest it be struck, and shrink. Ogödai still displayed nomadism by moving his residence from time to time, but already he planned to settle, and make the camp of Karakorum the capital of the empire, a capital of tents and wagons, but surrounded by a wall of bricks. He would not abandon dynamism, however. Dynamism meant war, and even if war were disguised as pacification of unruly occupied territory, it would give the military complete supremacy over the civilians and upset the precarious balance of power. It was in the Great Khan's interest that the government agencies continue their rivalry. Ogödai may have thought so himself, for he tried a compromise solution, proclaiming the formal incorporation of all parts of the former Kin realm into the Mongolian patrimony. But when Subotai insisted that the proclamation be followed up by another invasion, Ogödai issued marching orders and sought solace in a colossal orgy.

What had been expected to be a walkover turned into a difficult campaign. Kin generals of Chinese stock opposed Subotai with large, well-equipped armies and excellent strategy. It took the Mongols three years, from 1231 to 1234, to reduce the country. Subotai deliberately violated Song Chinese territory, yet the Song government not only took the incursions without a protest, but even organized auxiliary groups to assist the Mongols.

Victory was celebrated in Karakorum, proclaimed capital in 1235. The Mongolian war machine was in motion. Yeliu could not have stopped it, nor could he have prevented a Kuriltai from adopting a plan to conquer Song China.

Not even Yeliu could claim that the Djenghis Khan had been pacifist-minded; and war in the Mongolian manner was a source of revenue no less abundant, though not as lasting, as taxation of peaceful populations.

Subotai drafted the strategy of the great campaign in China, but he did not assume command, nor had he taken charge of the previous expedition to chastise Khwarezm.

Preliminary operations against China took place on the eastern fringe of the realm. Minor Mongolian forces swept the Korean peninsula to anchor the main army's left wing safely by the sea. Early in 1236 three corps broke into the Song realm; in the wake of fast-moving armies came administrators to take over provinces as they were captured. The territory was expected to be under complete Mongolian control by the fall of 1238. The Mongolian armies defeated numerically superior Chinese in every single engagement, and they occupied many provinces, but the Chinese generals startled their opposite number by a new procedure: Whenever the bulk of the Mongolian forces moved on from captured provinces, the Chinese surged back, and forced their foes to return and fight another battle for an objective they had already thought secure. Subotai's pattern was upset; the Mongolian administration of Song China had not established itself when Ogödai died, five years after the opening of the lightning drive. In fact the struggle continued on and off until 1279.

In Khwarezm, however, the Mongols had no trouble wiping out the vestige of a national government. Exiled Djelal ed Din Manguberti returned from Delhi and proclaimed himself King. The common people were apathetic. Nobles and remnants of the ruling officers' clan, however, and even Mongolian appointees for public offices, clamored for special favors, sinecures, and a share in the spoils of liberation. Oblivious of the threat from the crusaders in the west, and from the Siberians in the northeast, they struggled among themselves and neglected the country's defenses.

The Mongols returned to Khwarezm in the year they reinvaded Kin China. Subotai chose General Tshormakan to lead the expedition. Tshormakan gave no thought to conservation of men and resources, and his men—20,000 veterans—enjoyed the massacre. King Djelal was among the first victims. He made no attempt at resistance; but a peasant who recognized him stabbed the fleeing ruler and handed the dying man over to a Mongolian patrol.

Psychological warfare was used to the limit. Criers and runners were hired to tell fear-crazed people of the futility of resistance and the inevitability of death. The victims, most of whom had agonizing memories of past horrors, were paralyzed. The Mongolian rank and file relished their prey's mortal fear. Mongolian units usually were a silent lot, but as they now rode through the lands, they chatted merrily, laughed, frolicked, and practiced shouts of derision. *"Allah-il-Allah."* Mohammedans intoned their confession of faith. *"Allalahi,"* the horsemen shrilled when they closed in on targets of their man hunt. *"Allalahi,"* they bellowed, surrounding the trembling creatures. *"Allalahis"* showered the doomed as the hunters drew their knives, and to the sounds of *"Allalahi"* soldiers cut throats with quick, well-trained motions.

Ibn-al-Athir, one of the chroniclers of the punitive expedition, tells the following stories: "A man from the Nissibin district said that he had been hiding behind a cracked wall and had watched events outside. Whenever the Mongols were set to kill, they shouted mocking Allalahis. After finishing the massacre, they looted the market town, and dragged a few surviving women away. So great was the terror that God had planted in everybody's heart that a lone horseman killed the inhabitants of a populous village, one after another, without meeting resistance.

"At another place, a Mongol wanted to kill a prisoner, but, carrying no knife and unwilling to use a different weapon, he told the man to lie down and wait while he would go and fetch a knife. The man waited, motionless, until his captor returned with the deadly tool."

And this was told by a fugitive: "I had joined a crowd of homeless—there were seventeen of us. A Mongolian horseman ordered us to line up to have our hands tied behind our backs. 'Can't you see that he is all alone,' I told the others, 'let's kill him and run.' 'We are too frightened,' one said. 'Maybe Allah will save us,' said another, and 'You cannot kill a Mongolian,' said a third. They lined up, hands crossed on their backs. But I managed to seize the Mongol's dagger, stabbed him, and ran away."

It was a story of death and destruction, the rape of bodies and minds, in which the average Mongolian slayer did not distinguish among races, nationalities, and creeds, of which there were many in that part of Asia.

Ogödai showed a distinct preference for Christians, which might have been the result of Tshinkai's influences. He assigned Simeon, a Christian from Syria who had somehow come to Karakorum, as an adviser in Christian affairs to General Tshormakan. Simeon did his best to keep the Mongolian commander from dealing with the Armenians as he had dealt with their neighbors of Khwarezm; and even though he could not entirely prevent massacres of Christians in Armenia, the scope of atrocities was reduced.

Grudgingly the general accepted the Armenians' and Cilicians' formal acknowledgment of Mongolian suzerainty. But no adviser restrained him in his extended action against the Mohammedan Seljuks. The Seljuks had not rebelled, for they had not yet been under Mongolian rule, but they had failed to offer surrender, which was no better than rebellion. The proud Seljuks, who had successfully fought crusading knights from all European great powers, were incapable of resisting the Mongolian onslaught. Their armies were scattered, their peoples trampled underfoot. Asia Minor was open to Siberian invasion, and by 1243 the Mongolian Empire had spread to the Eastern Mediterranean. Mongolian conquest laid the roots of Mohammedan hatred against the Armenians, which exploded time and again, as late as during World War I and the period immediately afterward.

The Mohammedans contended that the Armenians had incited the Mongols against the Seljuks and all Mohammedan peoples of Asia Minor.

While the shouts of "Allalahi" sounded the knell to hecatombs in Western Asia, events of even greater portentousness took shape farther to the north.

Prince Batu, the bastard's bastard, had established his residence in the big steppes that extended from Southwestern Siberia into European Russia. He governed his fief in the name of the Djenghiskhanides, and sent messages in most obedient terms to his uncle, the Great Khan. Nowhere, not even in China, he explained, were aspects of expansion more auspicious than in the part of the world he administered; nowhere were strategic conditions as favorable. He had but a small cadre of Mongolian elite troops, but had had recruited a great number of auxiliaries from among roaming tribes; they were readily adaptable to Mongolian tactics, and capable of bearing great hardship and privation. Some 150,000 men were under arms and, equipped with modern, Chinese-made heavy material, they could add immense territories to the empire.

Yeliu could but welcome any suggestion that diverted some of the Mongols' conquering energy to areas far away from China, but a man of his wisdom had to realize that Batu had personal ambitions of his own. The aging Chinese was opposed to separatism. He, too, had visions of a universal empire, of a civilized, Sinofied world, in which all vestiges of barbarism would wither away. By virtue of his rank and office Batu would be in command of armies engaged in a drive toward the yet unconquered West, and the prince who had trained fourteen tümen of auxiliaries might increase his forces to an extent that made him independent, politically and militarily.

Subotai was in favor of any campaign that did not draw on Mongolian reserves; yet he had no desire to see Batu conduct independent operations. Political considerations were alien to the old general, who felt that such matters had been settled, once and for all, by the Djenghis Khan's law, but he wanted to have his share in victory.

For once Yeliu and Subotai agreed. The Western campaign should be undertaken, and Subotai should be Batu's chief of staff, in charge of operations in the field.

Ogödai approved of the suggestion. But he, too, wanted to tie Batu's hands. There were so many court intrigues against his nephew, so many insinuations of his untrustworthiness, that the Great Khan ordered two of his sons to go to Batu's headquarters to watch their cousin.

Subotai's generalship, matured by experience, was supplemented by a thorough knowledge of geographical conditions in Eastern and Central Europe. The army intelligence service co-operated with foreign informers and with agents who secured data on European armies, equipment, strategy, and tactics as well as intricate entanglements of European politics, the West's shaky system of alliances and smoldering national antagonisms. Subotai formed a diplomatic staff to assist and advise him in a new psychological campaign.

The head of the diplomatic staff became an Englishman, who long ago had left his native islands as a fugitive from justice, had led a quixotic life among Eastern European peoples, and eventually joined Subotai and Djébé during their first drive into Russia, as an informer. Ahead of the Mongolian army now went envoys asking kings and princes to surrender on honorable terms, such as the opening of all fortified places, and the delivery of 10 per cent of all property as taxes, and of 10 per cent of the population as slaves. In case of refusal, so they were told, nobody could predict what would happen.

But before the first Mongolian envoys called on Russian princes, strange ambassadors visited the mightiest rulers of Western Europe. They were Saracens, the fiendish infidels, the archenemies of Christianity who had battled the crusaders. The Saracens offered peace and permanent friendship to Frederick II of Germany, to Louis IX of France, to Henry III of England, explaining that the worst enemy of mankind was about to descend upon the civilized world. United, they could repulse the attack; divided, they were bound to succumb. The aggressors were savages, mounted barbarians, as fast as lightning;

but a huge phalanx of heavily armored knights should be able to resist their arrows. The Saracens would join the knights' armies with light cavalry.

An alliance with the Saracens was distasteful to the pious monarchs, who, however, had no scruples to deal with the Sultan of Egypt and the Bey of Tunisia, or, as in the case of Emperor Frederick, to hire Moslem mercenaries to bring pressure to bear upon the Pope. The German ruler in particular was contemptuous of ignorant barbarians, whoever they might be. The Christian rulers knew nothing about the Mongols from sources other than the Saracen ambassadors.

They did not believe that the savages of whom the Saracens told could be identical with the mysterious raiders the savants had said were Asiatic horsemen rather than King David's host. These raiders had vanished more than a decade before, and would certainly never reappear.

The Saracens, insistent and desperate, were still pleading with the monarchs when in 1239 Subotai led Batu's army across the Volga, decimating the Bulgars, who had meticulously kept their obligations under the tribute agreement.

Again the blooming steppes of Southern Russia turned into highways of misery, over which floated a stream of fugitives, some of whom had heard before the gruesome sound of galloping invaders' horses. The fugitives poured into the Wallachian and Moldavian plains and crossed the rugged Transylvanian mountains to seek refuge in the Hungarian heart lands of King Béla IV. The King granted asylum, but he was in no hurry to mobilize his army. No Saracen ambassadors had come to his court, but he knew of their strange proposal, which he considered either oriental trickery or an outgrowth of unworthy panic. Béla and his nobles agreed that if an invader really existed he might loot some of the weaker Russian principalities, but he never would dare to challenge the great, consolidated realms of the continent.

Next, events seemed to bear out Béla's fallacious assumptions. Mongolian diplomatic teams went to the courts of Russian princes and princelings, pressing surrender demands, asserting that their claims were legal according to the will of the Eternal Blue Sky. The Mongols, trained by the English chief diplomat, were haughty and threatening. The Russian nobles were cocky and rude, and several envoys were put to death. But there was no unity among the Russians; nobody wanted to use his army outside of his realm. And this time the Slav rulers wanted to outwit the Mongols. They would not give battle in the open field, where the horsemen could use their superior speed; they would concentrate on the defense of impregnable towns. It did not matter if peasants perished; there would soon be plenty of them again—the yokels were fertile. The princes ordered that livestock and rural food supplies be destroyed on the approach of the invader. The Mongols should ride for a beating under city walls, and afterward starve to death.

The Russians did not know the Mongolian supply system, the iron rations of dried milk that could support the soldiers until train columns caught up with fast-moving troops of the line, and they ignored Mongolian armored battering rams, explosives, and cannon.

In December 1238 the city of Ryazan succumbed to Mongolian attack. One fortified place after another crumbled under the impact of the Chinese-made siege machines. The destruction of Muscovy in February 1239 was only a minor event; Muscovy then was but a small settlement and its ruler a man of little consequence. In the town of Vladimir the populace crowded the churches when the Mongols entered through a breach in the wall. The invaders set the wooden building aflame, and watched, laughing, as the Russians burned alive. Batu's auxiliaries, many of them Slavs, were no less ruthless and cruel than Mongolian elite troops.

The rigidity of the Russian winter did not affect the conquering armies. A field force hastily gathered by the Princes of Tver and Yaroslavl was destroyed in a belated effort to co-operate and change strategy.

Then, a hundred miles south of Novgorod, the Mongolian drive halted abruptly. Novgorod was a rich prize, and so were the Baltic regions, but Subotai knew that in Russia thaws constituted a greater obstacle than frost, walls, and men. Thaws turned the land into a quagmire in which his speed of maneuver would be reduced to a crawl, and his heavy machines would stick fast.

During the summer of 1239 Mongolian horses grazed in Russian land, and preparations were made to resume the campaign as soon as the first frosts hardened the ground.

The initial Mongolian fury turned in the direction of the fertile regions that are now the Ukraine. Again one fortified city after another fell to the high-precision war machine. Kiev was taken on December 6 and only two hundred houses were left standing; next, the Prince of Halicz abandoned his realm and fled to Hungary. Nothing could stop the march of the Mongols, whose strength seemed monolithic.

The army, varied as its men were, was truly monolithic. But the house of the Djenghiskhanides, which owned the army, was disunited, split by rivalries and quarrels, some of them pettish to the point of ludicrousness. Subotai chose to ignore the brawls that occurred under his very eyes in Batu's headquarters, in which more royalty from Karakorum had lately arrived. To the old general nothing mattered but victory, and his only concern was to keep the querulants from disrupting his campaign. In fact the princes who had come to share in the military triumph showed less ambition to shine in action than to acquire personal power at the expense of the bastard's bastard.

Kuyuk, Ogödai's oldest son, was most vitriolic in his abuse of Batu.

The prince-governor of the western provinces reported to Ogödai on an incident that brought the latent conflict to a head: "By the favor of Heaven, and good fortune, O Great Khan, my Uncle, the eleven nations [eleven Russian principalities] have been subjugated. When the armies affected their junction, we held a celebration and all the Princes were present. As the oldest, I drank a goblet of koumiss or two before the others started drinking. Büri [a grandson of Djagatai] and Kuyuk behaved unreasonably. They got up and walked out of my tent, abusing me. I followed them, and as they mounted their horses, Büri said: 'Batu does not wield any authority over us; why did he drink first? To me, he is just an old woman with a beard. I could throw him over with one kick, and trample on him.' Kuyuk screamed: 'I shall order that he be cudgeled.' And then, some of their adherents came out and said things like, 'He ought to have a wooden tail tied to his ass as a disgrace.' Such language was used by princes when we were about to discuss important issues and to celebrate victory. There can be no serious discussions under the circumstances. This, I must report to you, O Great Khan, my Uncle."

Express messengers foundered horses to carry complaints, denunciations, and admonitions back and forth over thousands of miles, from the Ukraine to Karakorum.

Batu's complaint made Ogödai aware of the seriousness of the family crisis. He recalled his son and consulted with Yeliu about the possible consequences of the conflict between Kuyuk and Batu. Yeliu took a dim view of the matter. Such a rift, he said, could not heal. Batu would never forgive the abuse, and Kuyuk would certainly not apologize. The heir presumptive did not seem fit to rule a universal realm. It would be advisable to choose another prince as a successor to the Great Khan. Kuyuk had informers at his father's court. He learned of Yeliu's counsel, and of Ogödai's inclination to accept it. Still he hoped that the Great Khan would make no immediate decisions, and that he would succumb to exhaustion by debauchery before another candidate had been chosen.

In Hungary nothing was learned about dissensions in enemy headquarters; but it was known that the Mongols showed no signs of breaking up their campaign. Refugees from stricken regions posed problems that irked the King. Béla called his paladins into conference and, on its eve, Kotyan, a pagan Kuman chieftain, arrived at the Hungarian capital to testify about the horrors of the invasion and the Mongolian army's terrific strength. Kotyan's tribe numbered 40,000; he pledged allegiance to the King of Hungary, and offered to enlist with all his male subjects. High clerics objected against the inclusion of pagans in a Christian army, but Kotyan said that he would have his people converted and, after the Mongols were thrown back, he would see that all heathens in the European steppes embraced Christendom.

This pleased the clergy, but annoyed the nobles, who did not want the King to have a large army of converts at his disposal. The sovereign should depend on the levies of nobility for national defense. The aristocracy argued against hasty measures. What had happened in Russia, they claimed, could not happen in Hungary; the country was protected by the Carpathian range, a barrier too formidable for a mounted army to cross. Kotyan's Kumans should be drafted for labor, and build fortifications in the mountain passes, while a diet of nobles and clergy considered further steps.

The Kumans were sent to the Carpathians. Béla made an inspection trip to watch the progress of their work, and expressed satisfaction with the impregnability of the abatis he saw. Local Hungarian peasants, however, said that the Kumans were spies, thieves, and subversive elements altogether, and assumed a threatening attitude toward laboring foreigners.

In Buda members of the Diet arrived with huge retinues. There were elaborate, clumsy ceremonials, gala receptions, and smaller but pompous parties. The capital was crowded by hordes of servants, tradesmen, adventurers, whores, and spies. Entertainment delayed the Diet's negotiations. It took several months to pass a preliminary measure: the draft of frontiersmen.

Then an uninvited delegation came to Buda: bowlegged, black-haired, colorfully overdressed men, led by a fair and tall individual whose features contrasted strangely with his oriental garb. He spoke fluent Latin, which the clerics and some of the mundane grandees understood, and explained that he was born in England but was now a subject of the Great Khan, on whose behalf he had come to talk to the King of Hungary.

King and Diet received the Mongolian delegation with a mixture of curiosity and contempt. The Englishman lodged a complaint. Hungary, he said, was harboring notorious criminals who had treacherously assaulted and assassinated Mongolian envoys. He was not specific about the identity of either killed or killers, but he hinted that Kuman refugees were involved in the sinister affair, and that, by having the Kumans work for the Hungarian military establishment, Béla had most seriously violated the rules of neutrality. Coming down to the principal purpose of his visit, the chief delegate asked that Hungary recognize the suzerainty of the Great Khan, "to whom heaven has awarded all lands of the earth as his property."

The Diet roared angry defiance. The Englishman, temporarily abandoning his part as a threatening challenger, pleaded with king, nobles, and clergy. He asserted that he did not want Hungary to be destroyed, and pictured the horrors of Mongolian invasion. He gave a fantastic overestimate of Mongolian numbers, and suggested that the Hungarians gain time by sending the Mongols presents that could pass as a tribute, and that they meanwhile reconsider their untenable position.

The assembly gave no thought to the possibility that the delegate's change of attitude could reflect a Westerner's sympathy with a country which culturally was closer to the West than to the East. The Diet interpreted it as evidence of fear that Hungary would call the Asiatic bluff. Bishops and gentry shouted disdain; the Englishman cursed and abused. The session broke up in tumult and the Mongolian delegates barely escaped with their lives.

More refugees kept arriving from the Western Ukraine and from Western Poland. The Hungarian population turned against the alleged spies. The main objective of their violent wrath remained the Kumans. So many Kumans were murdered that defense construction had to be discontinued and plans to draft refugees were abandoned.

Hungarian experts said that the Mongolian forces reduced in number as they advanced; that every army had to leave security forces behind; and that the armies which had swept through Russia were not identical with those investing Polish territory. The name of Tatars turned up in the refugees' account. Nobody in Hungary had ever heard of Tatars.

In fact the name sounded puzzling. It was still used by Chinese in speaking of their aggressive neighbors, and maybe some psychological warfare experts who preceded Subotai's army spreading gruesome tales had called the invaders Tatars.

The Diet continued in session. The first nobles' contingents arrived under the walls of the capital, raising the spirits of the King's men, who had been slightly worried by reports that the draft had produced disappointing results. Recruits looted arms magazines and formed robber bands instead of joining their regular outfits. And, waiting for recruits to arrive, commanders did not march north to man the mountainous border line.

King Béla exchanged circumstantial messages about joint military operations with the King of Poland, the Dukes of Silesia and Oppeln, and the Margrave of Moravia. He was in correspondence with the King of Bohemia, the German Emperor, the King of France, and the Holy See. The express riders who carried the messages of Christian princes were not as fast as their heathen counterparts, and courts and chancelleries who studied the weighty documents were slow to reply. The invasion from the East posed a difficult problem: the unity of Europe.

Europe had known alliances, compacts, and mutual pledges, but the only instances in which partial unity had been achieved had been conquests by powerful rulers who merged countries into short-lived realms. Statesmen pondered over military collaboration among equals and wondered how future conflicts over spoils could be avoided; the Tatars' land was too far away to be divided among the European victors (there was no doubt in the statesmen's minds that Europe would defeat the intruders) and territorial acquisitions were absolutely necessary.

Suggestions turned up to distribute Russian principalities after they had been freed. The Swedes, the Lithuanians, and the Grand Master of the Teutons in the Baltic areas, jealous of the Westerners, prepared to gather their share in the spoils of Asiatic disaster before the West could reach an agreement on the subject. The shadow of a free-for-all among Christian rulers fell over the picture. Pope Gregory IX considered a crusade to achieve unity of purpose without selfish flaws, but he did not launch the appeal when he learned that the overbearing, despotic German Emperor would not fall in line. Rome made long-term policies; the Mongols or Tatars would soon be gone, and the trouble with the redoubtable Germans would continue. The King of France, who did not want to denude his territory of soldiers in face of a bothersome neighbor on the Rhine, decided to refrain from an expedition to the east, and instead sent his best wishes to the other Christian kings; and the German

Emperor, anxious to watch both France and the Holy See, sent similar wishes of his own.

Meantime King Boleslav of Poland made military preparations. The Vistula River was an obstacle of great magnitude; covering cavalry forces could frustrate any attempt at crossing. Polish horsemen patrolled the left bank of the Vistula. The river froze in winter, but despite the Russian experience it was thought that the Mongols could not campaign in the cold season.

Henry, Duke of Silesia, gathered an army which included Teuton and Templar knights, and infantrymen selected among mineworkers, a tough, hardened outfit of 30,000; he was joined by 10,000 knights and professional foot soldiers from Oppeln and Moravia; from Bohemia, King Wenceslaus was on the march at the head of 50,000 picked warriors.

There were no joint plans of operation. The host of Silesia, Oppeln, and Moravia would not co-operate with Poland. Nobody would co-operate with Hungary. But this was thought to be all to the good; it would force the invaders to split their armies, if, in fact, they would try yet another offensive. As the year 1240 grew older without the horsemen moving west, it was widely believed that the drive had petered out and that the bowlegged aggressors, faced by the Christian determination, were on their way back to their barbaric land of origin.

Heavy ice was drifting on the Vistula River, yet there was no sign of Mongolian activity. Only from Eastern Poland came reports of small raids on open communities. January 1241 went by, and the Polish cavalrymen had not seen a single enemy. The Christian forces did not disband; their leaders said that never before had so powerful a host been assembled. But their alertness relaxed, and King Wenceslaus' march bogged down to a snail's pace, punctuated by prolonged rests in comfortable urban quarters.

Subotai seemed to have eyes and ears everywhere in Europe. The mysterious Englishman, vexed by his reception at Buda, must have organized a superb intelligence system in courts and army headquarters, for the Mongolian general's planning made no error in either disposition of troops or timing of operations. The old soldier kept working in his tent, letting the princes brawl and write to the Great Khan. Time was not against him. Not within a decade would his opponents agree on effective measures, and meantime he could work on improved tactics against the knights' heavy armor, of which informers had delivered a few samples. He might have preferred to be already in Buda, if not headed for Germany and the Rhine; but he would have to wait until royalty was forced into line. Temudshin would have done so in a matter of hours, but Ogödai was not the Djenghis Khan—Subotai knew it well enough, and, somehow, he blamed Yeliu for the Great Khan's lack of energy. Obedience to the head of the Djenghiskhanides being sacred, however, he could not remonstrate against delays. From Karakorum came orders to give major assignments to princes. Subotai had a high opinion of the military abilities of Baidar, son of Djagatai, and Kaidu; he put them in charge of the first army that would drive straight west, while he maintained command of the second army to head south.

On February 11, 1241, at last, an estafette arrived on the last leg of the journey from Karakorum, his mount's coat covered with snow-white ice. The messenger handed Subotai the Great Khan's order to strike.

On February 12 the first army crossed the Vistula River near the bend of Sandomiercz, destroyed the city, and halted. Polish covering forces fell back beyond Chmielnik, thirty-odd miles to the west. King Boleslav's generals insisted that the rape of Sandomiercz, regrettable as was the loss of lives and property involved, was of no consequence, merely another hit-and-run raid. The Mongolian army stalled. The Poles amended their opinion by saying that the raid had been a rear-guard action to cover the complete evacuation of Polish territory.

Vague news arrived from Hungary, about three Mongolian cavalry sections crossing Carpathian passes and disappearing without a trace. Another rear-guard action, apparently. King Béla was still sitting with his Diet and the nobles' contingents were now gathered in strength.

On March 18, at dawn, a hail of arrows struck the Polish camp at Chmielnik, where King Boleslav was now staying with the bulk of his army, ready for a glorious return to the devastated parts of his country. The Poles saw little more of the attackers than ghostlike contours of fast-moving horsemen. There was no fight. Mongolian arrows mowed Poles down before they could rally. The King and his suite escaped in the direction of Moravia; scattered remnants of the army joined their sovereign's flight.

The Duke of Silesia had concentrated his men near Liegnitz, some two hundred miles to the west. It took over two weeks for the disastrous news to reach the Silesian. Wenceslaus of Bohemia was said to be only five days' march away, and there seemed to be plenty of time to group the joint forces for action before the attackers, with the strong fortress of Cracow and the Oder River line in their path, could overcome the distance.

The Silesian ruler did not know that the Mongols had already broken into practically undefended Cracow and sacked the city; that they were crossing the Oder on bridges built by Chinese army engineers; that a movement had started to encircle his camp.

Never before had Siberian horsemen battled knights in full armor; never before had Batu's mercenaries met such warriors. But they had been shown a knight's armor and had been told how to deal with its wearer. Arrows would hardly pierce helmets or breastplates, but the archer should aim at the unprotected parts of horses; dismounted, the riders would be helpless, unable to walk under the weight of iron.

On April 9 Mongolian vanguards skirted the Duke's camp. The alarmed Christian commander ordered an immediate retreat to meet Wenceslaus' tardy forces. The camp had been fortified, but the junction seemed more important than the cover of earthworks. When the army debouched from the camp, the Mongols charged, in complete silence. There were no battle cries, nor the newly introduced trumpet blasts, nothing was audible but the thunder of galloping hoofs. The horsemen broke into rear-guard infantry; the miner-soldiers were gallant people, a match for the attackers, man by man, but they were overwhelmed by enemy tactics that precluded individual action. Fleeing infantrymen poured into the knights' columns. The duke ordered his knights to charge through the routed infantry. From his command post he overlooked the enemy formations and found that they were not very numerous. Actually Baidar and Kaidu had 30,000 men against the Duke's 40,000. The Mongols turned around at once in one of their standard maneuvers, but the knights, who knew nothing of enemy tactics, jubilantly raced on. The Mongols shot their arrows backward, with gruesome accuracy; and wherever knights caught up with the enemy, they had to realize that their long swords had no telling effect upon the many layers of cowhide the Mongols wore. Still the Mongols fell back when, as a chronicler told: "there was raised a bearded human head of hideous appearance, mounted on a long lance; the head spat ill-smelling vapors and smoke, throwing Duke Henry's army into confusion, and hiding the Tatars from their eyes."

In 1241 Europe experienced the first gas attack, and the first smoke screen. However, the report seems to contain some inaccuracies. The smoke machines and "stinkpots" were not mounted on lances, and the "hideous head" probably was a Mongolian standard, with the cat-o'-nine-tails attached to it.

Confusion led to complete rout. Horsemen on swift shaggy ponies made routine outflanking moves. A few hours later only a handful of half-crazed Silesians were left to tell of one of the worst debacles in European military history.

Two days after the disaster of Liegnitz another catastrophe occurred, well to the southeast of the Silesian town.

Prince Batu was with Subotai's second army, which the general divided into three groups to cross the Carpathians in sections far apart. They converged toward the plains with a speed that seemed, and still seems, incredible in difficult terrain: the vanguards covered 185 miles in 72 hours. The Palatine of Hungary, who commanded the frontiersmen, established contact only with the central groups, without, however, being able to delay its advance. On March 15 the mountain range was Mongolian-controlled from the Beskides to the Transylvanian Alps, and Mongolian patrols invested the outskirts of Buda. The heavy siege machines were still far away, in Eastern Transylvania, and Subotai would not attack the capital unless his potent weapons were ready for operation. His patrols put the torch to rural settlements; they looted and raped, but they tried to evade superior Hungarian forces. King Béla's nobles and clergy vied "hunting up the elusive barbarians." Bishop Ugolinus, the most militant of European prelates, donned a helmet instead of his mitre, and led his fighting diocesans in sharp thrusts against the Mongolian cavalry in two or three of which the Mongolians suffered some casualties.

The bishop outfought the magnates of the realm, including Koloman, the King's brother; and he had an even more important achievement to his credit: the improvisation of an intelligence service. A refugee from Russia acted as Hungarian chief spy. He reported that the Mongols, only 20,000 strong, were assembling at the confluence of the Sájo and Tisza rivers. Their communications were harassed by marauding bands of Hungarian deserters and Kumans. The Hungarian war council scoffed at the barbarians' strategy: only a crude general could choose such an assembly area. The King's army would deploy on the heath of Mohi, its flanks protected by the two rivers, compress the barbarians into the marshes of the swollen Sájo, and this would be the end of the invaders. Ugolinus and Koloman would jointly lead the final drive. Couriers stood by to carry the news of enemy disaster to the capital, ahead of the victory bulletin that was expected to come from Poland or Silesia.

The morning of April 10 saw the Hungarians assembled. A bridge across the Sájo was intact; over this bridge rode Mongolian horsemen and were promptly attacked by Ugolinus' soldiers. The Mongolians fled, almost losing their way into the marshes. This was an auspicious beginning; caution required that the decisive Hungarian drive wait until the men were rested. By nightfall most units were gathered in a camp, surrounded by heavy wagons which were linked by iron chains. Only small vanguards and rear guards were stationed outside.

At the first dim light of dawn the Hungarian vanguards were struck by an awesome phenomenon. The sky was cloudless; yet sudden rumbling sounds and glaring flashes came from beyond the Sájo River, like in a thunderstorm. Before the startled men had time to think, howling rocks hit, like immense hailstones, spreading death and destruction.

The first cannon had made their appearance in a part of the world that claimed priority in all technical achievements.

The Hungarians ran, shouting about hell and sorcery. Bishop Ugolinus roared the soldiers into making a stand, and while men inside the wagon fortress, aroused by the ghostly noise, assembled, the valiant cleric held Mongolian units which were crossing the bridge. The Hungarians counterattacked thirty minutes after the first cannon missile had struck. But the Mongols, supported by continuous artillery fire, did not abandon the bridgehead, and more Mongols crossed to the far bank. By 9 A.M. the Hungarians retreated into their *laager,* still in reasonably good order and determined to fight. But then Subotai threw his main forces, which, with reserves unnoticed by Hungarian spies, numbered nearly 100,000, into action. Cavalry crushed Hungarian rear guards outside the camp and then blocked every path of approach. Archers and artillerists poured a steady stream of missiles into the *laager,* and they were joined by catapult crews throwing burning naphtha into the deathtrap.

Bishop Ugolinus, who had suffered heavy burns, and Prince Koloman, who had been wounded by an arrow, led monastic knights in a mad sortie. They were forced back by enemy fire, but charged again. A gap opened. A stream of desperate, howling soldiers raced for the breach. Bishop and prince, realizing that the apparent opening was a Mongolian ruse, tried in vain to restore discipline to the crazed mob. The enemy massacred the fleeing men in what turned out to be a gantlet.

Ugolinus died, sword in hand. Koloman, wounded, made his way to Buda. King Béla inspected the rear guards when the Mongols circled the camp, and fled toward the border, Mongolian pursuers at his heels. Koloman made an attempt to rally the citizenry of the capital for a determined stand, but already psychological warfare demoralized the burghers; the only way of escaping death, they said, was surrender. The prince went to the southern part of the country to gather an army, but died of his wounds before achieving his aim. One Mongolian flying column chased the fugitive King through Croatia, into the Balkans, to Spalato, and Cattaro. Other columns reduced fortified towns of Transylvania and cut levies of German colonists into ribbons.

Upon learning of the Liegnitz disaster King Wenceslaus of Bohemia crossed into Saxony, then went to his own realm, and in slow, zigzag marches neared the borders of Moravia, careful not to enter that rich province now being ravaged by Baidar and Kaidu. The Mongolian commanders did not care to go out of their way and engage his army, whereupon the King sent a boastful message to the German emperors, saying that he had scared the Tatars away.

The Mongols' first army was under orders not to waste time in Moravia, but to proceed to Western Hungary and join Subotai for a co-ordinated sweep west. Kaidu and Baidar left one Moravian fortress unconquered: Olomouc, defended by Count Yaroslav of Sternberg.

The junction was established late in April. The way west lay open. Subotai's horsemen invested Austria, by-passing Vienna. They met with no resistance and saw hardly any people; villages and market towns had been abandoned by a panicky population.

King Béla sent frantic appeals for help to the Pope and to major European courts. His experiences in distress had been most discouraging. He had entered Austria, but the Austrian duke held Béla up for cession of three Hungarian provinces in return for free passage, and he wanted the King's cash and treasures as payment of a sum allegedly due to him.

Béla altered his route of escape rather than be left penniless. Dalmatia Province, where he eventually went, was part of his patrimony. But from Venice came a note informing him that the Republic did not recognize Hungarian sovereignty over Dalmatia, or any other lands on the Adriatic Sea; the Venetian Government, however, would generously permit him to stay there until claims to the territory were formally presented.

Emperor Frederick told Béla's messengers that his imperial shield was raised against barbarian destruction, but that he would have to suppress regional rebellions in Italy before taking the field against any other enemy. He requested bluntly that the Hungarian delegates swear fealty to him in the name of their king.

The Pope admonished all Christians to hold out firmly against the Tatars, while, simultaneously, encouraging rumors that Emperor Frederick's agents were negotiating with the barbarians to split the rest of Europe between the Reich and the Tatar hordes.

Frederick, in turn, wrote to the Kings of France and England, denouncing alleged papal support of rebels against his authority and claiming that he could not devote his strength to the struggle against the enemies of Christianity while the Pope himself was making secret agreements with the foe. As an evidence of his own noble intentions, however, the Emperor told the Western monarchs that princes and prelates of his realm were gathered at Magdeburg and Herford to examine the situation and to encourage resistance against the heathen.

Ponce d'Aubon, a French Templar and adviser on German affairs to the French Court, told King Louis that, by the Lord's will, Germany might fall to the Tatars. This could but please the King, who saw in Frederick the embodiment of aggressive wickedness. Louis's ponderings about the state of affairs produced a jest: "We have the heavenly comfort that, should the Tatars come, We shall either send them back to the Tartarus whence they came, or else, shall We be admitted to Heavens and the raptures awaiting the chosen there." Courtiers parroted the King's words and praised his wit, which, as they said, was a solace to Christianity. It was, in fact, the only contribution France made to the defense of the continent.

A Bavarian chronicler recorded about Hungary: "That Kingdom, after existing for three centuries, has now been annihilated by the Tatars." And no European power would take up arms for the sake of a country that did no longer exist.

While Europe talked, intrigued, and joked, the Mongolian armies stalled. Mongolian vanguards even evacuated Lower Austria and fell back to the March and Leitha rivers. The Western grandee's rantings could not impress Subotai, Batu, and the Siberian princes, but Béla IV was still at large, and the Djenghiskhanide law required that resisters be punished. Not even Subotai, anxious as he was to continue his drive toward the Atlantic Ocean, could bring himself to conquer other realms unless the ruler of Hungary was made to suffer the penalty which the Yassak provided.

Prince Kadan went to step up the hunt for Béla; he reported from Cattaro that the King had escaped to the island of Rab (Arbe), and that fishing craft were being requisitioned to take up the pursuit at sea. But the best navigators had fled with their solid boats, and the Mongols took some time to reach Rab, only to find that Béla had gone.

Throughout the spring and summer of 1241, Mongolian horses grazed on Hungarian pastures, and Mongolian-appointed administrators began organizing Hungary. Peasants came out of hiding places; their homesteads were destroyed, but they were permitted to till the soil. Market places were established. Copper coins, of Chinese mint, began to circulate as occupation currency. There was even budding corruption. Never before had the Mongols met more attractive women than the Hungarians. A Hungarian peasant who had a sturdy wife or daughter—blondes preferred—could send her to talk about his problems with the local administrator, and he would obtain allotments of cattle, or even tax exemption.

Fall went by and the army was still waiting. To keep his army busy, Subotai had assaulted and taken the only remaining Hungarian fortress, half-starved Esztergom (Gran). He was now drafting a two-pronged drive which in a matter of four days should sweep through Austria into Bavaria, 250-odd miles away. The campaign was to open as soon as Béla was disposed of. Kadan's messages at last indicated that he had located his prey, on the island of Trau.

A hundred forty thousand soldiers waited for the signal to advance. Every private knew that it would come as soon as news of Béla's capture arrived. Guards strained their eyes, peering into the distance from where the dispatch rider would come. In Batu's tent waiting generals silently emptied goblets of kumiss; anything that mattered had already been said.

In the first week of January 1242 a mercenary guardsman near the eastern rim of the Mongolian camp saw a horseman approach the site. The man, carrying a pole with the Mongolian field badge, as only couriers of great importance would carry, rode right into the camp. He had a fine mount whose pace was breath-taking. From the saddle he shouted something the mercenary could not understand. Mongolian officers gave him the right of way to the commander's tent, which he entered, running.

Minutes later soldiers prepared to break camp even though there had been no alert. Sentries outside of Batu's tent saw generals emerge and proceed to their own abodes, poker-faced and noncommittal. Only the courier, the princes, and Subotai remained inside.

Still there were no orders. But Mongolian officers supervised their men's preparation for departure: cannon, battering rams, and other heavy equipment were aligned in marching order; storehouse crews were busy loading supplies in carts and wagons, and there was a scramble about booty, some arguing that spoils should be left behind to make the army travel light, others insisting that this was against regulations and that no amount of spoils would keep them from going fast.

Two thirds of the tümens were already in marching order, facing west. A stiff breeze blew in from the east which should accelerate their march west. Suddenly a shout arose. Trumpets greeted Batu and Subotai as they came out of the tent. The prince raised his arm. Units started moving. But then there were shouts, a commotion of sounds and signals which at first few could understand and which made no sense to those who did.

Turn about; turn east.

The enemy was west. The unconquered universe was in the direction of the sun that was about to set. Men stopped and stared. Officers raced to have orders clarified. This could only be a misunderstanding. Kumiss was a potent drink. But Batu and Subotai looked sober and as gloomy as no general remembered having seen them before. There was little talk, little motion.

And then, tümen commanders assumed direction of their units. Forward—march—direction eastward—back . . .

CHAPTER SIXTEEN The message had traveled day and night, as fast as horses could run, 6000 miles from Karakorum to the western border of Hungary. The Great Khan was dead: Ogödai had passed away on December 11, 1241. A Kuriltai had been convoked to nominate his successor. All princes of the blood were duty-bound to attend; and the army, being the princes', had to go with its owners. Such was the law.

Nobody lamented Ogödai, but officially he would be mourned with the bloodcurdling rites required by the law. Temudshin had been an ogre; and yet some men had appreciated his wicked greatness and lamented his loss. Ogödai had been an uninspiring epigone, a symbol of the most violent law of conquest ever devised, who, dreading the arduous task of symbolism, had drowned his qualms in kumiss. He had but a fraction of the number of Temudshin's victims on his conscience, and he had not wanted to count them for a report to Tängri and to the soul of the Djenghis Khan that would wait for him. Ogödai had had no personal admirer. In brief but crucial talks at headquarters preceding the retreat Batu had contended that there was one issue more portentous than attendance at a funeral, and more urgent than a Kuriltai: the conquest of the universe. No ruler of the universe should be chosen until the universal realm was constituted. It would take no more than one year to reach the Atlantic, but it might take several years to resume the campaign and carry it through should it be interrupted.

The younger princes were sufficiently versed in intrigues not to realize Batu's ultimate aim: The western part of the lands under Djenghiskhanide rule was his fief. Already he was the strongest among them; with Central and Western Europe under Batu's tenure he would be more powerful than any Great Khan. He would be the maker of Great Khans, and pass this power on to his descendants, the chiefs of the Golden Ordu. The younger princes no longer abused the bastard's bastard. Politely and respectfully they talked about the necessity of going to Karakorum first. It could be that the Kuriltai cut Batu down to size. Batu, however, had insisted that the universal empire should have priority over the universal ruler.

Subotai, too, would have wanted to complete the campaign. He was too old to lead another drive several years hence. But to him the Yassak could never be subject to captious interpretation. There should be a Kuriltai after a Great Khan's death, and nowhere did the Yassak say that the meeting might be delayed for any reason whatever. The law was immutable, and it had to be obeyed unquestioningly. This was probably the longest speech the general had delivered since he had kept repeating his battle report to the late Djenghis Khan. Through Subotai the Djenghis Khan seemed to speak. Not even Batu challenged his authority.

In March 1242, Western rulers learned that the Tatars were no longer in Central Europe. They did not even wonder whether this was a miracle or another dangerous strategem; they accepted it as an established fact, and their zealous correspondences centered on the question who had done most to frighten the barbarians away.

By that time Mongolian princes and Subotai were already inside Siberia, halfway to Karakorum. The army that went with them, however, was reduced to a fraction of its former strength. Batu, pleading poor health, had gone to his old camp in the Volga Valley, taking his men with him and promising to follow later.

Ogödai had not formally deposed Kuyuk as a crown prince at the time of his death, but he had stipulated that, pending the Kuriltai's decision, his widow Turakina assume the regency. It was not unusual among the Mongolian women to carry high authority, but Yeliu had strenuously objected to the appointment. Turakina was a vicious and resourceful woman who would use her powers recklessly and to no good effect. Ogödai had once acquired her from a Märkit chieftain of ill-repute to whom she had been married and who told him that there was no more lustful and imaginative woman in the world. The lewd Great Khan had turned a deaf ear to Yeliu's warnings; old Yeliu could not know what a treasure Turakina was.

Turakina had a favorite, a Persian slave girl whose relations to her mistress were the object of whispered gossip. The slave girl had also a man lover, a Mohammedan who had been involved in high-smelling financial machinations, the proceeds of which he shared with his mistress. Several times Turakina had rescued the Mohammedan from troubles. She considered him an extremely clever man. She did not dare to vex Yeliu outright, for the older generation still venerated him as Temudshin's counselor; but, to annoy the old man into withdrawing from public affairs, she appointed the Mohammedan chief of the civil administration. Angry and disdainful, Yeliu retired to his small house. The new chief of the civil administration discharged all persons hostile to Kuyuk and Turakina and replaced them by partners in his own dubious affairs.

Dismissed Sinofied civil servants, elderly dignitaries and merchants urged Yeliu to come out of his hiding and cope with corruption and mismanagement that would soon destroy what he had helped to build. Yeliu was taciturn and absent-minded; callers wondered if the great old man was not getting senile. Soon Yeliu refused to see visitors. Rumors spread that he had abused his office for many years to gather immense riches at the expense of the Djenghiskhanides, and that he would not receive anybody for fear that visitors would find, and steal, some of the jewels heaped up in huge buckets. The rumors could be traced to the Mohammedan's office, and they were gleefully quoted by Turakina and her favorites. Some said that "the old Chinese," as Yeliu was now called by disparagers, would be tried for untold crimes. Only an aging servant entered Yeliu's tent to bring him food. The servant said that his master was ill. A few months after his retirement Yeliu was found dead.

Crowds gathered in front of his habitat, as a token of respect or out of curiosity, to cast a glance at the buckets full of jewels. But the curious were disappointed. Nothing was found in the home of the man who for a long time had directed the economic affairs of a colossal empire but a number of books, a few Chinese musical instruments, and sketches of poetry. Nobody had known Yeliu to be a poet or a musician. And not even the many who had trusted his honesty had ever thought that the all-powerful secret counselor had been poorer than the Siberian herdsmen who lived under the Djenghiskhanide sway.

Nothing is recorded of Yeliu's obsequies. Turakina may have seen that dead Yeliu would not be talked about too much. Already the Kuriltai attracted general attention.

The regent's candidate for the throne was Kuyuk. Princes and princelings looked west for support against Turakina's choice. Only Batu could oppose the mighty woman. Batu would soon come to Karakorum. The opposition stalled, and the Kuriltai's sessions, very much to the annoyance of Turakina and Kuyuk, degenerated into prolonged bouts. But Batu stayed in his Russian domain, determined to make it practically independent should his foe be raised to exalted rank. He believed that the nomination of Kuyuk was well nigh inevitable. The civil administration was in the hands of Turakina's creatures; Subotai and the other old generals would soon be superseded by new appointees; and Turakina would corrupt and blackmail the electors.

It was more than two years, however, before the Kuriltai understood that Batu would not join them, and elected Kuyuk. Turakina proclaimed the bastard's bastard guilty of disobedience to the Yassak and no longer qualified to interfere with Djenghiskhanide affairs; but no steps were taken to oust Batu from office. He was too strong to be challenged.

But another, most unexpected, group of travelers arrived at Karakorum; the strangest-looking men the gathering had ever laid eyes upon. The foreigners were two Franciscan friars: Benedict and Plan Carpin (also called Piano Carpini), later the Archbishop of Antivari. They brought a message from Pope Innocent IV, a "letter to the King and People of the Tatars," reprimanding the addressees for unprovoked attacks on Christian territory and threatening that renewed aggression would bring the wrath of the Lord and His damnation upon the offenders, but offering friendship and good will should the Tatars mend their ways and embrace Christianity.

The Pope distrusted the Christian kings' claims that they had frightened the Tatars away. Through his legates he advocated joint action to keep the intruders permanently out of Christian territory. This letter was the result of his own endeavors with royalty's contribution, consisting in aid and advice to the papal deputation. No Christian ruler had more than vague notions of the whereabouts of the Tatars; it was decided that two expeditions should try to make their way to the mysterious regions, one through Asia Minor, the other along the route the invaders had taken in their attack through Poland and Silesia. The Asia Minor group never reached its goal, but Plan Carpin's indomitable energy eventually carried him all the way to Karakorum. The friar was a potbellied man in his middle years who had never ridden on a more formidable mount than a donkey. But he trusted that the Lord would give him sufficient steadfastness to ride horses and go to the end of the earth. They were three when they set out on the long trip.

The first leg of the Franciscans' voyage carried them to the residence of King Wenceslaus, who, however, refused to provide escorts to the land of the Tatars and passed the friars on to the Duke of Silesia, who issued letters of protection, to whom it may concern. From Breslau, where the duke lived, the voyagers continued to Cracow, from there through Galicia Province to Halicz, and farther east toward Kiev. They traveled through scenes of death and desolation, fields strewn with bones on which wild animals had feasted; they met survivors reduced to the level of haunted beasts of prey, who lurked in woods and ruins to kill and loot less destitute fellow-men. The Franciscans had several narrow escapes as they moved on through untilled fields. German colonists, well fed and well armed, were moving in to settle the land. Survivors of the cataclysm, too weak to engage the intruders from the west, watched the east for renewed disaster.

Ten months after leaving Italy the delegates arrived in the ruins of Kiev without having met a single Tatar. They had a sleigh, and thanks to the efforts of Benedict, who was of Polish origin, they even got horses every now and then. Their provisions were running low, but German colonists would sell food at stiff prices.

The land east of Kiev, through which they drove in midwinter, was sparsely settled but less ravaged than Poland and the Western Ukraine had been; and the peasantry, though obviously frightened, was working on restoration of their huts. Horses were available at regular intervals. Coachmen were taciturn, but they seemed to know where the Tatars lived, for they went straight on, and their passengers were confident that the long trip would soon be over.

Nineteen days out of Kiev the sleigh was stopped by heavily armed riders who shouted hoarsely and looked like devils incarnate. The coachmen talked to the horsemen and offered to the Polish friar to act as an interpreter: they had just met Batu's first cavalry patrol; horses and coachmen who had conveyed them during the past weeks had all been in Batu's well-organized transportation services.

The Franciscan was asked to explain the purpose of their trip in detail; then the patrol leader ordered a search of sleigh and riders. The bread in the friars' bags was confiscated (the Mongols considered bread a delicacy). The papal messengers were ordered to proceed on horseback. Cavalrymen took the lead; the Franciscans wondered wryly what would happen next, as the soldiers refused to answer questions. The trip continued for several weeks, with three to five changes of horses a day, searches for food, frugal meals of porridge, and night quarters in ramshackle huts, with soldiers monopolizing the space near the fireside. Patrols kept changing, the Franciscans were passed on from one group of sullen devils to the next without ever learning where they went and how long they would still have to go.

On April 6 they arrived at the fringe of a camp of colossal round tents mounted on wagons with axles thick as a ship's masts, standing fifty feet apart, and to be pulled by teams of twenty-two oxen harnessed in two rows.

The friars were made to walk between burning stakes so that they be purged of evil spirits, and then they were marched a full hour to the entrance of a tent which was even bigger than the others. They had to make obeisance before entering, be careful not to step on the threshold, and were ordered to prostrate themselves as they reached the interior and not to rise in the presence of the potentate. So intimidated were the Franciscans that they did not even dare to look at the face of the potentate whom his servants called The Magnificent and The Merciful.

Batu listened to the Russian, Saracen, and Mongolian translations of the Pope's Latin message (he understood only the last) and decreed that Carpin and Benedict be sent to Karakorum; the third friar would have to stay behind because he looked too frail to stand the strain of the voyage. The two friars had just enough time to take a good look at Batu's family quarters before they were whisked off.

The Merciful and The Magnificent had twenty-six legitimate wives, each of whom had one giant tent of her own and about a dozen smaller ones for her children, female servants, and retainers. Between one hundred and two hundred carts, loaded with provisions and household implements, surrounded every wife's accommodations. Carpin did not lay eyes upon Batu's ladies.

The 4000-mile distance to Karakorum was covered in fifteen weeks. "Horses were changed between five and seven times daily," the friar reported; "remounts were always fresh and vigorous. From morning till nightfall, we got nothing to eat, and when we reached night quarters behind schedule, we had to wait for our meal until dawn. The way led across deserts, where skulls and human bones lay in heaps, through regions full of ruined towns and fortresses, across lofty snow-covered mountain passes, through countries and past cities the names of which, as well as the language of their inhabitants, are unknown in Europe."

Carpin's party seems to have traveled the southern route to Mongolia, possibly through Khwarezm, Afghanistan, and Pamir. To cover for more than a hundred days a daily average of almost forty miles, with little rest and food, must have been a serious ordeal, but other papal messengers who had tried the route through Asia Minor fared even worse.

They were stopped by Baichu, a Mongolian civil administrator who officiated somewhere near the Syrian border. Baichu requested that the delegates render homage to him in the name of their master. Friar Ezzelino refused to comply. "The Pope," he exulted, "ranks high above all Kings of the world." The Mongol wanted to know how many countries the Pope had conquered, how many people he owned, and how many nations between the eastern and western seas trembled at the sound of his name. Ezzelino replied proudly that the Pope was the sole authority established by the Lord's will, anywhere, and forever. Baichu sneered and asked what presents the Pope's men had to offer. The Pope's men snapped that there would be no presents for an infidel whose name nobody had ever heard. This the Mongol took for a joke rather than an insult; he and his staff, joined by the local garrison, forced the friars to don fools' costumes and act as clowns. But then somebody opined that the clowns were spies. The friars were subjected to brutal interrogations and sentenced to death, but the execution was delayed because experts could not immediately agree on the best method. The general opinion turned in favor of skinning the culprits, stuffing their skins with chaff, and sending them to the Pope, when a general from Karakorum arrived on an inspection tour. The general, who had witnessed Carpin's reception, said that the government seemed to be friendly-inclined toward the Pope, and eventually the clergymen were returned, whole, though hardly happy.

As long as the Kuriltai was in session, foreigners were barred from Karakorum. Carpin and Benedict joined 4000 envoys waiting in the plains outside the capital. Among the envoys were princes from China, Russia, and Korea; a Seljuk sultan; rulers from the Middle East, as far away as Aleppo; and an oddity, a meek, effeminate-looking young man, who sought the company of similarly looking boys, and who was, in fact, an envoy from the Grand Master of the Assassins. All waiting nobles recognized the Great Khan's suzerainty; they waited to learn who the new overlord was, upon whose mood their own fate and that of their subjects depended.

The sight of Karakorum stunned Europeans and Asiatics alike. The capital was like an ocean of tents extending as far as the eye could see in all shades of the rainbow. The brightest spot was a white marquee, site of the Kuriltai.

Only the highest-ranking Mongols were permitted to approach this marquee of brocade, in which almost 2000 members of the mushrooming house of the Djenghiskhanides met, drank, played ball, and talked politics. Marquee grounds were surrounded with a fence which Chinese artists had decorated with pictures of Temudshin's victories, many of which were Chinese defeats. The fence had two gates, one apparently unguarded, the other heavily guarded by elite soldiers with drawn swords, bows and arrows in readiness. Through this guarded gate royalty, lesser nobles, and generals on official duty were admitted. Unauthorized persons trying to slip through were subjected to severe beatings or used for target practice with blunted arrows. The unguarded gate was reserved, to be used by the Great Khan after he was elected. It was unthinkable that profane individuals would pass that gate.

The average Mongol's curiosity was insatiable. The guard's rudeness could not prevent crowds from pressing as closely as possible to the marvels of might and wealth that were displayed during the Kuriltai. A tremendous array of wagons, 500 in all, was lined up around the golden tent that had been Temudshin's and Ogödai's and was now waiting for another dweller. The wagons carried the late Great Khan's personal treasure: gold, silver, silk, and brocade. It would be distributed among the princes of the blood, who in turn would give part of it to their soldiers and servants. These were spoils taken from half of the people of the earth. The Djenghiskhanides could afford to give most, if not all, away. As long as the conquered toiled for them, they would gather treasures faster than wagon builders could make conveyances to hoard them.

The soldiers got the lion's share. A soldier's profession was the most remunerative of all, but it was no longer easy to join the military. The army did not want unnecessary influx. It was strong enough to deal with every enemy. There was no need of enrolling more men—more greedily outstretched hands to be filled.

But every Mongol could watch the spectacle of his ruler's might, the most barbaric pomp on earth, and feel elated about being a member of the nation that ruled the universe.

A few slaves joining the crowds were derided by natives who, in turn, were snubbed by guards. Carpin talked to Russians and Hungarians who were serfs of the Mongolian military. Their lives, they said, were not all too miserable, but extremely unsafe. Their master's frown could spell death.

The Kuriltai lasted four years. Kuyuk's nomination was assured, but the princes enjoyed festivities and postponed the vote to play games, to drink kumiss brewed from the milk of 10,000 white mares, and to spend long hours in exciting female company, comparing the merits of Persian houris, Chinese courtesans, and Russian wenches with home-grown talent.

Kuyuk was not averse to orgiastic entertainment. He was a smallish man in his early forties who sported a grave look and was anxious not to smile in male company. Flatterers said that he had a sagacious expression. Kuyuk never announced a decision otherwise than in the name of Tängri. Prior to his enthronement he displayed deep respect to Turakina and patronizing benevolence to her favorites; everybody trusted that, as a Great Khan, Kuyuk would remain loyal to the regent and her appointees.

Carpin was among the first foreign delegates admitted into Great Khan Kuyuk's presence. The friar was not in a happy frame of mind. One of his slave friends had been listening to his master, a tümen commander, talking to another general. It appeared as if a plan were being prepared to subjugate the Pope and all Christians in an eighteen-year campaign. Other Christian slaves had heard similar things. They told of details that ordinarily would have aroused the friar's scepticism, but which, in the atmosphere of Karakorum, sounded entirely plausible. Prior to the audience Carpin's and Benedict's plain brown Franciscan garb was inspected by a courtier, and found unfitting for the occasion. The friars were made to change into Chinese ceremonial robes in which they felt extremely uneasy, and because this uneasiness was reflected in their bearing, masters of the Mongolian protocol placed the papal delegates in the last row of ambassadors ready to prostrate themselves before the new ruler of the universe.

The Djenghis Khan's historic tent, into which the foreigners were herded, was a pavilion of gold-embroidered silk and was covered with gold plates. Inside the tent, on a golden throne, sat Kuyuk, stiff, without a smile. Envoys had to make four genuflections before offering their presents. The Pope, however, had sent nothing but the letter, which Carpin handed to a disdainful official who in turn presented it to the Great Khan.

It is not ascertained how long the delegates were made to wait for a reply, and only 600 years after the events in Karakorum was the Mongolian answer found among long-forgotten documents.

The original was drawn up in Persian. "By the power of the Eternal Heaven, We, the Khan of all Khans of the universe, issue this command, and send it to the great Pope, so that he take cognizance and heeds to what it decrees. We understand, that, after holding counsel with the monarchs under your suzerainty, you did send Us an offer of submission, which was duly delivered by our envoy. If this is your intention, then you, the great Pope and all these monarchs, shall come in person to pay homage, and to learn the commands of the Yassak. You have said that it would be propitious for Us to embrace Christianity. In fact, you have couched it in terms of request. This, I cannot understand. You also write me: 'You have attacked all the territories of the Hungarians and other Christians. Do tell me of what offense they had been guilty.' This, too, I cannot understand. Djenghis Khan and Ogödai Khaghan did reveal the commands of Eternal Heaven. Those, of whom you write, however, did not abide by these commands; they were presumptuous and slew our envoys. Therefore, it was in compliance with the Eternal Heaven's command, that they were chastised. And if this would not have been Heaven's will, how could they have been conquered? You state: 'I am a Christian. I worship God. I accuse and condemn those who don't.' What makes you think that you are in God's good grace, and that you know what pleases God? Upon what judgment are your words based? Through the power of Eternal Heaven all the lands from sunrise to sunset have been bestowed upon Us. How could anyone achieve our accomplishments without Heaven's consent and order? After considering this, does not your own heart tell you that you must become our subject, and put whatever power you may hold at our disposal? Not unless you, in person, at the head of all your monarchs without exception, come to pay homage, and to offer your services, shall We recognize your submission. If you don't abide by the commandment of Heaven and by Our orders, We shall know that you are Our foe. This is what We have to tell you. Should you fail to act accordingly, how could We foretell what will happen to you? Heaven only knows the answer."

The voice of Siberia had spoken to the West. It had used distortions, perversions, and hypocrisies taken from conquered cultures to bedeck its innate crudity, just as Siberian rulers used Chinese paintings to adorn the site of a Kuriltai; but the message it conveyed expressed the immutable Siberian resolve to conquer and to consume creatures, goods, and creeds, and to do so without scruples.

Plan Carpin delivered the message, but the "great Pope and his monarchs" did not go to Karakorum. They probably considered the letter that bore Kuyuk's seal an oddity that did not warrant action, or contemplation, a document of the heathens' confusion.

The God-fearing messengers were shipped west on horseback, with no more convenience than they had on their express trip to Karakorum. Carpin's account on his mission winds up with the story of hardships suffered along the Tatar line of communication.

The eighteen-year plan of aggression, of which the slaves had spoken, remained a phantom.

CHAPTER SEVENTEEN There was one word in the vocabulary of the conquered for which the Mongols had no use: gratitude.

Gratitude did not figure in Mongolian mentality. No Siberian would do something unless ordered by a superior, or unless he considered it to be profitable. Neither required gratitude.

But Turakina had expected Kuyuk to think it profitable to act as her puppet. Through her slave girl's Mohammedan she controlled the civilian administration; and during the Kuriltai she had established solid ties with princes and other dignitaries who had wooed her and had lavishly greased the paws of her favorites.

After the Kuriltai was dissolved, however, Kuyuk broke with the regent. Abandoned by all her former cajolers, Turakina made a unsuccessful attempt at fleeing Karakorum, and then retired into her tent in fear-ridden obscurity until she was killed by intruders who could only have been the Great Khan's henchmen.

Her slave was accused of being a bearer of evil spirits, and sentenced to be drowned. The girl's Mohammedan lover, having denied his corrupt activities, was put to death as a liar. The executioner was ordered not to leave one drop of blood in the liar's body, so that his soul would be completely destroyed.

All the civilian functionaries nominated during Turakina's regency were charged with having given false accounts on their corrupt activities, and summarily executed as liars. All civil servants dismissed by the fallen administration were restored to office.

The military enjoyed the civilians' disgrace, which they trusted would eventually lead to a concentration of all administrative powers in the hands of the army. But soon they were rudely awakened from their happy dreams, when Kuyuk ordered them to render account on gathered loot. Lack of exact recollections, or denial of personal responsibilities, was not accepted as a valid excuse. Whoever could not present proof for what he had ever said or signed was a marked man. The purge of the army was almost as violent as that of the civilian administration, and while the latter followed a clear and altogether rightful pattern, the former turned into an arbitrary, whimsical butchery.

Princes who tried to interfere in favor of officers were asked to give accounts on the collected revenues of their fiefs, and invariably charged with mendacious misappropriation of funds. Several members of the ruling house were put to death at the side of the brocade tent in which they had played ball games only a few short months before.

Terror spread through the realm; but this time the masters trembled, not the chattels. Nobody knew who the next victim of Kuyuk's mania would be.

The new Great Khan was haunted by two nightmares: the breakup of the universal empire, and the loss of his virility.

The princes were still paying lip service to the Yassak, but they were pursuing selfish ends. The spirit of separatism, perennial empire wrecker, raised its frightening head. Kuyuk's fear-inspired frenzy did not generate separatism, but it stimulated already existing tendencies to carve sovereign dominions out of the empire. With lucidity born out of hatred Kuyuk had realized that Batu would not remain loyal, and Batu's bad example might encourage apostasy. He, Kuyuk, would have to answer for the empire that heaven and Temudshin had bequeathed upon his family for eternity. Batu had been closely associated with Subotai; Subotai was the army's idol; Kuyuk did not know that Subotai had overruled Batu in Hungary, but he did not dare to dismiss Subotai; yet he would crush his admirers who might nurse rebellious thoughts.

The Great Khan yearned for Yeliu. Tshinkai always invoked the memory of the wise Chinese when offering suggestions. But Tshinkai was not Yeliu, and he too might be unreliable. Kuyuk wanted to establish a system of government in which every man in office would be watched by an informer, and all informers by secret stool pigeons, and all stool pigeons by yet another group of informers.

Tshinkai suggested the establishment of limited national autonomy in obedient provinces. Former rulers should be reinstated as puppet kings, and pry on Mongolian governors. Local magistrates should watch Mongolian district administrators. National officials would denounce Mongols and vice versa, and both would court the Great Khan's favors. Kuyuk called the proposition inadequate, but decided to try it, adding a touch of unmitigated brutality to the pattern. Officials were dismissed, tried on trumped-up charges, and invariably sentenced to death, either bloodless death, by being wrapped in a rug and trampled upon by horses, or death with loss of blood and soul, by being chopped into small bits, according to the Great Khan's whims.

These whims depended on Kuyuk's sexual mood. His debaucheries turned into tribulations for the women and tormenting trials for himself. The Great Khan went to his orgies like a jittery student going to a test. Would he, or wouldn't he succeed? If he did, courtesans would get a carload of jewels; if he didn't, girls would be strangled in Karakorum; and thousands of miles away thousands of officeholders would meet violent death. Nervous irritation affected Kuyuk's virility. To him virility was not only a source of delight, but the basic quality of a universal ruler. The women toiled to stir the Great Khan's sensuality, constantly inventing new tricks and perversions. Kuyuk found them lacking, stupid, dull. . . . He wanted stronger impulses, just as he wanted better administrative designs and tougher army control.

Affairs of state and affairs of lewdness became hopelessly entwined, and beclouded the ruler's mind. Kuyuk longed for an outlet for his mounting frenzy—an act of violence that would once and for all destroy his antagonists and restore his self-confidence.

The objective of his violence could be but Batu. Once Batu was destroyed, all rebels would knuckle under. It would be Kuyuk's supreme triumph, and it would raise his potency.

The army, he trusted, would not save Batu from the Great Khan's wrath. The day before Kuyuk made his decision, Subotai died. No other general, not even Subotai's son, would defy the Great Khan's orders.

Batu was a transgressor of the law. His absence from the Kuriltai had been a serious infringement, but more serious even was his failure to do homage to the new Great Khan. All Djenghiskhanides had appeared before Kuyuk, their caps and belts removed as a sign of submission; only the bastard's bastard had stayed away.

Kuyuk's central administration requested that Batu present the accounts of his fief. From Batu's camp the messengers returned empty-handed. They had been told to leave; that was all. The supreme command of the army, requested to give an estimate of Batu's forces, reported that they were equal, if not superior, to anything at Kuyuk's disposal. This sounded like a conspiracy, but Kuyuk could not lay hands upon ringleaders. He ordered secret investigations among officials, officers, priests, and princes of the blood.

Shamanist wizards, smarting under the increased influence of other religions, attempted to talk the Great Khan into banishing all other clerics from his court. They insisted that this would restore everybody to the traditional

Mongolian way of loyalty, veracity, and obedience. Kuyuk listened grave-faced, and then announced that he was from that day on protector of the Nestorian faith. The frustrated shamans retired without a word. Nestorian preachers, however, who triumphantly tried to proclaim their faith as the official religion of the universal empire, were warned that Kuyuk's protection gave him exclusive power over Nestorianism, but did not give its preachers special privileges. Besides Kuyuk indicated that the great Pope would also be granted the Great Khan's protection after taking the oath of fealty.

The Great Khan was about to assemble his soldiers for a drive toward the setting sun. Generals would be briefed that this was a resumption of the campaign interrupted by the death of Ogödai. Batu would be directed to send his auxiliaries to an assembly point east of the mouth of the Volga, and to wait in his camp several hundred miles away for further orders. But as soon as Batu's men were incorporated into his army, Kuyuk would march to Batu's residence, kill the bastard's bastard and all his family, and seize his fief.

But the Great Khan felt that he would have to take somebody into his confidence. The most distinguished personality in Karakorum was the ranking Djenghiskhanide dowager Sorgaqtani, widow of Prince Toului. The lady had never tried to promote her own offspring in the scramble for the throne, or even for exalted appointments. She was above distrust.

The Great Khan paid the dowager his respects and in a heart to heart talk, the first he had had with anybody since the Kuriltai, he told her of his intentions and his worries about disloyalty. Sorgaqtani deplored the lack of tradition among the young generation and the older princes' shortsighted egotism, and offered her own son, Mongka, to act as Kuyuk's confidential man and secret informer.

Mongka, without cap and belt, renewed his homage and was welcomed by the Great Khan.

Through him Batu learned of Kuyuk's intentions.

Sorgaqtani, incensed at seeing her family by-passed in the selection of supreme rulers, had been the rebellious prince's ally and informer for the past two years.

Batu took his auxiliaries, twenty tümen strong, to the assigned assembly point, ready to attack and to treat Kuyuk as Kuyuk had intended to treat him.

Both armies broke camp in March 1248 but did not meet. In April, Kuyuk died from exhaustion, after a sadistic orgy in his headquarters. His forces escorted his body to Karakorum. Batu's tümens, however, did not stop their march.

They turned east, toward the Siberian lake of Issyk-Kul, and from a camp set up at the shore, Batu summoned all Djenghiskhanides to a Kuriltai.

According to the Yassak, a Kuriltai had to be called by the acting regent, on the site of inauguration. The legitimate offspring of Ogödai and Djagatai indignantly protested against the outrage. They insisted that one of Kuyuk's widows was the rightful regent, that she would convoke a Kuriltai to Karakorum. Quotcha, Kuyuk's young son, was first in line for the throne. Royalty at Karakorum requested Djenghiskhanides to boycott Batu's illicit gathering. Sorgaqtani and Mongka were cordially invited to join the loyalists in their action to make the Yassak prevail.

But the dowager and her son ignored the invitation and traveled to Issyk-Kul. The *coup d'état* Kuriltai was formally presided over by Batu's younger brother Berké, a man of great energy and swift decision. The white marquee, in which rebellious princes gathered in increasing numbers, was surrounded by hardened veterans of the Polish and Hungarian campaigns. The brocade marquee in Karakorum stayed almost empty. In what seemed to be a surprising change of heart even members of Ogödai's and Djagatai's families journeyed to the distant lake; escorted by a pompous host of warriors. But these warriors were not guards of honor as their masters said, but regulars assigned to seize Batu, Berké, Sorgaqtani, Mongka, and all the other conspirators. However, their attempt at quelling the rebellion was drowned in blood; Berké was quicker than his opponents.

Batu and his brother could have had any member of their family chosen as Great Khan, but they decided in favor of Mongka, who ascended the Golden Throne in 1251.

His enthronement, by the grace of a rebel governor-prince, marked the end of the legacy of the Djenghis Khan, of his vision of a centralized universal empire. Not even a quarter of a century had passed since the remains of Temudshin had been laid to rest. But more victims than all those the Djenghis Khan's campaigns had claimed were still to fall, more realms to totter under the blows of the horsemen, and the picture of even greater barbaric strength to emerge before the eyes of fear-stricken nations, until, centuries after it was created, the remnants of a phantom empire would crumble into dust, leaving behind a dragon seed that keeps sprouting and destroying to the present day.

Batu was the first prince who did not believe in the solidity of the Djenghiskhanide empire. Living in splendid ostracism, far away from the Great Khan's court, where everybody was under the spell of sheer indestructible splendor, camping in the lonely steppes of the Volga, between yet unconquered lands in the distant West and an unscrutable suzerain in the Far East, Batu pondered about the mechanics of might. No man, he thought, was powerful enough to rule the universe. He would have to delegate powers and depend on men who exerted them in his name. And law was an inanimate thing, subject to administration by men who would apply it as they saw fit. Batu did not covet the universal throne, nor did he want responsibility for the Yassak. He wanted to be the strongest of all governors, to make his realm as large as he could control it, to use the law at his own discretion, to make Great Khans dependent upon his support, and never to depend upon a Great Khan's good will. He would turn his fief into a hereditary realm that would outlast the deceptive throne of the universe.

Consolidating his realm, Batu laid the foundations of modern Russia, just as Rurik, another foreigner, had laid the foundation to ancient Russia. Slavic princes under the Mongolian sway were unified by shackles of common bondage to the Mongolian prince and his Golden Ordu; their subjects no longer faced each other in arms during internecine strife; they all served as auxiliaries in the armies of the foreign ruler.

Batu, to the Russians, became Tsar Batu, a Caesar who claimed as his property even what was rightfully the Lord's. Tsar Batu did not delegate powers, but he gave assignments which, carried out in his name, procured power and wealth. Batu and his successors appointed tax collectors, princelings who gleefully fleeced princes, and made good for their sovereign and for themselves. The rulers of Muscovy collaborated with the Mongols to squeeze dues out of other puppet rulers. Without Mongolian taxation Muscovy might never have become a predominant factor in Russia and without the Golden Ordu, seven hundred years ago, there might be no Russia today.

Mongka's mother had adopted the Nestorian faith and had raised her son in that creed. As a Nestorian, the Great Khan did not believe in Tängri; as a ruler of the universal empire, he had to trust in the mission bestowed upon him by the Eternal Blue Sky. This was a dilemma which not even the most ingenious men could have solved, and Mongka was not really ingenious. The shamans evaded his court, but they became ever more popular with the common people, who wanted no part in religions whose gods were incorruptible to the point of not making rain in exchange for rams and kumiss, most of which was consumed by the applicants for precipitation.

Mongka claimed to rule according to the Yassak, but his subjects whispered that he ruled according to Batu's orders. The new Great Khan was forty-three years old, when the Kuriltai of Issyk-Kul nominated him; he was a professed purist, sober, not easily seduced by courtesans, and not tempted by treasures.

His reign started with another purge of the administration. Mongka had to settle Batu's old scores and those of his mother. He appointed a special investigator who was also chief prosecutor and supervisor of executions. Eldjigidai, the appointee, was a meticulous man who did not believe in either innocence or attenuating circumstances, but in the collective guilt of families. If one person was found guilty, his next of kin would be executed without charges.

Tshinkai was among the first victims of the purge. Few civil servants survived, but the Great Khan was careful not to hit the army too hard. He needed well-trained soldiers, and he made the army the top of the social edifice. But simultaneously he tightened the rules of discipline to an extent that made service in the ranks no more pleasant than forced labor. The Mongolian nobility's traditional tax exemption was revoked. The princes' discretionary powers were curtailed. They were ordered to spend most of their time at Karakorum, where they were not entertained with fine food and drink, games and girls, but kept busy hunting, strenuous ancient Mongolian style, and participating in army maneuvers with all the rigors of actual campaigning.

The princes grumbled, and they were particularly angry because Mongka did not include the bastards of the Golden Ordu in the disciplinary routine.

Tsar Batu never went to Karakorum. He used the last years of his life to consolidate his fief, which reached from the vicinity of Lake Balkhash to the shores of the Black Sea. In 1255 he died, leaving behind a domain and an army that Mongka could not hope to bring solidly under his sway.

But the Great Khan had other plans. He would complete the subjugation of all of China, and he would found another Greater Persian Empire under Mongolian sovereignty. After this was achieved, the Golden Ordu would have to abandon its separatist attitude.

The new aggression should start without delay. However disciplined, a waiting army was bound to turn stale.

Mongka's younger brother, Kubilai, would be invested with all of China; Hulägu, another brother, would govern the Middle East. Both would be the Great Khan's liege men and their combined fiefs would assure the house of Toului lasting hegemony among the Djenghiskhanides. The Great Khan was careful not to involve Batu in the coming struggle and to keep the main Mongolian armies as far away as possible from the Russian domain.

Batu knew every detail of Mongka's plans, but he had no objection. It seemed to be to his advantage that the forces of Karakorum were engaged in costly and prolonged warfare, conquering devastated land which would not be rebuilt as well-cultivated farmland with prosperous cities. Meantime he would consolidate his domain, making it a going concern, and a source of increasing strength.

CHAPTER EIGHTEEN Both Kubilai and Hulägu pledged themselves to conquer territories not yet under the Mongolian sway and to organize them in accordance with the law of Temudshin as parts of the indivisible, universal empire. But neither Kubilai nor Hulägu intended to serve as liege man of a Great Khan, be he their brother or any other Djenghiskhanide, after their own fiefs were consolidated.

Kubilai had spent many years in Ho-nan Province. He had been reared by Chinese educators and cared more for Chinese art, agriculture, and industry than for Mongolian tradition. Yet his Mongolian blood clamored for forcible seizure of what he loved; he coveted all of China, not just the parts he had been administering. Even these sections had shrunk during the years that preceded Mongka's order. Mongolian occupation forces had been reduced; Song Chinese generals had boldly seized the initiative and recaptured some ground. This grieved the Mongolian prince, whom his tutors had told about a Greater China, comprising, not only Kin and Song territories, but also Yu-nan, Tibetan, and Annamese land. He wanted to be the unifier of China, and rule the empire in its own tradition rather than as an immense horse pasture.

Kubilai had a number of auxiliaries, some Chinese, others Siberians who had served with Kin, Song, or anybody who paid fees. Not all these men were as proficient riders as Batu's Southern Russian mercenaries, but they made better war-machine crews than those ignorant Slavs.

From Karakorum came the son of Subotai at the head of the Great Khan's shock troops, to supervise operations in China. The general had inherited part of his father's strategic dexterity, but not Subotai's tempestuous, sweeping speed. His men were welded into a high-precision fighting machine, better organized but less fear-inspiring than the host that had borne down on the Kin forty-one years before. The tümens still carried the dreaded Mongolian standard, but even the soldiers from Karakorum were no longer a solid national force. Many of them were foreigners whose fathers had been slaves and who now were regulars.

In October 1252 the Mongols opened the drive. They did not speed into Song China, as had been expected in Karakorum, but invaded Yu-nan instead. After defeating Yu-nan the army proceeded to Tibet and subjugated the Tibetans, tribe by tribe. Five years later Kubilai was still operating on the fringe of the Song Empire, conquering Annam and its capital of Hanoi.

Karakorum inquired why the army was engaged in such time-absorbing moves. Kubilai replied that his strategy aimed at covering his flanks, which was part and parcel of Mongolian regulations. More puzzling even than Kubilai's military procedure was his attitude toward subjected sovereigns. Instead of mercilessly tracking him down, he permitted the King of Yu-nan to retain his throne as a maharaja, and appointed an adviser to the Maharaja, who was not even a Mongol, but a Chinese. He did not slay Tibetan chieftains, but accepted their oath of fealty and offered the same treatment to the ruler of Annam.

Kubilai's maneuvers indicated arbitrary designs; interfamily separatism would frustrate Mongka's plans to establish his family's hegemony. Already notables at Karakorum talked about Kubilai's enigmatic attitude. After the conquest of Annam, Mongka called a Kuriltai to discuss current issues. The gathering of princes, the highest ranking of them Ariq-Bögä, another brother of Mongka, did not consider a demotion of Kubilai, but hailed Mongka as the commander in chief of all armed forces and as a genius who would always lead armies in the right direction. The Great Khan ordered his brother to stop flank-securing operations, and attack Song China without further delay.

Kubilai complied, having achieved his aim at conquering the lost parts of Greater China. Soldiers carrying the Mongolian banner invaded China from three sides, in an operation reminiscent of the Hungarian-Silesian campaign. Mongka himself joined the army in the field. But the Chinese did not fold up under the impact of Mongolian weapons as the Europeans had done. The suppliers of Mongolian equipment were familiar with its effects, and they even had a few machines of destruction of which the Mongols knew nothing. The drive, however, gained momentum and by August 1259 the invaders besieged the heavily fortified town of Ho-ts'iuan. Under the walls of this city Mongka died of dysentery.

Kubilai at once signed an armistice and a preliminary peace with the Song Emperor. The terms were mild if not gentlemanly.

In 1259, Kubilai was more determined than ever to conquer China, but he realized that he could never achieve this goal as long as another man sat on Temudshin's throne, a Great Khan who could assume command of his armies, depose him, even try him for disobedience. In order to become Emperor of China, Kubilai would have to become Great Khan first.

Mongka had died at a most convenient moment. Four years before, Batu had passed away. Batu's successor would shun the Kuriltai that would nominate the new Great Khan, and he did not yet wield sufficient influence with the Mongolian princes to direct their votes. And Hulägu, another candidate, would also be absent. Hulägu had styled himself Khan of Greater Persia, after subduing the Khalifates of Bagdad and Mesopotamia and reinvading Syria, countries that had enjoyed limited national autonomy under Kuyuk's reform and were startled to learn, by fire and sword, that autonomy was rebellion under a new, unpublicized reform. Hulägu wanted Persia to be his hereditary realm, and, to retain it, he did not consider it necessary to seize the throne of Karakorum.

There remained Ariq-Bögä and Kaidu as contenders. Ariq-Bögä was a pompous yes-man; this, at least, he had seemed to be at the last Kuriltai, of which Kubilai had confidential reports. He would not gain much support. Kaidu, a member of the house of Ogödai, would not be popular with Djenghiskhanide princes, who usually sided with the branch of their family that held the empire's purse strings and distributed sinecures.

Kubilai rode toward Karakorum in a happy frame of mind. He expected to be Great Khan and to return to China before the winter was over.

Ariq-Bögä was nominal commander of the Guards. The Guards virtually forced their commander to stage a coup. Kubilai was rudely awakened by a dispatch from Karakorum notifying him of Ariq-Bögä's seizure of the throne. A small band of frightened princes held in custody by the Guards had voted for the nomination of Kubilai's brother.

But the successors of Temudshin's invincible elite were a braggart lot of overfed, overdressed, blackmailing seekers of sinecures. On learning that Kubilai was nearing Karakorum in forced marches, with his cavalry racing toward the Yenisei River to mop up Guard-officered units, they made overtures to the elder prince, but Kubilai was in no mood to bicker and bargain. His vanguards made short work of the troops on the Yenisei. Karakorum opened the gates of its brick wall to the home-comer; Ariq-Bögä fled, apparently resigned to the loss of the throne.

Kubilai entered the capital as a Great Khan. Anxious as he was to dispatch formalities, he had gathered royalty serving in his army into a mobile Kuriltai and had them vote for him as a ruler of the universe. This was a travesty of the most sacred command of the Yassak, but Kubilai had no respect for Temudshin's law unless it served his purpose. He did not even invoke the Yassak to prosecute Ariq-Bögä; Kuriltai would not waste time hunting the impostor, or waiting until all the princes had rendered homage. Kaidu had not yet bowed, head bared, belt over his shoulder, when Kubilai, after spending a few pleasant nights under the golden tent, left Karakorum, leaving but a small unit of his most faithful men behind.

But Kaidu had already joined Ariq-Bögä; the prince of the house of Ogödai had a well-trained military force of his own, and he assured the fugitive that he would support his bid for recapture of the throne and make him the rallying center of a Djenghiskhanide drive for law and family unity. Ariq-Bögä stalled, scared by the thought of another *putsch* which, if successful, would make him a puppet of the indomitable Kaidu, and expose him to the vengeance of Kubilai, should it fail.

Disgruntled princes of Djagatai's clan went to the eastern foothills of the Altai Mountains, where Kaidu pleaded with the ex-Great Khan and enlisted recruits from neighboring tribes. The descendants of Djagatai also had soldiers, not the flower of the Mongolian army, but tough mercenaries who would neither ask for, nor give, quarter. Princes and officers jointly insisted that Ariq-Bögä assume command of all anti-Kubilai forces; and Ariq-Bögä, more frightened of his adherents present than of his absent foe, took the helm of the makeshift army and raced toward Karakorum in a desperate effort to get over with the risky adventure.

Karakorum again opened its doors. Kubilai's faithful were massacred by soldiers and civilians, and Ariq-Bögä moved back under the golden roof.

Kubilai had been regrouping his forces for a resumption of hostilities against China when he learned of the revolution. Only a fraction of his army was ready for a swift counterblow, but Kubilai gathered whatever tümen were available, and swung north toward the fringe of the Gobi Desert, while from Karakorum the bulk of the revolutionary army moved in the opposite direction to meet him.

On the arid grounds of the Gobi where, half covered by shifting sand, bleached the bones of tribesmen slain by earlier Mongolian great khans, descendants of victims, born into a tyranny which was the only way of life they knew, fought and died so that one tyrant would prevail after another.

Kubilai won the battle, but did not press the pursuit. Was it impatience to return to China that caused the Great Khan to hold his forces back? Was it a sudden horror of fratricidal strife? Or had the victorious army suffered severe casualties?

Whatever the reasons for Kubilai's reluctance to inflict the coup de grâce, it almost resulted in his own annihilation. Ten days after the battle the defeated returned to the blood-soaked grounds; and this time the tide turned against Kubilai. Already his Chinese mercenaries were rushing off in disorder, abandoning heavy equipment. His cavalry was thrown into confusion. The high-precision war machine no longer responded to its operators' motions. Already enemy patrols circled Kubilai's army, showering it with deadly arrows. But while their soldiers were winning the battle, princes in Ariq-Bögä's command post quarreled about the spoils, and before Kubilai's men were annihilated, a prince of the house of Djagatai went over. This defection turned victory into a draw. Exhausted and greatly reduced in numbers, both armies camped on the battlefield.

Not until 1262 did the internecine campaign resume. Kubilai got the upper hand, but still another two years went by until Ariq-Bögä threw himself at the mercy of his brother, the undisputed Great Khan.

The Yassak did not mention war among the Djenghiskhanides. If ever the thought of internecine strife occurred to Temudshin or Yeliu, they probably dismissed it from their minds as sheer heresy. It was the essence of the law not to give mercy to the defeated; yet Kubilai spared Ariq-Bögä and held him in custody until his death in 1266. Antagonistic officials, guardsmen, and nobles of all ranks were summarily executed, however. The younger generation of Djenghiskhanides depended upon advisers for important action; with no experts left to counsel insurgents, Kubilai trusted, there would be no insurgence.

It took Kubilai until 1265 to replenish his armies. And still their strength seemed not quite up to requirements when he invaded China without a warning. Song Emperor Ton-t'song had more efficient generals than most of his predecessors. These officers had kept telling him ever since the signature of the preliminary peace that the Mongol would strike again; they had indicated that, after half a century of constant warfare against the barbarians ways and means had been found to cope with enemy strategy. Given a reasonable military budget and regular draft laws, they promised to defeat the perennial invaders. The generals wanted to tie a substantial part of the invading armies into prolonged sieges of fortified communication hubs and to use small, superbly trained and equipped mobile units to engage roving Mongolian cavalry wherever the odds were favorable, whittling down enemy strength, disrupting enemy communications, and decimating the foe without fighting hazardous major battles.

Ton-t'song was an easygoing, pleasure-seeking monarch who detested the discomfort of war. He had an innate disgust for saber-rattling individuals, and loathed to see public funds go into clumsy fortresses and ugly machines of destruction instead of the beautification of imperial palaces.

His minister of state and personal favorite, Kia Sseu-tao, exploited his master's aversions. He upset the military planning, skillfully playing general against general and the Emperor against anybody who did not predict that there would be peace for the lifetimes of many generations. Ton-t'song gave Kia Sseu-tao unlimited power to deal with public finances and matters of national defense. Nefarious statesmen were no novelty in cabal-ridden China; under the circumstances, however, it could have been that Kia Sseu-tao was not just another intriguer, but the ancestor of modern villains who, in the pay of foreigners, set out to grab their countries, sabotaged resistance, and undermined morale. He withheld allotted funds for construction of a river flotilla. He refused to promulgate new draft laws and to extend the validity of existing recruiting orders.

When Kubilai struck, the Chinese could not disrupt the Mongolian supply and communication system. Several fortresses resisted tenaciously, but Chinese mobile units, under strength and lacking fast-moving artillery, did not inflict much punishment upon their opponents.

Kubilai's aides, Atchou, grandson of Subotai, and Bayan, "The Fortunate," did not share the Great Khan's secret concern over the welfare of China. To them the Yassak was still the one and only basic law of war, and the Mongolian tradition of destruction the only correct way of executing it. They let their men sack, loot, and kill to their violent instinct's content. Kubilai did not interfere with the outrages. He could not hope to keep his men under control without destroying their martial spirit.

Chinese engineers serving in the Mongolian armies were told to build stronger siege engines. The Chinese, fearful of retribution but even more horrified at the prospect of sped-up butchery, experimented with a few changes of design, but did not produce better weapons. Kubilai probably understood the motives behind this unexpected inefficiency, but he wanted to finish the conquest and summoned Mohammedan engineers from Mesopotamia. The Mohammedans were outstanding experts, but they were startled by the strength of Chinese masonry. It took until 1273 to reduce strongholds blocking the Mongolian advance to the lower Han Valley. Chinese river captains performed feats of epic valor to supply besieged garrisons. Emperor Ton-t'song turned most of his powers over to Kia Sseu-tao. As the Mongolian armies poured through the Han Valley toward the strategic Yangtse, the cities on their way, having received controversial orders from the government and running short of provisions, surrendered quickly. In 1275 the Chinese Emperor died, or, at least, this was the year in which his death was announced by Kia Sseu-tao, who prevailed upon the Empress to have her four-year-old son crowned, to nominate him his tutor, and to discharge all generals. Next he had the dowager and the boy Emperor surrender to Bayan, who sent the precious hostages to his master. Kubilai treated them with perfect civility.

After the army disintegrated, Chinese patriots kept up guerrilla resistance. They used river craft to infiltrate Mongolian-held territory, and applied raiding tactics learned from earlier invaders to keep the conquerors off balance. But, owing to Kia Sseu-tao's sabotage, Chinese shipyards had been idle for several years, leaving the country with inadequate shipping; and when they resumed operation after 1275, it was for the benefit of the Mongols. In 1279, when Kubilai gained control of the inland waterways, the guerrillas abducted the boy Emperor and led him aboard a seagoing fishing vessel which was part of a flotilla based on outlying islands, assembled to continue the struggle at sea. But a Chinese-built Mongolian armada tracked the boat down and the little prince, of whom the saying goes that he struggled valiantly against Mongolian boarding crews, was drowned.

For the first time Greater China was united under one conqueror. In sixty-eight years of war the population of China had been reduced by about 60,-000,000, roughly 60 per cent of the combined population of its territories.

These are the highest casualties, in absolute number, and percentagewise, recorded in any war in world history. The figure includes civilian casualties, which outnumbered military losses by 100 to 1.

Kubilai, grandson of a nomad, offspring of "those who lived in felt tents," shed the redoubtable name of his family and even fancied a new personal name. He had embraced China—an embrace that cost hecatombs—and he wanted to be adopted by China as national ruler. The Djenghiskhanide styled himself founder of the ruling Chinese house of Yuan, a new dynasty to continue where the previous nineteen dynasties had left off, and to last forever. Chinese courtiers called him Emperor She-tsu, and he enjoyed being so addressed.

As an emperor of China, Kubilai's principal designs were peace, reconstruction, and prosperity. Nobody within the boundaries of his empire could challenge the monarch's sincerity, but had some suicidally inclined individual called Kubilai's professed love of peace hypocrisy, the Emperor would have been genuinely indignant, for he believed in his peacefulness. It was a Siberian's notion of concord, unaffected by the mollifying influences of sedate cultures and creeds.

Already during the first phase of his campaign Kubilai had dispatched cavalry to Korea to make that ancient kingdom knuckle under to his rule and ready itself for incorporation into conquered China. In 1268, while his armies were stalled because of deficient siege equipment, the Great Khan requested Japan to recognize his suzerainty. But the Regent of Japan, Shogun Hojo Tomi Kune, declined and repeated his refusal three years later.

The Chinese campaign was not quite over when, in 1274, the future Emperor organized an expedition to chastise Japan. The annexation of Korea having been proclaimed, Korean recruits were drafted into the expeditionary force; so were Chinese prisoners of war. Mongolian horsemen were not available in number, and there was no adequate shipping space to carry their horses.

After looting the islands of Tsushima and Ikishima, Kubilai's mercenaries invaded Kyushu. The Japanese were taken by surprise by Chinese-built cannon, but recovered quickly and, after a sharp encounter near Mizuki, the landing parties took to their boats and left ingloriously. The Shogun used contemptful language to turn down a final request for surrender that came in 1276.

Five years later an unforgiving Emperor of China mustered the strongest combined force his men-of-war could carry, to avenge humiliation. Kubilai She-tsu had 45,000 Mongols and 120,000 Chinese and Koreans shipped to Kyushu in June 1281. Only part of the Mongols were mounted, they were ill at ease among their unscrutable comrades-in-arms, and most of them were affected by the voyage through unseasonably rough seas. The Chinese and Koreans fought badly. The huge army remained hemmed in a narrow perimeter and, under constant Japanese attack, it could not unload its artillery. On August 15 a typhoon scattered the invasion fleet and with the armada the soldiers were doomed. The victorious Japanese killed or captured most of them. Among the few who escaped the fury of the storm was the commander of the expeditionary force. Kubilai had him tightly sewn into the hide of a freshly slaughtered buffalo and left in the sun to be crushed to death by the drying and shrinking hide.

The battle of August 15, 1281, has become a legend in Japan, with various versions. One of them calls it a naval victory, which it certainly was not; another tells of the destruction of Kubilai's men, horses, cannon, and boats by the storm, which does not give due credit to Japanese soldierdom.

Kubilai did not attack Japan again.

Another sea-borne expedition which the aged Emperor sent against Java in 1293, to seize the fabulous island for China, did not attain its objective either. The Chinese soldiers, under the command of Chinese officers, captured the capital city, but eventually were ousted and forced to evacuate.

Land campaigns for the aggrandizement of China were not always successful either. An attempt to annex Indo-China in 1285 failed, and another invasion two years later was also repulsed. Kubilai's son Toghon, in charge of the first invasion army, displayed poor generalship.

Two invasions of Burma, immediately preceding the Indo-Chinese venture, did not crush Burmese resistance. It took ten years and a third offensive to force the Burmese to recognize China's suzerainty. Marco Polo, Kubilai's most enthusiastic chronicler, gave a glowing account of the Emperor's archers prevailing over Burmese war elephants. The merchant from Venice was no eyewitness to the battle of the Irrawady Valley, but his story was not disproved by other reports.

And there was yet another war that plagued Kubilai. Kaidu, the implacable foe, had escaped Ariq-Bögä's disaster; Kubilai had not interfered with his flight to southern Central Siberia. There the prince had gathered new forces, carved out a fief that included parts of Kazakstan and Dzungaria, and in another internecine war seized large territories from the Djagataide fief. From a fugitive Kaidu turned into a powerful prince, again a pretender to the throne of Karakorum. Kubilai was still fighting in China when Kaidu, with the support of other Djenghiskhanide royalty, assumed the title of Khagan.

Kubilai dispatched Mongolian princes of the blood serving in his army to hold Karakorum with whatever reserves were available. But the princes handed the Mongolian capital over to Kaidu.

The dust had not settled over China's battlefields and victims were not yet buried when General Bayan at the head of Kubilai's cavalry raced north to wrest Karakorum from the pretender. The rebels were garrulous mediocrities and offered little resistance; Bayan was under orders not to execute captives. And much as the general might have wanted to dispose of the lot, Kubilai pardoned them all and even permitted Kaidu to return to his fief, where the defeated prince set up felt tents on huge wagons and gave a display of traditional Djenghiskhanide rusticity that contrasted with the refined, Sinofied way of living adopted by Kubilai and his clan.

Leniency was wasted on Kaidu, who, in the tradition of his country, had no sense of gratitude. He plotted with relatives who had been endowed by Kubilai with lands in Eastern Mongolia and Manchuria. In 1288 the seventy-two-year-old Emperor of China had to take to the field to crush their rebellion. The Chinese were equipped with the finest weapons Chinese and Mohammedan engineers could build. They were supported by a superb river flotilla, the guns of which were trained at chariots blocking the lane of attack against the rebel camp. Kubilai, who as a boy had watched Temudshin direct battles from horseback, looked on from an armored turret carried by four gaudily harnessed elephants, as his armies broke through the line of chariots; he saw the lightning-fast rebel archers gallop away in the direction of the Siberian plains and vanish, just as ancient Siberian raiders had occasionally vanished from the sight of slow Chinese infantry.

Kubilai did not transplant Siberian military virtue to Greater China, and the members of the Yuan dynasty were more Sinofied than their predecessors of Chinese origin. Kubilai would have been horrified had he known that, less than one century after he established his rule, the last Yuan emperor, ignominiously chased from his residence, had nothing to offer but a rhymed lament: "O my great city of Taidu [Peking], adorned with colorful splendor; Chang-tou, my deliciously fresh summer-residence; and all the aureous plains, charm and relaxation of my divine ancestors, what evil did I commit to lose my Empire like that . . . !"

CHAPTER NINETEEN Kubilai was thirty-six years old when he reached for his coveted objective. He was sixty when Chinese organized resistance came to an end and the throne of the empire was his, by the law of the club, which was, and has always remained, the foundation of Siberian rule. He had to make up for many years lost, and for many frustrated expectations. But he was still healthy, and able to harvest the personal delights that ripened for him from crops of the blood of many million men, women, and children.

"The Emperor," Marco Polo tells us, "is of middle stature . . . his limbs are well formed, and in his whole figure there is a just proportion. His complexion is fair and occasionally suffused with red, like the bright tint of the rose, which adds much grace to his countenance. His eyes are black and handsome, his nose is well-shaped and prominent."[1] This description is typical of the bad old custom of calling the mighty handsome, youthful, and altogether romantic-looking. Yet there exists no other description of Kubilai's appearance.

The Lord of Lords, as his title as the head of the Djenghiskhanides implied, was of fantastic ostentatiousness, and his thirst for pleasure was insatiable.

He established his residence at Peking, which had risen from the ashes, and had the capital lavishly adorned with all the marvels that Chinese art and architecture could provide. When Chinese astrologers and soothsayers indicated that misfortune might be brewing on the site of the old city, Kubilai had the new city of Taidu built across the river, and ordered his subjects to move into the new town, which, however, was not large enough to accommodate them all. Therefore, Peking and Taidu eventually merged.

Taidu was laid out as a square, its sides each six miles long. The city was surrounded by thirty-two miles of walls and deep ditches, and inside the fortifications were eight military storehouses holding the equipment for an army of 300,000.

Inside the city an enclosure twenty-five feet high and four miles long protected an imperial game preserve in which deer and roe were kept.

The grounds of the Imperial Winter Palace, where Kubilai lived for the greater part of the year, reached from the northern to the southern gate of Taidu. A huge wall of white marble, built like an immense terrace, surrounded the parks, fountains, and buildings of the residence. Marble was Kubilai's favorite building material, and white his favorite color, but he would have the roofs of buildings brightly colored in red, green, azure, and violet. The house in which Kubilai slept, and held intimate parties, contained more rooms than the Emperor would ever care to visit, but they were all steadily patrolled by his bodyguard of 12,000—the Knights Devoted to Their Lord. One fourth of them was on day and night duty in their lord's habitation, while others were riding rounds through the city to arrest disorderly individuals. Prostitutes, of whom there were 25,000 in Taidu, were considered orderly, but persons who stayed out after the third stroke of the great city bell were arrested, subjected to the bastinade, and occasionally died under the procedure.

[1] *The Travels of Marco Polo,* New York, 1934, the Heritage Press, The Limited Editions Club, Inc.

The palace furniture included the most fabulous samples of carving, embroidery, and skins of exotic animals, in a barbaric pell-mell that was the Emperor's most personal note.

The most outstanding technicians were put to work to invent new aquatic marvels to supplement the existing variety of aquatic showpieces in the imperial gardens. Beautiful ponds were stocked with the rarest fish of the realm and spanned by ornamental bridges the color and form of exotic plants. Chinese botanists traveled thousands of miles to find roots and herbs, trees and flowers worthy of being planted in the imperial parks. Elephants carried the heavy loads; occasionally it might take a shrubbery caravan more than a year to bring some rare botanic specimen to Taidu, only to have the loads dumped because the chief gardener did not consider it worthy of adorning the grounds over which the Emperor might walk on his way to one of his four principal wives.

Every principal wife had quarters of her own, where she lived with an attendance of about 10,000, including 300 lovely virginal personal maids, pages of aristocratic ancestry, and hordes of eunuchs of whom the saying went that they were not all genuine castrates and that some of them had uncastrate-like kinship to one or other of the twenty-two sons of the principal imperial wives.

The Emperor was entitled to any number of concubines and to all courtesans the empire could produce.

Mustering candidates for the voluptuous service of His Majesty, and training of the draftees, was a highly respected and assiduous public office. Twice a year specially appointed male experts toured the most distant provinces of the empire in search of feminine beauty; maidenhood was officially required, but unofficially dispensed with. Twice a year they delivered their choice, between 400 and 500 ravishing girls, to a committee of ladies of the court. The ladies picked aspirants who were most likely to please the Emperor. The elite was carefully checked for bodily imperfections, including odor, sleeping habits (snorers were ineligible) and adaptability to the Emperor's special desires. The ladies of the court were thoroughly familiar with His Majesty's secret whims and fancies, which grew more numerous and intricate as he grew older. At last the selectees underwent a rigid practical training conducted by the ladies, whose devotion to their Emperor obviously overcame possible aversions to Lesbianism. Hardly one out of ten candidates eventually made the grade. But to have been among the aspirants, and have passed some of the tests, enhanced a girl's prestige; the girls were most anxious to be introduced to the hard-to-please ladies, because this alone made them desirable in the eyes of the most choosy nabob.

When the Emperor was not visiting his principal wives, which he did with diminishing frequency, and if he were not in the company of concubines, he was attended by teams of ten courtesans, who were constantly present in his chambers. The groups were supposed to rotate every day, but Kubilai was content to retain one set for three days.

This was regarded as overly modest by his successors. One of them had the teams enlarged to sixteen, and the girls had also to perform as a ballet to the accompaniment of an orchestra of eleven eunuchs.

Emperor Kubilai still considered hunting an entertainment at par with sex, and, as it were, less strenuous.

He no longer pursued the fleeing game on foaming horses, but sat in a wooden pavilion lined with gold embroideries and covered with tiger-skins, carried by a pair of elephants which were adorned like dancers, and watched trained hawks kill cranes, eagles hunting wolves, and tigers fighting buffaloes and bears. The Emperor also had a hunting tent which was taken along on trips from his summer residence. It was the only tent the Djenghiskhanide still used; it was not of felt however, but of leopard skins and lined with ermine and sable. It was rainproof and had a top of gilded bamboo on golden poles painted with China's heraldic dragon. A hundred silken cords served as ropes of the structure.

Kubilai retained the Mongolian predilection to kumiss, while his courtiers and younger princes preferred wine and liquors. Ten thousand mares, all spotless white, were kept in special stables and officials made the brewing of milk a scientific job. Pages who served the drink to their master had to wear tight tissues covering their mouths and nostrils, lest their breath affect the flavor of the kumiss. Only royalty was permitted to drink the imperial beverage.

The Emperor enjoyed ceremonious parties over which he presided, sitting on the north side of an elevated table, to the right of the Empress, the senior principal wife. His sons and grandsons were placed near him, their heads at the level of the Emperor's golden-shod feet. To the feet of the princes of the blood sat princes of lower rank, wives and children to the left of heads of their families. Members of the nobility, officers, and civilian dignitaries were seated in rows of tables, terraced according to the rank of their occupants. The lowest-ranking nobles and officials sat on carpets below the tables. From his vantage point Kubilai could see every person in the hall, but he never addressed anybody of non-imperial blood.

In the center of the hall stood a square buffet exquisitely carved with gilded figures of animals, and in a hollow about fifteen feet in circumference was a kettle of gold, filled with the Emperor's special kumiss; in each corner stood a vase containing various soft drinks, including camel's milk.

Liquor was poured from golden flagons, one flagon for two guests; but not even ten men could drink a flagonful of liquor without being intoxicated.

Attendants saw to it that diners' plates were never empty. The quantities of meat on hand were inexhaustible. Attendants warned guests not to touch the threshold of the hall with their feet; offenders were stripped of their garments and made to redeem them for a stiff sum. Only the Emperor was entitled to walk across the threshold as he pleased. He was guarded by the two tallest soldiers of the Guard, glum giants always ready to use their swords. When Kubilai asked for a drink, the page in waiting presented it, then backed three steps and knelt down. This was a signal for everybody present to kneel, and for musicians to start, and keep playing until the Emperor put down his cup. This ceremonial was repeated every time the Emperor drank; missing the cue was a grave offense, not excusable by drunkenness.

After the meal tables on lower echelons were removed, and lesser guests made to line up along the walls to make room for jugglers, comedians, and dancers, who performed until the Emperor rose and left.

The greatest celebrations were held on the Emperor's birthday and on New Year's Day. Every New Year 5000 elephants paraded through the streets of the capital, carrying the imperial treasury, from jewels to dinner plate, and from bullion to garments. More or less voluntary gifts from every community of the empire, from liege men, officials, foreign sovereigns, and traders who did flowering business with China (or "Cathay," as they called it) augmented the fabulous wealth of the monarch.

Kubilai was a lavish spender, but not even the most extravagant munificence could have disbursed a revenue that defied imagination. As the empire recovered from devastation, commerce prospered and tribute kept pouring in. Kubilai, supreme authority in budgetary matters, invested huge sums in the improvement of communications, in relief for areas stricken by disaster, and a variety of public works and assistance. The Emperor enjoyed making presents to favorites.

He used to wear thirteen sets of apparel, all in different colors, adorned by different jewels, for official functions. Kubilai knighted 12,000 deserving men, and donated thirteen garments like his own ceremonial robes, only with somewhat less precious jewels, to every one of his new knights.

Chinese financial experts initiated the Emperor into the black magic of paper money. For centuries already bank notes had been legal currency of the realm, and Kubilai, to whom it was a new and thrilling toy, preferred it to gold coins.

Paper manufacturers made pulp from the inner part of the bark of mulberry trees, and from the pulp produced black paper that was cut into pieces, sizes varying according to the denomination of the bank notes. The notes were signed by treasury officers, and the head of the department affixed the imperial seal on the imperial money. Refusal to accept bank notes at nominal value was a capital crime.

Kubilai made his own purchases of pearls, jewels, and precious metals in paper currency. Merchants visited the imperial court and displayed their precious objects before the Emperor, who had them appraised by treasurers, and then allowed the dealer a margin of profit which was always fair, and occasionally extremely generous. Even foreigners did not object to payment in bank notes. The black bills were accepted throughout Asia, and if they were damaged, the Chinese mint would exchange them into new bills at a discount of 3 per cent.

Europeans and people from the western parts of Asia who had never been to "Cathay" before Kubilai opened its borders to foreigners were inclined to attribute many of the marvels they saw to the genius of the founder of the Yuan dynasty. The art of printing, however, had long been established in China; the first Chinese encyclopedia was published in or about 980, and movable type of baked clay was first used after 1040. Even the Great Wall was occasionally mistaken for Kubilai's achievement, and so was the Great Canal linking Peking with Canton, which was only completed under the Emperor, its construction having been delayed by Mongolian invasions. The security of transportation, however, was largely a Mongolian achievement. Banditry had been rampant even in China, in particular in sparsely populated areas through which caravans had to pass on their way to and from trading centers.

The Chinese were traders by tradition; the Mongols were sponsors of trade by imagination. Kubilai, Batu, Hulägu, and their kin were stirred by the prospects of fantastic profits and wondrous objects that trade would supply. Roadhouses were built along the ancient silk road, through the Middle East, and on the approaches to India. Stables kept fine riding and wagon horses for the use of travelers, and the treatment given to foreigners differed favorably from that experienced by Carpin. From Northern China, through the steppes of Siberia and the foothills of the Ural Mountains, across the Volga and Don rivers rolled wagons loaded with silks, spices, and a great variety of other Oriental valuables to the Crimean peninsula, where Italian merchants took over to distribute the wares among their Western customers. Italian factories on the peninsula were protected by the soldiers of the Golden Ordu. During the previous period of insecurity of communications European consumption of Oriental goods had been reduced to a trifle. Levantine agents had monopolized the traffic; they charged immense rates of profit; governments levied prohibitive transit taxes, Egypt leading with a 300 per cent due; and wares, desirable as they remained, were priced beyond the reach of most customers. With the appearance of Chinese caravans in the Crimea and at Tabriz, in the present province of Azerbaijan, business figures rose rapidly. Kubilai did not permit local taxation of transit goods, and the Chinese were more reasonable in calculating profits than their Levantine counterparts.

Chinese warships resumed patrolling sea routes to the West. Chinese navigators explored new lanes of maritime traffic, which were soon regularly traveled by merchantmen. Chinese boats carried goods to and from the Spice Islands and Hindustan; they went to Java to load black pepper, nuts, clove stalks, and cubeb; they proceeded to Ceylon; they did sprawling business with India, where they sold raw and finished silk, satin, and brocade, and purchased Hindu cotton, pearls, and diamonds. "Cathay" wanted the finest that other countries produced. Persian manufacturers of rugs, saddlery, enamel, and fancy armor experienced a wave of prosperity.

China delivered the finest—in all lines except weapons and special mechanical supplies. Neither Chinese cannon nor water clocks or astronomical instruments were sold abroad. Foreigners were barred from arsenals and places of manufacture of other "secret" items. But the visitors were permitted to see things and processes that seemed miraculous to them. They could watch salt being extracted from brine and, most marvelous of all marvels, the mining of black stones which the Chinese used as fuel—pure coal.

European economists studied the China trade and wrote learned essays on the subject. One of them, *La prattica della mercantura,* by Francesco Balducci Pegolotti, had this to suggest: "Everybody who wants to travel to Cathay should supply himself with linen which he will be able to sell with a profit as soon as he reaches Gurganj [east of the Caspian, in Siberia]. There, he should buy silver ingot which the ruler of Cathay will always exchange into paper money, while storing the metal in the treasury. With the paper money, you can buy whatever you please; everybody accepts it, nobody charges a higher price because you pay with script."

European merchants were reluctant to use the overland trade route to travel to the source of treasures. They would have preferred sea transportation. Venice and Genoa had a head start in the rivalry for sea communication. Egypt, with its 300 per cent transit tax, was a road block in the short overland route from the Mediterranean to the Red Sea, western terminal of the ancient route to the Far East. Even had Venetians and Genoese been familiar with historic shipping lanes, they would have had to discover a detour, bypassing the bottleneck of land that is now intersected by the Suez Canal. The race that eventually led to Columbus' trip opened on May 1291, when Ugolino de Vivaldo from Genoa left his home port with two galleys, in search of a seaway to India. Vivaldo sailed through the straits of Morocco, down the west coast of Africa, but it was not learned whether he had reached, or rounded, the cape. The explorer's ultimate fate is unknown. In 1320 Genoese factories were established on the coast of the Gulf of Cambay, and of Malabar. But these regions were reached by land, after agents of the Vivaldo bank made exploratory land trips eastward, and eventually reached the Hindustan port city of Ormouz.

Kubilai built a universal empire of trade which, however, was no more durable than most Siberian creations. Fifty years after his death the land route from Europe to the Far East was again as unsafe as it had been before Temudshin created his empire. The Middle East was in foment, and while Chinese merchants kept off waters that were again pirate-infested, the period of European exploration for trade's sake came to an end. Merchants would eventually be superseded by conquistadores. The colonial era dawned.

One segment of Cathay's foreign business was not affected by the vicissitudes of the thirteenth and fourteenth centuries: the fur trade. Whoever ruled China, united or divided, wanted precious furs for himself and his favorites. Sables, ermines, and foxes came from the vast, silent forests on the banks of the huge rivers that flowed northward toward an ocean vaulted in shining ice —the abode of Erlik, the realm of the dead. Small clans of hunters roamed the forests; they were as poor, ignorant, and untidy as the ancient mendicants had been. Each year they waited at predesignated places along the rivers for the Chinese traders who would give a few sugar bits, trinkets, or pieces of poor-quality silk in exchange for Siberian peltry. Neither Kubilai nor his successors of the house of Yuan requested Siberian fur suppliers to accept their rule. Never did Kubilai, who was keenly interested in whatever people from the West had to say, express the desire to talk to the nomads of the North.

The Emperor, not a devout man according to the law of any creed, enjoyed listening to casuistic debates between learned clerics of different faiths, as if these were tournaments different in form rather than substance from the duels between wild beasts. He would award prizes to whom he considered the winners, valuables that would have gratified Roman gladiators but were hardly rewarding for the seekers of human souls.

Kubilai asked Pope Gregory X to send one hundred theological scientists to China, where they should engage in competitive arguments with Buddhist sages. In 1254 a distinguished Franciscan, Guilleaume de Rubrouck (William of Rubriquis), ambassador of King Louis of France, who no longer believed that the Tatars were necessarily creatures of the Tartarus, had come to Karakorum, where the Great Khan Mongka made him take part in a debate with Mohammedan doctors and Buddhist philosophers. The Franciscan had stood his ground, or at least this is what he reported to King and Pope. But the Pope did not want embarrassing situations. He did not deny Kubilai's request, but put the matter off indefinitely. Nothing useful came from Rubrouck's diplomatic efforts. Mongka had wanted the King of France to acknowledge vassalage, and when Louis did not comply, a clumsy, slow correspondence developed between the rulers of France and the Djenghiskhanide sovereigns.

Christian diplomats were perplexed by the etiquette of Oriental correspondence. Size and form of the paper, margins, measurements of the characters, and the length of lines had to be in accordance with the dignity of the addressee. The first message which the French King received was written in small characters on stationery-sized paper similar to the message Carpin had transmitted to the Pope; but eleven years after Kubilai's death King Philip the Fair, of France, received a piece of mail nine feet long and thirty-six inches wide from Djenghiskhanide Persia, most of the space was taken up by oversized characters expressing the unlimited esteem of the Persian Khan for the French King.

Kubilai granted religious freedom to many creeds and exempted churches from taxation. But whenever clergymen tried to obtain recognition of their faith as the empire's official religion, Kubilai asked for amendments of their canon, subordinating the religious law to that of the Emperor. Buddhism in

China was perverted in compliance with imperial demands, but did not profit from the concessions.

Chinese courtiers flattered Emperor She-tsu, Chinese scholars wrote lavish epistles of praise, and poets exulted in the love of the Chinese people for its ruler. Kubilai accepted it all as his due; his awards granted to zealous scribes were insultingly trifling. The Chinese people respected the victor; they appreciated his furtherance of security and economy, but they did not love him. There were even plots against the Emperor's life, and people whispered that he was under the evil spell of a sorcerer, a vicious Mohammedan. After the Mohammedan's unlamented death rumors had it that the spell was not broken, that the Emperor was bent on turning the Chinese into second-class citizens and making their country a true Mongolian domain.

When Kubilai was young, and later, during the war for China, and in the decade that followed his seizure of the throne, he wanted the Chinese to keep their traditional ways, and he felt little attachment to his own kind. But when he entered the eighth decade of his life, his ideas seemed to change.

It started with an order to his chief gardener for a huge flower bed planted with grass seeds from the lands south of Lake Baikal. The startled official, who had racked his brain how to find ever more colorful, fragrant, and exotic blossoms, fulfilled the Emperor's wish. He was positive that Kubilai would have the grass removed again, but the Emperor would stand there fondly looking at the blades, and pay no attention to exotic plants.

Then he invited Mongolian tribesmen to migrate to China. Almost 300,000 came; they were richly subsidized, clothed, and quartered. But while far fewer than that number had subdued the country in war, 300,000 peaceful settlers were but a few drops in the Chinese ocean. The Chinese sneered at the newcomers, at their coarseness, their ugly idiom, and the ridiculous way they looked in Chinese garb. But Kubilai began to distribute sinecures, and even responsible offices among Mongolian petty nobles. And assignments that Mongols could not fill went to Mohammedans and Nestorians from the Middle East.

In Kubilai, like in most Siberians, a strong element of distrust prevailed. He developed a sense of inferiority to the Chinese which was not mitigated by flattery. By adopting the Chinese way he felt to have become dependent on Chinese good will, and he wanted to assert his independence.

His twenty-two legitimate sons, and the twenty-five offspring of concubines were all-out Chinese; and Temür, whom Kubilai had assigned heir presumptive, after the death of his favorite son in 1286, attributed his father's attitude to mental disintegration caused by licentiousness.

In fact Kubilai's debaucheries grew excessive as he aged; yet his vigor prevented rapid physical and mental decline.

A provision in the Emperor's will came as a blow to his successor and the camarilla. Kubilai decreed that his body be laid to rest near the tomb of Temudshin, in the land he had not visited for decades. After he died, early in 1294, the pompous funeral vault prepared for him in his winter palace remained empty, while through the blizzard of February 18 a long and somber procession marched out from the capital toward the Siberian heart lands. Huddled in sable furs, a miserable and seedy Temür accompanied his father's coffin. But he would not go to Karakorum afterward. There would be no Kuriltai. The Djenghiskhanides no longer selected a Great Khan. They were either rulers in their own rights and of their own realms, or wretches and rebels.

Old, weather-beaten, and rugged, Kaidu still roamed steppes, forests, and mountains of Siberia at the head of armed bands that resembled the raiders of yore rather than Temudshin's and his successors' disciplined armies. He called himself Great Khan and Ruler of the Universe, but his domain was confined to the outlands of the new Djenghiskhanide empires, and his feats of arms to patrol skirmishes, not all of which he won.

Temür, who considered reference to his descent embarrassing, would have preferred to let Kaidu pose as Mongolian Great Khan had it not been for the implication that the cranky man from the steppes was his sovereign. Following the camarilla's advice, Temür adopted the title of Great Khan without the traditional ceremonies, and had light troops search for Kaidu—a task which proved to be extremely difficult.

Only after yet another decade of feud did the princes of the houses of Ogödai and Djagatai send embassies to Peking to accept the overlordship of the new Emperor. This was, however, not tantamount to restoration of Mongolian unity and centralized government, but an expedient to gain time and, if possible, Chinese support for new separatist ventures.

The Yuans had relinquished all tradition, but the Sinofication of the scions of Siberian nomads did not obliterate the fundamental barbarism that tainted their carousals and their policies. Yuans turned dipsomaniacs and sex maniacs, and murder was the alpha and omega of their stratagems. Ever-wilder orgies undermined the emperors physically, and the intricacy of cabals affected their mental equilibrium. But the world they and their creatures wanted to dominate did not really extend beyond the walls of the palace.

A small group of Chinese notables whose influence at court was greater than the wisdom of their judgment cajoled Temür into exerting his prerogatives as a Great Khan over territories such as Siberia and Turkestan. This would provide a bonanza of governorships and sinecures for distant relatives not eligible for court assignments.

The expansion of Chinese rule turned into a liability and a source of trouble.

A few years after Ogödaites and Djagataides had rendered homage to the Yuans, Tshäpar, of the house of Ogödai, attacked Kébék, Khan of the Djagataides. Both applied for Chinese assistance, but the Yuans were just engaged in fratricidal struggle and had no soldiers to spare.

A shadowy Temür had died of exhaustion and Prince Kaichan seized the throne that legally would have belonged to his brother. There was bloodshed, and it was not until late in 1307 that Kaichan was solidly established as third Yuan Emperor.

Kaichan wanted to enjoy an emperor's life, and he succumbed to women and alcohol four years later, at the age of thirty-one. His brother-successor lasted until thirty-five, and his brother's son was assassinated by a gang of dignitaries shortly after his seventeenth birthday. The murderers enthroned the victim's cousin, of whom later Chinese chroniclers said that he was inept, slack, virtually a prisoner of an extravagant court, and succumbed to the strain of debauchery after five years.

Five more emperors were pushed off the throne in so many years, two of them boys of six and ten respectively. Only in one case was the cause of death recorded: "Dissipation."

Even grown-up emperors had no word in matters other than their entertainment. Splendor got a touch of ridicule, and Chinese mechanical ingenuity was used for odd purposes. The ninth Yuan had a dragon ship launched on the biggest lake on the palace grounds, the head of the dragon nodding, and its tail wagging, as the feet waddled to set the vessel in motion.

At the age of thirteen, Toghan Temür ascended the imperial throne that had become a deathtrap; he seemed too puny an objective to the camarilla for daggers and poison vials. The youth who, haunted by visions of a torturous death, sought distraction with women, drinks, and lewd exhibits, and consolation through the ministrations of Tibetan lamas. He never learned that for a full seven years a courtier named Bayan had established a quasi-dictatorship; that Bayan had been murdered, and that factional warfare turned the court an object of scorn and disdain to the Chinese people. Nor did concubines, musicians, and servants, who were the only people Toghan Temür met, tell him that civil war had broken out in the lower Yangtse Valley and was spreading north; that imperial armies were siding with various parties; and that governors were engaged in internecine struggle. The young Emperor, forgotten by his courtiers, was suddenly remembered by his people, however —remembered with boundless hatred. To the masses he was the symbol of foreign rule, the Tatar, the usurping barbarian, the rapacious mendicant. Not even the many Chinese who had profited from the Yuan regime had a good word or a friendly thought for Toghan Temür. A wave of riots engulfed China. Adventurers styled themselves offspring of Chinese royalty, raised partisans, and drove governors out of office with the ardent support of the populace.

The most popular of all partisan leaders was Tshou Yuang-tshan, a Buddhist bonze and son of a laborer, whose power of speech and comparative moderation in action won him general acclaim. Guerrillas surrendered to the new leader, who proclaimed himself Emperor of the former Song realm and founder of the Ming dynasty.

Courtiers and generals in Peking made no attempt to dislodge the Ming Emperor. The domain of the Kin, which remained under nominal Yuan rule, was still big enough to support parasites. The camarilla trusted that the revolution would stop at its border. But the revolution completed the cycle, and disunity among the courtiers and the military hastened the inevitable end. The Kin domain was caught between pincers. A prince of the Ogödai family who lived in Siberia but knew more about events in China than his kin in the imperial palace assembled a makeshift army and crossed the Great Wall, and while border guards delayed his advance, the Ming Emperor's troops, the best soldiers China could muster, started out from Nanking to seize the Yuan realm. Enthusiastic crowds cheered the Ming armies as liberators. On September 10, 1368, the new Emperor entered a delirious Peking.

During the night that preceded the entrance Toghan Temür fled. He had learned of the collapse of his regime in the afternoon of September 9. His first reaction was the draft of the disconsolate farewell poem; his next and last was the gathering of what remained of the imperial treasury, after governors and clerks, generals, guardsmen, and servants had helped themselves to as much as they could carry.

The salvaged treasures were still substantial enough to assure the deposed emperor a fairly large company of men and women who expected to live on his funds in comfortable exile.

But Toghan Temür did not flee to a comfortable place. The route to seaports and, from there, to civilized countries was blocked by the Ming army and navy. The fugitive went to the steppes of Mongolia and Siberia. He was no longer haunted by fear of murder lurking in his palace, but, wandering through the wilderness that had been the home of his ancestors, he became frightened by the specters of deceased khans cursing him as the squanderer of their sacred inheritance. Local shamans stirred his fears, and charged high fees to pacify angry souls. His treasures diminished; his companions stole as much as they could and disappeared. The last of the Yuans wandered past tents of scattered tribes left behind when his progenitors decamped in quest of the universal empire. He did not stay at the camps lest the ungainly, high-smelling nomads despoil him of his holdings, but he stopped just long enough to barter treasures for food. The sullen hunters had little use for pearls and precious metals; they would have preferred bits of sugar, yet the ex-emperor had not learned of their preference, nor did he ever learn the language of the glum woodsmen whose progeny survive to the present day.

The West learned of Kubilai and of Yuan greatness mainly through Marco Polo, the fabulous merchant from Venice.

In 1260, Maffeo and Niccolò Polo left their home town to trade with the Golden Ordu and, after having made substantial profits, proceeded to Karakorum in quest of even better business. They carried various credentials, one allegedly by the Pope, another by Batu's brother Berké, who had been their best customer. In 1263 the Polos met Kubilai and, so they said, showed him the Pope's letter to induce the Mongol to adopt the Christian faith. But even though Kubilai treated the visitors with great distinction, he refused to be converted, suggesting instead that Rome send the 100 theologians. Returned to Italy, the men from Venice were received in audience by the Pope (successor to the pontiff who had signed the credential); they were supplied with another letter to Kubilai, and again left for the Far East in 1271, this time accompanied by Niccolò's son, Marco. Twenty years went by, and when nothing was heard of the Polos they were officially pronounced dead. Relatives took over their *palazzo* and their mercantile establishment.

But in 1295 three tattered wanderers presented themselves at the gates of the palazzo. They claimed to be Maffeo, Niccolò, and Marco Polo, but the heirs to their name and property had them arrested as impostors and turned over to the authorities. The men knew many amazing details about the Polo family prior to 1271, but their strange accent did not seem to indicate that they were Venetians. It was presumed that they had learned a great deal about the Polos to prepare their act. However, magistrates granted them permission to establish their claim in conformity with the city republic's noble custom. A sumptuous banquet was arranged for the grandees of the government, who did not want to miss the spectacle. The claimants appeared in splendid Oriental garb, and after the meal was over they produced the rags they had been wearing on their arrival, ripped open the seams, and poured onto the tablecloth a collection of precious jewels more astounding than even the wealthiest European monarchs had hoarded in their treasuries. The men's wealth was accepted as evidence of their identity, and Marco, speaker of the Polos, told the fabulous story of how they had acquired these riches by serving Kubilai and trading in Oriental realms.

Soon the city resounded with tales of the wealth of the East. It seemed that everybody could become a nabob in that part of the world simply by following the trail outlined by Marco Polo. The East seemed to be made of gold, diamonds, pearls, and rubies. Venice was in the grip of greed and adventurousness, and the tale spread to Genoa. Relations between the two cities had again been strained to the breaking point. Pirates using the flags of Genoa and Venice were preying upon the other party's merchantmen. After the Polo story made the rounds, the Genoese, furious at having been outsmarted by Venetian traders, stepped up the pirate war. Venice introduced a system of naval convoys, and Genoa countered by letting its warships patrol the seas; several pitched battles occurred, and in the summer of 1298 the bulk of the Genoese Navy entered the Adriatic for an all-out attack on Venice.

On September 9 the two navies met off the Dalmatian coast. The Venetians were defeated, and among the skippers who surrendered their craft was Marco Polo, who, restored to his status, was made honorary commander of a galley.

He was interned in Genoa. On learning of his presence huge crowds flocked to the ancient palazzo where he was held, clamoring to see the miracle man and to listen to his story. Authorities permitted Marco Polo to address the

Genoese; soon the city piers and wharves were deserted, as everybody hung around the palazzo. The lectures were discontinued, but the Governor authorized Polo to write his memoirs. Being not good at writing, Marco Polo asked a fellow-prisoner, one Rusticiano, to help him with his task. Rusticiano's Italian was poor, but he spoke French. Polo's French was no better than his helper's Italian. The result of their endeavors was an opus entitled *The Book of Signor Marco Polo, the Venetian, concerning the Kingdom and the marvels of the East*. It certainly was no literary masterpiece, but its contents made up for the shortcomings of presentation.

The book told of the marvels of coal mining: "Black stones extracted from rocks, that burn like sticks of wood; they are so effective as fuel, that nothing else is used in Cathay." (Strangely enough, the knowledge of coal that had been general among the Roman occupation troops of Britain had vanished in medieval Italy.) Marco Polo raved about China's inland waterways: "On the Kian [Yangtse] more boats carry goods than are used to ship merchandise on all rivers and seas of Christianity. Every year, 200,000 barges sail upstream, not to mention those who sail the other way." Peking, which the author calls "Canbalu," was described as the center of the silk industry, from where more than one thousand carloads of the finest tissues were shipped every day in every direction. Hankou, we are told, was the Venice of China, where innumerable vessels discharged spices from India and loaded silk for that empire and the Mohammedan world, and where many foreigners, including Arabs, Christians, and Mohammedans, were engaged in fantastically prosperous activities. Foutshou (Foochow) appears to have been the center of trade in pearls and precious stones, and there, as in many other cities, abundance defied the imagination of Western man.

The Polo account tells a great deal about Tatar military achievements and Kubilai's strategies, which, however, were basically Subotai's. Polo also described the process to supply the soldiers with iron rations of dried milk: "They boil the milk, and, skimming off the rich or creamy part as it rises to the top, put it into a separate vessel as butter; for so long as that remains in the milk, it will not become hard. The latter is then exposed to the sun until it dries. Upon going on service, they carry with them about ten pounds for each man, and of this, half a pound is put, every morning, into a leather bottle, with as much water as is thought necessary. By their motion in riding the contents are violently shaken, and a thin porridge is produced, upon which they make their dinner."

City by city, country by country, and land by land, all were described, one wealthier than the other, all of them secure, and connected by communication lines safer and more ingeniously organized than anything in the Western world.

The book gives glowing accounts of exploits performed by the Polos, of crucial assignments given to them by a benevolent and appreciative emperor —and it also tells of strange creatures and black magic.

The Polos, it says, helped the imperial armies to build "mangonels," super siege machines, vastly superior to anything the Chinese had known. In fact so little did Marco Polo know about Chinese equipment that he failed to mention its most amazing feature: artillery.

The Venetian merchant told of bats as large as vultures; of Rukh birds, "whose wingspan is 16 paces," and which can lift and kill elephants; of hunting dogs two of which could run down a full-grown tiger. He extolled the faculties of idolator priests and quoted the Emperor as saying: "When I sit at table, cups come to me, spontaneously, without being touched by a human hand. They [the magicians] have the power of controlling bad weather and obliging it to retire to any quarter of heavens. . . . You are witnesses that their idols have the faculty of speech and predict whatever is required. . . ."

But it was not the tales of elephant-killing birds or talking idols that aroused the indignation of readers of *The Book of Signor Marco Polo,* and they did not seem to mind his extravagant claims to personal glory; it was the description of the wealth of Cathay and other marvelous countries in the East that eventually enraged the men who had but recently raved about the Polo jewels and the story of their acquisition. Curiosity was superseded by envy, and envy shattered the belief, not only in what had been told, but even in what had been displayed. If Venice or Genoa or any other European trade center could not produce the wealth attributed to the East, Polo was a liar, for there could be no wealth greater than that of the cultured West.

When Marco Polo, who had been a prisoner of war in Genoa, was released from captivity Venice received him with scorn and admonitions to repent and correct his false statements. "Messer Millione," urchins jeered outside his palazzo, which the people now called "Corte di Millione." Carnival crowds carried a harlequin, "Marco Millione." Merchants, some of whom engaged in Oriental trade, evaded Polo as an "unsound character" whose advice nobody should trust, and even the few people who still saw the outcast kept asking him to recant. Marco Polo died in 1324, at the age of seventy. On his deathbed he told the priest who administered the last rites: "And yet, I did tell the truth—and I have told but half of what I have actually seen."

CHAPTER TWENTY Kubilai's task of conquering China was more difficult, militarily, than Hulägu's objective to raise the Mongolian banner in the Middle East; however, Hulägu was faced with political, economical, and religious problems of bewildering intricacy, and there was nobody who could really brief him on the subject. Not even Yeliu could have foreseen the contingencies lurking in a territory in which militant Christendom, rising Mohammedan fanaticism, mercantile rivalries of the old world, and annexationist ambitions of the most ancient and the newest ruling houses met in a vortex which could have been controlled only by united, overwhelming power. But Hulägu's power was not really overwhelming and Mongolian disunity was never before as clearly evident as during the Middle Eastern campaign. Mongka had been careful to prevent friction between Hulägu and Batu; he had clearly demarked spheres of interest, and yet he could not eliminate jealousies and distrust between the two clans which eventually exploded into open war. And even though Kubilai did not actively interfere in the fratricidal struggle, he played a diplomatic game that made reconciliation virtually impossible.

Mongka's message to Louis the Saint, King of France, "There is but one God in Heaven, and one sovereign on earth: Djenghis Khan, son of God," sounded like a travesty in the light of conditions prevalent in the house of Djenghis Khan as Rubrouck traveled to Karakorum through "European Mongolia," the realm of Batu. "Tsar" Batu, whom the French Franciscan visited in his tent, had "a piercing look, and a ruddy complexion, and a great number of previous goblets full of kumiss standing before him," and he did not talk unity. He was as little afraid of insurrection as of a distant Great Khan's interference in the affairs of his realm. He had a fine army of 100,000 horsemen, only 4000 of whom were Mongol, but the others, Kiptchaks, Bulgars, Turcs, and Russians, were in the grip of an iron discipline that turned them into fighting robots. Russian princes wide and far rendered homage to him. Alexander Nevsky considered it a privilege to help protect Mongolian Russia's Baltic flank against intruding Teutons, and other Russian grandees watched the western approaches of the land against the rising might of Lithuania. Batu and his brother Berké were determined not to let another great power arise on their southeastern border.

Hulägu's orders were "to make the customs and usages of the law of the Djenghis Khan prevail from the Amu Darja to Egypt." "Everybody who abides by your order," the directive said, "shall be treated with kindness, but those who disobey must go down in humiliation."

The Prince received the orders in 1251, and Mongka, who did not believe in his brother's diplomatic talents, gave him a political counselor, a Christian noblewoman who impressed Hulägu so greatly that he married her before completing his preparations in 1256. Hulägu, a Buddhist who had been sponsoring Nestorianism and after his marriage extended his religious sympathies to all Christian denominations, distrusted the Mohammedans on religious grounds; but he had no proper judgment of political and military impulses generated by the Mohammedan faith.

Twice Western Asiatic Mohammedan countries had ignominiously succumbed to Mongolian invasions, but twice they had recovered, disobeying Mongolian local administrations, and occasionally ambushing Mongolian occupation detachments. The Abbasside Khalif of Bagdad had but a small temporary domain, Iraq; but he claimed spiritual power over the entire Islamite world.

Hulägu's armies marched through Persia into Iraq without meeting organized resistance. But the gates of the city of Bagdad were closed, and the walls manned by well-armed soldiers.

"You know what fate befell the world that defied Mongolian armies since the day of Djenghis Khan. How could you deny us the keys to your city—to us, who have all the strength and all the might? Beware of challenging our banner!"

The Khalif received this message on February 1, 1258. "Oh, young man, who has hardly begun a career, you, who are intoxicated with a few days of glory, what makes you think that you are superior to the entire world? Don't you realize that from the Orient to the Occident all the worshipers of Allah, Kings and beggars alike, are my subjects, and that I can order them to stand up and unite against you?" the answer read.

But the worshipers of Allah did not stand up—not yet; and Hulägu ordered his armies to attack. The walls of Bagdad crumbled under the siege machines; on February 10 the Khalif surrendered his city, his realm, and his person.

The city was pillaged for seventeen days, and then put to the torch; 90,000 people died in the holocaust; the Khalif was put into a sack and trampled to death by cavalry horses.

Terror struck the hearts of Mohammedans, while the Christian world rejoiced. Old tales of King David were revived, and Hetum, King of Armenia, mobilized Christian soldiers to join the host of Hulägu Khan.

The Armenian monk Vartan gave a glowing account of Mongolian piety and kindness; it was eagerly believed by Christians whose parents had experienced Mongolian horrors. "The Mongolians of Persia," Vartan wrote, "carry a tent, the shape of a church. Every day, ordained priests say mass in the tent and the *djamahar* [an instrument producing loud, rattling sounds] calls the faithful to prayer. In the lands ruled by the Mongolians, Christian clergymen of all creeds and nations live in peace and security. The Mongolians' foremost objective is peace, and when it is granted to them, they offer rich presents in return." The tent, in fact, was the private church of Hulägu's wife; only she, her husband, and their attendants were admitted to services, and the Mongolian version of peace had not undergone basic changes since the day of Temudshin. Hulägu appreciated the psychological effects of Vartan's writings, however, and had the priest admitted into his presence five years after the rape of Bagdad. "This mighty monarch," Vartan exulted, "exempted me from bowing my knee, as etiquette would have required. He knows that Christians should prostrate themselves only before God. He asked me to bless a cup of wine, and received it from my hands. 'I wanted you to meet me,' he said, 'for I wish you would pray for me.' He made me sit down, I was joined by Syrian, Greek and Georgian Christians, and together, we sang hymns. 'Monks from everywhere have come to bless me,' he said, and 'God favors me.' His Christian sympathies opened a gap between him and his Djenghiskhanide cousins, the Khans of Russia, and Turkestan, who favor the Mohammedans."

Not his Christian sympathies accounted for Hulägu's war with his cousins, but political rivalries, which would ultimately pave the way for another conqueror, a man whose Siberian origin was not clearly established but who would nevertheless rank with Attila, the Djenghis Khan, and Kubilai as a Siberian vanishing despot.

Immediately after the conquest of Iraq, Hulägu's armies continued west. Armenian auxiliaries raced toward a junction with the Mongols; The Metropolite of Aleppo, Bar Hebracus, who considered this to be a crusade from the opposite direction, traveled to Hulägu's headquarters to render homage to the Prince, or Khan, of Persia, as he was more frequently called. "King" Bohemund VI, whose crusader ancestor had once captured Antioch, only to lose it again to the Mohammedans, joined the Mongols at the head of a small band of Frankish knights. Hulägu's campaign toward the Mediterranean opened in best Mongolian tradition. His cavalry swept battlefields. Mongolian-Chinese machines pulverized walls, towers, and battlements. Aleppo was looted, and its population massacred. Damascus fell; the Christians of that city forced the Mohammedans to assemble in the famous mosque, drink wine, and prostrate themselves before a cross held up by a priest. The victorious armies reached the isthmus between the Red Sea and the Mediterranean, the border of Egypt, which Hulägu intended to annex. Bohemund obliged by negotiating with the French barons of Acre about their joining operations against the country of the pharaohs, which had become the country of the Mamelouks.

The Mamelouks (Arabian for "purchased slaves"), descendants of prisoners of war of Turc and Caucasian origin, supplemented by recruits from Southern Russia, had been Egypt's lansquenets, then they rose to the King's elite troop and his palace guard and later became the pillar of Egyptian rule; the dominating power of the empire. The Mamelouks made, and disposed of, kings; they determined Egypt's policies; and in 1250, Kutuz, a Mamelouk, murdered the King and seized the throne. Mamelouk sultans and emirs were to rule the country of the Nile, on and off, until 1517.

The Egyptian army was stronger than Hulägu's previous opponents combined. Not only did the Mamelouk Sultan intend to defend his domain against any aggressor, he was determined to restore Egypt's dominant position in export and import commerce. The Egyptian ruler was doing business with Batu and Berké, who were selling able-bodied slaves to the Mamelouk armies. Batu had made it plain to Egyptian agents that they had no wish to side with their Persian relatives in a conflict with Egypt. There had even been some talk about Russia co-operating with Egypt, but Batu did not want to go to war during the lifetime of Great Khan Mongka.

While Hulägu crossed the Sinai peninsula, and Mamelouk forces assembled on the western shore of the Gulf of Suez, Great Khan Mongka died. Berké meantime succeeded Batu. Berké was more aggressive than his brother and with Mongka out of the way he encouraged the Sultan to seize the initiative. Hulägu had no delusions about Berké's attitude. His cousin had established a "Khanate of Kiptchaks" at the back door of the Persian fief. Not unless the border against the Khanate of the Kiptchaks was secure could large-scale operations against Egypt be resumed.

Hulägu left Kibutka, an aging Mongolian general in charge of 15,000 horsemen, to hold the approaches to Egypt in co-operation with the Christian forces; and withdrew with the bulk of his army to block intrusion by his relatives from Russia.

The barons of Acre, who had just proclaimed readiness to fight Egypt, made a prompt about-face, charging the Mongols with border violations, with the sacking of the city of Sidon, and with various other acts of aggression that made the Mongols appear "more barbarian even than the Mohammedans." They granted Sultan Kutuz free passage through their territory and all the supplies his army would need. Bohemund and his knights vanished from Kibutka's camp under cover of darkness.

On September 3, 1260, the Mamelouk army charged. The Mongolian-Armenian forces, outnumbered 10 to 1, were annihilated in a few hours of combat.

Kibutka, wounded and tied like a bundle, was carried before Sultan Kutuz: "Here you are," the Mamelouk scoffed, "yesterday's conquerors of many nations, trapped wretches today."— "It's not you who defeated me," the general is said to have replied. "It's the will of God. I am not, as you are, my master's assassin; I will remain his faithful servant to the end. When Hulägu will learn of my death, his wrath will boil like the surging waves of the sea, and the horses of his army will trample asunder the land of Egypt."

The Sultan motioned his chief executioner. The general died courageously, but Hulägu's horses did not trample on Egyptian soil; an inadequate force that Hulägu dispatched to stop the Mamelouk advance was dispersed, and the Egyptian army patrolled the approaches to Mesopotamia.

Berké and Baibars, the successor to Kutuz, who suffered a stroke, exchanged ambassadors as a token of friendship, and Berké opened verbal hostilities against Hulägu by declaring in the presence of the Egyptian ambassador: "Hulägu has sacked the cities of the Mohammedans, and he has killed the Khalif, he has never consulted his relatives on the matter; with Allah's assistance we shall take him to answer for the innocent blood he has criminally spilled."

Two years later Berké declared war on his cousin, on the grounds that Hulägu had executed the Khalif without his consent.

The internecine struggle turned into an exchange of much violent abuse and a few half-hearted blows, upon a background of ineffective political machinations involving practically all great powers.

The war between Egypt and Persia continued under the motto of Christianity versus Mohammedanism, but no religious issues were at stake. Egypt wanted Palestine, Syria, and Mesopotamia, and the re-establishment of its Far Eastern trade hegemony; Hulägu, and Abaka, his successor, hoped for a deal that would bring Egypt under their sway, with the help of the European Christian powers.

Kubilai disapproved of his Persian cousins, but he also intended to keep the Egyptians out of the Far Eastern business. He did not actively intervene in the internecine feud on the other end of the immense continent. Experience should have taught Kubilai a great deal about the essentials of power. His power was largely based on prestige. The Yassak presumed that the strength of the Djenghiskhanides would remain unchallenged and that fear of this strength would beget hypnotic obedience. When Kubilai was a boy, this seemed self-evident; in his late middle age, however, it had acquired a touch of unrealism. China had resisted to the bitter end; Japan scorned his calls for surrender; Egypt had not been affected by the spell of fear. It would be ruinous to Mongolian prestige to have the Great Khan try vainly to force his relatives into line, right under the eyes of Christian great powers.

Damage to Mongolian prestige, nevertheless, was great and irreparable. From 1273 to 1277, Abaka's ambassadors toured Italy, France, and England, calling on kings, princes, and city governments to forge a great Christian alliance against the Mamelouks. Ambassadors were asked embarrassing questions why their sovereign's armies could not subdue the pagan lansquenets of an upstart sultan. Nothing they could say would impress the Christians, and the Mongols were not sufficiently initiated into European game of political-religious-commercial intrigue to exploit inter-Christian cabals to their own advantage.

At last Abaka tried to impress the enigmatic foreigners with a demonstration of his own power. He assembled his horsemen and technical troops, 50,000 in all; from Armenia and Georgia came 30,000 volunteers; and a handful of Frankish adventurers joined the army. Abaka virtually bared the approaches to his hostile kin's territory, and threw every available man, horse, and war machine against the Mamelouks. The armies clashed near Homs, on October 30, 1281. Georgians and Armenians gave a noble account of their fighting qualities, but the Mongols, the mailed fist clenched to shatter the Egyptian array, flagged, wavered, and disintegrated in abysmal panic before the day was over. Abaka survived the disaster by only a few months.

Mongolian fortunes were at a low ebb. The only achievement since Hulägu's advance to the Sinai peninsula was the suppression of the Ismaelites early in the war.

Under the iron rule of its Grand Master, the Old Man of the Mountains, the order of the Ismaelites had terrorized Persia and neighboring countries for the better part of two centuries. Victims dubbed the fierce knifemen Hashishins, because they were drugged with hashish during initiation ceremonies.

Onomatopoeia converted the name into Assassins, thus coining a word that was to be incorporated into French and English vocabularies.

The Ismaelites posed as purifiers and keepers of the right faith, but their doctrine was never comprehensively disclosed. To the profane they were uninhibited murderers whose daggers always found their mark: wealthy or otherwise influential men who had refused to yield to the order's exactions. For several generations crime did pay. The Grand Master's wealth and the splendor of his abode were proverbial throughout the Middle East.

Every year a number of carefully sifted young men, perfect physical specimens thoroughly indoctrinated with the dogma of absolute obedience, underwent the rites of consecration as the far-reaching arms of the Grand Master, the Old Man of the Mountains. They were taken to the Eagle's Nest, his castle, high up in the mountains, accessible only by a small bridle path, but surrounded by the lushest and most elaborate gardens of Persia. The Old Man played host to the youngsters, told them of the delights that waited for the faithful, and poured drinks into which hashish was mixed. When the young men were sufficiently benumbed not to distinguish reality from imagination, but still capable of enjoying physical delights, they were led into the gardens and left there in the company of beautiful houris and lascivious pervert boys who ministered to their lusts. At last they were returned to the table of the Grand Master, and while the effects of hashish vanished, the Old Man explained that they had been dreaming of the paradise where they would be admitted in reward for services if they were faithful under all trials, and to the end. Eagerness to return to the site of their dreams made the youngsters defy death, and, if caught, to remain silent under torture.

The Eagle's Nest was vulnerable to Mongolian equipment. As soon as Hulägu's engineers appeared at the foot of the mountain, the Grand Master was deserted by his attendance and surrendered a few days later. So savage was Persian hatred against the terrorist chieftain that Mongolian cavalry cover could not prevent the crowds from seizing the Old Man and tearing him to pieces.

The order deteriorated into a poorly organized gang of professional murderers whose services were neither efficient nor reliable enough to keep them a going concern.

A quarter of a century after the last Mongolian success in Western Asia the once-dreaded conquerors were a bickering clan of defeated generals, hapless diplomats, and jittery administrators. Tenkonder, who succeeded Abaka, made a bid for local support; and because Christianity was not popular in Persia, the new Khan, though raised in the Christian faith, embraced Mohammedanism, changed his name into Ahmed, and adopted the title of Sultan. The Persians watched the convert's moves with distrust and hardly concealed scorn.

Sultan Ahmed made a bid for alliance with Egypt, but Mamelouks' reaction was discouragingly discourteous. Ahmed attributed the slight to the state of affairs in his army and administration, and undertook to purge these bodies of all "unreliable," i.e., Christian or pro-Christian, elements.

The generals, anxious to recover on Ahmed's palace grounds some of their reputation, lost at Homs, rebelled against the Sultan's purge orders, and victoriously had him slain.

His nephew Argun, a son of Abaka, was installed by the military as Khan, and as the champion of Christendom in the realm. Argun, who was a Buddhist, did not object to the political-religious line, but, feeling that economic advancement of the country was an urgent problem and that neither Christians nor Mohammedans were sound economists, he appointed a Jew as chief consultant in economic matters. Saad-ed-Daloué was a physician by profession, but his administrative and business skills were as remarkable as his medical knowledge. Christians and Mohammedans, however, charged that Saad-ed-Daloué misused his office to give all the members of his family remunerative assignments as tax collectors.

In 1285, Pope Honorius IV received a letter from Argun Khan. Oversized characters on gigantic stationery explained that the Khan was extending protection to "the lands of the Christians," in the spirit of his immortal grandfather Hulägu and his eminent father Abaka, and inspired by the shining example of his distinguished relative Kubilai, Great Khan of the Djenghiskhanides and Emperor of China. The letter also stated that Argun's armies were set to invade Syria, where, joined by an army of crusaders which the Khan expected to land there, they would, "with the help of God, the Pope, and the Great Khan, chase the Saracens away."

The Pope was getting accustomed to the Mongols' braggadocio rising to a pitch whenever they were in distress. He did not believe that Kubilai's help would be forthcoming and had no desire to resume frustrating negotiations for a crusade.

After vainly waiting for a satisfactory reply Argun delegated Rabban Sauma, his top expert in Christian affairs, to Rome. Sauma was a ranking prelate of the Nestorian Church and therefore, in the eyes of the Roman hierarchy, a heretic. The Nestorian reached the Eternal City in the summer of 1287. Pope Honorius had died shortly before, and no successor had as yet been elected. The Cardinals, who gathered for the conclave, were both polite and curious. They gave Sauma a hearing, as an ambassador from Persia, not as a Christian priest.

Sauma, born near Peking, was familiar with the Far East, and the Princes of the Church always appreciated information on these lands. But Sauma was not the man to sidetrack his own faith. "Take heed," he shouted, "that my forefathers, the Nestorian missionaries, have traveled to the lands of the Mongols, of the Turcs and of the Chinese since the seventh century, to teach the heathens and convert them. It is due to Nestorian perseverance and courage that today many Mongols are Christians, baptized, and confessing their trust in Christ; Kings and Queens are among them. King Argun, my master, is on friendly terms with the Patriarch. He wants to take possession of Syria, and he requests your support to rescue Jerusalem."

The cardinals cleared throats, put on thin, enigmatic smiles, and made veiled hints at the variability of the fate of Syria, which had so often changed hands, and at their concern about the right believers to be established in Jerusalem. Then they excused themselves: nothing could be done as long as the papal throne was vacant.

Rabban Sauma continued to Paris and Bordeaux to try his eloquence on Philip the Fair and Edward I. The kings were inquisitive but noncommittal.

The undaunted ambassador returned to Rome. The new Pope, Nicolas IV, more anxious to save a heretic soul than to engage in hopelessly hackneyed diplomatic deals with bankrupt conquerors, admitted Sauma to the ceremonies of the Passion Week, made him partake the Sacrament from his own hands, and gave him a seat of honor at the pontifical table. The Nestorian was not converted, but he had to concede failure of his mission.

Argun woefully came to the conclusion that the Orient was not up to Occidental standards of shrewdness. But an Italian could outsmart everybody, even a Frenchman. The Khan called in a Genoese merchant who had been to France. Jointly they drafted an epistle which, Argun trusted, would induce the King of France to side with him. "By the power of the Eternal Blue Sky," it opened in Djenghiskhanide style, "and under the auspices of the Great Khan, this, O King of France, is Our message: We propose to depart from our capital in the last month of winter in the year of the panther [Chinese version of January 1291], and to set camp outside Damascus in the middle of the first month of spring [February]." At this point the Italian took over: "Provided you will dispatch troops of your own army to join Ours at the predetermined time, We shall take Jerusalem, and hand it over to you. However, should you fail to meet the appointment, We would not set our own army in motion." The French did not meet the appointment and Argun died, a very disillusioned khan, in March 1291.

The military clique had already planned to have the Khan assassinated. Argun never learned that, as he lay ill in his tent, Saad-ed-Daloué had succumbed to the swords of a group of young officers, and that street orators already were briefed in addresses denouncing the Khan as a perfidious monster whose villainous misrule had been terminated by valorous, devoted soldiers.

The addresses were actually delivered, somewhat modified to meet the facts of Argun's demise.

Gaikatu, Argun's brother sidetracked to governorship of a remote province, was the natural choice of the generals, who quickly seized all the key offices, including the civilian. Having been relegated to obscurity by his calumniated brother, the new Khan existed under a halo of persecuted virtue. In fact, however, Gaikatu had been sent to semi-exile because of his corruption, his shiftless pederasty, and many other vices.

Gaikatu Khan never interfered with the abuses of the generals and their appointees in office, and otherwise went his bad old ways. These ways were expensive, and so was the rule of the military, who were extravagantly overstaffing offices with relatives, friends, creatures, and the creatures' creatures. Printing bank notes seemed an excellent expedient to cover up a skyrocketing deficit. Corruptionists and carousers had money fabricated on a fantastic scale. Uncontrolled inflation reduced the purchasing power of Gaikatu's currency to a small fraction of its nominal value. The Persians had accepted foreign domination, taxes, forced recruitment, and religious turmoil, but they would not stand for a debased currency. Pandemonium broke out in bazaars and spread through city streets; crowds rioted, merchants closed their shops and announced that commercial operations would be discontinued. Soldiers joined the rebels, roaring protests against depreciation of their pay. Rabble-rousers harangued the throngs, telling them that Persia was being sucked dry by a band of perverts. Frightened Mongolian generals tried to placate the people by invading the Khan's palace and strangling Gaikatu with a bowstring.

Ghazan, son of Argun, was the next in line to ascend the throne. The generals had no other candidate, and they coaxed and blackmailed the young man into assuming the now undesirable office of Khan, while outside the palace rioters gave noisy evidence of their disrespect.

The Mongolian military still had a supply of bowstrings with which to execute khans, but they had no means to curb the populace. With the officers' blessings Ghazan made a bid for popular support.

During the riots the figure of a demagogue had emerged in the capital, and the demagogue's pupils were successful in the provinces. Noruz was the man of the day, the symbol of Persian nationalism, of Mohammedan zealousness, and of rebellion against foreign mundane and religious rule. He spoke Persian with a strange accent that orators all over the country were eager to imitate; hardly anybody realized that this was not a cleverly studied act, but a necessity: Noruz was himself foreign-born.

He was appointed Ghazan Khan's nationalistic prime minister. The Khan adopted the Mohammedan faith for himself, his family, and as the official creed of his realm. Officeholders hastened to follow suit. For any man who did not wear the Mohammedan turban it was highly unsafe to show himself in the streets. He would be insulted and attacked; and nobody would be prosecuted if the victim happened to succumb to the treatment. The Nestorian patriarch was hanged with his head down, while "patriots" looted Nestorian shrines. Nestorian refugees barricaded themselves in the cathedral of Maragha, but the prime minister had Kurd mountaineers assault the cathedral and express their "indignation" by butchering the Nestorians. Anti-semitism became rampant. Acclaimed by khan and military, Noruz's agents spread the tale that, not only the late Gaikatu and the drones in office were responsible for the inflation, but also Saad-ed-Daloué, the Jew who had destroyed the foundations of Persia's currency to deliver the country to his usurer-coreligionists. Pogroms provided a safety valve for the crowd's craving for violence. Riots, rape, and looting undermined Persia's economy even further, and Ghazan Khan intimated cautiously that Noruz introduce an element of moderation in his government-by-consent-of-the-rabble. The Prime Minister ignored the Khan's hints, turned a deaf ear to the nominal ruler's subsequent admonitions, and established a dictatorship of his own. This frightened the Mongolian generals, who knew that they would have to run for their lives if Noruz purged the army. The generals and the Khan conspired against the dictator. They secured funds from foreign merchants who wanted to establish themselves on Persian markets and used them to bribe the army rank and file into loyalty. In the early spring of 1297 a military coup deposed the government. Noruz fled to his native Afghanistan, but was extradited and publicly executed. With him died all the members of his cabinet. Immense crowds applauded the executions. Crowds are volatile, always and everywhere, and the hanging of a tyrant provided no less merriment than the hanging of his victims had provided.

A new prime minister undertook to steer Persia's ship of state out of troubled waters. Rashid-ed-Din was a famous historian, an expert on mistakes made by past rulers, and a scholar of problems never solved. First of all, Rashid-ed-Din explained to the Khan, the people of Persia should get acquainted with the glories and achievements of the ruling house, so that it would no longer oppose it for narrow-minded reasons. The people of Persia had learned an object lesson about the Djenghiskhanides, but the scholar, who was commissioned to write a chronicle of the Mongols, performed his task with brilliant adroitness. He did not try to distort obvious facts and to make biased comments that would antagonize intelligent readers, but he managed to convey the impression that the destructiveness of Mongolian campaigns had been counterbalanced by the wholesome effects of Mongolian pacification, unification, and the inclusion of once-impoverished areas into an empire of prosperous trade.

Reaction to the chronicle was strong and favorable. Prosperity, missed since the dark days of inflation, became the watchword of the government.

New coins were minted, showing the profile of Ghazan, who stood for coined, not printed, money. Traders were encouraged in every possible way. Again bazaars were resplendent with exotic wares—silks and pearls from China, glassware from Venice; and even people who could not afford such expensive objects could still make a few coins by helping merchants in their trade.

Rashid-ed-Din tried to solve the agrarian problem, and this is what he recorded: "Ghazan undertook a land reform. He encouraged the reclamation of soil by decreeing that settler-colonists be granted the fruits of their labors under fair terms. Crown land uncultivated for a certain period would be allotted to those who would till it; they would be tax-exempt during the first year of ownership. Patrimonial lands abandoned by their absentee owners for the same period could be appropriated by colonists without the former owner's consent, and without compensation."

The greater part of migrant peasants, however, preferred a precarious living in thrilling urban surroundings to hazardous reclamation of fallow land; many of those who made use of reform decrees could not hold their own and flocked back to the towns, and not all of the few successful colonist families stayed permanently on appropriated estates. The second and third generations of wealthy new landowners displayed strong tendencies to absent themselves from their holdings and enjoy their riches in cities. Rashid-ed-Din's and Ghazan's land reform could not solve the agrarian problem, which has but two alternatives: compulsory labor, or free play of economical powers which carry their own laws.

Nationalism, too, has its own immutable laws and, even born out of wretched misery, the stream of nationalism flows toward aggression.

The old objective of Hulägu's mission loomed, unfulfilled, as a new goal of Persian nationalism. "Avenge the disgrace of Homs" became a slogan so strong that in 1299 Persian armies marched out toward the scene of past disaster. A Mamelouk force guarding the boundaries of Syria was attacked and dispersed. This was triumph, but did not last four years. Kutluk Shah, the most incompetent general ever to lead an army that included Mongols, was lured into a trap by this Mamelouk opponent in sight of Damascus.

Another great Djenghiskhanide design had failed, but the regime continued. Ghazan died of undisclosed causes which might have been natural. His younger brother Oldjatou succeeded him, and inherited the Rashid-ed-Din cabinet. Oldjatou resumed letter-writing, addressees still being the Pope and the Kings of France and England. He made no specific suggestions about joint action against the Mamelouks, but he extolled his brotherly relations to the Emperor of China, and even to the Djagataide Khan of the Kiptchaks. Kings and Pope replied with brief generalities.

Persia disintegrated. The army turned into a motley band of disgruntled adventurers. The civilian administration was wrecked by a new trend to separatism. Even trade receded as communication lines became exposed to banditry, and a new mercantile power, the Hanseatic League, diverted an increasing part of European business to the north of the continent.

In 1317, Oldjatou's son, Abu Said, was called upon to rule the ruins of an empire. Looking for a scapegoat, he found it in Rashid-ed-Din, who was tried on trumped-up charges. His execution was a foregone conclusion. But the emirs, nobles who had risen to a predominant power in decadent Persia, wanted more victims and started blood purges all over the country, turning provinces into autonomous territories. Many emirs were of Mongolian descent, sons of generals and officials who had donned the turban in unceremonious haste. For almost eight years Emir Tshopan held Abu Said a prisoner; then the Emir was murdered, but Abu Said could not reorganize his government. Few people would care to accept cabinet posts, and nobody would assume governorship of seceding provinces. Abu Said straggled along without a cabinet, abandoning rebellious districts to independence. Among the independent provinces was a district in Anatolia inhabited by Seljuks and ruled over by Turc chieftains whose distant origin was Siberian but who had adopted a nationalism alien to Djenghiskhanide perceptions. Out of that province emerged a new dynamic power, the Ottomans.

Abu Said's death in 1335 sounded the knell to the rule of Hulägu's descendants.

The office of khan had lost its meaning. The Khan's power, like that of any other man in the land, no longer extended beyond the range of his sword. Nobles, petty and high, usurpers, and pretenders, with smaller or larger bands of hangers-on, all made bids for individual sovereignty in a free-for-all for territories of any size.

A Mongolian governor proclaimed himself king of a province adjoining the budding Ottoman state, and opened war on another neighbor, which ultimately benefited the Ottoman fence-sitters. A new Kingdom of Bagdad was proclaimed, with no spiritual design but with unlimited territorial claims. A Mongolian prince of the blood who charged his dethroned relatives with having cheated him out of his birthrights called himself khan and, looking for a khanate, found it close to the Armenian border, in a district whose people had the largest per-capita tax arrears in the former empire. A score of miles away from this district a highwayman established himself in a mountain hideout, and from there raided all territories within range, which refused to recognize him as their prince. The bandit prince, claiming that he was the only Persian among all the new rulers, even claimed the throne of all Persia. His claim was violently contested by various aristocratic families, among them the Mozafferides, who really were of Persian stock, and the Kerts, who were Afghans. The squabble about who was genuine Persian was not yet solved when the bandit prince was slain by his brother, and the head of the Mozafferides was strangled by his son. The Kerts called themselves kings; they became the monarchs with the lowest life expectancy on record. The early Kert kings lasted an average of five months.

The involuntary buffoonery of the cast turned the drama of fourteenth-century Persia from tragedy into a comedy that lacked all elements of heroism, devotion, decency, and even Neronian folly. The ogre face of Djenghiskhanide Siberia was distorted into the grimace of a cannibal-clown.

In China degenerate successors of Kubilai concentrated on dragon ships and the courtesans' performances, and paid no attention to the affairs of close relatives who lived, and were killed, in distant lands. These people were not Chinese and therefore not worthy of attention.

In and around Karakorum forgotten Mongolian nobles who had missed the exodus to China, Persia, and Russia wondered about their overdue pensions for which no solvent relative assumed responsibility. They grew savage and aggressive, and had it not been for the depopulation of regions that had supplied the ancient Mongols with implacable legions, a new Temudshin might have decamped for another universal invasion. But the hundreds of thousands of Mongolian soldiers, settlers, and fortune hunters who had gone south and west were not yet adequately replaced.

Farther north, and all along the broad belt of silent woods, mighty streams, marshes, and prairie passing into tundra, Siberians lived as they had from time immemorial, probably unaware of, and certainly indifferent to, the transient glory of men and tribes they might hardly have considered their kin. There was no magnificence for Siberians from the silent belt; there never had been. Changes were almost imperceptible, and never to the better. The strange voyagers who gathered Siberian furs, and occasionally metal wares, were the determining factors in man-made affairs. They would pay in silk or candy, sometimes a little more, often a little less. During the last four or five generations some foreigners had turned up in the northwestern part of Siberia and had taken pelts without compensation, indicating that this was their due. And because these foreigners were strong and violent the Siberians had surrendered sable skins and foxes. This had become a local custom in some regions, but in general the trade went on: a piece of candy for a sable or two. No fur hunter or trapper had ever heard of Persia.

The descendants of Batu were losing control of their fief. For this reason they had let the family war fizzle out and were now watching events for favorable signs.

Chaos in Persia seemed to augur well for trade. Caravans evaded the ruins of the southwestern Djenghiskhanide fief, its bandits, and tyrants-for-a-day; they traveled through the Khanate of the Kiptchaks and established transshipment and market places. Prosperity would make the Khans of the Kiptchaks strong enough to consolidate and to conquer. But prosperity was a will-o'-the-wisp: the volume of East-West trade shrank into insignificance, and new markets turned into places of desolation.

In 1355 only did Djani-beg, Khan of the Kiptchaks, tired of waiting for good fortunes that would not come, gamble for control of neighboring countries. He seized Azerbaijan, deposed and killed the usurper-King, a relative of Emir Tshopan, the keeper of Abu Said, and installed his son as governor. But the campaign did not proceed beyond the border of Azerbaijan, and by 1358 the intruders were thrown back across the Caucasian range.

For almost three years it seemed as if this ill-conceived campaign had precipitated the fatal exhaustion of the Golden Ordu, and put an end to Mongolian influence west of the Ural Mountains. Yet there would still be another upsurge of Siberian power in Russia, and there would also be a fantastic, gruesome epilogue to the drama of Djenghiskhanide Persia.

CHAPTER TWENTY-ONE "Journeying eastward, you find yourself surrounded by flat grasslands, occasionally bordered, to the right, by an expanse of the sea, and under a dome of blue sky, amidst lonely grandeur, only rarely animated by troops of nomads with their herds. This is European Mongolia."

Thus Ambassador Rubrouck had described Southern Russia after his return from Karakorum.

Batu's fief, however, also included cities, market places and farmlands inhabited by populations culturally, economically, and even ethnically heterogeneous, ruled over by rivaling Russian princes, held together by Mongolian sovereignty.

One by one Russian princes made the pilgrimage to Batu's camp to prostrate themselves before the couchlike throne on which the "Tsar" would receive homage and dictate his terms in the presence of one of his wives, and of courtiers, soldiers, and officials.

The Mongolian Khan granted former hereditary realms as *yarliks* (fiefs) until further notice. Vassals paid high tribute and contributed recruits, auxiliaries, supplies, transportation, and whatever else the Mongols would claim.

Pleas for reduction of dues were to no avail. Even if a territory remained "vacant," Mongolian governors would make it a going concern regardless of what happened to its people, who with dull fatalism accepted extortion as another plague by the Lord's will. Few territories, however, remained vacant. The Russian princes had been locked in armed conflicts on issues so elaborately twisted by generations of antagonists that they defied solution. Ever since their armed might had been surrendered to the foreigners, they kept struggling through mutual denunciation, and outbidding each other for yarliks. By letting the Russians fight among themselves Batu obtained increasing revenue and an expanding spy net. Many accusations were trumped up and Batu knew it. Nevertheless he would occasionally stage "punitive expeditions" against alleged offenders: campaigns of devastation to which other Russian princes gleefully contributed men and materials, hoping to get their mite from the spoils.

Batu knew how to make a dominion pay. And he paid his soldiers and administrators handsomely, too. Mercenaries and officials, hardly more than 4 per cent of them pure Mongols, understood that the more Mongolian rulers extorted from Russia, the better they themselves would fare. This consideration determined the zeal even of Russian nationals who knew patriotism no better than the Mongols knew gratitude.

Russia had little molding effect upon its Siberian conquerors. The Mongols adopted vices, luxuries, and patterns of sinister machinations from countries of ancient high cultures. In "European Mongolia," however, they found little to lure them into new ways of life. But Russians and Mongols did interbreed; Russian nobility married members of Mongolian military and official families, and Mongolian soldiers freely begot children in towns and villages, on post routes, and in steppes, which eventually gave the Russian a Mongoloid touch not to be found among other Slavs.

"Tsar" Batu leisurely moved his tent city up and down the Volga Valley, from Samara (now Kuibyshev) to Serai on the Caspian Sea. This was his acknowledgment of nomad tradition and his way of watching a section of his domain. In fact he had eyes and ears everywhere through a Russian "confidential man": Alexander, Grand Duke of Vladimir, an alleged descendant of Rurik.

Alexander never pleaded for a reduction of yarlik dues, always delivered more auxiliaries than requested for punitive expeditions, knew the financial status of all the other vassal princes, as well as their resources and intentions. Batu appointed the useful man collector of taxes and tribute in Mongolian-dominated Russia. And Alexander did collect, ruthlessly and recklessly. He obtained payment in gold, silver, furs, cattle, and also in men and women slaves. The treasury was satisfied, and the operation left no mean profit for the collector and the Mongolian officials assigned to check his accounts.

Already corruption corroded the administration, but awe of Batu's authority held it within bounds. Under Berké's rule it spread; after Berké's death the lid was off.

The later heads of the Golden Ordu were no longer unconditionally recognized by all members of the family. Princes struggled for rights of succession and greater power, and they engaged in races for profits regardless of their sources.

Grand Duke Alexander catered to the princes' greed. He would act as their agent, selling influence for adjustment of taxes, interventions in local feuds, arrangement of punitive expeditions against detested rivals, and again cancellation of such actions. He helped to hold up communities for extra dues for the benefit of some tenth-line Djenghiskhanide. Alexander was the most indispensable person for extortionists and ransomers alike. His sons, Andrej and Dmitri, assisted him in his operations. They too were liked and trusted throughout the Volga Valley, yet they became instrumental in the decline of the Golden Ordu.

It started with Grand Duke Alexander's death. One man only could be ruler of Vladimir. The other might have received another yarlik, but both stubbornly clung to the patrimony, and both bribed right and left to get the award. Andrej won an important point by making the higher bid to the prince in charge of the armed forces, but Dmitri knew that Nogai, the Mongolian governor-viceroy in charge of provinces along the Black Sea including the

Crimean Peninsula, was considering revolt against Toula Bouqua Khan, the rather weak chief of the Golden Ordu.

To the Crimean Peninsula Dmitri went, his luggage bursting with gold and silver, and was promptly proclaimed Grand Duke, in unprecedented defiance of the Khan's authority. Nogai was positive that a showdown with the ruler was at hand. He mobilized his troops and marched off to Serai, where Toula Bouqua had just decided to ignore the incident. Nogai never learned of the Khan's decision, and this misunderstanding produced a number of unfortunate events.

Nogai's troops seized the Khan. The Viceroy had him strangled and filled the vacancy in great haste, trusting that Toktu, his choice for Khan, was an easily manageable young prince. Only belatedly did he notice that Toktu did not want a tutor. Before Nogai could interfere, Toktu had gathered his own men, ordered his vassals to join his army, and turned against the startled khan-murderer and khan-maker.

For several years Toktu battled Nogai. Thousands of Russians perished in the conflict. From the Volga to the Dnieper villages went up in flames and people starved. In 1299 Nogai was defeated and killed by a soldier who expected a high reward, but instead was put to death on orders of Toktu, who wanted to prove that he was not a vengeful man.

Throughout the struggle Russian princes did not rise against Mongolian rule. They accepted orders as they came, and after the internecine war was over they waited for further orders. They would never unite unless under a dictator, and they would have a Mongol to force them into strait jackets much rather than any one of their own ilk, least of all the hated Grand Dukes of Vladimir.

Victory made Toktu feel almost as strong and safe as Batu, but trouble was brewing in areas where he had least expected it. Genoese merchants in the Crimea used their quasi-autonomy to engage in a kind of traffic the Khan could not tolerate. Instead of confining themselves to bartering Italian luxury items against Russian furs they had adopted a new line: export of slaves to Egypt.

Genoese black-marketeers supplied the Mamelouk Sultan with human contraband from Toktu's domain, and shamelessly undersold the Khan's agents. The chief Genoese contrabandists were arrested. Yet the traffic continued, and in 1307 the incensed Khan ordered a punitive expedition against the infractors of his monopoly. The Genoese, warned by their own informers at court, had just enough time to destroy their buildings and staple goods and to go aboard ships ahead of the Khan's vanguards.

But as he considered punitive expeditions against princes suspect of informing the Genoese, and another campaign against Persia, he learned from reliable sources that the eastern part of his empire was about to secede. The part of the fief extending from the Aral Sea deep into the Siberian lowlands had never been governed by Russian, but by Mongolian, princes. Berké's own brother, Orda, had been installed as the first governor, and Orda's family, who called itself the White Ordu, continued to administer the sparsely settled but fertile territory for several scores of prosperous years.

Toktu bade the head of the White Ordu report at Serai, but there was no reply, and informers said that the defiant house was even planning to invade Russia.

Fearful of an invasion from the Siberian plains, and haunted by the specter of Russian insurrection, Toktu turned into a maniacal tyrant, brooding in fear that the gods had forsaken him; that Tängri was against him, and also the God of the Nestorians; and that the God of the Russian Christians did not like him either. He needed a deity to support him against celestial enemies. He had had few conflicts with the faithful of Allah. Toktu convoked his family and announced that he was adopting Mohammedanism, and that they would have to join him at once.

The Mongolian princes accepted the conversion ceremonies in perfect obedience. The Khan put his favorite nephew, Uzbeg, a young man with the mind and temper of a deceitful goon, in charge of religious affairs. Uzbeg became a Mohammedan inquisitor and executioner; his terrorism reduced the Golden Ordu into a herd of frightened sheep and paved the way for his succession to the khanate.

Toktu died in 1312, a madman, shaken by nightmares and outbursts of fury. He left no document nominating a successor to the throne, or, rather, no such document was found. Uzbeg, who had free access to the Khan's tent, may have destroyed Toktu's will.

His henchmen reported a plot by Mongolian princes to assassinate Uzbeg during the banquet celebrating his investiture as Khan. Uzbeg waited until all the guests were assembled, then he appeared in the hall, and executioners entered from side doors. Not a single real or alleged conspirator survived the carnage.

Uzbeg Khan ruled, surrounded by cringing chattels who outdid each other in protestations of admiring loyalty and adulation of his actions. He was a wanton sadist, but intelligent enough to realize that a tyrant should not needlessly antagonize foreign powers.

He readmitted Genoese traders and used them as his own agents in the slave business. He obliged Venice by granting its merchants concessions on the mouth of the Don River, and he entered into the closest relations with Mamelouk Sultan Nassir, signing a pact of friendship with the Egyptian ruler and giving him a princess of the Golden Ordu in marriage. Egyptian women were far more attractive and refined than the Mongolian, but the Sultan thought it good policy to become related to a khan.

Mohammedan zealots among the Golden Ordu were startled to see that Uzbeg, the murderous foreign champion of Mohammedanism assumed a benevolent attitude toward the Russian Church. In fact the Khan brought the Church under his indirect control and used it as a tool for the spiritual subjugation of his vassals. There were still no more reliable stool pigeons and extortionists than the descendants of Alexander of Vladimir. The Khan gave them temporal overlordship over the Church and ordered that the metropolitan establish his see in the city of Vladimir. The grand dukes saw to it that the metropolitan served the tyrants first and the Lord only in his spare time.

The grand dukes traveled back and forth between their yarliks and the Khan's court. Other Russian princes and *boyars* (nobles) who met the grandducal coaches and wagons stayed aloof, for a single incautious word reported to the Khan might spell their doom. Nine princes had already been executed without a trial because the grand dukes insinuated that they had been conspiring against the Mongolian government.

The holders of yarliks, however, were still too scared to engage in conspiracy. Fear was the mainspring of their actions. They would never trust a fellow noble though their plights were identical. They were ready to calumniate others in order to obtain pardon for offenses with which they might themselves be charged. They would help sack their neighbors' lands to get a respite for their own yarliks. They would sell their peasants into slavery to prolong their own precarious physical freedom. They would keep journeying to Uzbeg's camp as to the temple of a fierce idol; but the idol, rapacious and exacting as it was, was not as horrible as its satanist high priest, the Grand Duke of Vladimir, whom not even abject surrender could pacify.

The grand dukes themselves were fear-ridden. They had lied to their masters, they had cheated the Khan and co-operated with corrupt officials. The Khan might call upon the victims of their crimes for a punitive expedition against Vladimir. Nothing but reduction of other princes to sheer helplessness could assuage the nightmare; it would keep lingering as long as a Mongolian khan wielded the power to destroy.

The grand dukes knew about the White Ordu's ascendancy, but they did not dare to conspire with those upstarts. Those Mongols might be different and unite against foreigners. Mongols were not different, but this the Vladimirites did not yet know.

Cautiously, deceitfully the grand dukes engineered their drive for power. The princes of Tver were the most dangerous rivals of the grand dukes of Vladimir. One ruler of Tver had been Grand Prince of all Russia; a titular rank rather than a real office, but commanding respect even after that grand prince had been killed by earlier Mongolian invaders. It would be easy to have another prince of Tver executed under false charges, but it would not quiet Vladimirite apprehension. Tver would have to be obliterated.

Early in 1327 visitors to the city and the land of Tver whispered of portentous events ahead. People would be forced to become Mohammedans, they said. The men who spread the rumors never stayed long, and nobody remembered having seen them before; yet their story was widely believed. Men and women of Tver had given lives and properties to placate the savage rulers; but they would not sacrifice their souls by adopting the infidels' creed.

Late in June messengers of doom returned to Tver. They announced that August 15, the day of Assumption of the Blessed Virgin, would see the people either adopt Mohammedanism or accept martyrdom.

Also early in 1327 the treasurer of the Golden Ordu received reports on large tax arrears in the yarlik of Tver. The people of that domain, it was said, defrauded collectors of revenue and withheld important contributions. Officials from Vladimir did not directly confirm the report, but they sighed that Tverites were, and had always been, an arrogant lot, deceitful, dishonest, and defiant. Collectors from Vladimir, they contended, had done their best to keep accounts straight. But a thorough checking should establish the facts. The checking, carried out by grand-ducal experts, produced a lengthy report which charged Tver with disobedience, violation of the terms of the yarlik, and general tax fraud. The Khan decreed that the matter be investigated on the spot. His own cousin was sent to Tver to head the investigation commission. But conversion of Tver to Mohammedanism was never really considered.

Late in July the Mongolian commission arrived in the city of Tver. The Prince paid a humble call to the Khan's cousin and was treated with icy disdain; he was not told about the subject of the investigation and the Mongolian refused to listen when the Russian tried to plead for indulgence for his people's religion. Burghers of Tver gathered their most treasured valuables to bribe the Mongolians into tolerance, but the rumormongers warned the townspeople that the mere attempt at bribery would result in mass executions.

Every morning members of the commission would ride and drive to the government palace. Every evening the investigators would return to their requisitioned homes. Streets were deserted during their rides and drives to and from the palace. No conclusive evidence of fraudulent operations had yet been unearthed. Mongolian investigators were getting angry at their assistants from Vladimir, who kept ranting about cleverly concealed fraud; already the Mongols sympathized with the people of the silent city.

On the morning of August 15 streets were thronged by dense crowds. Mongols in carriages and on horseback cast surprised and friendly glances at the milling men and women in holiday garb, but the people stonily stared back. The square in front of the palace was congested; coachmen and riders were unable to reach the entry; throngs held the members of the commission hemmed in an iron vise. One irritable Mongol drew his sword . . . a simultaneous outcry of thousands of people burst over the square, spread all over town, reverberated from the city walls; a few seconds later thousands of hands rose holding knives, sticks, and rocks. The Mongols, their servants, and guards, and even their horses were slain, and their carriages broken to pieces. From side streets citizens emerged; carrying pictures of the Holy Virgin, they trampled on the corpses until they were no longer recognizable.

But when the crowd turned toward the palace, they found the gates locked. The Khan's cousin and some of his men had spent the night in the building and were barricading themselves. The citizenry had no siege machines, but it battered the doors with their bodies; the Mongols rushed through a gallery that linked the palace to the fortress, to hold out there. Besiegers heaped huge piles of timber around the fortress, the besieged hurled missiles at men and women who tried to kindle the piles, and killed many of them, but then there rose a column of fire.

The frenzied crowd knelt down to praise the Holy Virgin. This was her miracle. The unfaithful were burned at the stake; the people of Tver would remain Christian forever. Messengers from Tver raced to neighboring principalities to announce that the people had prevailed over its oppressors, and to appeal to all true believers to join Tver. From the highest roofs of the city, and from undamaged fortress towers, people held a day-and-night vigil to watch out for allies to join the blessed of the Mother of God. For several days the huge plains around Tver remained deserted. Then, at last, a cloud of dust became visible on the southeastern horizon, and from the cloud emerged contours of marching and riding columns, large as not even the most faithful citizen had hoped to see arrive. Another miracle seemed about to happen: righteous Russia uniting under the banner of the Virgin.

The columns carried banners veiled by dust from the cinder-dry ground. From the city's walls and forefield, and from roofs, banners waved, welcomes and blessings sounded. The approaching host marched in silence. A sudden breeze drove the clouds apart: banners became clearly visible—the banners of Vladimir.

A joyous throng still blocked the city gates as from vantage points shouts of distress announced coming disaster; the cavalry under the hated banner fell in trot, and then into gallop; they charged into opened city streets adorned with flowers and pictures of Mary. Tver was obliterated, its people decimated. "Throughout the Russian lands there was affliction, distress and bloodshed," a contemporary chronicler recorded laconically.

Ivan I, Grand Duke of Vladimir, had been hunting not far away from the Khan's court since the beginning of August. The people of Vladimir called their grand duke "Kalita," meaning "moneybag," because he was a penny-pinching, ducat-saving usurer to whom coins meant more than the Cross. The Vladimirites had no love for their ruler and Ivan Kalita reciprocated their disaffection. He transferred the seat of his government to Muscovy, a rickety settlement risen from a similar place leveled by the Mongols less than one century ago, and adopted the title of Grand Duke of Muscovy.

The "moneybag" was an empire builder in his own way, which was more crooked and violent than that of his Mongolian sovereigns. His agents had done well in Tver; and they had not done too badly in the Khan's treasury department. And he had made some thorough preparations, undetected by the Khan's agents.

On August 17, Uzbeg summoned Ivan; the Khan was foaming with rage, as he told the Grand Duke that Tver was in revolt, that Mongolian royalty had been killed, that terrific reprisals were indispensable, but that it would take months until a punitive expedition could get under way. No adequate Mongolian or vassal forces were ready for action. Russian princes were not entitled to maintain a standing army, but Ivan explained with proud modesty that he had just mobilized his contingent of auxiliaries to hold it at the Khan's disposal: 50,000 men, assembled near Muscovy.

Khan Uzbeg ordered Ivan to punish Tver. The "moneybag" suggested that since such conspiracy undoubtedly involved other cities and principalities, the entire plot should be nipped in the bud. The Grand Duke left Uzbeg's camp with unprecedented powers.

No previous ruler of Vladimir had had such an opportunity to destroy rivals; never before had the hegemony of Vladimir and Muscovy been as firmly established in Russia.

Novgorod resisted the Muscovite besiegers. Ivan detested the Westernized town, with its democratic form of government and its enterprising merchants who did prosperous business with Germany, Scandinavia, the Low Countries, the Balkan Peninsula, and who obviously obtained furs from some distant lands in the northeast to which he had no access, at prices which made his own fur trade unprofitable. It was a blow to the Grand Duke that his men could not take Novgorod by storm, but he gave vent to his urge for destruction in other parts of the land. Pskov, another well-to-do city, suffered the fate reserved for Novgorod, and many more towns became scenes of devastation.

Long after Ivan's death, and after the rule of the Golden Ordu had come to an end, complaisant historians would attribute the destruction to the Mongols, but the blood of hecatombs of Russian Abels cried to heaven against the Muscovite Cain.

From the Baltic, Lithuanian armies penetrated Polish and Ukrainian territory, invading regions that were part of the Khan's realm. Warnings reached the Mongolian court: The grand dukes of Muscovy were planning a deal with Lithuania betraying the Mongols in order to split their European realm. But the Muscovites did not side with the new great power of the Baltic. Either Lithuanian terms were unacceptable, or the grand duke expected to acquire all the lands of the Golden Ordu for himself. The "moneybag" assured the Khan of his unwavering loyalty and of his determination to fight the Lithuanians.

Uzbeg and Djanibeg, who became Khan in 1340, accepted the pledges at face value. The Golden Ordu still prospered; treasury chests were bulging with valuables, the Khan's wives and concubines, his officials, and officers, courtiers and relatives of royalty received lavish gifts. However, Muscovy wanted privileges in return, and they were granted without objections, apparently as a matter of courtesy; but as time went on, applicants turned claimants, and claimants exactors.

In 1361, shortly after the end of the fruitless campaign against Persia, when

Mongolian power and prestige were at a low ebb, the throne of the Golden Ordu became vacant. A horde of contenders struggled for the right of succession; it seemed as if the end of Mongolian rule in Russia were at hand, but an energetic, intelligent young khan seized the reins and made a determined attempt to restore his family to greatness. Mamai Khan was not averse to blood purges and rule by terror, but sober realism, conspicuously absent from the minds of his predecessors, told him that his position was too precarious to permit violence. He did not want to rely on Muscovy, and turned a deaf ear to grand-ducal protestations of loyalty as well as to requests for privileges and he even discontinued the tax-collecting agreement. He noticed soon that other Russian princes were no more reliable than the grand dukes of Muscovy. He knew that the White Ordu was irreconcilably opposed to the Golden Ordu. The power of his government was limited to the Volga Valley, and sections of the Black Sea coast policed by the army of the Golden Ordu, in which Mongolian enlisted men were as rare as bluebirds. And the government itself was not merely infiltrated by corruption; it was a sheer impenetrable body of corruptionists.

Mamai had to rebuild his administration and executive from scratch, from people without experience and of untried loyalty. But with indomitable determination he recruited soldiers, trained officers, and established new bodies of officials. In the east his hostile cousins of the White Ordu watched his doings; in the west the Muscovites were taking off the already threadbare mask of obedience. Reorganization would have required many tranquil years, and there was little time and no tranquility.

Russian princes refused to pay dues to Mamai's own collectors. The Khan had not yet enough men to stage a punitive expedition. Reluctantly he wrote Grand Duke Dmitri of Muscovy, requesting that he undertake both collection and punishment. The Muscovite replied bluntly that he had more pertinent business to attend to. With dwindling revenue Mamai continued to build up strength, hoping that by 1380 he might be able to chastise the arrogant Grand Duke. But in 1373 already Dmitri told Mongolian commissioners that he no longer considered himself the Khan's vassal.

Mamai gambled. He made an improvised attempt to crush the Muscovite by one lightning blow. But Dmitri's intelligence was on the alert. Russian soldiers under the Mongolian flag were met and thrown back by a superior number of countrymen under the flag of Muscovy. Mamai made an attempt to gain Lithuanian support. He offered to recognize all the Lithuanian conquests at Russia's expense, and even to cede more Russian territory in return for assistance against Dmitri. But the territories he offered were not actually under his control, and Lithuania regretted: it was too heavily engaged in struggle against the Teutonic knights to consider military ventures elsewhere.

From the south and east alarming reports poured into Serai, on the mouth of the Volga. A new, sinister power had arisen, and Mamai's shrunken realm was at the doorstep of a new empire that claimed universality. The Khan had no man to spare; and, as a Mohammedan, he was a fatalist. If it was Allah's will that he be destroyed, he would be destroyed; and if it was Allah's will that he prevail, he would prevail.

He decided to concentrate on the Muscovite foe. Dmitri had not invaded the Khan's inner fortress in 1373; Mamai wondered if the hated Grand Duke were not afraid. But Dmitri was only bidding for time. In 1376 he marched toward the Black Sea, outpost of Mongolian-controlled territory. The Mongols struck first, but the campaign resulted in several Mongolian setbacks; the Khan's armies were slowly pressed back toward the Sea of Azov. Not until the fall of 1380 did the great encounter take place, near Kulikovo, on the Don River.

Mongolian strategy still culminated in the traditional flank attack. The Muscovite was ready for that move. He held crack cavalry units ready to drive into the rear of an enemy flanking group. Mamai was defeated. Dmitri emerged as Dmitri Donskoy, victor of the Don; the scion of oppressors of Russia in the service of the Mongols was dubbed Liberator of Russia from the Mongolian yoke.

The battle of the Don was not a battle of liberation. Muscovy, having been prison guard, wanted to become warden in its own rights. Mamai survived his defeat. Like the Mongols of old, he led the remnants of his army into the wide steppes.

CHAPTER TWENTY-TWO Another man ascended and came like a storm, and covered the land like a cloud—he, and all his bands and many people with him.

The human storm grew out of minor disturbances, like an atmospheric tempest, and it took infinitely longer to assume catastrophic proportions than it would take natural disasters. Yet the son of man, as often before and afterward, did not deal with the human disturbance when it was but a nuisance, and he did not cope with it when its dangerousness was obvious though not yet overpowering. Complacency, fear, and the hope of profit by fellow-men's disaster paved the way for a new holocaust, which will forever be linked with the name of Timur, also called Timur Lenk and Tamerlane.

Timur has become a symbol of monstrous might and grandiose recklessness. He was pictured, in turn, as a giant ogre, a chosen of destiny, a hero, and, of late, as a titan of romantic adventure.

The most lasting memorials left behind by Timur are immense expanses of deserted, barren land reduced to desolation by his own savagery and that of all his bands.

Timur expected a glowing biographical account by his appointed historiographer to be the only document perpetuating his memory. He held long sessions with his favorite chronicler, directing him how to treat the topic of his life, including augury heralding his birth, bombastic claims to awe-inspiring ancestry, and tales of precocious exploits. No business of state, however pertinent, could keep the conqueror from discussing details of his biography with the man who wrote it down, adorned it by idolatrous phrases and interpretation of obvious infamy as evidence of sublime virtue. The most distinctive feature of Timur, as it emerges from the chronicle, is that of fantastic vanity.

Nothing indicates, however, that Timur had an exalted gift of genius. His cabals and intrigues, his deceit, his recklessness were extraordinary only because of the effect they produced in settings in which such qualities were not unusual. Sinister conjunctures turned him into an instrument of catastrophe, the germs of which were sprouting under the surface of lands, smarting under the effects of earlier Djenghiskhanide furor.

Timur was lame. This his biographer attributed to injury suffered in heroic action. It cannot be established when and under what circumstances Timur was crippled. Since Alexander of Macedonia's day infirmity has been known to stimulate tyrannical violence. Timur's lameness may have reflected upon his state of mind.

This eager chronicler tells of a marvelous foreboding of Timur's birth. When his mother was pregnant, Teragai, his father, had a dream: "A handsome Arab handed him a sword, and as Teragai brandished the weapon its brillant flash illuminated the entire world." "A son will be born to you," an augur interpreted the dream, "a man mighty by the sword; chosen to conquer the world, purge it of error and evil, and to convert all man to the true [Mohammedan] faith."

As the mother was in labor, Teragai studied the Koran and his eye fell upon the word *tamarru*, which means iron or, according to another version, shock. The future "mighty by the sword" was named Timur.

Timur's father was a Turc of recent petty nobility. Yet his biographer claims that Timur was a direct legitimate descendant of Temudshin. In 1336, when the boy was born, Djenghiskhanide polygamy accounted for legions of unrecorded progeny. Almost anybody could be a distant relative of Mongolian royalty, but apart from this conjecture there is no evidence that Timur was related to the Djenghis Khan.

The biographer claims that when the boy was nine his favorite pastime was war games, and he excelled all his playmates in devising amazing maneuvers. At twelve he sought the company of wise men and believed in the value of erudition. At fifteen he was a distinguished horseman, and at sixteen a philosopher who said, "The world glitters like a box of gold, but it is filled with snakes and scorpions. I despise deceptive glitter."

The city of Kerch, birthplace of Timur, was situated near Samarkand, in Transoxiana, which, in the process of disintegration of the Persian Djenghiskhanide realm, had become quasi-independent under the rule of an emir, who in turn depended on district governors, city magistrates, and rural leaders to put their orders into effect. Weak as the government was, the country was prosperous. Land reclaimed from the ravages of war was carefully tilled, crops were abundant, and livestock was increasing rapidly. Cities were bustling with craftsmen's shops and merchants' booths, trade caravans did thriving business in towns and market places. Its resources turned the land into a bone of contention of rival individuals and factions.

When Timur was in his teens, Emir Kuzgan, the one-eyed, called himself ruler of Transoxiana even though his actual power was narrowly confined and often did not reach beyond the walls of Kerch. Father Teragai served Kuzgan in a minor job, with as much loyalty as was required to hold on to his salary. This was like walking the tightrope: emirs did not last long, and rarely died of natural causes. Officials had to be careful not to antagonize the Emir's potential successors; they had to use counterintrigues to fight off their fellow-employee's cabals; they had to know from whom to accept bribes, and to whom to pay clandestine gratuities. There were so many intricate things a public servant had to know, and do, that there was almost no time left to perform his functions.

The state of affairs was not considered disreputable. Timur's historian proudly tells how his hero entered the Emir's employ: In his late teens the youth wanted to organize his former playmates into a conspirational body that should install him in public offices, but as the frightened lads hesitated to join, Timur bade them farewell, went straight to Emir Kuzgan's palace, and allegedly managed by deceit to be hired.

His first job was with the Bahadour guards, a mischievous lot always ready to make a dishonest coin by aiding conspirators. The chances are that Timur did not even obtain it by deceit, but by his father's intercession.

Shortly after the youth joined the Bahadours, rebels bribed the officer in charge to have his men look the other way while a group of murderers would invade the Emir's residence. As was the custom, the officer split the fee with the men on duty. Timur happened to be one of them, but his share was trifling. He asked for more. Had the officer given him a denar or two, the youth's greed and ambition would have been satisfied, and there might never have been Tamerlane, conqueror of India and scourge of two continents. But after his request was scornfully denied, he chose an informer's fee instead, and denounced the plot to the Emir's family. This denunciation started him on his gruesomely fabulous career.

The grateful one-eyed Kuzgan had Timur promoted to officer's rank, gave him one of his granddaughters in marriage, and in due course appointed him vice-governor of Kerch.

Generosity did not considerably prolong the Emir's life. In 1357 he succumbed to assassins' daggers. Timur was not present when the murder occurred, and his thousand Bahadours were off guard when the followers of

Bajazet Islair and Hadji Berlas, the chiefs of the conspiracy, invaded the palace.

Timur at once rendered homage to the duumvirate, who proclaimed themselves joint rulers of Transoxiana. And he also managed to maintain his intimate friendship with young Prince Hosein, his brother-in-law. The Mohammedan clergy, whose willing tool the murdered Emir had been, wondered about the attitude of the duumvirs; they assigned Timur to spy upon the Emirs and assured him of their support should he run into trouble. Hardly three years after the murder of Kuzgan the Emirs adopted Timur as a partner in government.

But Timur was not the man to put all his eggs in one basket, even if it be a joint emirate.

A few months after Timur's elevation Toghluk, Khan of Turkestan, a prince of Mongolian nationality, invaded Transoxiana. Bejazet Islair surrendered at once and was granted governorship of Samarkand Province; Hadji Berlas crossed the Amu Darja for safety and with him went all public cash. Timur's historian states that "sound policy can accomplish more than heroism, and bright ideas are stronger than armies." And this is what he tells about his protagonist's policy and ideas: Timur gathered the holdings of the treasury other than cash and traveled to Toghluk's headquarters. On his way he was occasionally stopped by marching Turkestan units whose commanders charged ransom before letting him proceed. Timur gave them what they wanted; the only things he would ask for in return were letters signed by the officers, recommending him to the Khan!

Equipped with a bundle of letters and reduced treasures, the ex-Emir reached the Khan's camp. He handed over credentials and valuables, deploring, as it was a traditional civility, the gift's unworthiness of its august recipient.

But Timur elaborated on the civility by telling the Khan that Turkestan officers had despoiled him of what actually belonged to their ruler. The Khan ordered his generals to return their loot, the generals objected that they had already split with the officers and the officers with the men. The irate Khan threatened to demote ranking officers, and subalterns withheld soldiers' wages to get back what they had given to their men. Rebellion shook the army. Toghluk was forced to withdraw part of his mutinous forces for reorganization, but before leaving Transoxiana he appointed the honest Timur viceroy.

An angry Bajazet Islair called Timur a cheat, and Hadji Berlas, who had purchased a safe conduct back to Transoxiana, spoke of fraud and misuse of office. The Viceroy denounced both men as heads of a Turc conspiracy to overthrow "legal Mongolian rule over Transoxiana," and the Khan, whose army was again under control, had Bajazet and Berlas put to death.

Until then Timur had never claimed Mongolian parentage or denied his Turc nationality; but after inventing a Turc conspiracy he hastened to assert that he was not, really, related to a people that plotted against its khan. Scribes and legal experts of dubious reputation produced documents to prove that Timur was of pure Mongolian stock, but they did not yet dub him a Djenghiskhanide, which the Khan would have taken as an act of imposture. Toghluk did not quite trust the documents, and put his son, Ilyas, in charge of Transoxianan military and civilian affairs, leaving Timur only his pompous title.

Occupation forces behaved outrageously. Raping, kidnaping, looting, blackmailing, and selling slaves were common practices. The higher a native ranked, the more he was exposed to the soldiery's abuse. Ilyas refused to interfere, and Timur hypocritically lamented his own weakness, which prevented him from helping his countrymen.

Clergy, nobles, and civic leaders began to regard Timur as a patriot who had been deceived and sidetracked. Timur, the faker, betrayer, and calumniator turned into a myth; the prospective liberator of Transoxiana.

Timur was not the man to lead a struggle for liberation unless sure of success. He was not dissatisfied. He still held an exalted title, drew a high salary, and was better off than almost any of his countrymen. Yet the myth was stronger than the man. Conspiratory groups formed throughout the country and proclaimed him honorary leader; clergymen blessed the rebellion and urged Timur to seize the reins; Bahadours slighted and discharged by Ilyas pledged allegiance to Timur; bards of national resurrection—unaware of Timur's claim to Mongolian descent—extolled his noble deeds. Some of their Timur ballads are still sung by Siberian shepherds in Kazakstan and around Lake Balkhash.

Timur stalled and wavered, but temptation grew as the occupation troops, hardly 10,000 strong, turned into undisciplined hordes of spoilers. Prince Hosein implored him to avenge iniquities suffered since the death of Emir Kuzgan; 6000 Bahadours were ready to serve as shock troops; more than twice that number of volunteers waited for the word to rise.

At last Timur acceded to the demand. The putsch should start with the arrest of seventy ranking occupation officials, and this was as far as the operation was carried out. The next phase, seizure of all Turkestan by Bahadours and volunteers, did not come off. Misunderstandings and poor organization delayed Transoxianan action. Ilyas recovered from his surprise and regained control. Timur was ready to deny his part in the plot, but intercepted a dispatch to Ilyas, saying that he was the leader of the rebellion. Therefore, according to his biographer, he followed the word of the Koran: "When you cannot come to terms with enemies who are stronger than you; try for safety in escape."

Timur fled, and with him went his brother-in-law. For two years, from 1361 to 1363, the two young men served petty emirs, chieftains, and clan leaders as advisers, soldiers of fortune, or experts on a colorful variety of affairs. The official biography reads like a flowery but utterly inconclusive tale of Timur's knight-errant heroism.

Actually Timur had not left his country empty-handed. His wealth permitted him to recruit and equip a fighting force of his own which for some time he hired out to the highest bidder and which he eventually used to make a bid for Transoxiana. The underground there still considered him their leader, and Hosein fervently insisted that legitimacy be restored to Transoxiana. Hosein, the legal heir to the throne, promised his brother-in-law the highest office in the government.

Late in 1363, Timur's mercenaries crossed the border; this time the underground rose at once, and so did the Bahadours. Turkestan soldiers, harassed by rebels, led astray by civilians, deprived of most of their equipment by fires set in storehouses, were routed. Timur and Hosein made a triumphal entry. Hosein assumed the title of khan. Timur was renominated emir.

The Khan was head, and the Emir his minister of state. The Khan had known destitution; poverty had turned him into a miser who collected every penny of dues regardless of the taxpayer's rank. Taxes were high, and had to be kept high to rebuild the army and repair the damage wrought during the occupation. The Emir was still a rich man and he had the reputation of being generous. Timur shrugged his shoulders when ranking officers, titled officials, and landowners complained about financial hardships, saying that he was a faithful servant of Hosein Khan, his sovereign, and could not interfere with taxation, but would lend money to those who needed it badly. Quietly he built up a ring of grateful debtors in key positions. Whenever it came to a showdown between him and his brother-in-law, the debtors would side with him.

Armaments continued to be the highest item on the budget; Hosein considered reduction of armaments. The Emir objected: With the collapse of Greater Persia continuing the army could be gainfully used to snatch large slices of neighboring territory and make the conquest pay. Land grabbing was easy in the 1360s and 1370s, and Timur had no use for disarmament that would relieve the taxpayer and deprive him of a pillar of his power: his mercenaries who had been incorporated *en bloc* into the Transoxianan army.

Hosein yielded to Timur's argument of ease and profitableness of conquest. The army was put to work. It seized parts of Afghanistan, it entered Turkestan, it even penetrated deep into Southwestern Siberia, the realm of the White Ordu. Timur accompanied the legions. By his rank he was the superior of all officers; he took credit for every success, of which there were many. He studied traditional Mongolian strategy and tactics, supply system, transportation, and military engineering, and acquired sound working knowledge of generalship. The first mention of his lameness is made in accounts of these campaigns.

One version tells of an arrow hitting Timur's knee while he was leading a cavalry charge. Another has it that the Emir battled a horde of aggressors, singlehanded, to cover the rescue of a wounded soldier, and suffered a serious leg injury. Neither account would explain his almost total lameness.

Meeting conquered chieftains, governors, and princes, Timur entertained them lavishly, accepted their vows of fealty, and enlisted their soldiers in the Transoxianan army, in the section of his own ex-mercenaries. The conquered hardly heard of the Khan. They accepted Timur as their sovereign. During the opening phase of the campaign against Afghanistan, Hosein inquired about Timur's method of treating defeated tribes. Timur replied with a protestation of enthusiastic, everlasting loyalty. The Khan had accepted the protestation, but his apprehensions rode again, when he learned of Timur using priests and demagogues to propagandize himself in the army, in occupied countries, and even at home.

As the soldiers penetrated into southern Afghanistan, agents addressed gathering crowds, telling of Emir Timur's noble generosity and calling him "Lord of the Auspicious Constellation," a byname that could but enhance his prestige in Oriental minds. The agents urged men to enlist in the Emir's forces, participate in his conquests, and share the spoils. Response was strong, and the troops of Transoxiana grew into Timur's private army. And throughout the Khan's realm Timur was eulogized wherever people gathered. In bazaars, mosques, and in market places men who had hardly ever profited from Timur's bounty praised the munificent Emir and cursed the greedy Hosein, who was trying to relieve the tax burden from proceeds of conquest.

In Kerch and Samarkand people staged noisy demonstrations against the Khan, who transferred his residence to the fortress city of Balkh, and assembled 7000 horsemen for his own protection. In an urgent message to Timur he requested assistance against rebellion. The Emir replied with another declaration of loyalty, not as emphatic as the previous protestation, yet still unequivocally worded. He did not refer to the bewildering propaganda mentioned in the Khan's message, but he did say that he could not spare a single man as a big battle was looming, and that 7000 soldiers should be sufficient to hold Balkh.

No battle was looming in Afghanistan, but Timur had another locale in mind: he was on his way to Balkh with all his men and a small fraction of his treasures. He used treasures to bribe the Khan's officers, and the presence of his army to frighten the Khan's men. In the year 1370 he encircled the fortress and summoned his brother-in-law to surrender. Deserted by his small army, the Khan yielded to the demand.

Timur charged him with a variety of crimes: oppression and exploitation of the people, offenses against the law of Islam, and betrayal of his country. To show his lenient generosity, the Emir told his victim that he would be spared provided that he resign his throne, surrender his property, and depart for a pilgrimage to distant Mecca to ask Allah's forgiveness. A guard of trusted nobles was assigned to accompany the bewildered ex-Khan. Hosein never reached Mecca. "By depriving Hosein of his life," Timur's biographer recorded, "his companions prevented him from fomenting further trouble and starting more wars. In the Book of Fate was written the time and place preordained for Hosein; no man can alter his destiny."

Timur did not at once adopt Hosein's title; even as emir he was the ruler of Transoxiana and many conquered lands. The people acclaimed him; his soldiers looked to him for guidance toward easy spoils; and the Moslem clergy extolled him as the Protector of the Faith.

Timur accepted the clergy's extolment, but his habits were anathema to Mohammedan law. He never had his head shaved; instead of the turban of the faithful he wore a gold-inlaid helmet or a Chinese-type hat; he consumed huge amounts of wine and, worst of offenses, his women were present at the warriors' banquets, and unveiled.

At the age of thirty-four his thinning hair and beard were turning white, his swarthy skin was slackening and wrinkling slightly. His men would call him Timur Lenk, Timur the Lame (later perverted to Tamerlane), but the stern Emir frowned at a byname that had not yet acquired a heroic flavor.

A portrait Timur had painted shortly after Hosein's death showed him as a grave-looking man, but otherwise the painting was as fanciful as the biography: it pictured an apple-cheeked gentleman with a huge pitch-black beard.

Timur's career had been based upon always having superiors or, at least, equal partners against whom he could conspire and against whom he could turn popular discontent. He had been thriving on rebellion against supreme authority; but now he had supreme authority, and he would have to suppress malcontents and look for other sources of power. In the past luckless Hosein had been his only friend, but he had had a number of intimates who had collaborated with him and helped him. However, intimacy generated betrayal. Timur, distrustful of former associates, deliberately antagonized these men and became afraid of their antagonism.

The harassed Emir realized that nothing but brute strength could protect him against cabals and violence. His army was big. A big army was expensive. The people he had incited against high taxes would get refractory. An even bigger army was needed to keep rebels under control. But such an army was in itself an element of rebellion. Generals were usurpers to the throne, in the pay of the object of their evil plans.

Timur wavered and pondered. He increased the army, and kept it out of mischief in small-scale campaigns. He no longer fraternized with subjugated petty rulers, because there was no khan against whom to turn their resentment. With every new conquest he acquired new enemies. Timur treated new subjects harshly, and worried about the effects.

Six years passed, and Timur still pondered over a secure policy. His popularity was low, and the army was dissatisfied.

Across the border, in the Siberian steppes, the White Ordu was locked in internecine struggle. Djenghiskhanide princes battled for the khanate. Timur had met several grandees of the White Ordu during his hegira, he had served them and had no opportunity to betray his masters, or, at least, he had not deceived Toktamish, a distant relative of ruling Urus Khan. Toktamish had staged an unsuccessful putsch against the Khan and fled before Urus' wrath. He crossed the Amu Darja (Oxus) into Transoxiana, and applied for Timur's assistance.

An invasion of the land of the White Ordu would satisfy the army's ambitions, bring rich spoils, and solve a few of Timur's pertinent problems. The Emir's almost-forgotten claim to Mongolian progeny was revived. Toktamish accepted it unquestioningly. He did not even object when Timur pretended to be a direct descendant of Temudshin. The Prince accepted vassalship in return for Timur's pledge to mobilize one cavalry corps for an invasion of Siberia.

In 1377, Timur's horsemen defeated Urus, and in the following year Toktamish was established as Khan of the White Ordu. The avalanche of conquest did not stop at the Russian border. Toktamish entered the realm of the Golden Ordu, claiming that, owing to internal discord, the descendants of Batu could no longer properly administer their fief, that unrest in Russia threatened peace and security of the domain of the White Ordu, and that it was Toktamish's duty to restore law and order in all parts of the Djenghiskhanide empire. Timur's cavalry, joined by remains of Urus' forces now under Toktamish's command, crossed the lower course of the Volga and advanced toward the Don. Mamai, head of the Golden Ordu, defeated by Grand Duke Dmitri, emerged from his hideout to halt the invaders. His pathetically small army disintegrated at the first contact with Toktamish's forces. Mamai fled to the Genoese trade colony in the Crimea in quest of asylum. But the Italians had no desire to become embroiled with an up-and-coming conqueror because of a defeated wretch. It was *vae victis* in the worst Roman tradition; Mamai was slain, and as Toktamish swept the northern shores of the Sea of Azov and the Black Sea, Genoese and Venetians applied for extension of commercial treaties and, as a token of their submission, minted new coins bearing the likeness of Toktamish and the words: "The Just Khan, the Helper of Religion, and of the World."

The Just Khan, still supported by Timur's troops, established himself on the throne of the Golden Ordu. He disdainfully accepted jittery homage from nobles of the realm, drafted a great number of men into his own army, and dispatched delegations to all Russian princes, requesting, in terms not heard since Batu's day, that they take his orders, which included immediate payment of tax arrears with interest. Muscovy got no preferential treatment.

Dmitri Donskoy, "liberator from the Mongolian yoke," and claimant to the title Grand Prince of all Russia, refused to comply. So did other Russian princes, who had become forgetful of Mongolian fury.

Another hurricane broke. From the southern Ural Mountains, from the steppes of Southwestern Siberia, from the hot shores of the Aral Sea, and from the vastness east and west of the Volga savage riders on fast ponies swept Central and Western Russia, spreading death and destruction.

No Russian armies could stop the horsemen, no Russian pleas could assuage Toktamish, and Timur's troops outdid their allies' savagery.

Vladimir succumbed to the devastators. Yuriel and Mozhaisk went down in ruins; one city after another fell. Muscovy was last on the invaders' schedule. The city was razed on August 13, 1382.

However, the drive did not conquer the Ukraine and Northwestern Russia. Lithuanian armies cushioned the shock from the East, Toktamish's vanguards were repelled near Poltava. And had it not been for the latent conflict between Lithuania and the arrogant Teutonic Knights, the Khan's men might not have retained control of Central Russia.

Mongolian rule was restored between the Dnieper and the Amu Darja, but it was no sovereign rule. Toktamish was still Timur's vassal, and Timur's troops still formed part of his army.

Timur's pretense to descendancy of Temudshin turned into an ominous menace. If the impostor were nominated Great Khan by corrupt Djenghiskhanides, he would establish a legal claim to Russia and Western Siberia, stronger than an oath of fealty obtained under duress. But should Toktamish become Great Khan, Timur's lands would be his own, as another fief. The Djenghiskhanides would support the stronger man regardless of legitimacy.

During the early phase of his campaign Toktamish received messages of encouragement, promises of increased assistance, and a great deal of praise from Timur. Later, however, little was heard from Transoxiana, no reinforcements arrived, nothing came but a few directives that conveyed the impression that Timur only wanted to remind the Khan of his status.

This status Toktamish was determined to change by force. He remembered Timur as a painfully limping, slack man who had been careful never to fight a really strong opponent. The Khan's realm was greater than Timur's.

The devastated cities of Russia were no longer sources of lavish incomes, farmland was again deserted, craftsmen's shops were destroyed. Again hundreds of thousands wandered through areas of desolation—idle, famished, useless. It would take many years to rebuild the country. Toktamish did not have much time. He was a conqueror rather than a builder; he could improvise, bolster the strength of his army, and gamble for all—or nothing. Timur was engaged in incessant campaigns; strangely enough he did not seem aware of Toktamish's intentions. He ignored the Khan's preparations, he did not request tributes and accounts, and continued his military operations, apparently unconcerned over the situation in Russia and Western Siberia.

Such complacency was either stupid or disparaging. Toktamish grew nervous. He would have needed another year or two to reorganize his forces and absorb the Transoxianan corps that was still with him, but in 1386, when Timur's armies marched up at the border of Azerbaijan, the Khan proclaimed his title to the province, and invaded Azerbaijan territory. In the following year the two armies clashed. It was a minor battle, the main forces were not engaged, and the Khan's men suffered a setback, but the victors did not advance beyond the battlefield.

Timur ordered that the prisoners be returned to Toktamish, and with the prisoners came an admonishing message from Transoxiana: "Why should you, whom I consider my son, invade and ravage that land of mine? You ought to refrain from such unseeming actions in the future, and faithfully abide by our treaties. Why would you revive needless rivalries of the past, in which neither I nor you were personally involved?"

The Khan read the message with elation. It did not sound like a proud conqueror's language. Doubtlessly Timur was weak, and getting weaker, so also his advisers seemed to think. Even Transoxianan officers in his camp also told Toktamish that Timur would have struck had he been able to do so. The Khan resolved to complete his preparations for the decisive attack without needless hurry.

However, Timur was strong, and getting stronger. He would never forgive Toktamish, nor would he forgo his claim to all Djenghiskhanide lands. But he too wanted to gain time.

Like many despots before and after him, Timur had decided to solve all his problems by aggression. Successful aggression would keep his armies content; it would satisfy his own violent instincts and his craving for grandeur.

He did not have generals with great vision, but he preferred craftsmen to geniuses. The Transoxianan army kept nibbling away on neighboring lands. It hit Khorasan, Ispahan, Kars, Kerman, and bit ever deeper into Afghanistan. It was not a national armed force. Timur preferred lansquenets to regular draftees; men who would be shiftless outside the army were not likely to desert, and foreigners could not easily conspire with natives. Former chieftains, and adventurers with military backgrounds, received commissions. Nomads, vagabonds, and runaways were trained as elite fighters. The army was honeycombed with informers; unreliable men were purged, and so were incompetents. Timur would rather see ten innocents discharged than have one suspect remain in the services. The mercenaries were encouraged to loot and rape. This was their bonus, their incitement to violence, and also an effective means of psychological warfare. People should be made to tremble before Timur's men as they had trembled before the Mongols of yore.

Already the dreaded Mongolian banners appeared in Timur's army. The Emir, who assumed the byname of "El Kebir," the Great, ordered that all remembered paraphernalia of Temudshin's host be displayed, and that psychological-warfare agents sent ahead of his forces apply the same phrases the Mongols had used. He wanted his troops to be considered Mongols. The military's atrocities were planned no less meticulously than supply and transportation. The city of Ispahan first experienced the horror of the new planning. The citizenry had already paid a huge tribute, surrendered all hostages and slaves the invaders asked for; but when the soldiery continued looting, a handful of desperate men rose and killed a few of the spoilers. Timur's army numbered 70,000. The commander decreed that as a retaliation each soldier deliver the chopped-off head of one civilian.

Most of the men were busy looting and did not want to waste their time seeking hidden victims. Professional hunting groups formed, and sold heads for one denar apiece. So rich was the bag of skulls that the price went down to half a denar by noon of the hunting day and by nightfall no more takers for the dreadful goods could be found. The quota was fulfilled and more than 20,000 surplus skulls were dumped. The quota trophies were neatly piled up in pyramids for display on public squares. The remaining residents of Ispahan were made to parade in front of the ghastly pile, and runners spread the story everywhere in the panicky land.

Timur's officers were proud of their performance. The Great himself expressed satisfaction. Army engineers, however, called the procedure inefficient. Not even the most thorough Mongolian massacres had produced lasting effect. Men grew like plants as long as they were nourished. The technicians insinuated that the land be killed, so that it could no longer support men. They wanted to destroy the highly intricate system of irrigation which had fertilized the soil ever since antiquity, so the soil would be parched, the vegetation wither away, the land die, and even animals avoid the scene of desolation.

Timur's was not a scientific mind, but the suggestion struck his fancy. He had not yet rivaled Temudshin's conquests, but he could outdo the Djenghis Khan as a wrecker. The engineers were ordered to execute the land. Dikes and dams were smashed, canals filled up, streams and brooks diverted to courses in which they were of little or no use. Tools and mechanical devices with which to repair some of the damage were destroyed, cattle was driven away to deprive the farmers of manure. Crops failed, the soil hardened, groves withered, winds from the east carried clouds of sand to the stricken areas. Farmers fled or starved. Desolation settled over areas that had looked like gardens for a hundred generations. Regions of Persia and of already badly stricken Afghanistan turned into memorials of human wickedness. Desolation affected the minds of men. It generated vengefulness that outlasted the perpetrators of the infamy, and it still stirred destructive mania after the power of destruction had waned.

Homeless farmers applied for enlistment in the conqueror's army. Timur accepted them all. Experience convinced him that these people would not try to avenge their own sufferings, but that they would inflict even worse iniquities upon other people and profit from the spoils. Destruction boosted the army's growth, and human despair created desperadoes.

Recruits received an induction fee amounting to the value of a saddle horse, and their month's pay was about one tenth of this amount. They could earn extra premiums for outstanding performance running between two and four monthly salaries.

Noncoms in charge of ten soldiers drew ten times the pay of enlisted men. Junior officers, in command of 100, made twice a noncom's salary. Generals received the equivalent of the price of 50 to 500 horses a year, and one of Timur's corps commanders would collect more than the entire general staff of a modern European army. And there were still the spoils to supplement wages. "First-line" soldiers, members of units designed to head the general advance, drew premiums; but only after three years of training was a man admitted to the "first line."

Timur's army was also remarkably well supplied and fed. Inductees received harnesses, mailed shirts, bows, arrows, lances, swords, shields, dragnets like those used in ancient Roman gladiator contests, and daggers. Every unit of ten got a complete set of tools for whatever work soldiers had to perform, from construction of fortifications to sewing and cooking. The army had a priority claim to all cattle, grain, and fodder produced in Transoxiana and conquered territory. In Timur's warehouses supplies were stored to last an army of 100,000 for a full two years; carts and wagons were on hand to transport the goods to any destination. Timur's arsenals were bristling with ammunition and siege machines, but most of his mechanical equipment was of ancient design. Little progress had been made since the day of Djenghiskhanide engineering.

Every senior officer had an assistant who served as liaison man to the higher echelons and who was a member of a special force that constituted a net of stool pigeons, a body of political commissars that makes similar organization in the French Army during the Terror and in the Soviet forces today appear makeshift and amateurish. The ancestors of political commissars themselves were divided in several groups that were in turn locked in bitter rivalries, deliberately stimulated by the supreme commander.

Timur divided the civilian society of his realm into twelve castes, the uppermost of which were the sheiks and ulemas, ranking Mohammedan clergymen who received promotion as a compensation for unqualified praise of Timur's heresies. Conflicts between castes were encouraged, and so was discrimination. The monolithic structure of the state was based on enmity and bitterness among its citizens.

Litigations between the military and civilians were subject to the jurisdiction of specially appointed judges; court decisions widened the existing gap between the two groups.

Timur's subjects were too tightly entangled in individual and factional strife to rise against their despotic ruler, and the omnipresence of his informers discouraged rebellious designs.

Timur knew the crowd, its hysteria, and its sheeplikeness, from past experiences. He would not permit rabble rousers to harangue the masses, as his own agents had once done. The mere mentioning of the taxes that had been constantly rising since his assumption of power was a capital offense. But the ruler was secretly afraid of his army—and of the gods.

The army had never suffered substantial casualties. Its invasions of small neighboring countries had been walkovers, militarily speaking. But small targets being exhausted, the army's very size required large objectives, and the conflict with Toktamish could not remain latent indefinitely. Soon there would be big battles and big losses. How would the army react to such trials? Would not one single setback bring disaster upon Timur? And yet the army was a *perpetuum mobile*. Timur tightened the spy net, promised even better pay and fabulous promotions, and exhorted his soldiers to do their best under all conditions. He could do no more.

And then there were the gods. Tängri was an idol, subject of spite to a Mohammedan. But Tängri was the symbol of the universal empire, to which Timur laid claim. And the pagan Lord of the Eternal Blue Sky was the supreme deity of Temudshin, Timur's adopted ancestor. The pretender to the universal empire did not want to be at odds with Tängri. Adoration of the heathen god, however, might further antagonize Allah, who, Timur feared, might not be placated by the bribed priests' praise of his sinful habits.

He called Mongolian nobles, who staged a gathering of Djenghiskhanides, a mock Kuriltai, and asserted that Timur was Temudshin's rightful heir, the chosen of Tängri, and protector of shamanism. They rendered homage to the swarthy Turc as the reincarnation of the Djenghis Khan. It did not quite allay Timur's fears, but it gave him some relief.

Mohammedan prelates approved of the comedy. The ulemas, legal interpreters of the Koran, implied that Timur did not serve Tängri, but that idolaters accepted his guidance to true faith. To be on the safe side, however, they suggested that Timur undertake a pilgrimage to Mecca. Many things could happen on the long trek, and traveling was a great inconvenience; his lameness grew constantly worse, and Timur wanted to save strength for campaigns to come. But a pilgrimage would please Allah, and impress the army. In the dilemma Timur applied trickery. He left, allegedly for Mecca, and had the front-line soldiers gather to witness his departure, but he had his physicians pronounce him dangerously ill while he was still not far away from home. Timur stayed in his tent for forty days, which, according to the ulemas, would exempt him from continuing his trip. During his "sickness" priests held innumerable services to obtain Allah's blessings for the venture of Sultan Timur. Timur had at last adopted a title commensurate with the size of his dominion and objectives ahead of him.

As the year 1390 drew to a close, Sultan Timur was ready to make his bid for universal rule.

CHAPTER TWENTY-THREE After seeing their ruler off the shock troops departed for Turkestan Province, and there, on the banks of the Syr Darja, they deployed for an invasion of Siberia.

The shock troops were followed by a second-line corps, which thorough training and excellent equipment had turned into a fighting unit second to none that Toktamish could muster. Endless columns of carts and wagons;

immense trains of mobile war machines; reserve horses; herds of cattle, and innumerable hangers-on like whores, peddlers, gamblers, and fly-by-night operators, in the wake of the host, made it appear larger even than its actual awesome strength.

Toktamish's own forces numbered less than half of his opponents, and he could not hope for substantial reinforcements from his Russian vassals. Only in 1390 did the Khan fully realize that time had been Timur's ally. The Russo-Siberian army stagnated. Training did not seem to improve the men's fitness, discipline slackened, desertions increased; there were thefts of equipment and cases of treachery. Raids against Timur's territory had been unsuccessful, and the old Transoxianan generals, still in Toktamish's camp as trusted advisers, warned that Timur might have planted subverters and spies in the forces. The former Timurite officers never failed to express admiration for Toktamish, the liberator, and disdain for Timur, the usurper, but in fact they were Timur's agents, and among their collaborators were several of the Khan's own generals.

Three of the Khan's officers were dispatched on a mission of appeasement. They found Sultan Timur with his troops. An immense standard in front of his tent indicated that ceremonies were being held: they marked the inauguration of a major war.

The delegates brought costly presents, including a rare falcon. Timur watched the bird, while the kneeling officers expressed their master's humble apologies for his past unruliness and his everlasting gratitude to the Sultan, his fatherly sovereign and protector whom he would henceforth obey.

And this was Timur's reply: "We have heaped benefits upon Toktamish, who has come to our court to seek asylum and protection; we assisted him; we gave him men and money to recover what had been taken from him; we did not shrink from huge sacrifices to establish him as the master of a vast domain, and we kept treating him as if he were our son. But the treasures he gathered, the army he had under his orders, stimulated his presumptuousness and his arrogance. While we were engaged in a distant war, he chose to repay our munificence with ingratitude; he invaded and ravaged border regions of our realm. We were indulgent still, ready to absolve him, and to put the blame for his offense upon his courtiers, had he humbly begged for forgiveness. Yet, blinded by vanity, he kept attacking us and our faithful subjects, whom it is our sacred duty to protect. He made a mockery of his own solemn commitments. We were forced to break up our own campaign and hurry back to repel his invasion. He then fled, ignominiously, hoping that we would not pursue him. And now that he is at last aware of the storm gathering over his guilty head, he tries to trick us with promises. His deeds speak louder than his words. We shall unflinchingly carry out our just design. May the God of Battle decide between him and us."

On February 21, 1391, Timur's army decamped with bag, baggage, and camp followers, the most unwieldy host ever to invade Western Siberia. The advance led through the former domain of the White Ordu toward the Tobol River, where Toktamish's army had last been reported. But, as the Transoxianans, under the Djenghiskhanide banner reached the upper course of that river, they found no trace of Toktamish's men. The still-wintry countryside was completely deserted. Herds of cattle and columns of baggage carts slowed the pace of the advancing army and required large covering forces. Timur ordered that the cattle be left behind and the army fed on groats and game. The soldiers were heavy meat eaters and resented the diet. The advance slowed down even further as the men roamed the countryside in search of edibles: elk flesh, birds, and even birds' eggs. They fought over every bit of food. Hoarders were threatened with the death penalty. From time to time generals arranged parades in the snowy steppes to boost morale and discipline. Timur himself, a somewhat inhibited orator and conscious of his sickish appearance, harangued his troops to hold out, but could not tell them when and where they would meet the enemy, or reach inhabited land.

Toktamish kept falling back, establishing a pattern of Russian defensive strategy that eventually was to defeat Napoleon and Hitler. But when first applied it was but a desperate means of evading a battle that could not be won. The retreat led in a northerly direction; if continued, it would reach the Tundra, where neither friend nor foe could find means of subsistance.

For three months Timur moved north, slowly, reconnoitering left and right, hoping to find the elusive enemy or at least somebody who could tell him about Toktamish's men. Near the confluence of the Tobol and Irtysh rivers, in the forests east of the Central Ural range, patrols rounded up frightened nomads whose language no interpreter understood. A man who seemed to be the head of the roaming family indicated through signs that soldiers had been nearby a short time ago. Rounding-up operations, in which the better part of the invading army was engaged, produced ten stragglers from Toktamish's forces. The stragglers said that their army had changed direction and was now marching west-southwest.

Timur at once turned toward the Urals. The men trudged on, still impeded by remnants of their train, through forests and swamps. Another prisoner was brought in. Timur questioned him personally, with the aid of one dragoman. "You will get lost in the wilderness," the prisoner warned. "Your men will get weary, they will starve." The soldiers actually were weary and famished, and they talked about being lost in the wilderness. The Sultan had the prisoner and the dragoman executed so that his men would not learn what had been said. He ordered forced marches. The strain should revive his men's spirits and make them believe that they were not wandering aimlessly, but tracking down the fleeing foe. The Urals were crossed. As they entered the territory of the Golden Ordu, they found more people and stronger indications of Toktamish's nearness. The season was well advanced, but temperatures were unusually low, and in June a blizzard blanketed the plains near Samara. And then, as the clouds lifted, Timur faced Toktamish's army.

The Transoxianan marching array could not be easily changed into battle order, and heavy weapons lagged several days' march behind. Toktamish's men were rested. They had been encamped nearby, and their equipment was ready. Never before had conditions been more propitious for the Khan, and hardly ever again would they be as advantageous. There could be no further retreat. The God of Battle would decide between Toktamish and Timur.

The decision fell in Timur's favor.

The Sultan's historian gives a dramatic account of the battle of Samara. For three days, he claims, the armies fought like demons. Timur's men were outnumbered (which is hard to believe) and outmaneuvered by their fresh opponents. Their center was almost crushed, their left wing turned, but the Transoxianans held their ground. At dusk of the third day, however, it seemed as if Toktamish were about to win a decisive victory.

But then the Khan's standard, visible from every quarter of the blood-drenched field, was lowered, which seemed to indicate that he was dead. Disorder hit the advancing ranks, units stopped, others broke and ran. Timur's array rallied, and broke through wavering enemy lines, changing defeat into victory.

Actually Toktamish was not even injured. Timur's agents are said to have achieved their master stroke by bribing the standard bearers.

The truth of this account is not established, however.

The victors feasted on food and drink left behind by the defeated. From Samara they went to Toktamish's former residence. Sultan Timur was carried to sit on Batu's throne. He gave a banquet for his army that lasted twenty-six days and nights. All women who belonged to the Khan's legitimate and illegitimate family catered to the conquerors. Timur himself had the most attractive woman assigned to his personal entertainment, and she was advised to see that the white-haired, withered cripple be satisfied—if she wanted to live.

The enchantress did survive the banquet. The soldiers found plenty of spoils, but with most of their carts and wagons left behind it was almost impossible to transport the loot. The men refused to abandon the hard-earned objects. Every pack animal, every conveyance, was loaded. The army became less mobile than it had been when it crossed the Syr Darja and it would have been sheer folly to continue the drive into Russia. Squires of Toktamish's court rendered homage to the Sultan as the head of the house of the Djenghis Khan; Timur appointed them provincial governors of the territory of the Golden Ordu, in charge of levying security forces for their territories, which he was about to evacuate.

Not quite one year after his departure from Transoxiana, he and his army were back. The men squandered their wealth, and the Sultan prepared for further conquest in other directions.

This time the armies would not cover vast distances through wasteland; they would go to rather nearby regions, where supplies were plentiful and transportation of spoils constituted no dangerous problem.

Again the ancient city of Bagdad was visited by invaders. Again Armenia and Georgia were reduced to wreckage and ruin. Again Syria turned into a scene of desolation. Nowhere did the Transoxianan armies meet determined resistance. But everywhere the conquered were maltreated, raped, looted, and Timur's soldiery built pyramids of severed heads.

Devastating as these campaigns were, they did not follow the pattern of universal conquest, but turned in narrowing and widening circles around a fixed center instead of reaching out into the width, as had been Temudshin's goal.

Timur might have contented himself with moving in murderous circles through southwesternmost Asia had it not been for events in Russia, which required either another long-distance campaign or abandonment of his adopted design.

The governors Timur had left behind after the Transoxianans evacuated Russian territory had not taken great pains and risks to secure the land for an absentee tyrant. They watched the tide turn in Russia, and turned toward the coming man.

The coming man seemed to be Toktamish.

The Khan had gathered the scattered remnants of his forces and established an exile government on the upper course of the Volga, from where he opened negotiations with Grand Duke Vassilj of Muscovy. The Muscovite was not strong enough to establish his own rule over all of Russia, and he realized that no sovereign could be quite as bad as Timur—the powerful, deceptive despot. Vassilj offered support to the defeated Khan in return for new political and economic privileges and substantial grants of land, at the expense of rebellious minor princes. Such terms would have been unacceptable to a well-established khan, but to Toktamish they were a windfall. He accepted with alacrity and, joined by Muscovite soldiers, proceeded to reoccupy Southeastern Russia. Governors pledged allegiance to the returning Khan and asserted that they had never been faithful to Timur. Toktamish accepted their pleas. He needed every man, and accounts could be settled later. He sent envoys to the Egyptian Sultan. The Mamelouk, alarmed by the presence of Timurite troops in Mesopotamia and Syria, signed a pact of alliance with Toktamish, but the Khan would have to attack Timur first. Toktamish raided Derbent, the "Iron Gate" on the western shore of the Caspian Sea, an outpost lightly held by a Timurite garrison. It was a hit-and-run affair. The Egyptian ruler did not consider it a satisfactory performance and refused to engage his army. Couriers carried messages back and forth between Egypt and Russia; envoys made round trips from the Volga Valley to Muscovy. Sultan, grand duke, and khan argued about whose turn it was, and Timur's spies intercepted part of the diplomatic correspondence.

Timur already had lost prestige by ignoring the rebellion in Russia. He could not idly stand by while three parties bickered about who should assault him. Even Transoxianan generals, who had been doing magnificently for themselves in the thriving west, agreed that unless Russia were brought under safe control the security of the army was in jeopardy.

But this time the troops should not march into the Siberian steppes. They should not be overburdened with supplies. The army would invade Russia along the shores of the Caspian and across the passes of the Caucasus.

In the spring of 1395, Timur debouched into Dagestan Province. The Egyptians were still not ready for action, and Muscovy was slow in reinforcing Toktamish's troops. In vain did the Khan's emissaries offer surrender. In vain did Toktamish try to lure the invaders east into the deadly vastness by diversionary moves. Inexorably the enemy host marched on and forced the Khan to give battle on the Terek River, on April 15, 1396.

The action was brief and one-sided. Timur's chronicler, however, cannot refrain from telling of his protagonists' heroic feats. He let the Sultan, who in fact had had to be carried in a chair, ride a horse and charge the enemy, using his sword and lance until the sword was broken, the lance dented, and the gallant bearer surrounded by a swarm of howling foes. The enemies would have butchered Timur had it not been for the devotion of Transoxianan guardsmen, who rescued the Sultan and refused to accept rewards, saying that it was their sacred duty to give their lives for their beloved ruler. The unselfishness of the guardsmen is no more credible than the rough ride of Timur the Lame.

Toktamish escaped. Timur's squadrons could not catch up with the fugitive's fast horse.

Near the present site of Stalingrad the victors found precious furs, pearls, rubies, gold, silver, and "young girls and boys of rare beauty." Pederasty had become admissible at the Khan's court.

From Stalingrad, Timur continued toward Muscovy, but he veered off less than 300 miles from the city. Hostile troops were gathering on the Dnieper and on the Don. The enemy scattered at Timur's approach, but the victor made no move to set a course for Muscovy again. He was distracted by reports of heavily loaded columns trudging through the Russian plains. Governors and petty princes who had first sworn fealty to Toktamish, then to Timur, and then again to Toktamish were afraid of trying another about-face and, with their treasures and servants, made off to seek asylum. Many were caught and slain, some reached the Balkans, others Lithuania, and Asia Minor. It seems even that a few fugitives eventually made their way to Siberia.

The Timurite armies wanted still more spoils, and Timur's favorite son, heir, and next in command, was no exception to the rule. Rounding up wealthy stragglers was more remunerative than hunting runaway soldiers who owned nothing but skinny mounts and dilapidated clothes and weapons. For a while the victors followed a zigzag course, indicating the high command's vacillation; but then they headed for Tana, the Genoese factory. A delegation of merchants had called at Timur's headquarters, offered samples of the most precious goods stored in bulging warehouses, and expressed hope that the conqueror would further and protect their peaceful activities. This Timur promised to do, but then he seized Tana, and had his soldiers empty the Genoese factory and sell Christian inhabitants into slavery.

There was no lack of transportation, and the army was bountifully supplied with everything that spoiled lansquenets coveted, but marauding turned officers and men into a rapacious mob that could not be relied upon in serious battle. Timur did not resume his advance on Muscovy. He appointed a puppet khan for the lands of the Golden Ordu and the White Ordu, put his son in charge of the pillaging armies, and returned to Samarkand, where he had established his residence, to recover from the strain of the campaign and to ponder about his next move.

The Transoxianan soldiery rambled from the Black Sea and the Sea of Azov to the Caspian. Their beat was everywhere spoils could be gathered. Their robbery inflicted the death blow upon a once-fabulous commerce, and their maniacal urge for destruction ruined settlements that earlier invaders had spared. Serai, emporium on the lower Volga, showcase of Mongolian trade policies and the first European city where coffee had become a fashionable beverage, was leveled.

And while rabble under the Djenghiskhanide banner despoiled the land, Toktamish reached Lithuania and pleaded with the rulers of that country and of Poland, and with the Grand Master of the Teutons, conjuring them to depose the grand dukes of Muscovy and to drive out the looters. Lithuanians, Poles, and Teutons were responsive but distrustful of one another. They wanted to keep their main forces ready for the argument over their spoils. Only small contingents entered Russia and were beaten back by riffraff mercenaries. Toktamish was with the invading troops but did not flee. For ten years he kept wandering through his former realm, crossing and recrossing the Ural Mountains, exhorting nomads and settlers to join him, always unsuccessful, often narrowly escaping captivity. At last he fell victim to an assassin who did not know the object of his onslaught, but who had been attracted by the meager purse at the old man's belt.

Timur was past sixty when he meditated over his future course. His achievements had lost some of their luster. If he wanted to rule the universe, he would have to make haste, and to conquer states more ancient, richer, and of higher culture than Russia and the steppes east of the Ural Mountains. China had been the most coveted objective of Asiatic conquerors, but there was another land, more legendary than China: India.

To India he would go.

This would be supreme glory, and his intelligence agents asserted that it would not be hard-won glory. Big as India was, it was split and weak.

A reorganized Transoxianan army crossed the Indus River in 1398. A rotating system transferred undisciplined first-line soldiers back to the reserve and promoted eager reservists to first ranks. Not until late in that year could the rival Indian princes assemble a force to challenge his advance. But the Indian war elephants were no match for the Timurite cavalry, and the Indian infantry was helpless against the strange war machines. In December 1398 army officers carried Timur up the steps of the throne of Delhi and prostrated themselves as he solemnly assumed title and prerogatives of an emperor of India.

Again high pyramids of human heads marked Timur's road of advance. He seized the jewels Indian sultans and rajahs had amassed in many centuries, spent hours gazing at them, and then ordered them put away. He had captured war elephants trained to kowtow before him, and had them slain afterward. He got tired of the sight of Delhi and ordered the city demolished. He toured more cities, inspected their marvelous buildings, and doomed them to destruction because they were profane. He startled army chaplains by proclaiming a holy Mohammedan war against Hinduism. The spectacle of a sublime old culture aroused the upstart's most violent instincts.

The Timurite armies penetrated as far as the Ganges River and the Himalayan Mountains; then Timur left and went straight to Samarkand.

The army followed its commander in chief, an army in name only, looking rather like a migrating people. Individual soldiers had collected up to 100 slaves and 500 heads of cattle. All wagons, carts, oxen, buffalo and horses of the land were requisitioned to transport loot. The roads of India, poor and few, could not carry the mass movement of men, beasts, and vehicles at a reasonable pace. When weather was fair and the roads were dry, columns would cover a maximum of four miles a day; when it rained, the Transoxianan armies were mired and forced to wait in chaotic disorder until the sun dried them loose. It took the strange host more than a year to recross the border of India.

Timur made no provisions to keep the empire under control. Neither strong occupation forces nor a stable administration stayed in the devastated country. Nothing remained but the stench of death, the dust of ruins, and the shock of horror. Experience had taught the lame tyrant that people recovered from shock and that, as in Russia, the defeated who survived always came back. However, Timur did not seem to care. In him, as in other aging upstart conquerors, a mental lopsidedness emerged from the spectacular crust of efficiency, trickery, and stubbornness that is occasionally called genius. The old Timur was obsessed by a maniacal urge to invade foreign lands, to tramp them asunder as fast as horses could carry his soldiers, and to keep on invading without organizing past conquests.

Tamerlane, as he was more often called in his later years, had had no delusion about the changes that affected his army in the course of a victorious campaign. In India, as in Russia, wherever spoils could be found the fighting forces would dissolve into hordes of plunderers. He had another army organized while the Indian campaign was in its early stages.

Back in Samarkand he took command of the new army and led it west. They marched through scorched Mesopotamia, and in October 1400 descended upon Syria. After Toktamish's signal defeat the Egyptian Sultan had begun to put his Asiatic outposts in a state of defense. A substantial security force guarded the approaches to Aleppo, and farther to the south stronger forces concentrated between Damascus and the Red Sea. The security army was crushed before the walls of Aleppo.

On Christmas Day, Timur defeated the Egyptians near Damascus. The Mamelouk Sultan narrowly escaped capture. Tamerlane was still fighting what he called a Mohammedan holy war, and his ulemas still called it a sacred, rightful action, but the victims of his campaigns, the men and women whose heads formed pyramids along the easternmost shore of the Mediterranean, were observant Mohammedans, and the soldiers who slew them and pillaged their homes were often not even Mohammedans in name. They belonged to the Russian Church, or they were shamanites, or Nestorians, and regardless of their nominal creed they were a godless lot.

Timur could have marched on straight to the Nile before the Egyptians, scraping the bottom of their manpower barrel, could have raised a new army. But instead the victor turned and went to Mesopotamia. This looked like a major strategic blunder, but actually Timur's procedure of unguarding conquered areas paid sinister dividends. The people of Bagdad began to raid Timurite supplies, and intelligence reports told of preparations for revolt all along the road from Transoxiana to the Mediterranean. Timur did not investigate and staged no trials! He had the population further reduced in number and condition so that it would not interfere with his operations.

Not until 1402 was the work of destruction completed. Meantime another Mamelouk army re-entered Syria. But Timur headed into Asia Minor to crush the budding Ottoman state. The Ottomans were overwhelmed near Ankara; wide stretches of Asia Minor were covered by smoldering clouds as Ottoman cities and villages went up in flames; many thousands of noncombatants died a gruesome death. Timur's chroniclers did not record exact numbers, but kept on eulogizing his feats of valor in battles he watched at a distance, seated on a golden sedan chair, his face twitching with frantic impatience. Not even the pace of thunderous cavalry charges could satisfy the lame man's urge for speed. At the time of the battle of Ankara he had been out of Samarkand for a full two years, and the areas he had conquered were disturbingly small as compared with the regions not yet touched by his horses' hoofs.

The defeat did not destroy the Ottoman nation, but it delayed its rise to great power for almost half a century. The Emperor of tottering Byzantium expected his capital to be next on Tamerlane's schedule and, mindful of the Djenghiskhanide law, sent a message of submission. Byzantium was one week's cavalry ride away. But Timur never went to the ancient city.

He had decided to conquer China and, as his historian adds, to convert the empire to Mohammedanism. For seventeen years there had been diplomatic exchanges between Timur and the Ming Emperor. The ruler of China had opened the correspondence with a request that Timur pay tribute and pledge allegiance to him, as the rightful heir to the Yuan dynasty's suzerainty over the Djenghiskhanide realm. Timur had the carrier of the letter arrested, but then reconsidered, treated the man with courtesy, and sent an intricate, noncommittal reply, together with presents that could pass as a tribute. Embassies traveled from Samarkand to Peking, and from Peking to Samarkand. Timur sent more presents, wondering whether China was really as strong as his ambassadors depicted it and if it was worth while to humor its emperor. In 1395, when Emperor Yong-lo expressed thanks for Timur's gifts, Transoxianan legal experts interpreted this as a recognition of Timur's sovereignty. The correspondence slowed down, but not until 1402 had there been indications of Timur's intention to attack China.

The magnitude of the task should have awed a young and healthy man, and old Timur's health was deteriorating. Ruy Gonzales de Clavijo, the Spanish Ambassador to the Court of Samarkand, reported to his king that Tamerlane, who now wanted to be called Lord of the World, had become almost blind. The Lord of the World had requested that the Ambassador move so close to him that their faces nearly touched, and yet he had not been able to distinguish his features.

Transoxianan generals were horrified at their lord's decision to have an army of 200,000 combatants march more than 3000 miles through Siberia, attack the strongest standing army of the Far East, and, worse even, to start the advance no later than in 1405.

No soldier, regardless of rank, would have dared to make presentations to the Lord of the World, and no courtier or statesman had the courage to warn Timur against a move he intended to make. Officers and officials bid for time by trying to keep Timur busy. The Lord of the World fancied himself to be superarchitect, the greatest master-builder of all times. Samarkand had been built into one of the biggest cities in Western Asia, though not its finest. Timur preferred size to artistry. State ministers submitted plans for enlargement of Samarkand, for new, giant building projects; trembling architects drew blueprints, and Timur accepted nearly all of them. Construction work started at a breath-taking pace; nothing but new speed marks would satisfy the master-builder. Every day he had himself carried through the building sites. He would stop, the piercing look of his almost sightless eyes fixed in the direction from which the sounds of work came, and while frenzied laborers, foremen, and architects toiled for their lives, he would keep on staring. If the men were lucky, he would leave, mute and sullen; if they were out of luck, he would suddenly point in the direction of some man or group, and order that they be executed for laziness.

Among the buildings under construction was a mausoleum for one of Timur's grandsons, killed in action in Asia Minor. The despot could hardly perceive the contours of the edifice, but in a spell of violence he called it ugly and undignified, and ordered it torn down and rebuilt within ten days, or everybody connected with the project would be put to death. It is told that fear-crazed workers achieved the impossible. The Lord of the World spent long hours at the site, watching slaves labor day and night. He seemed to need very little sleep. In fact he forced himself to stay awake, harried by the thought that the hourglass of his life was running out.

His courtiers tried to tire the despot by staging banquets and carousals. Timur, still unconcerned over Islam's ban on intoxicating drinks, consumed terrific amounts of wine and hard liquor, but did not go to sleep. His hands, not too strongly affected by paralysis, would crawl, like hairy spiders, over the bare bodies of courtesans, who writhed lasciviously for their lives. The monster did not forgive sensual imperfection. Grave and morose, he listened to the sounds of the orgy: the roars and shrieks of carousers, the babble of drunkards, the snores of sleepers.

But nothing could divert him from his objective. In the fall of 1404 he summoned his generals and requested a report on the preparations of the great campaign. Cringing corps commanders asserted that everything would be ready in time, and that there would be no transportation trouble whatsoever. The generals threatened field-ranking officers with decapitation should their units not be ready by the end of the year; field-ranking officers voiced similar threats to their inferiors, who in turn passed the menace on down the line to the lowliest reservists. Two hundred thousand able-bodied men trembled before one mad cripple.

The army assembled on the banks of the Syr Darja, on the fringe of Siberian steppes. In Samarkand, Timur arranged a farewell banquet. All foreign ambassadors were present, the representative of the Emperor of China and the dean of the diplomatic corps among them. The Chinese sat on his accustomed place of honor. But the Lord of the World ordered him to take the lowest seat as "the representative of a robber." This was tantamount to a declaration of war.

December 1404 was an unusually cold month on the Syr Darja. Army tents did not provide adequate shelter against subzero temperatures; many men were suffering from frostbite, and in the following month the temperatures fell even further. Timur joined the army in January. His big silken tent was comfortable enough, but he inquired at once about the state of health of the army. After hasty deliberations the officers decided to tell him the truth. The men were freezing, and the number of casualties was running high. But the Lord of the World sneered; exercise would warm them up, and advance was the best exercise for a soldier. The great standard was unfurled and guards officers carried their sovereign across the frozen Syr Darja, ahead of the cavalry vanguards. An icy wind battered creatures and objects with a hailstorm of needle-sharp crystals.

Timur's limp body was racked by spells of violent pain, but he would not consult his medics, nor would he tell anybody about his sufferings. He did not want to show a weakness that would be a bad example to his soldiers and stimulate his generals' obvious desire to postpone the advance. The climate of

China was milder than that of Siberia; he would recover in China; the sooner he got there, the more complete his recovery would be.

Timur's sedan chair kept pace with the vanguards; cavalrymen saw their ruler's greenish, pale, twisted face, but did not talk about the Lord of the World: one uncautious word could spell death. The despot suffered physical agonies and mental anguish. It occurred to him that his life would have been in vain if he did not reach and conquer China; that to stop would mean to give up, but that to continue the journey would be unbearable. Pain and anguish struggled, but pain prevailed.

Timur ordered the advance halted. He was bedded on a cozy couch in his tent. But not even in this comfortable position did his torments abate. Physicians prostrated themselves before his bed, babbling about speedy recovery, but were helpless in the face of a disease they could neither cure nor even diagnose. The horrible patient seemed doomed, yet before he would succumb, he could have all his physicians put to death. But Timur ordered the medics out of his tent; he realized that no man could help him in his distress.

God only could save him. Allah owed him a great deal. Hadn't Allah's priests and sages eulogized Timur's merits? Hadn't they extolled his holy war and his religious zeal? Wasn't he on his way to conquer China for Allah? The imams, and the Islamite chaplains, who owed him their social standing, their abundance, and their power, would have to be instrumental in getting Allah's help. They would have to beseech Allah, and not relax until a miracle came to pass.

All army chaplains and imams were ordered to say the prayers for the dying, without letup, day and night. Every soldier should hear them recite the litanies; they should shout so loudly that Allah could not turn a deaf ear to the invocation.

The monotonous litany droned through the vast camp, its sounds battling the furious howl of gusts. Shivering soldiers listened, fear-stricken and bewildered, wishing they would face a real foe rather than the nightmare of storm and prayer.

The litany besought Allah. It shouted for mercy for the man who had built pyramids of heads, who had been deity's scourge, who had violated every divine command and committed more sins and atrocities than were mentioned in the Koran. Extortions brandished against the ramparts God had erected against transgressors of the law, wrested for the trophy of blissful deliverance for the most unrepentant of sinners. But the men who shouted themselves hoarse did not love the man who had made them the highest-ranking of his tools. They were mortally afraid of the dying man's wrath, and their own fear begged Allah for their own deliverance from a perilous duty.

Lying on his couch, covered by towering blankets and furs, Timur listened. He was attended by picked guardsmen, sluggish giants who acquitted themselves of their task with unfeeling accuracy. Generals were relieved to learn that their presence was not wanted, and so were the members of Timur's family who stayed away, meditating how to make the best of the tyrant's inevitable death. The sounds of the litany weakened, but the pains continued, unabated. Allah's fortress was stronger than any bulwark Timur had known. Allah did not want him to conquer a reward.

On the third day of the prayer storm Timur, speaking with intense effort ordered his wives, sons, and grandsons to gather in his tent. They came, screaming, rending their garments and performing all the mourning antics prescribed by an orthodox ritual.

The dying man harshly bade them not to behave like lunatics. He had a will to make, to dispose of an empire which, he assumed, still ranged from the western shores of the Black Sea to the Himalayan Mountains. His sightless eyes roamed the tent, then closed. He sighed, strained his hearing to listen to the crowd's reaction to his final decision: None of his sons was worthy of becoming the Lord of the World. Pir-Mohammed, a twenty-nine-year-old grandson, would inherit the title. He would be the head of the family, the sovereign over the holders of fiefs which he started to distribute among his other direct male descendants. Timur was running short of breath. The session had to be interrupted. It was resumed and adjourned several times, but the provisions of Timur's will were never completed. The last of the great Asiatic conquerors died in the night of February 18, 1405, as he was outlining the borders of a small fief.

Before he could ascend the throne, Pir-Mohammed was deposed in favor of his eight-years-younger half brother Kalil. The generals rendered homage to Lord of the World Kalil in return for his promise to abandon the Chinese campaign, which, as everybody felt, could but end in disaster. Kalil's rule lasted less than one year.

Timur's realm had never been forged into an empire. The countries he had conquered had only one element in common: destruction, and destruction was not a strong tie. The universal realm disintegrated almost at once. A few Timurites, however, who used their wealth and their gifts of diplomacy and corruption to good effect, maintained themselves in their fiefs and passed petty thrones on to undistinguished progeny.

One hundred two years after Timur's death the last of the Timurites lost the last city of his domain, Herat, on the Afghan-Indian border, to a horde of Siberian Uzbeks, who, under the leadership of a Mongolian prince, raided neighboring territory in quest of loot.

Two centuries of Mongolian-Siberian furor had thrown the greater part of the peoples of the Old World into convulsive labor in pools of blood. Ligaments of highly organized society had been truncated. A multitude of knavish, devious, and wily patterns of despotism had been established. But furor could not change human nature, and old basic social forms emerged practically unchanged by torment. But for timely slogans and deceptive philosophies the patterns of despotism applied 600 years after Temudshin was born can all be found in the records of the two catastrophic centuries. And because it is extremely unlikely that the modern dictators were familiar with these records and desirous to complete what defunct despots had left unfinished, it should be assumed that the calamitous patterns are just other—perverted—manifestations of human nature.

CHAPTER TWENTY-FOUR One thousand years of Siberian aggression had not carried the universe.

One disastrous cycle of history had come to an end, but the peoples of the world hardly noticed it. No era of peace dawned upon the scenes of devastation. Ruins germinated more struggles, drives to gather the flotsam of old wars through new wars, different in name and scope from their predecessors but hardly less destructive.

On the western end of the line of aggression, the Ottomans, rapidly recovering from the blows inflicted by Tamerlane, would set out to gather the spoils of Byzantium, and adopt Tamerlane's scheme of world conquest in the name of Islam. These heirs to Türküt belligerency, to Attila's lust of conquest and fanaticism, reared by a line of Siberian conquerors, were thriving on the weariness of less fanatical nations.

In Russia the decaying cement of Asiatic rule crumbled, and in the dust of collapse princes, chieftains, and petty khans engaged in a mad grabbing melee until sixty-five years after Timur's death, Ivan III, Grand Duke of Muscovy, emerged as the first "gatherer" of a Russia that was to pay a disastrous return visit to Siberia in the following century.

In western and central parts of Siberia, Mongolian princes made crude attempts at empire building by returning to the ancient pattern of gathering strong raiding forces and establishing themselves on rich lands within striking distance of alluring objectives.

People of Northern Siberia, who had never joined conquering drives but had been dealing with aggressive foreign tradesmen on less than equal terms, became increasingly exposed to a pressure that lost all pretenses of being only commercial.

While the Golden Ordu and the White Ordu, Muscovy, and their slaves were fighting, an unusual quiet had settled in the regions between Lake Baikal and the Great Wall, and far out to the west. In Karakorum great khans of dubious legitimacy held court, spending formidable remains of fabulous Djenghiskhanide wealth, but collecting few, if any, tributes.

Heirs of khans who had not settled in the lands they had helped to subjugate enjoyed inherited fortunes, unmindful of the military tradition that accounted for them.

Along the Djenghiskhanide post route guardsmen still lived in solidly built roadhouses. No longer did the Great Khan's couriers race back and forth; no longer were visitors to the court of Karakorum rushed along. Caravan traffic was reduced to a trickle. The profession of guardsman, however, passed on from father to son. Guardsmen cultivated land, sold equipment, and engaged in a prosperous trade with horses which theoretically belonged to the "ruler of the universe." Other descendants of transportation personnel formed cattle-breeding clans roaming around roadhouses and wandering once a year to Chinese and Tibetan markets to barter livestock against coveted luxury items.

The shamans were the only ardent keepers of Temudshin's memory. They exploited the Djenghis Khan myth by claiming to ride and fly to his tomb, by exhorting his spirit by chants which glorified his deeds, and by collecting from their customers whatever the spirit allegedly charged for assistance in matters of weather, health, and business.

The core of the Mongolian nation, a few hundred thousand people, spread over an area of more than one million square miles, without effective central administration and military cadres, did not constitute a potential threat to a consolidated neighbor. The Chinese, however, who remembered mendicants who had turned tyrants, did not want to give the peaceable Mongols another opportunity to turn into savage warriors.

And already while the aging Timur prepared another invasion of Russia, the Ming Emperor of China suddenly invaded Temudshin's patrimony. In Karakorum an alarmed great khan summoned his nobles to join the army with their contingents, and dispatched riders to call all able-bodied men to arms. The Great Khan's orders carried little, if any, weight. The nobles had practically no trained soldiers. Roaming cattle breeders and roadhouse farmers had few arms, and did not quite understand why they should take them up.

Had not the advancing Chinese army been overly careful to protect its long lines of communications and cover its flanks against surprise attacks, it would have occupied a large part of Siberia without meeting resistance. But while the Chinese inched on, the Mongols learned that the invaders inflicted property damage. This provided a stronger incentive to action than all appeals and decrees from Karakorum. A motley crowd of ex-mercenaries who had been aging in peaceful occupations, of bewildered herdsmen, serfs, and gaudily garbed nobles gathered to protect their possessions. The arsenals of Karakorum still contained Djenghiskhanide equipment. There were many cannon, but no cannoneers. Some men had heard that the iron barrels could belch deadly fire and smoke. They consulted shamans; shamans talked to spirits, and spirits asserted—for a fee—that the barrels would do their duty. When, at long last, the Chinese army came into sight near Bar Nor, the Mongols dragged the cannon out front and hopefully waited for thunder and lightning to take care of the enemy. But the cannon did nothing of the sort, and disdainful Chinese cavalrymen rode roughshod over silent batteries.

The campaign was a chase rather than a war; the Mongols recovered part of their ability to flee; yet they would have met their doom had not the

Chinese eventually discontinued their advance, not so much because of supply troubles or innate aversion against operations into space as because of new, psychological considerations.

Chinese statesmen reasoned that it would be unwise to reduce the prosperous Mongols to poverty. Prosperous people had a tendency to comfortable conservatism, but destitute people were dangerously refractory. The Emperor did not deign to sign a peace treaty with a great khan whose rule he did not recognize, but ordered his forces to return home and be careful not to inflict unnecessary damage on Mongolian property. In an act of condescending generosity he granted pensions to Siberian nobles who had suffered great hardship. Beneficiaries professed humble gratitude and unswerving loyalty to the ruler of China, whom they would henceforth consider their sovereign. They ignored the Great Khan, and kept ignoring other holders of the once awe-inspiring title, who succeeded each other at Karakorum and eventually disappeared in the middle of the fifteenth century, regretted only by their Chinese purveyors.

But other Siberian nations and tribes also lived within striking distance of China, and had been contained by the superior strength of their Mongolian neighbors. Now that the lid was off the people's caldron, they would again burst forth along the lines of least resistance, toward the most tempting spoils.

The Chinese gave no thought to the Oirats who had served China as mercenaries; they had been efficient fighters, but otherwise unreliable and obstinate. Several times they were discharged, and returned to the northern forests where they inured themselves against softness, regretted the lost fleshpots, and in due course returned to the Chinese border, as applicants or raiders, and occasionally as both. Still the first Ming emperors had hired Oirats, and equipped them with effective weapons, but the obdurate woodsmen kept behaving badly, and were chased away to the vastness beyond the Mongolian habitat. From behind the screen of scattered, chastened Mongolian tribes, however, the Oirats watched developments far to the south for another opportunity.

Their clan leaders and chieftains were primitive men but competent soldiers, and attributed the latest Chinese victory solely to Mongolian inefficiency. Prince Tonghon, a man of great energy, insisted that they should establish control over Mongolian tribes, forge an auxiliary force of mounted archers from that human material, and use its land as a springboard for attack.

The Oirats swept the wide land, seized all property, and drafted all men into their service before the Mongols had recovered from the shock of the Chinese invasion. The Mongols resigned themselves to their fate; Oirat brutality even struck a familiar note, and revived some of the traditional belligerent instincts. There were a few attempts at desertion, and several Mongolian princes did not hesitate to take the oath of fealty to Tonghon despite their pledges of loyalty to the Emperor of China. A few pensioners of the Emperor, however, escaped to the coffers of China. One year after the operation had started Tonghon's reinforced army stood on the Chinese border.

Emperor Ying-tsong abhorred the idea of preventive war. Instead he resorted to the machinery of intrigue and psychology to throw the upstart conquerors into paralyzing confusion. In the disguise of merchants his agents, interpreters, and informers told Oirat grandees of Tonghon's having sinister designs against his own nobles, spread rumors of Chinese invincibility, and won access to Tonghon himself, warning him against impending aggression from Western Siberia. The "Middle Ordu," they said, was preparing to seize control of the ancient Djenghiskhanide realm. Valuable Chinese gifts found their way into the Oirat camp.

The psychological offensive eventually wore off without seriously affecting the fighting efficiency of the woodsmen and their chattels. Tonghon used old-fashioned Siberian terrorism to deal with recalcitrant elements. He knew of gifts to his generals, and made it plain to the officers that victory was more rewarding than corruption. He also said that he who talked most, as the Chinese did, was most likely to be weak. The seriousness of the threat to his western flank was discounted.

In 1445, Tonghon led his army against China, seized Jehol Province, and began to sap the resources of that large territory. A stunned Emperor of China issued mobilization orders. It took four years to assemble an army which, the Chinese officers thought, should be able to defeat the Oirats and discourage future aggressors.

Tonghon had planned to continue his drive in the summer of 1446, after he had finished looting Jehol. But before the sordid job was completed, he grew apprehensive about the menace from the Middle Ordu. Caravan leaders who arrived from the Persian border told of a mighty conquering host gathered to strike out in every direction. Tonghon postponed further advances to watch developments. He kept watching and wavering until 1449. Had it not been for the aridity of the land between him and the Middle Ordu, he would have gone west to cope with the rising danger; but his soldiers wanted only spoils, and there would be no spoils all along at least 2000 miles of road, and Tonghon wondered what would happen if his personal orders were to stand against the vociferous will of 100,000 men.

He received with relief the news that Emperor Ying-tsong was leading an army against him. This would enable him to decide the Chinese war in one single battle in the vicinity of his camp instead of having to fight countless engagements on battlefields widely apart in the immensity of China. After the battle was won, he could have his soldiers loot to their hearts' desire, and then decide whether to keep on the defensive against intruders from the west, or to have an expeditionary force deal with the Middle Ordu.

The Chinese army was a pompous, decorative host that impressed civilians all along the long road to Jehol, even though the Chinese were markedly unenthusiastic about wars and sceptical about their outcome.

Tonghon's Oirat-Mongolian forces were a rather savage-looking array, but Oirat cannoneers knew how to operate their weapons; and Mongolian archers were good marksmen, even though there was little order in their volleys. The deadly precision of ancient Siberian war machines was conspicuously absent: cavalry units charged rather wildly; infantry columns neglected cover, and tactics that Subotai had developed were hampered by poor timing. Yet savagery and speed made up for many shortcomings, and the slow Chinese army was soon thrown off balance by sweeping attacks.

The one battle upon which Tonghon had pinned his hopes brought him victory, large booty, and many prisoners—among them, Emperor Ying-tsong. But it did not decide the war.

Confronted with new Chinese levies, stronger and better led than the Emperor's own army, Tonghon could neither penetrate deeply into the empire nor disengage his forces for a drive west. He held Ying-tsong as a hostage: but the Chinese high command was less anxious to ransom the Emperor than Tonghon had thought. The Oirats made one attempt to organize a Chinese puppet state in Jehol, but lacked administrative conception and the plan had to be abandoned. In 1453, Tonghon resigned himself into being a thoroughly unsuccessful victor. He stripped Jehol of whatever could be moved, and signed peace with China. The Oirats evacuated occupied territory and bartered the captive Emperor against a pledge that the Chinese armies would stay within their borders.

In these parts of the world, more even than elsewhere, treaties of peace were codified capitulations if a military decision had been achieved, or were circumscribed adjournments of a showdown if the campaign had been stalemated. The Oirats expected to return and subdue China after absorbing their Western Siberian rivals; the Chinese hoped that the impending battle of the Siberians would eventually destroy both sides, or at least break them up into a multitude of impotent tribes.

The Middle Ordu was the purest Djenghiskhanide clan still in existence when the Timurite empire folded up. Its founder, Cheiban, grandson of Temudshin and veteran of Subotai's campaigns, had been paid off with a fief away from the path of migration, trade, and invasion. The land between the sources of the Tobol River and the regions northeast of Lake Balkhash was a pittance compared with Batu's fief, Persian areas, and, of course, China; it would not have satisfied a man with imperialistic vision. But Cheiban did not have a fancy imagination. He had seen enough action to satisfy his belligerent impulses; he had witnessed too much trouble organizing conquest to make him wish to spend his time struggling with corrupt governors and with subjects whose mentality he understood as little as their language. Cheiban wanted to live in the style of a glorified country squire, which was quite unusual for a man of his race and era.

His domain was ideally suited for that purpose. It was succulent grassland, a horse and cattle breeder's delight, sparsely populated by nomads whose way of life did not greatly differ from that of the ancient Mongols except for their lack of military organization. Such nomads did not really require an administration, and not even strong security forces.

Cheiban bred horses and cattle, wandered about his realm, and had no further ambitions. He did not mingle in the affairs of his powerful neighbor kin, and warned his sons and grandsons against overstraining their resources. They should keep in the quiet center of a stormy world, as the sedentary Middle Family (Middle Ordu), and hold onto their patrimony. And because in Siberia warfare was the only noticeable account nations or dynasties could give of themselves, the Middle Ordu was soon all but forgotten.

Siberian grasslands experienced a period of peace, which lasted for about 150 years, but no accounts tell of its blissful accomplishments. Whatever its effects, literacy was not among them. Maybe the Pax Siberica was peace only in the sense that there were no foreign wars but that factional strifes continued.

The Middle Ordu was not involved in battles between the Golden and the White families. It kept out of reach of Timur's drives, and, even though the western boundaries of its realm were close to the Urals, the Middle Ordu is not known to have crossed that range.

The neighborhood of stronger powers constrained the Middle Ordu, but apparently did not uproot its violent urges. As Timur's realm disintegrated, the Middle Ordu, in a snowballing process, shaped into an aggressive horde. The human mass rolled on, over small tribes that had been under White Ordu and Timurite domination; it sucked them up, impressing their young men into military service.

Cheiban's ancient warning was cast to the winds. The new chiefs were no country squires, but old-fashioned barbarians, different from their forerunners only in equipment and garb. The Middle Ordu had an abundance of fine horses and old-fashioned arms, but already daredevil operators offered weapons from plundered Timurite arsenals in exchange for horses. The next object of aggression was the Uzbeks, who lived north of the Syr Darja, peripheral witnesses of the past grandeur of the Lord of the World, but not rich or numerous enough to be included in his itinerary of conquest. To the Middle Ordu, however, the Uzbeks offered a desirable strategic target.

These semi-nomadic Siberians were soon integrated into the new makeshift realm.

Less than forty years after an old and dying Timur had been carried across the frozen Syr Darja, at the head of a disciplined army of 200,000, a young and healthy khan of the Middle Ordu stood on the blooming bank of the river, reviewing a boisterous horde of some 50,000 horsemen. The Middle Ordu proclaimed itself legal heir to Temudshin's legacy and aspirant to universal rule in which its soldiers were eager to collect their share.

The horde invaded Afghanistan, chaos-ridden Persia, and Turkestan, robbing, raping, and relishing its apparent invincibility. The princes of the Middle Ordu had been trained to conserve a limited domain, but did not know how to build an empire. They expected conquered lands to coagulate by cruel beating, and hitting hard was the acme of their policy.

The radius of their raids expanded, but, contrary to reports circulating in China and Mongolia, the Middle Ordu was not yet set to invade Eastern Siberia, when an Oirat army marched west to forestall such a drive. The ruffians of the Middle Ordu were on their way to another looting expedition into Persia when they met Tonghon's veterans.

Both sides carried the banner of the Djenghis Khan; both outdid each other in savagery. Otherwise, however, their furious brawl did not resemble ancient Mongols' high-precision tactics. The Oirats won. The victors stayed on the battlefield to plunder the enemy baggage train, to barter captured soldiers against seized whores, who rated higher than men, and to consume all the food and drink left behind by the losers. This operation lasted several weeks. It left the soldiers with a hangover, and the chiefs with a thorny three-cornered problem: Should they continue in a westerly direction? Should they march to China? Or was it necessary to consolidate their conquest before trying either?

A reconnaissance in force revealed that the road to the Mediterranean was blocked by the Ottomans, a force already much more redoubtable than anything Siberia could muster. A checkup of army morale disclosed that orders to march back through no-loot-land might result in mutiny. There remained the organization of a domain that stretched from the eastern shore of the Caspian to the Great Wall, encompassing almost half of Siberia. In this task the Oirats were bound to fail.

The Oirat-Siberian Empire was a mosaic of ill-fitting, loose bits which only careful central planning and efficient administration could have adjusted and solidified. Tonghon's men were neither planners nor administrators. The mosaic fell apart; the Oirat-Mongolian army dissolved. Princes returned to distant roaming grounds, soldiers again became cattle breeders and roadhouse famers. The Middle Ordu retreated to its pastures, battered, disillusioned, but still pugnacious. Small domains were set up in strife and disintegrated in strife, and what remained could not resist outside pressure. The Uzbeks regained independence and used newly acquired military skills to plague Afghanistan and Persia.

China was triumphant. The empire had won a political victory of first magnitude; an age-old scheme had produced fabulous results. Siberian aggressors had fought each other, and both had succumbed; Djenghiskhanides had destroyed Djenghiskhanides. Siberia was no longer a breeding ground of aggression: it was the habitat of chastened nomads and has-been conquerors who depended on Chinese bounty for opulence. The people of China could, henceforth, go about its peaceful occupations, its technicians could concentrate on constructive projects instead of building tools of destruction. No more large standing armies were needed, those expensive sources of trouble. China's foremost weapons would be industry and commerce, and China would rule a world of its own. This time it was ultimate victory.

But this time, as in the past and in the future, total victory was but total delusion.

No other nation knew more about ominous symptoms and portentous manifestations than the Chinese, and yet Chinese wishful thinking prevailed over sound reasoning. Two writings on the wall were interpreted as happy omens rather than tokens of a twofold danger that would strike in a yet distant future.

A small-scale migration of people began north and northeast of the Chinese borders, and in Manchuria, where Chinese garrisons were centered around Chanyang (Mukden). The Tunguses, who had been missing from the Siberian scene for about 200 years, were suddenly back, seven tribes of them, some reduced to complete primitivity, others retaining traces of culture acquired in a legendary past. Not even Chinese traders knew where these people had been hiding. The Tunguses trudged toward the rising sun, with carts and cattle, on horseback and afoot, some carrying tents, others depending on natural shelter, fishing in rivers and lakes, hunting in forests, occasionally settling down in small groups, then again battling among themselves with more fury than skill, but careful to avoid friction with Chinese caravans.

The traders followed the trickle of migrants to remote parts of Manchuria, to the present Siberian Maritime Province, and to the approaches of Kamchatka Peninsula. Kamchatka was almost deserted; frequent outbursts of volcanoes frightened even bold hunters. But the Tunguses were not scared of belching craters. As shamanites, they did not attribute supernatural powers to anything not deriving from all-mighty heaven. Cattle-breeding Tunguses roamed the Amur Valley, and exploration-minded clans turned north to the Lena River as in an immemorial past the pursuers of the mammoth had done. A shift of tribes repopulated the eastern and northeastern sections of Siberia; Chinese experts considered it a wholesome development, one stimulated by the disappearance of Mongolian human road blocks and vanishing fear of Mongolian aggressiveness. The Tunguses gave every indication of peaceful designs. Historian-analysts asserted that onetime conquerors who had relapsed into impotent primitivity would never again turn dangerous aggressors. The learned men said that even if an unruly chieftain should become a local nuisance, a handful of caravan guards could take care of the matter. Chinese authorities, desirous of putting Tunguse submissiveness to a test, sent tribute collectors to fur-hunting clans, and the hunters paid assessments without as much as a grumble.

Merchants visited migrants in the Lena Valley and the foothills of the icy mountains of Verkhojansk. They divided territories among themselves, careful not to trespass on each other's beat, while Siberian hunters competed fiercely to dispose of their furs. The Chinese penetrated well beyond the

Arctic Circle. They told of unending night, and of other phenomena of extreme latitudes. They began to do business in reindeer hides, which, even though they were known in China, had not previously been a common commodity.

Hardly ever had caravan guards to interfere with Siberian misdemeanors; even hunters who had fared badly in barter refrained from violence. Merchants were full of praise of their docile customers; the Chinese administration issued permits for export of firearms so that hunters in the Amur Valley, in the Manchurian border forests, and in the Maritime Province might stalk the big bluish-gray tigers that infested the regions.

The Tunguses also spread over areas in which Mongols still went after unspectacular businesses. The Chinese noted it with satisfaction: the two nations would hold each other in check and would offer Chinese trade an even broader field of activity.

No importance was attributed to the gradual concentration of larger numbers of immigrants in eastern Manchuria, and only Chinese scholars were interested to learn that Lamaism spread among Mongols—Lamaism, even as practiced in Tibet in the seventh century, had not stimulated aggressive impulses, and, perverted by shamanism, as it was among late-fifteenth-century Mongols, it was just an oddity. Not even alarmists denied that China had good reason to be pleased with the state of affairs in Siberia.

Happy indulgence and heedlessness continued when, in 1557, a Mongolian khan, Tümen Sasaktou, called upon his nation to convert all men to a new creed. Tümen Khan did not speak of universal rule, and he advocated the use of persuasion instead of force. And it was taken as yet another innocuous oddity that Tümen Sasaktou's ideology was adopted by many Tunguses, who ordinarily had no proselyting ambitions.

Outbursts of internal struggles in China, caused by a decline of the power of the Ming dynasty, diverted Chinese interest from goings-on abroad, but it was taken for granted that Siberia would not seek to profit from China's troubles.

But in Siberia the ways of all ideologies lead to aggression. In 1606, Tunguse chieftain Nurkatsi proclaimed himself khan of all seven tribes; in 1616 he styled himself Emperor of Manchuria; in 1625 the Chinese were thrown out of Changyang, and the Manchus, as the Tunguse conquerors called themselves, began to incorporate all of present Inner Mongolia, most of Outer Mongolia, and sections of the Amur basin into a realm. The Chinese kept doing business with the Manchus, still bartering firearms for furs, and—supreme naïveté—offered to hire any available number of Manchu soldiers, when, in the course of Chinese civil war, an impostor seized the throne of Peking and the elderly, learned legitimate Emperor committed suicide by hanging. Manchu auxiliaries assisted Chinese loyalists in ejecting the impostor. Manchu soldiers occupied Peking and in 1643 proclaimed the six-year-old Chouen-tshe Emperor of China. By 1649 all of China was under Manchu rule. The Manchu dynasty, Sinofied like their foreign predecessors, lasted until the collapse of the monarchy in China, in 1912.

By the time the Manchus ruled China the second danger that earlier Chinese had so optimistically overlooked had become real: the Russian flood was rising in Siberia and engulfing the approaches to China.

Among China's fur suppliers were barbarians, whom the merchants called Nenez, and whom they had known for a long time. The Nenez lived in the extreme north, somewhere between the lower Yenisei and the frozen swamps that spread endlessly from the wild and mighty river to regions not even the most enterprising traders cared to explore, and their customers called the underworld. It was rough, barren land where, the Chinese said, the year consisted of one day and one night. The Nenez resembled the early Huns in many respects, including repulsive untidiness. They knew nothing about the outside world; their only concern was to fill their stomachs and protect their bodies against the cold. They worshiped primitive idols and the spirits of ancestors. They had shaman priests and saw no harm in cannibalism. The Nenez also ate fur animals, and had a notion of reindeer breeding. They used reindeer and dogs to draw crude sleighs, lived in bark huts and hovels made of boulders, and dressed like cave men might have dressed aeons ago. Their attitude toward the Chinese visitors was characterized by a mixture of suspicion and curiosity. They were entranced by brightly colored rags displayed by the merchants, and they would eagerly barter any amount of fine furs for the cheapest textiles, provided they were gaily colored. The natives also showed intense interest in weapons which the traders bartered somewhat reluctantly, wondering if the tools might not be used against them. However, indications were that the Nenez were not a bellicose type of barbarian. The Chinese paid very little for sable and ermine, but the trade was not lucrative enough to attract well-established merchants. The length of the trip and hardships involved made it a hazardous operation.

The venturesome operators who went to the inhospitable land expected to establish a purchasing monopoly, but much to their angry surprise they soon found that their purveyors were acquiring new luxuries, such as tents and big hunting knives, and that the fur supply was less abundant than before. The Nenez were either unable or unwilling to indicate, in the adopted language of signs, what had happened. It took the Chinese some time to find out that competitors from the far west were dealing with their customers, and still more time to meet their opposite numbers: big, fair-skinned men, who called themselves Novgorodians and referred to the savages as Samojeds.

The Novgorodians and the Chinese did not fight; but they outdid each other in friendly warnings about the aggressiveness of the people they were dealing with, and in lamentations about the unremunerativeness of a business which, they asserted, they would eventually be forced to abandon. Both parties continued their operations, but competition did not bring prosperity to the Nenez-

Samojeds, nor did developments revive a long-forgotten tradition of relative greatness.

The Novgorodians had been doing business with the Samojeds and their neighbors centuries before meeting the Chinese, but during the period of upheavals in Russia the trade was discontinued by legitimate merchants, who had other ways of obtaining furs. Russian pirates, however, who made Arkhangelsk their home port and continued their raids, unconcerned over war and destruction, continued where the respectable trade left off. They shipped through the coastal waters of the Barents and Kara seas, and entered rivers, including the Pechora, the Irtysh, the Ob, and the Yenisei. This was a remarkable navigating feat, for the route led up to the seventy-fifth parallel, but it did not seem rewarding. Pirates too had to take care of an overhead; they too had to take risks, and receivers of stolen goods and similar characters who acted as their brokers paid less than half of what the wares would bring on regular markets. Efficient buccaneers could still sell a know-how-to-acquire-valuable-goods to respectable merchants, and even turn temporarily respectable themselves, as appointed agents. Eventually Novgorodian firms returned to the Samojed business, and because sea transportation was unduly expensive, they rediscovered a formerly well-known land route across the Urals to shorten the trip and reduce costs even though their caravans were occasionally ambushed.

The first meeting between Chinese and Novgorodians probably took place as early as the days of Kubilai. Almost two hundred years later other Westerners appeared at the scene of barter. They resembled the Novgorodians and spoke a similar language, but were less polished than Chinese and Novgorodians. They substituted violence for skill, collected tribute, and tore reindeer skins from the tents of the natives if displeased. The violent men were Russians; agents of the grand dukes of Muscovy.

Back in Peking trade and security experts studied reports on the merchants' meetings with the strangers. Chinese cartographers in the service of Temudshin and Batu had mapped large sections of Russia, and copies of their charts were still available. The trade experts prognosticated that voluminous business with Russia would certainly develop along the ancient southern trade route, and security wizards insisted that no European army could ever reach the approaches to China. The encounter in the land of the Nenez was termed auspicious, and subsequent reports on the appearance of other foreigners in the distant northwest were greeted as indications of more and better business ahead.

The foreigners included one Pole and later one Englishman.

The Pole, Mathias de Miechov, is quoted as telling in 1517, long after his voyage to the Samojeds, that the people of the countries beyond the northern Urals had a huge idol, the Zlata Baba (Golden Hag), whose advice invariably benefited those who sought it. He gave a description of the statue which inspired four contemporary drawings; one of them shows a naked woman of shapeless clumsiness, holding a horn of plenty; the three others portrayed the Hag dressed in a floating gown and carrying some object in her right hand that looked like a crosier, an alpenstock, and a wrench respectively. Apparently Mathias de Miechov was not business-minded, for he tells nothing about sables, ermines, and natives' demand for the products of foreign industry. Some later visitors to the Siberian northwest also tell of the Zlata Baba, and of other idols decked out in primitive finery or daubed over with blood, and of faces carved in wood; the likenesses of ancestors.

But Giles Fletcher, a widely traveled Englishman, denounced the story of Zlata Baba in his book *Of the Russe Common Wealth* (published in London, 1591), claiming that the alleged idol was just a huge boulder. However, the Samojeds did have idols and kept worshiping them, very much to the annoyance of the Russian clergy, who, as late as 1827, turned iconoclast, seized some 440 idols, and had them burned or hewn to pieces, which in turn infuriated contemporary Russian scholars and archaeologists.

Another Englishman, Mr. Jenkinson, undertook five voyages to Muscovy, to Siberia, and to Persia in the middle of the sixteenth century. His assistant, Richard Johnson, wrote a report to the London Trading Company: "Upon the sea coast dwell Samoeds, whose meat is flesh of olens or harts, and fishe, and doe eate one another sometimes among themselves." The indignant globe-trotter also tells that Samojeds killed their children to treat visitors, and that the remains of a traveler who happened to die on the sea coast would be eaten by his hosts; and he has a great deal to say about the Samojeds' unattractiveness. The London Trading Company was also informed that Samojed sables were of superior quality. Jenkinson did not refer to Chinese dealings with the Samojeds.

Some Russians, however, previously less exploration-minded than other European nationals, did follow the traces of Chinese caravans, and at about the time of Jenkinson's first voyage actually went to China. The travelers were men from Muscovy, delegates from a ruler who had advisers of Mongolian ancestry and whose courtiers had more traditionally violent Siberian features than could be found beyond the Urals.

The Muscovite traveler's account is not remarkable for geographical and ethnological accuracy. Beyond the city of Isker they found the land of the "Mungals," which "extends from Bokhara to the sea." The Mungal men were dirty, but their women were neat, and beautifully garbed in velvet clothes with various adornments. The women, however, had no precious stones, only pearls of inferior quality. But there was a great deal of silver in the land of the Mungals, also fine horses, and camels, and every imaginable kind of grain and vegetables. A woman, Queen Machikatuna, issued transit permits to voyagers on their way to China.

However, the maps of Mungal, enclosed with the account, obviously are incorrect and the people who lived between Bokhara and the sea did not belong to the same nation.

In China the Russians were not admitted into the presence of "Taibun, Tsar of the Chinese," as they called Emperor Muh-tsung, because they lacked proper credentials and had no presents to offer. But they were allowed to walk freely through the streets of Peking. "The city is as white as snow," they wrote. "It is built in a square; at the corners are towers with embrasures, armed with heavy cannon. The gates have windows. There are many shops, all of stone, with wooden painted posters, where you may buy satin, silk, and cotton goods, but no woolens; and you also find all kinds of vegetables, fruits, flowers, a variety of sweets, cinnamon, and other spices, even precious stones. In the inns, a man can get all the drinks he wants, and the company of more harlots than he can manage. Thieves and robbers are publicly hanged, impaled, or beheaded; lesser offenders have their hands cut off. The jails are built of stone. The streets are paved. Nobles have large retinues, and they carry parasols."

The Russian delegates had all the drinks and all the harlots they could manage; and they spent in stores whatever money they had left after touring the inns. Their purchases are said to have included a special aphrodisiac made from the antlers of a deer that roamed the forests of the Altais.

Even though they were not admitted to court, the Emperor had the visitors watched, and the impression was gained that these people were poorly mannered but would never constitute a threat and might eventually become regular customers.

CHAPTER TWENTY-FIVE The vanishing Siberian tide had left Russia in chaos. The land was still as bountiful as when the historic message to Rurik had been dispatched, but there was even less order in fifteenth-century Russia than there had been in the ninth-century land of feuding, scattered Slavonic tribes. Except in Novgorod, whatever talents of orderly government may have existed among the Russians had been quelled by a succession of tyrannies. It seemed as if nothing but another despotism could cement a realm that had no strong ties of nationality, culture, and economy.

There was no want of despotic will in Russia, but in the earlier part of the fifteenth century no man was powerful enough to gather the debris of Batu's fief and to cope with erratic invasions.

Lithuania, victor over Muscovy in 1368 and 1371, had grown into an empire of 350,000 square miles, extending from the Baltic to the Black Sea. Lithuania had defeated the Teutons in 1410; it was closely associated with Poland. Immigrants from the West—scholars, craftsmen, and merchants—promoted the country's cultural and economic development. One bold bid by the rulers of Lithuania could have incorporated the Russian heart lands into the new empire.

Prolonged wars of hegemony in the eastern Baltic, the tremors of Timurite and Ottoman campaigns in the Black Sea basin, and the establishment of a violent Mongolian splinter horde in the Crimean Peninsula produced mass migrations of afflicted peoples and a motley flock of human vultures who prospered on the spoils of the wretched and turned them into savage outlaws. The fugitives did not till the soil and did not engage in other regular professions. Experience had taught them that they could nowhere stay long enough to reap the fruits of honest toil. Apparently beyond control, they roamed large tracts of the Ukraine and infiltrated adjoining lands. "Casaks," they were called, a name derived from the Mongolian term for wanderers. "Casak" (or "Cossack") indicated no nationality, for these people had none; but it defined the status of persons who had no family and no home and who were capable of anything, always ready to be hired for vile purposes. Casaks served highwaymen and river pirates, robber barons, petty conquerors, and slave dealers, learning such trades and, more often than not, despoiling their employers and taking over their sordid businesses. Not even the Lithuanians were able to check the "wanderers." Muscovy made no such attempts.

The downfall of the Asiatic conquerors seemed to sound the knell to Muscovy. The grand duchy was deprived of its income from tax collection, coercion, and bribe, and remained the focus of hatred and contempt. Furious neighbors harassed the land by small-scale invasions. Violent Mongols from the Crimea struck at Muscovy, adding to the destruction of its cities and to the violent transfer of its rural population into other servitudes. But the Mongols left behind in Southern Russia hardly noticed their brief opportunity of becoming the domineering power between the Dnieper River and the Caspian Sea. The Russian princes exhausted their rage in brief fireworks of vengeance, and it was their greatest triumph to see the most wretched of Muscovite grand dukes, Vassilj the Blind, captured by his foes and ransomed under humiliating circumstances.

They all lacked vision and power to unite the fragments of a scattered realm, be it under an orderly rule or under their heels. And Lithuania, foreign heir-presumptive to Russia, was soon shaken by internal feuds by the resurgence of the Teutons, who enjoyed the protection of the German Emperor, and by the establishment of the Ottomans, within striking distance of Lithuanian outposts.

And as Lithuania weakened and Russian princes relapsed into inertia, the grand dukes recovered. They throve on the distress of other nations. Even the capture of Constantinople by the Ottomans in 1453, which, almost two hundred years later would result in the near-conquest of Russia by Sultan Suleiman, seemed a windfall for Muscovy. It turned the ramshackle residence of Ivan III into the spiritual center of the displaced Greek Orthodox Church and into the mother city of all people of the Greek Orthodox faith, the creed of most Russians and many Lithuanians.

Still, the third Ivan had only a makeshift army, and his depleted treasury depended on the continued good will of a strange financier who had also lent the cash to liberate Blind Vassilj. But the Grand Duke did not want to see the scales switch again. In 1465 the Muscovite drive for domination of Russia opened.

The initial objective of the campaign was bound to be Novgorod. The city-republic had had no part in the attacks on Muscovy, but in a Muscovite realm of despotism there should be no islands of popular government and of prosperity by peaceful, individual endeavors. No subject of Muscovy should observe the workings of a system that was the antithesis of everything Muscovy stood for. However, the attack did not open against the city proper. The first blow hit—Siberia.

This was an odd decision, which only a Muscovite could have taken. It was the Grand Duke's traditional philosophy that the roots of strength of a state lay in the exploitation of other people's resources, and that, deprived of these resources, the strength was bound to wither away. Ivan knew that Novgorod was dealing with people who lived in the distant northeast, and from there drew supplies of fur, silver, copper, and iron. He had this information from men of the city of Yustyug, which lay astride the road used by Novgorodian caravans. The Yustyugians had preyed on trade convoys, served as convoy guards, and occasionally tried their hands in some violent business with the suppliers of the men from Novgorod. Yustyug was a ramshackle city with few legitimate resources, and the wealth from the northeast seemed colossal to its people.

Novgorodian chronicles told of the Iron Gate, which voyagers had to pass on their way northeast to the land of Ugrians, Obdorians, and Mangansees. The gate was said to be a giant rock in rough mountains, almost 1000 miles away from Novgorod.

But the Yustyugians saw that there was no Iron Gate. The Syrjane road led through the wilderness, a trail so called after Finnish tribesmen who had hewn it on their migration to the west. It was easily passable, contrary to this Novgorodian description: "The road leading through the mountains is blocked by abysses, snow fields, and more mountains are beyond, toward midnight."

The Yustyugians scoffed at yet another scare tale: "In the mountains beyond the bend of the sea (Kara Sea), one can hear the stringent voices of strange people who beg for iron to break through walls of rock. Already, they have carved a small hole, through which they will reach for axes and knives, and they will pay for these objects with furs. Even stranger and extremely dangerous are the neighbors of the immured men, an aggressive, poverty-stricken and unclean lot, the Ugrians."

Highwaymen from Yustyug said that these Ugrians had furs, silver, and metals, and that they were a timid lot, ready to pay tribute rather than face attack. And no more formidable were people who lived further toward midnight, of whom the Ugrians said that they were called Obdorians and Mangansees.

Ivan III would extort all the tribute he could get, and he relished the thought of seeing the Novgorodians cut off from their resources. He hired one Vassilj Skrajaba, an Ystyugian of well-deserved ill-repute, as a commander of a Muscovite expeditionary force of bandits, flotsam of past catastrophies, including Casaks, and a few tough regulars, all men of flawless brutality. Skrajaba's orders were to invade Ugria, Obdoria, and Mangansee, to seize these lands and whatever other lands he could find "toward midnight," to collect all valuables he could lay hands upon, and to bring the princes of these people before the Grand Duke. The assignment also included attacks on Novgorodian caravans wherever they would be encountered.

Skrajaba did not find Mangansee, he was somewhat vague about his penetration into Obdoria, the land on the Ob River, but he reported proudly to have conquered Ugria, to have leveled every settlement and several fortresses, and to have killed lots of people. The valuables he presented to Ivan were not really stunning, but the Grand Duke had not expected an honest accounting. What mattered most was that the Novgorodians would now go empty-handed. The conqueror of Ugria—and perhaps parts of Obdoria—introduced two captives, who gave their names as Kalpak and Tetschik, and said that they were Ugrian princes.

The captives pledged fealty to Ivan, acknowledged Ugrian tributary obligation to the Grand Duke and to his heirs and successors, and were eventually released to organize their country as a Muscovite province. This was the last that was seen and heard of these men.

Muscovy had made the first European conquest in Siberia. However, the boundaries of Ugria were not clearly defined; the land seemed to be situated somewhere astride the northern Urals and Obdoria was a phantom land, and Mangansee a nebulous notion. The fortresses of which Skrajaba told were, in fact, Novgorodian trade outposts, undefended by a few resident clerks.

Novgorodians, who liked to indulge in fancy in reports designed for general consumption, were strict to the point in confidential accounts to the administration of their city. Skrajaba's bands were still looting on the near side of the Urals when not only the fact of the campaign but also the objective behind the unusual drive were learned in Novgorod.

Novgorod was a city of opulence, refined living, and artistic ambitions. A few top-ranking families called themselves *"boyars,"* but that title of nobility was a social adornment and did not involve political functions. Novgorod had a statute, if not a constitution. Important decisions were taken by a citizen's assembly, the "Veche" (the "Watch"), and whenever a vital issue came up, a huge bell on the main square would toll to convoke citizens to attend. Debates were orderly, and generally on a level of competence and courtesy that would put modern parliaments to shame.

The Novgorodians were immensely proud of their government by orderly public debate and well-reasoned decisions. In the 1460s, however, hardly any matter would be taken up and less even decided by the Veche unless Martha Boretsky had been consulted. Her opinion carried more weight than that of any local magistrate or nabob.

Martha, widow of Boyar Isaak Boretsky, was the wealthiest person of Novgorod, the keenest mind, the most efficient organizer, and—last but not least—the most domineering of the city's matrons. She lived in her huge mansion, called Wonder Court, reputably the most sumptuous building in that part of the continent. Her banquet hall accommodated nearly one thousand, in settings of splendor that included luxuries from Europe, Asia, and Africa; the tapestries of her smaller reception rooms were curiosities which, when seen, enhanced the prestige of Novgorodians and foreign visitors alike. The vaults of Wonder Court were bulging with gold and silver. The jewels Martha wore at her famous parties would have made most queens blush with envy. She owned sixty-eight villages in the most fertile regions of Western Russia; nobody knew how many fisheries, complete with boats and men, she owned in the Baltic, and how far her mercantile interests extended. Lesser nabobs from Novgorod contended that Martha owned iron, silver, and copper mines in Ugrian lands, that her property in the Urals included forests swarming with sable, foxes, and martens.

To Martha Boretsky went foreign envoys. Distinguished merchants patiently waited in her anterooms until the mighty matron was ready to listen and give advice about important projects. To Wonder Court trudged debaters from the Veche, fur caps in hand, to present their case and that of the city. Martha was in her forties, but her overwhelming bearing, her massive appearance, and her ceremonial attire with dark sable dominating the picture made her look older.

The bell on the main square tolled when survivors from despoiled caravans told of Yustyugian and Muscovite bandits roaming the Syrjane road and attacking natives, and Novgorodians. The people of Novgorod had never trusted Muscovy, and they had the lowest possible opinion of Yustyug, but they abhorred war and did not think that war ever solved a problem. Yet some countermeasures had to be adopted, and, as usual, a deputation went to see Martha Boretsky. She knew more about the invasion than the deputies had learned. In fact her own trade posts had been looted, her Ugrian miners had been killed, and she realized that this was only a beginning. Ivan III had to be checked in his tracks. Gravely she announced that this was an international issue, not a matter of concern to the city only. Novgorod needed alliances, a defense system had to be built up without delay, and every citizen should contribute his share. The Veche thereupon adopted a high-sounding but otherwise rather vague resolution to take appropriate steps in close co-operation with like-minded states and cities.

Ambassadors gathered in tapestry-adorned reception rooms and listened to a measured address by Martha. She pleaded for an alliance between Novgorod, the Hansa cities, Sweden, Lithuania, and Poland; the formation of a Baltic Union of mutual assistance, a Super Hansa of trading and seafaring nations that could develop into a Great Northern Empire. The ambassadors promised to forward the project to their respective governments, and gave wordy praise to Martha Boretsky's pattern. They said that it was the finest plan ever conceived, found it strange that a Baltic Union had not been created long ago, and agreed that Novgorod had to be its center of gravity.

From Hansa cities came messages of congratulations. The Hansa would study an extension of its trade all along Northern European coasts. Sweden was complimentary too, and it would consider integration of its interests in Finland with the new combination. Poland praised the plan, and Lithuania approved of any measure to strengthen peace in the Baltic. But . . . there were too many "buts" for Martha's comfort. The worried lady talked to Novgorodian citizens of consequence; the matter did not suffer prolonged delay. Visitors from Muscovy told of continued military preparations and from the distant northeast came reports on uninhibited Muscovite lootings, carried out by grand-ducal agents who called themselves collectors of the "Iasak" (tribute).

Novgorodians listened respectfully; they would say that certain matters could not be rushed, and that Muscovy should not be provoked into attack against single presumptive members of the Baltic Union before all the others were ready to give assistance. They were convinced that, once the state of readiness would be achieved, Muscovy would hardly dare attack at all. . . .

The years 1466, 1467, 1468, '69, '70 went by; Muscovy did not attack. Novgorodians thought that Muscovy was economically weak and could not risk a protracted siege of their city. Other parties of the nebulous new union thought that there were many more pertinent issues than a woman's scheme.

The year 1471 came and almost went. It had not been a prosperous year for Novgorod. Caravan losses in the northeastern trade had been substantial; fishing was below average; trade with Lithuania was losing volume. People talked about reorientation of business interests and did not quite know what they actually meant.

One dark morning the bell started tolling. Christmas-minded crowds gathered on the square, wondering. Nothing grave, nothing serious, could happen that time of year. . . . But the man of the Veche who followed the routine of visiting Wonder Court looked grim and pale. It had been said that a Muscovite army was on its way. At first most people thought that this was just another rumor and that not even Muscovites would desecrate Christmas by an act of aggression. . . .

But Muscovites evidently had different views on the sacredness of Christmas. From estates of wealthy Novgorodian landowners arrived fugitives who all told of arsonists and looters under the approaching banner. The bell of the Veche tolled day and night. Novgorod needed volunteers. Resistance to the limit had been unanimously decided upon, and Martha Boretsky had ordered her first-born son, Dmitri, to enlist first. Novgorod's example, she was quoted saying, might inspire other Baltic nations to join the noble battle, and the emergency might be a blessing in disguise.

Novgorod had some 2500 professional soldiers—superbly clad and fed, and armed with the most spectacular swords the city's master craftsmen could produce. The men had never fought adversaries more formidable than highwaymen, and they had never operated in units larger than a hundred.

The enlistment drive produced 10,000 enrollees. This was not up to expectations. Still, everybody talked defense—in public. However, there was reluctance; noiseless brakes on a popular drive. In small clandestine gatherings citizens voiced cautious misgivings: Should a woman tell men how to behave in the face of attack? Were women not too emotional to make decisions? Was not peace, even at a high price, the noblest of all goals? Negotiations might clear the air. Even defense might be an act of aggression if it were not preceded by negotiations.

The citizens who spoke along these lines did not consider themselves poor patriots. They wanted Novgorod to be free; and they would have been indignant had anybody suspected them of promoting Muscovy's aims.

There were plenty of arms for the 10,000, and plenty of horses. The Novgorodians would not stay within their walls, Dmitri Boretsky proclaimed, and let the Muscovite ravage rural districts. Novgorod would meet Muscovy on the open battlefield. Dmitri was Novgorodian commander in chief. He had no military training, but, as Martha's son, he had to be supreme commander. Dmitri was a playboy of the late Middle Ages, but he had practically all the frustrations and inhibitions which the untalented child of an overpowering mother would have today. The Christmas war was his opportunity to assert himself before his mother. And so young General Boretsky rode out at the head of 10,000 blustering volunteers and not quite 2000 uneasy soldiers, to meet the hordes of Muscovy.

He did not have to travel far; Ivan III was one day's march away. The Muscovites expected to beleaguer a strong city, and hardly trusted their eyes when they saw a column of horsemen who, in sight of their enemy, started maneuvers which threw the column into disorder. The rest did not take long. Most Novgorodians were killed. General Dmitri, gesticulating, shouting, swearing, and crying in a crazy effort to bring his army into fighting order, was captured and beheaded on the spot.

The bell tolled disaster; it kept tolling to have the citizenry organize a last-ditch stand. But nobody wanted last-ditch defenses. The Veche was not in contact with the bereaved Wonder Court. Rabble rousers suddenly emerged, shouting that Novgorod's very survival depended upon peace. Muscovy needed Novgorod's assets: its commercial ties, its experience, its skills. And Novgorod could benefit from collaboration with the Grand Duke's backward realm. Novgorod could become the East's window to the West.

On January 15, 1472 a well-rested Muscovite army, drunk with easy victory, camped under the walls of Novgorod. On January 15, a Veche, with an unusually small attendance, voted unanimously to accept whatever terms would be asked, and also on January 15 the Grand Duke rode through the city gates.

The Muscovite soldiery installed itself in burghers' quarters. There was little looting; the citizenry surrendered without argument whatever the occupiers seemed to like. There was no arson, except for a few small-scale fires that might have been accidental. And Ivan, who left the town after a brief, gay holiday, did not decree any terms. Novgorod was Muscovy's. . . .

The Grand Duke did not deign to talk to former champions of nonresistance. He did not even order the historical bell removed, and did not object to convocation of the Veche. Optimists interpreted this as an act of respect for the tradition of the city and were relieved when, one year after the fall of Novgorod, the Muscovite resident general appointed Martha Boretsky's second son to a minor office. The agony of fear lifted. So Muscovy was not the raging blind despot it had been said to be. Already German, Dutch, and even English merchants flocked back to the city, and the Muscovites did not know how to manage the distant northeast. They would surely entrust Novgorodian old hands in the business with its reorganization and expansion. Social gatherings resumed and the "Window to the West" became the favorite topic.

The Veche did not make important decisions, but discussed local affairs. It could happen again that men, cap in hand, would ask Martha for her views. Martha's hair had turned white, but otherwise she was her old imposing self, who voiced her opinion on inconsequential problems with no less authority than she had once displayed on weighty issues.

Muscovy sent tax collectors. Novgorodians duly complained about depression, greased greedy paws, and hoped that the grand duchy would eventually relieve the burden. Muscovy did permit Novgorodian caravans to visit Ugria and the countries beyond; but there was always Muscovite personnel present to watch and imitate their commercial operations, and request, under flimsy pretexts, hush money from natives and Novgorodians alike. Grand-ducal personnel were boorish and clumsy in their dealings with the natives, and natives had not much left to sell after the Muscovites collected their spoils. Business with the northeast was no longer prosperous.

The matter was not mentioned at the Veche. Muscovite guards were around whenever the bell called the men to take counsel. To Ivan's stool pigeons the assembly seemed the travesty of a government. Small wonder, they contended contemptuously, that the city had fallen an easy prey to the first assault.

Ivan himself, advised by a man who held no title, drew no salary, did not defraud the Grand Duke, and even kept a generously filled purse ready to finance Muscovite ventures, did not think that the Veche was silly. But he was maddened by the assembly's procedures. He had intended to watch the Veche to learn the workings of self-administration, to be able to nip it in the bud should it pop up in his realm. Now these Novgorodian cheats were fooling him by letting the Veche appear a petty institution dealing with trifles. There seemed to be some other Veche—a hidden, conspirational assembly.

There was no hidden Veche. Novgorodians, brought up in security and freedom, had never learned how to conspire.

Delegates from Novgorod regularly visited Muscovy to profess loyalty and devotion to the Grand Duke, who had adopted the title of Gossudar—the equivalent of Grand Ruler—to take orders, guess wishes, and distribute handouts.

Novgorod was both worried and hopeful when Ivan, accompanied by a riotous bunch of boon companions, visited their town. The Muscovites occupied the finest mansions in town with the exception of the Wonder Court, and asked to be entertained. The wealthiest and most prominent people wooed to amuse the Muscovite crowd. The finest wines from France and Germany flowed freely, the daintiest delicacies were served in barbaric quantities; the Grand Duke liked devouring caviar served in ten-gallon silver buckets; luscious local wenches and others imported from Poland catered to Ivan's party. When the Muscovites were getting tired, they would put in an evening of "serious entertainment," in the house of a ranking clergyman or an elderly matron, where they would only get drunk and forgo whoredom.

Martha Boretsky dispatched one of her grandsons to solicit the honor of Ivan's visit and present him with a carload of gifts nobody in town could have duplicated. Rude guard officers took the gifts and told the young man to be off. Ivan did not visit Martha.

He stayed in town for more than two months, and left it seedy, moody, and convinced that his secret adviser was right: the Novgorodians were cheats: they had more money than they would admit to the tax collector, or else they could not have arranged such expensive festivities. And they were an impudent lot: trying to deceive and to corrupt their master. But he, the Gossudar, could not be deceived, and he was uncorruptible.

The citizens had spent more on Ivan's visit than they would formerly have spent for five years of public expenses. They expected preferred treatment in return, but instead their applications remained unanswered, the local governor was outright insulting, and delegates to Muscovy were abused by sneering underlings. In 1477 a Novgorodian application addressed to Grand Duke Ivan III, mistakenly omitted the title Gossudar. The application was thrown out as usual, and now Gossudar Ivan had his case against the city: He had been "deliberately insulted by Novgorod's official representatives."

Fear-stricken magistrates presented a humble, imploring apology, which was not accepted. An irate citizenry bent on appeasing Ivan before the bolt could strike turned against Martha Boretsky. Envy and resentment, smoldering under a thinning cover of respect, broke in the open. Martha had been a tyrant in her own wrong, raging orators claimed; she was the cause of the city's misfortune; she had defied the Gossudar, in 1471, and even thereafter. If the Boretsky woman were punished, the Gossudar would spare the city. Mobbists, turbulent and mean as they had not been known to exist in the sedate city, put the torch to Wonder Court. It burned to the ground, but Martha escaped unhurt.

The Novgorodians waited for a sign of Ivan's approval. Months went by; then in 1478 an armed column approached the town. The bell tolled to call out people to line the streets and offer flowers, refreshments, and presents to the Muscovite visitors. This was the last time the bell tolled, the last time the Veche convened. The bell was dismounted and carried off to Muscovy, and together with the bell went hundreds of wagonloads of valuables: all church treasures, every object of gold and silver from private households, including the goblets and plates used in banquets in Ivan's honor. Not only treasures left Novgorod. A roll of doom, prepared seven years before and kept up to date, listed the name of all undesirable citizens. It included virtually everybody who had entertained the Gossudar, every person of consequence. Martha Boretsky headed the roll. The victims were marched away. The Muscovite kept no records on the deportees, but Martha is known to have died in a nunnery, a pathetic human wreck.

Novgorod remained an empty shell. Muscovy did nothing to fructify the city's assets in the Western trade; Muscovy did not care for a window to exchange goods and ideas with the West. All it wanted was a sally port through which to rush out to attack Western neighbors. The grand-ducal treasurers were genuinely surprised when Novgorod ceased to produce a noteworthy income, but the Gossudar had other resources.

The schedule of gathering fragments of Russia and neighboring domains was stepped up. In 1485, Tver fell to the conquering Muscovites; then another drive to the northeast, disguised as a punitive expedition, pushed the Gossudar's realm beyond Ugria and, as a by-product, engulfed Kola Peninsula and the coast of the White Sea. In 1503 an old but still rabid Ivan III forced Alexander, King of Poland, the Gossudar's weakish son-in-law, to cede his provinces on the central Dnieper. In 1505, Ivan's successor, Vassilj III, made a conquering debut at Pskov, from where he proceeded to Ryazan, which he took in 1512; and two years later a sally west took Smolensk from the Lithuanians. Vassilj's Muscovy had no more skill in making newly acquired land pay regular dividends than Ivan's had had; but the gatherers of Russia did not need to produce interest as long as they could spend the principal that other people and rulers had saved up.

Muscovy still employed Novgorodians in the trade with Ugria and the lands toward midnight, but first-rate experts had been deported and second-stringers, who worked for the Grand Duke, were hampered by the stupid interference of brutish supervisors. The Muscovites had grievances against the Ugrians. Kalpak and Tetschik had not kept their word. Tribute from Ugria was overdue, and survivors of the first Muscovite invasion pretended not to know about commitments, and contended not to know Kalpak and Tetschik. Ivan wanted sables and silver, and attributed the Ugrian attitude to a conspiracy between the natives and the Novgorodian ex-nabobs. His trusted adviser, "who never wanted anything for himself," praised the Gossudar's wisdom. These Ugrians, he said, were disloyal; and you could never trust a Novgorodian. Not only did Novgorod agents induce natives to default on their obligation, but bands armed with weapons only Novgorod could have provided were crossing the Ural Mountains into the Eastern Russian plains. The adviser himself claimed to have suffered through those bandits; his loss was, by implication, that of the Gossudar, who depended on that man for ready cash.

In fact Eastern Russia was an open highway, the hunting ground of Crimean Mongols, infiltrating Casaks (Cossacks), and roving Muscovite lansquenets. But there were hardly any Ugrians among the highwaymen, and Novgorod had as little to do with the Western Russian chaos as it had had with the capture of blind Grand Duke Vassilj, which the scheming adviser posthumously attributed to Novgorodian instigation.

In 1483, Gossudar Ivan's short supply of patience had become exhausted. He hired a band of Yustyugians to invade Ugria, and appointed Prince Ssemjon Kurbsky commander in chief, and Ivan Saltik, from Yustyug, an expert in dealing with recalcitrant natives, his assistant. Kurbsky was a vegetarian; his features were ascetic, and he never failed to invoke God when issuing orders; later chroniclers arrived at the conclusion that he was altogether a saintly man.

The soldiers crossed the Ural Mountains, and returned five months later with as much loot as they could carry. They also brought an embassy from Ugria, timid men who sued for peace. Peace was granted, and, to make its terms sacred, they were dictated by the Bishop of Perm. The prelate administered the oath of fealty to the ambassadors, as plenipotentiaries of their nation; he made them pledge good and peaceful behavior and, last but not least, payment of an annual Iasak (tribute.)

The pledge of good and peaceful behavior became the Siberians' undoing. For there was still no peace in Eastern Russia. Ivan was convinced that the Ugrians were involved in all upheavals reported to him. And he had yet another indication of Ugrian incorrigibility: beaver had become fashionable, and the Ugrians did not deliver all the beaver furs he wanted.

Ivan wasted no time investigating whether or not there were enough beavers in his distant vassal land. He organized another expedition to drive the devil of rebellion from all provinces toward midnight. Kurbsky again assumed command. The Prince had the advice of a man familiar with transportation across the Urals, and in the plains beyond, or else he could hardly have equipped his force of five thousand so well. That man might have been a

Novgorodian, but it could well be that equipment and logistics were supplied by the Gossudar's always useful trusted adviser.

The expedition started in 1499. The men used small craft on the Pechora River where they built blockhouses to secure supply lines. The season was already advanced and they proceeded on snowshoes across the Urals into the Ob River valley. Supplies were carried on dog sleighs, and as the force penetrated into the domain of reindeer breeding, reindeer were used as draft animals. Prince Kurbsky proudly reported to have won a decisive victory over strong hostile forces and to have made numerous prisoners. In fact the commander had small roaming parties of Samojeds put to the sword, and his prisoners were not men but reindeer; two hundred of them.

Marching south on the frozen course of the Ob, the Muscovites scored similar victories over Ugrians, and Wogul and Ostjak tribes, whose racial qualities Kurbsky could not define but whom he called Obdorians. They captured more reindeer, furs of every kind, and even jewels, indicating that the natives had been trading with foreigners more generous than the subjects of the Gossudar. As the loot grew, transportation troubles arose. Mongrel dogs perished from exhaustion, and even the hardy reindeer did not stand up too well under the strain. The saintly Prince ordered that, with the help of God, and until further notice, seized natives be spared from death and put into dogs' and reindeers' harnesses.

Kurbsky would not miss Easter services in Muscovy. On Good Friday, 1500, he was back in the capital, to the delight of mundane and ecclesiastic authorities and of festive crowds who did not know exactly what the ascetic vegetarian had accomplished but cheered him anyway.

The Prince reported to the Gossudar that his expedition had covered a distance of 3000 miles and had weathered hardships beyond imagination. They had crossed chains of mountains whose peaks towered beyond the skies; they had defied the threat of fish which looked like men, and similar ghoulish creatures; they had fought off attacks by evil men and had faced, unafraid, humans who died every year on November 27 and came to life again on the following April 24.

Parts of Kurbsky's tales were obviously taken from ancient Novgorodian stories. Ivan ignored the Novgorod manuscripts, and he did not know that the maximum altitude along Kurbsky's road was 4752 feet; neither did it occur to him that Kurbsky had not been on the spot on November 27, or April 24, to watch humans die and resuscitate.

However, Kurbsky's campaign was the most extensive recorded expedition by Europeans into Northwestern Siberia, the deepest penetration ever made into Asia north of the silk road. A delighted Ivan assumed the title of Prince of Ugria and of Obdoria, and in the last year of his life styled himself Gossudar of "all of Russia," without defining the borders of his realm.

The Gossudar would never have acknowledged boundary lines. His realm should extend as far as his armies could penetrate and as far as his tribute collectors could go. It should include even lands not accessible to his official looters; Ivan considered himself Emperor of defunct Byzantium because he had married Princess Zoë, niece of the last ruler of the ancient empire, and he had Byzantium's two-headed heraldic eagle included in his coat of arms.

The Muscovite tax collectors were rapacious, petty conquistadores who would go beyond their assigned districts and, at the head of small bands, conquer Iasak-paying domains of their own.

Their accounts on collections were as inaccurate as their reports on visited districts. Of a thousand sable furs extracted perhaps one hundred would eventually reach the Grand Duke's coffers. Five times that number would be distributed among officials in charge of checking accounts, and the rest went to the collector, who had to bribe his assistants. The collectors went as far east as the Irtysh River, but did not memorize the outlandish names of people and settlements on their way. They called people and places as they seemed fit. The small castle of Isker on a hill, overlooking a river where a khan lived and sighed under Muscovite demands, they called a spot of poor weather: something like "Siwer." Registrars back at Muscovy entered that name. It did not occur to them that they were christening a realm the size of which they could not have conceived. The men from Muscovy were no mathematicians and no geographers; areas did not stir their imagination.

The gossudars were no mathematicians and geographers either. But at the dawn of the sixteenth century the tentacles of Muscovy reached into limitless space. The shadow of another universal empire emerged: an Asiatic conception, shaped and hardened by Asiatic conquerors, imbued with Mongolian notions of conquest, guided by Mongolian suggestions.

The Muscovite rulers did not have the wisdom once planted by Yeliu. Their universal empire was the realm of the hunter, not of the conservator, and this could eventually give the right man an opportunity as no man had ever had before.

The right man would have to wait, however. Impatience might destroy his chance. Anikita Stroganoff had all the patience required, and he considered himself the right man. This patience he had inherited from his ancestors; and the wealth and power the right man would need were another bequest. But the ruthless shrewdness was his own: Ivan and Vassilj were badly mismanaging their holdings and their successors would probably do even worse. May the gossudars keep conquering, may their hordes penetrate even deeper into that land toward midnight, of which Anikita knew a great deal even though he had never been there, but of which the Muscovite would learn nothing even if they visited all of it. Muscovy would always need the advice of the Stroganoffs, the advice of men who had counseled and financed Muscovy for generations without asking for anything in return, without even charging interest, but who had always planned to collect the greatest award in history. The Stroganoffs had been the driving power behind the third Ivan's drive across the Urals, their counsel achieved the downfall of Novgorod, they were expert diplomats, uncompromising rivals, and they had an Asiatic faculty of waiting. . . .

CHAPTER TWENTY-SIX

The name of Stroganoff derives from the Russian word *strogat,* meaning grated; and to be grated was the sordid fate of the ancestor of the family, a Mongol who was chopped into small pieces for having engaged in treacherous dealings with an early grand duke of Vladimir. The grated Mongolian is said to have been a kin of the Golden Ordu; and he is also credited with having introduced the *abacus,* an Oriental reckoning board, in Russia. The latter, however, makes it unlikely that he was of princely descent; Mongolian nobility usually did not bother with business appliances.

The surviving members of the family sought refuge in Vladimirite territory, and the fact that it was granted by a collaborationist grand duke proves that the Mongols did not pass on their ire from father to son. To be on the safe side, however, the refugees chose to live on the Dvina River, far up north of the traditional route of inspection tours by their former countrymen. They adopted the name of Stroganoff in memory of the defunct, whose mercantile talents were inherited by his successors. The financial success story, which started the Stroganoffs on the road to the greatest wealth ever owned by any individual or family in modern times, is not completely recorded, nor is it possible to compute the exact figure of Stroganoff property at its peak, more than three centuries ago. However, a rather free evaluation, combining contemporary estimates with present-day quotations, makes it appear as if the Stroganoffs had been worth forty or fifty billion dollars in present currency.

Landed property constituted their main asset: the family domain temporarily covered 600,000 square miles, about one fifth of the area of the U.S.A. But these Mongolian Midases did not shun industry and banking operations. They operated a fantastic number of salt mines and kept liquid funds on hand to cover all expenditures of their sovereign, and still invest in enterprises of colossal variety.

When the Stroganoffs went to live on the Dvina River, they probably owned some hard cash. Ready cash could bring high and immediate returns in that strange land of smugglers, black marketeers, pirates, agents of respectable trading firms, and not-so-respectable sovereigns. The grand dukes of Vladimir and later of Muscovy claimed sovereignty to the land; but so did other Russian princes, and nobody had full control over it. Officials, brutish scoundrels, administered estates in the Grand Duke's name and, also in his name, sold goods of dubious sources, and bought contraband items for smuggling into unspecified areas. Other promoters engaged in similar businesses, allegedly on behalf of other distant rulers. Novgorodian agents established warehouses and caravan hostelries along the river; they sold assistance against roaming bandits, and in turn did business with the robbers. Distinguished patricians from Novgorod emphatically denied dealing with outlaws, but they had their hands in many a business, and the left hand ignored the doings of the right. In itinerant fairs pirates and highwaymen sold furs, precious metal, and other loot from the northeast. Hardy buyers, who preferred to remain anonymous but had backing from North German, Dutch, Swedish, Danish, and English wholesalers, lurked for bargains in stolen goods. Bandit leaders looked for investors to finance trips into the lands toward midnight, or to acquire their businesses lock, stock, and barrel. Buyers also hired highwaymen to prey upon a competitor's property.

During the hundred-odd years in which the Stroganoffs did not keep records they must have done well indeed. For when, under the family rule of Spiridon, who died in 1395, they began to register events and proceeds, they had trade caravans of their own, which penetrated as far toward midnight as pirates and Novgorodians would go, and which were accompanied by tough guards. Feuds between Stroganoff's men and Novgorodians were frequent, on land and on water, along the 700-odd-mile course of the Dvina, and from Dvina Bay on the White Sea to the distant coasts of Western Siberia. Spiridon's records do not specify expenses, but he undoubtedly paid pirates preying on Novgorodian supplies, and fought a savage battle against buccaneers selling out to Baltic merchants. Spiridon could not yet match the financial strength of the old, established houses of Novgorod, but he was already determined to crush his arrogant rivals.

With fanatical stinginess he did not permit himself or any member of the family to spend one copper on luxuries; and luxury to Spiridon meant everything that went beyond the cheapest means of feeding and clothing oneself. He scoffed at the city slickers from Novgorod, who wasted sums, which could have kept a thousand highwaymen in operation, on such nonsense as tapestries, paintings, dainty food, and drink, and who clad themselves in materials and furs that could have been sold at a profit. Spiridon's greed, however, could not make up for Novgorod's head start, and on his deathbed the first bookkeeping Stroganoff admonished his son Luka to save even more. The younger Stroganoff was a sober man, yet, after having suffered through his father's avarice until his mature years, he did not want to continue depriving himself of all the pleasures money could buy. But victory over Novgorod had to be won. This fierce determination inspired Luka, first of the two geniuses who turned the Stroganoffs into princes of money.

As Luka knew, the agents of the grand dukes of Muscovy who managed their sovereign's affairs on the Dvina had never sent one ruble to the coffers of the capital. When Luka went to Muscovy, he traveled simply, without a large retinue, as it befitted a commoner; but his luggage included many precious sable furs—dark, long-haired, glossy pelts that could have been the delight of the Holy Roman Emperor. The Grand Duke of Muscovy was a lesser man than the Emperor; he raved about the sables which one Stroganoff sent him as a token of his humble devotion.

Luka did not apply for an audience. He merely told a sloppy chamberlain that he was staying in an inn nearby, and he did not forget to slip a purse into the chamberlain's greasy palm. Commoner Stroganoff was called to the palace, where the Grand Duke asked many questions about business up north. Commoner Stroganoff was guileful and cautious, the Grand Duke artless and impatient. The Muscovite wanted returns from his properties on the Dvina; the man from the Dvina did not say that such returns were hard to obtain, but insinuated that he himself was making money. When Luka left, he held a contract with the Grand Duke, appointing him tenant of all Muscovite property in the Dvina region, and manager of all Muscovite businesses including tax collection and transportation.

Luka paid a fee, the first income the Grand Duke remembered having drawn from the Dvina, and he even disbursed a generous advance on earnings for years ahead. The Grand Duke told his tenant to come to Moscow regularly; he wanted to consult him on state business; and, he shouted, so loudly that all courtiers could hear it, that all boyars were cheats, traitors, or drunkards, and that only simple people were honest.

Luka placated the courtiers by bows and more ducats. He had made the most substantial business investment in Stroganoff history, but it would produce more than privation could bring. He had become a power in his own right: he could levy duties and operate a monopoly of transportation in the Grand Duke's distant domain; he could do more than any Novgorodian could do. It turned out to be a sound investment, but not quite as outstanding as Luka had expected. The men from Novgorod occasionally evaded duties and by-passed districts, where he held exclusive transportation rights. He would have to incite the Grand Duke against Novgorod—but Muscovy was weak, and Novgorod was still strong. He would have to wait. He would not immediately return to Muscovy. As a power in his own right, he would go to the lands toward midnight. . . .

He traveled across the Urals, not in a style befitting a humble commoner, but with a large retinue of servants, and with the bearing of a conqueror. Luka visited Ugrians and Samojeds, talked with chieftains as a high and exalted ruler would talk to his vassals, yet with a grain of diplomacy that made the Northwestern Siberian natives believe that the visiting grandee might help them in some inscrutable way. The head of the house of Stroganoff did not make commitments, but his own trade with the Siberians rose sharply, and after he left several riots occurred against Novgorodians. It is even likely that tributes were collected by Stroganoff's caravan leaders.

Indications are that Luka also met Chinese merchants and arranged for an exchange of goods at the expense of Novgorodian trade. From the land of the Samojeds he traveled south, through Obdoria. He met strange Mongolian splinter tribes of whom not even Novgorod seemed to know. These ignorant people were ruled by naive khans who didn't belong to the Golden, White, or Middle ordus, but who, according to the eminent eighteenth-century historian, Professor Johann Eberhard Fischer, were descendants of an obscure Mongolian prince whom Temudshin himself had invested with a distant fief.

The khans felt honored by the visit of a man who, if not a khan himself, might be a viceroy appointed by some proud and mighty khan. Luka did not explain his situation to his hosts, who might not have understood the implications of his position as a grand-ducal tenant, but he told the Siberians certain things they apparently understood. For soon after his return to Muscovy, mounted hordes from the forgotten tribes swarmed across the Urals, raiding roads over which Novgorodian caravans traveled and starting upheavals in Eastern Russia. Luka had become a major factor in Siberian affairs, but the nature of his agreements with the Siberian chieftains and khans can only be guessed. Luka was not the man to keep telltale records.

The head of the Stroganoffs carefully dosed his speech. He did tell Grand Duke Vassilj of his Siberian travels, not only because the Muscovite intelligence service could hardly fail to learn about it, but also because he might need support in case Novgorod or the khans themselves would take action against him. He presented his journey as an exploratory expedition, undertaken at a great expense and terrific hazards in the Grand Duke's interest. There existed large territories and many tribes, he said, from which tributes could be collected. Luka refrained from telling about his arrangements with the khans, and he did not mention that on his way back to Muscovy he had paid visits to Eastern Russian cities, including Perm and Kazan, and, should Muscovite informers learn about the detour, he could always say that he had taken a rest in those relatively comfortable places.

But Vassilj's agents did not report on that phase of Luka Stroganoff's trip, and the Grand Duke, immensely pleased by the prospect of tributes, gave high praise to his devotion and honesty. Yet there was another business to discuss: Muscovy needed a loan. . . .

The devoted and honest agent investigated the situation. He was shocked to find Muscovy's treasury empty. Worse even, the barracks were empty also —but for small bands of rough recruits—and three-pronged attacks by hostile neighbors could hardly be checked. Angry Russian princes and savage Crimean Mongols battered the shaky realm. Had it not been for their poor strategy and lack of co-ordination Muscovy would already have disappeared from the map. Vassilj was a less than mediocre man, and his eyesight, always poor, had deteriorated to the point of blindness. This grand duke was certainly unable to cope with extreme odds.

Yet Luka granted the loan.

Bankers would have called Luka's decision insane. It turned out to be a master stroke, however. Luka had several talks with Vassilj, with no witness admitted. From Muscovy the Stroganoff coach headed toward the Dvina, but turned aside some fifty miles north of the city and proceeded in a different direction. . . . The coachman and the servants did not talk; neither did their master. But there can be no doubt that Luka went to Kazan. Reinsurance was not yet a business practice, but Stroganoff acumen was ahead of his time.

Suddenly startling events occurred.

First Vassilj gathered his disheveled bunch of recruits and, accompanying the band on a litter, invaded the lands between the Volga and the Oka rivers, which Kazan considered its domain.

Next an infuriated prince of Kazan, a man of Mongolian descent, attacked the Muscovites. The cavalry from Kazan destroyed the invaders and captured Vassilj. A message was sent from Kazan to Muscovy. It called for ransom of the blind Grand Duke and wound up: "Unless the amount is paid up in full and at once, we shall make a bonfire of the wretch." The carriers of the message, violent cavalrymen, rode through the streets of the city, bullying people and gaily shouting, "Cash or bonfire." Their attitude left little doubt that the log houses of the capital would also go up in flames should the amount not be paid.

The city had a population of between 10,000 and 20,000. Muscovites would certainly rather part with their grand duke than their cash, but they did not want to lose their houses. However, the ransom exceeded their means. There are several versions of the amount, ranging from 29,000 to 200,000 rubles. But in those days a solidly build farmhouse would bring no more than three rubles, and there was hardly one ruble of cash between every three Muscovites.

The Kazanites gave Muscovy one more day.

At dawn Luka arrived, and paid. This was an almost incredible solution of an otherwise hopeless problem; but circumstances of the last-minute rescue were veiled in mystery.

No Muscovite had informed the tenant from the Dvina of the unhappy event, and even had express couriers from some other place raced north to report the tidings, Luka Stroganoff could not have arrived in time. His visit could not have been accidental, for otherwise he would not have carried an amount of cash that could purchase at least 10,000 farmhouses through bandit-infested regions.

Vassilj did not ask his deliverer indiscreet questions. The blind Grand Duke offered a promisory note of twice the amount of the ransom. Luka wanted neither note nor bonus. He would charge the ransom against future rents or dues. . . . A Stroganoff wanted nothing but business: he did not ask for favors, titles, honors. . . .

A Stroganoff had played Muscovy against Kazan and come out in high favor with both; the reinsurance still stood; and, despite the Grand Duke's wretchedness Luka trusted the Muscovite star. He was the first to notice symptoms of creeping paralysis among other Russian princes, and the decline of Lithuanian and Polish power. If the West did not destroy Muscovy,

Muscovy would survive. Luka gave more loans and advice; Stroganoff put many eggs in the frail Muscovite basket.

The Stroganoffs acquired immense tracks of land at nominal prices. The Stroganoffs expanded their business to all branches of economy, acting, more often than not, as grand-ducal agents; this meant that, for a trifling duty, they had official backing for transactions which the grand dukes ignored. They had their own agents in more parts of Siberia than were marked on Russian maps; they maintained a staff of hundreds of employees, and a varying number of mercenaries, whose actions were veiled in secrecy.

Luka was not only a schemer whose trickery makes that of Niccolò Machiavelli, the Florentine who was born several decades later, appear dull and anemic; he was also an outstanding industrial pioneer. He advised his son, Fjodor, not to confine himself to traditional business, but to take up specialized production on a large scale.

The aging Luka proclaimed salt as the most lucrative object of modern industry. Muscovy levied forbidding duties on salt, which was imported from Belgium through the German Hansa and its Novgorodian agents. From the Black Sea small quantities of salt were smuggled into Muscovy, and even smaller quantities reached the grand duchy from somewhere in the north; duty collectors could not locate the place.

Luka located it. It came from lakes in the wilderness not far from the Urals, and it was produced by haphazard operators who did not know how to make the golden opportunity pay, in silver at least. Luka willed that the Stroganoffs move their residence to Sol-Wueshegodska, the center of salt production, strategically located on the road to Siberia, amid immense forests that might also yield a huge income.

Fjodor executed his father's will. The family established itself in a region of salt lakes. On the Dvina remained factories and depots which, however, were of relatively minor importance, since the Stroganoff urge to the east had found better base in Sol-Wueshegodska.

It was extremely difficult to recruit a labor force of a few hundred in fifteenth-century Russia, but Fjodor gathered several thousand men to clear forests, build roads and houses, to work in his industry, and he even managed to keep his men adequately supplied, which was perhaps the most difficult proposition. It was not difficult for him, however, to receive a salt monopoly in the grand-ducal realm, and it was equally easy to organize smugglers' rings to export Stroganoff salt to countries whose governments were not indebted to the industrialists.

Rock salt abounded on the bottom of lakes and rivers. Primitive operators staked small claims. The Stroganoffs did not contest such titles to property. There was more salt around Sol-Wueshegodska than the small fry knew. The small fry would no longer be able to smuggle their product to Muscovy; Stroganoff guards would see to that. They would have to sell their salt to the Grand Duke's own contractors, on the contractors' terms. The small fry drew buckets full of brine from lakes, heated it in rusty pans until it evaporated, and gathered salt by the ounce. The Stroganoffs hired specialists from Upper Austrian rock-salt mines, and had salt produced by the ton. Workers were ordered to labor beneath the surface of lakes: this was a difficult and dangerous job and the men were not slaves, in the judicial sense of the word. But the Stroganoffs knew how to make men toil, and if somebody was getting weary, guards could always restore him to diligence.

The Stroganoffs still traveled to Muscovy to advise the grand dukes and to direct Muscovite policies as they deemed fit. The fate of Eastern Europe was decided in the picturesque settings of the salt mines. The Muscovite rulers were not aware that Sol-Wueshegodska was pulling the strings. The Stroganoffs never asked anything for themselves; their suggestions invariably benefited Muscovy: they enlarged Muscovite territory, they boosted the grand-ducal ego. Boyars at court received gratuities from the salt manufacturers—furs and cash. They always nodded when the Gossudar sang the Stroganoffs' praise. The Gossudar too received gratuities: he would buy luxury objects from the wholesale house of Stroganoff: they would be properly billed, and then the wholesalers forgot to collect.

As the fifteenth century drew to a close, another Stroganoff took the reins at Sol-Wueshegodska, a seventeen-year-old youth—tall, lean, with dense dark hair and penetrating, slightly slit eyes. Anikita was an erudite young man. He could read and write, and he had learned to say Mass from the local *pope* (Russian clergyman). When he presented himself in Muscovy, the boyar ladies raved about his handsomeness and did not charge sable furs for their favors. Their bearded husbands, however, who thought that handsomeness was tantamount to stupidity, tried to collect higher gratuities than usual, and were satisfied that Anikita was dumb, when he gave them all they wanted.

Anikita was, in fact, the second and greatest genius of the Stroganoff family.

His first action seemed strictly commercial. He no longer wanted to deal with small operators, but offered to purchase all claims in his domain. He gathered salt mines, paying between three and twenty rubles apiece, according to size, and the bargaining skill of mineowners. The local *pope* was a poor bargainer: he received three rubles altogether.

Anikita married a nondescript girl of undistinguished parentage. Mavra Stroganoff bore him eight children, meekly abided by his command, and insisted that servants call him Highness. He was Your Highness also to his wife, at least in public.

Anikita had 600 servants. Boundary lines between clerks and grooms were not too tightly drawn as far as treatment was concerned. His mansion provided quarters for the family and the entire staff of men and beasts.

It was a tremendous wooden building, strong and ugly. The front side reminded of an oversized grange, flanked by twin round towers on one side and by an awkward turret on the other; the wings of the mansion were low and forbidding, and conveyed the impression of dungeons. Only the rear, where the stables were located, had a touch of habitableness. The mansion, center of a private domain of 22,000,000 acres, remained residence and business headquarters of the Stroganoffs for 253 years.

The spirit of dark, arbitrary violence and mysteriously malicious cunning that pervaded the building imbued the minds of Anikita's progeny; it bred feuds, cabals, betrayal, and mendacity, but it never again begot genius. When at last the spell was broken, in the late eighteenth century, a somewhat provincial *bon vivant,* Count Stroganoff, moved into another clumsy palace of nobility, like the Tsar's courtiers owned in Moscow and St. Petersburg, to live there like other wealthy noblemen, fond of cards, horses, wine, and women, averse to exertion, and leaving the administration of his estates to persons whose social ambitions did not prevent them from indulging in business.

The Stroganoffs lost their provincial tinge, the last reminder of Sol-Wueshegodska; and when a nineteenth-century tsar suggested that a Stroganoff take the office of governor general of Siberia, the Count said that he did not have the experience required for the job.

But in Anikita's day the Gossudar's mood was the basic law. The mood was more affable toward the commoner-Highness from Sol-Wueshegodska than it was toward anybody else, but it was still unfathomable. One mistake could bring the hangman or savage bears into the picture. Nothing could stop Muscovite violence but the limit of Muscovite power. This power had been saved and boosted by the Stroganoffs, and not even Stroganoff sabotage could have reduced it in the day of Ivan IV; however, Anikita wanted it to be strong, dangerous as it was, wielded by a madman. A weak Muscovy could not get back his seizure of the lands toward midnight. Yet establishment of a sovereign Stroganoff realm was the only thing no Muscovite, mad or sane, could possibly tolerate. . . .

Anikita walked the tightrope and, studious as he was, he devoted no less time to political contemplation than he gave to business.

He did not purchase the small salt claims for business reasons exclusively. These operators had had eyes and ears only for their petty sales. But they lived near the estate and might watch goings-on at Sol-Wueshegodska. Anikita wanted no outsiders to witness his doings. He had visitors from Ugria. The erudite industrialist knew more about Ugrian history, and Novgorodian history at that, than almost all contemporary historians, and certainly the Ugrians themselves.

The Ugrians and their kin had been quite formidable in the day of Rurik and during the two centuries that followed. The Novgorodians did have some reason to speak of an "Iron Gate" even though, geographically and geologically, it did not exist. On a pass in the northern Urals, Novgorodian militant merchants, led by one Uljeb, had been thrown back by Ugrian hordes in 1032; and sixty years later the Syrjane road was built as a sally port from Northwestern Siberia into the Russian plains. Later Novgorod gained the upper hand and imposed a tribute upon the Ugrians, and eventually switched from tribute collection to trade. When Anikita invited Ugrian and Samojed dignitaries to Sol-Wueshegodska, he explored the possibility of having the fur hunters stage a massacre of Muscovite tribute collectors, which would result in another punitive expedition. He would go to Muscovy and offer to make the expedition really pay. He might be appointed administrator, governor, general-tenant of Ugria, Obdoria—as a first step to total rule.

But the Ugrians, Obdorians, and Samojeds who came to the forbidding mansion did not understand His Highness's political hints. They seemed to think that furs were the most relevant objects in the world. Sables would bring up to fifty rubles apiece on Dutch markets, and you could get them three to five for one ruble from the hunters; Anikita already sent more pelts to Holland than he delivered to Muscovy, but the imperialistic merchant aimed at more important goals than sable sales.

Anikita questioned his visitors about Mangansee. They had heard of such a country, but they had never been there, nor had they ever met anybody from Mangansee. In fact the people who talked about the land were foreigners, and they believed that Mangansee was extremely rich in furs and metals.

Anikita did not believe that Mangansee actually existed. Neither Novgorod nor China could have failed to explore an extremely rich territory, and Yeliu would have told Temudshin about it too. He would not send his own people to look for Mangansee, but the will-o'-the-wisp of an Ophir toward midnight could delude a greedy Muscovite. Anikita did at first not mention Mangansee in Muscovy, and when Muscovite traders and collectors on their trips to Ugria stopped at Sol-Wueshegodska, he was satisfied to note that they ignored the Ophir toward midnight.

There were other territories beyond the Urals, farther to the south, that could become the lever to lift the Stroganoffs into sovereign power.

Ettiger (Jediger) Khan, who resided in Isker, and kept calling his place so after the Muscovites named it "Sibir," considered himself ruler of all scattered Mongolian tribes, a loyal vassal of the Gossudar, and a faithful correlate of the house of Stroganoff. He paid his tribute, wooed collectors, had wined and dined the members of the Muscovite mission to China, and traded with the agents of Sol-Wueshegodska. Ettiger accepted the state of affairs as not all too prosperous but reasonably secure; he might sigh about arbitrary raises of dues, coercive collectors, and Stroganoff's stinginess, but he was satisfied that, as long as Muscovy was well disposed toward him, no rival would attack his realm. He asked collectors questions about his liege lord, and his tastes; and, on learning that the fourth Ivan had a strange passion for squirrel furs, he sent a delegation to Muscovy to present the ruler with 1000 choice squirrel pelts, plus 1000 sables as a token of friendship.

Anikita was present when Ettiger's delegates prostrated themselves. He whispered in the Tsar's ear that the gift was a pittance, and, after hesitating briefly, Ivan told the Siberians that, in order to be warm, friendship had to be lined solidly. This was the first joke Ivan had ever made, and he was immensely proud of it. They hastened to promise that more furs including dark sables would be delivered. Ivan said he wanted them black; the delegates protested that they would be nearly black. Ivan wanted 1000 sables and 1000 squirrels every year; the delegates pledged themselves to that quantity, wondering how much they would have to deliver in order to have 1000 of each kind reach Ivan's coffers. Ivan was highly satisfied with the audience, in which he shone as a wit; if it were not for the outrageous rascality of his boyars, he thought, he would be a jovial, mirthful man altogether. He was not yet twenty when the audience took place, and he would live to be fifty-four, but he never made another joke.

CHAPTER TWENTY-SEVEN The delegates from Sibir-Isker had hardly left when Ivan IV informed his courtiers that, henceforth, he was Commander of all Siberia.

Commander was a strangely unpretentious title for a monarch who had styled himself Tsar-Caesar at the age of seventeen. But Ivan had already a collection of exalted appellations, he liked diversity, and if Anikita had suggested "Commander," his reasons for doing so were known only to himself.

The Tsar, Gossudar, Prince, and Commander, was commonly called Ivan Grozny—Ivan the Formidable. He liked the surname, and he might not have minded that foreigners later would translate it to mean "The Terrible." Ivan wanted to spread terror; he wanted other people to dread him no less than he dreaded almost everything and everybody. He was afraid of darkness, for darkness was the cloak of murder; he feared bright light, for it exposed him to hostile assault; he was frightened by food and drink, for it was the carrier of poison; he dreaded bigness, for it was strong, and smallness because it was elusive. He was terror-stricken when alone, and panicky when guarded—for guards were armed, and arms were tools of murder. He felt surrounded by murder in all species, animated and inanimated. Murder could be prevented by murder only; he had to kill in order not to be killed; and the more he killed, the more he feared that he could not survive for long. He was afraid of pain; and yet he was beset by a maniacal urge to inflict pain so that he could watch what frightened him. And he was afraid of the Lord, who might send him to the tortures of purgatory. Nowhere could he relax, nowhere could he find love, which he violently craved.

He had been afraid ever since he ascended the throne: a three-year-old boy whom the heavy headgear caused agonies, and who felt vertigo at the thought of being thrown from his high seat. The seat seemed to rock throughout the somber coronation ceremony.

He was surrounded by grave-faced, solemn boyars who kept him like a captive idol; they whispered to him to beware of evil people who might kill him. "Kill" became the leitmotiv of his days and nights, suspicion and fear his earliest impulses.

His keepers plotted against each other. Every boyar, and every boyar's wife, wanted to become the boy Gossudar's most trusted mentor and make him suspicious of everybody else. Ivan feared and hated them all, frantically, desperately, irreconcilably. And Ivan, who, at the age of three, had been taught to abuse domestics, saw in his servants the executors of the hatred that seemed to close in on him from all sides.

The idea that the servants are a master's most intimate foes was his first doctrine. The doctrine inspired his first administrative reform. Posthumous apologists presented Ivan's "land reform" as a somewhat amateurish and immature attempt at improving the status of rural serfs; and of late the Bolsheviks have granted the most evil of all tsars a niche in their hall of fame because allegedly he championed the cause of the landless peasants. The Bolsheviks realize well enough that summary damnation of the Formidable might reflect upon their own heroes whose methods of dealing with undesirables are somewhat similar. In fact Ivan did not propose to advance the cause of landless peasants, and the only status he was anxious to improve was his own. He hoped that by organizing rural domestics into an estate, the Dvorjane, and by having that estate establish the Land Council, the Ssemsky Sobor, to advise him on agrarian affairs, he could secure a workable pattern for the destruction of the boyars.

However, the Ssemsky Sobor was a disappointment. Its members conceived no ideas that would satisfy Ivan, and, worse even, they began to feel solidarity with the aristocrats after the reform had turned them from obscure mushiks into His Majesty's counselors. Whenever the Tsar demanded strong measures, they timidly suggested petty chicaneries and, cringing and grimacing as reverently but even less gracefully than the boyars themselves, they implored the Tsar to let his wisdom guide them on the path of duty. After sixteen years of sterile sessions the Ssemsky Sobor received a bill drafted by Ivan. It stipulated that part of the Russian Empire be set aside as "detached land," *apritchina,* the Tsar's personal domain, on which only persons approved by the ruler could settle.

The counselors rubber-stamped the bill, and Ivan colonized the detached land with his best-tried henchmen and their families, in an effort to create a refuge for himself, where he could stay, protected by his faithful, when every other abode would be dangerous. But he never went to live there. He did not trust his henchmen. They too might turn against him, and they would be even more dangerous than less thoroughly trained murderers would be. The Ssemsky Sobor survived the Tsar, and after Ivan's death turned into a redoubtable institution. Freed from the terror of Ivan's presence, the counselors grew bold, and, in a brief period of near-chaos, became tsar-makers—the strongest organized power in Russia. But not even in those days did the Ssemsky Sobor consider progressive rural reform. The Land Council stagnated after the establishment of the Romanov dynasty, and passed out of existence in 1682.

Ivan felt forsaken by the unimaginative and perfidious rural servants, but he still had recourse to the army and the Church in his maniacal struggle against the boyar archenemy.

However, the army was officered by boyars of Russian and Mongolian ancestry. To the Tsar the Mongolian boyars were an untrustworthy lot, the Russian boyars could have but one goal—regicide—and the soldiers were a dull mob, uniformed rural servants whom not even hatred of their master would stir into purposeful action against regicide. Ivan would have wanted to disband the army altogether, but he needed an armed force to defend him against domestic murderers and hostile neighbors. Ivan could not escape the vicious circle. . . .

He purged the officers' corps with sweeping ruthlessness and utter disregard of efficiency; he had hundreds of officers killed, and was a thousandfold frightened at the thought of vengeance. He had new soldiers recruited: roving adventurers, resentful convicts, violent city scum, and jobless mercenaries without inhibitions. He wanted them to hate the privileged, the accursed boyars. Adventurers and mercenaries obtained commissions; they were not very good officers, but staunch tools of violence. Ivan had a bodyguard selected from among the soldiers; only the finest marksmen were eligible. *Strjelzi* (marksmen), the guards were called.

Strjelzi were quartered in all Russian cities, but the bulk of the marksmen was stationed in the city of Moscow. A city district was assigned to the Strjelzi; they received commercial privileges usually withheld from civilian applicants; they were encouraged to exploit the population of their district, to plague the burghers, and act as the Tsar's terrorists, so that no friendship should develop between the never quite trusted soldiers, and the always distrusted citizenry. The Strjelzi scorned other people, and were thoroughly hated in return. They never turned against Ivan, and their organization, too, survived the Formidable and kept growing to upward of 50,000. Only some seventy years after his passing did the marksmen show signs of restiveness, and another forty-five years later they rebelled against Peter the Great, who disbanded the Strjelzi, and staged mass executions which would have enthused Ivan.

The purged army was still strong enough to conquer Kazan in 1552. The city had offered voluntary incorporation into Ivan's realm, but the Tsar did not believe in non-violent incorporations. It seized Astrakhan in 1557, and Perm in the following year. However, Ivan never quite trusted the Russian Army, and it almost gave him a grim satisfaction when his views were catastrophically borne out later when the Crimean Mongols descended upon his capital.

The army never alleviated Ivan's fears.

The Church was God's, and he, Ivan, was the head of the Church. He considered himself God's partner; but God did not seem to care for him, nor to recognize his ecclesiastic distinction. The clergymen were Ivan's servants, grudging, servile creatures. He could kill bishops and abbots. He could replace the higher by lesser clerics, but they too would be perfidious. The clergy, the Tsar reasoned, knew a way to God. He was a sinner, but the clerics were duty-bound to show him the path to the Lord's forgiveness; once God had forgiven him, he would no longer depend upon the priests. The priests of the court, who had taught him the Scriptures and whose solemn lingo he could never quite understand, were no comfort. They apparently withheld some basic truth. The truth should be best known to augurs, who lived in the seclusion of monasteries.

At the age of sixteen Ivan began to make pilgrimages to remote monasteries, where he frightened abbots and monks by requesting that they perform especially severe rites so that he could watch the effect. Asceticism, even extreme, was no fitting exhibit; Ivan wanted something spectacular: flagellation, self-mutilation, rough rides on wild mules through crowds assembled for the purpose. And because spilled blood did not cry out his salvation, Ivan raged, swore, and killed.

On his first pilgrimage as a tsar he had a village destroyed and the peasants tortured because the sight of huts and people irritated him. Three men in his attendance who voiced cautious objections were beheaded on the spot, and a fourth who muttered something the Tsar could not understand had his tongue torn out. And while this was being done, delegates from Pskov delivered a message of complaint against the local governor. Ivan had their hair singed and their bared bodies scalded with boiling wine. . . .

And he felt forsaken by the Lord.

At the age of twenty-one Ivan had the most reputable clerics summoned to his court. He appeared before the assembly, and tearfully confessed sins of his youth: lewd thoughts, gluttony, unchastity. . . . He did not confess murder. To him murders were no sin, for he killed only in self-defense.

The assembly granted subservient absolution, and hailed Ivan's subsequent pledge as exalted penance: the Tsar promised to rule his realm with justice and mercy, and to see that past mistakes, all owing to boyar malice, would not occur again.

But the Tsar's fears did not vanish, and fears were indications of the Lord's persistent discontent.

A few months after his confession Ivan called a council of prelates. He presented one hundred written questions on how to right prevalent injustice, and asked the prelates to answer them in straight, unequivocal fashion. The questions were couched in diffuse language and did not refer to the deplorable fact that the Tsar had broken his previous pledge. Fretting prelates produced wordy, involved theses, which Ivan's legal counsel's edited into confusing decrees.

And still Ivan remained a fear-ridden ruler whom the Lord refused to bless. Prelates, apparently, were no better than boyars. The Tsar appointed a humble monk as special adviser on church matters. The monk did not visibly improve his sovereign's standing with God. To Ivan he was a traitor; all clergy, secular and regular, were conspirators who mispresented the thoughts and actions of their overlord to the Lord. The people should help their tsar and beseech God with prayers to relieve their sovereign from the oppression of fear. He would recompense the people with untold benefaction.

But even if the crowds could not read Ivan's tortured mind, it was their duty to love their tsar as the father of the nation.

After the domestics, the soldiers, and the clerics the nondescript masses were derelict of their filial duties.

They did not even seem to trust his noble intentions. Ivan had stool pigeons mingle with crowds and report on overheard conversations. The stool pigeons said that the people did not believe that knavish boyars were the sole cause of wars, poverty, and other vexations; that the faithful did not consider mass murders of clergymen devout purges; and that burghers refused to accept the Strjelzi's outrages as legitimate actions of national defense. And, as for the Tsar, his subjects contended that he was a genius only at inventing more frightful methods of execution. Nobody seemed to pity Ivan; nobody grieved over the Formidable's own grievances. This could be but the effect of wicked propaganda, the boyars' conspiracy. Ivan would give the misguided people a period of grace, a last chance to reform. But he issued no proclamation: fathers do not sue for filial love. The people did not know they were on parole.

Throughout the period of grace the terror kept raging. On his fortieth birthday Ivan decided that the time of leniency had passed.

He would make an example of the disaffected populace. He would strike at the centers of unappreciativeness. Novgorod was a "natural," and so was Pskov, and there were more wicked cities. Up to 15,000 were killed every day: flogged to death, roasted over slow fires, thrown to trained bears. Friends and relatives of victims were forced to attend the massacre; many saw their tsar and the Crown Prince, rigid on horseback, preside over the horror. Ivan gave his son an object lesson in filial duties. The Tsar was the head of a family of his own, a monstrous husband, a destructive father.

Churches went up in smoke. Villages were flattened, monasteries stripped of their properties, including images of the saints.

Agents arranged "spontaneous" homages, pledges of love and allegiance by agonized remnants of decimated populations. The wave of mass murder abated. Ivan was proud of his generous moderation, and yet more scared than ever. He appointed an investigation commission to go to the roots of the conspiracy. The Oprichnina sentenced boyars, clergymen, burghers, and peasants to the rack, but the demons of Ivan's fears were not allayed. He ordered the Oprichnina to investigate its own members; the Oprichnina pressed charges against 300 of them. In the torture chamber all confessed to treason and conspiracy. Ivan had a vision of greatness and mercy: he would arrange for the most gruesome execution in history, but would pardon the culprits in the last minute. Yet an annoying personal letter he received from an exalted lady on the crucial day made him abandon the noble resolve. After the sordid spectacle was over, and the remains of the victims had been fed to the stray dogs of Moscow, eighty wives, and an even greater number of daughters of the executed men, had to submit to the executioners. The Tsar also claimed his share: he assaulted the widow of Prince Ivan Viskovaty, and ordered the Crown Prince to rape the Princess's unconscious daughter.

Moscow's main square had been almost deserted when the execution started; then the Strjelzi had rounded up several thousand people to hail the Tsar, but the crowd shuddered and remained silent with the exception of one emaciated, naked man who shrieked abuse. The Strjelzi tied and flogged him, and left him numb with pain, but alive.

Ivan did not leave his chamber in the Kremlin for several days after the execution of the three hundred. His fears were focused on one particular person, a lowly preacher who, as the clerics insisted, was not even ordained; a jabbering, ragged creature whom the people called Simple Vassilj. The people listened to Vassilj; he was ubiquitous, but the Tsar's guards pretended that he was elusive.

Simple Vassilj was preaching on Red Square, just outside the Kremlin. He addressed the walls, as if they were Ivan. The day before the great execution Ivan had listened to an address from behind a closed door: "If thou could silence all human voices," he heard, "the stones would cry out against thee, Ivashka. Thou art feeding on men's flesh and blood. God's anger follows thee; and for every torment thou inflicts upon innocent men on earth, thou shalt suffer ten torments in hell. . . ."

There were no guards around when Ivan yelled for the Strjelzi. They seemed to be hiding before Simple Vassilj. At last Oprichnina agents arrived. The Tsar ordered that the preacher be brought before him, unharmed. He wanted to persuade Vassilj that "Ivashka" was a righteous man, an innocent victim of conspiracy, he wanted to solicit the preacher's blessings.

The Oprichnina agents reported to have searched the whole city without having found a trace of Simple Vassilj. Neither the Tsar nor the Strjelzi who had beaten the naked emaciated man realized that he had been Simple Vassilj . . . and that the abuse he had shrieked was a prophecy of disaster about to strike.

Nobody knows the time and circumstances of the death of Simple Vassilj. Ivan evidently never met him again. But the Formidable Tsar probably regarded the ragged preacher as one of the three perfectly righteous men he knew: the others being himself and—Anikita Stroganoff.

Ivan called the head of the Stroganoff family by his first name; he told him of his personal tribulations, except that of fear. He spoke to the much older man in terms of emotional admiration, and Anikita replied with comforting dignity, and yet with a tinge of submissiveness that convinced the Tsar that his friend was the incarnation of unquestioning devotion.

Ivan would have been pleased to make Anikita a metropolitan, or general, or, better even, general inquisitor of affairs of church, army, and government, but the aging man had a strange faculty of keeping the Tsar from making extravagant suggestions, and besides, he was already extremely busy on Ivan's behalf in another field.

Trade with the West was almost dead; the Hansa shunned Russian markets, but Russia was far from self-supporting. Ivan swore that this too was the boyars' fault, that he would reverse trade policies. But the Tsar was at a loss how to encourage foreign commercial relations. He wanted imported luxuries for himself, he needed equipment for his armies, there were no manufactured goods available in his realm: his subjects, he raged, had only one skill, that of treachery; otherwise they were unhandy, incapable of producing the most primitive objects. The boyars did not want their serfs to learn anything useful.

Anikita supplied superb wines and palate-tickling delicacies for the Tsar's table; he delivered quantities of luscious eider downs, so that insomnia-ridden Ivan might, at least, rest comfortably on his couch; and he always had batches of furs ready to supplement the furriery gathered by collectors in Siberia. Ivan needed many furs; the sight of piles of pelts soothened him. And so few furs apparently came from the land whose commander he was. He did not have to bother about payment of goods from Sol-Wueshegodska. Whenever his treasury was drained, Anikita forgot to render bills.

Anikita found a solution to the manufacturing problem. He brought German craftsmen to Russia and financed the establishment of their shops in the Tsar's cities. The Germans could produce everything Ivan and his subjects needed. Most of all, the Tsar appreciated the gunsmiths; Russian foundries had not been capable of turning out a falconet. The foreign master craftsmen cast a cannon of almost two yards' caliber, adorned with wondrous figures; the admiring Tsar was a little scared by the bigness of his cannon. He had it carefully conserved and never learned that the monster was a showpiece that could not be fired. But the Germans cast other guns that could fire; they knew how to make muskets, and even how to build ships, solid river craft, armed and stronger than anything river pirates could muster. And, last but not least, those Germans were *niemezy,* mute ones, who could not converse with the Russians. Mute men could not plot.

Ivan had once made an attempt at independent mercantile action; in 1553 an Englishman came to Moscow and, received in special audience, told the Tsar that he was exploring possibilities of trade or barter with Russia. Ivan said that he would give every encouragement to trade or barter, and that he would deal with the matter on the highest plane—sovereign to sovereign. A correspondence with King Edward VI, and later with Queen Elizabeth Tudor, ensued, but did not produce commercial advantages. The Tsar was embarrassed and turned to Anikita for advice, who gave a few hints of how to make the venture more remunerative. Ivan admired them as another evidence of Anikita's superb capacity of improvisation.

However, his trade policy toward England did not consistently follow the course outlined by the superb improviser. English traders were granted privileges, with few sizable concessions given in return. The Tsar had another objective in mind: He was weary of being married to unworthy Russian women, one after another. Only the Queen of England would be a spouse worthy of the Tsar. Ivan wooed Elizabeth by trade concession, in addition to more romantic courting. He even considered soliciting Anikita's advice on that matter, but could not bring himself to talk about it, and later blamed himself for not having opened his heart to the righteous sage. With Anikita's help he would have won the shy Queen's love, and she would not have written the letter that infuriated him on the day before the Oprichnina executions. It had been a reply to a note in which Ivan, in an effort to win Elizabeth's affectionate sympathy, told her of treacherous plots against his life. Instead of confessing her affections or mentioning matrimony the Queen assured him of free ingress and egress to and from England, should he be in danger of losing his throne, and she promised to appoint a fitting place where he could stay at his own expense. This was an affront that could not even properly be redeemed by expropriating the English-owned Russian Trade Company. . . .

Anikita knew all about Ivan's dealings with England, and he was too cautious to get himself involved in the affair. After the English the Dutch had come to Russia to have a look at business opportunities. The traders from Holland were referred to the house of Stroganoff. Anikita's agents met Dutch skippers on the Dvina estuary, and eventually channeled their efforts into an attempt at discovering a sea route to China via the Arctic Ocean. English mariners, jealous of their Dutch rivals, joined in the unavailing attempts. The Stroganoffs did not want foreigners to explore land routes to Siberia; they even offered the foreigners some bargains in furs to keep them from being all too anxious to get to the sources of furriery.

The time was getting ripe for the Stroganoffs' master stroke.

A new force turned up in Siberia. Ettiger Khan sent a message of distress to Ivan, imploring him to assist him against an impostor. The Redoubtable did not reply. Ettiger's friendship had not been sufficiently well lined, and whoever the impostor may be, he would have to pay Iasak.

The impostor's name was Kutchum, and he styled himself Khan. He was a Mohammedan who presented a genealogical tree indicating his descendancy from Djenghis Khan and claimed to have the sacred mission to Islamize the peoples of Siberia. Ettiger insisted that Kutchum was an adventurer from Bokhara; later other sources indicated that the alleged descendant of Temudshin was in fact a dark-skinned Cossack.

Anikita praised Ivan's attitude. Ettiger had never been an asset, he said, and the struggle between the rival khans may have been decided before the message had arrived in Moscow. There was no order in Siberia; the Tsar did not receive his due. Anikita talked only about Siberia; at Ivan's behest he always deplored the disorderly state of Siberian affairs and its averse effects upon the realm. This time, he added cryptically, upheavals in Siberia were particularly unfortunate under the circumstances. The Tsar thought that circumstances referred to trade with England, and asked no further questions.

Ivan, who would usually scent conspiracy even behind adverse changes of weather, did not seem to suspect that Kutchum's venture had the support of a strange personality whose aims in Siberia might be sinister. The new Khan had a small army of horsemen trained in traditional Mongolian tactics; the men had no modern equipment, but, even so, recruiting and training such a force involved substantial expense, and nothing indicated that Kutchum had been a man of substance.

Soon Iasak collectors reported that at the time Ivan and Anikita had talked the battle between Ettiger and Kutchum had already been decided, Ettiger's pathetic bands were routed, and the Khan and all his male relatives put to death by the victor, who was now residing at Sibir. The Tsar could but admire the intuition of his friend, who saw even the invisible. He wished he could have kept him at his court, but Anikita had left in an unusual hurry, claiming fatigue. He had looked very old, and the Tsar worried at the thought of losing him.

He sent a note to Kutchum, reminding him that, as successor to Ettiger, he had inherited the obligation to pay an annual 1000 sable and 1000 squirrel furs. Civilities due to a sovereign ruler were carefully omitted.

Kutchum replied in kind. Instead of sending a distinguished ambassador with a load of good-will presents, he sent a courier with a message that should have infuriated the irascible Tsar: "This is from the independent Kutchum Tsar to the Grand Duke, the White Tsar. Allah is Great! Until this day, I have sent thee no note, for I was waging war against my enemy. Now, that I have prevailed, I shall make peace with those who desire peace, but I shall make war upon him who wants war. Let us make peace. Only if thou desirest peace, shall I recognize thee as my brother. I expect the messenger to receive a reply."

Allah's greatness was an insult to the head of the Russian Church; the assumption of the title of tsar by a mere khan was impudence, and the message did not even mention the tribute.

But Ivan was unpredictable, and he was at a loss how to treat the incredible Kutchum in the absence of Anikita. From Sol-Wueshegodska came indications that the friend was in need of a prolonged rest.

Kutchum received no reply, and he too seemed bewildered. He did not repeat his offer for peace, and was cautious not to molest a Russian party which lingered around Sibir-Isker, sketching maps.

The new Khan did not pay the tribute when the collectors came to his residence, but he treated the Russians with studied politeness. The Khan's brother and lieutenant, Mehmet Kul, was disgusted at Kutchum's spinelessness.

Mehmet Kul wanted a bold policy, and he was a better soldier than "independent Kutchum Tsar."

The military reins passed into Mehmet Kul's hands. He led the horsemen through Obdoria to the land of the Samojeds. The frightened cannibals described him as a giant who could uproot trees with his bare hands; they told of merciless killings and arsoning committed by the invaders. Far up north the cavalry ran into strongholds which defied their crude equipment, and were manned by men who looked like Russians. Mehmet Kul retreated, but not without informing the Samojeds that henceforth all tribute would have to be paid to Isker. The Samojeds were not sure about the location of Isker, but promised to comply. For quite some time they had paid exclusively to the people of Sol-Wueshegodska, who also collected in the Tsar's name, and who had established the strongholds.

Stroganoff's men from Samojed territory raced to headquarters to report the invasion and the imposition of tribute. They also told of having encountered a roving Englishman who talked to Samojeds through an interpreter.

The Englishman might learn that all tribute had gone to the Stroganoffs, that Stroganoff embezzled Crown property. Mehmet Kul might purchase equipment with funds obtained from Samojed tributes; he might return and dislodge Stroganoff garrisons. Kutchum, emboldened by his brother's success, might snatch the fur business from Sol-Wueshegodska.

The Khan might build a Siberian empire of his own, right under the eyes of the "Commander of Siberia," whose armed forces were still engaged in mopping-up operations around Perm, and who had no income from Siberia to lose.

On April 1, 1558, coaches and carts from Sol-Wueshegodska rambled into Moscow. Anikita rode in the most spacious coach, a smaller one carried his two eldest sons, who were followed by medics, menservants, and a long line of baggage wagons. Never before had the Stroganoffs come to the city with such pomp and cargo.

The three Stroganoffs called on prelates, ministers, generals, and other dignitaries, formally, as if they were making inaugural visits, and they brought presents that were worth fortunes.

On April 2 the family went to the Kremlin on foot. Old Anikita, still tall and erect, white-bearded, silver-haired, looked like a patriarch; his sons, walking at a respectful distance behind their father, had a bearing of dignity and civic virtue.

The strange procession startled Ivan; he was scared, so scared, in fact, that he believed to see Anikita's ghost, appearing to warn him of conspiracy. It took Ivan some time to satisfy himself that this was, in fact, the real Anikita.

But it was a changed Anikita—no longer the man who looked into the future as if it were an open book, the Tsar's guide on the road onward, through the underbrush of lurking treason. Anikita was a weary man who had come to take leave.

Anikita explained that he had reached the age of seventy, that his days were numbered, that he wanted to spend the little time left to him in pious contemplation. However, the Stroganoffs, aware of the untold benefits received from their lords, would always devote themselves to the service of their benefactors. Here were Anikita's eldest sons, at Ivan's beck and call, the heirs of Stroganoff loyalty. Loyalty was the most precious bequest Anikita could bestow upon his sons.

Ivan broke into loud sobs and his tears flowed freely as he ordered that all dignitaries be summoned to witness the finest proof of loyalty ever given to the unselfish ruler of an ungrateful land.

Anikita had seen the Tsar cry before. Ivan wept rather easily, usually with self-pity. Neither were the courtiers moved by their sovereign's twitching cheeks and tears streaming into his beard.

The old man resumed his address. He also had a bequest to make to his beloved sovereign. More than fifty years of his life had been devoted to investigations, explorations, and daring investments that absorbed a great part of his earnings, to contribute to the greater glory of grand dukes and a tsar. These noble princes, he recited as if reading a script, should no longer be impeded by trivial financial worries from carrying out their exalted designs. God had blessed his venture; at the threshold of the grave he could reveal his findings to Ivan, the anointed of the Lord. Far beyond the Ural Mountains, beyond the lands of Ugria, Obdoria, and Condinia, high up on the shores of the icy ocean, hidden by storms, darkness, and clouds, flanked by mighty rivers, was a land of stocky, short-nosed cannibals, who were the best archers and trappers in the world. The country swarmed with sables, the largest of which was the legendary king of fur animals, as big as a horse. This country was Mangansee, also called "Manganseeya" by people who usually had not been there, because they did not dare penetrate into the darkness and the storms. The people of Mangansee had more furs than could be counted, and there were also gold mines up in Mangansee. Possession of Mangansee would give its owner the greatest wealth of the world. The barbaric capital of Mangansee was resplendent with treasures. Mangansee was Anikita's farewell present to his tsar.

There would always be men in Sol-Wueshegodska to serve as the Tsar's humble organs in the administration of all Siberian lands, Anikita went on, so that peace be kept and safe communications maintained between the Tsar's new treasure chest and his capital. Already Stroganoff laborers were building a trafficable road to Mangansee, and Anikita's sons would continue where he was now leaving off. They would be Ivan's treasure diggers.

Ivan had stopped crying. He radiated with joy and pride. Courtiers could not help worrying that the delight might explode in an outburst of violence. Ivan's face suddenly turned a bluish red; he roared that only the Stroganoffs were honest people, and that all his so-called dignitaries were not only scoundrels, traitors, but also ignoramuses; none of them had ever found out the truth about Mangansee, while his friend Anikita had known it for fifty years. But he would not allow them to cheat and trick him out of his friend's legacy by their mismanagement of the affairs of his new domain.

"My new domain . . ." Ivan roared for a scribe, and had it recorded that he was now also Commander of Condinia, and lord over all the northern coasts. These titles should never be omitted in the correspondence with England. The thought of England diverted his mind from violence.

The courtiers meantime complimented Anikita, and when the lord of all the northern coasts, his voice skipping, presented Anikita as a shining example of unselfishness, they all bowed, approved, and admired.

There remained the question of how to manage Anikita's legacy. The patriarch asserted that Ivan's wisdom would certainly guide him in ruling his new domain, but as a small help, he had permitted himself to draft a few suggestions.

The suggestions turned out to be a complete charter, a document unique in Russian history. The Tsar's was not a judicial mind, but the fact that Anikita had devoted so much labor to his ruler's interests made him weep again, and everybody duly joined in his emotions.

It was a perfect show. Anikita played his part admirably, from his entry into Moscow to the signature of the charter, which took place on April 4, 1558. There were few changes of the original draft except for a preamble added at Ivan's request.

"In evil times, boyars and merchants made loans to their rulers, but they requested securities, furs and jewels, and pledges of fiscal income, and they charged high rates of interests. But the Stroganoffs never wanted anything for themselves."

The charter itself granted Grigory Stroganoff, the eldest son, all uncultivated land along the Kama River and its tributaries; it entitled him to build towns and fortresses, to maintain armed guards, to manufacture weapons, and use them as he deemed fit. He reserved a monopoly of trade with Siberia, exclusive mining privileges, and the sole right to maintain and operate communications with, and inside, Siberia. He was entitled to levy tributes within his sphere of operations to cover expenses. Tributes to Muscovy were not mentioned. Grigory Stroganoff was exempt from taxes and statutory obligations for the twenty-year duration of the charter, and was entitled to continue explorations into territories in which they would enjoy similar privileges.

The only restrictions imposed upon the holder of the charter concerned the kind of people permitted to settle in the domain: thieves, vagabonds, runaway slaves, draft evaders, deserters, and sons of boyars derelict of duty in their own land were barred.

For onescore years the Stroganoffs were the highest, if not the sole, authority in Siberia, and through the concessions on the Kama River even on the strategic approaches to Siberia; they had twenty years to turn the land into their sovereign realm. Their domain, of course, included Mangansee. Ivan overlooked that the charter omitted Mangansee, or perhaps he trusted that his friend's sons would not keep the treasures of Mangansee for themselves. The Stroganoffs did not intend to keep these treasures, for there were no such treasures; they knew that there was no Ophir of the northern coasts; there was just barren tundra.

Never before had an empire been acquired at so low a price.

Anikita lived on for eight years after the grant of the charter. His dying hours were troubled by the thought that the supreme prize was gliding from his grip—a glittering phantom.

Siberia was not yet the Stroganoffs' possession, and not even all stipulations of the charter had been put into effect.

CHAPTER TWENTY-EIGHT In the last years of his life Anikita spent much of his time in the main hall of the mansion of Sol-Wueshegodska, sitting in a massive, thronelike chair, deep in thought. He did not want more than two or three pine torches to be lighted in the hours of darkness, and when the glaring rays of a late winter sun outside, reflected by myriads of tiny ice crystals, turned the landscape into a blazing orgy of brightness, little light penetrated into the huge, somber room, whose walls seemed to fade into vacillating obscurity. The old man rarely rose to look out of the tiny windows at the splendor of undulating forests yonder. Nature's grandeur meant nothing to Anikita. To him forests were just timber and receptacles of fur animals; rivers were conveyors of merchandise and men. Men were tools, not always usable, and hardly ever worth much. Anikita had more marketable commodities than any other man, and the charter, crowning achievement of a triumphant life, gave him a thousand times more, and yet, as he stared into the semi-darkness, the aged Stroganoff may have thought, in a variation of what an aging Temudshin had told Yeliu: "I don't know if I have always done correctly. . . ."

And if Anikita, in contrast to Temudshin, did care for the opinion of men, he had no Yeliu to whom to confide his thoughts, and to receive inspiration in return.

Grigory was not as clever as his father. The heir to the Stroganoff domain was determined to assert his authority, but this authority did not rest on competence. Jakow, next in line, knew this and scoffed at his elder brother. But Jakow was no outstanding man either. Anikita attributed the shortcomings of his children to the mediocrity of their mother.

A brooding Anikita talked to Grigory only in curt terms, and in a tone that indicated doubts that his orders would be properly executed.

Grigory may have been instrumental in a capital blunder of the house of

Stroganoff. Or hadn't it been a Stroganoff blunder? Had it really been another unfathomable Siberian tide that swept Kutchum into the power he now wielded in areas which the charter awarded to Grigory? However, it is hard to believe that Ettiger lost his land and life to an impostor who had no outside support.

In fact Grigory had been to Siberia to look after the family business before Ettiger sent his message of distress to an unresponsive Ivan. Grigory had met people from Bokhara and Turkestan, and for some time a Stroganoff agent from Bokhara had been known to stay in Kutchum's camp. Grigory also had had dealings with Cossacks. If Kutchum was Grigory's choice to replace Ettiger, and to be the stirrup holder of sovereign Stroganoffs, this had been a blunder of incredible magnitude.

Kutchum recognized the authority of the Stroganoffs as little as he recognized that of the Tsar, but while he limited his challenge of the Crown to withholding a few batches of pelts, he dared the Stroganoffs by impudent raids against their holdings and chattels in Siberia, and even in outposts west of the Urals.

The Stroganoffs maintained an army, even though they were careful to call it guards and watchmen; they were not reluctant to recruit thieves, vagabonds, runaway slaves, and deserters from the Tsar's army, and to settle them wherever they pleased for training or garrison duty, but they had not enough men to wage war in Siberia for the defense of their Asiatic domain and its expansion into infinite vastness while simultaneously maintaining peace in their European territories against a surging wave of brigandage that engulfed many parts of Russia. The Cossacks were on the move, not as a synthetic nation, but as organized gangs who plundered the country. They gathered in hordes, several hundred, and occasionally even several thousand, strong; they built river flotillas and ambushed peaceful shipping. Instinct guided them toward rich loot, and nowhere could richer spoils be found than on Stroganoff estates, Stroganoff land and river transportation.

The Tsar had cannon-equipped river craft built in Stroganoff wharves and foundries, Ivan's men battled river pirates, captured their vessels, hanged captains and crews on deck, and let the ghost boats drift downstream as a warning to Cossacks settled near the mouths of the Don and Volga rivers. But the Tsar would also hire Cossack bands, have them fight against their own kin, and against whatever foreigners were on the warpath, and discharge them later—usually in running battles. Discharged Cossacks kept their equipment, most of it delivered by the house of Stroganoff, and went on raiding Stroganoff property.

Anikita had told Grigory to hire Cossacks and Grigory complied, but the Cossacks were a plague in garrisons, unreliable in battle, ready to run over, to fraternize with Kutchum's men, and to join them in looting and raping Siberians.

Sol-Wueshegodska enlisted fugitive Samojeds. The Siberians were reasonably good archers and knifemen, but an efficient sixteenth-century war required musketeers, and to train savage Siberians in musketry meant taking suicidal chances.

Grigory was a failure as a military man. But Anikita was weary, and could make no supreme effort to remedy the situation. Weariness forced him into inactivity, and inactivity extinguished him like a burned-out candle.

At their father's funeral Jakow derided Grigory for his incompetence. But Jakow could offer little more than derision. Cossacks kept raiding the estate, and Stroganoff forces east and west of the Ural divide could neither stop raiders nor regain territory lost to Kutchum and his arrogant brother.

To make things worse, a group of travelers from Moscow arrived at Sol-Wueshegodska; cartographers on their way to map the land of Condinia and the northern coasts for their commander, the Tsar, and to get a glance at Mangansee. Ivan now figured Mangansee as made of solid gold.

Mangansee, bait for a stupid Tsar, turned into a thorn in the Stroganoffs' side. It was not difficult, but rather expensive, to keep the Tsar's men in Sol-Wueshegodska, and have them draft imaginary maps at Stroganoff's headquarters. Grigory dispatched furs, wines, and eider downs to Ivan, labeled gifts from faithful Condinian subjects, but this added only to the expenses and did not advance the Stroganoffs' aims. Grigory suggested that they try to obtain the Tsar's military support; Jakow countered that the Tsar's troops, once established there, would stay in Siberia, and the charter, already half expired, would never be renewed.

In 1568 the arguing brothers visited the Kremlin. They carried gifts—on different wagons, and presented them separately, with many genuflections and invocations of the Scriptures, claims, and petitions too intricate for the Tsar's comprehension. All that Ivan realized was that Grigory and Jakow were at odds, and that they had trouble in Siberia. The charter of 1558 did not mention Jakow. Ivan decided that Jakow too should have a charter, and granted the second-born Stroganoff more land along the Tshussova River, enlarging the central family estate by five million acres, and he stipulated that the validity of both charters be prolonged indefinitely.

The brothers praised the Tsar's magnanimity and elaborated on their troubles with Cossacks and raiders. Ivan brushed it off. The Stroganoffs, he said, could build all the gunboats and cannon they wanted, which should enable them to hold their own. The Tsar's patience was wearing thin. He was sick of dealing with affairs of state while he had his mind set on matrimonial affairs. Elizabeth Tudor would surely consider him a fitting match if he were not married. Apparently she did not realize how little this status mattered in Russia. Nine years before Ivan's wife had died most conveniently, and his current wife would not stand in the way of his union with Elizabeth. He was making broad hints to English envoys, and accompanied hints by presents and trade concessions, and raged against those blockheads who did not seem to understand.

Two years went by after the Stroganoffs received the second charter; two years in which Stroganoff business was less lucrative than before and storm clouds gathered over Ivan's realm.

Crops failed, famine broke out, famine bred cannibalism, cannibalism was followed by plague.

War in the Baltic continued. Ivan was short of manpower. Famine and plague had claimed 300,000 victims, in addition to the hecatombs executed for not loving their Tsar.

And the Sultan of the Ottomans, ruler of the Turkish great power, styled himself protector of Islam and demanded that Kazan and Astrakhan be handed over to Mongolian Mohammedans, and that Ivan pay indemnities and tribute.

A fear-ridden Tsar replied with protestations of friendship and admiration for his Ottoman brother, who, however, did not care to acknowledge the message, but had a Crimean Mongolian puppet, Devlet Hirei Khan, equipped to attack Russia.

Devlet Hirei challenged Ivan to a duel to decide all pending issues. The Tsar admonished the Khan to be peaceful and reasonable.

In 1570 100,000 horsemen burst forth from the Crimean peninsula (Russian chroniclers refer to the Crimean Mongolians as Crimean Tatars); the Tatar hordes burst through a wavering screen of defense, and raced on toward the capital. Ivan left at once, claiming that his presence was required in the Baltic; and while the Tsar took cover in the headquarters of the northwestern armies, a small garrison remained in Moscow to defend the city to the last man, as Ivan had decreed. Ahead of the Tatars swept a wave of panicky fugitives, who brought to the capital stories of enemy ruthlessness, and of the spreading of plague. The Tatars closed in, the fugitives fled north; the tail end of their sordid column was still in sight when the Tatars stopped under the walls of the city. Devlet Hirei kept the bulk of his men outside the gates to keep them from contracting deadly diseases. Only incendiary squads entered the capital.

An English eyewitness relates: "The city burned down within six hours. Many thousand men, women, and children were burned or smothered to death by the holocaust, in dwellings, churches, monasteries, vaults, and cellars; few only found refuge within the walled castle of the Kremlin. The Moskwa River was clogged with people, who carried their property, and struggled, often in vain, to keep their heads above the water. Heat and smoke polluted the air. The garrison retreated to the Kremlin, the only area spared by the holocaust, and made no mien to fight."

Ivan sued for peace. He promised to accept the Sultan's every demand. The invaders evacuated Russia, with a booty of 100,000 Russian girls and women, who were in demand in Turkish harems.

But the Tsar hedged. He would not cede Kazan and Astrakhan, and he had no ready cash to pay indemnities; and all the time Ivan kept concentrating reserves drawn from the Baltic, south of the capital. The Sultan did not want to engage his own armies in the remote theater of war, but Devlet Hirei made another sortie in 1572. He came to within thirty-five miles of Moscow, where he met a Russian army under the command of Prince Michael Vorotinsky. The Russian soldiers, who believed that their commander was endowed with supernatural powers, fought better than ever before.

The Tatars were defeated. They continued to exist as a national group for another two centuries, but no longer constituted a threat to Russian security.

Vorotinsky was a boyar, and Ivan was afraid of him. Five years later the Tsar had the victor over the Tatars tried for sorcery in league with Satan, and roasted alive. . . .

The Tsar returned to his capital in a happy frame of mind. He rode through the ruins, past throngs of stunned survivors, and nodded approval. "This was God's punishment for my sins; the Khan was but an instrument of the Lord's wrath," he told his attendance. "The fire of the city has purged me of my offenses. I am absolved. But nobody else is absolved," he added maliciously.

Ivan received congratulatory presents from Sol-Wueshegodska; he looked the objects over with obvious satisfaction, but did not invite the brothers to Moscow, reconstruction of which was getting under way. He now had another adviser, a twenty-year-old man of petty Mongolian nobility, a handsome, powerfully built youth, whose name meant little to the dignitaries, and nothing to the people. The Godunovs had never played a noticeable part in Russian affairs, and it was difficult to see why Ivan appointed Boris Godunov to a position of trust and power unequaled in the court hierarchy.

The Tsar never explained his actions. The hierarchy had to accept the facts, and in the two years that followed the defeat of the Crimean Tatars, Boris Godunov wielded supreme authority in the realm. He transacted all state business with greater skill than could have been expected under the circumstances, and Ivan never interfered with his favorite. Boris Godunov called himself a loyal, humble servant of his imperial master, with no ambitions of his own. But the courtiers knew that young Boris was betrothed to Maria Skuratov, daughter of an assassin and debaucher who was Ivan's favorite; she may have been begotten by the Tsar. Boris's sister had married Ivan's second son. As a member of the ruling family, he would remain a power to be reckoned with, regardless of the vicious gambols of Ivan's mind.

The Tsar enjoyed two sabbatical years vacillating between sadistic debauchery and pious contemplation of renouncing the world and spending his remaining years in a monastery. Strong impulses were required to stir the Tsar's lasciviousness, and he had no patience with women who could not anticipate his desires. Prelates and abbots would have to guess Ivan's conceptions of penance and beatification, and tell him exactly what he could not have put into words, if they wanted to escape his wrath. The Tsar's virility and rueful reflections were enhanced by the spectacle of capital punishment; Ivan preferred the killing of men by angry bears even to roastings in supersized frying pans. The Stroganoffs kept supplying the Tsar with superbly ferocious bears.

Ivan had not seen the Stroganoff brothers for six years when they came to the capital in 1574 unannounced. Grigory and Jakow had a long talk with Boris Godunov, and then applied for an audience with the Tsar. The ruler was getting tired of both lewd and pious diversions and, for a change, resolved to govern Russia and to court the Queen of England. He received the callers from Sol-Wueshegodska with perfect graciousness.

The brothers found the forty-four-year-old Ivan greatly changed; his hair and luxuriant long beard were almost white; his regular but distinctly vulgar features were distorted by bluish veins and myriads of wrinkles; the obstinate eyes were bloodshot and tired. Ivan also thought that the younger Stroganoffs had considerably aged; then he remembered that they were about a score of years his seniors, and felt that they were too old to understand his problems, and that he was better off with Boris Godunov.

But he listened sympathetically to the worthy brothers' lamenting about Siberia's unruliness and the Cossacks' misdeeds. His victory over the Tatars (Ivan never thought of it as somebody else's achievement) had not benefited the men from Sol-Wueshegodska. In fact wars, plague, famine, and devastation had turned Southern Russia into a land of outlaws; homeless victims joined the hordes that threatened such opulent citizens as the Stroganoffs.

Ivan did not commit himself to assist the holders of two charters; but he would give them yet another one. This fantastic document entitled the Stroganoff family to annex Siberia in the name of the Tsar, with one fourth of the land to become Stroganoff private property. Only once had the Tsar mentioned, in passing, and with a glint of insanity in his bloodshot eyes, his city of Mangansee, from where he expected to get as much gold and fur as all his gunboats could carry. The brothers remembered their wild bears: they, too, might be thrown before the beasts. The Stroganoff empire had to be established before the madman's whims could destroy Grigory, Jakow, and their growing families. The common danger soothed old rivalries, but the reconciled brothers realized that they did not have the genius of their father, who would have known how to deal with the situation.

Ivan again forgot Mangansee; from Sol-Wueshegodska came sufficient valuables to keep him supplied, and he also kept toying with high-spirited reforms, by appointing outsiders to extreme power to give them an opportunity to work for the best of the nation.

Prince Federov, Ivan's equerry, became the first object of the Tsar's experiments. Once, in the presence of many nobles, the Tsar accused the aged Prince of treacherous dealings with Poland. "How could a man like myself, who stands with one foot in the grave, endanger his immortal soul by such an abominable crime?" Federov objected.

The gathering was numb with terror. Charges by the Tsar had to be accepted in silence as irrefutable truth. An incensed Ivan might have put to death, not only the offender, but all the witnesses. Yet the Tsar doffed his mantle and crown, seized the Prince's hand, and led him to the throne. "May a man mindful only of saving his soul rule Russia," he exclaimed. "I make you Tsar herewith." Federov crouched on the throne, cadaverous-looking and stunned. Ivan stepped back, grinned, and then performed a pompous act of homage, part ceremonial, part savage travesty. The audience, not certain which way the Formidable's weird thoughts would turn, bowed with fearful admiration, and, then again, rocked with shrill laughter. The act lasted for half an hour. Then Ivan roared: "I had the power to make you Tsar, and I have the power to crush you." He stabbed Federov's heart, and tore crown and mantle from the limp body.

And because he wanted his nobles to understand that he was not only a formidable but also an efficient ruler, he had the murdered Prince's family wiped out so that there would be no pretenders to Federov's succession.

Ivan's next guinea pig was a young Mongol, Ssain Bulat, whom Boris Godunov had brought to court. Ssain Bulat, whose name was Christianized into Simeon, was crowned by Ivan. For almost one year Tsar Simeon wore the crown on his trembling head, received petitions, and set the seal upon official documents. Sentences were passed in his name. He memorized diplomatic formulas and received foreign ambassadors, except the English envoy; Ivan still dealt with Elizabeth's representative. "I have seven crowns," the Formidable told the gentleman from London; "may he [Simeon] wear one; and I've still the key to the treasury." The travesty of Tsar Simeon had a happy ending, much to the surprise of courtiers and diplomats who expected Ivan's fertile mind to produce a ghoulish way of disposing of the young Mongol. Ivan simply told him to surrender the crown, and clear out. It was Boris Godunov's steadily growing power that shielded his conational.

In Sol-Wueshegodska the brothers, meantime, agreed to put Maxim, son of Jakow, in charge of the Stroganoff army that would conquer Siberia. The showy young Maxim recruited whatever outlaw or fugitive turned up at the estate, and in three years gathered almost 5000 desperadoes. Yet no number of individuals could make up for the lack of cadres and of experienced military men to handle the hordes. The Stroganoff bands were a nuisance and a financial burden. Only if Maxim were able to enlist a strong Cossack band could the rabble be merged into a fighting force.

One Ivan Kolzo, who called himself "Hetman," Supreme Commander, was overlord over the most formidable Cossack horde to plague Ivan's realm. He exerted absolute power over an estimated 7000 men, raided open cities only a few hundred miles away from the capital, and specialized in the capture of virgins, guaranteed untouched, for delivery to Oriental markets, where they commanded high prices. Kolzo also waylaid trade caravans; and in 1577 even laid violent hands upon Crown property, goods from Persia destined for Ivan's court. The goods were unpaid for, and obviously acquired through Stroganoff agents.

Maxim Stroganoff appealed to Kolzo to mend his ways and enlist in the Stroganoff guard as a respectable Christian soldier, and on fair terms. Ivan Kolzo scorned the appeal, but Ivan the Tsar, learning of the loss of his Persian luxuries, did not admonish the robber and did not offer enlistment. The Formidable dispatched some 10,000 men—some of them Cossacks, others Strjelzi, and also a number of regulars—to avenge the outrage. In a pitched battle on the Volga River, Kolzo's band was destroyed. Most of the men were killed in action, and prisoners, including Hetman Kolzo, were "violently racked and punished with death." The report on their punishment gave details of the racking, which satisfied the Tsar.

Five hundred forty Kolzo bandits survived, hidden in dense forests north of the battlefield. They had deserted their "hetman" on the eve of the battle because the Cossacks had no cannon and could not hope to resist Russian artillery.

The man who had told this to the 540, and who had led them into hiding, was Kolzo's chief of staff, the band's military scientist: Ermak Timofeitch.

Timofeitch stood for "son of Timofei." However, this was a fancy name, for the parentage of Ermak was not established. Unappreciative Cossacks used to say that he was the offspring of a witch and a toad. Cossacks were not usually handsome, but Ermak's ungainliness stunned even hardened observers; he was very big and his exuberant beard covered part of his grotesque features.

Ermak Timofeitch had been a river pirate on the Don, which made him eligible for hanging on some mast; he had served with the Tsar's regular army in the Baltic and deserted the army, which in turn should have netted him the frying pan. But he escaped the noose and the fire and joined Kolzo, telling him that he had been a captain in the Tsar's army. He had never risen beyond the rank of sergeant, but was a sound military man.

An ancient Cossack saying goes that a good Cossack had not only to be a staunch fighter, but that he also must be able to wiggle out of a tight spot. Ermak had gotten himself out of various tight spots, and his fellow deserters trusted that he would do it again.

Ermak knew of the Stroganoffs' offer to Ivan Kolzo; he led his band in the direction of Sol-Wueshegodska, hiding by day, marching by night, letting the men loot only what they needed most urgently, and insisting that other unlawful activities, even the virgin trade, be discontinued. It was getting cold when 540 ragged, underfed Cossacks reached the Stroganoff estate. Ermak tried to contact Maxim Stroganoff, but the young man kept him waiting until the band was almost frozen to death. Only after more than one month of misery did the commander of the Stroganoff army consent to assign camping grounds to the Cossacks, and some warm equipment. It took another month of waiting until Maxim permitted Ermak and his men to enlist. The chastened Cossacks pledged themselves to reform, to be good Christians, and to forgo banditry. Their camp was transferred from the fringe of the domain to a clearing of the woods in its center. They were provided with well-lined coats and ample food and drink, and equipped with muskets from Stroganoff arsenals.

Hardly were the Cossacks restored to vigor when they turned again into a boisterous, blackmailing lot, a threat to the bulging storehouses, and a plague to loyal Stroganoff employees. Ermak brazenly denied that his men had broken their pledge to reform. They had grievances, he told a furious Maxim Stroganoff and his uncle Ssemjon, who helped the young commander in his difficult task of restoring order within the "forces of order." Ermak said that their grievances would have to be settled; then the soldiers would behave. He did not specify the grievances, but mentioned that pay scales had not been established. He refused to make proposals and claimed not to understand scales computed by Stroganoff auditors. But he agreed to accept down payments for later accounting.

The down payments disappeared in Ermak's bottomless pockets and Cossacks raided Stroganoff warehouses, claiming that they were collecting back pay. Maxim no longer considered amalgamation of his 5000 idle mercenaries into the mutinous Cossack force; but the idlers—Russians, Germans, Poles, Lithuanians, and even Mongolian renegades from the Crimea—had their own ideas about amalgamation, and happily joined the looting expeditions.

The winter of 1577–78 turned into the worst in the history of Sol-Wueshegodska. Sometimes the Stroganoffs were besieged in their mansion by their own soldiery. Had Mehmet Kul launched a determined attack, Sol-Wueshegodska might have gone down in ruin; mansion, storehouses, arsenals—and charters.

Fortunately, however, the Siberians did not cross the mountain passes. Informers told the Stroganoffs that Kutchum's strength was on the wane. The Khan from Sibir did not understand how to manage his affairs; he was short of many essentials; and he would succumb to a determined, quick blow.

But the Stroganoff army was in no shape to inflict a blow on anybody but their own keepers.

A family council gave proof that the traditional Stroganoff spirit was not dead. It was decided that Maxim and Ssemjon should induce Ermak and his 540 thieves to invade Siberia; Cossacks and Mehmet Kul would cut each other into pieces, and eventually a reorganized Stroganoff army would collect the spoils.

Ermak listened to lectures on the promise of a Siberian campaign; he looked at maps, surprised the Stroganoffs and his own lieutenants by his ability to read them, and shook his head.

In May 1578, however, he notified his employers that he was ready to tackle the task. He wanted a flotilla, an advance on cash fees that should enable him to pay his men for at least one year, food, ammunition, and building material.

A few river craft, ready for delivery to the Tsar, were turned over to Ermak.

Maxim decided that it would be better to keep Ivan waiting than to delay the departure of the Cossack pest.

One week later the Cossacks manned the boats and navigated down the Tshussova River. Ermak had been briefed to act in the name of Stroganoff, not to damage Stroganoff property in Siberia, and not to stay on the western side of the Urals longer than absolutely necessary.

"Hetman" Ermak had just nodded. He had ideas very much his own. He would establish his own realm in Siberia, enslave natives, and rule them with a greedy, iron hand. His main concern was his Cossacks, and how to maintain discipline among them. In one point, however, he approved of the Stroganoff briefings. He would not stay on the near side of the mountains; he would move deep into Siberia to keep out of range of Russian forces.

Ermak was not as fine a geographer as his men had believed. He misread maps, led his flotilla into the wrong tributary of the Tshussova, and was still close to the crest of the mountains when winter came.

He had a solid cabin built for himself and ramshackle huts for the rank and file. Three of the Cossacks were runaway monks; they suggested that a church be built that would eventually be dedicated to St. Nicholas, and meantime could serve other dignified purposes. The Hetman agreed, which led later chroniclers to state that "he was not without religion." The ex-monks supervised the construction, delivered strange sermons, and went to live in the comfortable building together with a native wench whom they shared in brotherly fashion.

The Cossacks went "wench-hunting" among elusive nomad hunters; there were not enough women for all the men, and there were many brawls, even bloodshed.

It was a dreary time of hibernation, on short rations, little heat, and no pay whatsoever. Morale was low, discipline even lower. The Hetman issued strict orders. Fornication was punishable with "public washing," a humiliating and inconvenient procedure; culprits were kept in chains for three days, then their pockets were filled with sand, and they were forced to stand, waist-deep, in the freezing water of the Silva River.

A whispering campaign suggested that they all return to Russia. Dying at the rack did not take more than one hour or two, but death in the wilderness could take many agonizing months. Ermak decreed the death penalty for men who left the camp, and had three Cossacks drowned despite their assertion that they had only gone hunting. Twenty men, who left in the following night, were caught by Cossacks to whom the Hetman had promised extra bonuses, and also put to death. After the execution Ermak addressed his men, promising that they would soon be compensated for their sufferings. Discipline was restored, and in the early spring, when the Hetman led his horde on a looting spree into Samojed territory and had the proceeds actually distributed, his popularity was at a peak.

But no amount of the leader's popularity could make up for the shortages that beset the small army; a drive deeper into Siberia could but result in disaster. Ermak left a hundred men behind to hold the camp and the *ostrog* (fortress) into which the "church" had been converted, and returned to Sol-Wueshegodska for reinforcements, equipment, and supplies.

First, the Stroganoffs were dismayed to see the Hetman back whole, and at the head of still 400 bandits; but then it happened that Mehmet Kul, who had been watching the Cossacks and who considered Ermak's retreat an indication of Stroganoff collapse, threw whatever men he could muster into one bold raid on Sol-Wueshegodska. The Cossacks fought back and repulsed the Siberians; in a complete about-face Maxim and Ssemjon offered the Hetman command of their mobile forces, if he would promise to wipe out the "Kutchum nuisance."

Ermak was agreeable. All he wanted was a short rest for his own men, a brief training period for the mercenaries, and, of course, adequate transportation, ammunition, including artillery, and provisions for the army.

The Cossacks took their rest, enlivened by some stealing and an occasional raping; the mercenaries trained without much gusto. Ermak established headquarters in a wing of the mansion, conferred with candidates for commissions, and discussed supplies with Stroganoff clerks.

Maxim, anxious to show that he was still the supreme Stroganoff war lord, decreed that the army be organized after the Mongolian pattern, in sections of one hundred. Ermak said that he had been planning just that. Every section would need one *sotnik* (captain), two lieutenants, and ten noncoms; the army command should consist of himself, as commander in chief, of two *atamans* (generals), and four *jessauls* (aide-de-camp secretaries).

Maxim inquired somewhat sarcastically what rank Ermak proposed to assume. *"Vojvod,"* the bearded Cossack replied. Vojvod meant prince, supreme commander.

Maxim considered this sheer impudence.

Ssemjon, however, thought that it was a harmless extravaganza conceived by an upstart's mind, and that, whether vojvod or hetman, Ermak would never be more than a servant.

The house of Stroganoff approved of titles and commissions, and supplied some 200 gaudy fur hats for the officers. Supplies for the army included 100 muskets of a new model, heavy enough to kill a horse by one blow of its butt; 3 field cannon; many sacks of gunpowder; huge stacks of bullets; river craft, sleighs, wagons, and banners embroidered with pictures of saints. There was plenty of food: 3 poods[1] of rye flour, 1 pood of biscuit, 1 pood of salt, 2 poods of buckwheat and roast oats, and half a pig per capita.

The accounting department entered it in the books; the computed investment amounted to 20,000 rubles. Prices had gone up since the ransom of Vassilj the Blind. Nevertheless the figure was rather exaggerated.

---

[1] 1 pood = 36 lbs.

The Vojvod was informed of the expense, but he was not impressed, and did not say when the campaign would get under way. He claimed that his atamans and jessauls had not yet completed their staff work, that he had not checked intelligence reports, that some of his men were not feeling well. Maxim was getting exasperated, and the older Stroganoffs could but agree that the army should not stay in Sol-Wueshegodska through another winter.

Pressed for departure, Ermak named his terms. Since it did not befit a vojvod to act as an agent of merchants, no prince-supreme commander would take orders from a junior member of a merchant family. A vojvod was a conqueror in his own rights. He would build fortresses in Siberia, and all the land around the ostrogs (fortresses) would be his own. In gracious recognition of the Stroganoffs' contribution to his army, however, he would reimburse the brothers from the proceeds of his expedition. Ssemjon nodded. It was a deal. The Vojvod, drunk with power, was not surprised at the speedy approval. He held arms and supplies, he did not depend on shopkeepers; he thought it magnanimous of him, indeed, to offer payment for that lumber.

The Stroganoffs scorned Ermak's stupidity. Whatever spoils he might gather would be without value to him. He could not market the goods, and eventually would have to offer them to agents from Sol-Wueshegodska. He would not find enough sables all along the northern coasts to pay what the Stroganoffs would then charge for one sack of gunpowder. The Stroganoffs would cut the band and their leader down to size—and a small size it would be.

Ssemjon and Maxim on horseback saw Ermak's army off. Banners with pictures of saints waved in a light breeze as some five thousand shouting men marched past the two merchants, who waved measured salutes.

The host took to the boats on the Tshussova; destination was the Tagil River, or its approaches—the maps were somewhat inconclusive about a junction of the two rivers. From the Tagil they would proceed to the Tura, from the Tura to the Tobol, and eventually to the Irtysh. But again the expedition missed the right tributary, and Ermak had not realized that the level of rivers would get so low that dismounted sails would have to be used to dam up water to keep the ships from grounding. There was a great deal of confusion and almost no progress, and then the frosts arrived sooner than the Vojvod had expected. The army stopped at Ermak's first winter camp; the men working frantically to build shelter.

Again discipline slackened; Ermak and his favorite ataman, who adopted the name of Kolzo in memory of the executed band leader, organized a group of henchmen, better housed and fed than the rest of the army, who controlled all firearms and summarily disposed of rebels. Executions, hunger, diseases, and—despite tough control—desertions, took a fearful toll. When the thaws came, the army was reduced to 1636. Nobody knew the number and location of Kutchum's forces, and everybody was afraid of the Samojeds and other natives whom Ermak's men had been looting, raping, and murdering at random. They feared that the Siberians would unite against their torturers, assisted by their somber, violent gods. The men serving under the banners of Christian saints believed in pagan idols much rather than in their embroidered patrons.

Ermak dreaded the silent north and its vengeful ghosts. To him the Samojeds and other cannibals who lived in the wasteland were ghoulish keepers of treasures; he would much rather face Kutchum, Mehmet Kul, and all their men than ghosts and their incarnations.

Instead of proceeding through the land of the Samojeds the army turned in southeasterly direction, using dismountable boats and rafts. The bright greenish waters looked friendly, and so did far-flung sweeping hills, the luscious pine woods, interspersed with succulent meadows and adorned with flowers so bright that the soldiers wondered if these were not jewels. Some men insisted that the glittering sight was a deceptive vision devised by sorcerers to lure them into a trap. Whoever would set foot on a meadow would be caught in a swamp or even fall into a bottomless abyss. The ex-monks, who had spent two winters in the ostrog, had met shamans and told their fellow soldiers about the natives' black magic.

Ataman "Kolzo," the least superstitious of the band, urged the soldiers to abandon their fears and think of the riches ahead. The mentioning of riches stimulated the weary men. It did not dispel their apprehensions, but they would, reluctantly, disembark wherever required, and make reconnaissance drives into the splendid vastness. They never encountered men; and they were greatly worried at the absence of their likenesses whom they could ravish and loot, thus finding out that they were real.

From time to time a cannon was fired to break the mighty silence. But the balls would hit trees or disappear in the fifteen-feet-high grass, and then the silence would fall again, like the cover of a coffin.

Already they should have reached populated land, the center of Kutchum's domain, but the cartographers, whose maps guided the army, had obviously underestimated the distance. Settlements marked on the deceptive maps did not seem to exist.

The advance slowed down and eventually halted. It seemed sheer madness to continue into space. The Vojvod had a fortified camp built, surrounded by palisades and cannon emplacements. Patrols went out to scout the territory and returned without having encountered human beings. Then, one fine summer day, a patrol returned and reported having found fresh marks of horses' hoofs. Two sections went to the spot, firing a cannon as they approached the crucial areas. Not only did they see the marks, but soldiers who had been on the first patrol stated excitedly that the number of marks had increased, that more horsemen must have been around, and obviously were still nearby.

CHAPTER TWENTY-NINE In his stronghold of Isker a fretful Kutchum pondered about reports of Cossack outrages in Northern Siberia, of the rape of Samojeds and Woguls by Stroganoff men. But were the bandits really Stroganoff men?

Mehmet Kul insisted that they were just that, and several chieftains shared his view, but Kutchum had an inkling that the Cossacks were in the services of the Tsar. Already he regretted having discontinued the payment of tribute to Ivan and having written that unfortunate letter. He would let the mysterious army invade the heart lands of his domain rather than counterattack before it was established who the invaders were. This, he told Mehmet Kul, and Jepansae, *mursa* (chieftain) from the regions on the Tura River, who had come to Isker to report that his mounted scouts were circling the Cossacks' camp. The Cossacks should not be molested, Kutchum insisted, and he would permit only small cavalry garrisons from Jepansae's district to watch the strangers.

The Mursa did not want his villages to undergo the treatment the nomads in the north had suffered. If Kutchum did not intend to fight, Jepansae would act independently. His villagers were determined people and refugees living in the district would enroll in the forces of defense.

Ermak was almost as uneasy as Kutchum. His army could not stay in a camp, however well fortified, with unguarded, overextended communication lines and a mysterious enemy ahead; it would have to retreat, or advance into populated territory. The former meant frustration of all hopes, for the Stroganoffs would discharge him; the latter was extremely perilous, for the Siberians might outnumber the Vojvod's shrunken host and it was said that they did have artillery. Sotniks opined that it would be difficult to make the soldiers advance on land. The men muttered that if they could not stay where they were, they would rather take to the boats.

Late that summer the army shipped along the river. Soldiers were on the lookout for the enemy. First they would see vague contours, moving, at some distance from the bank in the early dawn and late dusk. Then contours changed into figures of horsemen escorting the flotilla day and night. The screen of horsemen grew, men afoot joined the cavalry, and then arrows began to hit rafts and boats; the Russians answered with musketry. Exchanges resulted in a few casualties on both sides. The expedition had a touch of the ludicrous; a travesty of a march of conquest. But Ermak's men were emboldened to find that their opponents had no firearms.

Five days after the trip began the Russians sighted a comfortable village: the residence of Mursa Jepansae. Ermak ordered his men off the boats. The

Russians established a bridgehead, fired their cannon; the impact of superior weapons put the defenders to flight. Only after nothing but smoldering ruins remained of the village did it occur to Ermak that he should have used the place for quarters and storage. At the next village he ordered to spare inhabitants who did not resist to be used as slave laborers, and not to commit unnecessary arson. The soldiers spared those women they could use, and removed all valuables from houses and huts before putting the torch to buildings.

Weather continued fair and mild, and Ermak postponed the search for shelter. Leisurely the invaders advanced through fertile land, well tilled by an industrious population which had long since abandoned nomadism. Granges and larders were chock-full, and the cattle were fat. The Russians feasted on the riches of the farmers, they butchered all livestock, and carried away what they could not gobble up. The army was still in rich, well-settled land when winter came, the third since a fugitive Ermak and his 540 had camped at the outskirts of Sol-Wueshegodska.

Quarters in Western Siberian farmland were comfortable. Ermak had armed parties roam surrounding settlements to collect tribute, and even though the Vojvod did not pay collection fees, the soldiers imposed contributions of their own, which nobody dared to refuse.

But the army was getting short of ammunition. Ermak sent a request to Sol-Wueshegodska for so and so many sacks of gunpowder, bullets, musket locks, and as many light cannon as were available.

Maxim delivered the goods. An accompanying note stated that this was a regular business transaction, and that Ermak now owed 30,000 rubles.

After studying the location of Ermak's winter quarters the Stroganoff family counsel had decided to treat the Vojvod as a solvent customer, and not to put the squeeze on him before he had met Kutchum Khan. The camp was closer to Sibir-Isker than the Cossack commander seemed to realize, and a showdown with Kutchum should be at hand.

In Sibir, meanwhile, a desperate Mursa Jepansae implored Kutchum Khan to call his people to arms. The Mursa had seen the enemy's banners; they did not show the Muscovite eagle; these soldiers were not the Tsar's! Mehmet Kul supported the Mursa, but he had to admit that his army was not in good shape. Epidemics decimated men and mounts, and about half the original strength was available for action. Three thousand fighting men seemed a trifling number to the Khan; and Mehmet Kul's and Jepansae's assertions that the figure could be boosted to 10,000 by enlistment of fugitives did not relieve his fears.

Jepansae was a shamanite, Mehmet Kul a Mohammedan. The Mursa suggested that the Khan proclaim a holy Islamite war against the Christian intruders. Kutchum did not want to hear of it; the faithful would say that Allah had forsaken him for not uprooting shamanism in his realm.

In the midst of winter, as Jepansae was still staying in Isker, and Mehmet

Kul had just left to inspect his army, ten noisy ruffians in heavy long coats knocked at the gates of the Khan's residence and fired a musket when the watchmen hesitated to let them in. Kutchum saw the party through a window, and ordered that they be admitted.

The ruffians said that they had come to collect tribute. They did not mention the Tsar and when a melancholy-stricken but bargain-minded Kutchum cautiously inquired in whose name they acted, they said that their vojvod was Ermak Timofeitch. The Khan expressed weary delight at meeting the envoys of so distinguished a prince, and distributed gold coins as welcome presents to the gang. But the men wanted no less than ten *soroks*[1] of sables. Kutchum distributed a few more coins, and offered one sorok. The envoys settled for two. And after being treated to strong drinks they did not object when one of Kutchum's officials accompanied them to Ermak's headquarters.

Such a companion was like a hostage when traveling through unsafe territory. In fact Sibir-Isker had not been on the party's itinerary; they had seen the city in the distance, and had just gone there. They did not even know who the melancholy man was who had given them furs and tips.

Ermak learned about the call to Sibir through Kutchum's official. The Khan's representative deplored his master's inability to present the Vojvod with more worthy gifts, but the country had been visited by disease and poor harvests; treasury and storehouses were empty. The Khan extended his friendly invitation to Vojvod Ermak Timofeitch to visit him later—after conditions had improved.

Ermak replied that he would be in Sibir early in the spring. He entertained his visitor in a banquet enlivened by lots of stolen kumiss, and the antics of girls spared from Jepansae's district. The Vojvod was stone-drunk, and in his drunkenness he made vague utterances, which the official memorized as best he could and later repeated to Kutchum.

Neither the Khan nor his advisers could understand the meaning of the cryptic sounds, but everybody realized that the Vojvod would come next spring, and spring was not far off.

Jepansae, still protagonist of active defense, had yet another suggestion. If Allah did not assist the Khan, why should not the shamans be consulted how to protect the people? By then Kutchum no longer believed that Ermak was the Tsar's general, and he even doubted that he was the Stroganoffs' man. Couldn't the wizards find out who the Vojvod really was?

The wizards mimicked rides to the highest skies, plunges into the deepest underworld, battles with ghosts, and interviews with spirits wicked and noble, and eventually announced that Ermak was an emissary from the darkest section of the underworld, destined to bring grief and misfortune upon all the lands on which he set his foot.

Mehmet Kul was present when the announcement was made, and so were

---

[1] 1 sorok = 40 pieces.

Jepansae and other mursas whose districts were menaced by the emissary from the underworld. The Khan could no longer stall, but ordered dejectedly that the army be concentrated on the approaches to his city, and that all tribes be summoned to contribute to the country's defense.

But Kutchum's fears of the Tsar revived. He could not bring himself to revoke his orders, but sent a message to Tsar Ivan, the first in many years. He no longer used blustering language. He refrained from an insinuation of being the Tsar's equal, if not his superior. He did not speak about war or peace. But he deplored, in terms of supplication, the unlawful activities of one Ermak Timofeitch, who called himself a vojvod and seemed to be the Tsar's subject. The message enumerated unlawful acts committed by the said Ermak: destruction of life and property, usurpation of sovereign rights, undermining of justice, exclusively embodied by legitimate rulers. It was a clever note, conceived to arouse a ruler's ire even if he were less irascible than Ivan.

The messenger proceeded to Moscow on a southern route to stay out of range of the invaders, and actually reached the Russian capital.

In May 1581, Ermak resumed his advance, again by boat, on the Tura River, and from there into the Tobol. The soldiers were well rested, the craft heavily loaded with supplies; the weather was fair and mild, and so was the countryside. Nobody talked about ghosts.

At the junction with the Tobol River a troop of Siberian volunteers on their way to join Kutchum's main forces spotted the ships. They shadowed the flotilla without being detected, and that evening when the boats put to shore, the Siberians attacked. Firearms were of little use in the darkness; both sides used knives, swords, and spikes, and finally the Russians prevailed over the outnumbered volunteers. But the number of the victors was reduced to 1060, and Ermak could not afford to leave rear guards behind.

The flotilla kept sailing—flying on winged ships, as scouts told Kutchum—but it would stop whenever prosperous villages came in sight. To keep the soldiers from looting would have reduced their will to fight. But looting jeopardized equipment; the mercenaries would throw ammunition, and even food, overboard much rather than leave booty behind. Ravaged villages went up in flames; destitute villagers formed bands of avengers who trailed the flotilla like packs of hungry wolves.

The left riverbank was steep, rifted, and screened by birch groves. When the Russian ships were being tied up for a night, avengers closed in with axes, knives, homemade bows, and with immense fury. They tried to keep the foe hemmed in a birch grove, and set the trees afire to roast the evildoers alive. Ermak, coolheaded and efficient, rallied landing parties which repulsed the avengers; but they were not completely destroyed, and remnants kept trailing the invaders.

Less than a thousand men continued upstream.

Mehmet Kul, at the head of Kutchum's army, wanted to give battle now.

Kutchum wanted to stay on the defensive until more potent weapons were on hand. The Khan's agents had already acquired two falconets, one sack of gunpowder, and a few iron balls, and were busy looking for gun crews. The falconets bore no manufacturer's mark, but looked exactly like Ermak's pieces. Eventually defenses were set up at the narrows of the Tobol. Heavy chains spanning the river a few inches below water level should stop the ships; volleys of arrows should harass the invaders into retreat or submission. There would be no pitched battle.

One mile away from the narrows Ermak's ships collided, because of faulty navigation, and while the boats disentangled, one small craft continued toward the chain, hit it, and was showered by arrows. The crew fired back; the sound of shots alerted Ermak, who, as an old hand at river piracy, knew the trick of underwater chains, and also a ruse to cope with it.

He had clusters of branches and bundles of straw draped with Cossack's coats and put on deck, to make the naïve foe believe that these scarecrows were the crew, drifting with their vessels toward the trap. But before releasing the craft the men went ashore to take an unsuspecting foe from the rear. The ruse worked and the Siberians suffered high casualties. But gruff Cossacks who searched the battlefield grumbled that corpses were worthless, that they wanted furs and gold, and that this unfriendly country was not even a place where a man could enjoy his wealth.

Ermak roared the unruly soldiers to attention, but when he ordered them to return aboard ship, the Cossacks stalled and wanted to know where they were going. The Vojvod did not call upon his execution squads; he had lost too many men already to arrows, knives, and disease. He waited until tempers had cooled off, and then said that they would sail straight to the Siberians' treasure chest. The Cossacks were not quite convinced; however, they had lost track of their own route and depended on their leader's sense of orientation. They obeyed glumly, and with their expressions heralding evil.

The voyage continued into the Tavda River, and in a northerly direction, away from the Khan's capital. Ermak was reluctant to call at Isker, as he had so boisterously committed himself to do in the spring. If Kutchum was an astute man, he might exploit the Cossacks' ugly mood and even reverse the tables, hire Ermak's band, and treat the Vojvod as an outlaw.

Only loot, plenty of it and quick, could placate the men. But the banks of the Tavda River did not seem to be promising hunting grounds, and reconnoitering patrols reported empty fields, woods, and streams all around. Ermak accompanied one patrol. They captured a lone man who had dismounted from his horse; he was well clad and spoke Russian. He said that they were close to the terminal of a road that led across the mountains into Russia. Ermak waved him off; he did not want his men to realize that they could find their own way without his assistance. The native mentioned Kutchum, his army, and his capital. The Khan was a wavering man, the army depleted by disease, and, strong as the fortifications of Isker were, they would crumble under the thunder and lightning of Ermak's arms.

Ermak was impatient. He did not want to attack Isker or to give battle even to a depleted Siberian army; he needed spoils without a fight. The prisoner knew the answer: a Mongolian squire lived some ten miles from the confluence of the Tobol and Irtysh rivers. He was the wealthiest man of the land, having inherited untold riches of gold, silver, and jewels from his forefathers, who in turn had gathered the treasures as Djenghiskhanide generals. The nabob was doing business with foreigners, and augmenting his holdings. But he kept no guards, for fear that they would rob him.

A rich man's mansion became the goal of the expedition that had set out to conquer the largest land on earth!

The Cossacks were unusually docile when they heard of their goal; but as they followed the captive's guidance, they saw crude signposts, pointing west, and even though Ermak kept the captive from talking, word spread that this was the way to Russia.

The men raved with delight. The wilderness had held them in shackles, bondsmen of the unknown. But now they could return home. These men had no home, and they had hardly ever cared to understand the meaning of the word, but the signposts evoked feelings alien to freebooters. Russia was home, the place where a man could enjoy what he owned. In Russia booty could be converted into rich clothes, stout women, strong wines; in Russia a wealthy man did not have to go to war. Nobody worried about the rack and the rope waiting in Russia; they had cheated the rope when they were destitute, they would cheat it after they got rich. The Cossacks roared that they would pillage the rich man's mansion, return to the signposts, and follow them right into the promised land of booze and whores.

Ermak pondered. Kutchum's cavalry might be on the lookout, and in their present state of mind his band might fall easy prey to organized attack.

In fact Mehmet Kul had obtained his brother's consent to engage the invaders. And while the Vojvod kept his host in an improvised camp, Mehmet Kul's vanguards staged a harassing raid. The shower of arrows brought the Cossacks to their senses. They fought back and repulsed the assault. The Siberians lost twenty men for every Cossack killed, but the Vojvod could ill afford further losses. No reinforcements were available; no news had come from Sol-Wueshegodska of late.

The loot eventually gathered at the rich man's mansion was even greater than expected. In one hour of savage plunder, treasure chests bulging with gold, silver, jewels, pearls, and furs were emptied, stables, granges, and storehouses cleaned of their contents. The conquerors feasted and boozed in a mad carousal. The Cossacks turned into a belching, gulping, vomiting rabble, and a handful of foes could have disposed of the human garbage.

Ermak stayed sober; singlehanded, he spilled all beverages he could find to arrest further excesses. Then he went to look for his three ex-monks; they were still uninjured, having always taken good care of their hides. Ermak disdained the loquacious cowards, but he needed them. The Cossacks might not listen to his harangues, but they would still heed advice by their own comrades. The Vojvod fished the three out from under heaps of snoring drunkards, and locked them into a closet. Twenty-four hours later they were able to understand their commander.

They should talk the Cossacks into obeying orders, and they would, in turn, receive one tenth of the Vojvod's share in the latest loot. The three said that religion was always the best medicine for sinners. Ermak had his doubts about remedy and prescribers, but he let the trio work on the soldiery; knocking heads of dozing men on floors, and trampling on aching stomachs. What the monks shouted into the ears of slowly awakening Cossacks about the Lord and His wrath made the Tsar appear a benevolent sentimentalist: God, the trio roared, would not put the sinners into a caldron and leave them to boil and rest in peace ever after. The God of the Cossacks would have them executed every day of eternity, and every execution would last all day long. The methods of executions they described were colorful enough to make even a seedy Cossack inquire about redemption. Nothing but obedience, they learned, could win them a reprieve, and they would have to abstain from drink throughout the period of Maria Lent, which, according to the lecturers, lasted two months.

Maria Lent lasted two weeks only, and the period had already expired, but the men promised to obey and stay sober indefinitely.

Their constancy was put to a severe test when Ermak ordered that all treasures be buried ten feet below ground. The Vojvod had kept his share, and permitted the monks to put theirs aside.

The Cossacks palavered; they wanted to keep at least as much as they could carry in their pockets. Ermak had a religious service performed and afterward repeated his order. Isolated shouts, "Let's take the goods, and return to the signposts," were quickly silenced. The Vojvod addressed his men. Long after the speaker and the last man to listen to his unrecorded oratory had died, Russian clergymen and lay patriots claimed that it had been a noble appeal to the finest sentiments of a soldier, a talk about the disgrace of flight, and the undying virtue to die for the greater glory of a larger fatherland.

And still later the communist government of Russia pictured Ermak as a proletarian patriot in the Red spirit.

Whatever Ermak may have said, he was successful. The treasures were buried, and the expedition continued.

Already leaves were turning and chilly mists fell at night. Not only had the spring been wasted, but the summer too was gone, and little, if anything, could be achieved in the autumn.

Ermak looked for winter quarters. They were now moving in circles; the men did not object, the picture of an Almighty executioner was still strong in their minds, and, besides, moving in circles kept them close to the buried treasure.

A small neck of land commanding neighboring regions seemed a good location for a winter camp. Vanguards found the area lightly held by archers dug in shallow trenches. Ermak did not attack. He withdrew behind the Irtysh-Tobol junction and mustered his strength. Five hundred twenty men were left, a sprinkle of paltry humanity in the immensity of glorious land. Ammunition supplies would have been catastrophically low for an army of the original number, but they would suffice for the small band. Food, however, was not even adequate for that number. Poor conservation methods and the men's tendency to destroy whatever they did not find convenient to carry accounted for a dangerous shortage. Attempts at foraging in the countryside were unavailing. The natives had fled, leaving nothing—in another early version of scorched-earth policy.

It was October. Soon heavy frosts would set in; hungry men could not well resist the cold. The end seemed at hand.

From the commanding neck of land horsemen watched the distant grounds on which Cossacks labored on dugouts and palisades. The man in front of the observers was pale under his swarthy skin, and shivered despite his heavy sable coat. These men and their weapons, the shivering man thought, were invincible; it had been sheer madness not to surrender.

The panicky Kutchum Khan wished he had never permitted Mehmet Kul, the stupid Mursa, and the corrupt shamans to talk him into resistance; and all the informants who had told of the invader's losses and troubles were fools and traitors. As he looked at the invading army, its number seemed legion.

Mehmet Kul contended that they still outnumbered the enemy. But what could some 2500 roving tribesmen, and hastily mobilized farmers, achieve against professional warriors?

Even though he would not admit it now, the latest decision to meet Ermak in the field had been Kutchum's. Late in September, when the Cossacks had not yet reached the vicinity of Isker, Mehmet Kul suggested that the army stay around the capital and let the invader struggle for cover. The Khan, however, unnerved and jittery, could not stand the strain of waiting.

Early in October he ordered the army out to a showdown battle. Mehmet Kul, his chief of staff, now proposed to attack the digging Russians. Kutchum, beset by an inferiority complex, decreed that the army stay on the neck of land to wait for the enemy assault.

Only one hundred of Ermak's men stood by for action should the foe attack; the others were out on forays or working in unarmed groups. The Vojvod had had no reply to his last appeal to Maxim Stroganoff, imploring him to send more men and more cannon lest Siberia be lost and a vengeful Kutchum Khan march on Sol-Wueshegodska. He could not help wondering if reinforcements would be of use under the circumstances. They would not bring his army up to a strength adequate to make the bid for Isker, and they might hasten starvation. Ermak was panicky too, and no less impatient than Kutchum had been.

On October 23, 1581, at dawn, the Vojvod undertook a reconnaissance in force against Kutchum's camp. He found the Tatars, as he called the foe, crowded into absurdly narrow space, two cannon emplacements right in the midst of groups of men who had practically no elbowroom, a crazy array, the brain child of Kutchum. The reconnaissance in force turned into a full-scale battle, all Cossacks stopping work and rushing to join the attackers; the enemy had food to keep their stomachs filled for months to come, and food was worth fighting for. The hemmed-in Tatar cannon opened up, but the balls tore gaps in their own ranks and did not strike onrushing Cossacks. The Cossacks' bullets and balls hit their mark; it was impossible to miss the milling crowd. Kutchum turned over command to Mehmet Kul, who attempted to extricate his forces from the deathtrap and charge into the rear of the Cossacks, an operation which could have produced a Russian rout; but before it was completed, the ranks of the Samojed volunteers broke. The savage hunters could no longer stand the splashing sounds of cannon balls hitting human bodies. Tatar squads sacrificed themselves to keep a gap of escape open, and as night fell a thousand men, all that remained of Kutchum's army, straggled back in the direction of Isker.

The Khan galloped far ahead of his defeated army. He stayed in Isker only to gather valuable belongings, and continued southward. The population of Isker, numbering less than one thousand, watched their khan's flight, and then gathered their own movable property to follow the fugitive, leaving only the sick, the aged, and small children behind.

During the first night of retreat the remaining volunteer contingents deserted Mehmet Kul. They did not think that their leaving for home constituted desertion. The war was lost, further resistance meaningless. Mehmet Kul made no attempt to stop the exodus, and he would not defend the capital.

Ermak had lost 107 men, and took a dim view of his victory. But after the enemy did not turn and counterattack, as he expected, the Vojvod made his boldest bid, and won. In forced marches 400-odd Cossacks raced for Isker. The captive who had shown them the way to the rich man's mansion still served as their guide, and showed them short cuts to the Khan's residence.

On October 27 Ermak saw the city for the first time. It looked well nigh unassailable, perched at the crest of a hillside that sloped almost vertically deep down to the banks of the Irtysh River. The hill was crowned by palisades and solid breastworks. Behind a sharp bend of the river the slope was not all too steep, but deep gullies cut by torrents formed natural defenses of forbidding strength. The Vojvod, remembering that tribute collectors had never told much about Isker's strength, reconnoitered the approaches from the land side, and found that they did not present natural obstacles. However, there were strong earthworks, trenches, and abatis, newly constructed and not easy to take by storm. But no arrow whistled as the Cossacks approached the fortifications; no Tatar rose to fight as they trudged their way across the network of defenses. The belt of uncultivated land in front of the walls was deserted, and the door of the wall stood wide open.

A few infirm, aged persons, and playful, small children watched Ermak and his patrol enter the city. A weary band of ragged, unkempt men poured into Isker, established themselves in abandoned houses, stored supplies collected at the field at the last battle, in empty storehouses, and wondered whether they were victors or prisoners of cunning Tatars who might soon return and besiege them in the city of the Khan. The Cossacks were not numerous enough to man the outer defenses of Isker. But under the circumstances they had no choice but to stay where they were.

Ermak and his atamans worked on another message to Maxim Stroganoff, boasting of their capture of the enemy capital while supplicating for more men, muskets, cannon, and gunpowder—an inconsistency which even more skillful stylists would have found hard to cover up.

The letter was not yet ready when, on November 1, sentries sounded the alarm. The citadel of Isker, on a circular-shaped plot 300 feet in diameter, surrounded by partitioned wooden enclosures, with brick-encased cellars, was manned for an all-out defense against the approaching column that could only be the Tatar army.

However, as a Cossack gun crew kindled the match to fire the first shot, a bareheaded, unarmed tribesman presented himself at the gate, asking permission to present his homages and his people's gifts to the new Khan of Isker. The caller and his followers, all unarmed and submissive, had brought a carload full of edibles, containers full of kumiss, and bundles of furs. The visitors were soon followed by other delegations: Tatar tribesmen, Samojeds, and other nationals—Kutchum's former vassals and freemen, a cross section of natives from Western Siberia, anxious to pay their respects to the conqueror and to purchase his good will in cash, food, furs, animals, and in whatever objects of value they had to spare, including women.

The Cossacks were delighted and supremely confident. They did not fret about the Lord executioner; they were in a robber's Lubberland, and they would stay there forever.

It dawned upon Ermak that he had won a war and conquered an empire. He did not know its boundaries, he did not speak its language. He did not know how to administer a country; but as long as valuables kept pouring in, the affairs of his state were in splendid shape. Everything was perfect but for one thing.

He did not want his men to learn what was bothering him now. And the men were apparently not anxious to know what the letter said which a courier from Sol-Wueshegodska had brought to Isker a few days after the first homage by the natives.

The courier had been the lad the Vojvod had sent to the Stroganoffs' mansion to ask for assistance. The lad told that he had been questioned about the army's misdeeds in Siberia, and whipped with the cat-o'-nine-tails in the presence of Maxim Stroganoff when he said that they had sailed and fought, and collected what was due to them, and that he did not know what misdeeds were. He bared his back, and the Vojvod saw deep red scars.

And the letter said that the house of Stroganoff would have no further dealings with Ermak Timofeitch (just Ermak Timofeitch, without title or rank) until such time as he would return to Russia to account for his misdeeds and be cleared by the Tsar's court. Meantime, however, he was expected to pay 30,000 rubles, plus interest, for commercial deliveries made to him.

All donations made by unsuspecting natives would not permanently keep a band of 400 in control of an empire; the Tsar's court would never clear a river pirate and deserter, whatever the judges thought of misdeeds in Siberia. He did not have 30,000 rubles. His debt to Sol-Wueshegodska did not actually worry him. But why did the Stroganoffs treat him like that? Didn't they realize that he was the victor?

CHAPTER THIRTY The message a desperate Kutchum had sent to the Tsar did not receive Ivan's full attention. The Formidable did not want to be bothered with affairs of Siberia, nor with any other trivial matter, while he was devoting his efforts to momentous dealings with England: trade concessions, portrait sessions, and other matrimonial affairs. He turned the letter over to a young court counselor for further study and report.

The counselor, a favorite of Boris Godunov, and, like Boris, a man of Mongolian stock, was a worshiper of the memory of the Djenghis Khan, and incorruptibly hostile to the Stroganoffs, descendants of a traitor to the Golden Ordu. The counselor's report, supplemented by testimony, some genuine, some fictitious, was devastating. The Stroganoffs, it said, were responsible for chaos in the east; through their arrogant greediness they had antagonized the Tatars who otherwise would have been enthusiastically loyal to the Commander of Siberia; Stroganoff brutality and covetousness had also exasperated the patient Samojeds and turned them into furious raiders. The Stroganoffs had consistently misused privileges obtained from their magnanimous ruler, and, as crowning misdeed, had hired and equipped a band of outlaws who were responsible to no legal authority. These bandits were ravaging the lands beyond the Urals, destroying His Majesty's sources of income, murdering His Majesty's faithful subjects. Not only was the employ of criminals a blatant violation of the basic charter; it should also be taken for granted that Sol-Wueshegodska shared the proceeds of the outrages with its perpetrators. A general uprising of the peoples of Siberia provoked by the Stroganoffs could have disastrous consequences for the Russian Crown and for Russian subjects. Under the circumstances a death warrant against all the male members of the Stroganoff family and their hirelings would be highly justified.

But even a preoccupied and deranged Ivan would not set his signature under a death warrant against the Stroganoffs. Instead the disappointed counselor was ordered to send to Sol-Wueshegodska a letter of censure and a request for justification.

The counselor affixed the Tsar's black seal to the document; the black seal was the expression of the monarch's extreme dissatisfaction, and usually tantamount to a death sentence. Never before had a black-seal letter been addressed to a Stroganoff. The contents of the letter did not relieve the shock.

The family was harshly reprimanded for having hired brigands wanted for untold crimes, for having armed said mob and used it to kill people engaged in peaceable occupations. By such action they had willfully deprived the Crown of legal income from Siberia. The Stroganoffs were ordered to desist from further criminal activities, to have Siberia evacuated without delay, to discharge the deserter-Cossack Ermak Timofeitch, and to have him and his band handed over to the Tsar's authorities.

Not even old fox Anikita would have dared to go to Moscow and talk himself out of such an indictment. His offspring closeted themselves in the hall in which Anikita had sat pondering about Siberia, and deliberated how to forestall disaster.

The results of their endeavors were several voluminous epistles. The first—antedated, to make believe that it had been written well before the black-seal letter was even drafted—consisted of eloquent and indignant complaints about predatory Samojed and Tatar hordes, rebelling against the sacred authority of their tsar and commander, invading Russian territory staunchly defended by Stroganoff guards, destroying lives and property destined for His Majesty's use. A fortified place authorized by the Tsar, and constructed at high expense by his loyal subjects the Stroganoffs, had been besieged by eastern brigands. The Stroganoffs were determined to invest their last ruble in the restoration of law and order, but they would be forever grateful should the generous Lord and Tsar assist his humble subjects with his invincible army.

The Stroganoffs did not expect Ivan to send his army into Siberia, but the petition should show the Tsar that his humble subjects had nothing to hide.

The antedated letter was followed up by epistles of apology, never trying to refute charges made above the Tsar's seal, but always insinuating that the Stroganoffs were, in fact, guiltless.

It is even said that several members of the family sent secret personal messages, putting the blame on their brethren and cousins, but no such messages have been recorded.

The maltreatment of Ermak's courier and the letter to the Vojvod were but links in the chain of the Stroganoff vindication.

In Sol-Wueshegodska the family waited anxiously for Ivan's reaction. They hoped that the Tsar could but restore to his full favor the men who had never asked anything for themselves. As no reply was forthcoming, the Stroganoffs felt forsaken and doomed.

In the late fall of 1581, when the letters from Sol-Wueshegodska arrived in Moscow, Ivan did not read letters. The Formidable's career of murder had reached a fitting climax. The catastrophe started with his checking the attire of his eldest son's pregnant wife. The Princess was found to wear two petticoats, while the Tsar insisted that an honest woman in her condition should wear no less than three. He beat the Princess and kicked her with his feet. Her husband interfered. There was a brief exchange of angry words. That evening, the Tsar, his son, and Boris Godunov had a talk; the Tsar bragged about his wealth and might, and told the Crown Prince how fortunate he was to look forward to his inheritance.

"Valor, as the King of Poland possesses," grumbled the younger Ivan, "can achieve more than wealth, and without gallantry, one cannot really be mighty." Stephen Batory, King of Poland, whose army of 26,000 had not received their pay for a long time, had recently defied the Tsar and his paid-up army of 300,000. Ivan was numb with rage, which gave the Crown Prince an opportunity to say: "Rather than bequest your treasures upon me, give me command of your army, and let me restore our prestige in the West."

A cupbearer, about to serve the Tsar another goblet of wine, fled, terror-stricken, when he heard those words. Boris Godunov did not flee; he rose to prevent a horror that would, in fact, pave his own way to the bloodstained throne. But he could not stop Ivan, who assailed his son with a sharply pointed iron rod, the effigy of a scepter, which he always carried. The iron rod had already killed several men; now Ivan thrust it into his son's chest, pulled it out, and hit his victim's head with the heavy handle. The Tsar roared like a wild beast, but as his son collapsed, roars changed into shrill screams. He threw himself on the ground, kissed the young man's bearded face, tried to stop the gush of blood, bawling: "I have killed my son—I have killed my son."

Trembling surgeons alerted by Boris Godunov found the Tsarevitch breathing his last.

At the state funeral Ivan tore his hair, moaning, groaning, a spectacle of savage grief.

Valets watched the Tsar wander through the halls of the castle at night, calling his son. He did not sleep in his bed, he did not wash, did not have his hair and beard groomed, and threatened with the iron rod everybody who attempted to smooth his deranged attire. Courtiers and officials summoned into Ivan's presence crossed themselves: they might not come out alive.

The Tsar called his courtiers and ranking officials into session. Fjodor, his second son, was also present. Fjodor was a slow-witted, gentle man of twenty-three, whose one and only pleasure was to ring church bells. The Tsar indicated that this son was not fit to rule the empire; he wanted the assembly to chose another successor; Ivan would pass the crown to the selected man at once.

The fear-stricken crowd deliberated, in whispers, speakers casting cautious glances at the Tsar, whose mien did not reveal the workings of his mind. At last a member of the court knelt down and stammered that the assembly implored Ivan, the Chosen of God, to keep ruling over them and to apply his own benevolent wisdom to design his successor.

Ivan snarled that the wish was granted.

He remained rather indifferent to the affairs of his realm, and the counselor, foe of the Stroganoffs, chose not to arouse the Tsar's ire by bothering him with Siberian matters.

Ivan was again pondering over marital problems. He wanted an heir to the throne better fitted to handle the affairs of Russia than the offspring of his dumb wives were. An English mother should bear him a son who combined English business acumen with Ivan's own lofty virtues. The Queen of England was too old to bear children, but she could assign an English princess to marry him, and after the Princess had served her reproductive purpose, she could always die from unestablished causes, like other tsarinas, and he would then marry the aging Queen.

The Tsar sent a special envoy to England to negotiate more commercial projects and an alliance between the two countries. The envoy should also present the Queen with dark sables, and discuss his master's intimate affairs.

Elizabeth accepted the sables, inquired about His Majesty's health, expressed sorrow at Ivan's bereavement through a "grievous accident," as she called the death of the Crown Prince. The envoy's mentioning of commercial affairs was well received, but the Queen was not co-operative in the crucial matter.

A candidate for marriage was being considered: thirty-one-year-old Mary Hastings, a relative of the Queen. The ambassador had seen her portrait.

"I do not find her beautiful," the Queen told the envoy, "and I cannot imagine that she will be found so by such a connoisseur of female beauty as my brother Ivan. She has but lately had the smallpox, and our painter gave her rosy cheeks, which, in fact, she does not have." Elizabeth suggested that the envoy take a hunting trip to Windsor Forest, and otherwise enjoy himself, rather than talk to Mary Hastings.

The Queen's ministers protested that Elizabeth's aversion to the match injured English commerce. A meeting between the envoy and Mary Hastings was arranged. "A tall lady, possessing a pale face, grey eyes, flaxen hair, and a well-built, slender figure," the Russian described her, omitting pockmarks and other flaws. Nothing tangible for the Tsar's reproductive desires, or for English commerce, resulted from the interview, however.

Because the envoy did not dare to return empty-handed, the Queen assigned Sir Jerome Bowes to accompany him and humor the Tsar by telling him that Mary Hastings could not presently undertake a long voyage, but that she was expected to be able to do so soon, and that the Queen had other, more attractive kinswomen. Sir Jerome was under secret instructions not to talk about an alliance with Russia, which the cabinet considered madness.

Ivan immediately mentioned the alliance. The Englishman replied that his powers did not cover such commitments: he could talk business or marriage, but nothing else.

The angry Tsar shouted abuse.

"Treat me ill—and good-by to all chance of Lady Mary," the staunch Englishman countered.

Sir Jerome's cold-blooded impudence exasperated Ivan. The Queen's appointee went even so far as to call Ivan's choice unsuitable: "She is an ill-looking woman, in poor health." The Tsar would have wanted to impale the offender, but he was afraid of the consequences. Fear, the perennial torment, pervaded Ivan's attitude toward England. After exchanges about Lady Mary's suitableness Sir Jerome arrogantly requested more commercial concessions.

The Tsar was beset by self-pity. His affection meant nothing to men, high and low, they wanted only material things—concessions, gifts.

He despised materialists. However, he would send more furs to England. But not even the Stroganoffs could provide enough furs to make all men love him.

Two thousand miles away from the Russian capital a fretful Ermak was getting gloomier every day. He did not share his band's delight about tribute that kept pouring into Sibir-Isker and improving the aspects of enjoying opulence on the spot. Kumiss was not a mean beverage, the men said, and the Tatar women were not so bad either.

Officers talked to Ermak, who let his top men into the secret. They were forsaken, abandoned by the Stroganoffs, outlaws to the Tsar; no later than in the spring even the stupid natives would notice that their conquerors were an isolated, abandoned lot.

The young ataman who had adopted the name Ivan Kolzo did not share the Vojvod's pessimism. All men were corruptible, he opined, and why not send a shipment of furs to one of the Stroganoffs and make him settle their dispute with his family? Ermak did not consider it practicable. The Stroganoffs were too rich to be impressed by furs, and they would keep the shipment as a down payment. Kolzo had yet another suggestion: "Why not try the Tsar? He is not as rich as the Stroganoffs, and we owe him nothing."

It sounded simple and sound to the other ataman and to older sotniks, and Ermak could but agree. There seemed to be no other choice.

The new Ivan Kolzo offered to go to Moscow, much to the relief of other officers who dreaded such an assignment.

A petition to the Tsar was drafted. Natives were ordered to supply transportation, and Ermak toured storehouses to select furs for the Tsar.

At Christmas 1581, Ataman Kolzo left Sibir with a column of long, narrow sleighs pulled by teams of dogs and reindeer. He arrived in Moscow in February 1582 and was at once arrested. The elaborate arsenal of the capital's executioner was waiting for highway chieftain and river pirate Ivan Kolzo. Protestations of mistaken identity would not have saved the ataman had it not been for the furs. They had been sent to the Tsar: 2400 dark sables, 2000 beavers, and 800 big black foxes. Ivan's wrinkled face brightened as he stared at the wealth. This should be irresistible to the English; he would generously reward the man who brought it to his capital.

Ataman Kolzo was released from the dungeon, clad in rich garments in which he felt extremely uneasy, and ushered to the Kremlin. He was coached to prostrate himself before the man with the iron rod, and then to read the petition. The latter was not feasible. The supplier of the furs could not read. A court scribe would read it in his place.

But the script was not in a shape that would please the Tsar; frantic stylists whipped it into a pompous document including the Formidable's favorite phrases.

At last a bewildered ataman plumped on his knees before a white-haired man with a high, pointed hat and an iron rod, and listened to highbrow vocables that made no sense to him. The white-haired Tsar grunted approval. Ivan liked to hear of loyal admiration, of repentance, of pledges of devotion. Siberia *was* an asset, after all, a fine Crown jewel. It occurred to the Tsar that he had never received so splendid an assortment of furs from Sol-Wueshegodska. Did the younger Stroganoffs short-change their tsar? He could always ignore charters and take all of Siberia for himself.

The scribe kept on reading: Ermak and his aides appealed to His Majesty to lend assistance to their endeavors by sending his grandiose army to Sibir, and to assign a governor to rule in his exalted name. The original draft said nothing of a governor; the court stylists had made this addition on their own responsibility.

Ivan meditated, his bloodshot eyes glaring at the iron rod, and then proclaimed that, in view of their patriotic zeal and their ardent endeavors to reform, full pardon was herewith granted to Ermak, Kolzo, and all the officers and men serving in their outfit. The Tsar paused. Such an act of grace should elate men of good will, but most men were materialists. Ivan called Kolzo, handed him a few coins from his purse—less than the price of one sable—and decreed that the man be given a piece of linen for his personal use. Ermak, as the leader, should receive another piece of linen, two sets of heavy armor, a drinking cup, and a piece of fur trimming from one of the Tsar's discarded coats. The leader should continue in charge of Siberian affairs until such time as a governor would be assigned to take over. Ivan did not mention his grandiose army. He liked to have it called so, but he was reluctant to commit it on so distant a theater.

In Sol-Wueshegodska word about the Tsar's reaction to Ermak's message was anxiously awaited. The Stroganoff information service was still functioning well. Ivan's proclamation and decree alleviated the family's gloom. A piece of linen, a drinking cup, harnesses, and a rag from an old garment would be of little help to Ermak, and whatever the Tsar undertook, he would always need the Stroganoffs.

Kolzo was not yet back in Sibir-Isker when the troubles Ermak had anticipated started in earnest, even though not quite according to the expected pattern. Local chieftains had rendered homage to the Vojvod. They had stripped their tribes of valuable possessions to buy his good will and they had stayed in the city. From the walled city Cossack patrols kept roaming the countryside, plaguing farmers and hunters. The Russians were insatiable, and the natives were leaderless. They had only hunting weapons and their organizational capacities were low. Mehmet Kul, the man who could have welded loose groups into a makeshift army, had gone into hiding after suffering a wound from the last bullet fired in the last battle.

But the natives' will of resistance grew, and as the winter progressed, yet another element spurred the Siberian men's vindictiveness: the attitude of their womenfolk. Instead of hating the invaders they did not seem to mind mating with Cossacks, and they developed a maniacal admiration for Ermak. Siberian idioms had no terms for hysteria, but the Ermak craze had every feature of sexual psychosis. Native women would run away to Sibir, and there fight among themselves for the favor of serving the Vojvod. Native husbands took up arms to avenge the shame.

In March of 1582 it had become unsafe for Cossacks to venture beyond the walls.

The chieftains who had stayed with Ermak realized that they would be killed as renegades should they return to their villages and camps. They had to cast their lot with the Cossacks, work for them as best they could by spreading tales of the victor's generosity and recruiting proselytes for the Vojvod. From Isker runners went out to enlist natives, to incite strife between anti-Ermak elements and neighbors who had not yet suffered much from the hands of the invaders. Miniature civil wars, with no quarter asked or given, flared up around the fortress, but the Cossacks were on the defensive and almost every day a man would be missing.

Cossack parties went out fishing; natives shot arrows at fishermen. The parties were reinforced by musketeers; for a while archers stayed away, but late in April a group of twenty Cossacks was ambushed and killed to the last man.

A woman spy reported that Mehmet Kul, still suffering from his wound but already gaining strength, had set up camp on the shore of Lake Kular, not far from the Irtysh River. He had fifty followers, and soon he might have several times that number; the ambush of the fishing party had been Mehmet Kul's doing.

She offered to guide a sotnia (squadron) of Cossacks to Lake Kular on a route unguarded by the Tatars. One crisp night sixty Russians, experts in nocturnal forays, followed the woman. When Mehmet Kul awoke, he found himself roped, and all his followers dead—their throats cut.

Ermak received the bundle that had been his main opponent, with expressions of cordiality. Mehmet Kul was untied and welcomed as a guest. The captors had expected to witness the most spectacular execution of their careers, but the captive was too valuable a price to be thrown to the Cossacks. After a few days of friendly treatment Mehmet Kul agreed to write his brother Kutchum—the Khan stayed in Bokhara—that he was being well treated and that he had abandoned all thoughts of further resistance.

In an accompanying note Ermak hinted broadly that unless the Khan appealed to all people formerly under his rule to obey the Vojvod as their legitimate overlord, Mehmet Kul would die of starvation. The Khan's prestige in Siberia was rising, since he had not actually surrendered. But Kutchum refused to sign the appeal.

Much more annoying than the attitude of the refugee Khan was the account received from Ataman Kolzo after his return to Sibir. Two thousand four hundred sables and all the other furs had brought a miserly return: a collective pardon that might undermine the men's morale, and a few objects for which the Stroganoffs would have charged one sable or two. And not one word about support.

As before Ermak was on his own to consolidate his rule, replenish his treasury, and keep the men from returning to the now safe land of Russia.

No chieftains went to Sibir that spring. Ermak wanted to dispatch expeditions to the silent tribes. There had been few attacks since the capture of Mehmet Kul, who was held in honorable custody; but the Vojvod was at a loss how to proceed.

Sotnik Bogdan Bräsgä volunteered to visit the natives, and contended that his own understrength sotnia would suffice to enforce their law. Bogdan Bräsgä had made a name for himself back in Russia as the toughest of cattle thieves.

Ermak appointed the tough sotnik to administer the oath of vassalage and tributarianism to all the natives he would find between the rivers Irtysh and Ob. Ways and means were left to the sotnik's own judgment.

At first the sotnia proceeded at will. The natives had rudimentary local administrations. The land was divided into *ulusses* (districts), the boundaries of which marked community hunting and fishing grounds. District magistrates acted as justices of the peace, kept family registers, and apportioned tribute liabilities. These magistrates administered the oath of fealty to Vojvod Ermak and acted as Bogdan Bräsgä's collecting agents. After the official action was completed, the sotnik would let his Cossacks have some personal fun. Fun resulted in casualties to the natives that could be made up for nine months later, thanks to the Cossacks' attentions to female tribute payers.

According to Bogdan Bräsgä's judgment, this was a benevolent, if not idyllic, course of action, and rising native unfriendliness evidence of the villainy of the Tatar character. The tough cattle thief would not tolerate ignobility. When he encountered opposition, he stormed settlements, "had able-bodied men hung by their feet and massacred in various manners," as a Russian historian recorded, "and forced survivors to kiss swords and daggers stained with the blood of their kin."

The deterrent effect of such treatment satisfied the sotnik. Back in Sibir, Ermak was pleased to receive substantial shipments of tribute collected by the expedition.

Near the site where Ostjak City now stands the Cossaks were stopped by a fortified place where an Ostjak magistrate had gathered fugitives and men from his own district. "Two thousand of them were inside," the sotnik reported. The fort could not accommodate more than one tenth that number, but even this gave the defenders a 3 to 1 edge over the Cossacks. The sotnik's men were repulsed as they tried to force the gates.

An Ostjak informer told Bogdan Bräsgä that the garrison had an idol, sitting in a basin of water; one gulp of that water rendered a man invulnerable for a certain period of time. As long as they kept idol and water, they would hold the fort.

The sotnik promised the informer a reward should he sneak into the fortress and steal the idol. The traitor returned, and said that, even though he had not been able to catch the idol, matters looked auspicious for the Cossacks. A wizard had put the idol on a table, surrounded by pans, with burning fat and sulphur, and was asking it whether or not they should keep fighting. Not only did the removal of the figure deprive the water of its magic qualities; the guardian spirits of that shaman were not usually in favor of boldness. They would probably tell the defenders to quit.

This was the sotnik's first experience with shamanism, and it turned out to his satisfaction. The fortress was abandoned by its defenders. The land near the junction of the Irtysh and Ob rivers was rather densely populated; local shamans consulted their idols, and the idols indicated that, at the approach of the foreigners, people should hide in the forests. The faithful took the oracle literally. They fled only when the Cossacks were nearby, and this left them no time to save their belongings. Bogdan Bräsgä collected whatever these people owned—a generous compensation for loyalty oaths not administered.

In November 1582 the sotnik was back in Sibir-Isker, with another big batch of furs.

At the same time, in Moscow, Ivan wanted more furs for marriageable English ladies and hard-boiled English merchants. Nothing had been forthcoming from Siberia, and little from Sol-Wueshegodska. The Stroganoffs wrote no letters and paid no calls, and even though he had not requested it, he had expected Kolzo and Ermak to produce revenues.

The Tsar ordered that 500 soldiers and a group of administrators be dispatched to Siberia to turn the country into a going concern. At second thought he decreed that the Stroganoffs should muster an auxiliary force of fifty mounted men to join his troops. Commander of the expedition would be Prince Simeon Bolkhovsky, a smug, averagely incompetent young officer who had earned his present rank of major in the bedchambers of influential ladies. The Prince should be installed as Governor of Siberia and administer the country in the name of the Tsar and Commander. His instructions were: "Hold what is already conquered, expand holdings wherever feasible, and always keep collecting."

One Ivan Gluchov, a rather obscure Russian civil servant, was appointed *golova,* chief secretary, to Simeon Bolkhovsky.

Except for the contribution of fifty horsemen the Tsar ignored his charter commitments to the Stroganoffs. However, the men from Sol-Wueshegodska were relieved not to have been entirely left out of the venture. They made no effort to advise the bureaucrats in Moscow working on details of the expedition; the more the bureaucrats would blunder, the more stupidly the Governor would act, the better for the Stroganoffs. The Tsar should realize that he depended on the holders of the charters as the final instance in all Siberian matters.

Mossback generals who had never been beyond the Baltic planned equipment and logistics. The Tsar might review troops. Ivan had a fancy for artillery; the expeditionary force should have the heaviest pieces foundries could cast; Ivan liked mounted men. Most of the 500 would have to be cavalrymen; the Tsar was impatient with long columns of ugly carts; the small army should have few huge wagons.

Ivan did not inspect Prince Bolkhovsky's army. By the time the host, joined by the Stroganoff contingent, had reached the western foothills of the Urals, part of the unwieldy cannon had been abandoned by exhausted crews, many horses were lost in snowdrifts, and most wagons littered the long track from Moscow. Logistics called for river transportation; the generals did not seem to know of the land route across the mountains, but part of the flotilla had been crushed by huge ice floes before the army reached embarkation points.

In the late summer of 1583 a dispirited band of disease-ridden soldiers straggled into Sibir. They had lost all their mounts and most of their artillery; and their supplies would not last another week. But the Siberian capital was not the promised city of fleshpots, leisure, and safety Bolkhovsky's men had longed for.

The garrison subsisted on short rations; many men were sick, and there would be little rest for the weary new arrivals. After several months of deceptive peace native insurrection had flared up again. Kutchum, the last man Ermak expected to engage the invaders, had returned from Bokhara with a band of mercenaries, and the Khan became the rallying center of resisters in Siberia. Kutchum had a new military adviser, Karatsha, a chieftain, whose tribe had been hard hit by Bogdan Bräsgä's band.

Karatsha had tricked Ataman Kolzo and forty crack Cossacks into an ambush, and none of the Russians escaped alive. Karatsha, co-operating with magistrates, had tribute collectors slain; Karatsha's patrols raided Ermak's columns with telling effect.

The Tsar's soldiers were urgently needed to bolster defenses and secure supply lines.

Prince Bolkhovsky left military matters to Ermak, and civilian affairs to Golova Ivan Gluchov; his sole concern was how to get back to Moscow soon.

Ermak, who had been elated when news of reinforcements on the way had reached him a few weeks before the column of misery trudged into the city, was steeped into deep gloom when they arrived; but the Vojvod would not allow himself to keep deploring a situation indefinitely. If the Tsar had sent these men, he would send more, better supplied, and more efficient troops, provided, of course, he would consider it profitable. Only precious objects and tidings of victory would be accepted as evidence of profitableness. There were still plenty of furs in Sibir's otherwise depleted storehouses, and even though Ermak had suffered setbacks throughout the year, he held one token of success; Mehmet Kul. Sables, and the Khan's brother, should induce the Tsar to help Ermak.

Again Ermak picked a shipment of furs; the darkest sables, the biggest fox skins. Cossacks fought with fists and knives for the boon of joining the column to Moscow.

It got safely through, but shortly after it left, a siege ring closed around Sibir. From the west bank of the Irtysh River, Karatsha directed operations to starve the city into submission. Kutchum Khan toured his former realm and urged Mohammedans to destroy the archfoes of Islam.

Not one grain of food reached Sibir. Russian fishing parties were decimated by Siberian arrows. Blockade runners never returned.

By Christmas the last crumbs of food had vanished from the storehouses; most of it had been consumed, the rest stolen and hidden away by soldier-thieves. The garrison chewed bits of leather from their boots, ate weapon grease, and searched furs for decaying flesh. Caught hoarders would be torn to pieces by their comrades and devoured. Cannibalism was rampant; Tatar collaborationists were consumed without exception. Bolkhovsky's soldiers were no less savage than Ermak's. The Prince himself was dying of scurvy; the Golova, more fortunate than his master, managed to survive, probably with the assistance of food thieves. Ermak was sick. Practically everybody was sick with scurvy, typhoid fever, intestinal diseases, and poisoning. Bellies were grotesquely swollen, heads distorted by oedema. The stench of decay hung heavily in the stagnant icy air. Nobody buried the dead. They were eaten.

The thaws came; the besiegers did not move. They did not want to incur unnecessary losses. Scouts roaming the approaches to Russia without interference reported that no reinforcements were in sight.

May 9 was the day of St. Nicholas, whom Cossacks sometimes called their patron saint. On May 9, 1584, Ermak, badly shaken but unbroken, made a roll call: 300 men answered, a harrowed-looking mob of half-crazed ogres. The Vojvod explained that St. Nicholas had told him to guide them to a place where they could find food: right in the enemy's camp.

The Russians were hardly able to walk, but the fury of hunger gave them power. They followed the Vojvod, and fell upon the Tatar camp. Karatsha was caught off guard. Hundreds of besiegers were butchered, among them Karatsha's two sons; the rest fled.

The victors stayed in the camp, voraciously devouring whatever food they could lay hands upon. The orgy of gluttony continued for several days, and the sudden intake of excessive quantities of food resulted in the death of one out of ten men.

It was Ermak's good luck that the Siberians did not turn and enter Sibir while his men feasted on abandoned supplies.

And more good luck: The news of Karatsha's defeat spread like wildfire throughout the country. Ermak did not need to forage; submission-minded chieftains sent furs, food, drink, and one petty khan even sent his daughter as a prospective bride for the Vojvod. After a brief inspection, however, Ermak returned the girl.

Native scouts told him that a caravan with the finest Persian goods was approaching Sibir to trade the wares against sables. Ermak's highway instincts were aroused. Why should he give up sables if he could waylay the merchant? The leader of the scouts could speak Russian; he seemed familiar with the route the caravan would take. The Vojvod donned his armor, alerted one sotnia of Cossacks, and ordered the scout to act as their guide.

He would not have suspected that the caravan did not exist, and that the scouts were in the pay of Kutchum Khan.

Trade caravans never traveled in the darkness. Ermak spent his nights resting comfortably. The night of August 6, 1584, was cloudy, with low visibility. The Vojvod was sound asleep when Kutchum and his mercenaries closed in. The mercenaries cut the throats of sleeping Cossacks; the Khan had reserved the right to dispatch Ermak. Near the bank of the Vagai River, Kutchum perceived a faint glitter. He made a quick step; a branch broke with a brisk sound; a tall figure rose—Ermak, in full armor. It took the Vojvod but one split second to realize what was happening. A small boat drifted a short distance away. He tried to reach it with one broad jump, but the weight of his breastplates bore down on his powerful body.

Ermak plunged into the river and tried to swim. But the Tsar's gift dragged him to the bottom.

CHAPTER THIRTY-ONE Ivan felt low, and miserable as the year 1583 drew to a close. He ordered his physicians to give him powerful medicines, but he did not drink them for fear that they might be poisonous, and then raged against the medics' treacherous incompetence. He called in astrologers to foretell the date of his death.

"March 18, 1584," the astrologers announced.

Ivan shuddered. At night he had a giant soldier who could crush a man with one bear hug lie in front of his bedroom door to keep assassins away. He asked for, yet did not take, more medicines. He did not perform any state business except for the unavailing wrangle about an English marriage—which he would not have been able to consummate. Ivan waited for March 18.

On the eve of the crucial day he appeared before his courtiers and announced triumphantly that he had never felt better; and that at sunset next day he would stage the most spectacular show the capital had seen since its reconstruction: the public execution of the mendacious astrologers. Clad in a loose gown, open shirt, and linen trousers, he started a game of chess with Boris Godunov, the courtiers attending. As the Tsar set the pieces, the chess king fell to the floor.

At this moment Ivan fainted and slumped backward.

"There was a great outcry," an eyewitness related. "One sent for aqua vita; another rushed to the apothecary for marigold and rose water; a third alerted physicians and priests. But the Tsar was already choked—stark dead."

The Metropolitan arrived, at the head of the clergy. The prelate's figure was bent by age and by fear of the abomination he was about to commit. But such had been the Tsar's will, and he did not dare disobey even the dead Tsar.

"Thou art not Ivan Grozny," he addressed the corpse. "Ivan Grozny is alive, a monk in a secluded monastery; thou art Johan, a God-fearing monk whom Ivan Grozny has appointed to rule in his place and thou hast devoted thy brief rule to acts of piety."

The Metropolitan's voice faltered as he continued according to the traditional rites. Nobody in the audience spoke. They understood what the address meant. The Lord should be deceived, made to believe that it was not blood-drenched tyrant Ivan, but God-fearing, humble Johan who appeared before the judgment seat of the Almighty.

A pudgy man with a sallow complexion, a huge hooked nose, and bloated cheeks ascended the throne, weak-limbed and with an unsteady gait. He made a pathetic effort at smiling. The courtiers did not return his smile. They stared reverently at a tall, husky man with a huge beard and broad cheekbones who, magnificently garbed, stood at the foot of the throne: Boris Godunov, the real power in the realm.

The coronation formula was read: Fjodor, now called Theodore Ivanovitch, was Tsar of Russia, Commander of Siberia. . . .

Commander of Siberia . . .

At the time of the coronation nothing was known in Muscovy about the state of affairs in the distant domain. Nobody knew that Sibir was under siege, Prince Bolkhovsky dead, the garrison starving, and not until many months after it occurred did Boris Godunov learn that Ermak had drowned.

Ten days after the Vojvod's disaster Tatar runners brought the news to Sibir. Golova Gluchov, the highest-ranking Russian in the city, gathered one *sorok* of sables, which back home would buy him a fine estate and a mansion, and made off for Russia as fast as native guides, horses, and oarsmen could transport him. One hundred fifty men, all that remained of the conquering army, departed almost simultaneously for the same goal.

Six months after he was proclaimed Commander of Siberia, Tsar Theodore Ivanovitch did not control one square inch of Siberian territory.

The immense land was free—free for the first time in ages; not even a home-grown tyrant held the colorful maze of people in his iron grip. Yet for the first time Siberia was unified. The liberator, the unifier, was Kutchum Khan.

But Kutchum's Siberia lasted less than one year.

The Russians played no part in the disintegration of the realm. During the winter following Ermak's death and the abandonment of Sibir, when Boris Godunov had no reports from the Russian expeditionary force, he had small reinforcements sent across the Urals; one hundred musketeers and one heavy cannon, under the command of Ivan Mansirov. Kutchum had little to fear from that tiny band, but there were other elements he could not control.

The people of unified Siberia were violently split among themselves. The population was divided into collaborationists and resisters, but the border lines were hazy. Alleged collaborationists either flatly denied all charges or called their relations with the invaders clever means of protecting their tribes against exorbitant tribute and wholesale slaughter. They scoffed at alleged resisters and called them swindlers who wanted rewards, such as public offices or valuables. In fact the resisters did claim power and privileges for themselves and their families, and the testimony they presented to support their claims was not always convincing. A bewildered Kutchum ordered investigation of *uluss* magistrates and chieftains; dignitaries and officials defied the authority of the Khan to look into their private affairs and eventually requested increased powers which, if granted, would have made central government illusory altogether.

Controversies turned Siberia into a whirlpool of petty feuds and furious animosities. To make things worse, national antagonism raised its Medusa head. Tatars despised Samojeds, Ostjaks scorned Woguls, Ugrians hated everybody else. Ill-defined nations refused to take orders unless they were endorsed by an established conational; and clans and tribes raided one another for the greater glory of nationalism.

It would have taken many years of patient endeavors and superb statesmanship to quiet the storms in a thousand teacups. Kutchum was not a statesman; and his hourglass was rapidly running out.

He was back in Sibir, surrounded by his mercenaries, a lot of alien cutthroats whose ideas about prerogatives of an army in occupied country did not essentially differ from those of the Cossacks. He had extreme difficulties recruiting his subjects; his spell of popularity was over. Already people talked about his early record of non-resistance against the Russians and about his foreigners. The epithet Khan-Liberator, which had greeted him in Sibir, was not heard again.

It was not a Siberian habit to talk about people, be they rulers or neighbors; Siberians, regardless of national marks, were not gossipy, and their primitive idioms were no media for loose talk. But rabble rousers, never before seen in the steppes, forests, and prairies, toured the land wide and far and harangued taciturn men and women with vehement denunciations of the Khan at Sibir, and mystical promises of a great khan who would come to punish the offenders and make everybody else prosperous and happy.

The demagogues were in the service of a new pretender to Temudshin's heritage, a resident of Bokhara who had amassed a big fortune in devious business transactions, and was investing it in a bid for rule of Siberia. This Uzbek, imitator of the Stroganoffs, had neither the immense wealth nor the astuteness of old Anikita, but conditions in Siberia and Russia seemed to favor his venture. He had been in business under the name of Sejid-jak; when he made his bid for Siberia, he had a genealogical tree prepared by Bokhara fakers, and styled himself Great Khan Seidak, most direct of all direct descendants of Djenghis Khan. In the Mongolian tradition brought up to date he opened the attack on his rival by propaganda, on a pattern that has been developed, but not essentially changed, by Asiatic-minded conquerors of our time. And while the itinerant heralds of Great Khan Seidak roamed camps and settlements of Southwestern Siberia, their employer recruited an army of about 1000 for a march on Sibir-Isker.

Worked over by agents of the new impostor, Kutchum's cutthroats deserted their master, taking part of his treasures along. The Khan made an attempt at organizing the defense of his capital by his family and loyal citizens. But most of the members of the Khan's family were women and children, while the citizens who had recently returned after a lean period of hazardous exile did not intend to chance their lives. As the new impostor approached the capital unopposed, Kutchum led his kin out of the doomed residence and to the countryside where peasants lived, whose traditional Mongolian belligerent spirit should not be entirely dead. He would give these true descendants of the greatest warriors of all times two goals worth fighting for: freedom and unity.

Kutchum's earlier life had been marked by grievous pitfalls and scant, short-lived achievements, by wavering, and deceit. In the thirteen years of affliction that followed his second exodus from Sibir, however, the aging Khan grew into a towering, tragic figure, a man who, briefly supported by few, permanently forsaken by many, homeless, outlawed, derided, exploited, and deceived, never abandoned faith in a mission conceived in the agony of distress: to make the people of that land enjoy the blessings the Lord had so richly bestowed upon it.

In the fair season of 1585, when Kutchum set out on his hegira, he headed a sizable column. The size of his family was considerable. He had servants, and the objects left behind by the deserters still filled many carts. The aura of opulence surrounding a well-supplied column attracted shiftless elements and fortune hunters who stole, or lived on, Kutchum's treasures and made off when they were satiated.

Carts emptied as the column proceeded through Siberian farmlands without predetermined itinerary. Kutchum stopped at every settlement and he talked to roaming herdsmen wherever he met them. People listened, and turned their backs to the man who wanted them to take up arms. They would not fight the Great Khan, who had already arrived at the head of an army, for the sake of that man who had no army, and had not done well before. And they did not strain their imaginations to understand what Kutchum told them; to the Siberians all rulers, impostors, and aggressors had the same objective: to dominate and to collect.

Pursuers tracked the column; the drones never fought; they would steal as much as they could carry, and desert. The fugitive's property dwindled, but what hurt Kutchum even more was that members of his own family no longer believed in him. In the beginning they had struggled whenever he ordered it; they had listened to him whenever he addressed them. One of Kutchum's sons and two of his grandsons had died in action. But now they no longer wanted to fight, no longer cared to listen; they did not seem to trust his sanity.

More than five years had gone by since Kutchum started on his track. Russian agents, back again, trailed him and his family, who camped in collapsible tents, had but few, half empty carts left, and had long since been abandoned by their servants. The Russians related the story of Mehmet Kul: Tsar Theodore Ivanovitch had welcomed Kutchum's brother as a ranking foreign dignitary and offered him a commission in the Russian Army; now Mehmet Kul was General Altaulovitch, expert on affairs of the Crimean Tatars. The Tsar, they said, was a generous master who rewarded those who served him well.

Kutchum's family was weary; all three remaining sons and their women and children surrendered to a Russian patrol. They were taken to Russia, allowed to take up residence in the capital; pensions were allotted to them, their descendants were titled, and eventually became the Princes Sibirskoy.

It has been said that an emissary offered Kutchum the opportunity to serve Russia in an exalted station: as a viceroy, or even a vassal emperor of Siberia. The Russian state archives do not contain documents to support such claims, but it would not be surprising had the fugitive received tempting offers, and turned them down with the unswerving determination that marked his declining years.

Ragged and hungry, his eyesight failing, and all alone, Kutchum continued his meaningless wanderings. He was last seen in 1598, a Siberian Lear, his white hair waving, frail but upright, groping his way eastward, completely blind and apparently also deaf, for he did not respond to the observer's call. The people who had had no use for the living Kutchum Khan turned the vanished blind man into a mythical hero; one of the rare items of Siberian folklore tells of Kutchum becoming king of a distant land that nobody had visited before, and ruling over it for forty glorious years.

Back in 1585, Ivan Mansirov and his forces navigated toward the Irtysh River, spending nights on what they considered friendly land. In the vicinity of Sibir they learned from natives that Ermak was dead and Kutchum back in the capital, but that yet another man was about to depose him. Mansirov did not have Ermak's boldness and gambling instinct; all he could think of was to get back to safety. But nights were already getting crisp and Mansirov was frightened by the weather no less than by the khans. He doubted that he could be home before the snowstorms came. The natives indicated that events in and around Sibir had not affected territories far up north. The Russian officer decided to take up winter quarters in high latitudes. He navigated into the Ob River, and continued downstream. Low water level eventually stopped their voyage.

Mansirov's troop landed in hilly, wooded country. The woods provided material for the construction of a solid ostrog. The soldiers went to work; Mansirov wanted the fort surrounded by high palisades and watchtowers. He hoped that there were no natives around, but soon scouts reported having found a settlement nearby. Mansirov's haunted subaltern mind pictured the settlement as a huge fortress manned by thousands of determined, well-armed soldiers. He wanted to leave, but the water level was still low. He ordered construction sped up, and every working soldier had to keep his musket ready.

Actually those natives were poor Ostjaks who lived in shacks and were no less afraid than the Russians on learning that foreigners were near. The property of the villagers consisted of a small herd of reindeer and some dry fish stored for the winter. But they knew that invaders did not disdain humble spoils if nothing of substance could be had. The Ostjaks consulted their shaman; the shaman told the gullible to build a fence around their huts and place their biggest idol in front of a birch tree outside the palisade, to take care of the aggressors.

And while the Ostjaks built a primitive fence and carried their idol, a crude wooden monstrosity, to the tree, the shaman went to Ivan Mansirov.

The natives waited for the idol to chase the Russians away, when they heard a detonation and whistle; then tree and idol were shattered by the impact of a missile. The Russians had fired their cannon.

The pot shot put the natives to flight. Several days later their elders, joined by other clansmen whom they had told of the invader's idol-shattering powers, appeared outside the half-finished ostrog, waving dried fish and herding their finest reindeer.

Mansirov accepted fish, reindeer, and gestures of surrender. The natives received letters of protection which they could not read, but which they accepted as indications of the commander's willingness to spare them for the time being. The Russians did not kill natives that winter, but many Ostjaks died of starvation as the invaders consumed their edibles. The letters of protection said that the respective recipient—*knaesez* (princeling), as the elders were addressed—had to pay tribute to Russia. Mansirov was proud of this idea. It would be one achievement to point out in case superiors in Moscow would ask embarrassing questions. And, meditating about his record, the officer remembered that foreign dignitaries rendering homage were welcome in the capital. He had a few notables rounded up, and sent them to Moscow with a flowery report on the letters of protection.

The Muscovite bureaucrats found the report to their liking; the procedure set the pattern for Russian dealings with Siberian tribes for some time to come. A knaesez who did not have a letter of protection was an outlaw, and those who did have the document were destitute, forever exposed to extortionist demands.

The Ostjaks who lived and starved near Mansirov's ostrog had little, if any, furs; this did not prevent the Muscovites from taxing one Lugui, highest-ranking knaesez from the region, with an annual tribute of 280 fine sables. Boris Godunov approved of the procedure, and he told his brother-in-law, the Tsar, to add "Ruler of the Great River Ob" to his other titles.

Boris took a lively interest in the Siberian affairs. He realized the difficulty of occupying all the lands because of their immensity, and he was well aware of the Russian official's stupidity and corruption. The Stroganoffs, too, were corrupt, but at least not stupid. Boris Godunov fastened the ties with Sol-Wueshegodska. He did not wish to have the Stroganoffs collect all that was due to them under their charters, and even less to have them carry out their secret designs, which he could see through; but he intended to secure their co-operation as long as he would need it and get off the hook of the charters later.

Dmitri Stroganoff, the keenest mind of the family, negotiated with Boris. Dmitri is said to have addressed him as "Your Majesty." Boris Godunov wondered whether this was an exaggerated expression of submissiveness or rather an impudent hint at his own secret aspirations. He countered by talking about

Mangansee, in the existence of which he did not quite believe. Dmitri Stroganoff boldly asserted that his family wanted nothing more urgently than to incorporate the city of splendor into the Siberian realm, and that this would have been achieved long ago but for the interference by muddleheaded boyars in army and offices.

Mansirov and his tiny band, on their way back from the Ob River, were just resting in Sol-Wueshegodska, ill-clad, ill-equipped, and altogether no asset to Russian prestige in Siberia. The Stroganoff boss casually remarked that he would bill the government for rehabilitation of the band; Boris Godunov insisted that the Stroganoffs were committed to supply the expeditionary forces with all necessities; Dmitri produced a long list of infractions and breaches of charter committed by the government, and gave a figure of damages which, if paid, would have bankrupted Russia.

Eventually Boris Godunov pledged himself to supply an adequate number of elite soldiers for consolidation and expansion of the Russian occupation; the Stroganoffs were committed to provide food, weapons, transportation, and advice. The validity of the charters was not questioned. Whether or not Mangansee should be part of the Stroganoffs' 25 per cent share in Siberian territory would be decided after the city was captured.

Dmitri Stroganoff smirked at the Mangansee clause, a brain child of the aspirant to the throne, who obviously wanted to use it against the Stroganoffs. The head of Sol-Wueshegodska did not doubt that Boris would eventually be Tsar; but he trusted that his rule would be too brief to see this question come up. For the time being, at least, the Stroganoffs were back in the Siberian picture.

The first contingent of a new expeditionary force left in the summer of 1586. Boris had talked to both Mansirov and Golova Ivan Gluchov and was disgusted with their cowardice. He would assign the toughest characters to spearhead the new army: 200 Strjelzi, the scum of Ivan's guards, and 100 Cossacks, professional criminals facing the hangman's care but released for the purpose. The commanding officers, Vassilj Sukin and Ivan Maesnov, were depraved swashbucklers; the administrative officer, Tshulkov, a municipal clerk with hard fists and soft brains.

Dmitri Stroganoff supplied the men well enough, and his advice, tantamount to orders, was that they march in the direction of Sibir but avoid a battle for the capital, and start building a network of ostrogs to cover a territory some fifteen days' march in diameter, and use the ostrogs as springboards for further expansion and as collection centers. A Stroganoff trustee joined the troops, and they were given to understand that supplies would be cut off in case of disobedience.

The Strjelzi and Cossacks came within sight of Sibir without meeting resistance. They were informed that Great Khan Seidak and his soldiers were in the capital—how many soldiers the informers could not tell.

From the top of the fortress Great Khan Seidak watched distant campfires, wondering whether the Russian expedition was not actually a godsend. His investment had not paid the dividends he had expected. Half of his army from Bokhara was gone—vanished without combat. He had sent sections to take possession of provinces; the lansquenets plundered and did not return. Tribal chieftains who had seemed manageable, if not yielding to his rule without question, and who came to Sibir to do homage, had turned sullen, unresponsive, mutinous. All but two had left him; those two were petty leaders of doubtful standing with their clans, and the titles of sultan he had bestowed upon them seemed exaggerated in view of the "army" they had brought him: a combined total of twenty-five loafers.

Great Khan Seidak wondered whether the country under his control extended as far as the view from Sibir-Isker in fair weather. He had heard that the Russians wanted ranking Siberian collaborators, and hoped they might hire him at generous terms. He decided to wait for an offer, and meantime refrain from any action that might antagonize the gentlemen from Moscow.

The Russians built the first ostrog, the center of the proposed network, near Sibir, and called it Tumen, a name derived from the Mongolian term for an army unit of 10,000. Nobody could mistake the 300 for a host of 10,000, but the Russians later bragged to have tricked a superior foe into refraining from attacking them.

Ostrog construction continued on the rivers Tura, Pishma, Iser, Tavda, and Tobol; the last would eventually become the nucleus of the city of Tobolsk. The fortresses were manned by only a few soldiers, but could still have resisted the primitive weapons of the natives in case of attack. But there was no attack. Great Khan Seidak waited for an offer; and the feuding tribes did not even unite in the face of an enemy trickling in. One by one, clans and tribes were faced with demands for tribute; one by one, they paid up, satisfied to surrender to foreign oppressors rather than forgo their domestic arguments.

Three hundred intruders established the foundations of tyrannical rule in a territory larger than all European empires. The Stroganoff trustee was a transportation expert. The Russians were inherently inept as road builders, so the expert concentrated on waterways. Voyagers would have to build their own craft; they would find logs and tools at predesignated points. Trips downstream presented no problem; upstream, however, the rafts and boats would have to be pulled by men marching along the banks, where thicket often turned every step into a difficult plight. But official voyagers would be informed where they could enlist natives at musket point.

Natives supplied the ostrogs with whatever the garrisons requested; there was nothing else they could do, for muskets were an irrefutable argument. As the network of domination expanded, 500 more soldiers arrived from Russia via Sol-Wueshegodska, and joined the tyrannical builders to establish a government by, and for the purpose of, extortion.

The Russians ignored Sibir for two years. Five hundred more soldiers had crossed the Urals into Siberia; the network of ostrogs kept enlarging at a rate that added to the Russian holdings upward of a hundred thousand square miles of territory annually. Boris Godunov approved of the system of expansion and took credit for its rapidity. The Strjelzi and Cossacks were anxious to provide cover for themselves by erecting forts at top speed; once established, they were in great hurry to loot the surrounding countryside. Small patrols raided natives. Their spoils were supposed to be surrendered to ostrog officers who, in turn, would forward them to group commanders; group commanders were directed to deliver valuables to the civilian administration, to be forwarded to the Tsar's treasury. But patrols cheated their officers, officers cheated their superiors, and so forth, all along the line; after the Tsar's treasurer had taken his bite, almost nothing remained for the Crown. The Stroganoffs did not make out badly, even though they had no part in the line along which the riches of Siberia moved into naught; embezzlers had no way to dispose of their loot but by selling it to agents from Sol-Wueshegodska.

By 1588, administrator Tshulkov was a wealthy man; the Stroganoffs paid him slightly better prices for his stolen goods than they would pay the military. But his peace of mind was disturbed by the perennial bugbear of Russian officials: the *revisor*. A revisor might check his accounts and denounce him to the Tsar, or at least claim a fearful share of the ill-gotten goods. Tshulkov would have to gratify the ruler by some special achievement, to keep the revisor away. If he could dispose of the Great Khan this should impress the Tsar, or rather Boris Godunov, and it would be less expensive than bribery or honest accounting.

Tshulkov invited Seidak and his dignitaries to visit him in his residence, the ostrog of Tobol. Seidak assembled his petty sultans and soldiers, made them wear whatever Mongolian warrior's gadgets could be found in the city, and set out to Tobol, confident that he would receive a tempting offer for collaboration.

The Russian guards did not permit more than 100 men to enter the ostrog; the other 400 waited outside. The ill-reputed merchant from Bokhara and the corruptionist clerk from Moscow met at a well-set banquet table, trying to enact impressively their respective parts of Great Khan of Siberia and the Tsar's plenipotentiary. Tshulkov opened discussions in a condescending tone; Seidak was smug and glib. But soon the administrator changed his tone into insolent abuse, calling his guest a stupid plotter against the Tsar's government. Seidak affirmed that he had never plotted against the Tsar, pointed at his record of non-resistance, offered to enlist with all his men in the Russian Service.

Tshulkov demanded that the Great Khan and sultans submit to trial by drink. Only should they empty in a single draught a huge goblet, filled to the brim with strong kumiss, would he believe in their innocence. No man could pass that test.

Seidak stammered desperately that the consumption of intoxicating drinks was abhorrent to any Mohammedan and the sultans joined his plea, which was not convincing, because they had been drinking at the opening of the session. The three were chained and would have faced fatal torture had not the Stroganoff agent explained to Tshulkov that it would be better to send the prisoners to Moscow as a token of victory than to have them killed on the spot.

The 100 men who had been admitted to the ostrog were killed to satisfy the administrator's bloodthirst, and from the palisades Strjelzi opened up on the 400 waiting outside, displaying fine marksmanship.

The story of Seidak had a happy ending, however, to his own extreme astonishment. He and his two companions were taken to Moscow, where Boris Godunov was looking for more Siberian nobles, phony or genuine, for proselyting. Seidak wound up with a town house, an estate, Russian serfs, and a pension, in return for pledges of loyalty. The two sultans did not collect that much for their oath of allegiance, but they were well satisfied with minor commissions in the Tsar's army.

For several decades Siberian renegades were indiscriminately well received in Moscow; few, however, reached the Russian capital. The dull, ignorant, and poor average native had no idea of startling opportunities in the homeland of his conquerors. Chieftains, and not yet impoverished notables who might learn of these prospects and were bold enough to venture the long voyage, had to meet extortionist demands for safe-conducts by ostrog commanders all along their way, and usually they would wind up destitute, devoid of conveyances and draft animals, before reaching the Urals, or be murdered despite safe-conducts. Only every now and then did an aspirant for an assignment in Russia get through, most of them through the good but exacting offices of Stroganoff agents, who were back in numbers in Northern Siberia.

The lot of the Siberian natives who stayed within the widening range of the ostrogs was steadily worsening. Earlier conquerors had struck once, or in twin blows, like the Mongols. Those who survived would keep on living afterwards. The Russians kept striking; every one of them was a petty tyrant, imaginative in abuse and ill-treatment.

To the Cossacks and Strjelzi, who still constituted the bulk of the garrisons, slaughter of natives was a recreational activity, infliction of torture a sport, and looting a legitimate business. Civil administrator Tshulkov, who, ever since the capture of Seidak and the subsequent occupation of Sibir, had considered himself a finer soldier than the professionals, outdid the military in brutality. His methods of taxation were highhanded sadism; his ever-changing decrees were enforced by fire and sword upon the natives who ignored kaleidoscopic changes of law; rare raids, carried out by not yet conquered tribal bands, were avenged by mass executions of hostages.

Tshulkov was responsible for a ruling against marriages between soldiers and native women. The natives, according to the administrator, were "unclean pagans," not worthy of legal bonds with Christians.

The soldiers requisitioned women as they would requisition reindeer, dried fish, furs, and firewood. The requisitioned women served as all-purpose laborers and receptacles of the soldiers' virility. Begotten in the dimness of ostrog basements, in sticky, smoke-filled barrack rooms, in refuse-cluttered yards, under the eyes of other men and women, by mates who did not care to look at each other's faces, the progenitors of the modern Homo Siberiens came into being; a mixture of ethnically indefinable, uniformed vagabonds, and Ostjak, Wogul, Samojed and Mongolian women continued haphazardly, eventually shaping into a nation whose tradition and inheritage became humiliation, abuse, and blind vindictiveness.

Few of the Cossack ancestors of the Homo Siberiens had been baptized; not all Strjelzi were Christians even in name; neither they nor the Cossacks had any conception of the Christian spirit. But they relished a ruling that established their superiority, and they were even more pleased when Tshulkov, upon the Stroganoff agent's advice, amended his anti-matrimonial decree by introducing a heathen tax, a Iasak to be paid by unclean pagans. As usual, ostrog garrisons acted as collectors. Girls were accepted in payment, and soldiers traded the women, untidy Samojed females rating between one and three red foxes, plump and skillful Tatar wenches bringing as much as one sable of medium quality. Officers had a first choice of requisitioned and collected women.

The Russian Church demanded that the soldiers' offspring be Christianized: the occupiers did not want their revenue reduced by baptism, and the monks and nuns who began to arrive from the West were no fighters for the faith. They did not hunt for neophytes. This left the early Homo Siberien subject to his begetter's discriminatory taxation. The Siberian clergy made no effort to stop the spreading of shamanist doctrines among the soldiers who were attracted by the antics performed by wizards and wizardesses.

More Russian troops entered Siberia in 1592, to secure continued progress, according to the official explanation, but for an entirely different purpose, according to Stroganoff intelligence.

Commanders were Princes Gortshakov and Trochaniotov, the only Russians among the officers. The others were international adventurers, veterans of various armies and prisons. The rank and file were Cossacks, in no way different from earlier contingents.

Local Stroganoff agents subtly insinuated that the central course of the Yenisei River was the focal point of progress, but the commanders brushed the agents aside and headed north.

They left ostrogs at Pelym, on the Tavda, Sosva, and Lesiva rivers, behind, and continued toward the tundra.

A pathetic log fort held by a small band of Ostjaks collapsed under a cannon ball; hit-and-run attacks by Ostjaks could not halt the Russian advance even though the Ostjaks had a few muskets.

Shamans followed the marching army. They told of dangers ahead, of the vault of ice from which spirits of the underworld would emerge to destroy the intruders; they insisted that good luck and prosperity awaited the soldiers in the south. The commanders had several wizards executed and forbade their men to listen to pagan nonsense.

The army entered the tundra: in midsummer the vastness of short-lived, brilliantly colorful vegetation under the rays of a sun that did not set; in midwinter, the savage barrenness of arctic expanse under a nocturnal sky never lit up by dusk; in the fair season infested by swarms of sanguinary mosquitoes; in the rough season blasted by ghoulish ice storms. And beyond that glacis of magic and plague lay the gateway to the underworld. Had it not been for the glittering promise the Cossacks would have broken into headlong flight, but their goal was the wealthiest place on earth—Mangansee.

Gortshakov and Trochaniotov were looking for Mangansee. Boris Godunov wanted to locate the mystery city or expose the Stroganoffs' deceit. This the family in Sol-Wueshegodska had learned, and this they had tried to prevent through agents, hired Ostjaks, and shamans.

Agents, Ostjaks, and shamans had failed, but nature fought the Stroganoffs' war. Not until 1595 did the Russians penetrate as far as the estuary of the Ob River, where they built another ostrog, Obdorsk, as a take-off point for the final assault of Mangansee. From the top of the towers of Obdorsk sentinels claimed to see contours far up the bay. A huge city, it seemed to be. The Russian princes ordered the advance; the march turned into a race; officers and men struggling to be first to set foot on the golden city.

They did not reach the promised El Dorado. Nobody saw even contours of a city. Wide, endless, incredibly desolate, extended the ice-flake-studded waters and the barren shores of the bay.

The Russians were stunned. They could not believe in the completeness of their failure. In this moment of supreme disappointment they believed more fervently than even during the march that El Dorado did exist. They used spades and knives to dig into the ground where somebody had said the city had been hidden by wizards. The ground was solidly frozen a few feet below the surface. Bare fists hammered at rocklike soil; hoarse voices shouted obscene curses. Cossacks who had never cried before wept with maddening self-pity. But the tundra did not open to release the bewitched city of gold.

After several weeks of battle with the soil the troops marched back, determined to avenge defeat by pagan spirits upon pagan men.

The road to Tobolsk was littered with smoldering ruins and mutilated corpses. Deep inside virgin forests fugitives were hiding. Letters of protection purchased at fantastic prices from other invading hordes could not have protected their holders against the wrath of the defeated.

Prince Gortshakov did not voice doubts in the existence of Mangansee in the presence of his Cossacks; they would have torn him to bits. But he and Trochaniotov reported at Court that Mangansee seemed to be a phantom, and that the most venerable Stroganoff family had been misinformed by its agents. However, the expedition had covered an immense territory. New ostrogs had been built, and several hundred thousand miles added to the realm of the Commander of Siberia.

Boris Godunov did not think that the venerable Stroganoffs had been victimized by mendacious underlings. He took the family to task, and requested an immediate and fully satisfactory account on the missing city.

The Stroganoffs had had more than three years to prepare an explanation: they declared that the map that had guided the Russian commanders had been drafted without consulting experts from Sol-Wueshegodska. Had the princes consulted the Stroganoffs before rushing into the wilderness, they would have learned that Mangansee was not where the map marked it, but more than 500 miles farther to the east. Mangansee did exist, and it was a treasure chest unless, of course, lawless elements permitted to enter Siberia without knowledge of the holders of the charters had sacked the city as they had done with other settlements, to the disadvantage of the Crown and its unselfish servants, the Stroganoffs.

Did Mangansee exist? Boris Godunov did not believe it. There was no way of refuting the claim other than by another expedition. The Stroganoffs were positive that the Russian Government, shaken by internal and external troubles, would adjourn such an expedition indefinitely. But five years after the hopes of the first exploring Cossacks had been dashed to the ground, another Russian troop reconnoitered the regions along the lower course of the Taz River, 500 miles east of the Ob estuary. They found coy, primitive Samojed nomads who, questioned through interpreters, answered "yes" to everything they were asked. "Yes," this was Mangansee. "Yes," it was bulging with gold. "Yes," the treasure was nearby. The inquiry about the exact location of the treasure drew another "Yes." High rewards were promised to the first soldier who would find the city, its debris, or, at least, some of its gold. The men rushed around in exasperating, unavailing hurry, and eventually they found a strange, half-finished construction that looked like a primitive ostrog. "Yes," the natives said, this was Mangansee. "Yes," it had always been there. "Yes," it had been built but recently—by natives? "Yes." By foreigners? "Yes."

Thus ended the search for Mangansee.

But the Russians did build a Mangansee of their own, an undistinguished place on the Yenisei River, latitude 66° N from where they plundered natives under the pretext of trade and cheated higher authorities by embezzling dues and behaved no differently from other conquering organs.

CHAPTER THIRTY-TWO After the miserable Theodore Ivanovitch had been forced to pose as a Tsar, instead of acting as a sexton, as was his one and only desire, one person remained between Boris Godunov and the throne: Dmitri, youngest son of Ivan's last wife, born not quite three years before the Formidable's death at the chessboard.

The Tsar had never shown much interest in the child, and few people knew of his existence. Boris was Dmitri's chief guardian; the other appointee and the boy's mother had no word in the boy's affairs.

Among the first documents Boris Godunov made his puppet tsar sign was a decree banishing Dmitri Ivanovitch to the monastery of Uglich, 120 miles from the capital. The decree gave no reasons for the banishment, but it is claimed that Boris told the frightened Tsar that his half brother was a tool in the hands of dangerous plotters, and that he showed indications of unreliability and rebelliousness.

Except for Dmitri's irate mother and the helpless other guardian hardly anybody in Muscovy learned of the deportation of the three-year-old "potential rebel"; no written report from Uglich confirmed the boy's arrival. Soon, Boris presumed, even the few who had known Dmitri would have forgotten him, and there were ways and means to silence mother and guardian should they keep protesting. They did not protest, in fact.

Boris Godunov was well familiar with the workings of courtiers' and dignitaries' minds, but he did not quite know the romantic vagaries of the soul of humble Russian peasants, and the unfathomable ways of news reaching the mushik.

The peasants who lived near the forbidding monastery and worked the lands of the church seemed to know that Prince Dmitri lived in a secluded cell, that the monks treated him well and raised him to be a merciful Tsar, but that sinister forces were out to destroy the boy so that he may never rule according to the law of God.

Five years after the people of Uglich had begun to talk about "Little Father Dmitri," the bells of the monastery started tolling. It was early dawn; from huts and shacks, from stables and granges peasants flocked to the walls, took off their caps, and, as the ringing continued, they said prayers for the departing soul of "Little Father Dmitri," who had just been murdered by evil men.

The lugubrious chimes from the belfry continued for a long time, and after the sounds had died away, the peasants still stood outside the walls, bareheaded, absorbed in pious mourning.

They resumed their labors, and kept invoking Little Father Dmitri in their devotions and weird contemplations. Dmitri Ivanovitch became their adopted patron.

From Uglich the tale of the little Prince spread to neighboring estates, and gradually peasants all over the Russian heart lands murmured about Little Father Dmitri, redeemer of the people. Most peasants began to believe that he was not really dead, but only hiding, to emerge from his concealment when the time had come.

A worried Boris Godunov belatedly announced that Prince Dmitri Ivanovitch had been stricken by a virulent disease, and that despite the best of care he had succumbed on May 15, 1591. The peasants did not believe this story. The mightiest man of the realm was powerless against a dead boy. A commission went to Uglich to investigate the apparent conspiracy at its source.

The abbot denied knowledge of rumors concerning the little Prince. He could not remember the tolling of the bells on a certain day. The bell ringer asserted that he had never rung the bell out of turn. The monks denied having ever substituted for the bell ringer, and they did not recall the matter at all.

Peasants were asked who had told them about Little Father Dmitri.

"The bell," they replied unhesitatingly.

The members of the commission called them criminal morons and had them flogged. The peasants wailed and cringed, but when questioned about the man who had talked about Dmitri, they cried out that it hadn't been a man, but the bell. Threatened with worse if they kept prattling nonsense, they protested that they would be forever quiet and that they would turn deaf ears to anything the bell had to say.

The bell was found guilty.

Boris Godunov, not yet Tsar but the keeper of the imperial seal, which Theodore Ivanovitch was no longer capable of handling, affixed it under an edict which charged the bell of Uglich with incitement to rebellion and high treason. The clapper of the bell was cut off by the hangman, and the mutilated instrument shipped into perpetual exile to Pelym, east of the Urals.

The first deportee to Siberia was the bell of Uglich.

Soon it was joined there by the abbot, monks, and peasants who lived in the vicinity of the monastery. The next notable arrivals in exile were Dmitri's other guardian and the guardian's brother.

The living deportees were put to draining marshy land, together with natives sentenced to penal servitude. The combined number of the exiles was not recorded, but it is known that in 1621, when the ostrog of Pelym was destroyed by fire, thirty people from Uglich were still vegetating there.

The bell was silenced, but not so the peasants of Russia. Millions waited for Dmitri Ivanovitch.

At the time of his coronation the twenty-seven-year-old Theodore Ivanovitch looked almost twice his age; at thirty-five he was a decrepit wreck, slack of body and sluggish of mind. But still his functions continued, and Boris Godunov, several years older than the Tsar, became impatient with the stubborn beating of the crowned wretch's heart. But he could not have the Tsar killed. Dmitri's shadow protected his half brother. Boris could not create another martyr of royal blood. The huge, bearded despot came to fear even the death of the Tsar from natural causes. It occurred when Theodore Ivanovitch was past forty.

A national assembly was convoked to elect a new tsar. The nobles had been whispering about action to eliminate the aspirant, whom they all feared, but

Boris had his *sbirrs* everywhere and the mere mentioning of another candidate could bring disaster over the rash speaker, and an anguished body of yes-men proclaimed Boris Tsar.

The ruler of Russia and Commander of Siberia arranged ceremonies of barbaric pomp. Deputations from every district of Russia prostrated themselves before the monarch, as they had been ordered; they were struck by the savage display, but they thought of Little Father Dmitri.

In Tomsk the Russian administration arranged a Siberian contribution to the festivities. They had caught one Tojan, chieftain of a small tribe of 300 from the lower Ob River, hiding in the depths of the forests. Tojan was impressive-looking and easily manageable, in contrast to some other princelings, who had to be battled into not always reliable surrender. The instrument of surrender was a petition for the overlordship of the White Tsar.

Chieftain Tojan was illiterate, but he expressed his consent with such alacrity, and acknowledged so solemnly that a signature affixed under the document by a scribe was his own, that he was whisked away to Moscow, along a newly opened, tortuous land route, as a delegate, not only of his own tribe —promoted to a nation by the scribes—but also of five other Siberian nations whose petitions to the White Tsar constituted the voyagers' official luggage.

"White Tsar" did not refer to the ruler's complexion. Like other Orientals, some Siberian people used terms of colors to describe the station of a person. White stood for independent, clear of tribute, and altogether felicitous; black signified submission and a sad state of general affairs. It would have been discourteous not to add White to the title of the ruler.

Boris Godunov looked with inquisitive wonder at the man from Siberia, who was his distant kin, but whose spineless, silly submissiveness was the antithesis of Mongolian heritage. Tojan was received with greater distinction than his rank warranted. He accepted it with awkward satisfaction; he bowed and grinned when the White Tsar approved of the petitions and promised consideration to pleas Tojan would make.

Tojan made no plea; the splendor of the palace, which he now shared with the whitest of men, made him forgetful of visitations back in his native woods, inflicted by men of lesser splendor upon his drab tribe.

Tsar Boris wanted the Siberians to be on his side. He too was a ruthless impostor, a murderer, a wicked despot, but, unlike the Formidable, he did have a grand design. He wanted Russia to be greater, more powerful, and more prosperous; he even wanted justice in the empire in all issues which did not conflict with his purposes. The people should help him, but no help could be expected from poorly trained stooges.

No assistance would be forthcoming from the Russian people.

The spirit of Little Dmitri had arisen; it rallied the country against Boris. Under the very walls of the capital preachers and demagogues told the peasants that Dmitri, saved by faithful monks from the daggers of Boris Godunov's henchmen, was on his way to liberate his people. The forces of the executive were powerless; the demagogues would invariably disappear before the soldiers arrived at the spot, and would re-emerge as soon as the soldiers had gone. A central organization seemed to exist, such as Russian agents would hardly have been able to set up. It undermined villages and spread into cities; worst of all, it operated in the army, concentrated against Poland. Generals attributed recent setbacks to the disloyalty of their soldiers.

The coronation festivities were not quite over when it was announced in Poland that Dmitri Ivanovitch, rightful Tsar of Russia, now under the protection of the King, was assembling an army of Russian patriots in exile, to liberate his country. In the wake of the announcement came reports from the Baltic that Dmitri's army was on the march, and that clashes had resulted in mass desertions and a general rout of Boris Godunov's forces.

Tsar Boris could not well claim that he had had Dmitri murdered more than a decade before, but he repeated his statement about the Prince's death in 1591, to prove that the "liberator" was an impostor. Nobody seemed to believe it. Besides Dmitri himself, a story had it that Dmitri claimed that another boy, at Uglich, had been murdered "by mistake" and that his mother knew of it. As his mother had been poisoned since, the tale could not be checked.

Boris appealed to the nobles to stand by him; he sent rescripts to local governors and magistrates, instructing them to incite the patriotic zeal of the common people against the Polish archenemy and his stooge. But there was no response.

King Sigismund of Poland was the driving power behind "Dmitri Ivanovitch." Sigismund, whose grandiose imperialistic scheme encompassed claims to the throne of Sweden and reduction of Russia to vassalage, exploited the saga of the vanished Prince. The true identity of his Dmitri has not been reliably established. German scholars tend to believe that he was one Grigory Otrepjew, an obscure novice from Tshudov Monastery.

Slowly, inexorably the liberation forces pressed the disintegrating Russian Baltic armies back. There were few Russian nationals among Dmitri's soldiers; the majority were Poles, and there was also the usual admixture of international tramps.

Tsar Boris realized that the capture of his capital was inevitable, but he did not live to see it happen. In 1605, when the victors closed in on Moscow, he died—a sudden death that could only have been more merciful than what would have been in store for him had he been captured alive. Boris's son Fjodor, who assumed the title of Tsar with a helpless gesture rather than defiance, was taken prisoner.

Thus ended the short-lived prospect that, in a new version of Djenghiskhanide rule, a Mongolian dynasty would govern a united Russia and Siberia.

"God is with Dmitri," the peasants hailed their idol.

"He is invincible," exulted the nobles who had no mystical delusions but were convinced that Dmitri, whoever he really was, would give them better opportunities than had Boris Godunov.

Dmitri entered Moscow as a tsar, in a ceremony that resembled a devout procession rather than a military triumph. He was careful not to irritate the citizenry by ostentatious parades of his Polish soldiers; he surrounded himself with Russian advisers, and emphasized his Russianism at every turn. Polish soldiers stayed in barracks and improvised shelters in strategic locations. The people, raving about their righteous young tsar, ignored the ominous presence of the armed foreigners. Dmitri had only Russian soldiers on duty in the Kremlin, and his discretion in dealing with his Poles was truly remarkable.

But Tsar Dmitri had also a Polish fiancée, and this became his undoing. Marina Mniszek, a glamorous noblewoman with a shining crown of golden hair, noble features, and the figure of an antique goddess, was King Sigismund's personal choice for Tsarina. She would dominate her amorous husband, keep him from deviating from the path of submission to Poland, she could outshine Russian women who would woo the Tsar's favor. Marina Mniszek was a fervent Polish nationalist who disdained the brutish Russians; she would always be loyal to her native land. Dmitri was too blindly in love with Marina to consider the political hazards involved in a marriage which he wanted to have performed as soon as possible. He did not seem to mind when he learned that Marina would come with an attendance of many, many Polish nobles.

The royal fiancée and 2000 Polish cavaliers rode through Russia, a procession of beauty, splendor, and arrogance. Along their road peasants and burghers stood watching, in wonder first, and soon in wrath, the bearing of the Poles who treated them like chattels not worthy of licking their boots. Ahead of the cavalcade traveled the breath of surprised indignation, which grew into a cloud of furious doubt: how could this woman who did not deign to look at her subjects, and who was escorted by a host of foreigners who used horsewhips to chase people rendering homage out of their way, be the chosen of their Dmitri, the anointed of God? Who was she, and—fatal question—who was he, whom they had idolized?

When the cavalcade arrived at Moscow, the legend of Dmitri, the anointed, the liberator, was all but destroyed. But popular passions were still at a pitch and clamored for an emotional outlet, be it love or hatred.

Crowds that had been milling around the gates of the Kremlin grew even denser after the beauteous woman and her escort had entered, but their previous adoring radiance changed into glumness and their minds were set at destruction.

Inside the palace the 2000 Poles, seconded by Marina, requested offices, civilian and military, in all parts of the country, that would have turned Russia into a Polish colony. They were scornful and insistent; they could always appeal to the Polish soldiers in the city should Dmitri try to stall; and Dmitri would need their support, for already the milling crowds outside were grumbling loudly enough to be heard through the walls of the Kremlin.

Dmitri did not quite understand the change of mood of the populace. He had not offended his people; no public executions had taken place since he had come to the capital, even the collection of taxes had been temporarily suspended. He did not realize that his unfathomable subjects reasoned that he was not *their* Dmitri, that the real Dmitri was yet to come, and that he stood in the way of *their* true tsar.

The wedding ceremonies were arranged, and lasted for more than ten days. But while inside the Kremlin priests chanted their blessings, people outside shouted their curses. And while the guests of the wedding, the 2000 Poles, and a handful of Russians sat down to a banquet, the people battered the gates, and Russian guards did not oppose them. The Polish nobles escaped through a back door to the barracks, to which their soldiers were confined; the clergy and the few Russian dignitaries made for the safety of the church. Dmitri and Marina alone remained in the banquet hall; and he fell victim to frantic assassins.

The people besieged the Polish barracks but could not conquer the garrisons.

A rump assembly elected Prince Vassilj Shuisky Tsar, but Vassilj, a man with a sketchy record, was eventually deposed by Polish reserves and Russian collaborators, which re-established control of the capital only to be, in turn, attacked by a peasant army led by another Dmitri, allegedly a thief. The second Dmitri was defeated by the Poles and murdered by his own men, who reasoned that a genuine prince, as God's favorite, could not have lost a battle.

And there was yet a third Dmitri, one Isidor Sidorka, who seized the town of Pskov by a coup in 1611, and from there set out to conquer Muscovy.

He reached Moscow two years later, in chains, and lived there for twenty-four hours—the time the hangman took to complete the elaborate tortures reserved for the last "False Dmitri."

Once more Russia was in turmoil. In the south Cossacks organized large bodies of troops for orgies of rape and loot. Prince Trubetzkoy, a soldier of fortune, and Ataman Zarutsky, who under different circumstances might have become another Ermak, organized the sanguinary bands into a motley army to seize the capital and to make Russia a Cossack domain. Ironically enough the Poles protected Moscow against the besiegers, who eventually quarreled among themselves and disbanded into smaller hordes which descended upon lesser towns and villages. Citizens organized home guards to battle the Cossacks. The home guards struggled among themselves until a strange nobleman, Dmitri Mikhailovitch Posharsky, conceived a plan to weld them into a national army that should subdue the marauders, and wrest Moscow from the Poles.

Kosmo Minin, a butcher from Nizhni Novgorod, became Posharsky's assistant and treasurer of the army, in charge of collecting contributions for the national army. In April 1612 most of Central Russia was cleared of Cossacks, and the way to Moscow lay open, but Posharsky, who called himself a prince, was in no hurry to advance. He was negotiating with Prince Charles Philip, brother of Gustavus II Adolphus, King of Sweden, about terms under which Charles Philip would be offered the Crown of Russia. But the Swede refused to guarantee that Posharsky would be Chancellor for life, and thereupon, in August 1612, the national army continued to the capital. On November 27 the Polish last-ditch defenders of the Kremlin surrendered.

In the following year a national assembly elected seventeen-year-old Michael Romanov Tsar. The ancestor of the Romanovs, Andrej, also called Kobyla, the Mare, had come in 1341 to Russia from the province that would later become East Prussia. His son, Koshka, the Cat, entered the service of the grand dukes of Muscovy. His offspring intermarried with higher Muscovite and lesser Mongolian nobility. They were titled and eventually created princes. One Romanov princess figured on the roll of Ivan Grozny's wives. Like other spouses of the Formidable, she remained a somewhat shadowy figure, lamentable in the settings of glum, brutish pompousness. But she did succeed in establishing members of her family in prominent positions at court, and this brought Boris Godunov's disfavor upon the family. A Romanov bishop, Ivan, also called Anikita, was nominated the second guardian of Dmitri. Boris would have disposed of the boy under all circumstances, but the appointment of a Romanov speeded his action. It might even have been that to him the name of Romanov evoked visions of conspiracy.

Bishop Ivan, and his brother Vassilj Romanov, were marched to Pelym in 1598, where Vassilj died in 1601. But Bishop Ivan Romanov survived, returned to Muscovy after his nephew, the first Romanov Tsar, ascended the throne; and the Bishop lived until 1630.

What he told the Tsar about the lot of deportees did not cause Michael to discontinue either banishment or punitive transfer to Siberia, and among the men he sent beyond the Urals was Posharsky.

Nobleman Posharsky (the Tsar never called him Prince) had received a town house in Moscow and three estates, complete with mansions and peasants, as a reward for his patriotism. This did not satisfy his ambitions, however, and he spun threads to Lithuania, offering his services in return for the domain and the princely title of Smolensk.

Tsar Michael learned of it and gave the schemer an assignment that would keep him from plotting with foreigners: as a clerk in the administration of Tobolsk, Siberia.

After eight years of subaltern work Posharsky induced the local governor to send him on inspection tours. He posed as the Tsar's own *revisor*, collected bribes, seized contraband, invested in traffic with native girls and moonshining products, and was well on his way to become a respectable nabob when he turned overly bold and faked the signature of the Archbishop of Tobolsk on a paper authorizing Prince Posharsky to seize all furs collected within the archdiocese.

The angry prelate had the faker arrested. Posharsky's Siberian property was seized, and so were his awards for past patriotism back home.

Posharsky died in 1638. His monument and that of Minin now stand in Moscow, and Soviet rulers have awarded him a niche in their Walhalla, perhaps because there is no other suitable revolutionary patriot available for that period.

CHAPTER THIRTY-THREE At the turn of the century the Russian Government took stock of its conquests in Asia. Reports on the farthest points of advance reached by January 1, 1600, were confusing, and the maps on which they were marked offered no clear picture of the controversial locations. But officials delighting in high figures estimated that the Tsar's Siberia already covered some two and a half million square miles.

This was a wild overstatement, but Boris Godunov accepted it and map designers hastily adapted their delineations. This eventually resulted in a discrepancy of thirty degrees in longitude between Siberia's actual eastern extension and its delimitation on Russian maps, which was to be grudgingly rectified only late in the eighteenth century.

Tsar Boris's experts produced a pattern to exploit Siberia in accordance with its expansion and potential wealth.

A rescript was signed by Tsar Boris in 1600, ordering that "in view of the size and steady expansion of the Russian holdings in Siberia" annual tributes for the Crown should be "no less than 200,000 sables, 10,000 black foxes, and 20,000 beaver furs, all flawless, and from fully grown animals."

This minimum did not include such gifts (*pominkis*) as the people and chieftains of Siberia would offer His Majesty and his appointed officials.

The rescript did not say which officeholders were entitled to soak the natives, but not even the lowliest clerks, not even Russian coachmen, would refrain from soliciting their share. The small fry were expected to split with their superiors who, in turn, collected on their own and split with higher-ups all along the line to the Governor General, who took care of the gentlemen in the capital in charge of Siberian affairs.

It was an intricate network of catch as catch can, everybody trying to cheat everybody else and, in turn, expecting honesty from the next man; a ring held together by savage determination to bleed the natives white.

The minimum figure of tribute was completely unrealistic. High as the number of fur animals was, it did not come anywhere near the assumptions upon which the rescript had been based. The *pominki* would bring the demand for sables at about one million annually; this would have exterminated the population of sables in no time, and there were never enough men to hunt such a number of animals, skin them, and ship the pelts to their destinations. Besides the international market for costly furs was narrowly limited, and a sudden oversupply would have reduced the price of a sable to that of a rabbit.

Never was the contingent delivered. Russian accounts were sketchy, but it can be assumed that in no year did 10 per cent of the figure reach the Tsar's treasury. The rescript, nevertheless, remained in power for a full two centuries.

The Siberian Chancellery in Muscovy, the central agency in charge of Siberian affairs, proclaimed the fur trade a government monopoly. But government monopoly could not prevent violators from disposing of contraband. Black marketeers operated in the remotest spots of the land, maintained direct communications with foreign buyers, and if caught in illicit dealings, which happened rarely enough, simply paid bribes.

Another trade rescript proclaimed that traffic in commodities other than furs was free; no duties would be levied; traders from Bokhara and the Nogai district should be encouraged to take their wares, horses, and cattle to Tumen, Tara, or Tobolsk; delegates accompanying caravans should be invited to visit Moscow as guests of the Russian Government, and to negotiate profitable trade agreements. Russia, which never during that period had more than 1500 soldiers in Siberia, including native volunteers, offered military protection to trade caravans throughout the long route. The rescript also directed governors to build Tobolsk into an Asiatic trade center. Tobolsk, expanded into a primitive settlement 630 Russian fathoms (4410 feet) in circumference, was proclaimed capital of Siberia in 1607.

The Stroganoffs did not protest against infractions of their charters; the disregard of their commercial privileges was soon followed by the establishment of a government near-monopoly for land transportation; Sol-Wueshegodska had foreseen the rise of Boris Godunov; Sol-Wueshegodska realized the imminence of his fall, and would not argue with a doomed man. For the record the house of Stroganoff filed a claim for 600,000 square miles of Siberian land, subject to exact delimitation and extension as Russian domination expanded.

Officials were just drafting another edict proclaiming all of Siberia Crown land, and military governors, churchmen, and mercenaries were freely allotting land to themselves and their friends and associates when the Stroganoffs filed their claim. Action was postponed.

The Stroganoffs did not go empty-handed, however. They operated the black market in furs; they controlled the trade of Tobolsk through their agents. Stroganoff agents were the only Russians in Siberia who had ready cash to buy valuables from soldiers and officials, who owned a wealth of goods but had no cash to buy an imported bottle of wine. Hardly ever had the traditional policy of keeping liquid funds on hand paid such dividends as in Siberia around the turn of the seventeenth century.

Sol-Wueshegodska was in no hurry to specify details of its claim to the 600,000-square-mile estate. The Russian Government was working on an agrarian settlement program; it would take a long time to achieve results, but the Stroganoffs could wait. Only after certain areas were being cultivated would they stake the boundaries of the domain. As Russian soldiers, Cossacks, and irregulars rushed eastward in a mad drive into space, the nominal Stroganoff domain kept growing. With Siberia supposed to encompass all the lands beyond the Urals and the plain between these mountains and the northernmost shore of the Caspian, the estate would have grown into more than twice its size of 1600; but, expanding, it grew into a phantom domain.

No additional claims, no specifications of the first claim were ever filed. The Stroganoffs were no longer of Anikita's caliber; they no longer could conceive the establishment of a sovereign realm of their own, but they were realists. They had no delusions about the impossibility of administering such oversized possessions; they were aware of the manpower problem involved, and they also knew that such a territory could not be sold. No individual or group had the means to acquire that land and there were not enough free farmers in Russia to buy it in smaller parcels, nor even to settle it as tenants.

The Stroganoffs were not like Johann August Sutter who, 250 years later, would establish his Californian empire and hold onto his title of property to the ruinous end. As Russian governments pondered about repeal of Stroganoff charters, the family pondered about poachers, suggested negotiation, and eventually chose the bird in hand: a mere 10,000,000 *dessjatines* (27,000,000 acres) of the finest farmland adjoining their patrimony, complete with as many souls as were needed to operate the estate.

"Souls" were peasants who lived on a property as part of its inventory, and whom Russian terminology did not call serfs even though this would have fittingly described their status. In the underpopulated Russia the number of souls on an estate rather than acreage determined its value.

Throughout the seventeenth century the Russian administration took no Siberian census. But governors and captains, clergymen, clerks, and Cossacks could but notice that there were not enough "souls" in Siberia to keep them comfortably supplied.

There seemed to have been no famines in the central and southern districts of Siberia before the Russians penetrated the area. But, as native farmers and cattle breeders neglected their skills and turned hunters to satisfy Russian demands, and tribes became nomads in the woods to escape Russian violence, the fur output declined steadily, while thievery, wastage, and general mismanagement constantly increased Russian consumption. The administration and the military resolved to round up natives for forced farm labor. Before the operation went under way, General Prince Jelezkoj, a favorite of Tsar Boris, and the civilian officials quarreled about who should get a priority, and eventually the roundup became as wasteful as everything authorities undertook in Siberia. Useful groups of native farmers were exterminated. The army switched from recruiting to tax collecting, hunting for tribute evaders in remote vastnesses, and re-emerged from virgin forests with a booty of a few light, shabby sables. Once natives told the Prince about the Pegaja (Dappled) Ordu, Tatar tribesmen whose skin was dappled like the hide of a horse, and Jelezkoj wrote to Muscovy that he would soon present the Tsar with a batch of dappled subjects. Hunting for the Pegaja Ordu, the army penetrated the glorious wilderness of the Altai Mountains, but was unable to find a single living man, plain or spotted. However, with regulations requiring that conquered territories be safeguarded by construction of ostrogs, Jelezkoj spent almost one year constructing fortifications in the unpopulated mountains and eventually returned to Tobolsk, without provisions or labor draftees, but with the draft of another letter to Muscovy, explaining that the Tsar's dappled subjects were a tricky and elusive lot, whom he would track down and fine for misdemeanor.

Food shortage was acute and menacing. Overextension of conquest for the sake of a silly hunt was insanity. Jelezkoj's tales never reached a tsar, for they arrived in Moscow during the interregnum. Officials, however, who carried on, drafting regulations and filing incoming documents, chaos or order, read about the Dappled Ordu and put the report in the files of defaulters on tributes.

Several decades later this entry spelled disaster for a tribe on the Indigirka River whom neighbors called "speckled" because of the reindeer skins they wore. Those unfortunate tribesmen were dubbed Dappled Horde and fined eleven sables per capita for every year of arrears. They were unable to produce the furs and the fine was commuted to decimation.

The civilian administration of Siberia could not wait until bureaucrats back home worked out an agrarian program for Siberia. Their frantic calls for assistance continued throughout the reign of Tsar Boris, the interludes of the false Dmitri and Prince-Tsar Shuisky, and all the time governors of Siberia tried to muster native manpower to produce food. Official stupidity and viciousness accounted for the deportation of natives to barren regions, such as Pelym, instead of fertile districts.

Experts on population policies and agrarian production would have considered a debacle inevitable. The Siberian problem was further complicated by Russia's own shortage of manpower and by the turmoil into which the land had been thrown. The Siberian venture seemed doomed. But experts' reasonings did not apply to Russia, where unsoundness successfully substituted for logic, and chaos brought consolidation.

Early in the seventeenth century, when Muscovite officialdom at last produced a master-plan of settling one hundred peasant families in the region of Tomsk, this seemed to be a travesty. But already nature had set a course to conserve Siberia for the invaders. This resulted in another of those miracles which, combined, account for the existence of Russia, past and present. And also, not unlike other Russian wonders, this one was based upon a false premise: old Anikita's tale of Mangansee.

The people believed that the Siberian Ophir had been located, and pictured it according to their own visions of wealth. Gold meant little to peasants, and furs other than sheepskin meant nothing. Their Ophir was a land which produced rich harvests without as much as fertilization, and where crops belonged to the men who planted and harvested them. Mangansee, to them, was an immensity of fat, black earth.

Venturesome men defied all obstacles to get there. Man-made hindrances marked the beginning of their pilgrimage: few Russian peasants were nominally free, but even the freemen needed permission to leave their dwelling places. Local authorities refused to grant permits for immigration to Siberia. Landowners used drastic means to prevent the loss of souls. Illicit immigrants who managed to sneak away had no animals, provisions, or tools, and they were outlaws. Outlaws who stayed on trodden paths had little chance to escape the posse; men without provisions who made their way through the wilderness would often starve. Nature, too, took a fearful toll of the ragged wanderers, and yet a trickle of peasants reached Siberia. They did not find their Ophir, but they did reach fertile land, and they had no choice but to work it. The blessings it lavishly bestowed would not make the peasant wealthy; the crops belonged to men who held it in their sway. The waste of peasant lives was terrific: out of a hundred illegal immigrants to Siberia, perhaps ten ever reached the land, and another five or six died there prematurely from undernourishment and overwork. But the proceeds of their toils kept the conquerors alive, and Siberia under Russian rule.

The hundred authorized peasants, immigrants who eventually arrived at Tomsk—afoot, since conveyances were reserved for cargo—were fed and sheltered during their voyage, but did not get allotments of land they had been promised, nor did they find the abundance of seeds, cattle, horses, and implements of which Russian officials had been talking. The land was the Tsar's and his organs treated the immigrants like the Spanish conquerors in America had treated their peons. The settlers made crude implements, lived in primitive huts, raised abundance, and subsisted on crumbs and mystical expectations.

Around 1605 Tomsk consisted of a solid ostrog, a network of fences behind which cattle and natives were held, and a grange where the official coachmen lived together with horses, a gaily painted cart, and one sleigh.

The environs of Tomsk were an agronomist's paradise. An early report, unearthed 150 years after the peasants settled, said: "The soil is black, fat, and loose, and it requires no manure. In fact, an experimental fertilization of the soil produced adverse results: the seeds produced overgrown stalks and less grain. The region is ideally suited for horse breeding, and cattle raising. The rivers are teeming with fine fish. Much of the district consists of virgin soil. The land was never heavily taxed. There was always more soil than people could till; and after working one plot for several years, Siberians let it lie fallow, and turned to another lot."

The fine fish in the rivers attracted discontented farm laborers, who would try their hands as fishermen in waters which, as they thought, were no man's personal property. Rivers, lakes, and ponds were the Tsar's, but the Tsar was as remote as the heavens. "Heaven is high above, and the Tsar is far away," was one of the earliest proverbs coined by Russians in Siberia. The Tsar's disloyal servants, however, were nearby, within the range of their muskets. Fishermen were stripped of their catch as thoroughly as peasants of their grain. Desperate, destitute ex-farmers and ex-fishermen joined strange bands which roamed the lands; but new immigrants took their places to till the fertile, sheer inexhaustible soil.

Russian officers and noncoms drew their pay, not only in money and in kind, but also in *pomestie*—allotment of domains. *Vojvods* (army commanders) received upward of a million acres, and even a *dvoraen* (captain) would collect scores of thousands of acres. Accountants padded pay rolls and had large estates apportioned to fictitious soldiers; Cossacks claimed and received similar allotments.

Governors helped themselves to immense estates, and parceled out millions of acres to their favorites as recompense for alleged merits.

The King's man controlling the land from his strong *burg* and the landman tilling the soil under his protection and absolute rule were a standing feature in the early development of rural estates in the Old World, where the arbitrary powers of the lord of the burg were subsequently superseded by statutory assessments and by tenancy. In seventeenth-century Siberia, however, rural estates did not follow this trend of development.

The holders of immense domains had no affinity to the soil. They were neither builders nor preservers, and an acre of an agronomist's paradise, like a pelt or a stolen musket, was considered but a means of payment for a coveted commodity that could not be had by robbery. No Cossack, no army regular, no clerk or governor wanted to wait for returns; they would sell today for one bottle of wine rather than wait until tomorrow for a chance of obtaining two bottles or three. The urge for drink and debauchery was imminent; tomorrow was remote and unsafe.

Fertile land was in turn tilled, abandoned, and worked again; peasants changed, and titular owners; there was no system in Russian farming in Siberia, no stability, and no progress for which men could claim credit. However, the procreative power of the soil was stronger than the destructiveness of man. Enough food grew to support a population, which half a century after Ermak's death may have numbered about one person to every five square miles.

The government in Moscow did not really want its appointees to establish themselves permanently and indulge in nepotism. Highhanded as these officeholders were, they would strive for powers reserved to the sovereign and his Siberian Chancellery. And Moscow had no delusions about honesty in office. Unable to find honest servants, however, the Tsar's government set time limits to a man's opportunity to steal.

There would be a rather quick rotation of officeholders, and men called back to the capital should be squeezed out of part of their ill-gotten property. Tshulkov became the first victim of the rotating system. Three harsh messengers summoned him to Moscow and informed him that the expected duration of his sojourn there required that he take his mobile belongings along. Tshulkov departed with his grim companions and a fortune in furs, jewels, and precious metals. This was the last Siberians saw of him; there is no record of his ultimate fate.

The governors of Tobolsk, raised to the rank of governor generals of Siberia, were authorized to wield the seal of the Tsar in Siberia and to act in the Tsar's name. Keepers of the seal made inspection trips and found corruption and incompetence wherever they went; but, on returning to Tobolsk, their personal baggage had grown by several carloads, and their reports to His Majesty bristled with anecdotes of spontaneous manifestations of loyalty, of progress in every field of human endeavor. They did not mention setbacks or the necessity of purges.

Purges did take place, however, with no other effect than changes of physiognomies. The system and the character of its instruments were not affected.

A commerce department, set up in Tobolsk in the day of the Polish occupation of Moscow, compiled records of its achievements. New market places, it said, were mushrooming all over Siberia; foreign merchants had taken up residence in Tobolsk, Tomsk, Tara, and Tumen; they were never unduly molested, and were treated with such courtesy that more tradespeople were flocking into Siberia to establish agencies and factories. Business figures were rising, and there were no complaints about irregularities.

In Verkhoturie, on the Russo-Siberian border, the Siberian administration had established a clearinghouse for imports and exports from and to the West. The customs office of Verkhoturie collected an increasing amount of duties and storage fees, which would benefit the Russian treasury.

The Siberian administration boasted that Russian expansion no longer depended upon military conquest alone. Nations and tribes who lived beyond the confines of outlying ostrogs sent deputations to Tobolsk, to apply for Russian sovereignty and Russian administration. The Telenguts, the Kirghizes, the Kalmucks, the Umaks, and many more allegedly important Siberian peoples were flocking to the Russian orbit, as did workers, volunteer soldiers, suppliers of furs, and peasants, all inspired by a desire to enjoy the blessings of the Tsar's rule and to offer their lives and skills in return.

In fact the Telenguts were but an unimportant nomad tribe; the Kirghizes who went to Tobolsk were representatives of two small splinter groups who lived far apart from the bulk of their kin; the Kalmucks were a fraction of their nation; and the Umaks were a wretched lot from Northern Siberia. The "many more important Siberian peoples" existed only in a gubernatorial secretary's imagination.

Tsar Michael Romanov, to whom his Siberian Chancellery submitted such reports as edifying reading matter, had learned enough about Siberia from his uncle, the ex-exile, to doubt the veracity of the men who had composed them. The members of his family, who advised Michael, were not familiar with the complexities of Siberian ethnology, but experience gathered at Pelym indicated that the conquerors had not yet encountered coherent, numerous peoples, that natives were not anxious to barter their skills against foreign domination, and that applicants for Russian rule were often coerced or bribed, and always nonentities.

The older Romanovs were sensible men: they saw that the rise in business volume was falling behind the rate of territorial expansion, and they understood that the establishment of a customs house in Verkhoturie was detrimental to the incorporation of Siberia into the Russian economic system, another indication of separatism among the *tshinovnitzi*, the officials, who would fraudulently exploit whatever independence they could achieve.

Godlessness was the mainspring of wrongdoing; nothing but rapid expansion of the Church could create the foundations of virtue in Siberia. The Cossacks and rootless adventurers there believed that God could watch men's doings only through the "eyes of his churches." Where there was no church, God was blindfolded. If there were many churches, Cossacks and their like would come to fear God's watchful eyes; and even officials would be restrained by the presence of many good priests.

The man who told this to Michael was his father, Philaret Romanov, Metropolitan of the Russian Church.

On behalf of Tsar Michael, Metropolitan Philaret requested a conclusive account on the state of religious affairs in Siberia, much to the embarrassment of the authorities who kept few records on subjects they did not consider profitable.

It was said that sometime about 1604, Jonah, a monk, had built the first Siberian monastery near Verkhoturie and dedicated it to St. Nicholas. But it was not known whether Jonah had been a saintly visionary, a repentent offender, or an itinerant friar. He was already dead or had otherwise vanished and the monastery was abandoned. A church, however, had been built nearby, with the authorization of Boris Godunov, who had made a donation toward construction, lumber left over from the building of an ostrog. There were more churches and monasteries, as of 1615, the report added, but no data as to their creation and activities was available.

"In the days of yore," a distinguished Russian scholar wrote later, "Siberian churches and convents were established by common monks, some of them not even ordained, without order or authorization by the proper authorities."

The Metropolitan realized that correspondence with Tobolsk would not promote the advancement of virtue and religion in Siberia, and in 1621 he had Cyprian, Archimandrite of Chutinsoy Monastery near Novgorod, appointed Archbishop and Primate of Siberia, with residence in Tobolsk.

"Turn Siberia into a clean, God-fearing domain," the prelate was briefed. This was a herculean task, and Cyprian was a mild man, equally afraid of boisterous soldiers, pagan natives, and exacting superiors.

The new Archbishop was horrified by what he called the wicked, disorderly life led by the Russian population of Siberia in general, and the loathsome behavior of the Cossacks in particular. In a letter to the Metropolitan he complained that men transferred to foreign lands acquired different habits and even looks, like herbs transplanted into another soil. The Cossacks' faces had changed after they succumbed to paganism, and they had no morals. They even induced "unmarried persons of the female sex to come to Siberia," and did not marry them but treated them as slaves, and even worse. The immoral Cossacks would not listen to the admonitions of their pastor, and therefore the primate had advised the military authorities to take disciplinary action against the vexation.

But the authorities refused to antagonize Cossacks and regulars by what they called hypocritical chicanery. The prelate invoked the Metropolitan's directives; the officers quoted Tsarist rescripts, authorizing them to use their own judgment in local matters.

Cyprian wrote more letters to Philaret Romanov, bitterly complaining about Siberian viciousness and entreating the Metropolitan to have the Tsar chasten blasphemers in office.

In Moscow, however, not even the clergy wanted to provoke a mutiny in Siberia, and after waiting several months to let the Archbishop cool off the Metropolitan replied that rashness and violence were neither wise nor virtuous, and that Cyprian should concentrate on the Christianization of the people by missionaries, of which there were many in Siberia, on encouragement of meritorious local clergy, on construction of churches, and that he should cure souls by spiritual means rather than by punishment.

The Archbishop knew already that there were no missionaries active in his primacy. However, several religious institutions existed and carried on despite lack of subsidies. Cyprian undertook a long, uncomfortable voyage to visit monasteries and to thank and comfort steadfast monks and nuns.

In Uspenskoj and Troyzkoj he found cloisters built in the first decade of the century. The residents were busy in various, not strictly pious, endeavors to make a living. They said that they had no time to spare for observance and divine services, but should the Archbishop provide them with enough supplies they would arrange for services. Cyprian continued to Spaskoj on the Tara River, and to Pokrovskoj near Turisk, where he found similar conditions but was relieved to learn that Mass was being regularly said in another convent at Turisk.

When he visited the convent, he found the place inhabited by men and women wearing monk's and nun's garbs, who intermingled with complete lack of chastity and raised flocks of offspring. The person in charge of religious activities was a coarse layman who enjoyed saying Mass his own way. The monks and nuns were in dire need of conversion to repentant virtue, and the building would have to be reconsecrated. The dwellers did not object to reconsecration of their habitat, but they did not want to hear of separation. Unable to control the sinners, Cyprian assigned his vicar Marcarius to guide them toward the path of duty, and left for Tobolsk, where he wrote yet another letter to Philaret about his findings.

The Metropolitan found such abuses intolerable. He prevailed upon his son to draw up two rescripts, directing his officers and governors to lend all support to the Archbishop and to comply with every request he would make. Officers and governors were incensed. Under the rescripts the Church would gain the autonomy in Siberia for which they had been striving in vain. Hardly had they recovered from the shock of the rescripts when yet another decree ordered them to allot land to the Church and cover the expenses of religious institutions. The local masters of Siberia did not want another party to share the spoils of the land, but the smoldering mutiny did not break out: there was too little unity among the dignitaries, and too much mutual distrust.

The prospect of prebends lured invalid Cossacks, aging poachers, and shiftless elements, including many women with strictly non-religious backgrounds, to join religious institutions. More convents sprang up, and even a number of devout and intrepid individuals entered orders. Few natives applied for admission. To them the God of the invaders was a Russian, from whom they could not expect much good. They would placate the Russian in heaven by subservience, but they would otherwise try to evade him. And because the majority of the new clergy had neither the aptitude nor even the desire to go out and teach the non-believers, the heathens did not meet many evangelizers.

Marcarius used an allotment of land to solve the problem of purifying Turisk. He offered the monks a big estate if they would move there, alone, and after some bickering and bargaining the male sinners established themselves on their new domain, leaving nuns and children behind. Into the vacated quarters moved other nuns, whom the indignant archespicopal vicar had found living in private quarters near barracks, under conditions that defied detailed description in a report to the primate.

Relations between Cyprian and the mundane authorities were improving, but this was not caused by a change of heart of the laymen. The Archbishop no longer wanted to live in bare, narrow quarters, but requested that an archepiscopal palace be built. In 1626 the building—largest in the town—was completed, and 8000 acres of land were parceled out as the primate's domain. Peasant immigrants were assigned to work the land for the benefit of its master. Next the primate requested, and obtained, construction of a cathedral. Then the authorities donated to the Archbishop another estate teeming with game and fish. Cyprian accepted it graciously, and during inauguration ceremonies of the cathedral clerical and mundane dignitaries exchanged pledges of everlasting friendship.

A brief entry in the records of the Siberian primacy concerns enlargement of the ecclesiastic domain to 100,000 acres.

Cyprian's reports to the Metropolitan now omitted references to unsatisfactory Siberian morals; they elaborated on spiritual progress, on the migration of farmers, and on—historiography.

The primate took a lively interest in Ermak, and most seriously considered having the former river pirate canonized. Substantial awards were pledged to persons who could testify on actions bearing out Ermak's saintliness. Cossacks who were not yet born when Ermak drowned claimed to have participated in some virtuous exploit or other performed by him. But combined false testimony did not quite justify canonization. Cyprian eventually contented himself with having Ermak's name, and the names of his men killed in action, engraved in a mural tablet on the new cathedral, and holding annual special services in their memory.

Cyprian lived like a wealthy squire; his religious zeal gave way to magnanimous tolerance. Transplanted to Siberia, the Archbishop had undergone a remarkable change indeed.

CHAPTER THIRTY-FOUR

"The saying 'As you sow, so you reap,' does not apply to Siberia, where you reap what you sow tenfold," a Russian agricultural expert raved in the day when Cyprian was still sowing religious zeal, and had not yet reaped personal prosperity. "Standing crops are a marvellous sight, with the ears of corn as large and full as never seen elsewhere. Little toil produces harvests, which dwarf anything that can be obtained inside Russia.

"Salt springs are being found in the northeasternmost corner of Siberia, on the Yenisei River and in the steppes adjoining the Irtysh. The brine, gushing forth from the springs, evaporates almost instantly, leaving behind growing piles of the purest rock salt." Experts dispatched to the spot to check this account found it exaggerated as to the ease of production, but correct as to the abundance of salt.

In 1628 the Governor of Turisk reported the discovery of large iron deposits, which had been known to natives for a long time. Within the next decade silver, copper, and lead were discovered in quantities.

Supplies were needed, transportation and equipment; peasants were needed, so were miners and salt laborers, and experts, experts, experts.

Siberia could have been Ophir but for Russia's lack of laborers and organizers.

Moral requirements for immigrants, as listed in the Stroganoff charter, were no longer mentioned. Deportation of Russian criminals to Siberia had become common practice since the exile of the bell, and in 1649 it was officially instituted as a penalty. Thieves, vagrants, deserters, pederasts, coiners, heretics, dealers in stolen goods were liable to deportation. Under the law of civilized Western countries such men would have faced the rope, the stake, or even the kettle with boiling oil. Russian justice was not merciful, but it was found more efficient to have a man work in the Tsar's salt mines than have him roast in the Tsar's frying pan.

Exiles were marched to their destinations under despicable circumstances; yet the strongest survived the ordeal and transport commanders had a way of making up for losses en route. The number of their wards was listed, but not their names, and if fifteen were missing, fifteen natives, wanderers, or even children were tracked down and added to the transport before it was delivered to the receiving agency.

Not only convicts were liable to deportation. The Tsar, his ministers and governors, and lower officials down to provincial magistrates could have persons sent to Siberia for no reason other than personal dislike. And landowners could have "souls" deported without as much as an investigation of their alleged offences.

Deportation in these days was tantamount to forced labor for life. Only much later were time limitations and differential treatments introduced, and not until the early nineteenth century did exile to Siberia acquire the aura of martyrdom, tragedy, and glory, which has become an essential notion of Siberia to many people of many countries.

Deportees assigned to work in the Tsar's mines were quartered in *katorgas*, prisons as rotten and filthy as most Russian dungeons. They were guarded by Cossacks and marched to work by overseers who stole and sold part of the captives' food, and even more of the Tsar's salt, iron, copper, silver, and lead. Captives who cleared forests and drained marshes slept in barracks and were less heavily guarded, but otherwise they enjoyed no privileges.

The intelligentsia among the exiles, however, men prominent enough to have fallen into disgrace with the Tsar, his generals, and ministers, were treated with distinction by Siberian officials who enjoyed rubbing shoulders with notabilities even if they were no longer in good standing. Such men would be house guests of ostrog commanders, provincial governors, and ranking clergymen; they never joined labor gangs.

Many common deportees gained freedom through escape. They were rarely branded, and, when stopped, and asked to identify themselves, they would invariably reply that they had lost their memories. "The Forgetful" became a familiar Siberian character, and he remained unmolested until a governor general put a price of three rubles on the head of each fugitive deportee, and peasants, Cossacks, and burghers went hunting forgetful human prey.

Boris Godunov, a student of the ancient Mongolian system of communications, had ordered that a network of transportation be established in Siberia. *Tshinovnitzi* went to work on the tremendous project to link major ostrogs, market places, and outposts of expanding conquest for the benefit of authorities and authorized settlers—not including convicts. The new system of communication should use land routes. The *tshinovnitzi* brushed aside the idea of systematic road construction and somehow there would be roads—later. Most tracts of Siberia were flatland; flatland would always be traversable by carts, thousands of teams of horses would be needed to maintain services and horses needed food and care. The bureaucrats could not figure exactly how many animals and helpers were required, but there would not be enough of either in Russia, and so they left the matter to nature, which might take care of it to the benefit of the Russian Crown. Carts and carriages, sleighs and wagons were the next item on the agenda. The Russian military had no conveyances to spare, but the tshinovnitzi's trust in nature knew no bound. A solution of that part of the problem was also taken for granted.

Eventually a project unequaled in scope since Roman construction of communications narrowed down to the hiring of coachmen to carry out transportation in accordance with regulations, drafted by busy scribes—"ink souls," or "office scrolls," as their sophisticated countrymen called them.

Together with the first hundred authorized peasant families fifty *jamstshiki* (coachmen) left for Siberia. The coachmen, protected by some thirty Cossacks, went to the distribution center of Turisk. En route they got an object lesson of what a Russian could do to Siberian natives provided he was part of the authority. The Cossacks requisitioned and collected as a matter of routine, and the jamstshiki realized that they too could impress the "pagans" into their own service.

The coachman was an official; he requisitioned as many horses, or, far up north, reindeer, as he wished; and he ordered the beasts' former owners to service the stock. The jamstshik needed conveyances. He ordered natives to build what they did not have, and confiscated what they did have. Natives were flogged and kicked into doing the work to the taste of the jamstshik, and they were forced to repair vehicles battered by hobbling over creeks and bumps on roadless ground.

So brutish were the coachmen that a foreign explorer who traveled through Siberia almost one century after the first transport reached Turisk noted in his diary that the most savage tribesmen he had encountered were those the Russians called jamstshiki.

The jamstshik was committed to transport persons on official business, holders of special passports, and their personal belongings. Timetables did not exist. Departures were to take place "when warranted by the circumstances." Only holders of special horse-relay allotments were entitled to "immediate transportation." The coachmen were illiterate. Words on documents meant nothing to them. Officials requesting transportation soon found this out. The government issued documents of different colors to mark the sort of paper the holder presented.

The coachmen, however, had already noticed the advantages of not understanding certificates. They had been grudgingly tipped by holders of official papers who could not wait until the jamstshik was convinced of their title to transportation. The coachmen now claimed that they could not distinguish colors, and they kept coercing customers into paying illegal dues.

Legitimate peasant settlers were in no hurry, but they carried tools and household implements which the coachmen refused to consider personal belongings. The peasant immigrants would part with some of their objects at every jamstshik station to have the greedy coachman carry the rest; they would be destitute by the time of their arrival at the assigned plot.

Merchants on their way to and from Verkhoturie were soaked by the coachmen. Cossacks sold moonshine-booze and nauseating tobacco to natives; they would stab or shoot everybody who interfered with the trade, except for the jamstshiki, who were more violent than Cossacks. The coachmen became partners in other people's illicit businesses and they established many of their own. They were brigands, murderers, smugglers, white-slavers, cheats—yet, they did drive conveyances, thus bearing out the optimistic negligence of Boris Godunov's *tshinovnitzi*.

A system of transportation came into being, cartwheels turned, men and objects were taken to their destinations, unsafely, haphazardly, of course, but transportation turned into another odd Russo-Siberian miracle. Prior to the construction of the Trans-Siberian Railroad at the turn of the twentieth century it could take anywhere from three months to three years to cross Siberia from west to east or in the opposite direction, depending chiefly on the magnanimity of the traveler.

Nominally transportation was a government monopoly, but the government would not give such services to natives under process of "resettlement." Muscovite *tshinovnitzi*, whose names are not recorded, accounted for a coercive population policy, such as forced collective shifts. Not since Biblical times had such practices been applied to conquered people. Siberian governors were authorized to stage mass deportation of entire tribes and people to areas in which they could be usefully put to work. The deportee's status was inferior to that of most serfs: they had no title to life, property, and justice. They were driven to their destinations by mounted soldiers who carried cat-o'-nine-tails; the exhausted were left to die from exposure; survivors soon succumbed to ill-treatment; none of the objectives of deportation, either economic or military, was achieved. But, however futile, this population policy was a momentous practice, for it set the pattern for later conquerors. Hitler used it, among others, against the people of occupied Russia; Stalin applied it to get rid of the "Volga Germans" and similar undesirables, and in the course of events it came to range high among the means of extermination of men by men.

The resettlement decree was issued under the rule of Boris Godunov, almost simultaneously with another official enunciation which termed the conquest of Siberia "legal" because Siberia was the land of Kutchum, whose ancestors had attacked Russia without justification; thus the Russian campaign was proclaimed a legitimate retaliation, and Kutchum was called the one who had opened hostilities.

The recognition of Kutchum's descent was as surprising as it was belated; it was fantastic to call him the aggressor, but when the enunciation was made, the conquerors had already penetrated far beyond the part of Siberia formerly under Kutchum's control. When publicized, the document seemed inconsequential; however, the formula was inherited by Red Russia, whose government keeps denouncing victims of its encroachment as provocators and aggressors.

The alleged legitimacy of conquest would not have induced anybody to immigrate to Siberia, however. Residents of Russia who considered immigration usually wanted to get beyond the range of the law.

Bands of deserters and escaped prisoners of war roamed the Russian northwest, including men who had no conception of their nationality and who spoke an idiom of lansquenets, based on obscene onomatopoetical terms for genitals, food, drink, and arms. They were Germans, Lithuanians, Poles, and, of course, Russians. They went east in gangs strong enough to loot villages and to fight their way out of traps. Moscow outlawed the marauders, but, Russia being in turmoil, the ban had little effect inside the European realm and none whatsoever in Siberia.

Prince Jelezkoj had had an "army" of 141 when he advanced toward unconquered parts of the former Djenghiskhanide realm; he gladly enlisted whoever could carry arms. His host of 1500, which eventually went hunting for the Dappled Ordu, included many hundreds of ex-prisoners and deserters. With the help of such men he reached the sources of the Irtysh and Ob rivers, then turned southeast to invade the Baraba Steppe, building ostrogs as he advanced.

The Baraba Steppe is a vast expanse of land stretching from the fertile grounds around Narym and Surgut to the foothills of the Altai Mountains. Only in its extreme northeastern and southeastern rims is the Baraba Steppe inhospitable to men. In the northeast treacherous swamps suddenly swallow creatures not as light-footed as the animals of the fields; and fir forests so thick that the sun does not penetrate the entangled branches even on bright midsummer days defy clearing. In the southeast a caprice of nature reduces precipitation to a point at which there is never any relief from drought.

Elsewhere, however, the good earth pulsates with fecundating clear waters; good-sized rivers arise in the steppe; lakes rest in settings of profusely blooming meadows and lovely birch groves. Nature adorns the steppe with a profusion of wild fruits; an untilled soil produces edible herbs, inviting all creatures to feast from God's own larder.

Jelezkoj's ruffians did not appreciate the fascination of beauty and abundance. The natives they encountered went hunting and fishing, and offered beaver furs as a barter against anything. Glittering trifles they owned indicated that they had been bartering before. Chinese traders occasionally came to the steppe to acquire fine beaver for next to nothing. It did not occur to the Russians that they might encounter representatives of a great nation in so remote a region, and they did not want to barter. They stripped the natives of their furs and fish, and of 482 pairs of *lueshi,* skis that came in handy in Siberian winter campaigns. The soldiery learned to ski, but never to farm. They built ostrogs, manned fortresses, and later they would deny the use of the land to Russian immigrant farmers unless they accepted the military's feudal rule.

European Cossacks went to Sol-Wueshegodska in search of opportunities in Siberia. The Stroganoffs no longer set up forces of their own, but would sell provisions and weapons to applicants and offer advice on routes to the land of furs. The customers had no cash; their signature under a bill would have been worthless even had they been able to write, and their word was no better than their signature. However, the men would gather furs and dispose of them illegally, and by doing so they would invariably have to deal with Stroganoff agents, who would make a 10,000 per cent profit.

"Civilian Cossacks," as these prospective fur hunters were called, had been guided from the Stroganoff estate to the rim of the Siberian tundra since the early 1590s, and it seems likely that they built the first trappings of Mangansee. The gathering center of the immigrants became Beresov, an ostrog on the Ob River from where they spread through the habitat of Ostjaks and Samojeds.

The civilian Cossacks shunned stable domicile. They never worked in construction, mines, or trades. They did not even become efficient fur hunters, for it was more remunerative to despoil natives than to stalk wild animals. The civilian Cossacks plundered Ostjaks and Samojeds, and sold the spoils to merchants, with no questions asked. And while the house of Romanov was beset by a shortage of sables, the house of Stroganoff had plenty of supplies on hand, and marketed the goods with no more regard for the monopoly of the Russian Crown than the Crown had lately shown for their charter.

Expansion of the Stroganoff business required new routes of transportation. Russian navigation was still in its infancy; prior to Peter the Great's ascension to the throne in the late seventeenth century authorities showed no interest in naval exploration. Russia had more land than she could manage. It could leave the sea to the land-starved British, Dutch, and Portuguese. But the ostrog commander of Beresov displayed a sudden and lively interest for the exploration of arctic waters beyond the estuary of the Ob.

The man from Beresov had strong ties with Sol-Wueshegodska. The great-grandsons of Anikita had a vague conception of a northeast and a northwest passage. The Stroganoffs, mindful of Ermak's earlier profession, considered Cossacks expert shipbuilders and navigators.

In 1600 the ostrog commander hired civilian Cossacks to build ships and start exploring.

A contemporary chronicler records that the Cossacks were by no means the equals of Europeans in naval construction or seamanship. Crudely built Cossack boats, *kotchi*, were twelve Russian fathoms (eighty-four feet) long and flat-bottomed. They had a deck structure on which armament was fastened with pegs. No parts of iron were used. The boats could be rowed and sailed, but the Cossacks knew only how to run before the wind, and could not properly utilize side winds. To the Russians this was the acme of navigation; and having never seen products of western navy yards, they considered their boats the seaworthiest things afloat. Natives had been rounded up to serve as oarsmen, but they would accept quick death as a penalty for disobedience rather than rowboats headed for the vault of eternal ice.

Eventually ninety Cossacks manned a flotilla under the command of the ostrog commander's assistant. The trip was an abysmal failure. The sea was wind-swept, the boats were overloaded, supplies and gunpowder were soaked and had to be thrown overboard. Then the right wind did not spring up, and the rowmen could not handle their craft in ice-studded waters. Eventually pilots lost their bearing, and after drifting in choppy waters north of the Arctic Circle the ships made for an estuary surrounded by desolate tundra. The skippers did not want to put to sea again, crews went ashore with what was left of bag and baggage, spending several weeks to round up Samojed porters. The mistreated porters stole weapons, ambushed their taskmasters, and, unable to fire muskets, they used butts with telling effect. Only sixty Cossacks returned to Beresov.

Another attempt at exploring arctic waters, made by civilian Cossacks in 1612, did not produce tangible results, but convinced the commander of Beresov and many other people in and out of office that the *kotchi* were ideally suited for trips in extreme latitudes. The *promyshleniki*, another type of Russian conquistador, adopted the kotchi for their daredevil expeditions.

The *promyshleniki* apparently were from Russia. Otherwise nothing is known about the earlier lives and origins of these men who became pioneers of Siberia, as diffcrent in temper, designs, and habits from the American pioneers as Russian freebooters were from the Anglo-Saxon trail blazers. The Russians were scornful of family ties; the law of the land meant nothing to them. They did not even establish a code of their own, for law was the antithesis of their way of life. If they had ever heard of God, they did not even seem to think that He could see through the eyes of churches, and they had no conception of powers higher than that of the trigger. To them mining and farming were not activities worthy of a man who owed his freedom to his wit and versatility. They were averse to construction, but almost ten years after their first appearance in Siberia they would learn to build *kotchi* and *sinowie*, dismountable winter huts.

Originally the Siberians called the intruders "poachers," which was a fitting term, for poaching fur animals was their foremost objective. However, the poachers developed such ingenuity in their nefarious operations that Cossacks dubbed them the "circumspect ones," which, in the contemporary jargon, meant *"promyshleniki."* Later, however, the word came to mean "industrialists," a parodying description of the men whom a Russian historiographer describes as "unruly vagabonds, the scum of many provinces, who would venture into the remotest wilderness where no soldier had previously been, to prey upon fur animals."

As compared with the promyshleniki Cossacks appeared timorous.

Cossacks would stick together; the promyshleniki were fundamentally rogues. Only reluctantly would they form small groups and accept temporary command by a ringleader. The Cossacks were always careful to keep lines of communication open; the promyshleniki despised links with the rear; they wanted to advance, and never to turn or even look back. The Cossacks had somewhat perverted notions of comradeship; the promyshleniki had not even perverted ideas of loyalty.

For more than two hundred years batches of promyshleniki arrived in Siberia, living on their wits and their total lack of inhibitions. They produced few notable leaders, no folklore, no writings, but they spearheaded Russian expansion, battled tribes, and roamed through spaces that would long afterwards remain white spots on the map.

However, they accounted for two important events in the history of Siberia under Russian domination: the ultimate settlement with the Stroganoffs, and the migration of sables.

The Stroganoffs had been the first to notice that the invasion of the promyshleniki would eventually create terrific ravages. The poachers killed sables at a rate that tipped the scales against survival of the precious animals; and, worse even for the people of Sol-Wueshegodska, they did not deal with Stroganoff purchasing agents. Deportee dealers with stolen goods escaped from transports, established themselves in their traditional business, and dealt with the poachers. Not even the Stroganoffs were certain where the furs went, but it was presumed that the buyers of stolen goods established contact with China. The poor prospects of fur business may have been a major factor in the decision of the Stroganoffs to settle their claims. The sables, however, were not exterminated by the promyshleniki; they migrated. Aeons after the mammoth had left their habitat the sables left the forests on the lower course of the great Siberian rivers and went south-southeast, over distances of 2000 and 3000 miles, to the Shilka and Amur river valleys, to Manchuria, and the mountains east of the Sea of Okhotsk.

Manchus and Chinese also hunted sables, but not as ruthlessly as the promyshleniki, and the sables eventually survived. Sables are not gregarious animals, and they are not renowned for their intelligence, but an unfailing instinct guided these aristocrats of the martens toward relative safety. "Had the sables fled north," Professor Johann Eberhard Fischer wrote regretfully, "the damage would not have been so great."

The damage was irreparable, but the Russian Government did not show much concern. The "ink souls" merely authorized Siberian governors to issue hunting licenses, for a fee of 10 per cent of the proceeds. The governors shrugged off the decree and the poachers hardly ever learned of their title to acquire a license. But even had they learned of it, they would not have understood what a license meant.

Ostrog commanders talked to promyshleniki; the poachers knew more about distant native tribes than Russian vanguards, and they would sell information for supplies of ammunition. Information on native conspiracies rated several pounds of gunpowder higher than other data, but it had to be borne out by actual rebellion and raids against Russian establishments. Native conspiracies were not frequent, and therefore, promyshleniki incited rebellions of tribesmen who lived within the poachers' hunting grounds, offering Samojeds and Ostjaks to guide them to Russian storehouses. Bright poachers acquired some knowledge of the natives' idioms and used their skill to rabble-rousing effect. The natives staged raids which were invariably denounced to Russian commanders and nipped in the bud.

Hangmen were busy through the good offices of the poachers, and soon also through the sinister activities of shrewd Ostjaks and Samojeds, who turned provocators of, and informers against, their own people. Tax evaders, grumblers, thieves, contrabandists—the Russians had them all executed without a trial. About half of the hangman's fee went to the informer in booze and tobacco. Addicts kept informing.

The military admired the promyshleniki's linguistic gifts. In fact the native vocabulary was small; there were no rules of syntax, and the Samojed and Ostjak words were of barking brevity: Tree was *pa*, lake was *tu*, the bow—*ja*, midday—*tjel*.

The promyshleniki were explorers by the very nature of their activities. Eventually their discoveries in the east would serve Russian expansion, but involuntarily they also contributed to the improvement of land communications across the Urals.

One Artemi Babinov, a ringleader, looked for a track on which his gang could negotiate the border without running into military patrols, and found it north of the established road. But his discovery could not be kept a secret, and eventually Russian transports used Babinov's road, which was shorter and safer than the ancient route.

The poachers usually advanced north of the beaten track and there they met nomads who had once been taxed by invading parties but left alone since. Mindful of past experiences, and unable to distinguish between authorized and unauthorized conquerors, these natives offered reindeer, furs, and girls. The promyshleniki accepted what they were offered, and seized whatever else they considered worth taking. As they learned to understand Siberian utterances, they realized that there were dues to collect, and proceeded to impose their own Iasak, which was never evaded. The promyshleniki came out of their winter huts in time to catch the natives still squatting in their own primitive winter quarters, with all their pitiful possessions gathered in the shelter.

Hunting for furs, and Iasak payers, the promyshleniki advanced at a surprising speed through the northern plains; in 1610 they swarmed across the mouth of the Yenisei River. The migration of the sables was already well under way, but the poachers were not aware of it; they could outwit native men, but they did not understand that animals could score over the "circumspect ones" in a struggle for survival. The promyshleniki were, as chroniclers say, the first foreigners the natives had ever seen so far east. However, the same chroniclers tell of "strange merchants," with whom the promyshleniki did business in the expanse of the tundra, which stretches 125 miles inland from the shores of the Arctic Ocean. It is impossible to say who these strange merchants actually were, but their presence in the treeless vastness can be accepted as a fact. Had not the promyshleniki been able to trade spoils against goods, such as ammunition and building materials, they would not have advanced at such a speed.

Life in Siberia had its effects even on the promyshleniki. Their aversion against staying together lessened, and expediency taught many of them to make their rings a lasting institution; leaders, however, changed frequently and no permanent authority could establish itself.

Next the men, most of whom had never been aboard a ship, learned to build *kotchi* and to operate the boats. Four years after the spearhead of their ilk reached the lower Yenisei, a kotchi built and manned by promyshleniki left the estuary of that river for an exploratory trip.

It was June when they sailed, but it was still chilly. For a full five weeks the novice seafarers struggled against drifting ice, and icebergs ranging two hundred feet above the surface of the sea, but eventually they fought their way into open waters and discovered distant shores where Samojeds dwelled. After despoiling the Samojeds of their valuables they undertook further sea voyages. During the next six years promyshleniki reached the Kara Sea, then went to Novaja Zemlja, and from there to the Barents Sea, and as far southwest as the White Sea, unaware of the fact that this brought them into European Russian waters.

The sea-borne raiders traded several dangerous narrows, they landed on the Maximov Islands, the island of Beloi, and other terra incognita, but they did not chart maps, nor did they name newly found lands. And even though they did not report their findings, news of their journeys reached the Russian capital. It produced another decree, prohibiting further voyages because of unlawful activities, such as black-marketeering and the evasion of customs duties involved.

Russian authorities could not enforce their order; shipping expeditions continued, but were overshadowed by a tremendous advance by land.

One Penda, ringleader of forty poachers, probably the largest group of that kind, arrived in Turukhansk in 1621, and requested impudently that his band be supplied with ammunition. The local governor was just having trouble with his garrison of Cossacks and regulars. Previously he had kept the restive men in check by playing Cossacks against army men, but now the two were ganging up against him; the promyshleniki could serve as a "third force" to fasten the governor's shaky regime. Penda got what he wanted, and he fulfilled the commander's expectations so well that he and his band received supplies, conveyances, and ammunition that would last them for several years. The superb equipment caused smaller bands of promyshleniki to join Penda's forces, which went east, robbing, poaching, taxing, trading with strange characters, hibernating comfortably, using frozen watercourses in the spring to advance with quick ease, and occasionally fighting ambushes without noteworthy losses to themselves. Sometime in 1624 the men reached a mighty stream, bigger than any waterway they had known, and met strange people who seemed different from natives they had seen and plundered before.

Penda had little sense of distance; he did not know that he had already penetrated a thousand miles farther to the east than any of his predecessors, but, finding no black marketeers, he decided to return to Turukhansk, and dispose of his furs.

The river they had reached would eventually be called Lena, and the strange people were the Yakuts. Within the lifetime of one generation Russian conquerors, starting in the Urals, had covered a distance almost equal to the east-west expansion of the United States.

More impressive than Penda's account of his travels were the silent witnesses of his endeavors: 3000 sables of superb quality, in addition to many other furs of lesser value. Never before had such riches been seen in Turukhansk. Cossacks and regulars admired the treasure, and stole as much of it as they could. An enthusiastic governor helped market the bounty and offered to promote the ringleader to military rank. The highest rank of which Penda had ever heard was that of a corporal; he asked for that title, and corporalcy was awarded to him.

The story of Penda's sables reached outlying ostrogs, and promyshleniki bands. Cossacks deserted their fortresses, promyshleniki deposed their leaders, soldiers quit their units and flocked to Turukhansk to join the host of Corporal Penda for another drive east. The Crown never got one pelt from the big catch, but the Governor opened his arsenals so that all members of Penda's army could help themselves to the Crown's ammunition.

A legion of 189 promyshleniki and 123 Cossacks and regulars raced back to the source of furs. The Governor of Turukhansk sent a flowery report to Moscow telling of extension of the rule of the Tsar over many more Siberians, the pacification of immense territories, and the enlargement of the hunting grounds that produced fur animals for the Crown.

The host reached the Lena River and sailed to a point no more than 400 miles north of the Manchurian border as the crow flies. It ranged the banks of the Tunguska and Angara rivers and collected furs. The yield was good, but not quite as good as members of the expedition expected. Cossacks and promyshleniki accused each other of cheating and there were several brushes; this made the corporal discontinue his advance, which otherwise might have reached China no later than in 1630.

Penda was a wealthy man, but what became of his wealth and what eventually became of him have not been established. Nothing personal was recorded of that promyshleniki conquistador but for his "extreme untidiness."

In 1632, Cossack officers organized a third expedition to the lands of the Yakuts and the Tunguses. They enlisted veterans of Penda's campaigns as scouts and guides, and Cossacks as fighting men. The Lena River was reached without incident. A new ostrog was built at the site of Yakutsk, and the officers established "Iasak Offices," to collect tribute from natives who lived on the far side of the mighty stream. Exactly how far Cossacks and promyshleniki then penetrated east of the Lena is impossible to say, but there can be little doubt that advance groups crossed the Aldan River and probably reached the foothills of the mountains of Verkhojansk. The explorers were robust men. It hardly occurred to them that they had penetrated the region of the "cold pole." Iasak was collected the usual way, and proceeds disappeared, also as usual. Officers gave Cossacks and promyshleniki a share of the spoils, and left it to the groups to split it among themselves. Cossacks and promyshleniki made an arrangement on a 50–50 basis, but when the promyshleniki went to a place where a buyer waited, the Cossacks waylaid their former associates and stripped them of all they carried.

CHAPTER THIRTY-FIVE Siberian military tradition was the most terrific of the world, but ancient Siberians usually held the initiative: they had fought when and where they pleased; often they had paused for generations until their host was hammered into firm shape and a leader had emerged who could operate the instrument of aggression to disastrous effect. Even in the few instances in which Chinese armies staged counteroffensives the horsemen could always fall back to sanctuaries, not far away from the Chinese as compared with the distances Russian invaders of Siberia had covered within a few short years.

Faced with the problem of defensive warfare in a period of dissent and weakness, the attacked were unable to rally and expel invaders who could have been wiped out by a single of the Djhenghis Khan's divisions equipped with thirteenth-century weapons.

However, there were manifestations of valor by small groups, in particular in the southern regions of Siberia. Russian records, the only available source material, tend to distort defense into rebellion, astuteness into guile, and courage into savagery. Still some Siberians did fight, and, better led and equipped, they might have prevailed.

In 1596, Prince Jelezkoj had been told that well-armed natives were gathering at a place called Tunus, and he had staged an expedition against this alleged fortress. Four hundred soldiers found a building resembling a roadhouse for caravans, with neither palisades nor battlements. A Tatar who met the Russians outside explained that twenty families lived there, who had paid up their taxes and sworn allegiance to the White Tsar, and who had peaceful designs. Jelezkoj had the Tatar beheaded and summoned inmates of the building to come out, singly. But the men made a desperate sortie, armed with nothing but their knives. In the ensuing struggle seventeen Russians were killed and several more wounded. No Tatar survived. Jelezkoj did not say what became of their women and children. He wrote, however, that "the conquest of Tunus is an important step toward the pacification of Siberia; no lasting peace can be established as long as the barbarians are in control of places suitable for defense."

Shortly thereafter Ostjaks, incensed by the Cossacks' methods of tribute collecting and by the manner in which extortionists treated their women, ambushed Cossack patrols, forty strong, and killed them all. The insurgents could not be identified, but the commander of a neighboring ostrog opened a campaign of extermination of natives over an area of several hundred square miles. In pitched battles maltreated Ostjaks displayed formidable fighting spirit, and inflicted vexatious casualties upon the Cossacks.

In 1608 an uprising occurred that gravely threatened Russian control of wide areas: "The War of the Sable Coat." It started when a Kirghiz dignitary, Prince Nemi, paid a courtesy call at Tomsk to accept the overlordship of the White Tsar. His visit had been announced to the Governor through a messenger who carried good-will gifts. The Prince was accompanied by his stately wife. They both bowed as they entered the room in which sat the Governor and his officials. The Russians neither rose nor otherwise acknowledged the greeting; they did not offer their visitors cups of welcome and seats, but one official made for the Princess and brusquely stripped her of her sable coat. This was an insult her husband could not accept.

The couple managed to leave Tomsk. The Prince alerted his people, and in a matter of days Russian patrols and convoys found themselves hit by furious Kirghiz raids. Communications between Tomsk and other ostrogs were temporarily severed; no reinforcements were available to quell the emergency. However, Siberian wrath could not substitute for planning. Instead of concentrating on the Russian foe, the avenger of his wife's dignity turned against Kalmuck tribes who had collaborated with the invaders. This gave Tomsk a breathing spell. The hard-pressed Kalmucks applied for Russian assistance. The Governor of Tomsk charged a stiff price, payable in horses, cash, and furs; he collected and eventually produced a "letter of protection" which, however, afforded no help against the Kirghizes.

The angry Kalmucks eventually associated with the still-infuriated Kirghizes. Blithely unconcerned about the spread of the uprising, the men from Tomsk antagonized another tribe—the *kusnezi* (smiths), who produced kettles, arrow points, and tripods, and sold them to Cossacks for less than nominal prices. The Governor notified the smiths that henceforth they would have to deliver their produce without compensation, and the decree was emphasized by confiscatory raids. Destitute smiths joined Kalmucks and Kirghizes, and, according to Russian accounts, the number of native fighters rose to 5000.

A Russian proverb says that "fear has big eyes"; the Russians were getting frightened, and eventually they "saw" more enemies than were under Nemi's command. Yet an immediate attack by the Siberian allies would have resulted in Russian disaster. But while Nemi wanted to avenge the robbery of the sable coat, a few Kirghiz tribal chieftains preferred to settle scores with Iasak collectors. Tatar farmers had grievances against *jamstshiki,* and the Kuznezi wanted to recover kettles.

In 1611, Kirghiz tribesmen arrested Iasak collectors, and inflicted a public flogging upon the culprits. Then it was the jamstshiki's turn; they fared worse than the collectors; every other coachman who fell in the hands of the foes died miserably, and eventually 300 Cossack kettle thieves were routed. But the attack against Tomsk, the big prize in the war of the sable coat, was put off time and again. The average Siberian saw no point in assaulting a fortress as long as they were successful in their vendetta. By 1614, Russian Iasak revenue was cut in half, native bands ravaged farming areas, burning the crop of the black earth before it could be harvested.

Nemi encircled Tomsk seven years after his wife had been stripped of her coat. He staged an all-out assault, but reinforced palisades, walls, and watchtowers resisted the onslaught. Without artillery and siege machines the attackers, decimated by Russian fire, withdrew to siege encampments. Still they could have starved the town into submission had not the setback destroyed whatever concord existed among the Siberians. Agents of the Governor infiltrated the camp, promising amnesty and tax relief to chieftains who would withdraw to their domains. One chieftain after another accepted the offer; group after group marched away, some of Nemi's own Kirghizes joined the quitters.

Eventually only Prince Nemi with his most loyal warriors, and a few tribal leaders who did not trust Russian promises, stayed in the forefield of the fortress. They were joined by their women and children. The besieged turned besiegers; the natives made a spirited last-ditch stand. Nemi's wife, clad in another sable coat, died, sword in hand, at the side of her husband. Consecutive assaults carried the three remaining encampments.

"All men were cut down, and, as it is the custom in war, women and children were led into captivity. Thus, Kirghiz refractoriness was restrained, and the innate unruliness of these people changed into a peaceable attitude. The victors triumphantly returned to Tomsk. And this took place in the year of the world 7124." (This was 1616 our time.)

This was the wording of the official Russian communiqué at the end of the War of the Sable Coat.

When the victors returned, they were in a less than triumphant state of mind. They had suffered great hardship and collected next to nothing. The town, stripped of most commodities, was not a comfortable place to live in, and the Governor refused to pay the Cossacks fees and premiums, claiming that obligations could not be met until new revenues came in. The angry ranking Cossack, Ataman Tumenez, charged the Governor and his assistant with fraud and deceit; the civilians retorted that a single regular could have disposed of a hundred natives, and that the Cossacks were bragging cowards. Tempers flared, but were soon restrained by incoming intelligence reports indicating continued unruliness among the natives and the possibility of renewed action.

Only the dead were reliably pacified, and there were still a considerable number of Kirghizes alive who were no longer overawed by Russian might. Then there were the Buryaets, who were said to have an army to be reckoned with. Adjoining the territory of Buryaets lived Kalmucks and other tribes, apparently less meek and frightened than people from the north and the west of the land; and still farther to the east dwelled the Altin Khan, the Golden Khan of the Mongols. Should the Golden Khan assume the protectorate over all adversaries of the White Tsar, some Russians thought, consequences might well be disastrous.

Ever since 1606, Russian authorities had heard of that Mongolian ruler. First they had tended to discount the flowery accounts as products of Oriental fancy. But foreign merchants kept telling of the Golden Khan, of his power and wealth; and even Russian scouts contended that they had either seen the Prince or been in the vicinity of his residence. They would tell of parleys between Russians and the ruler of the Mongols, partly friendly, partly perplexing, but without producing results.

Ataman Tumenez was illiterate, and the Governor was no erudite man, but the word Mongol had a sinister ring in the ears of any Russian and the big eyes of fear pictured the Golden Khan as a titan.

Governor and ataman grudgingly agreed that the Golden Khan should be won over to their side, but they did not know how this should be done. They discussed a plan to keep smaller groups from uniting under Mongolian overlordship, but could not conceive a pattern, either.

The first merchants to arrive at Tomsk since the siege offered advice. They said that the natives were split by age-old animosities. The Kirghizes loathed the Tatars who had given them their name, which meant "crude wretched scamps." The Kalmucks had similar grievances: they wanted to be called Urjaets, in reference to caps they proudly wore, but the Mongols refused to do so. Resentful cap wearers laid claim to hegemony in the steppes, and everybody else ridiculed the pretense. The shamans all over Central Southern Siberia were locked in a mad struggle with Mohammedan ulemas, who wanted to proselyte the people; and chieftains who had quit the siege of Tomsk were now charging each other with treason. The merchants recommended playing both ends against the middle, as it was the Siberian tradition.

Had it not been for the merchants, Cossacks and civilians would have resumed their brawl, this time over the question of who should assume the diplomatic task. The ataman claimed that natives detested the Governor's henchmen and would never listen to their talk; the Governor insisted that the reputation of the Cossacks was such that they would be considered wolves even if they put on all the sheep's clothes in the world.

Eventually the merchants decided the issue by telling that the standing of the Cossacks was even lower than that of the civilians.

The Governor's men contacted Kalmucks, and contended that Kirghizes were ganging up with Tatars against them, and that Russia wanted to supply the objects of this conspiration with means of defense. The Kalmucks accepted equipment for 290 men—and marched straight on to Tomsk. They penetrated into the suburbs and were repelled with some difficulty. The Russians did not press the pursuit. Next the Governor's diplomats tried the Kirghizes with a crude story of Tatar plottings. Feuding Kirghiz chieftains buried the ax, obtained Russian muskets, and invaded the province of Kusnezk, raiding Russian establishments.

The Governor of Kusnezk protested to his colleague of Tomsk, other governors and ostrog commanders also asked that the nuisance of arming natives be stopped. The administrators conferred, and drafted a policy of persuasion. Russian officials reminded chieftains and petty princes of their oath of allegiance to the White Tsar, and admonished them not to offend the Great Lord by manifestations of disloyalty. The native dignitaries countered with charges of robbery, rape, and pillage committed by the Cossacks, extortion by collectors, and acts of ruthless lawlessness of which the governors themselves were guilty. They requested permission to bring their complaints before the White Tsar; the governors worried lest a refusal produce more uprisings, agreed on principle, but laid down their rules: petitions to the Tsar would have to be prefaced by pledges of loyalty; the wording of complaints would have to be in accordance with the official style; petitions should be drafted by scribes from gubernatorial offices, and, most important, only reliable persons would be admitted to the capital; and Russian officials were sole judges of reliability. A number of chieftains accepted these terms; others withdrew from the negotiations. Scribes filed petitions, omitting every word that referred to grievances, trusting that the natives, who could neither read nor speak Russian, would never learn of the editorial changes.

The first Siberian delegates stood mutely by as court functionaries read the petitions to the Tsar, they performed kowtows and retired, mute and dull.

But then, not long after the end of the War of the Sable Coat, Siberians spoke up at Court, interpreters translated their accusations, and the Tsar and the members of his cabinet obtained a shocking picture of the situation in Siberia. Tsar Michael, a handicapped man, had a physical aversion to violence, and his ministers were opposed to corruption that harmed the treasury and did not benefit them personally. Ruler and court were aroused, but this did not bring relief to the Siberian victims of fraud, despotism, and arbitrariness. Siberian governors were requested by decree to treat the natives with justice and to refrain from "practices not in accordance with the principle that conquered peoples should not be enslaved."

For almost seventeen years similar rescripts were issued at irregular intervals. Governors acknowledged receipt and failed to report execution; they never asked for elaboration on the term enslavement, nor did they assert that extreme taxation and resettlement orders issued in Moscow actually turned Siberians into slaves.

The Siberian Chancellery in Moscow contented itself with reiterating admonitions. In 1637, at last, the government lost patience with the inefficiency of this office. The Chancellery was reorganized as a new branch of the government, under the old-name Siberian Chancellery (Prikas). The reorganized agency drafted changes of provincial borders, switched gubernatorial powers, recodified economic rules, and regulated a thousand other things, from the tshinovnik uniforms to the number of relay horses available to traveling accountants; but after thirty years of paper work it had not gotten around to the fundamentals of how to treat natives. Russians, from governor general down to roving *promyshleniki,* invariably went as far in the oppression of natives as circumstances would permit.

At last the inept Prikas was stripped of its authority, and its essential functions transferred to the Empire Council, while the Chancellor of the Exchequer took charge of Iasak collection. Changes were made in higher echelons of Siberian officialdom, yet reforms affected individual beneficiaries of tyranny and defalcation, and did not remove the roots of evil.

The authorities in Siberia, who watched the rising flood of refractoriness, could not wait for rescripts to deal with their predicament.

Ataman Tumenez sneered at the failure of the civilians, and insisted that the Cossacks would have solved the problem long ago; they would have gone right to the Golden Khan, made him see the light, and had him help restore peace and order all the way from his domain to Tomsk.

The governors made yet another attempt to pacify the natives before passing the task on to the Cossacks. Foreign merchants were promised trade privileges if they talked the Kirghizes into a deal with the Russians. The merchants returned to Tomsk conceding failure of their mission and reporting on negotiations between the Golden Khan and Siberian groups who were ready to pay half the statutory Iasak for Mongolian protection, which would free them from obligations toward Russians.

At this point Ataman Tumenez took charge. Still the dispirited civilians insisted that a Cossack could never win the natives' confidence and that the illiterate Tumenez was the last who could overcome the element of sophistication that had become noticeable among native chieftains.

An incident, however, raised the Cossacks' prestige.

A Cossack patrol ransacking a Kalmuck village seized an aged man for the fun of plucking his long beard. An oldster was not considered an object of value, but, to the Cossacks' surprise, an excited Kalmuck notable offered to redeem the captive for five good horses. One good horse was worth several plump girls. As was their habit, the Cossacks tried for more, and the Kalmuck bettered his bid to fifty mounts. The Cossacks collected enthusiastically and kept their prey, whose obvious importance could net them a special bonus from their ataman. The ataman had the victim "severely questioned." The old man admitted being a *bakshi,* an adviser on spiritual affairs to several tribes. He was still able to say that more of his kind were acting as advisers to natives before succumbing to the interrogation, which was highlighted by the application of a metal-plated knout.

The ataman did not know what a bakshi was, nor had civilians, officials, and foreign merchants made that discovery, and governors grudgingly acknowledged that the Cossacks had scored.

Authorities were summoned to round up bakshis and to gather more information on these mysterious people.

The bakshis, it was learned, were "able to understand all idioms spoken anywhere, to contain fleeting words [to write], and to read minds." They were teachers of peoples, spiritual leaders of princes. To the governors and to the ataman, these bakshis seemed to be the instigators of all troubles by which the Russians had been beset, and the cause of reduced revenues.

But it was not easy to get hold of a bakshi. The natives were hiding their teachers, and if one were found, they would offer such stunning ransoms, payable after the captive's return, that Cossacks could hardly resist the temptation of getting a bunch of horses and girls for their own use instead of turning an old wizard over to their commanders. And even if the Cossacks did hold a bakshi, they might still barter him en route to their ostrog against more enjoyable commodities. The rounding-up drive was not really productive, but as native resistance bogged down, the prestige of the bakshis was reduced, and Siberia ceased to be a goal for itinerant teachers.

Later Russian scholars found that the bakshis formed a caste, halfway between priests and sages; and that their remarkable erudition was derived from Tibetan, Indian, and Chinese sources. Young aspirants for caste membership founded families, but, as they grew older and their learnings progressed, they deserted wives and children, and became lamas, to prepare for the last and highest stage of initiation. After graduating they set out singly, to advise peoples.

The ataman did not propose to wait until the rounding-up operation was completed. He now had an educated assistant, a Cossack whom he wanted to head the Cossack diplomatic mission to the Golden Khan. Captain Ivan Petrov had lately arrived in Tomsk, where he surprised everybody by his ability to read regulations and to sign his name. Petrov had used his skill to raise his rank, as recorded by the papers, from sergeant to captain; but this was discovered only later, and by then nobody seemed to mind the forgery.

Not all governors approved of the Cossack mission. The administrator of the district of Yeniseisk took violent exception to Cossack diplomacy. From Kusnetzk came acid objections, and more protests were coming in as an undaunted Tumenez mustered Petrov's party and bickered with local treasury officials about presents for the Mongolian prince.

These gifts were eventually listed in the treasury records of Tomsk as including: ready-made men's and women's wear of various sorts and value; sheets of various colors and qualities, cloth for caps, silken-embroidered bed curtains, plates and dishes of tin, brass kettles, knives, small and large mirrors, rings of brass and tin, tin buttons, large corals, stationery, raisins, honey, butter, and groats—an assortment indicative of Cossack tastes.

Guided by natives, messengers rode ahead of the mission, which Tumenez joined personally. They announced that the White Tsar's ambassadors were on their way to visit the Golden Khan, and requested that the Khan assign guards of honor to escort the party on the last lap of their journey, which, incidentally, would lead through territory inhabited by restive Kirghizes.

The Golden Khan sent thirty horsemen, led by a noble in gaudy Chinese attire, to meet the Cossacks and guide them to his court, on a detour through territory where the Mongolian prince was held in high esteem. The Khan's cavalrymen had refined manners, which startled the small band of Cossacks and baggage carriers, and they were linguists who acted as interpreters between the Russians and tribal chieftains.

Petrov made notes on their adventures; scribes at Tomsk compiled the entries, adding official polish, and Muscovite officers put the report in shape for the attention of the Tsar.

"When we arrived in the land of the Sajans," the Tsar read, "their big-chief Black Beard inquired what kind of men we were, and who our King was. 'We are the men of the Great Lord Tsar and Grand Duke Michael Fjodorovitch, self-ruler of all of Russia,' we told him. Thereupon he supplied us, voluntarily, with food and fresh horses, and asserted that he had no more urgent desire than to sacrifice himself in the faithful service of the Tsar. Next, we visited the Prince of the Maci who received us joyfully and accompanied us to the residence of the Golden Khan, where we were welcomed by the heir to the throne and the highest nobility of the realm. As a token of the respect for the Tsar of Russia, a tent had been raised for us next to the Khan's own tent. The day after our arrival, we were received in audience in yet another tent, which belonged to Kutuchta, the primate of the Mongols. The primate attended, and so did a vassal prince, the Khan's top officials and ranking courtiers, and the men who had escorted us. 'You are unlike all other ambassadors who visited this court,' the Khan hailed us, 'for you have come from the Great Lord, the Tsar.' He inquired about the Tsar's health, a choir of priests sang for us, and then we read to the Golden Khan the full title of the Great Lord, Tsar and Grand Duke, described his eminence, and told of the countless Kings, Princes, and lesser rulers who were vassals of His Majesty. As we were reading, the Golden Khan slightly raised his cap, and all others present took off their headgear. After we had finished, the attending vassal prince claimed: 'I am ready to serve the Great Lord, Tsar and Grand Duke, Michael Fjodorovitch.' We addressed the Golden Khan to persuade him to accept the sway of the Tsar, together with all his soldiers and subjects. This, the Khan pledged to do; the oath of allegiance was administered, while the priests intoned a choral and raised an idol.

"The Golden Khan told us the story of his prelate, who came from the land of the Lamas and could read and write at the time of his birth. The child died at the age of three, and lay buried for a full five years. Afterward, he resurrected, could read and write again, and recognized people whom he had met in his short previous life span. Everybody considered him a saint, and he was chief overseer of Gods, bells, and books.

"The Golden Khan, whose name is Kunkantshei, and who was wearing a robe of golden satin, accepted our presents with great thanks for the Tsar's magnanimity, and he directed his Chamberlain to see that the ambassadors of the incomparable White Tsar be honored, served, and supplied with everything they wanted."

The land of the Golden Khan was situated on the border of China, again torn by upheavals, yet able to maintain contact with neighbors and check on events in their territories. By judging from fragmentary Chinese records, the Golden Khan never swore allegiance to the Tsar. The chant of the priests and the raising of the idol were parts of greeting ceremonies, and the Mongol never went to Moscow to pay his respect to the Russian ruler, as it was alleged by Muscovite chroniclers.

The dreaded union of various Siberian peoples under Mongolian protection did not materialize. The reasons can hardly be found in the impression created by the Cossack mission. It is sound to assume that the Golden Khan, despite legends of his wealth and might, was but a pompous, Sinofied prince whose actual powers were very limited, and who had no desire to make dangerous commitments. And as native tribes drifted apart during the two decades following the War of the Sable Coat, Kunkantshei was probably not too strongly urged to assume a role for which he was ill-fitted.

Another report by Petrov was not edited for presentation to the Tsar. It was either sketchy or parts of it disappeared from the files when Russian historians compiled available material a hundred-odd years later. Indications are that the Cossack party received ample information on China by subjects of the Golden Khan, and that the Russian ambassadors actually proceeded to "Ki-tai," the empire on which other Russians had set foot before and which was all but forgotten in Muscovy when the Romanov dynasty rose to power.

"We met subjects of the Golden Khan," Petrov relates, "who dwelled in tents of felt, that were loaded on camels, during migrations. Their weapons are bows and arrows, and we had an opportunity to watch their way of living [no description of this way of living is enclosed] . . . . They told us of a Kingdom, called Ki-tai, which is situated on a bay of an ocean. The King's name is Taibin [this could refer to the House of Tai-Ming], his capital is built of bricks, and it takes a rider ten days to circle the town. [This was an obvious exaggeration. However, one century later the circumference of Peking was found to be forty miles.] The people of Ki-tai use fire barrels and cannon. Huge ships with crews up to 300 sail to and from Ki-taien harbors. The men are clad like merchants from Bokhara. It takes one month to reach Ki-tai from the residence of the Golden Khan; the way leads through virtually flat lands [indicating that the Khan's residence was situated in the Mongolian plains] and there are no big rivers to cross. On our trip to the court we saw stone houses, built in rocks, and people told that they had been inhabited by men from Ki-tai [probably abandoned trade outposts, or lamas' dwellings]."

Other parts of the report are even more fragmentary: "Men from the Topin Empire were present at Court. They told us that their country was being ruled by two Kings, Ishim and Bagatir, that their towns were built of stone and timber, that they used fire barrels and cannon. . . . Other people, born in the realm of the Yellow King, said that their ruler was Kalatshine, that their capital was built of bricks, and that they, too, had fire barrels and cannon. . . . Ultimately, we met people from Kalka, whose tents are carried by camels, and who have no fire arms. All these nations live at peace with each other, they exchange embassies, and trade among themselves. With the exception of Kalka, which is located toward the morning, all other people mentioned live toward midday."

Still other fragments of the document deal with names of lakes and rivers and geographical data, all of them confusing.

A Russian commentator suggests that the Cossacks had been to Korea, another thinks that Topin is Tibet, or Toepoet, as the Mongol pronounced it; and the men who loaded their tents on the backs of camels should have been roving Mongols. But whatever interpretations and guesses could be made, it seemed obvious that there were nations in the distant east who lived in houses of stone and brick, which meant the ultimate in comfort to the Russians; whose men dressed like merchants from Bokhara, which the Russians considered the most costly garb a person could wear; and who had objects to trade with. Russian expansion into indefiniteness got to one major objective: Ki-tai.

Available accounts indicate that the prospect of meeting numerous people equipped with "fire barrels and cannon" did not intimidate the invaders, who, after an interlude of worry, seemed to think that they could conquer all nations along their path.

But instead of stimulating the advance toward their goal the prospect of rich spoils retarded the forward movement, and led to Russian civil war in Siberia.

CHAPTER THIRTY-SIX The accelerated turnover of officials brought another governor to Tomsk even before the Cossacks returned to that base after a stay of only ten days at the Golden Khan's residence. The new appointee was Ivan Ssemyonovitsh Kurakin, a nobleman with a less-than-noble record in the administration, a man unburdened by scruples, who, after reading and listening to Petrov's account, resolved to conquer Ki-tai as his private domain.

At first Cossack leaders from Tomsk were prepared to collaborate with the Governor; but as Kurakin insisted on holding the reins of the venture, they made a dilettantic attempt to organize their own campaign into Ki-tai. They held top-secret palavers with lesser Cossack luminaries, made clumsy overtures to administrators of Russian arsenals, and retained the guides who had served the embassy to the Golden Khan. The secret leaked out: Cossacks, clerks, soldiers, promyshlenikis, prison guards, destitute peasants, runaways, and new arrivals all pinned their greedy hopes on Ki-tai. Veterans from the embassy raved in tall tales of a country shaped according to their imagination. Ki-tai was a land of gold; more gold could be found in Ki-tai than all the horses of Siberia could carry; the women of Ki-tai were clad in silk, and smelled sweetly; and their caresses were infinitely more exacting than those of the shabby, malodorous Siberian girls and Russian prostitutes who had come to the new land to satisfy their own rapacity rather than the lusts of the conquerors.

Groups from Tomsk left for Ki-tai, got lost in the wilderness and killed each other for food, or simply tried to keep the other party from winning the lead in the race. From Tomsk the story of Ki-tai spread to Yeniseisk. Cossacks formed a small army, but went astray and wound up collecting inferior furs from poor natives who did not seem to know about Ki-tai.

The Governor of Yeniseisk blamed his colleague from Tomsk for the failure of "his" Cossacks, and staged a punitive expedition against Tomsk. Bands from both cities, Russian regulars, native draftees joined by vagabonds engaged in hit-and-run battles and pillage. The newly founded city of Krasnojarsk, envious of older rival towns, mobilized flying columns to raid both Yeniseians and Tomskians. Few natives joined the brawl among Russians, but they all ceased to pay the tribute. Loss of revenue brought Kusnezk into the battle. The Governor of this province turned against Yeniseisk, where, as he believed, 3000 sables were stored. When he did not get furs, he seized convoys of fresh food for Krasnojarsk; a devastating epidemic of scurvy broke out in that city. Cossacks from remote ostrogs deserted their forts and joined the free-for-all; few, if any, had heard of Ki-tai, but they wanted a share in Siberian spoils. Promyshleniki raided Russian settlements no longer guarded by their garrisons, which had gone warring.

Meantime the Governor of Tomsk attempted to find a waterway to Ki-tai. Fugitives had told him of a huge lake, the bottom of which was clustered with transparent stones, and of a big river flowing out of the lake toward midday. Parties explored watercourses, but did not find the lake with the glittering bottom. Others also tried rivers in search for Ki-tai, or any other place of plenty. An expert whom Moscow had assigned to explore silver mines in Siberia reported to the capital that his work had to be discontinued because of the insecurity of waterways.

Stoppage of search for precious metal made Moscow aware of the seriousness of the upheaval in Siberia. In 1629 express messages to all Siberian governors threatened court-martial procedures should order not be restored at once. Substantial police forces were said to be on their way to Siberia to enforce the decree. Actually the police forces were not yet ready, and the government had but recently ordered the recruitment of 500 men and "150 unmarried wenches," as an expedition force to Siberia; soldiers should not scatter in search for female company.

The governors did not wait for the arrival of the mixed host. Civil war in Siberia was getting out of hand. No longer did the heads of provincial administrations pull all the wires; subalterns staged expeditions of their own, defying their superiors' orders; alliances formed between uncontrollable elements; anarchy was spreading; within another year or two the governors would be powerless in their own districts and outlaws anywhere else. To cease hostilities upon the orders of the Tsar prevented loss of face; it permitted officials to use whatever armed men still obeyed their orders to put down the forces of chaos. So the governors did all they could to make peace.

In 1631, when the police forces marched, rode, and sailed through Siberia, they found ostrogs, cities, and walled settlements reasonably quiet and provincial administrations functioning busily. It took another decade to repopulate deserted Krasnojarsk.

But outside the urban places peace was not yet restored. Outlaw Cossacks, promyshleniki, deserters, and natives enrolled in Russian bands and kept on fighting well into the 1640s. Those of the men who had once heard of Ki-tai had practically forgotten the land of gold and sweet-smelling women. They had no grievances against the men they were out to slay. They were unsteady as wild beasts, yet, unlike the beasts, they did not select their prey, but devoured whatever could not resist their onslaught.

The end of hostilities was brought about only by the end of the men who engaged in them. It seemed that by the mid-seventeenth century more dead Russians littered the woods, steppes, and meadows of Siberia than quick Russians trod on Siberian soil.

Moscow commended meritorious governors for their patriotism, which had restored the blessings of peace to the Tsar's eastern territories. It ordered reconstruction to be precipitated by encouragement of business. The house of Stroganoff no longer functioned in the official pattern of Siberian business. Cossacks received five-year trade concessions and bonuses of a half-year salary to provide investment capital. Foreign merchants were assured that traffic with Siberia was sound and secure with the armed forces actively established in business.

Cossacks would invite merchants to ostrogs, have them show their wares, grab them without payment, and turn the visitors out. But the merchants did not always take insult and injury without retaliation. According to Russian records, they sometimes displayed their goods outside the walls, had the Cossacks come out with whatever they had to sell or barter, and the merchants had them ambushed and looted by hired ruffians.

The power of the governors over natives, absolute as it had been in fact, was legalized. Death sentences could be meted out by governors against which there was no appeal. Fear of the natives, rampant from days of insurrection, innate cruel despotism, and the determination to silence potential complainants forever produced a drive of legal extermination by mock trial. Certain tribes were subject to persecution by unprecedented means. One harmless splinter people, which irritated the Governor of Krasnojarsk, were stripped of their hunting and fishing implements and had to dig wild-lily roots for food; the Governor seized the utensils the hungry used for that purpose, and eventually had the helpless people isolated by Cossack patrols until the gruesome end.

The government later denounced the procedure as "dastardly," but from the records it does not appear that the Governor had been punished.

Yet another governor officiated in Tomsk. He knew that at some time or other his predecessor had dispatched a secret embassy to Ki-tai, and that yet another embassy had left for the same destination with credentials signed by Cossack Petrov. Neither embassy had been heard from again. The official tended to discount the saga of Ki-tai. In Siberia men did not live long and had no time to wait for sagas to come true. Scouting, discovery, exploitation, and enjoyment had to follow in rapid succession. Nobody worked for the benefit of successors.

With the vision of Ki-tai paling another objective for treasure hunters came in sight. Silver—loose mountains of silver . . . wealth that did not have to be mined, could be picked up: all you needed was two big hands and many big sacks.

The silver craze broke out soon after the civil war abated. Governmental search for silver mines was one of the reasons for the mad rush; others were tales of Buryaet wealth, of hoards of silver stored by these men, and the omnipresent will-o'-the-wisp of abundance.

The Buryaets lived around the southern shore of Lake Baikal, near the cradle of ancient Siberian strength. They were trading with China, bartering furs, horses, and cattle against sugar, silk, and silver accessories, with which they adorned quivers, saddles, and harnesses. The Buryaets did not mine silver, nor had they ever found it in their domain.

Cossacks, promyshleniki, black marketeers, runaway peasants, escaped deportees, officials and officers, clerks and scribes turned prospectors. Staking of claims was a yet unknown procedure, but prospectors were determined to defend what they held and to conquer even more.

They had no tools, but plenty of weapons. Again scantily replenished arsenals emptied; a stolen musket would produce tenfold, a hundredfold its weight in silver.

The race to the silver mountains led through stretches of unexplored territory. Some parties got lost; some impressed natives into their service as guides. Siberians who denied knowledge of the location of the mountain were summarily killed; others told the Russians that nobody who reached the silver could hope to survive, for the Buryaets were the most ferocious people on earth, half men, half ghosts, and they invariably slew intruders.

The prospectors refused to accept the story of Buryaet savagery at face value. They wanted silver, and no fabulous creatures should stand in their way.

The Tsar's government continued its own search with the assistance of experts, who did not believe in shining mountains, and with labor forces of deportees and chattels who perished in droves for a phantom they could not have enjoyed even had it been real.

In the early dash for the silver mountains Yeniseisk had a head start over other Siberian cities. Governor Jakow Chripunov hired and equipped fifty Cossacks, had river craft built, resigned from office, and set out to conquer treasures and their keepers. Chripunov's band navigated on the Tunguska and Oka rivers and encountered a number of Buryaets riding on silver-plated saddles and carrying silver-adorned quivers; the Russians opened fire, the Buryaets fled. But Chripunov ordered all men aboard ship again. There he died.

The circumstances of his death were not disclosed by the few Cossacks who returned to Yeniseisk, without silver but with a catch of twenty-three Buryaet women; neither did the Cossacks explain how these persons had fallen into their hands. The new Governor confiscated the prey because their capture constituted a violation of anti-slavery directives, and released them, at three sables apiece, to another Buryaet tribe.

More expeditions, four to fifty strong, met and mistreated Buryaets, who would fight only to protect their lives. Among leaders of expeditions were two demoted Cossack atamans, one ostrog commander, a lieutenant of the regular army on a punitive assignment in Siberia, a black-marketeer who specialized in stolen Crown property, and a promyshlenik with a criminal record extraordinary even for poachers' standards.

Except for a few trifling silver adornments their loot consisted of sable furs and fox skins. Disappointed freebooters cursed the "tricky, mendacious, abusive natives," who not only led conquerers astray, but also insulted them by delivering summer sables instead of the finer winter specimens, and by mixing scabby fox skins among the better ones.

What had started as a diversion from the original objective, Ki-tai, carried the Russians closer and closer to China, and resulted in the discovery of territories and waters leading toward the Pacific—the ocean of which the Russians did not yet know that it delimited Siberia in the east.

As Cossack parties went hunting for Buryaets and silver mountains, they kept building ostrogs; a line of forts sprang up between the Tunguska and Lena rivers, branched out in the direction of Lake Baikal, and promyshleniki, racing ahead of Cossacks, added to the chain of bulwarks by setting up winter huts surrounded by palisades.

In 1637 one Kopylov, a Cossack officer from Tomsk, was ordered to Yeniseisk. Instead of proceeding to this garrison, he took his fifty men on a looting and "tax-collecting" spree, raided Yakuts, seized furs and livestock, gave battle to a company of Russian regulars who policed Yakut Province, lost his cattle, had thirty natives sabered in retaliation, and turned south.

In the Aldan River valley, as Kopylov told later, he encountered Tunguses, who offered to guide him to prosperous people who tilled the soil and bartered its products against furs of which the Cossacks had a supply. Under Tunguse guidance the Cossacks reached a people "called Naktani," whose language was difficult to understand, who owned silver objects, corals, and huge copper kettles, and who obtained silk, woolens, and flour from other people who raised hogs and chickens and distilled brandy in metal boilers. The distillers and the Naktanis "were trafficking by water on the Great Black River that empties into the Great Sea."

Black meant Omur; the Russians misspelled the word into "Amur," and thus the majestic river received its present name.

Kopylov and most of his men stayed with the Naktanis, having a good time at the expense of the newly discovered Siberians. A scouting patrol on a raft proceeded down the Shilka River to the Amur. Tunguses who went with the scouts deserted them later, "out of sheer wickedness," as the Russians contended, and eventually the scouts were stranded with neither spoils nor information. However, they found their way back to the location of the main group, where Kopylov had decided to march to distant Yeniseisk, in quest of reinforcements, and to resume the expedition.

In Yeniseisk, however, his discoveries were not accepted as a valid excuse for the delay of more than one year caused by the anabasis. Siberian authorities usually were not severe about highhanded diversions, but by deposing the Cossack officer they expected to cheat him out of benefits of his discoveries.

Veterans of Kopylov's expedition boasted of their exploits, of treasures, of merchants in silken garments, of trade-minded princes they had met, of an abundance of furs they had seen. Tall tales were part and parcel of veterans' talk. However, Chinese merchants wearing silk visited the Amur River valley, which would form part of the Siberian border with China for centuries to come. The migration of sables had reached the Amur at least one decade ahead of the invasion of the Cossacks.

Neither the ataman who succeeded Kopylov or this ataman's successor reached the Amur again, much to the annoyance of the Governor of Yeniseisk, who, like his colleague from Tomsk, had been placed under orders of the Governor of upstart Yakutsk. Failing to outshine Yakutsk by expansion of Russian territory, the two officials ganged up to starve Yakutsk, which depended on food supplies from the two older towns. The Governor of Yakutsk searched archives to find other sources of supply, and he found an account on the "Dawriens," prosperous farmers whose habitat seemed to lie south of his city, a goodly distance away. But the small garrison of army regulars refused to leave Yakutsk in search of a mysterious people and local Cossacks made exaggerated demands to be met in advance.

The Governor appealed for volunteers; freebooters turned up in number; their command was entrusted to Vassilj Pojarkov, an office clerk with a sense of ruthless adventure. Pojarkov had two scribes join his mob to record whatever laudable deeds they would perform.

In 1640 a river flotilla sailed to "Dawria." In Yakutsk an anxious governor waited for grain and meat; and when none had arrived three years later the expedition was considered lost. But since sabotage of food shipments by jealous subordinates had meantime ceased, the loss was not considered grievous.

In 1646 fifteen haggard men loaded with sables trudged into Yakutsk. Whitehaired and worn, Pojarkov had returned. First the Governor did not recognize his former clerk, but then he was less anxious to hear his account than to lay claim to the furs in the name of the Crown. After a heated controversy the Governor settled for 500 sables for his personal use, 500 for Pojarkov, and 100 sables per capita for his men. What was left should be the Tsar's. Nothing was left, of course.

And this was the essence of Pojarkov's story as recorded in Russian archives:

After leaving their base the boats had a "tedious trip" over sixty-four rapids, cascades, and cataracts. In September 1640, when ice formed on the river, the men had not yet seen a single Dawrien. A search party looking for edibles found a village where peaceful people lived, who fed the strangers and offered them three large huts for shelter. The hospitable people were farmers and cattle breeders. Pojarkov went to see the peasants, and asked if they were Dawriens. This the natives answered in the affirmative and presented the clerk-commander with ten oxen and forty basketfuls of groats. Pojarkov made an inspection tour of Dawrien territory, finding the people "moderately prosperous," and of "timid friendliness." He split his forces and quartered them in various locations; the party that had first established contact with the natives was assigned to the village they had found. These men, however, "were not satisfied with their good fortune. Their greed knew no bounds; they thought that natives who were friendly on their own free will would accede to every demand presented with an imperious gesture." A nearby Dawrien building looked like a storehouse. The Russians staged a threatening parade around the fence, and seized a number of Dawriens who stood watching. They threatened to torture their prisoners should the natives refuse to hand over the building to the Russians. The Dawriens objected "that the place was too crowded to admit visitors."

Thereupon the captives were subjected to "monstrous torments." Some Dawriens tried to free their countrymen; from neighboring villages armed farmers arrived on horseback; they came too late to save the victims, but killed ten of the fifty Russians, injured several more, and captured five. The five were eventually released "even though almost none of them escaped injury," and they rejoined their remaining comrades for what turned into a prolonged ordeal. The natives penetrated into the Russian camp, took away oxen and groats, and held the garrison under siege. One nocturnal sortie carried the besieged close to the place where Pojarkov stayed. But Pojarkov refused to admit his countrymen. He had learned of their misdeeds through natives whose early friendliness had changed into hardly veiled hostility. The group fought its way back to the camp. None of the culprits survived the winter. Hunger, disease, and cannibalism accounted for their end.

Pojarkov's own party spent a miserable winter of want and fear. In the early spring he gathered the remnants of his men to resume his voyage. The natives refused to give them supplies. The food which the Russians eventually took on their trip included "flesh from human bodies."

The next people they reached were the "Dutcheri," whom they "tried to convince that payment of Iasak was in their best interest." For three consecutive weeks the Russians sailed from village to village, collecting as they went. But the Dutcheris were an "unreliable lot," and when a force of thirty-five went ashore to reconnoiter the region east of the junction of the "Seja" and "Shingal" rivers, they were set upon by natives. Only two escaped the ensuing massacre. "Undaunted by the incident," Pojarkov continued the voyage. Six days later the flotilla reached the mouth of the Usuli River. The Natkis, who lived there, expressed surprise at the Russian demand for Iasak; they had never paid tribute before. But eventually they did pay in fine furs. (Pojarkov failed to explain how he communicated with a variety of peoples; all he has to say about the language of the Natkis is that they never used the letter *"r,"* which would point at Chinese linguistic influences.) "Where the land of the Natkis borders that of the Gilaeks" the Russians reached the Amur. "The domicile of the Gilaeks extends a fourteen-day voyage down the Amur to the sea. These people's clothes are made of fish skin; they catch fish in the river, as well as in the channel between the Amur estuary and an outlaying island whose name is Shantar."

Shantar was Sakhalin; the Gilaeks controlled at least part of the long-stretched island. Pojarkov was not aware of the momentousness of his voyage that would have made the glory of Western explorers.

"When we reached the Amur estuary," his account continued, "I had lost half the original number of my men and winter was at hand. I wondered what to do next. Should we return upstream? This would be hazardous, and we might not get far before the water froze. Should we set sail, and ship into the ocean? Stormy seas would have smashed our craft, and, at best, we would have been left stranded in a hideous wilderness. The winter in these regions is rough, and I decided to spend the cold season among the Gilaeks."

The "hideous wilderness" was, in fact, a shore of serene beauty, but the Russians took a strictly utilitarian view of landscapes; those that provided food and shelter were beautiful; those that offered little of either were hideous.

They found shelter and food at the expense of the Gilaeks, whose primitive dwellings they crowded, whose preserved food they ate, whose fur clothes they put on for the winter, and whose fishskin garments they seized for use in the warmer season.

In the spring the Russians took to the sea. They sailed north, 500 miles across the Sea of Okhotsk, to the estuary of the Ulbeja River, near the present site of Okhotsk. It was a "dull trip," according to Pojarkov's journals, and it lasted a full twelve weeks. The journals do not indicate what caused the Russians to sail straight north in what seems to have been the first trip by Russian craft in Pacific waters.

But it appears that Pojarkov was rather disappointed by what he found on the northern shores of the Sea of Okhotsk: Tunguses dwelt there who claimed to pay dues to the Tsar and objected to twin collection. Pojarkov "convinced" the Tunguses that nobody but he himself was authorized to levy taxes; the natives paid up, and agreed to feed and shelter a small garrison that would see that no other tributes were paid to "impostors."

These impostors could only have been ubiquitous promyshleniki. Nobody knew the farthest penetrations of the poachers, and since they had learned to build and navigate ships, the possibility cannot be ruled out that promyshleniki craft had sailed the Sea of Okhotsk even before Pojarkov arrived.

With the remnants of his expeditionary force Pojarkov went inland to locate fur-rich people said to live in the wooded mountains to the northwest.

The report makes no further mention of such people, and it does not give the sources of the sables Pojarkov took to Yakutsk. But it tells of Russians reaching the sources of the Maja, their subsequent trip on rafts on this river, and on the Aldan, and their eventual return to the Lena and Yakutsk.

The shores of an ocean first reached in 1513, by European men, had again been reached some 130 years later, and some eight thousand miles away. But while Vasco Núñez de Balboa, who saw the Pacific from the coast of Panama, received everlasting credit as its discoverer, Pojarkov's travels passed into oblivion. The 500 sables retained under his agreement with the Governor remained his only award for a sequence of robberies and wild dashes into space, which added several hundred thousand square miles of land to the Tsar's realm and explored waterways for continued expansion toward an even farther East: the outposts of a new Far West.

The Governor of Yakutsk passed Pojarkov's report on to the Siberian Prikas, brazenly adding that he had planned, subsidized, and directed the operations. The officials in the capital adorned the story with flowering comments, making it appear as if the lands and seas visited by the Tsar's adoring subjects would be settled, exploited, and consolidated within the next decade, and not, as it turned out to be, only a solid two centuries later.

It was not only egotism and the urge for ever wider authority—standard features of governmental agencies not only in the Tsar's Russia—that caused the Siberian Chancellery to exalt the achievement and to add that it had been stimulated by the Chancellery's own careful planning. Tsar Michael had died, and his son Aleksei was "Western-minded." Only constant plugging of accomplishments in Siberia could prevent Tsar Aleksei from considering the "Sibirskoie Prikas" an altogether unimportant office.

The best stylists of the Prikas prepared memoranda on the expansion of Siberia, the discovery of new sources of wealth, of springboards for even more fabulous territories, waters, and nations. Mapmakers reveled in designs that showed oceans shaped like fantastic monsters, towering mountains with galleries indicating mines, and expanses of land which, as accompanying memoranda would explain, were densely populated by the Tsar's newest subjects, all rich, all loyal, all enthusiastically devoted to the cause of Russian greatness.

Artists and authors, however, missed an essential trait of Aleksei's character. The second Romanov was scared by big open spaces, a victim of what might be called claustrophilia, which made him afraid to leave the Kremlin.

The very size and distance of Siberia frightened the Tsar; the West was not so far away and not so unlimited as his enigmatic Asiatic realm; this stimulated his Western-mindedness.

Events on the western borders of Russia actually deserved attention. The cohesive powers which had held Poland together were dwindling: most of the Ukraine, including the ancient city of Kiev and the town and district of Smolensk, had fallen, a ripe fruit, to Russia; and the shadows of Sweden and of Turkey were portentously cast over Russian western territories. The Tsar read reports on Poland, Sweden, and Turkey more carefully than epistles pouring forth from the desks of the Siberian Chancellery; but he would never visit even Smolensk, about 250 miles away.

The Siberian Chancellery had an embassy from Siberia shipped to Moscow.

The last Mongolian embassy that had come to Moscow in 1639, six years prior to Tsar Aleksei's coronation, had been a failure. The Mongols had silently listened, as they had been instructed, to the master of ceremonies reciting their address of homage; and they had performed all the required antics of submission during the presentation of their gifts to His Majesty. But then, when asked whether their masters had particular wishes, they had not, as instructed, said that "to serve the White Tsar was the highest gratification a Prince could hope for," but had produced a long list of objects which their principals back in Asia expected to receive. So outrageous were their demands that the protocol listed them in detail: one prince wanted 1000 ducats, canvas for tents with a total capacity of 1000, 108 big corals, one dark fox, one solid armor, and one sword; another asked for 300 big corals, 2000 big pearls, 300 pieces of amber, a sword, 10 linen sheets 20 yards long; a third aspired to 108 precious stones of various colors, 5 sheets, 10 gilded cups, one saddle and harness with silver mountings, 3 good sabers, 2 pieces of silver-and-gold-brocade, 100 black and 100 red foxes. "Had the Russian treasury paid such prices for Mongolian vassalage," a court official noted, "Russia would have been reduced to poverty." Actual donations to the Mongolian princes, however, did not produce such effect. The ambassadors received three letters, one for each prince, in which the White Tsar expressed not clearly defined feelings toward the addressees.

The Mongolian embassy to Tsar Aleksei did not ask for corals, bed sheets, amber, and sabers when they appeared at court in 1649. "These were not the type of men Russians need be afraid of," an eyewitness recorded. And a court historian, uneasy at the thought that the ancestors of these bewildered, timid-looking men "could have conquered most of Asia," rewrote the story of Djenghis Khan, claiming that it had not really been the Mongols who defeated other nations, "but an immense Chinese army of deserters who had been bribed into the services of Temudshin and had taken their equipment along." The treatise concluded that the former glory of the Asiatics had vanished, that they were reduced to the use of bows and arrows, and that they could never stand up against the terrible thunderbolt of Russian muskets and the roar of the Tsar's cannon.

Tsar Aleksei sat through the audience, absent-minded and obviously unimpressed. Ki-tai was not mentioned, nor were the newest conquests in Siberia elaborated upon.

The Siberian Chancellery did not repeat the performance. Embassies were apparently less effective even than memoranda and maps. However, there were other means of self-assertion in a monarchy whose ruler was fundamentally apathetic. The members of the Prikas continued to send memoranda, but they indulged in a short-lived, unreported Siberian policy.

CHAPTER THIRTY-SEVEN In 1628 an informant had told Governor Chripunov of Yeniseisk about the Holy Sea of the Mongols, but with the civil war raging the Governor was in no mood to explore holy sites, and afterward would not waste time on a lake when there were mountains of silver to conquer. But eventually the story of the mysterious waters was conveyed to Cossack Captain Kubat Ivanov, who, remembering the tale of the lake with the shining bottom, thought that the holy waters and the mysterious source of silver were one and the same, and that the glimmer came from a silver mountain submerged under water.

In 1643 the Cossack captain and seventy-five well-armed and well-supplied men left Yakutsk with their goal veiled in secrecy. The troop proceeded up the Lena River, through settings of gently rolling hills and fertile steppes. Ivanov had expected to find the region densely populated by Buryaets or Mongols, but the only living creatures were monsters dwelling in dense underbrush, which were invisible in daylight, but would emerge in the darkness and fall upon Russian livestock with so terrifying a roar that sentinels took to their heels. The men's imagination pictured the nocturnal raiders as demons larger than steers and faster than horses, with furs of silver and gold, who guarded the silver and after devouring the invader's cattle would devour the men. Hardened brutes timidly suggested that they return to safer regions, but the captain insisted that they march on. The men did not attempt to fight the mysterious foes, which were, in fact, Siberian tigers, the largest and most ferocious of their species.

For several days the marchers watched a dark blue silhouette growing on the eastern horizon; in the morning it seemed lined with silver, and at dusk it had contours of gold. As they approached, the dark blue mass evolved into a gigantic chain of mountains. A few Russians claimed to have seen fiery rays shooting up from the foot of the mountains; others said that they had heard sounds of hammering.

One midmorning in July the specter-ridden men reached the crest of a low hill and, marching down the incline, they saw an immense expanse of dark water. To their left the waters were rimmed by mountains veiled in a delicate shade of blue; in the center the curving expanse was covered by a protruding chain of high, wooded hills; to their right another range of mountains shot skyward. The huge, varicolored walls overwhelmed the wanderers by the sheer impact of their suffocating mass and nearness. Snow-sprinkled boulders crowned dark green belts of woods on an incline so steep that it seemed impossible for a tall tree to take roots, and made the Russians fear that the trunks were suspended in mid-air and held by demons who could release them to crush down on the intruders. From high above came foaming torrents, racing through the mysterious forests, dashing over light moraines, and into the dark expanse of water, furrowing it with stripes of iridescent spray. The waters reflected a multitude of colors and shades; rainbows, large and small, seemed to mark mystic spots on the expanse.

This could only be the Holy Sea of the Mongols. The men stared at a wooded island a few miles offshore, wondering if this was not an anvil in the forge of the pagan gods; then they heard shouts, sounds of running feet, and, expecting to meet sledge-hammer-carrying deities, they found themselves faced with a horde of natives, set to protect their homes and fishing grounds against the invaders.

Ivanov claimed to have defeated a thousand Buryaets in a great battle for control of Lake Baikal; and by the time his report had been edited by the Siberian Chancellery, the victory was said to have yielded a hoard of treasure. Moscow took gracious cognizance of the good news and requested additional information, substantiated by samples of the yield.

At this point Ivanov dropped out of the picture. Another Cossack from Yeniseisk, at the head of a hundred men, went to the shores of the grandiose lake and returned to his base in 1647 carrying several bowls of silver and pieces of gold. These objects, he told the Governor, were not a produce of Baikal mines, but gifts from a Mongolian prince who had bought them from merchants whose caravans came from Ki-tai.

The discovery of Lake Baikal renewed the Russian urge to Ki-tai. Siberian governors and counselors of the Prikas weighed ways and means to conquer the land of plenty.

An inevitable interlude of feud between spiteful governors brought more Cossack troops from Yakutsk and Yeniseisk to the lake and to the Mongolian roaming grounds beyond, with few discoveries made but many tributes collected at random and women and men enslaved. The Siberian Chancellery had its "ambassadors to Muscovy" rounded up by the irregulars of the Governor of Yeniseisk.

More information on Ki-tai was obtained by Cossack Ivan Poshabov, who had intended to pillage the tribe of a Mongolian khan, but changed his mind when he found his band heavily outnumbered by grim-looking tribesmen. Instead of attacking Poshabov paid a friendly visit to the Khan and even apologized for the intrusion. The Mongol and his white-haired father-in-law told him about Ki-tai; of recent conquest of this great land; of its new ruler, the Divine Khan who was ready to receive distinguished visitors; of rich mines that could be found in Ki-tai; of silk and sugar that traders from Ki-tai sold in war and peace. But when Poshabov asked for guides to take him before the Divine Khan the Mongols made excuses, claiming that this was not the good traveling season, that they did not have skillful interpreters available, and that the Divine Khan may take it amiss should the Russians arrive at his court with Mongolian guides.

Poshabov never reached his goal.

He was still palavering with the obstinate Mongols when another expedition left Yakutsk under the leadership of Jerofei Chabarov, a promyshlenik, according to official records, but quite different from any other bearer of this designation. Chabarov may have been a man with an unusual education and noble background, who went to Siberia for reasons unknown. He too was later adopted by the communists as an early champion of their ideology, but actually, whatever his origin, Chabarov was the earliest Siberian representative of free enterprise and free labor.

Chabarov was first heard of when he found a salt mine and had it operated by vagabonds settled for the purpose, to whom he paid regular wages. The efficiency of Chabarov's operations as compared to that of the Tsar's own pits annoyed the authorities; he was deposed, and his workers organized into lamentable chain gangs.

Undaunted, Chabarov gathered destitute, landless peasants and began to till abandoned lands in the vicinity of Yakutsk in another free venture that brought the Governor so much relief from food troubles that at first he did not interfere with these unorthodox, if not rebellious, activities. However, he did not want Chabarov's farms to remain under the leadership of so bold a man. Soon he cajoled and coerced Chabarov into leaving the farms on the banks of the Lena River in care of a supervisor, and to try his talents in another field: the discovery of treasures in the distant south.

Treasures, in the Governor's opinion, were gold, silver, and furs. Chabarov thought of precious things in terms of grain, salt, and other consumer goods. The Governor suggested that Chabarov proceed to the Holy Sea of the Mongols, but Chabarov remembered having heard of Prince Lawkai who ruled over fine lands beyond the mountains toward midday. Whatever briefing he may have received, Chabarov headed straight in the direction of Lawkai's land.

None of his peasants was permitted to accompany him. He assembled a motley horde of camp followers, left Yakutsk, and reached the Amur River on the shortest route ever established. The first building they found on the left bank was a fortress with palisades, embrasures, moats, covered trenches, and sally ports. The place was deserted, and so was another fortress farther downstream. After a prolonged search the Russians sighted five men on horseback on the opposite bank of the Amur. Interpreters shouted to the five that here were peaceful Russians wanting to do business with the people of Prince Lawkai. From the other bank it came back that all Russians were thieves and murderers, that Prince Lawkai in person was here to say so. Then the party galloped away while interpreters roared desperately that protection of all natives by the White Tsar could be had for a bargain price. Prince Lawkai, a Dawrien, did not care to listen.

The only other native the Russians saw on their trip downstream was a half-witted woman who blabbered that she was Lawkai's sister but would not answer further questions.

The Dawriens, mindful of the horrors suffered a few short years before, had taken refuge south of the Amur; Chabarov and his men did not know that Manchu patrols were watching them from hiding places a short distance away, and that their every move would be reported to the ruler of Ki-tai long before Russian authorities would learn of their whereabouts.

Chabarov was amazed at the high level of cultivation he saw on nearby fields. The soil was fat and fertile, and the river abundant with fish, including "giant sturgeons between fourteen and twenty feet long and as thick as the body of a strong man." No finer location for an agricultural settlement could be found, but Chabarov's band was not of settling and pioneering timber. The men clamored for something substantial, and went roaming forests to hunt sables.

Poachers would never turn farmers. Chabarov returned to Yakutsk to recruit peasants for a grandiose venture on the Amur River. He did not expect much support from the authorities, but when he arrived in May 1650, nobody in office would listen to farm-talk; and exploration by land route was out of date. The great treasure was said to be on the arctic shore, far to the northeast, where only specially built ships could go. Such ships were on their way and Yakutsk waited for the happy tidings. The city was overcrowded with operators watching for opportunities as they would arise after the treasures arrived; with hangers-on and black-marketeers; and with a pathetic mass of human flotsam waiting for opportunities.

Chabarov called for volunteers to go farming in Dawria. He would not accept anyone who was not of peasant stock and had not had recent farming experience. Desperate fortune hunters were turned away. One hundred seventeen men and women were admitted eventually: the first Siberian colonists, who were neither freebooters nor soldiers, but settlers and builders. On the eve of their departure Chabarov was called to the Governor's office and notified that he would receive a "protective force" of twenty Cossacks. His objections that the peasants could take care of their own security were overruled. The Governor was not concerned with the safety of the settlers, but determined to keep their leader under control. Chabarov realized that his expedition would be disbanded should he press his opposition, but, if he anticipated trouble with the Cossacks, his worst misgivings were borne out by later events. Despite his and his peasants' desire to establish a peaceful agrarian colony the venture did not succeed and the violence of "guardian Cossacks" and bandits associated with them precipitated war between Russia and China.

For a good many years the Governor of Yakutsk had been pondering over exploration by sea; he had already studied its aspects when he first sent Chabarov south.

One Bursa, who styled himself a retired army captain and operated a rickety ship on the Lena River and on arctic waters beyond the estuary, had first told the official of the treasures that could be reached only by ship. Bursa, a deserter who had never held a commission, hoped to obtain the Governor's material support for extensive trips that should carry him to the goal of every Russian in Siberia: the mysterious hoard not yet raised. Bursa had been as far east as the Yana estuary, where he had found sables, walrus teeth, and ivory, and he had met what he called a new nation, the Yukagiris.

The Governor was impressed by the boastful stories; but, being an educated man, he studied accounts on arctic navigation since 1553 when Sir Hugh Willoughby had tried to sail all the way along the Russian and Siberian coasts. Sir Hugh had failed, and so had other noted English and Dutch seafarers between 1553 and 1616, and lesser seafaring foreigners since. But Russian seamen who hunted seals, seahorses, and polar bears had covered the 4000-mile distance from Arkhangelsk to the mouth of the Lena, and some had even returned to their base. Their *kotchis* were smaller and less solid than English and Dutch craft, yet results seemed to indicate that they were even more seaworthy than Western boats.

The Governor requested *promyshleniki,* and Cossacks who had been north, to report to his office and tell him about conditions in arctic waters. Promyshleniki who had been well east of the Yana River said that the coast was rugged, that ships that kept close to shore would be smashed on the cliffs, and that the waters farther out were infested with drifting icebergs as big as ostrogs, as sharp-edged as hatchets. These icebergs did not even melt in midsummer, when the sun never set. However, Cossack rangers who claimed to have outrun the promyshleniki insisted that the coast became smoother and the climate milder farther east.

Bursa, whom the Governor told of the Cossacks' report, was doubtful. He did not want to chance his craft sailing through drifting ice, but he insinuated that, sailing up the Yana River and its tributaries, a short cut to the eastern sea could be found. Such an attempt, made with the Governor's blessings, carried the skipper to the site of Verkhojansk, but the trip did not proceed farther because no tributary leading east could be located.

Bursa attributed his failure to the lack of a *kotchi* that could be transported over land until the right watercourse was found. The Governor argued against inland navigation, but eventually advanced some money so that Bursa could build a dismountable boat.

News from abroad took a long time to reach Yakutsk. Not until several years later did the Governor learn that in 1639 a splendidly equipped Dutch expedition had sailed "to discover the east coast of the Great Tartary, and the famous gold and silver islands." He requested that Bursa sail east at once, to prevent the Dutch from reaching the hoard first. Bursa asked that the Governor take charge of all expenses and content himself with a modest share in the proceeds, on the basis of Bursa's own accounting. The two men quarreled, and parted as irreconcilable enemies.

The Governor appealed to all merchants and financiers within and outside his province to invest in a fabulously lucrative venture which he, the Governor, would direct.

Merchants and financiers—actually black-marketeers, smugglers, and usurers—consulted with backers and associates; once more the grapevine told of impending discovery of the legendary riches. From a thousand miles around people flocked to Yakutsk; a variety of fortune hunters and desperadoes as only Siberia could produce. Partnerships formed and dissolved; crews were hired and left stranded without pay; every day people would drop out in despair, but more than their number would arrive. Yakutsk turned into a stock exchange of exploration with booms, busts, and fortunes changing hands without visible progress toward the achievement of the big goal.

The Governor played budding syndicates against each other, made and broke commitments, issued and revoked licenses, bickered and bargained with prospective partners and competitors.

Outside of the gubernatorial mansion a hoarse Bursa addressed audiences, calling for backers of an expedition which, he insisted, only he could undertake on his dismountable kotchi, which he had on display in the square. But no responsible man wanted to deal with a rebel. Eventually Bursa's kotchi was burned and its owner disappeared.

Sometime in 1647 three expedition leaders were selected, all Cossacks: Ataman Gerafim Aukudinov, Ataman Fjodor Alekseev, and Simon Deshnev.

Deshnev was the Governor's personal appointee. The names of those who backed the two atamans are not recorded, but it appears that the Governor had secret partnership agreements with them, insurance against the possible failure of his own choice.

Nineteenth-century writers who first discovered Deshnev as a topic insinuated that he might not have been a Cossack but rather a promyshlenik; and, searching for fitting adjectives, they could do no better than call him "simple." Deshnev was certainly not an intellectual, but, simple as his speech and manners undoubtedly were, he must have been a methodical man and an expert navigator. The terms of Deshnev's contract are not fully revealed, but it is known that he was pledged to deliver at least seven sable furs per capita of inhabitants of the Anadyr Peninsula.

Siberian archives do not indicate that any Russian had been to that northeasternmost tip of Asia by 1647, nor that mapmakers had gone beyond the Yana River. However, more puzzling even, the Governor did have a map of all the northern coast of Siberia, showing rivers, gulfs, isles, and peninsulas, all officially unexplored, with an accuracy that contrasted strangely with the inexactness of maps available in the Russian capital. The mystery of the Governor's map was never solved.

In the winter of 1647–48, Deshnev, Aukudinov, and Alekseev left Yakutsk for the mouth of the Kolyma River—a white spot on maps in Muscovy, 163° east of Greenwich and latitude 69° north, 1000 miles from Yakutsk as the crow flies.

Deshnev had a crew of sixty men; the two others had thirty men each. They had three kotchis, dismountable craft similar to that Bursa had built; the parts were loaded on reindeer sleighs. Again no metal had been used in construction; men could not touch iron with their bare hands in regions where winter temperatures may fall below minus 80° F.

In April 1648 the three groups arrived at the mouth of the Kolyma with their craft ready to sail. Not until later, in 1649, did the first report reach the Governor of Yakutsk: the promontory of the Kolyma River was described as very big, and altogether different from promontories farther to the west. "It bends, in a circular course, toward Anadyr; on the western side, there is a rivulet, close to which native Chutskis have built a pile of whalebones. There are two islands opposite the promontory, both inhabited by Chutski, people who have pieces of sea-horse teeth thrust into holes in their lips."

Deshnev did not yet disclose that he was at odds with the atamans, who suggested that, now that they were beyond their backers' and sponsors' reach, they continue their explorations for their personal benefits.

The "simple Cossack" had unusual ideas about loyalty; he wanted to keep his contract and insisted that others do the same.

The Governor was not interested in natives' lips inlaid with walrus teeth. He had been told of a Dutch flotilla sighted off Taymyr Peninsula, sailing east. Taymyr was still some 50° west of the Kolyma, but if Deshnev did not hurry the Dutch might overtake him.

The report on the Dutch flotilla remained unconfirmed. Captain Kvast, who had left for the "Great Tartary" twelve years before, had chosen a southern route of exploration. Kvast's own account told of his reaching the "Southern Sea, where, at 37.5 degrees north, and 28 degrees east of Japan," he had explored "a very great and high island, inhabited by fair-skinned, handsome, civilized people, extremely opulent in gold and silver."

No such island was later found to exist, and Kvast never tried to find the Northeast Passage. Captain Vries, who after Kvast sailed to explore "the famous land of Jesso near Japan" (obviously Hokkaido), "the Kingdom of Kata" (China), "and—the West Coast of America" on behalf of the Dutch West India Company, hardly could have gone to Siberia, even though a paper, issued in 1675 by the Illustrious Royal Society, insinuated that he may have explored the Northeast Passage and reached the Lena estuary. Nobody saw Vries in Siberia, and the actual results of his voyage are veiled in mystery.

Back in Siberia, Deshnev's arguments with his fellow Cossacks did not delay their naval operations. The seas were still partly frozen when they arrived; only on June 20 were the waters clear for the voyage. However, it appears from the position of the kotchis on that day that they had been cautiously moving on to a sheltered bay well east of the Kolyma estuary.

The next report, written by the only literate member of Deshnev's party (Deshnev himself could neither read nor write), tells that "with a good wind it is possible to sail from here to the Anadyr estuary in three days, and it should take no longer to reach the Anadyr estuary on land, by sleigh."

The three kotchis accomplished just that. Between June 20 and 23, 1649, they turned the cape from the Chuckchi Sea into the Bering Sea, the crucial section of the Northeast Passage. This route, considered almost impracticable by naval experts, was effortlessly traded by naval dilettantes, who were not even aware of the significance of their trip. Rounding a cape meant nothing to them unless they found the hoard beyond it.

For the better part of three months the voyagers scouted the coast for objects of value, but the yield was unsatisfactory: some walrus teeth, a few fur animals, not enough to cover the Governor's contractual minimum share or to compensate the sponsors of the enterprise for the loss of Aukudinov's kotchi, which had run aground and had to be abandoned, with its crew taken aboard Deshnev's craft. September came with fogs and storms. The Russians tried a landing south of the Anadyr, but were engaged by natives. Alekseev was wounded, and the party ignominiously driven back to the vessels. Visibility was poor; a storm came up. The skippers lost sight of each other, and never met again.

October saw Deshnev cruising near the Anadyr estuary, uncertain what to do. Another raging storm wrecked his kotchi. Together with twenty-five survivors the skipper reached the shore only to be attacked again, but this time by Russian prospectors who had somehow reached this region, 2000 miles east of Yakutsk. The engagement resulted in a stalemate, both sides entrenched in improvised fortifications.

A messenger from Deshnev sneaked past hostile countrymen, and, evading equally hostile natives, made his way to Yakutsk to request the Governor's assistance against irascible elements trying to cheat the authorities out of furs and walrus teeth. The Governor assigned two Cossacks and a score of volunteers to help Deshnev protect his stores and to collect Iasak. The Cossacks helped disperse the prospectors, but insisted on taking charge of further operations. Deshnev refused to resign; again Russians were locked in struggle against Russians. Deshnev retained command, built an ostrog, and explored the land only to find it poor, barren—not the place he had been sent out to seize—and at last started on the long trek home, afoot.

He arrived in Yakutsk in 1655. The financial backers of his voyage found their investment a total loss. The Governor, who did not seem to have put up cash, collected the sables, and all the walrus teeth, the latter as compensation for the deficit in furs. After some consideration the official decided to send a report to the Siberian Prikas. The Chancellery might reward him for his contribution to expansion. Deshnev was to dictate a detailed account of the voyage to a scribe, and the scribe should forward the paper to the Prikas.

The Cossack was no skillful storyteller. The scribe was no industrious man. The Governor had yet other businesses to mind.

Deshnev died, with his story not yet completely dictated. The Governor passed away. So did the scribe. An orphaned file gathered dust.

In 1736 a historiographer from St. Petersburg, the new Russian capital, toured Siberian cities to compile material on early Russian settlements. In Yakutsk he found little reliable data, even fewer conclusive figures, just a heap of contradictory protocols on internecine feuds. But in a back room he detected a pile of yellowing sheets, with leaves missing, obviously torn out as note paper. The cover was addressed to the Siberian Prikas, which no longer existed. The curious historiographer checked the sheets: they contained Deshnev's report.

It reached the Russian capital eight years after Bering had sailed on his famous voyage. And the Russian authorities decided that the credit for the discovery of the Northeast Passage should rest with Bering, who was born twenty-five years after Deshnev's return to Yakutsk, but that a minor cape be named after Deshnev. This done, the report was filed again, and left dormant ever after.

The yellow pages did not contain information on whether Deshnev sighted America on his trip through the arctic straits; whether he learned that Chutskis were trading with the people of America.

What would have happened had the report reached the capital in time?

It is likely that before long, certainly under the rule of Peter the Great, the Russian Government would have resumed exploration of the extreme northeastern territories on a larger scale, and the discovery of Alaska would have followed in a matter of years. The Pilgrim Fathers had landed on Plymouth Rock only thirty-five years before Deshnev began to dictate his story. At the rate of Russian penetration into newly discovered territory the conquerors of Siberia might have reached the American Middle West and established themselves as the dominant power in America before the colonists could have seized control of vital areas.

It could be that the laziness of an obscure scribe, who officiated in a city of which few Americans have ever heard, and which almost no American ever visited, preserved the North American continent for non-Russian immigrants and that Siberian carelessness gave American history a decisive turn.

CHAPTER THIRTY-EIGHT Chabarov and his peasants spent the winter of 1650–51 in an abandoned Dawrien village, while a few hundred yards away the Cossacks dwelled in a comfortable ostrog they had forced the peasants to build.

Early in March Chabarov ordered the peasants out to work, while the Cossacks still idled in their overheated, abundantly supplied fort. Chabarov hoped to have the spring sowing completed before their ruffian guards could start mischief. The Cossacks showed little interest in farming activities as long as mud and chill made it unpleasant to stay outdoors, but then trouble arose from unexpected quarters. Bands of tough characters kept arriving at the village. They did not say from where they came and who had supplied them with the weapons they carried—including three fairly new field cannon; they sneered when asked either to work on the fields or to leave, but requested a voice in the affairs of the community. Chabarov asked the Cossack commander to chase the intruders away, but the man refused to interfere. He even fraternized with the goons, who molested laboring peasants, robbed them of their trifling possessions, and feasted on their rations. More bands arrived in April 1651; farm work slowed down, stopped. In a stormy meeting in which the Cossacks joined with the intruders in shouting down Chabarov's pleas for resumption of agricultural operations a resolution was adopted to break camp and proceed downriver in quest of better opportunities.

Chabarov gave in after the Cossacks threatened to burn down the village and take tools away from peasants who refused to join the expedition. The peasants shrugged their shoulders; 117 men could not argue against three cannon. Chabarov was forced to lead the expedition. He had rafts built, and in the second week of May the troop of Cossacks, freebooters, and peasants was on its way downstream.

After a short trip they reached triangular fortifications. The main blockhouses were stronger than Dawrien forts; earthworks were of recent construction, and when the Russians steered toward the riverbank troops rushed out of trenches to meet them. Chabarov wanted to parley with the Dawriens, but the Cossacks opened fire and the fight was on. The duel of musket bullets and cannon balls against arrows led to the inevitable result: the fortifications were overrun and so were the residential dwellings they covered.

Chabarov reported to Governor Peter Golovin of Yakutsk that 641 Dawrien soldiers had been killed, 243 women and young girls, 118 children, 237 horses, and 113 head of cattle had been captured, at a loss of 4 Russians killed and 45 wounded.

A strange party watched the engagement from the opposite bank: unarmed men wearing bright silken gowns and dark fur caps. After the walls had collapsed, the spectators crossed the Amur in canoes, and asked to see the Russian commander.

They spoke an idiom Chabarov's interpreters said they could not well understand. It appeared that the foreigners were delegates of some khan and they had come to trade with the Dawriens. After an unavailing exchange of confusing phrases the foreigners took to their canoes, indicating that they, or their kin, would return for further negotiations.

The Russians still camped on the battlefield strewn with Dawrien corpses when another foreigner came to visit their commander. "His cap was of bluish sable, his long gown of richly embroidered silk, and he talked a great deal," a Cossack officer is quoted. "But interpreters could hardly understand half of what he said."

It was learned, however, that the visitor was a delegate from the Shamsha Khan, a Manchurian prince and alleged sovereign of the Dawriens; that the Khan had warned the Dawriens not to open hostilities against the Russians, but that the Manchu did not intend to tolerate the Russian infringement on his right of suzerainty.

The rest of the address the Russians did not understand—or rather they claimed not to have understood it, for it is hard to believe that Dawrien interpreters serving with Chabarov's army had serious difficulties in understanding the language of a nation with whom their people had had intercourse since time immemorial. The Russians probably learned that the Manchurians wanted them to evacuate Dawrien territory, but they did not intend to comply; and after their march of conquest did not turn out as expected they wanted to blame the interpreters.

Chabarov signed communiqués eulogizing achievements; he is said to be the author of orders drafting Dawriens into military service, and of outrageous Iasak assessments. "He gave ample proof of his commercial and military talents," an official chronicler recorded, "but unfortunately he was not a master of the art of exploring human emotions; he did not understand that people, attacked without provocation and deprived of their freedom, could not be trusted, however submissive they appeared to be." However, there is reason to assume that Chabarov loathed his role as a military commander, that he tried after the battle of the triangle to organize farming ventures, and that small collective farms were set up by his peasants. The fact that he was eventually called home to report indicates that Chabarov never made the about-face insinuated by chroniclers. The chief wirepuller was Golovin, the sinister Governor of Yakutsk.

The avalanche of events was stronger than men who signed communiqués or pulled wires. The dice were cast: there would be war between Russia and China, now ruled by the Manchus.

The Russians seized hostages and held them in strong stockades, yet more than half of the detained escaped with the help of Dawrien villagers. Natives were held for questioning; they stood up under torture, and hostages kept escaping. Cossacks captured a prince and put him on the rack to force him to order his countrymen to give up resistance. The Prince held out until the henchmen were tired, then snatched a knife from a Cossack and cut his own throat.

The Russians became jittery. They were more afraid of the Dawriens than they would admit even to themselves. Unwilling to retreat, they fled forward, down the Amur toward the lands of less fanatical peoples.

The journals of the expedition record a smooth trip downstream past Gilaek and Dutcheri villages, and reaching the domain of the Atshanis, a tribe not mentioned by earlier explorers. The Russians spent the winter with the Atshanis. They had the natives build winter quarters and supply them with food, drink, and fuel. But hardly had they moved in when the Atshanis attempted to put the torch to the buildings. "This rebellion was quelled in blood, and until March 26, 1652, the natives kept at a safe distance of 'Atshanski Gorod.' "

March 26, 1652, dawned—damp, chilly, heavily overcast. The Amur still was icebound, its banks were covered with deep snow. Drowsy Russian sentinels hardly peered into the lingering haze; not since January had they laid eyes upon non-Russian people. Suddenly there were sharp detonations; a few seconds later the slumbering garrison was aroused by the crash of missiles hitting palisades and log walls. Barefoot and disheveled, the men tumbled out of dormitories as another salvo roared from out of the haze, and contours of men in assault formation emerged near the palisades.

Two hundred six Russians rushed to battle positions, not knowing who and what had hit them.

The Manchus had arrived, to carry out the threat the Russians "did not understand."

Two thousand Manchus attacked Atshanski Gorod, according to Russian journals. They used light cannon: two-pounders with a range superior to that of Russian rifles; bomb throwers, hurling "pinarts": earthern vessels filled with forty pounds of explosives; and "lockless fire pipes with three barrels apiece." This formidable artillery kept pounding the fortress; by noon the walls were breached, but the besiegers did not force their way through the gap, and waited for the Russians to come out and surrender.

However, the Russians concentrated their cannon on crucial targets, and a bold sortie routed the attackers. "We counted 676 enemy dead, and captured 2 cannon, 17 fire pipes, 8 standards, and 830 horses, at a loss of 10 killed and 78 wounded." No Manchu report on the battle is available.

The Russian journal goes on to say: "We captured a man, who was a native of a country which the Manchus call Nikan; and which they want to bring under their sway. But this should be difficult, for the Nikanese are a numerous people, they have gold, silver, pearls, jewels, silk and cotton, and they can manufacture damask, satin, velvet and various other goods."

"Nikan" and "Nikanese" were Manchu terms for China and the Chinese. But in 1652 the Manchus did not "want to bring Nikan under their sway." For a full eight years already a Manchu emperor had occupied the Chinese throne, and only in remote sections of the empire did partisans of the deposed dynasty hold out against the conquerors. In 1661, when their position became untenable, the last diehards left the mainland in quest of some island where they could recuperate and eventually return to their home as conquerors. They found an ideally suited place called Tai-Wan (Formosa).

Thirty-seven years before, Dutch merchant-conquistadors had established themselves on the big island and built Zeelandia Castle as a stronghold for colonial expansion. But the Chinese partisans took the castle in 1662, and forced the Dutch to evacuate Formosa. The first Chinese conqueror of Formosa bequeathed the island to his son, with the solemn admonition to return to China and restore the legitimate rule of the realm. The design was never carried out, and eventually Formosa fell to Manchu-ruled China.

The battle of Atshanski Gorod marked the beginning of a war between Russia and Manchu China. Chabarov was not aware of the grave consequences of the engagement but very much concerned with mounting losses. Practically all the wounded died of infections. No longer did the remnants of former Cossack guards and tough newcomers rant about continued advance. The Russian peasants who had valiantly fought talked about going out to the fields. A number of them actually left the camp and went farming.

Late in April Chabarov decreed that the men take to the ships and sail back toward Dawria. A favorable wind sprang up and carried them rapidly away from the scene of their last fight. The wind saved the men's lives, for hardly had they left when Manchu scouts arrived on the spot, vanguards of a large force the Russians could not have hoped to defeat.

Sailing up the Amur at good speed, Chabarov missed bands who marched down the river valley: reinforcements from Yakutsk.

Governor Peter Golovin had performed yet another mental gambol. With Deshnev apparently not yet in possession of the hoard he would concentrate on Ki-tai. Golovin had a cousin in Moscow, a high government official. Their relationship was not strictly friendly, but one of the rare letters from his faraway kin indicated that the usually self-centered authorities in the capital were getting more alert to events in Siberia and gubernatorial activities. Careful not to arouse his government's suspicions, the Siberian Golovin would not recruit volunteers for a drive into China, but would stir up another craze to make shiftless elements flock to the Amur, where Cossack officers would take over command.

Word-of-mouth propaganda spread another tale of gold, silver, fur, and silk in the distant southeast, and—a new touch—of the fantastic fertility of the soil, which meek and industrious natives would cultivate for the benefit of their Russian masters.

Applicants formerly not accepted by Chabarov were the first to clamor for equipment, and leadership. They massed in front of the Governor's mansion, but were not admitted. Through a rude clerk Golovin made it known that he was busy with serious matters, and that he might even leave town for a year or so. Desperate applicants knelt in front of the Governor's window, camped outside the mansion, shouted pleas, recited prayers. In vain. The clerk announced that His Excellency was not available, and that intruders would be hanged. At last a Cossack officer turned up and offered some equipment and guidance. The crowd struggled to lick the boots of their benefactor, and soon the first troop was on its way south, followed in rapid succession by similar troops organized under similar conditions.

The new craze got out of control. From Yakutsk it spread to other provinces. Freebooters and vagabonds flocked to the Amur River, not for the greater glory of their fatherland, as members of the Prikas later insinuated, but to escape a land that, to them, was a stepfather, taskmaster, and perennial prosecutor, and to go to a country where they would be taskmasters themselves. Anguished reports by provincial governors on looting of arsenals and massacres of scattered farmers' families alerted the Prikas to the fact that the drive to China was on, and that China might fall to highhanded adventurers, in or out of office, unless the Russian Government seized the reins.

Meantime Chabarov continued his voyage upstream, back to the village and ostrog where the past winter had been spent. As the disheartened party eventually went ashore, they were met by an express courier from Yakutsk, with stern orders never to retreat.

The band stayed in its quarters, while bands kept arriving from the interior of Siberia and from Yakutsk, some marching past, others, under the command of Cossacks, staying on. The Cossacks defied Chabarov's authority. Newcomers and veterans brawled and refused to take orders from anyone.

Bands marching past had neither competent guides nor interpreters. Many of them vanished farther downstream; others—marauding, sacking, and being in turn hunted like mad dogs by emboldened natives—eventually reached the shore of the Sea of Okhotsk. Only small remnants returned to the interior of Siberia.

Chabarov considered leaving his mutinous horde, but then word spread that an immense Russian army was approaching the village and ostrog. Instead of another horde of undisciplined ruffians a squadron of regular army cavalry rode up in front of the ostrog. An officer in full kit requested to see the commander. When Chabarov came out, the officer introduced himself as Boyar Dmitri Sinoviev appointed by Tsar Aleksei Mikhailovich to inspect His Majesty's territories and provinces on the Amur River.

Behind the advance squadron came other Russian troops, in smart uniforms, marching in formation with flags and standards and a train of carts and artillery, officers out in front, noncoms flanking the ranks as on the maneuver field—all regulars who looked at Chabarov's tattered ruffians with disgusted curiosity. The ruffians glared back with the hatred of mongrels.

The boyar had Chaborov's horde arrayed outside the ostrog, and addressed the glum gathering in terms that sounded strange to them: words of patriotism and gallant deeds performed in the service of His Majesty. The Tsar, he announced, had graciously decided to give invaluable gifts to all old fighters. The gifts turned out to be gilt medals worth perhaps a copper apiece. The array of regulars was formidable enough to keep the men from pressing their anger in a drastic manner.

Chabarov was notified that his presence at the capital was urgently required; the Tsar desired to have a firsthand account on events on the Amur. He was forthwith relieved from his command, and this was the end of his military career.

There are two versions of Chabarov's further experiences. According to one, he went to Moscow, was received in audience by the Tsar, was titled, and spent the rest of his life in and near the capital under favorable circumstances. The other says that Chabarov was sent to Yakutsk, where he was kept waiting for a full six years, until told that his presence in Moscow was not desired, and that a magistrate's job was waiting for him in a district on the Lena; but that instead of going to his district he went back to the Amur to found an agrarian colony at the present site of Chabarovsk.

One hundred years after his death the Russian Academy of Science gave the following appraisal of Chabarov's activities: "As long as he was in charge of military operations, the Russians scored weighty successes in the Amur campaign, and after his relief, things took a turn to the worse. However, he could have performed a greater service to his country had he handled the plow rather than the sword, and organized the settlement of peasants. Soon after Chabarov was recalled, the Bogda Khan [a Mongolian term for the Emperor of China, whom the Russians avoided calling Emperor] evacuated all Dawrien peasants from the Amur River valley, and thus the Russians, deprived of food supplies, could not maintain their strongholds along the river."

As was his habit, Governor Golovin sent glowing reports to the Prikas, telling of the establishment of a fabulous farming domain in the Amur region, where "trees bear apples as big as melons, cattle fatten in less than half the usual time, and even peasants wear garments of gold-embroidered velvet." When this stylistic exploit was drafted, the Governor expected the officials in the capital to have another map designed, adorned with pictures of overdressed gentlemen riding on fat steers and playing ball with melon-sized apples; to present the map to the Tsar; and have the matter shelved. But, viewed from the mansion at Yakutsk, world affairs did not look as they then did from the vantage point of a European capital, even if it was glum, ignorant, and superstitious Moscow; and when the Moscow Golovin made the Siberian Golovin aware of the Prikas's increasing alertness on Siberian affairs, the Governor of Yakutsk did not yet realize that his "discovery" of China was grievously obsolete, that the Western seafaring powers were already manhandling "his" empire, and that influential men in Moscow offices were busy organizing an expedition to turn China into a Russian province before Dutch, Portuguese, Spaniards, Englishmen—or Siberian governors—could take over.

Chabarov, his 117 peasants, and their 20 nefarious Cossack guards had been on their way to Dawria when one official in Moscow persuaded the Tsar to put his seal under a decree ordering a military expedition to the Amur Valley, to restore law and order in the interest of Crown and population. It would have been well nigh impossible to have Tsar Aleksei Mikhailovich sign mobilization orders for a war against China, but once a military expedition went east the champions of conquest of China could see to it that their intentions were carried out. It was up to the Tsar to assign one of his aides as commander of the "Army of the Amur." The Tsar had many aides, some of whom he loathed, some of whom he liked, and many more of whom he could not remember having met. He would not part with a man he liked; he would never promote anyone he loathed; and he did not trust people he could not remember. The presumptive conquerors of China expected Aleksei Mikhailovich to ask for suggestions and appoint their own candidate. This the Tsar did: Prince Ivan Ivanovich Lebanov-Rostovskoy became commander in chief of an army of 3000, to be recruited from among veterans of Baltic campaigns. In the West the Thirty Years War had recently come to an end. Losses of population ran as high as six million out of sixteen million in Germany, and two out of three million in the Kingdom of Bohemia, but armies engaged in major battles on either side had numbered only between 30,000 and 45,000. Yet it seemed absurd to expect a force of 3000 men to conquer the Chinese Empire.

Boyar Sinoviev's men were the vanguard of Prince Rostovskoy's Army of the Amur. Before engaging his main forces the commander wanted to survey general conditions, and went to Yakutsk to discuss matters with Governor Golovin. He should have been able to cover the distance from Moscow to the Lena in no more than three months; however, it took him a full year to complete the voyage. Wherever he came carts and carriages seemed to be undergoing repairs; horses were lame, *jamstshiki* sick, ships leaking. When the weary voyager eventually arrived at Yakutsk, he was met by a hospitable, smiling, congenial governor who asserted that, had he only been notified in advance, he would have arranged for the smoothest, speediest transportation of his "assistant in military matters."

The Prince insisted that he was not the Governor's assistant in any matter, but commander in chief of the Army of the Amur, responsible only to the highest authorities in the capital; and that Golovin's assumption of military powers was usurpation. Apparently unperturbed, Golovin assured him that, as a patriotic official, he would abide by orders, even though the gentlemen in Moscow were apparently not fully aware of the situation in Siberia and on the Amur. More than a striking force would be needed to seize, hold, and fructify the land: a migration of artisans, peasants, clergymen, and traders would have to follow in the wake of the conquering vanguards; and to organize such a migration was within the province of local civilian authorities.

The Prince did not expect matters to be auspicious, but he was soon flabbergasted to notice that he had inherited chaos. Not even Golovin would have been able to control the sinister tide built up by his own mischievous propaganda for the golden southeast. The people of a large part of Siberia were on the march. Tattered, destitute ruffians stole whatever they needed: arms, supplies, beasts—and men. They respected the property of Crown and Church as little as they spared private possessions. No arsenal, no convent, no storehouse was by-passed in their looting spree. Peasants who by prodigal power of self-preservation had established farms of their own found their huts invaded, their tools seized, and able-bodied young men and matable women deported at knife or gun-point. Cossacks left their ostrogs to go to the Amur and drafted craftsmen to go with them. Carpenters recently arrived from the West, among them several Germans who were the best shipbuilders in Siberia, were impressed into the bondage of Cossacks. Settlers on their way to assigned locations were captured, together with their belongings and marched to the Amur and slavery. From out of the woods came promyshleniki and outlaws; black-marketeers and rogues assumed leadership of the woodsmen. Bands trailed the Army of the Amur, stealing supplies and ammunitions, harassing rear-guard soldiers, and urging them to desert and join the bandits. No supplies from the hinterland reached soldiers and immigrants.

Prince Rostovskoy found the Army of the Amur drifting forward without aims other than to find food to subsist for yet another day of trial.

The Prince ordered that the advance be halted, ostrogs built, communication lines secured, and that scouting operations explore the land ahead of the army. Scouts found abandoned Dawrien and Gilaek villages, scant buried stores, and no trace of soldiers. A few natives left behind by their kin were apparently half-wits and could not answer questions. The commander in chief sent them on to Moscow to humor the court, and he also applied for further instructions.

From the Prikas came a baffling reply: Natives were not subject to shipment to the capital. The Prikas did not issue instructions.

Boyar Sinoviev bluntly said that all they could do was to gather what was left and get home. The Prince discharged the defeatist and appointed one Onufrej Stepanov, a professional soldier, as Sinoviev's successor. Stepanov had the men raid bandits' quarters to recover whatever food and ammunitions they had stolen from the army. There was a great deal of grim skirmishing until the Army of the Amur, already reduced in number, assembled in quarters to spend the rough season on small rations and heavy guard duty. Around the soldiers' camp formed a ring of huts in which the outlaws vegetated, preying upon their countrymen, who, having food, were their archenemies.

In the spring of 1654 the Army of the Amur opened another drive. This time it would not "drift forward," but march in formation with artillery and other heavy equipment carried by *kotchis*. The suddenness of the army's departure surprised both outlaws and natives. The outlaws, who were worn out by privations, missed opportunities to steal, and Dawriens who had flocked back to villages during the cold season had no time to carry their possessions to safety. The first days of the advance were a Russian soldier's dream: plenty of spoils and no combat.

The army turned into the Sungari River valley and continued upstream toward the old Manchu-Chinese border and toward an overland short cut to the Great Wall.

From observation points on treetops, from hideouts in rolling hills, from holes dug on riverbanks native scouts counted men, cannon, ammunition boxes, even muskets. Runners transmitted observations to Chinese and Manchu officers who compiled the data into an over-all picture as complete as the most pretentious general could want. The Chinese and Manchus were in no hurry; they would give the Russians time to blunder. Already the trip upstream was a major blunder. The kotchis were not sufficiently maneuverable to operate in the shallow waters of the upper Sungari. The Russians did not know that Chinese light and fast river craft were trailing them, and that natives officered by Manchus marched up the Sungari Valley, ready to hurl themselves against the invaders once their mobility was impaired.

Stepanov's ideas about strategy and tactics were rudimentary if not stupid. Prince Rostovskoy was away on a mysterious inspection tour when Stepanov chose a narrow in the upper Sungari River to unload heavy material.

The Russians were off guard when the light Chinese vessels appeared, and shortly thereafter native soldiers swarmed over their improvised camp.

Stepanov's artillery was of heavier caliber than that mounted on Chinese boats; several attacking craft were sunk; their hulks, however, constituted further hazards to the kotchis, and more Chinese boats kept arriving.

Native infantry hit the Russian flanks, the Army of the Amur was hemmed into an ever-narrowing space, and Stepanov ordered all men aboard kotchis. Had the natives pressed their advantage, the Russians would have been annihilated. But the attackers stopped on the riverbanks, and eventually the kotchis broke through the thin belt of Chinese vessels and escaped downstream.

A communiqué to Moscow over the signature of Prince Rostovskoy announced a "naval victory."

The "naval victory" cost the Russians a number of ships and the greater part of their artillery; and it reduced the strength of the Army of the Amur to a mere 500 combatants.

Manchu China had defeated the Russians by proxy. With the exception of a small number of officers, artillerists, and boat crews the Dawriens had borne the brunt of the battle.

The shattered army trudged toward the Amur River to establish winter quarters at Kamarskoy Ostrog and to secure communication lines between that fortress and the interior of Siberia by construction of small ostrogs.

The grimness of defeat had impaired discipline; however, the aspect of spending a winter in heated accommodations restrained nascent refractoriness. Buried supplies would last the decimated army until early spring. A square of earthworks with four bastions was built, surrounded by palisades and by a moat fourteen feet wide and seven feet deep. The forefield was sown with concealed traps that would catch a wolf or a man. Three cannon —all that were left after the "naval victory"—were put on emplacements from where they could sweep the approaches. Wells were dug, water pipes laid; the fortress turned into the strongest yet built in the region.

The winter was not yet over when the enemy arrived, with men and horses and a colorful collection of siege weapons. The assailants had fifteen two-pounder cannon, not sufficiently powerful to break walls, but effective against earthworks at a range of 700 yards. Ammunition was carried in two-wheeled barrows, covered with leather-coated wooden shields. Assault troops used similar barrows to cover their advance toward the walls. The enemy also had many "fire tubes," some of them with locks.

For three weeks Chinese artillery pounded the ostrog. Several times armored barrows shepherded infantry within a few yards of the palisades, but, finding the bulwark intact, the infantry made no attempt to scale it.

As suddenly as they had laid the siege the enemies lifted it. The Russians did not rejoice, and Stepanov issued no victory bulletin. The men who had once looked down on Siberian freebooters with disgust turned into marauders who clamored for spoils without fight. The delegate commander had no delusions about having lost the war. In a palaver that resembled a stormy political meeting rather than a military gathering it was decided that the Army of the Amur should spend the fair season collecting Iasak in districts not patrolled by hostile soldiers.

When Prince Rostovskoy arrived in Yakutsk, he knew of neither the decision nor of the battle of Kamarskoy Ostrog. Governor Golovin sneered when the Prince requested ammunitions for the Army of the Amur. There was no material available for an army that was abandoning it to the enemy, he said.

The Prince threatened to have Golovin deposed. Golovin was scornful and abusive, and the hapless Prince dashed off to Yeniseisk.

Governor Pashkov's assistant behaved no better than Golovin. He relished insulting a prince, an army commander, one of these Muscovites, big people who considered Siberian officials an inferior lot. The Assistant Governor snarled haughtily that Yeniseisk was currently supplying the real Siberian-raised Army of the Amur, under the leadership of a Siberian governor who would repair the damage done by incompetent European soldiery who had turned into itinerant tax collectors.

To Rostovskoy, Siberia seemed to turn into a ghost-ridden madhouse. He went straight on to Moscow, where he was unceremoniously discharged.

The "itinerant tax collectors" found Dawrien settlements a most unrewarding bait. The Dawriens had carried out a thorough scorched-earth policy that caused the Russians to curse their own hard luck and the trickery and black magic of the natives. Hunger plagued the men amid fertile fields and Stepanov led his men, who now herded together like frightened sheep, to the east, at safe distance from the Manchu-Chinese border, toward regions inhabited by Gilaeks, and smaller neighboring tribes.

Soldiers slew, raped, robbed, and eventually collected 2500 sable furs. But when their commander requested that all these furs be used to buy the good will of the Tsar, the Prikas, and Siberian governors, pandemonium broke out. Stepanov pleaded, promised to promote reasonable men, pictured their fate if no supplies reached them. They could not subsist on Gilaek food alone during another winter, and you could not eat sables. Eventually some 600 furs were surrendered under condition that this would be the last sacrifice they would be asked to make.

Stepanov eventually shipped the batch to Yakutsk, care of the Governor, accompanied by a long list of goods required by his army, from cannon balls to groats. By the time the sables arrived Golovin was living in retirement, and the new Governor signed a receipt for tax arrears and ignored the requests.

Pashkov's new Army of the Amur did not fare well either. Outlaws suddenly promoted to mainstays of law and of conquering patriotism stole and sold to black-marketeers whatever material reached headquarters; soldiers assigned to guard communication lines waylaid friendly supply columns. The dejected former Governor eventually led his army to the eastern shores of Lake Baikal.

There, separated by towering mountain ranges from the great river, the Army of the Amur lived idyllically on the proceeds of native labor. At lengthening intervals Pashkov would answer inquiries from Moscow concerning his activities with boisterously vague allusions to momentous events ahead. The Tsar and the Prikas were far away.

Official Iasak collectors, however, were not as remote as the Kremlin. They were unable to obtain payments in the regions in which the Army of the Amur had established itself; their angry reports were summarized in memoranda denouncing plunderers who appropriated to themselves what was the Tsar's, who had established robber barons' ostrogs as storehouses for stolen property which they sold to smugglers who in turn supplied the Chinese enemy.

The section of the Nerchinsk storehouse reserved for the commander's property was never empty; as the year 1658 drew to a close the former Governor received urgent warnings from well-wishers in the capital: Unless he achieved something respectable, quick, his days in office, civilian or military, were numbered.

Three choices were left to Pashkov: he could make a desperate attempt to lead his robbers to distant battlefields; he could ignore the warnings; or he might gang up with whatever was left of Stepanov's army and establish a condominium of looters from the great lake as far to the south and east as the Chinese would permit. The first choice was hopeless, the second extremely hazardous, and, the more the ex-Governor thought of the third, the more auspicious it seemed to be.

Runners from Nerchinsk went to locate Stepanov and invite him to a friendly parley with His Excellency Pashkov. They found him neither in the mountains nor in the distant Amur River valley. However, they sighted such a number of Chinese river craft that they chose to return to their base.

Ahead of them a rugged horde of Russians arrived in Nerchinsk to tell the story of Stepanov.

After a few buccaneering years the former professional soldier decided to make a bid for the jackpot. His men were willing to stake their unsatisfactory fortunes on one bold stroke. Stepanov's fleet sailed to the Sungari River and upstream, with watches shouting defiant challenges at an invisible enemy.

The day after Stepanov took course upstream forty-seven Chinese boats caught up with him. The Chinese craft was better built than their Russian counterparts and equipped with heavier guns of superior range.

The second Battle of the Sungari lasted only a few minutes. One hundred eighty Russians, who abandoned ship after the first salvo hit home, were the only survivors of Stepanov's armada. The commander himself was never heard of again.

The survivors fled to Pashkov's headquarters, where they hoped to find food, shelter, and less hazardous but more profitable assignments.

Pashkov received them well enough, but as soon as the stragglers had their stomachs filled, their humility changed to raucous insolence. They requested commissions and the final word in decisions affecting the Army of the Amur. After a number of severe brawls the savage horde helped itself to supplies stored in Nerchinsk and left to resume pillage on their own account.

They numbered still 172 when they marched out of the ostrog. In the fall of 1661 six survivors reached Yakutsk, loaded with furs. The others had died of hunger, or exposure in untold struggles for survival. Their wealth in furs could not provide them with the necessities of life, and the Governor of Yakutsk confiscated them at once—"for the benefit of the treasury."

The loss of supplies in Nerchinsk sealed the doom of Pashkov's bands. The men slaughtered their horses and their dogs, ate the flesh of foxes and wolves, scurvy broke out, cannibalism became rampant. In 1662, Pashkov was left with his personal servants. The other men had either died or deserted him— only to die in the wilderness.

The ex-Governor and ex-commander eventually went to Moscow, where he presented an account bristling with high-principled professions of noble purpose and charges of disloyalty and general denunciations of anybody who had not promoted his worthy endeavors.

He received no reply. Even in Moscow it was now realized that the war against China was lost. To the Russians losing a war was tantamount to demotion of the commander in chief, and preparation of another try for the same goal "soon," which could mean next year, next generation, or a little later.

CHAPTER THIRTY-NINE Jesuits were the first Westerners to provide recent elaborate information about China to an Occident where most people had never heard of the empire, and the few who had considered it either a Marco Poloian hoax or an elusive treasure hoard to be looted by a lucky robber.

Members of the Society of Jesus took a special vow of obedience to the Pope in matters of foreign affairs; they became the instruments of a global policy aiming at recovering, through conversion of the great nations of Asia, the ground lost and still to be lost by the Reformation. Sixteenth-century

Rome had ancient maps showing the caravan routes to India and China; and over these routes, by-passing Siberia, the first Jesuit padres traveled to Peking.

The emperors received the ecclesiastics with great distinction. Jesuits who acquired a perfect mastery of Mandarin Chinese, the language of the court, became official advisers in many matters, including that of military equipment. Jesuits designed the cannon that later destroyed Stepanov's *kotchis*. Jesuits were promoted to mandarins, wore the silken robes of their rank, associated with Chinese dignitaries, and had it not been for celibacy, a new caste of Jesuit-Chinese aristrocracy might have emerged.

Jesuit reports on China's wealth and its military weakness stirred the greedy imagination of expansionist-minded merchants and governments that had not previously realized what advantage the Portuguese had gained by sending their ships to the Far East ahead of other seafaring nations.

The Portuguese, who had been more secretive about China than Jesuit missionaries, had done business with China since 1516, and their mercantile imperialistic procedures would eventually set the pattern for Dutch, English, and French rivals. It started with friendly trade, continued with the establishment of factories on Chinese territory, to be followed by lodgments on strategic outposts from where the invaded land could be put under pressure. In 1557 the Portuguese seized Taipa and Coloane, small islands on the mouth of the Canton River, as nucleuses of their later colony of Macao, and later established themselves on Macao Peninsula, right across a narrow strip of sea. The Dutch, who were poor seconds in the race for the China trade, waited until 1607 to make their bid for Chinese territory. In that year the Dutch East India Company, chartered in 1602 with a capital of 6,600,000 guilders, had its men invade Canton. The Chinese did not offer resistance, but the Portuguese from Macao foiled the attempt. A retaliatory Dutch attack on the Portuguese stronghold, staged in 1622, was repulsed.

Until the end of the sixteenth century the English considered it sound policy to let other people struggle for Oriental wares and to buy the goods from those who made the precarious purchase. But in 1599, when the price of pepper on the London market skyrocketed from three to eight shillings a pound, indignant merchants resolved not to let anybody else manipulate prices of colonial groceries. The East India Company was organized to deal with the Orient directly, and on English terms. France, less efficient in matters of commerce, eventually followed suit.

From the eastern shores of the South China Sea, Spaniards watched events across the waters with arrogant *grandeza*. Spain did not act through trade companies and for the sake of commodity prices. Spain conquered in the name of its king and for the sake of raising the Cross. And if hecatombs were committed under the process, conquistadores felt that the avowed ends justified the means.

Gerónimo Román, Factor of the Philippines, made a study of the Chinese

Navy, and summed it up as follows: "The King of China maintains a numerous fleet; the vessels go to sea only in perfect weather, and stay in port at the least wind. They have small-caliber iron cannon, but their gunpowder is no good, and they use artillery mostly to fire salutes. Their sailors have arquebuses, but they are so poorly manufactured that the bolts could not pierce an ordinary cuirass."

This report was included in a voluminous document, jointly signed by the Governor of the Philippines, the Archbishop, and the superiors of religious orders established there, and submitted to the gracious attention of the King of Spain. It was suggested that His Majesty conquer China. "Between ten and twelve thousand Spanish regulars, joined by an equal number of Filipine and Japanese mercenaries," the Governor explained, "are superior to anything the Chinese can put into the field."

His Majesty did not engage in the conquest of China, but the Governor waged a private war when in 1603 large numbers of Chinese settlers arrived on Luzon in an effort to escape the horrors of feud on the mainland. The Governor charged that the immigrants were plotting to seize Manila. With the assistance of Japanese residents he staged a massacre in which not only the new arrivals but also the old established Chinese local community were exterminated.

This exploit, however, did not induce the government of Japan to react to feelers about joint action against China, nor did the government amend its anti-emigration laws to permit volunteers to join a Spanish-Filipino expeditionary force. Japanese citizens who left the country faced execution upon return. No such Draconian measures, however, were taken against Japanese pirates who harassed the sea lanes as far as Java and Sumatra, and whose robberies were viewed with favor by an ultraisolationist Japanese government.

The disappointed Governor of the Philippines eventually decreed readmission of Chinese to the islands, with the provision that the number of Chinese in Manila should never exceed 6000. Soon men and women began arriving at the scene of the massacre of their kin. To the Chinese massacres, like storms, droughts, and floods, were elementary disasters to be taken in stride.

Matteo Ricci, an Italian Jesuit who became Ambassador of the Roman Catholic Church to the Court of Peking, was among the most thorough European observers on the scene. He lived in China until his death in 1610, was made a mandarin of the first class, wore Chinese attire, and translated the Ten Commandments into Chinese. Ricci was an admirer of China's culture and science, but had nothing but scorn for its military institutions and the military spirit of its people.

"The Chinese are poor warriors," he wrote in his journals, published in 1615. "The military are one of the four castes that are considered mean. Nearly all soldiers are malefactors, sentenced to perpetual slavery in the Emperor's service. They are, at best, fit to war with thieves. . . . It is the most difficult thing in the world to consider a Chinese a fighting man. . . . They spend two hours every morning combing and platting their hair. To run away is not considered disgraceful. They do not know what an insult is. . . . If they quarrel, they shriek abuse like women; like women they pull each others' hair; when they are weary of scuffling, they are friends again, and there is no bloodshed. Civilians are not permitted to keep as much as a knife in their houses. The Chinese are formidable only in number. More than 60 million people are inscribed on the Imperial registers, and this does not include holders of public offices and persons too poor to pay taxes."

The soldiers Ricci saw were demoralized, and were the subject of general disdain. However, the papal ambassador, shocked by the contrast between Chinese cultural achievements and Chinese military prowess, did not seem to realize that the fighting efficiency of Chinese armies was subject to sudden and amazing changes, that the rise of a dynasty of warriors could produce a rise of military standards; and—more puzzling even for a European observer to whom an army was a soulless, fighting machine—the same Chinese army that would run away before one enemy would give an impressive account of itself against another, provided it was an archfoe.

European seafarers, regardless of their flag, were no archfoes, but it was a mistake to interpret the generally passive Chinese attitude toward foreigners as a suicidal disregard for strangers. In later entries in his journals Ricci referred to Chinese contempt for foreigners, strange enough for a man to whom the Chinese had shown so much consideration. Such contempt concentrated on untidy raiders, dishonest merchants, feuding competitors, and corrupt blackmailers, who constituted the bulk of foreigners gracing China in the seventeenth century. And it did not enhance foreign prestige with the Orientals that, armed with nothing but their wits, they could outsmart merchants who did business while the guns of their vessels were trained at the market place.

But Chinese civil engineering aroused the admiration of foreign observers. "Their highways are superb, very well laid out, and paved with stone. Bridges are kept in admirable shape, and the width of city streets is incredible. Fifteen horsemen can ride abreast on them," one account stated.

Oriental corruption, frequently ridiculed by aliens who had, and still have, no better argument to support their own claim to superiority, did not seem to have permeated Chinese courts of law: Juan Gonzáles de Mendoza, an Augustinian friar from Toledo who compiled reports from missionaries to China, found this statement: "The Emperor pays his magistrates adequate wages. Acceptance of bribes or gratuities from litigants is considered a major crime. The judges are directly responsible to the ruler, and subject to strict regulations. Magistrates, sitting in court, have to be absolutely sober; and even the intake of food prior to trials is to be held at a strict minimum. The judge shall not rely upon scribes or notaries to take down essential evidence and testimony. Whatever is pertinent to the case must be written down by the judge himself. He must give careful consideration not only to the wording of testimony, but also to the personality of the witness, and the circumstances under which he testifies." Only in rare cases "will there be complaints about ill-considered or unfair decisions."

Learned Europeans who watched the Chinese tragedy of weakness, fratricidal feuding, and disloyalty, against a theatrically sinister background of regional famines, heralding the downfall of the Mings and the establishment of the Manchus on the throne, could not conceive the survival of the empire. No Western country could have stood up under a similar holocaust, and observers agreed, some regretfully, others with malicious joy, that the dissolution of China was a matter of time: a few years perhaps, or at best a few decades.

Such opinions stimulated the seafarers' conquest-by-trade activities. Foreign intruders tried to beat their rivals first, and get the complete spoils of China afterward. Their cutthroat competition boosted Chinese trade in the midst of a political calamity which otherwise would have produced depression; and while the Ming Emperor could not have prevented a single European landing detachment from marching wherever it pleased, rival Westerners blocked each other's way.

And when the Manchus emerged victorious, China had not, as it had appeared to Jesuit padres, simply fallen to a foreign conqueror; it had exchanged a decaying dynasty for a dynasty of warriors, and with all their outward appearances of crudeness these warriors were ready, and even waiting, for Sinofication.

It took the amazed Europeans more time to understand the strange processes of amalgamation that characterized violent changes of regime in China than it took the Manchus to provide their new realm with a competent military caste, and in turn to embrace the essentials of Chinese administration and the unadulterated Chinese way of life.

The new emperors introduced their system of conscription. Men between sixteen and sixty were subject to draft; China was organized into 2208 recruiting districts, each of which could raise ten companies, each 150 strong. Officers were taken from families in which the military profession had been hereditary. And because few Chinese men could meet this requirement, the officers' corps became essentially Manchurian. Manchurian were the eight "Elite Standards," which constituted the hard core of the army. Not all other countries of the world combined could have raised an army of 3,300,000 in the seventeenth century. However, this Chinese strength remained on paper only. At no time could the government equip 10 per cent of that number; and, more disappointing, even the moral damage done by discrediting the soldiers as an inferior caste could not be fully repaired.

Even so, European observers still underestimated the actual fighting power of China, and they did not see what objectives the Manchu-Chinese military could have had beyond repelling disorganized invasions from Siberia.

However, Manchu generals, co-operating with Chinese statesmen, devised a long-term program to establish control of those regions now known as Outer Mongolia, Inner Mongolia, and Tibet; to capture Formosa from émigré partisans, and to hold the Russians in Siberia at a safe distance, outside the forefield of the empire.

Control of Mongolia and Tibet was achieved in an elaborate process of step-by-step infiltration, which taxed Chinese statecraft higher than Manchu strategy. Formosa was incorporated in 1683, and by brief shows of force and circumstantial diplomacy the line was held against Siberia for about two centuries.

But to conquer and to expand as far as possible remained Russia's irrevocable objective, and nothing could alter the law of Russian gravity that would not keep within boundaries, however wide, unless forcibly contained.

New human elements of Russian expansion were forming while the first Russo-Chinese war was still running its strange course. The aftermath of Stenka Razin's legendary Cossack revolt saw several thousand desperadoes determined to get beyond the range of the government's vengeful arms. The church reform, introduced by Patriarch Nikon in 1656, led to schism (Raskol). Old Believers (Raskolniki) seceding from the reformed Church set out in quest of lands where they could worship God according to traditional rites. Rabid outlaws and hardly less rabid zealots went to Siberia. Their total number was trifling: one man or two to every thousand square miles of land. But they did not want to stay under the sway of mundane or ecclesiastic authorities, and pressed on eastward, a violent trickle that local adventurers would use to make their mills grind.

With the Amur turning into a strong barrier pressure would seek an outlet beyond the range of Chinese power. The eventual Russian drive to America was in logical sequence to Cossack rebellion and church reform, even though long delayed by the strange fate of Deshnev's papers.

But still, peace on the Amur River did not last.

Raskolniki and Cossack rogues swarmed the Baikal regions, leaderless. Not even promyshleniki and adventure-minded black-marketeers wanted to deal with them. A few salt mines were operating in the vicinity of the lake; the workers were mostly prisoners of European wars whom the Russians had shipped there without giving a thought to repatriation. The prisoners, Poles and German lansquenets among them, were supervised by fellow-prisoners. One Polish overseer, Nikifor Chernigovsky, assisted by hard-hitting Germans, seized control of a large mine. Russian guards joined the prisoners. Runaways from other mines, Cossack rogues and Raskolniki, flocked to Chernigovsky's band. The salt mine was abandoned. The men went straight to the Amur. Where they found the weapons they eventually carried, and who had told them about the abandoned Russian ostrogs in the river and the intricacies of the Iasak system, remained Chernigovsky's secret.

The adventurers rebuilt the ruined ostrog of Albasin and collected Iasak from natives who were apparently taken by surprise. The Raskolniki eventually left, disgusted with such a profane way of life, but newcomers joined the band.

In 1671, Chernigovsky was a wealthy man, and his men were well to do—in sables. But prosperous markets for sables were not accessible to the freebooters, and the leader, who had complete authority over his men, made a bold bid for prosperous respectability. He shipped a load of the thickest and darkest furs to Moscow, accompanied by an exuberant message that he was about to carry the Tsar's flag to the extreme east of the continent, and that all he needed was His Majesty's gracious approval. The Tsar's blessings, he hoped, would bring him gubernatorial powers and access to the market of the capital, where fabulous prices were paid for selected pelts.

The reply received, by courier, was brief and frustrating: By the Crown's rescript the fugitive Chernigovsky was sentenced to death for his arbitrariness, and every member of his party would be "severely flogged." Nothing was said about the furs received.

The Pole was still pondering over whether or not to tell his trusting followers of the dismal rescript, when another visitor arrived from the capital. Military Governor Tolbuzin, as he introduced himself, was a ranking dignitary in charge of affairs north of the Amur and on the Shilka River. Tolbuzin knew of the rescript and had a word of comfort. The sentence was suspended; they were on parole as long as their action did not result in another war with China.

In fact Moscow had trade with China in mind, and trade was the object of Tolbuzin's voyage. Practically all Western nations were doing business with China, importing silk, tea, porcelain, and rhubarb, and selling the oddest commodities of their own land. Russia wanted a share in the China trade, not a batch of sables once in a while.

The Chinese had never been deterred from doing business even with people with whom their country was at war. But at no time in their previous history had trade with fundamentally antagonistic nations been as prosperous as it was in the seventeenth century. Chinese officials, not as virtuous as the magistrates described by Jesuits, profited from operations they were assigned to regulate for the benefit of the treasury. Mandarins sold import licenses and discounts on duties, organized Chinese trading companies, and granted regional monopolies to their business fronts. Mandarins created airtight trusts and fixed prices at a level assuring a minimum of 50 per cent profit on the sales figure after expenses and nominal taxes. Manchu conceptions of trade did not go far beyond the notion of primitive barter; the Emperor could not understand the machinations of his mandarins, but he admired their intricacy and would put his seal under whatever ordinances the officials submitted. However, when the officials urged trade with Siberia, the Emperor consulted his generals who cautioned against close relations with the Russians unless the borders were clearly established and Russia gave proof of its intention to respect them. The soldiers knew of the presence of Chernigovsky's band at Albasin, and of Tolbuzin's visit.

Diplomatic threads were spun between China and Siberia, cautiously on the part of the Chinese, clumsily on the part of the Russians. China put feelers out in Siberia and in Russia with foreign merchants acting as unofficial intermediaries.

The Chinese suggested the establishment of boundary lines, and did not exactly say where they should run; they wanted evidence of Russia's peaceful intentions and did not say what would be accepted as evidence. The Russians reiterated that they wanted peace and trade, but did not state their terms.

Tolbuzin and Chernigovsky reinforced Albasin, the former taking charge of operations, appointing the Pole his next in command, and co-operating with him as if he were an officer in good standing, and not a fugitive under suspended capital sentence.

Years went by, and no Chinese patrol ventured close to the fortress, but in 1685 a Chinese force encircled Albasin. A few days later, under constant hammering by Chinese artillery, panic broke out among the garrison, and the military governor meekly applied for surrender terms.

The Chinese were generous. They permitted the garrison to march off, with their flags, sabres, and Tolbuzin's *ikons,* and even provided some food and carts. Tolbuzin had to promise solemnly never to return to Albasin, and he watched the victors burn down the fortress.

Two tsars and one regent were in office when news of the capitulation reached Moscow. Tsar Peter (later called "the Great") shared the throne with his feeble-minded stepbrother Ivan V, and Ivan's sister acted as Regent. The government precariously jogged along with cabals obstructing all activities. But even to the obstructors it was obvious that further disasters in the east had to be avoided, and that a real expert on Siberian affairs, a man not unfamiliar with Chinese mentality, should assume the delicate task of disentangling the Far Eastern mess.

Tsar Peter knew such a man: his onetime tutor, Fjodor Golovin, close kin of the controversial Governor, who had spent his boyhood and early youth in Siberia, in an atmosphere of buccaneer intrigues and predatory romantics, and had come to Moscow later. The Tsar thought highly of Golovin, who had studied reports on China and during the period of "diplomatic feelers" had told him that the etiquette-minded Chinese Court would much rather accept a less favorable proposal submitted with pompous deference by a ranking dignitary than the most advantageous suggestion made by mediators of inferior station. The Tsar had several government counselors discharged, scapegoats for past disastrous policies, and appointed Golovin Ambassador Extraordinary to negotiate all pending questions with organs of the Emperor of China, Kiang-ti.

Through neutral channels the Court of Peking was notified of the Tsar's desire to settle all pending issues in an amicable way, and of the impending departure of accredited plenipotentiaries to a meeting place to be determined by mutual understanding. Emperor Kiang-ti's reply was circumstantially courteous and agreeable. Had it not been for Golovin's overly painstaking adherence to what he considered essentials of diplomatic dealings with China, there might have been no further hostilities in the Amur region.

But Golovin insisted that impressive garb was as important for success as bargaining skill, and he would not leave the capital unless his costume and those of his staff were up to the highest requirements of style and etiquette. Designers consulted Bokharian merchants, who had been doing business with prosperous Chinese and with European visitors to China, to find out what raiment could outdo Chinese splendor. It took them a long time to devise a coat that looked like a cross between a Turkish caftan and a Cossack's jacket, and to agree on the material: gold brocade with sable lining. Tailors and furriers were equally slow fashioning the coats. Next the bootmakers had their day, and then the saddle and harness makers meditated about adornments matching the costume. And one could not travel fast if he wanted to keep the splendor undimmed. Not before 1687 at the earliest could the meeting take place.

Meantime Tolbuzin pondered about possibilities of retaining his rank and regaining the initiative. He had nothing but contempt for Chernigovsky, but he could not rid himself of that man before he had found a better *condottiere*. The better condottiere introduced himself while fashion designers in Moscow did not yet know whether to use brightly embroidered silk or brocade. He gave his name and rank as Afanas von Baidon, major in the Russian Army, but his thick accent revealed that he was, in fact, German. Germans were said to be superior soldiers. Herr von Baidon had several hundred alleged Germans under his command, a colorful outfit of thugs. He knew of Tolbuzin's predicament, and pulled panaceas out of his hat like magic rabbits. He said that China was in trouble; a new chieftain had recently unified Kalmuck tribes; the Kalmucks would attack China from Eastern Turkestan to the Mongolian border; the Chinese would have no men to spare should the Russians return to Albasin and from there launch a determined attack south, or, preferably, east. There was no reason to worry about inadequate numbers and equipment. Many bold men roamed the countryside who would all join Tolbuzin if Baidon gave the word; and they knew where to find muskets and cannon. Baidon also had definite ideas about an alliance with the Kalmucks, to be concluded later, after he and Tolbuzin were advancing and the Kalmucks would have spent much of their striking power. He had visions of another Djenghiskhanide empire under his and Tolbuzin's joint rule, with the Kalmuck chieftain their faithful stirrup holder. For the time being he would be satisfied with becoming the Military Governor's chief aide. Chernigovsky, of course, should have no place in the plan.

Chernigovsky disappeared promptly, without leaving a trace. Major von Baidon's real rank is said to have been that of lieutenant. His title of nobility was as dubious as the authenticity of his name. It seems that he had enlisted in the Russian Army and deserted, together with a number of countrymen. But what he had said about the Kalmucks was not quite unsound, and he was right about the available reinforcements. Several Kalmuck tribes were, in fact, in revolt against China, even though Chinese armies were not too heavily engaged. Hordes began to flock to Tolbuzin's and Baidon's band after they had reached agreement; they carried arms pilfered from arsenals in the remotest regions of Siberia. When, a little over one year after his solemn promise never to return to Albasin, Tolbuzin issued orders to advance on the town, 1500 men equipped with twelve cannon answered the roll call.

In May 1686 a new fortress had risen from the ashes, but in July a Chinese army invested Albasin again. A Russian sortie failed to break the siege ring, and Tolbuzin was killed in this costly operation. Baidon, who had talked him into leading the sortie, assumed command. After ten months of siege the garrison was exhausted. But by then a "peace party" at the Chinese court had prevailed over the champions of victory. With the Russian embassy on its way the partisans of peace claimed that further hostilities would needlessly embitter the Tsar's men and procrastinate negotiations. The siege army withdrew, with the capitulation of Albasin within grasp.

Golovin arrived only in 1689. Contrary to Baidon's expectations the Kalmuck insurrection against China had not continued. The tribal leaders had turned around, and invaded the Baikal region, causing little military harm, but disrupting communications and forcing the embassy to make long detours.

On one of these detours, the Tsar's ambassador learned of the latest battle of Albasin, and sent a special messenger to Peking, offering to make peace now and discuss terms later at Albasin. The message arrived after the siege had been lifted, and the Chinese accepted the proposal. But they refused to meet at Albasin. The Russians should evacuate that place. Golovin, unperturbed by that Chinese attitude, headed for the fortress. The head of the Chinese mission, Prince Som-go-tu, Commander of the Palace Guards, Palatine of the Interior Palace, Counselor to His Majesty, and Mandarin of the First Class, led his own men toward Nerchinsk, where he wanted the parley to be held.

According to Russian standards, Golovin had a large staff, and he gathered the remainders of the garrison of Albasin to increase its number to almost 2000. Herr von Baidon, who was now bragging about having repelled a Chinese attack, joined Golovin. His career, which seemed to have come to an abrupt end in 1687, was happily resumed; the German eventually became Military Governor of Verkholensk, and survived Tolbuzin for three lucrative decades. But not even Baidon's swagger could cushion the shock of the announcement that the Chinese delegation numbered 15,000. Grudgingly Golovin went to Nerchinsk.

Golovin's gala and that of his aides were in glorious trim; their horses pranced as if they came right out of seignorial stables. But the Chinese outshone their Western counterparts. The ranking Eastern dignitaries were dressed in golden cloaks trimmed with sea otter and lined with beaver—more expensive in those days than sable. They were carried in elaborate palanquins almost as pompous as thrones. The Russian diplomatic staff was several hundred strong; the Chinese had a thousand scribes in addition to experts, copyists, priests, chamberlains, cooks, physicians, interpreters, sword bearers, umbrella bearers, and pipe bearers for every ranking dignitary. And while Golovin was the only top official of his delegation, the head of the Chinese embassy was joined by an uncle of the Emperor, four bonzes "of the very highest class," and other illustrious figures. Baidon's unkempt soldiery compared most unfavorably with the Chinese military whose hair-do might well have taken two hours a day.

Conference tents were set up under the walls of Nerchinsk. Golovin was under instructions to accept the Amur River line as a permanent boundary between Russia and China, and to make a trade agreement of some kind. He opened the parley with an address in praise of traditional Russo-Chinese friendship and brotherly love. Prince Som-go-tu, unperturbed by that historical fallacy, answered in the same vein and exulted that heaven had blessed that friendship by drawing a natural boundary line between the two loving empires: the Lena River.

The Russians were stunned. Nobody in Moscow had ever thought of the Lena River. The Lena Valley was considered deep inside Russian territory that should and could not be relinquished. It sounded unacceptable, if not absurd. Even the Jesuit chief interpreter, Golovin contended later, could not conceal his surprise.

Mentioning the Lena was a trial balloon. Should Golovin return to next day's session, Prince Som-go-tu would present him with maximum demands; should he choose to sulk in his tent, he would be given to understand that the other party was ready to hear his own proposals.

Much as he prided himself with understanding the Chinese mind, however, the Russian was in no defiant mood. Sullen and dejected, he appeared at the session only to learn that the Chinese-projected border would run from the Sea of Okhotsk, over the ridge of the Stanovoi Mountains to the sources of the Gorbitsa, along this river to its junction with the Amur, from there to the Argun-Shilka junction, and to the source of the latter river, and eventually down the Lena. This would strip Russia of almost one third of Siberian territory; it would virtually ban Russia from the Amur, and from the outlet to the Pacific.

Golovin sat, bent over a map, and after long reflection grumbled that he could not find the line, and that the issue should be clarified. Prince Som-go-tu replied with sarcastic amiability that clarification would be forthcoming.

The next morning a Chinese officer received the Russian embassy in the conference tent and gave notice that unless the gentlemen accepted boundaries as outlined the ostrog of Nerchinsk would be stormed.

Golovin did not request further elaboration. He found everything marked on the map, and on August 27, 1689, the Treaty of Nerchinsk was signed, according to the Chinese terms, with the provision that regular and direct trade relations would be taken up.

After conquering roughly five million square miles in one century, Russia lost one and one half million square miles of Siberia in one conference. Golovin returned to Moscow, unmindful of his attire, wondering what method of execution was in store for him. He found his former pupil, now the sole ruler of Russia, in a forgiving, if not outright friendly, mood. Tsar Peter said that advantages resulting from trade with China could more than outweigh territorial losses. Neither the Tsar nor Golovin realized that China would never actually establish forces along the Lena line; that this would be contrary to the tradition of not scattering the army in remote territory. As long as the Russians could be scared into respecting that border, the Chinese would be pleased; once the Russians chose to trespass it, the Chinese would ignore it. Golovin was eventually created a count, and, to his relief, he did not receive the assignment he dreaded above all: to return to the conference tents and arrange for trade relations, which to him could be but a puzzling source of additional frustration.

Tsar Peter would not entrust a Russian with a commercial mission if he could help it. He chose a Westerner, Isbrand Ives, to go to Peking to draft trade clauses and put them into effect.

In 1692, Ives made the agreement to the effect that Russian official trade caravans were admitted to the Chinese capital, that their travel expenses on Chinese territory would be defrayed by the Chinese treasury; and that profits belonged to the Russian Crown. Private Russian merchants were permitted to attend annual fairs held in Chinese border towns.

Soon Russian traders became notorious for their drunkenness and violent excesses on fairgrounds. Provincial authorities drafted indignant complaints to Peking, where for similar reasons feelings against the personnel of official caravans ran high.

The Chinese were not prudish, nor were they teetotalers. Peking prided itself on catering to the most extravagant tastes of sexuality and carousal, but the vulgar brutality of Russian customers aroused even tavern and brothel keepers. Even Western sailors, whom Chinese had come to consider the scum of the earth, were better behaved than Russian trade envoys.

The Court of Peking made Russian indecency the topic of a sharply worded note to Moscow. This was not so much a moralist action, however, as another trial balloon to find out whether official Russia was still under the spell of the display of Chinese might, or whether it had already recovered some of its impudence. Moscow at once sent a special agent and an assistant to China to appease the Court.

The special agent signed a long protocol establishing rules of conduct for his countrymen visiting China. The protocol did not only deal with decency and sobriety, it also laid down rules of honesty, which had been lacking in Russian commercial operations. The Russians cheated in weight, measure, and quality; they presented false accounts; and in outlying regions they even tried to browbeat customers. The agent left his German assistant in charge of supervising Russian visitors to China.

Yet another aspect of Russian foul play incensed the Chinese Government in the early eighteenth century: subversive activities.

The same Russians who oppressed, robbed, and exterminated natives of Siberia styled themselves protectors of their victims' kin who lived under the uncomparatively milder sway of China. Parts of Mongolia had been slipping from Peking's suzerainty during the war between the Mings and the Manchus, and while Chinese soldiers and officials exerted themselves to restore this authority with a minimum of violence, Russian talebearers in merchant's disguise toured among minor Mongolian chieftains south of the Siberian border, telling them that Russia wanted to establish an independent Mongolia united under the Tsar's protection, that Russia would double pensions and prebends previously paid to chieftains, and improve the lot of tribesmen. The Mongols would not even have to fight to make a Russian-sponsored millennium materialize; carefully planned disobedience to Chinese orders and sabotage of Chinese transportation would disrupt the administration; occupation troops would be forced to withdraw, and the Russians would move in as liberators.

Tribesmen whose wanderings had taken them into Siberia could have no illusions about the blessings of Russian rule, but the talebearers did not talk to nomads who had no word in the decisions of their chieftains. The chieftains received handouts from Russian agents that convinced the corrupt dignitaries that collaboration with the Tsar's men would be remunerative.

The handouts came from funds accumulated as profits in the China trade, and administered by the German supervisor of Russian behavior.

Not until 1719 did Chinese adminstrators in Mongolia report on widespread and apparently well-organized disobedience in their respective districts, but then alarming accounts accumulated rapidly. China was faced with an elaborate conspiracy. An investigating commission left Peking for Mongolia. The commission had not yet finished its work, when in 1722 several Mongolian chieftains issued a joint declaration abnegating Chinese suzerainty and applying for Russian protection. Chinese occupation troops, however, did not withdraw, and no official Russian reply was forthcoming on the application.

The investigating commission hurried back to the capital. Its findings indicated that the German assistant to Russia's former trade envoy had fomented the insurrection, that he was the mastermind behind the plot. Summoned before the Court of Peking, he did not deny dealing with the Mongolians, and he outraged the Chinese even further by his refusal to apologize. The treaty of Nerchinsk, the German lectured, did not apply to Mongolia.

Mongolia was not mentioned in its articles, Russia was free to protect, or to annex, Mongolian territory. He also insisted that political activities were not incompatible with his status as "assistant trade agent in China." The contentions were presented with sneering rudeness, unheard of in the Imperial Palace, where even damnations were pronounced with studied civility. The basic claims were uncontestable: Mongolia was not mentioned in the treaty, and the impudent man's credentials did not say that he would not engage in non-commercial activities.

Such logic, based upon omission, poured oil onto the flame of Chinese wrath.

The Court pronounced immediate severance of all relations with Russia, commercial, diplomatic, and otherwise. Russian agents were expelled, Russian nationals barred from entering the empire, including Mongolia.

The Tsar was unofficially notified; no formal communication would be made. The Emperor of China considered it beneath his dignity to enter in correspondence with the ruler of Russia.

This was a terrific insult to Peter the Great, who had just defeated Sweden in a twenty-year war for hegemony in Northern Europe, and who had adopted the title of "All Russian Emperor," and had even further solidified his primacy over the Russian Church. In St. Petersburg, capital of Russia since 1713, the city the Tsar had had built in the swamps of the Neva estuary, literally upon the bones of hundreds of thousands of mushiks pressed into hard labor, courtiers shuddered at the thought of Peter's unbridled rage. But the autocrat chose to ignore the indignity. He had known humiliation before, and time had always worked in his favor.

Peter had not enough time left to wait for the tables to turn; he died three years after the insult. However, the complete severance of Russo-Chinese relations lasted only a few more years.

CHAPTER FORTY Among the many oddities of the human species that developed in Siberia was the "forgotten *tshinovnik*," the petty civil servant, usually appointed for a roving assignment by some faraway, and often meanwhile deceased, official in the capital, a struggling wretch whom no governor wanted on his pay roll and who spent his days hunting for someone who might pay him a salary or at least give him an opportunity to share in the proceeds of some swindle, and his nights dreaming of grandiose wealth and splendor.

Vladimir Atlassov was one of those forgotten men, and not until he reached the age of forty were his experiences essentially different from those of other people of his kind. He had started as a "government agent for fur collection," traveling in Northeastern Siberia. Atlassov liked those regions; his fancy was stimulated by their lonely grandeur, and, more important even, the farther away a man got from his superiors the easier should it be to do a thriving illicit business with the Tsar's furs.

Nature lavished its magnificence upon the petty tshinovnik, but superiors in office would not permit an underling to do well for himself. Harassed by roaming accountants, pedantic bookkeepers, and haughty bosses, Atlassov rarely managed to put a few furs aside. Officials refused to pay his salary; black-marketeers got stingier by the day; Cossacks and *promyshleniki*, contemptful of the tattered tshinovnik, did not make him a partner in their shady businesses; the best they would do was to hire him as a guide, for Atlassov was more familiar with tracks through woods and wastelands than any other person around.

The Treaty of Nerchinsk gave Atlassov his first chance in many lean years. Roaming the Yana River district, he met a Cossack who told him that the valley had become part of Ki-tai, that actually all the land that side of the Lena was now Ki-tai. The Cossack ventured that there might be better opportunities under Ki-taian rule. Atlassov pondered about this as he wandered through the Yana, and then through the Lena Valley. To him it was inspiring land: immense forests that seemed to harbor grandiose secrets, and beyond the forests rugged wasteland that looked like an immense graveyard or a garden of silent, titanic ghosts, who held the keys to unexplored marvels. Somewhere among tall trees, marshes, and frost-fissured barren earth seemed to run an invisible line dividing reality exploited by men from an unreality shielded by deities of the forests and the ice. A downtrodden shaman offered prophecies. The forgotten tshinovnik had no high opinion of wizardry, but in these surroundings even the poorest shaman tricks assumed significance. He had almost nothing of value to spare, and the forecast was in accordance with the meager fee. The shaman advised his customer to return where he had come from and get himself more money.

Atlassov went to Yakutsk, which under the terms of Nerchinsk had become a border town. No Chinese patrols had been seen in the vicinity; no Russians had emigrated from the east to the remainder of the Tsar's Siberia; but the mood was gloomy, and almost everybody predicted disaster. The forgotten tshinovnik called at the Governor's office. An angry clerk waved him off, snarling that he wasn't on the pay roll, but Atlassov explained that he had not come to collect, but to apply for an assignment in the distant east. The clerk sneered at the fool who obviously did not know of Nerchinsk. The clerk's superior roared with laughter, when he learned of the application; the Assistant Governor slapped his buttocks with malicious glee; and the Governor said that this was one of the funniest stories he had ever heard. In a mock ceremony in 1696, Atlassov was nominated district commander of Anadyr. Everybody but the appointee grinned when it was read out that the district commander would receive his salary from the sovereign who ruled the district.

Atlassov was confident that he would not depend on a salary. He found his seat of office, 2000 miles away, populated by a disorderly bunch of seventeen Cossacks, untidy female accessories, and hordes of savage children. The Cossacks did not care who their ruler was. The Emperor of China was almost as far away as the Tsar, God was still high above, and he who had the gun ruled the land. The Cossacks had guns, and their storehouse contained sables, ermines, black foxes, and sea otters. Back in Yakutsk black foxes commanded four times the price of sables, and sea otters five times the price of black foxes.

The Cossacks of Anadyr ignored market quotations; they seized what they could lay hands upon and sold it for whatever it would fetch to a black-marketeer who called once a year. They did not personally hunt foxes and otters, but took them from neighboring natives who were said to stalk their prey somewhere farther south. The Cossacks would not have surrendered their furs to any official unless he arrived at the head of a strong military unit; Atlassov had no soldiers, and he did not request the Cossacks to give up "property of the Crown." But he offered to reorganize and to expand the fur business for the benefit of everybody concerned. He would open new markets and seize the hunting grounds on which valuable animals could be found. In the winter of 1697 ten Cossacks, led by their one and only noncom, left for the Korjak Mountains to tighten their rule upon the otter-hunting natives. In the past the Korjaks had sent Iasak to Anadyr, but they had otherwise shunned the Russians even more carefully than the vicious men-eating brown bears in their forests. In the winter, however, they were off guard; the Cossacks found the first Korjak village inhabited and an altogether cozy place to stay. The ten warriors spent a comfortable season, and returned in the spring with fifteen Korjak ladies and five sea-otter furs, claiming that they lacked sufficient ammunition to run to the end of the world.

Even a disappointed Atlassov realized that his forces were hardly adequate to achieve ambitious aims, and he decided to make the long journey to Yakutsk in quest of support. The Governor no longer thought that an assignment in Anadyr was altogether funny. The Chinese had not yet come, and it seemed as if business in no man's land was better than in a realm of a ruler who might get the idea of enforcing law. He offered to give official approval of every conquest the district commander would make. But this was as far as he would go—in return for a share in the proceeds of the conquest. Atlassov should take care of his own supplies. The district commander toured moneylenders; they refused to accept his claim to a salary as a security, and he did not have other collateral. Eventually, however, a black-marketeer agreed to lend him 160 rubles (roughly the equivalent of 200 dollars in 1954 purchasing power). Interests were a "reasonable" 100 per cent per annum. However, principals were payable in furs at prices so far below the market quotations that this boosted the rate of interest to some 500 per cent.

A hundred sixty rubles did not buy much ammunition, and some had to be set aside as hiring fees for mercenaries. But Atlassov was a glib talker; forty-five adventurers joined him on his way back to Anadyr.

He found the neighbors of his territory, Korjaks, Yukagirs, and Kamchadals, locked in a furious feud over one head of reindeer, which the Korjaks insisted was their property, while the Yukagirs said it had been stolen from their herds, and the Kamchadals contended that the beast was theirs. Atlassov intervened. He defeated the Korjaks, stripped them of all their reindeer, and distributed their herds among Yukagirs and Kamchadals. Grateful natives showered him with gifts and attention, and the Kamchadals made him their honorary cheftain.

Chieftain Atlassov did not know the area and population of his realm. When he set out to explore it, he found a small group of natives, a little taller but otherwise not different from the average, who spoke a queer but altogether understandable Russian dialect. They said that their progenitor had been one "Fedotov," who, with a number of companions, had once come to live on the Kamchatka River. Fedotov and his men had married Kamchadal women; they had been formidable warriors who kept intruders away and they had been liked by everybody; had they not had the unfortunate habit of stabbing one another, they might have lived much longer. Fedotov seems to have been Alekseev—Fjodor Alekseev—shipwrecked participant on Deshnev's expedition, and the intruders he and his fellow warriors had kept away could only have been Russians. Yet Atlassov did not seem to know of Deshnev's voyage, and apparently the Cossacks of Anadyr had never heard that kotchis had sailed around the huge cape north of their ostrog half a century before.

Russian-speaking natives told Atlassov of immense territories beyond the Kamchatka River. He could not take possession of it all with only sixty Russians, including Cossacks, under his orders, but he would not go to Yakutsk again; he would not deal with the Governor or with usurers; after all, he was a district commander in the service of His Majesty, Tsar Peter. And to the Tsar he would go.

In 1701 he surprised protocol officials in Moscow by requesting admittance in private audience, in his status of dignitary of the Siberian administration. The name of Atlassov was nowhere listed on the files, but since the applicant claimed to have glorious announcements to make and valuable presents to offer, an audience was arranged.

Atlassov brought several hundred sables, ten otters, and one Japanese man. The furs were half the proceeds of his first tax collection, and the Japanese was a shipwrecked pirate whom Kamchadals had turned over to their honorary chieftain.

The Tsar needed heartening news. The Great Northern War was off to a start that did not augur well; the Turkish menace was growing; and China was not a source of happy tidings either. Peter's face brightened as he saw the furs, and he listened gleefully as Atlassov recited his account, which had been edited by the Tsar's staff. He explained that the furs were but a first installment of great revenue to come from the Tsar's new subjects, the Korjaks, the Yukagirs, and the Kamchadals, who had embraced the True Faith, adopted the Russian way of life, and were building cities to please the Tsar, the master builder of the world. The Kamchadals called Atlassov chieftain, this being their version of administrator appointed by the Tsar. Atlassov wanted the title chieftain to stand for itself, but officials insisted that nobody should be more than an appointed official. Peter asked a few desultory questions about the welfare of the natives; he could not recall the names of these tribes, and he wanted to know exactly how many sea-otter furs they would produce. Atlassov replied cautiously that taxes had not yet been finally assessed, but that the proceeds would be very high. The Tsar was diverted from the sea otters to the Japanese, the first he had ever seen, and, he did not doubt, the first ever to reach Europe. The castaway was a soft-mannered man who had learned some Russian during the long trip to Moscow. His demeanor was more dignified than Atlassov's, and this pleased the Tsar so much that he ordered the "ambassador" to stay at his court, to teach nobles the Japanese language and Japanese manners so that they be ready to go to Japan when the time came.

Atlassov was nominated "Chieftain in His Majesty's Service"; he would draw an annual salary of 10 rubles—the furs he had brought were worth roughly 10,000 rubles in Moscow—and a special allowance for clothing of 100 rubles plus a piece of German cloth. He was authorized to recruit men in Siberia, and Siberian governors were directed to supply him with ammunition. The Tsar did not allot recruiting fees and made no provisions for administrative expenses. Atlassov considered His Majesty a miser, but he kissed the miser's hand and muttered professions of everlasting gratitude. It did not seem to bother the Tsar that by sanctioning Atlassov's land grab he was violating the territorial clauses of the Treaty of Nerchinsk.

The Chieftain in His Majesty's Service returned to Siberia. In Yakutsk he settled his affairs with the usurious financier. A group of determined-looking brutes who accompanied Atlassov induced the creditor to accept half the principal and no interest, all in cash. The brutes were members of Atlassov's new army, and, like most of their comrades, they had been highwaymen operating in small bands along roads, waterways, and trails over which traveled Chinese trade caravans. Chinese merchants were regular visitors to Siberian ostrog cities and markets. They usually traveled in well-guarded convoys; small gangs could not attack such convoys, but there were stragglers and an occasional small caravan to be waylaid.

Atlassov's army numbered 200; once assembled and equipped, the men suggested that they try for one big haul on the spot before going east. The chieftain was open to sound suggestions. When he learned that a flotilla of heavily loaded Chinese river craft was approaching Yakutsk, he led his host to a spot on the bank of the Lena where merchants used to spend the night prior to their arrival in the city.

The raid was a complete success, with spoils of silk and tea evaluated at 16,000 rubles. This was the figure claimed as damage by an irate Chinese caravan leader who managed to escape and presented his complaint to the Governor.

The Governor was delighted. He had tried to get some cash or furs from Atlassov, but the impudent man had refused to pay him off, even with a pittance. But now that a crime had been perpetrated, he would make him pay off heavily.

Atlassov was not ready for interrogation when the Governor sent for him; neither were his men. They were celebrating their success with prodigal quantities of kumiss blended with Russian home-brewed spirits. The Governor had the party thrown into jail. When Atlassov eventually recovered, he protested furiously that a chieftain was not subject to arrest by a mere governor. He did not want to hear of a friendly arrangement either in terms of thousands of rubles or of a partnership in Kamchatka. The Governor insisted that barons, counts, and princes were entitled to privileges, but that chieftains were not immune. He had Atlassov and ten of his men flogged on a public square, and, when the chieftain still refused to pay up, he sentenced him to life in a dungeon.

The ten flogged robber soldiers were discharged. One of the Governor's lieutenants assumed command of the other 190, to lead them to the Kamchatka River and continue in the name of the Governor where Atlassov had left off.

But when they eventually arrived, they found that the natives had killed all of Atlassov's former men and put the torch to their buildings. The Korjaks, who had recovered from the shock of the seizure of their herds and were now at peace with their neighbors, were the most formidable of all natives. More troops were required to subdue the wild men. Reinforcements arrived, chastened the Korjaks, and forced them to build a new settlement for their captors, who called it Verkhne Kamchatsk, and from there resumed tax collection.

But guerrilla actions continued. Several tax collectors were killed, and so was the assistant commander of Verkhne Kamchatsk. It was impossible to penetrate beyond the Kamchatka River. An outraged Governor of Yakutsk, convinced that his officers and officials were making good for themselves and cheating him of his dues, eventually visited Atlassov in the dungeon and again talked partnership. Four years of imprisonment had not broken the chieftain physically, but his spirit was no longer indomitable. A deal materialized. Atlassov again took charge of operations; the Governor granted him a full pardon for all criminal offenses, past and future, and would in turn receive 50 per cent of the proceeds.

The Crown's title to revenue from the domain was not mentioned in the partnership agreement.

In 1707, Atlassov was back with his tribes, who gave him a turbulently unfriendly reception. The honorary chieftain retaliated by meting out capital sentences against rioters, and staging a punitive expedition against the Korjaks, who suffered another defeat and were stripped of whatever belongings the victors could carry. But victory turned into a boomerang; the soldiers refused to surrender the spoils, and when Atlassov tried to enforce his orders, the men turned against him, and he had to run for his life. Officials from Yakutsk went east to restore order, but then feuded among themselves and could neither bring the unruly soldiers under full control nor at first smother recurrent native rebellion. The natives, who had once believed that "Fedotov" and his men were invincible, and vulnerable only to assault by their own kin, had long since learned that Russians, powerful and well armed as they were, could be killed and wounded even by the primitive arms of weaker natives. With furious determination they defended themselves against the aggressors. But after Russian superiority became crushing, they had to retreat beyond the Kamchatka River and farther south. The Russians penetrated the narrow neck of the Kamchatka Peninsula, deep and ever deeper into the 100,000-square-mile territory. In 1711 the conquerors reached the southern tip of Kamchatka and native resistance deteriorated into disorganized, hopeless raids.

Atlassov himself had gone into hiding in an abandoned ostrog, where he lived on crumbs provided by descendants of Fedotov, and made grandiose plans—again a Forgotten Tshinovnik. The Japanese he had taken to Moscow had told him of his own country, of many more islands, and chains of islands, and of another big continent beyond the ocean toward the rising sun. These islands, and this continent—America—Atlassov wanted to make his beat. Forgotten by the Tsar, forsaken by the Governor, chased away by his soldiers, he was still the honorary chieftain; and just as some men still fed him, others, more numerous and powerful, might still follow him.

The southern tip of Kamchatka had just been reached when a frail and white-haired Atlassov emerged from his abode. A party of Cossacks who saw him did not know who he was, but his high sable cap became the object of their covetousness. The presumptive empire builder refused to part with his headgear. His body was later identified by an official from Yakutsk who chanced to travel through the region.

The wonders of Kamchatka remained forever hidden to the Forgotten Tshinovnik, who would have admired them no less than the man who gave the first description of the peninsula: Georg Wilhelm Steller, a German, assigned in 1737 by the Russian Academy of Science to explore the Three Realms of Nature in Kamchatka, and who a few years later played a fateful part in Vitus Bering's last voyage.

Steller tells of deep lakes set in elevated plateaus, braided by fantastically shaped mountains, like chatoyant jewels on fanciful gigantic China plates. "Streams, draped by delicate white caps, are fast-moving mirrors reflecting light verdure, the velvety somberness of forests, and the glaring colors of blooming meadows along their banks. The landscape of Kamchatka, the clouds above, and even the clear skies, radiate a wild symphony of colors. But the most stupendous features are the mountains: 63 volcanoes, up to 16,000 feet high, glaciated, yet still partly active. When one of them erupts, a burst of infernal heat smashes the crust of ice that encases the crater, and turns the shallow parts of the upper glacier into a boiling cataract, tumbling down over deep layers of ice, over moraines and boulders, storming the barricade of woods below, and, with a deafening roar, rising a fire flag of iridescent vapors which turn purple, as torrents of lava pour down the glacier, filling creases and crevasses, yet never melting the primeval masses of ice. The victorious struggle of primordial congelation with the furor of unleashed heat manifests itself 1000 miles in the round by a red beacon, almost too bright for eyes to behold."

The natives of Kamchatka were not overawed by a spectacle that lent wings of poetry to the pen of a man used to drafting papers in the pedestrian language of eighteenth-century science. They did not seem to fear the volcanoes. The mountains stood where the Creator had placed them, and the floods of lava did not deviate from paths shaped by previous eruptions. Men could evade the angry elements. But men could not escape the hardships imposed upon them or dragged in by vicious fellow-men.

The Russian invasion cost the lives of between one and two thousand Kamchadals; of whom a total of about 10,000 lived on the peninsula when the mercenaries from Yakutsk reached its extreme point. Fifty-seven years later, the smallpox, imported by Russians, claimed 5368 victims. By then few freeborn natives were still alive. A generation of chattels, raised to serve their masters, had come of age. The Tsar's authorities kept records of their bondsmen, and regretfully noted that less than 3000 survived the epidemic, mostly women and children: "There are only 706 tributary males left, and, consequently, last year's intake has diminished to 279 sables, 464 red foxes, 50 sea otters, and 38 sea otter cubs, not sufficient to meet administration expenses." The apparatus of the administration of Kamchatka included one chancery, four district authorities, one magistracy, and a permanent garrison of 300 Cossacks.

The authorities also listed damages caused by eruptions of volcanoes. In 1768 "two Kamchadals drowned in the cataract of hot water; combustible matter spread over 250 miles in circumference, including cultivated areas where cabbage, turnips, radishes, beets, carrots and cucumbers are grown; there was some unspecified damage to buildings."

When this was recorded, Kamchatka had become the springboard of Russian penetration beyond the eastern seas, to the islands north of Japan, and to America.

Peter the Great was the godfather of a scheme of Russian expansion over three continents: Europe, Asia, and America. The Tsar, who styled himself a Westerner, who in rare moments of tenderness called his crown prince *zoon* (Dutch for son), sought the company of members of democratic institutions, but would turn panicky when he actually met them. Once, when facing a respectful municipal council in Holland, he had pulled his hat and wig over his eyes and taken to his heels. Peter, the fickle absolutist, was a "Forgotten Tshinovnik" at heart. His phantasy was the haven of his fear-stricken mind, the domain of the frustrated. Peter longed to shape his own realm—an empire in which the appreciative would outnumber the inappreciative, the doubting Thomases, and the cringing rebels.

He had long forgotten Atlassov, but he had not forgotten the regions of which he had told him. And the Japanese ex-pirate, whom he had kept at Court, was an eloquent man who seemed to have been everywhere, and to whom the Tsar liked to listen. Members of the Academy voiced cautious disparagement of the ignorant stranger; and the Tsar ordered them to show their own wisdom by accounts on the eastern seas and America beyond. The professors drew maps, drafted reports, made suggestions, all dealing with the subject.

Much as he read and raved about America, Peter had so much day-by-day business to transact that he could not attend to the object of his dreams. But when he was dying, his last thoughts concentrated on his old fancy. With an unsteady hand he drafted a note to Apraxin, which, redrafted, became the gist of the order issued by Peter's widow, Empress Catherine I, to Vitus Bering:

"You shall cause one or two convenient vessels to be built at Kamchatka, or if this be not practicable, somewhere else. You shall endeavor to discover, by coasting with these vessels, whether or not the country toward the north, of which, at present, we have no knowledge, is part of America. If it joins the continent of America, you shall endeavor, if possible, to reach some colony belonging to some European power; or in case you should meet some European ship, you shall diligently inquire about the name of the coast, and all such circumstances as are within your power to learn. This you shall convey to us in writing, so that we may get certain facts by which a chart may be composed."

CHAPTER FORTY-ONE The Empress was subsequently glorified as a protagonist of Russian exploration, as the exalted heroine who had opened Russia's way to the New World.

The first Catherine made no pretense at such extollment. She had little enthusiasm and even less understanding for the objectives of the order she had signed, much as she had heard of America from the late Tsar. Peter had tolerated Catherine at his flare-ups of phantasmagoria as a convenient object to have around rather than as a conscious listener to his pell-mell oratory. She had considered such outbursts as part of her man's maze of whims, which elated and tormented him. Whenever she felt that Peter was being hurt by the strain of delusion—to her it all seemed delusion—she put her big, warm hand on his forehead, and even if at first he pushed it back, he would eventually relax and calm down.

America—America—Peter had roared, muttered, chanted it over and over again. More than once had she quieted him when he was haunted, tormented, by the name. Catherine would have preferred not to hear it again after she became a widow, but Prince Alexander Menshikov insisted that the American project was an essential part of her husband's sacred legacy, and she trusted Menshikov unquestioningly.

Catherine was forty-one when she signed the order, a matronly, graying woman who looked like a farmer's sturdy wife in royal regalia.

It could be that the Empress of Russia was of peasant stock, but not even that much was ever ascertained. Her original name was not Catherine, but Marta, and she was not Russian, but Lithuanian-born. She had kept company with mercenaries roaming the Baltic regions, ever since soldiers had accepted her as a female. She slept on baggage carts, together with other women of her status, and at eighteen "belonged" to some Swedish dragoon. The baggage train was captured by Russian soldiery, and, together with carts and cargo, Marta fell into the hands of the Tsar's men. The young woman satisfied the crude and hurried lusts of her captors, who changed her Lithuanian name of Marta into the Russian Katja. Word got round that Katja had qualities other girls of her profession did not have, and she was passed on to officers, rapidly rising from a lieutenant's wench to the favorite of the young general Prince Menshikov.

The Prince did not keep Katja long, however. Courting the Tsar's favor, he donated her to his sovereign, who was looking for a woman with a perfectly even temper, who was a strong and healthy specimen and did not mind the strain of campaigns, and knew what a man really wanted. Katja, now Catherine, was as powerful as any able-bodied soldier; she had an infallible flair for male desires, and she was not even inhibited by awe for the Tsar. In camps men were more alike than in settlements, and even though she now lived in a fine tent of her own, she stayed in the field with Peter, as she had stayed with the Swedish dragoon and all the others. She bore Peter three children in the first few years of their association, two daughters and one son, the last of whom died young. She was imperturbable on the brink of disaster, soothing in the turmoil of triumph, at hand when needed, self-effacing when her presence was not convenient. She accepted lavish presents with a childlike ingenuous joy, and returned them without flinching when Peter needed precious objects, as happened once, when the Russian Army was surrounded by superior Turkish forces and the Sultan's generals charged several hundred thousand ducats for opening the trap. Catherine was a better person to have around than the prim generals' ladies who followed the army in luxury carriages and would rather see a battle lost than have their heavy cavalry escort diverted into action.

After her ten years of concubinage Tsar Peter married Catherine, but not until more than another decade had passed, when he felt sick and weary, did he have his consort crowned. And all the time Prince Menshikov was with them, Peter's favorite, and his field marshal; Catherine's mentor first, then her confidant, and her mentor again during the two years of her reign.

Menshikov's loyalty to the woman whose youthful charms had played a major part in his career eventually caused his downfall. After her death in 1727 she was succeeded by a stepson, Peter II, who detested her and gave vent to his hatred by demoting the Field Marshal, confiscating his fabulous property, and exiling him to Siberia.

Bering, as expedition leader, had not been Menshikov's choice, but that of the Imperial Academy of Sciences in St. Petersburg, with the approval of General-Admiral Count Apraxin. To choose a Russian for the mission would have been incompatible with the policies of Peter I; Bering's Danish birth was a major asset in the opinion of dignitaries in the capital.

The explorer, whose name figures prominently on geographical maps, has left no notes from which as much as his psychological silhouette would emerge, and historiographers still leave some of his features undefined. "A fundamentally timid man, the very antithesis of a conquistador," an Englishman called him, and went on to say: "He had no personal ambition, no objective beyond the one defined by his assignment. He would do his best to accomplish his task, but he would suffer disgrace rather than to make false pretense. He would use the authority vested in him as far as regulations permitted, but he would not arrogate to himself illegal powers. It did not once occur to him that a voyage of discovery on Her Majesty's orders could be turned into a marauding expedition as some of his officers and Russian crew members expected. He did not propose to look for natives that could be subjected to Iasak; nor was he interested in sables, otters, jewels and gold. He made this clear to his men, who were disappointed and grumbled about their commander's 'outlandish views.' "

Georg W. Steller, who gave so emotional a description of the scenic beauties of Kamchatka, had only sober though contradictory words for his commander, Vitus Bering, toward whom he assumed an attitude of questionable loyalty: "Bering was born in Denmark, in 1681, an honest, decent Christian, smooth-mannered, quiet, friendly, and well enough liked by subordinates and superiors alike. After participating in two voyages to India, he enlisted in the Russian Navy in 1704, as a lieutenant, and served, devotedly, until his death in 1741. He reached the rank of Captain Commander. His assignments included expeditions from Kamchatka. Impartial observers will agree that he tried, to the limit of his strength and ability, to carry out his task as best he could. Yet he himself admitted that his faculties were not quite up to requirements of such difficult expeditions; that the expeditions should have been broader in scope than he was able to arrange, and that it might have been advisable to relieve him from command as he grew older, and put a more youthful, present-minded man in charge. As it has been recognized since, Bering was not apt to make hard and fast decisions. However, it remains a question to what extent a person of more fiery disposition would have overcome obstacles and discomforts, without devastating lands and peoples. Bering, a man of remarkable composure and given to mature consideration, a person of unflinching loyalty and unselfishness, could hardly restrain his men. His overly mild attitude caused no less harm to the venture than the fierce, and often wanton, actions of his subordinates. He had too high an opinion of the intelligence and skill of his officers, and this boosted their conceit, led them to scorn everybody including their commander, and made them inappreciative, if not unmanageable."

Bering had been briefed by experts from the Academy of Sciences. The Academy had French maps available, which indicated that the American mainland was approximately sixty miles due east of the neck of Kamchatka Peninsula, and that outlying American islands were but twenty-five miles away. The Russian scientists opined that the distance between America and Kamchatka might be somewhat greater than their learned colleagues in Paris assumed, but that it appeared likely that the two continents were linked by an arc-shaped isthmus farther north.

Nothing seemed to have been known in St. Petersburg of the maps Governor Golovin had used fourscore years before, and no reports had been received about exploration trips Eastern Siberian Cossacks continued to make in leather-covered rowboats from Anadyr and adjoining coastal regions toward the islands off the American coast and, quite likely, to the mainland.

Bering's apprehensive queries about shipbuilding facilities in Kamchatka drew protestations of confidence in the general excellence of Kamchatkan installations after so many years of Russian rule. St. Petersburg had, of late, adopted higher standards of naval construction. The new Russian Navy included several first-class fighting ships, all, however, purchased from Western, mostly English, yards. The members of the Academy believed, or wanted Bering to believe, that craft of similar quality could be built by home-grown talent, serving in the extreme east of the Tsarina's realm. Bering was advised to leave for Kamchatka without delay, and to travel light; crews, weapons, and food were to be had on the spot in abundance, the peninsula was an area of plenty—except for information on America, which the Academy claimed to have monopolized.

Bering, accompanied by another Danish-born officer, Lieutenant Spannberg, rushed to Kamchatka, using all sorts of transportation including dog sleighs, and arrived in Avatcha, near the present site of Petropavlovsk, still in 1725. The shipbuilding facilities he found there were certainly not as they had been described in the capital. The yards hardly deserved that name and the only material available was timber. Cordage and sails had to be brought from Yakutsk, via Okhotsk, by land and sea. The only larger type of ships built on Kamchatka were *shitiki*—sewed craft—so called by the Russians because the planks were sewed together by thongs of leather. The boats were two-masters, with crews of forty or seventy, armed with whatever the skippers could obtain.

Bering wanted two shitiki with crews of seventy each. The local administrator regretted: all he had on hand was one boat for forty; but if Mr. Bering would care to wait a while—no more than three years—he might have yet another ship.

Bering resigned himself to starting his expedition with one craft, the *Fortune*. He wanted a seasoned crew of Russian sailors, but this was against the local rules. Half of the crew members had to be natives, whose pay was but a fraction of that of the Russians, who subsisted on small rations and who were less susceptible to scurvy which, he learned, was bound to hit his expedition sooner or later. Bering requested supplies from government stores; he had been told that Kamchatka's warehouses were bulging with food and ammunition. The local official lost patience; he would not contribute one morsel of food or one ounce of gunpowder. He neither wanted the people of his district to starve nor would he face mutiny with inadequate armament. Kamchatka had nothing to spare.

Kamchatka might have been a land of plenty, even though its northernmost regions, about 62° latitude, were severe, with an annual average temperature of 20°. In the valleys of the central and southern parts, however, the climate was mild and the soil fertile. As in most parts of Siberia, the rivers of Kamchatka were well stocked with fish; wild goats and reindeer were abundant. The Russians were too indolent to hunt wild goats, but they slaughtered the herds of reindeer and forced the natives to track fur animals and neglect farming. Iasak was not payable in food; it had to be rendered in otter, ermine, sable, beaver, and fox furs, and—small coin— in bear or wolf skins. And because otters, ermines, and beavers lived in outlying islands, native fishermen had little opportunity to catch salmon in rivers; they would have to row to the islands instead and have half the furs they delivered credited to their tax account; the other half was considered rental fee for the boats which the occupiers claimed to be their property. Every Cossack noncom, every smalltime mercenary, was a petty tyrant in his own domain, wielding absolute power over property, life, and death of the natives. Local tyrants had all the food they wanted. What remained went to the black market first, and was used only later to keep natives from starvation. Kamchatka was almost starving, but the administrator's allegation that it was on the verge of revolt was no longer correct: the Kamchadals would accept ignominy rather than famish.

Bering had to deal with black-marketeers to supply the *Fortune*. The prices they charged for food were 300 per cent above those in the capital. Bering purchased the minimum quantity he would need for the trip under ideal weather conditions. The black-marketeers claimed to have any number of cannon and ammunition, but Bering's funds were short and he still had to pay his crews. The *Fortune* was not heavily armed.

The most serious of all troubles started when the crew was at last assembled: twenty dejected Kamchadals and twenty Russian ruffians, several of whom produced officers' patents with seals and signatures which could hardly stand scrutiny.

The "officers," seconded by Russian sailors, refused to sail straight north. The north was no place to go, they said; there land and sea came to an end; there was nothing but ice, inhabited by the souls of the dead and their evil guardians. Bering called this crude superstition; one officer replied that every uneducated Cossack knew more about the real facts than the erudite ignoramuses in the capital. Not even naïve Cossacks would waste time going north; they would all go south and southeast to the rich chain of the "Thirteen Islands," which stretched as far as the jewel-rich Empire of Japan, and on which a clever man could make good in business. Business was the object of all discovery, the officer added; and the Tsar needed the proceeds of business no less than any of his subjects.

The Captain reiterated his decision to go north; the trouble-makers emphasized theirs to go to the "Thirteen Islands", or nowhere at all. They produced maps to bear out their geographical assertions. Bering called the charts stupid botchery. The officers sneered and refused to board the ship. The Russian seamen did not budge either. The Kamchadals stood by, indifferent and mute.

More than one year had been lost, and 1727 had come. Bering had a ship, stores, and crew, but he could not sail. The local administrator suggested that he hear experts before deciding upon his course. The experts were people who claimed to have traveled extensively through the eastern ocean. Having no other choice, Bering agreed. The administrator produced a number of odd characters who introduced themselves as officers, trade officials, and tax collectors, and kept repeating with slight variations that there was absolutely nothing to explore in the north, but that the "Thirteen Islands" were real, and that there might be more and bigger islands nearby, the discovery of which should profit all concerned. Bering did not know that he was talking with Cossacks, black-marketeers, and *promyshleniki,* but he realized that they were plotting against his voyage, and could not quite understand the reason. In fact the Cossacks from Anadyr, who obviously knew a great deal about the approaches to the American mainland, did not want an appointee of the distant government to learn of their discoveries and their illicit business with natives; Cossacks were duty-bound to report on discoveries, and the fur trade was still a government monopoly. The black-marketeers, who engaged in operations on the islands, wanted to corrupt Bering and have him put his ship and his prestige at their disposal, in return for some share in the proceeds of expanded trade. The promyshleniki had no vested interests, but they drew fees from other parties for their "testimony."

Bering did not flinch. He did not want to hear of the "barren north," shrugged shoulders when phony trade officials raved about the islands, and turned down an offer by a black-marketeer to take him and his wares abroad so that he might at least have a chance to barter with natives should the *Fortune* run out of supplies. The Captain snapped that he had goods for barter: pins and needles from Russia, and that he could handle matters himself.

The exasperated skipper resumed palavers with the officers. Russian Lieutenant Tshirikov, visibly impressed by Bering's steadfastness, intimated that a display of rude energy might produce results. Bering assembled all officers and men and roared orders to go aboard. All of a sudden, as by the touch of a magic wand, sneering officers, sloppy Russians, and sullen Kamchadals began to move toward the gangplank, singly first, then in groups. The *Fortune* was ready to sail, straight north.

The weather cleared after a few days of navigation in dense fog, and on August 8, at a latitude of 64°30′, they sighted a boat rowed by eight natives. The eight were taken aboard the *Fortune;* and explained that they were Chutskis, from Siberia, and that they knew of a big island, not far away. Two days later Bering found the island and assigned Spannberg and Tshirikov to "examine" the place. The men found dwellings, obviously evacuated by their occupants a very short time before; otherwise the territory did not seem remarkable.

August 10, 1727, is not memorialized as the date of the "Russian discovery of America." However, the landing party had set foot on American soil: on the island of St. Lawrence. Yet, it is doubtful that Tshirikov was the first Russian to visit St. Lawrence. Savages are inquisitive; the fact that they fled at the approach of the Russians indicates that they had met men of that type before, and that their experience with them had been discouraging.

On August 15, Bering's party reached a latitude of 67°18′, well beyond the straits that would be named after him. He seems not to have sighted the Diomede Islands, however. He could see no land to the north or to the east. Yet there was land stretching west, great boulders and rocks, with snow lying in crevasses and covering tops. After five days of cruising Bering took stock: The French map had shown the American mainland sixty miles due east of Kamchatka; according to his calculations, they had been as far as 372 German leagues, approximately 1700 English miles, east of their point of departure. America was not where the French map makers had marked it. He would have to report this to the Russian authorities, who might, in turn, convey this statement to the "Company of New France," chartered by Cardinal Richelieu, and in control of Canada.

Bering's cruise took him around the northeastern tip of Siberia, rediscovering the Northeast Passage that Deshnev had negotiated.

Bering's laconic logbooks tell of forty Chutskis who had been crowded in four small boats, boarding the *Fortune* and bartering dried fish, meat, fifteen fox skins, four narwhale's tusks, and fresh water contained in whale bladders against pins and needles. Natives are quoted as having said that they had never attempted to cross the northern seas and that they had been to Anadyr, where they had been extremely well treated by the garrison.

Bering had to rely upon two translators to communicate with the Chutskis, which may explain the otherwise astonishing remark about Russian good behavior toward natives.

On August 28 the *Fortune* was buffeted by high winds; heavy fog blanketed the sea; the vessel suffered damage, but eventually made port.

Bering took a dim view of the results of his voyage. This view was shared by Spannberg, and also by Tshirikov, who had become a trustworthy companion and who suggested that they make another attempt to find America. If it was not located in the north, it should be in the east, and it would be sound policy to explore the "Thirteen Islands" and also to implement inadequate official maps.

Bering spent much time collecting data on shortcomings in the Siberian administration and urgently needed reforms, and interviewing Kamchadals selected by Tshirikov about the great continent that was America. The natives said that the great continent was straight east of their peninsula and "not far away." The Captain had hoped that the boat would be refitted and ready to sail by May 1728, but not before June 5, 1729, could he leave Kamchatka for his second trip. Struggling against adverse winds and foul weather, he reached a point 130 miles east of the coast, and when conditions kept growing worse he abandoned hope of reaching America, rounded the southern tip of Kamchatka, and set his course for Okhotsk, where he arrived on July 23.

Okhotsk was firmly held by the Russians; the Chinese made no attempt to dislodge the violators of the Treaty of Nerchinsk. The port was developing into a new base of expansion. Bering's second voyage had led him through the Kurile island chain, steppingstones between Kamchatka and Hokkaido, and it convinced him that there was more to the story of the "Thirteen Islands" than he had thought two years before when he had struggled for the departure of the *Fortune*.

In 1730, Bering was in St. Petersburg to report to the Academy, the Admiralty, and the Tsar. He did not see the ruler of Russia. Peter II was dying of smallpox.

The Academy received Bering's report without enthusiasm. The scientists did not like to be told that their calculations had been wrong. A map of the northeasternmost shore of Siberia, drawn by Bering with Spannberg's and Tshirikov's assistance, was accepted as a basis for further exploration, but nothing was said about a future assignment.

Nothing about a future assignment was said by members of the Admiralty, either. Bering was given to understand that his voluminous account was not according to regulations; naval officers were expected to confine their narration to naval matters and not to elaborate on land transportation, cattle breeding, and similar landlubber business.

Had it not been for Admiral Count Golovin, son of the man who had signed the Treaty of Nerchinsk, Captain Commander Bering would have been sidetracked to a desk, if not retired from active service because of advanced age. But Golovin saw in Bering the Russian explorer *par excellence,* the man who had negotiated the Northeast Passage, and had sailed in waters which not even the Dutch, Portuguese, or English had ever reached. The more seas, islands, straits, and promontories were named after Bering, the more the Western world would have to realize that their naval superiority was a matter of the past, and that Russia was now at least the equal of the old, established seafarers. The vessels of the Russian fleet were foreign-built, its skippers including Bering, foreign-born; its armament was of foreign type, but this did not smother Golovin's rabid nationalism. The Admiral had inherited a sense of mortification about developments along the Chinese-Siberian border, and mortification found an explosive outlet in a frenetic urge of eastern expansion through default, deceit, and daring.

Golovin did not obtain a monetary reward for Vitus Bering, or even a promotion, but he secured another Eastern assignment for the weary Captain Commander, one broader in scope and involving greater powers; and he also had the Admiralty retract its earlier criticism of Bering's account.

The Captain Commander's observations, and recommendations on public works, industrial and agricultural production, cattle breeding, cartography, overlapping of, and vacuums among, Siberian administrative domains, were passed on to experts' committees for surveys, which would provide two generations of civil servants with remunerative paper work, and produce nothing practical.

But even in the good graces of the Admiralty it was a frustrating task for Bering to prepare the exploration of the sea that was to bear his name. The naval experts of the capital agreed that he needed solid ships, fine crews, abundant supplies and construction materials. But when the Captain Commander, seconded by Spannberg and Tshirikov, wanted to know exactly which vessels he would get, where he could muster crews and check supplies, the gaudily uniformed gentlemen from St. Petersburg contended that such details were beyond their control. All they could do was to approve of Bering's requests; but they could not spare ships; they were short of crews, even in the Baltic; and had not the Captain Commander himself reported that Siberian transportation was in bad need of development? How could he carry immense loads of supplies over such inadequate routes? But weren't Russian shipbuilding facilities in the east superior to those of other European nations? Wasn't there food and timber in Siberia? And there should also be crews on the spot. Bering was not an eloquent man; a sudden outburst of energy, as it had saved the day in Kamchatka, was to no avail in the Admiralty Palace.

Bering, ground by the mills of bureaucracy, wearily pleaded for strongly worded orders to Siberian governors to assist him to the limit, and implored the naval brass to recruit craftsmen, engineers, and retired sailors with whom he could fill the gap of skilled labor that existed out east.

The authorities handed grandiose credentials to Bering, and issued pompously worded orders to whom it might concern—governors, coachmen, or fortress commanders—but the recruiting drive did not come off as Bering had hoped when the Admiralty consented to assist him.

There seemed to be few skilled men in the capital; the only category of manpower in unlimited supply were convicts. Bering received permission to enlist whoever would enroll, convicts or freemen. He did find volunteers, Russians and foreigners, some inquisitive, some enterprising, some adventure-minded, and many more rapacious brutes. Eventually the Captain Commander and his aides rounded up specialists, but their number was small and their qualifications were dubious.

It took until 1733 to assemble 900 men. They traveled afoot, on sleighs, or, as the season advanced, on carts drawn by requisitioned horses, and on river craft.

The size of Bering's troop, and the weight of the papers he carried, impressed local authorities west of the Ural Mountains. The expedition was still treated with distinction as it trudged through the eastern foothills of the Russian continental divide, but the farther they proceeded, the less co-operative governors and military commanders became. They scoffed at the "foreigners" and refused to approve of Bering's requisitions. He had to struggle for every carload of food, every draft animal, and every piece of material. Siberian Cossacks engaged in brawls with members of the expedition; discipline slackened; there were casualties through injury and desertion.

Bering ordered that they split into three groups. It would be easier to supply bodies of 300 each than one unit of 900. Spannberg was to lead the vanguard, travel as fast as he could, and engage in preparatory exploration from Kamchatka, scouting the Kurile Islands, and have three ships readied for the main expedition. Bering stayed with the last detachment, trying to gather ammunition as he proceeded.

Spannberg reached Kamchatka in 1736. The second group, under Tshirikov, followed in the spring of 1737, its ranks thinned by mass desertions.

The Governor of Kamchatka was less unfriendly than his Siberian colleagues, and offered Spannberg and Tshirikov every possible assistance in securing ships. The Governor was not motivated by a Golovin-type of patriotism, nor had his ideas on explorers from the capital changed, but he wanted to rid himself of several hundred mouths to feed, and he hoped that the intruders would eventually perish at sea or, even better, turn into his tools and those of his black-market associates.

The *Fortune* was no longer seaworthy, but an old schooner was patched together, a shitiki was refitted, and yet another built. The *St. Peter*, the *St. Gabriel*, and the *Archangel Michael* constituted a fleet not fit to bear out claims to naval excellence, yet they were formidable for the standards of Kamchatka.

Spannberg and Tshirikov took the *St. Peter* and *St. Gabriel* out to sea; they explored the Kurile Islands, coasted Japan, drew maps, and waited for Bering.

Meantime Bering battled governors, argued with officials, threatened, conjured, requisitioned, begged, and advanced at a snail's pace. The Siberian administrators sent express couriers to St. Petersburg to complain about Bering's alleged misinterpretation of orders, his arrogation of powers, and illicit appropriation of government property. Siberian administrators had friends in the capital, and there were still people of consequence in the Admiralty who resented Bering's fame.

In 1738, Bering received a message from the capital, censoring him for misuse of requisitioning powers, and notifying him of a reduction of his salary for the purpose of restitution. Bering did not care for money, and he did not even mind the unjustified accusation. He was positive that he would not live to return to St. Petersburg, but he would carry on in the eastern seas, whatever happened in the distant west.

It took him two more years to reach Kamchatka, years during which he had no contact with the outside world, during which he kept struggling for ammunition to be used on his voyage—to America.

Late in 1740 he received Spannberg's and Tshirikov's reports, and examined cartographical work done on the coast of Japan. The yield of all the years that had gone by since he had reported to the Admiralty was rather meager, but there was a great task ahead.

CHAPTER FORTY-TWO Vitus Bering was sixty when he started the exploration of a new continent and the seas thither. In an age of brief life expectancy he was an unusually old man to engage in so momentous a project. He had not had a permanent abode in fifteen years, no relief from nerve-racking chicanery, physical discomfort, and mental anguish; he had known brief periods of insecure eminence, and long spells of insult. He had battled against iniquities and had never been defeated, but in turn he had never decisively prevailed over stupid injustice. A person of lesser fortitude would have succumbed to the strain, but the aging Captain Commander was still determined to achieve an objective that had not even been of his own choice fifteen grueling years before, but to which he had now unflinchingly dedicated the remainder of his life.

He was determined no longer to pay heed to the vicissitudes of cabals in the capital, to overlook ignominy inflicted upon him by Siberian officials, to write off an adopted stepfatherland as it fell behind, and to concentrate on the loyal small world of his ships and crews, which should carry him to an unlimited world of discovery.

But the small world waiting for him in Avacha harbor was not as loyal as he had hoped. Tshirikov was faithful, but many officers and men were affected by the destructive spirit of Siberia. Bering soon enough realized that he would not find a sufficient number of reliable sailors to man three ships.

And there was yet another element he had not taken into account: he would have an unexpected passenger. Mr. Steller's credentials entitled him to accompany Bering and to do scientific research. Bering must have had a foreboding of evil as he read the papers, for an uneasy, if not unfriendly, feeling prevailed between him and the German almost from the outset. Steller was much younger than the Captain Commander and considered youth an asset; he was a man of higher learning than the old officer, which gave him a sense of superiority, and, having spent several years in Kamchatka, he was convinced that he knew more about the lands in those latitudes than Bering.

Steller probably did not speak or act in a disreputable manner as long as they were in port; he was too clever to provoke the commander into leaving him behind, despite his credentials. But he obviously had a sarcastic way of expressing respect, which irritated the officer.

The winter of 1740–41 was spent with preparations. Bering would use only two of his three vessels, and even though he still had almost 600 men, selectivity made it difficult to find the 140 crewmen. The *St. Peter* and the *St. Gabriel*, the latter rechristened *St. Paul*, were relatively well supplied with food and ammunition; Bering chose the *St. Peter* as his flagship, and Tshirikov was in command of the *St. Paul*.

The expedition left port on June 4, 1741. Logbooks do not indicate that Bering was in poor health. Steller's journals, however, tell of the Captain's chronic indisposition, which confined him to his cabin most of the time.

"After our departure," the journals say, "we sailed with south, west, and southwest winds, and on June 11, we were 135 Dutch miles [more than 600 English miles] from Avacha, at a latitude of 46°47'. On the following day, we perceived indications of land nearby: marine plants, flocks of ducks and sea gulls. In latitude 51°, we were separated from the *St. Paul* in dense fog, and even though we sailed down to the 46° latitude, we did not find her again. On the 18th of June, we changed course and steered northeastward, covering up to 2 degrees of longitude and 1 degree of latitude per day."

The course of the vessel was not determined by orders of the skipper, however. Bering wanted to sail north, but his officers, arguing that America should be east, overruled the commander. "Overruling the commander," as Steller called it, was but a slightly veiled wording for mutiny.

For more than one month the *St. Peter* furrowed the waters of the Eastern Sea, circumnavigating the Aleutian chain almost in its full length. The crew fretted about the emptiness of the ocean, which was contrary to what Kamchadals had said about the location of America, and altogether frightening.

On July 15 the watch at the top of the mast saw a light spot on the horizon, which developed into a snowcapped mountain; later a "much broken coast, dented with bays," came in sight.

"It is easy to understand the general rejoicing caused by the detection of land," Steller noted. "Everybody congratulated the Captain on the discovery, which would be held to his credit. But he received congratulations with marked coldness, and when we were alone in his cabin he told me: 'They think that we have now completed our task, and may entertain big expectations. But we are a tremendous distance away from our base, we don't know the country ahead of us, we are short of water, and contrary winds may upset our further voyage!'"

In a sudden change of mood the crewmen abandoned their rejoicing. Sailors bewailed their misfortune at being mortifyingly far away from home; others argued about how and where to collect the awards to which they felt entitled. Some asked that they sail into a natural harbor; others shouted that they should keep off the coast where unknown dangers were lurking. Everybody shouted his opinion, nobody asked for orders, Bering, in his cabin, was not even consulted.

"Previously, even trifling issues had been decided by orderly consultation. But now there was no understanding on crucial matters; the only unity was that of being confined to one and the same craft," Steller complained.

On July 18 the ship approached the coast. The land was dotted with large tracts of forests. The shore was flat, level, and sandy; but fear of lurking dangers prevented a landing on the mainland. Leaving the continent to its right, the *St. Peter* sailed northwest, toward a "lofty island consisting of one wooded mountain."

The next day was spent with debates. Steller wanted to enter a strait between the mainland and the island, and from there proceed toward a river, the color of which promised clear, fresh water. The crew objected, and the vessel eventually cast anchor in "a great bay" close to the island.

The outermost tip of land—the discoverers were not certain whether it formed part of the continent of the outlying archipelago—was called Cape St. Elias, because it had been passed on St. Elias's day. St. Elias also gave its name to the range of high mountains the Russians had first sighted from a latitude of 58°28′.

This "second discovery" of America by the Russians carried Bering to the vicinity of the Pacific coast of Canada. But apparently he did not realize that he was close to a European colony, and he met no ships whose captains would have answered inquiries about the land.

"No landing was attempted on the continent," Steller raged, "and the reasons for this were indolence, obstinacy, an unreasonable fear of unarmed, terrified savages, and dastardly impatience to return home. After ten years had been spent on preparations of the voyage, ten hours were spent making observations on an island about 3 Dutch miles long, and half a mile wide."

The place was Kaye Island. A landing party was sent to fetch drinking water. Steller joined them: "It seems that we have come all the way from Kamchatka solely to carry water from America to Asia," he quotes his own jest.

The German scientist walked one verst (0.66 mile) inland and there "found a hollowed trunk, in which there were stones, and the bones of a land animal, apparently a reindeer. In Kamchatka, the natives cook meat on hot stones in hollow trees. I also found Yukola, dried fish, as Kamchadals eat instead of bread, and sweet grass prepared in the Kamchadal manner. Also nearby, I saw still glowing embers, and a wooden tinder box, different from those used in Kamchatka only by the kind of tinder: white moss, bleached in the sun. This indicated that the island was inhabited, and that the natives were of the same origin as the Kamchadals. We should assume that the continent of America is much nearer to Kamchatka further up north, for it seems impossible that the natives could cover distances of 500 Dutch miles in their absurdly primitive craft."

Another two versts away Steller saw trees, stripped of bark, the bark being used as building material for boats and dwellings. He also found what he called homesteads; cellarlike excavations supported by wooden poles, with walls of bark, and layers of stones, and covered by heaps of grass. Primitive household utensils, such as vessels made of bark, had been left behind, and so was cooked salmon, and sweet herbs. Other discoveries included hemp for fishing nets; dried layers of bark of pine and larch, similar to what "is used as food in many parts of the Russian Empire"; solid straps of seaweed; and large arrows of Tatar design, obviously fashioned with iron tools.

Steller did not meet a native of Kaye Island. But he left a few presents behind: a rusty iron kettle, one pound of tobacco, a pipe, and a piece of cloth.

Many years later, when the island was revisited, an old native told of objects left by some foreigners; he did not indicate whether these foreigners had been the first white men to visit their island.

Steller drafted a cursory survey of the land and its produce:

"The climate of this part of America is superior to that of the northeastern coast of Asia. Here the coast and outlying islands are dotted with mountains, some of them very high and covered by eternal snow. But while northeastern Asiatic mountain sides mostly consist of bare rock interspersed with stunted trees and scanty herbage, the mountains of America are covered up to considerable altitudes with fine trees and rich herbage.

"American plants grow earlier in the season, and are more abundant than those of Siberia; rich forests cover parts of the coast up to a latitude of at least 60°. It is my opinion that the American continent expands from Cape Elias to beyond lat. 70°, and that it is protected from northwinds by high mountains.

"I found all varieties of common berries, and also a new kind of raspberry which, because of its size and taste, deserves to be transplanted to St. Petersburg.

"Of land animals, I observed black and red foxes, and there should also be reindeer; of birds common in Siberia, I found raven and magpies, but I also saw upward of ten new species, distinguished for their brilliant plumage. One of these specimens reminded me of a picture I saw in a recent report on Carolina [apparently the blue jay].

"Shoals of fish come closer to the coast of America than to the coast of Kamchatka. Whales, dog fish, and sea otters are found in prodigal numbers.

"As to minerals, I saw only sand and grey rock. This, however, does not indicate negligence on my part. It must be taken into account how little a man can achieve in a bare ten hours, and without assistance."

Steller's journals berate Bering for his stubborn insistence on weighing anchor without further exploration.

Bering had sound reasons for wanting to return. Immensely far away from Siberia, and unable to regain full control of his vessel, he may have hoped to find the *St. Paul* and later resume his voyage on that ship with its better crew. He left no word on his vain attempts at steering back to Kamchatka. Steller remains the sole source of information:

"On July 21, Bering appeared on deck, and without consulting with his officers, expressed anxiousness to return home. A few days later, he suggested again that we be satisfied with our discoveries, and set sail for Kamchatka; it would be hazardous to remain in unknown waters, close to unfamiliar lands, exposed to weather conditions of which we knew nothing; the vessel might run aground in the darkness, or be wrecked by autumnal storms, and leave us stranded on a desolate cliff."

But the Captain's "suggestions" and pleas were no better obeyed than his previous directives.

Bering never learned of the adventures of the *St. Paul*, of which *Mueller's Account of Russian Discoveries* says that the vessel reached the American mainland on July 15 at a latitude of 56°, finding a steep and rocky coast. "Ten men were sent ashore in the long boat to look for water, and reconnoiter the country. When they failed to return, it was presumed that they had been attacked by hostile natives. Six more men were dispatched to their rescue, but they too did not return, and probably were massacred together with the first party." After cruising along the coast for several days Tshirikov returned to Avacha. Owing to adverse winds the voyage lasted from July 27 to October 9; five men died of scurvy; the last victim was Louis Delisle de la Croyère, a French astronomer and geographer who had joined the expedition. Tshirikov was ill, but he recovered in the following spring to make an unsuccessful attempt to find Bering, who had not been heard from during the winter.

The voyage of the *St. Peter* continued. On July 26 they came in sight of Alaska Peninsula, Steller noting that the mountains were high and capped with snow. Steering west, they reached a group of wooded and mountainous islands, and saw herds of seal, sea lions, sea otters, porpoises, and "sea bears." By August 18 the officers seemed weary of further discoveries and set course toward the open sea. On August 26 a violent storm broke. For two days the *St. Peter* drifted haplessly; then it was decided to sail back to the American coast to refill the water tanks. On August 29 they discovered five islands. Steller tells of arguments with officers who insisted on filling casks with brackish water, which, he said, promoted the outbreak of scurvy.

Six days later, when the ship had not yet left, the first sailor aboard the *St. Peter* died. The man, one Shumagine, was buried on an island, and the group was named after him.

Adverse winds delayed the departure, when at last, and quite unexpectedly, as Steller noted, "We saw some Americans."

"We heard an outcry, which we first believed to be the roar of a sea lion, but then two *baidars,* felt-covered one-man canoes, approached our craft. At a distance of ½ verst, the rowers opened a long oration, which our Korjak interpreters did not understand and which, to us, sounded like a prayer, a conjuration, or a welcome as it is occasionally heard in Kamchatka. We beckoned them to come nearer, they answered with gestures, inviting us to come ashore. 'Nitishi,' we shouted, which, according to Baron Lahoutan's *Description of North America,* means 'water.' The men in the canoes repeated the word several times, and again pointed toward the land. One of them rowed close to our ship. He drew pear shaped marks upon his cheeks with earth, stuffed his nostrils with grass, and thrust a thin bone through his nose. He brandished a three ell long red stick, apparently a calumet, fastened two hawk's wings to it and, laughing, threw it toward our craft. Thereupon, we tied two Chinese tobacco pipes and some glass beads to a board, and threw it toward him. He examined it and handed it to his companion who put it upon his baidar. Growing bolder, they ventured closer; one of them tied the disemboweled body of a hawk to another stick, and held it out to our Korjak interpreter who reached for it. This, however, alarmed the American who let the stick go, and paddled back. We threw a piece of silk and a mirror at him; he caught it, but he and his companion paddled back to the island, from where other natives were shouting at them.

"It was resolved that Lieutenant Waxel, myself, the interpreters, and nine crew-men row ashore. We were armed with lances and had guns concealed under a sail cloth; we also carried bisquit, brandy, and various trinkets as presents. As we approached the rocky coast, a crowd of natives motioned to us to come nearer, but the surf was so violent that we could not land. Our interpreters stripped and waded through the water; the islanders received them in a friendly manner, supported them under their arms which indicates respect, and guided them ashore. They handed our men a piece of whale blubber and, constantly talking, pointed at the far side of the hills, as if to indicate the location of their dwellings.

"A native lifted his baidar into the water, rowed toward us to help us ashore. We welcomed him with a cup of brandy; he swallowed and spat it out with gestures of indignation. Our sailors offered him a lighted pipe of tobacco, but he was disgusted with smoking and rowed away with indications of vivid displeasure.

"As the wind increased, we called our interpreters back, but the islanders attempted to retain the men by offering them more whale blubber; when this did not produce the desired effect, they held them back by their arms, as others made for our boat to pull it ashore. Our dissuading gestures were to no avail, and so we discharged three muskets over their heads. They fell down, terror struck. In the ensuing commotion, the interpreters freed themselves, and rushed back to the boat.

"Recovering from the shock, the angry natives motioned us to leave, and some even made mien to throw rocks. We were happy to reach the ship.

". . . The baidars of the Americans are about 12 feet long, two feet high, and two feet in breadth; the frames are made of ribs, and fastened by cross bars; they are covered with seal skins. . . .

"The people are of medium stature; their arms and legs are very fleshy; their hair is straight, and of glossy darkness; their faces and noses are flat, their complexion is brownish; they have black eyes, and thick puffed up lips; their necks are short, their shoulders broad, their bodies square but not fat.

"Men and women were similarly dressed. They wore shirts, sewed with thread made from the intestines of whale, hanging loose or tied around the waist with a string; their boots and breeches resembled those worn by Kamchadals; they were made of seal skins and dyed red with alder bark; iron knives, in poorly manufactured sheaths dangled from belts.

"Watching a native cut a whale blubber, it occurred to us that the knife was not of European manufacture. However, the knives were hardly produced by the natives; they could not have been imported from Kamchatka either where no iron is found, and natives are not familiar with smelting processes. I learned from reliable sources, that the [Siberian] Chutskis were trading with America."

Steller did not elaborate on his sources, but there is no reason to doubt his information. Indications are that trade routes led across Bering Strait, then via Anadyr to Alaska; and also from a western terminal near the neck of Kamchatka to the Aleutian Islands and the Alaska Peninsula. It cannot be ruled out either that Chinese merchants and Japanese pirates did business with Americans, dumping their inferior goods upon people whose living standards were much lower than those of the old Asiatic nations. Spanish buccaneers may have ventured far up the American West Coast, but Steller's account of the knives seems to preclude the possibility that they were of Spanish origin.

A more elaborate account of Western American overseas trade could have produced invaluable information on age-old ties between America and Siberia, but Steller had only this to say: "The main objects of barter between

Chutski and Americans are knives, hatchets, spears, and arrow heads, and skins of sea otters, foxes and martens. The Chutski now purchase metal objects from Russians, who charge very high prices, and still make a handsome profit selling the objects to Americans."

The expedition met more Americans on September 8, a short distance away from the Shumagine Islands.

"Nine of them came in baidars, drew up in a line, and performed ceremonies as described earlier. They wore hats of bark, dyed green and red, open at the top, and shaped like candle screens. Some hats were adorned with hawks'-feathers and grass, reminding of the way Brazilians adorn themselves with tufts of feathers. It seems that the natives of this part of America are descendants of Asiatics; Korjaks and Kamchadals wear similar hats. We acquired two headgears in exchange for a kettle, five needles, and some thread. These people deem it attractive to make holes in various parts of their faces and to insert stones, and bones into them. One man carried an object more than two inches long through his nostrils and a bone, three inches long, stuck between his chin and lower lip. Americans have little or no beard, in which they resemble Kamchadals and other Siberians. It occurs to me that they stay on the continent during the cold season, and visit the islands during the summer to collect birds' eggs and to hunt whales and seals."

The seasonal migration of natives seems to have begun when the *St. Peter* coasted the approaches of Alaska Peninsula in mid-September. All was quiet on board. In his cabin the skipper was brooding: it would take at least two months to reach Siberia; even if September continued mild and October were less tempestuous than he expected, it would be extremely difficult to navigate in November. But to spend the winter in America, depending upon enigmatical savages for supplies, with the frail ship exposed to elements, would be even more hazardous than the voyage back. Bering had no control over his ship, but he still had all responsibility.

Meantime Steller, out on deck, sketched, recorded, made scientific observations, apparently oblivious of the passing of irretrievable time.

The officers were indifferent to science and surveys on sands, rock, and birds. They considered spending the winter in America, and, to make it a comfortable season, drafting natives into building solid huts, bartering pieces of thread against bales of edibles, and otter furs for needles—one needle to the pelt. The natives seemed a soft lot, but even if they stalled, the Russians had their muskets; three shots fired into the air had frightened Americans into a near panic; a well-aimed volley would certainly force them into blind obedience. By spring every officer would own a fortune in furs, and should the *St. Peter* be wrecked, natives would be put to work on another ship.

The ship's crew, dumb, illiterate, and superstitious men, was corrupted by the spirit of latent insubordination, yet they were too dull to turn a rebellion at the top into a mutiny of the lower echelons. The men lingered under deck and at their stations, beset by fear of horrors yet unborn but long begotten, and by an impotent hatred against the instigators of calamities that would rise from those quiet waters, calm air, and rocky islands that dotted the sea like clenched, bony fists.

The men's portentous tenseness shook the officers out of complacent dreams of comfort and prosperity. Once ashore, the sailors' tenseness might explode into devastating rebellion. They consulted Steller, but the German had no better suggestion than to offer to talk to Bering.

The Captain Commander had his mind made up. The *St. Peter* should return to Kamchatka without delay. Any attempt to spend the winter elsewhere would lead to disaster.

Looking tired, speaking slowly, and with an expressionless voice, he did not attempt to issue orders, however, and the officers took his words as an opinion, which they were not bound to accept. One suggested that they talk to the crew, but they could not agree who should address the sailors, nor what he should tell them. Bering's advice seemed sound; but even if they did get to Kamchatka and were not court-martialed for insubordination, they would be left penniless after a voyage out of which luckier men would have made princely fortunes. On the other hand, even if they stayed in America, would the sailors idly hover by, while the officers gathered the spoils? Would not the men take it all and murder their superiors?

It was agreed that, pending another decision, the *St. Peter* should sail west —in the direction of Asia. Sails fluttering in a lazy breeze, the ship navigated through a maze of islands, which time and again seemed to block the route.

September went by, calm and fair. The ship was still in sight of the Fox Islands. As long as they were so close to the New World, they could still spend the winter there.

Came October, still calm and fair. The *St. Peter* reached the fringe of the open sea. The route continued west.

Quite suddenly clouds rose, like dark chariots, driving up on the sky's pale blue expanse. A storm broke, a shrieking prelude to winter. The sailors considered it a chorus of fiendish ghosts and grew panicky; they would try to reach a deserted cliff ranging out of the spray of foam rather than face the gruesome wrath of ghouls.

The shouts of the crazed seamen were louder even than the howl of the hurricane. Helpless officers requested that Bering quiet the men. The Captain Commander wanted to place the instigators of the panic under arrest or have a boat hoisted and have them make for the cliff. This the officers refused to do, and eventually Lieutenant Waxel talked to the crew. His speech is not recorded, but eventually the storm abated, and the *St. Peter* continued toward Asia.

For several weeks the ship sailed on. The weather was much better than expected. On November 6 land was sighted. Uproarious sailors insisted that this was Kamchatka, and they would land there even if they were a long way from Avacha.

Landing operations seemed difficult. Again officers went to Bering's stuffy cabin and requested that he take charge of the operation. Bering pointed to a map. The *St. Peter* was still about 150 miles away from the nearest point of the Kamchatkan coast.

They could be in Avacha in no more than three days. It was sheer madness to disembark now. The officers shook their heads. The crew would not stand for a continued voyage.

The aged commander rose. Defied, disobeyed, derided as he had been, in this moment he still was the sole legal authority. His orders were to continue to Avacha, and if the officers did not have the spirit to convey them to the sailors, he would go on deck and see that they were carried out.

Officers blocked the exit. They claimed that Bering's prerogatives were limited to conducting landing operations. Should the Captain Commander refuse to co-operate, they would act alone.

Bering was a skillful seaman and duty-bound to the last. He issued directives how to make port.

"Soon after sunset," Steller recorded, "we cast anchor one verst offshore, in nine fathoms of water. The evening was crisp and clear, and the moon shone with extreme brightness. Half an hour later, a sudden dreadful swell tossed the ship around like a ball, it seemed, as if the *St. Peter* would be cast ashore and dashed to pieces. Soon the vessel was adrift, one anchor lost; but then the waters quieted, and we could cast anchor again."

There were many sick men aboard; on November 7, when Steller directed the unloading of men, baggage and stores, a number of the stricken had to be carried. However, there were no complaints. All sailors seemed firmly convinced that they were back in Kamchatka. And even though none of them had been born or raised there, Kamchatka was the incarnation of home to those distressed castaways. At home all men recovered. Their superstition pictured Bering as a mighty sorcerer; hadn't he conjured home for the wayward and the weary? Hadn't he calmed the deadly squall, the last blow of the ghouls? And yet they would not hail Bering; a sorcerer was always dangerous.

Bering went ashore, supported by three servants. He had suffered agonies during the past weeks; his limbs felt leaden, his mouth ached, and it had a strange taste—a taste of death. Steller waited for the Captain Commander with a paper he asked him to sign: a certificate to the effect that the landing had been necessitated by the "sickly state of the crew." "I am not qualified to attest that," the skipper said casually, and made for a rickety tent. Steller put his own signature under the document.

Two of his servants abandoned the Captain Commander at once and joined the sailors. From them the crewmen learned that this was not Kamchatka, and that Bering had known it all along.

A wave of immense hatred burst forth against the vicious sorcerer. Nobody, however, dared to lift a hand against him. He could still save them; only he had the power to do so.

Vitus Bering was the only man on the island that would later bear his name who did not notice that the sailors believed that he was endowed with black magic. He stayed in his small tent, suffering "from a tertian ague, and a swelling of his feet which spread to his vital parts and developed into gangrene, to which was added scurvy." Lieutenants Waxel and Kyrov visited him, both anxious to be appointed commander by the doomed man. Bering understood that even mutineers had to have a leader. But Waxel's health was failing too, and Kyrov was so detested by the sailors that his appointment would have resulted in chaos. Steller told this to Bering, who had not been aware of it. Steller promised to take care of the thorny problem of command, and of other problems as they would arise.

No natives were found on this island astride the fifty-fifth parallel. But there were quite a few animals; moor hens, otters, and black stone foxes. The island swarmed with foxes—droll and fat beasts, the least shy of all wild creatures the men had ever seen—and the most voracious, as they soon had to realize.

The men were trailed by foxes. Foxes watched their doings with bent heads and pricked-up ears. From time to time the animals performed acrobatics, accompanied by funny mimics which made everybody laugh. Laughingly the men butchered foxes with hatchets and knives, more than sixty on the first day. The fur of stone foxes had a nauseating smell; they were shabby, and nobody would have traded sixty skins against one sewing needle, but killing was the crew's way of getting acquainted.

On the second day more than a hundred foxes perished. Yet for every animal killed ten and more would turn up, as if attracted by the smell of the blood of their fellow-creatures. They swarmed all over the camp, pilfered provisions, sniffled, doglike, at sick men lying on the ground, and at carcasses of their own kind.

The crew built three dwellings, which were neither solid nor comfortable, but the men were not sufficiently strong and skilled to erect better accommodations. It was considered to use the *St. Peter* as floating quarters, but two weeks after the landing the ship was cast ashore in a blizzard and broke up.

At home men recovered. But in foreign lands they died. The sick muttered it and cursed Bering. Scurvy decimated the crew. One of the buildings was turned into a ward where, according to Steller, "the sick lay promiscuously on the bare ground, with no other covering than their clothes; and nothing was heard but outcries and groans accompanied by imprecations on the instigators of their misery. Moor hens and otters provided fresh meat. Yet the men were starving, as scurvy made their gums swell over their teeth, and bulge like sponges."

Healthy men stayed out of the building that was permeated by the sounds and stench of death. But the sick still had company: the black foxes.

From outside sailors put foxes' carcasses on air holes to keep the nocturnal cold from penetrating into the "hospital." The playful black animals removed the carcasses, sneaked inside and jumped down, sniffled at the living, and mangled the dead. The foxes devoured provisions, but they also ate leather, woolens, and textiles. They stole coats, gloves, and boots, stripping the living and the deceased with droll motions, as if mocking their distress.

The Russians, inside and outside the death house, were haunted by the foxes. Their tortured minds pictured the beasts as demons, forerunners of even more savage evil spirits to come and put them on the rack, laughingly. The devil himself was castigating them, and Bering was the assistant of the Prince of Hell.

But Bering, as Steller now entered in his journals, "was an upright, devout Christian, resigned to God's will, determined to give every possible encouragement to others, and to bolster the hopes of the stricken." Still unaware of his part in the men's nightmares, and with incredible indifference to his own excruciating pain, he staggered to the ward to give comfort to the sick.

An inhuman howl of fear and hatred drove him back to his tent. He would never again leave that tent alive.

"He might have survived," Steller's journals record piously, "had he reached Kamchatka and enjoyed warm dwellings and fresh provisions. Hunger, thirst, cold, fatigue, and despondency brought him to the grave."

On December 8, 1741, Bering died. His last loyal servant had succumbed to scurvy the day before. Foxes, gnawing at his garments, held the death vigil.

The black foxes stayed with the Russians. No storage place was secure from their ingenious intrusion. The men hunted otters in number; the furs would have been worth a fortune, but the foxes found them and chewed them until they were ruined.

Crazed men engaged in weird hocus-pocus to exorcise the beasts; the breath of insanity lingered over the camp.

As a presage of madness, a plan was hatched to deter the foxes from further mischief.

Around Christmas time catchers seized some twenty foxes, tied their muzzles, and carried them to flat grounds where a stake had been set up, and where knives, tongs, and spears were displayed.

Two groups formed around the ground, a narrow semicircle of all the thirty-odd men who could still walk, and a large circle, of hundreds, if not thousands, of lively beasts.

One seaman addressed both gatherings, explaining that the muzzled foxes would now be punished for their misdeeds, and that a similar fate was in store for every fox who would, henceforth, invade the camp.

Volunteer tormentors worked on the animals. They gouged out eyes, tore out tails, roasted legs over a bonfire; they outdid each other in inflicting untold tortures upon the foxes, careful not to kill them.

The muzzled beasts could not bark their pain, but their onlooking kin barked in a weird chorus, and performed funny antics, as if to entertain the victims. But they did not attack the torturers.

Henchmen released horribly mutilated animals which dragged themselves toward the large circle, which opened, admitted them, and closed again.

The Russians had no stir of pity, no notion of the repulsiveness of their doings. They carried on until the last of the muzzled foxes had suffered all tortures ingenious madmen could inflict. Dusk was falling when the men made for their lodgings.

At this moment the wide circle broke. A host of foxes swarmed over the camp, dragged away whatever they could hold in their snouts, befouled tents and huts with their excrements, and retired, performing clownish drolleries. Then, several hundred yards away, they rallied in a silent cordon. Animal fortitude stood up under human bestiality. The day was the foxes'.

On New Year's Day the number of dead had risen to thirty, almost half the total population of the camp on November 7. But indications of lingering insanity were no longer alarming, and it even appears as if man and beast had found a pattern of co-existence. The journals no longer elaborated on the stone foxes. They record that the state of health improved after January 1, 1742, and that among others Lieutenant Waxel recovered from scurvy.

Flesh of sea animals proved to be wholesome and even tasty. The meat of the sea lion was delicious, and its fat was said to taste like the marrow of an ox bone. Great quantities of driftwood relieved the shortage of fuel.

In May the castaways began to build another ship, using largely material salvaged from the wrecked *St. Peter.*

Steller explored the island and made measurements that confirmed an earlier assumption that it formed part of an archipelago—later to be known as Commander Islands (Ostrova Komandorskie).

On August 14, 1742, the new *St. Peter,* commanded by Lieutenant Waxel, left Bering Island. Three days later, as Bering had estimated, it reached the Kamchatkan coast.

CHAPTER FORTY-THREE In Siberia tragedies were chiefly considered from the angle of profitable opportunities involved. Hardly anybody pitied Bering's, whose disaster was fraught with profitable aspects. Siberian supplies of otter were running low, but there were otters galore in the region of the island where Bering had died. Americans were bartering their produce against sewing needles; America could be a gold mine for clever men. In consolidating Siberia it became difficult to set up domains complete with native labor; in America he who got there first should be able to establish kingdom-sized domains, and not even the Tsar could interfere.

However, risks involved in a voyage to America were great and required high investments. Operators and speculators in Kamchatka calculated that it would cost between 15,000 and 30,000 rubles to acquire, equip, and man a solid vessel for a trip that could last upward of three years. The purchasing power of the mid-eighteenth century ruble was incomparably lower than that of the ruble of Anikita Stroganoff's day; yet no single merchant in Kamchatka could have put up such an amount. People who had made so much money in the "Wild East" would return to regions where they could enjoy it in comfort and relative security.

Kamchatkan businessmen contacted their counterparts throughout Siberia. Several months after the return of the remnants of Bering's seamen the land hummed with planning, considering, computing. The co-operative pattern was popular among Siberians. Ingenious speculators invited investors to buy shares in corporations which would build and man *shitikis* to explore America. A share sold at between 300 and 500 rubles. A single voyage could bring fantastic dividends. The Chinese paid up to 140 rubles for a fine otter skin. A few hundred otter skins would bring twice the investment, but there should be thousands of otters, tens of thousands. Primitive Siberian mathematics could not conceive the figures involved.

A few years after foxes had held the vigil at Bering's deathbed modern "Ermaks," more efficient and independent than the legendary Cossack, set out for America.

Official Russia lagged far behind its citizens.

Not until the spring of 1743 did the Admiralty learn of the return of the *St. Peter,* and it took even longer until Steller's account of the results of the voyage was received.

The term "unsuccessful" was not part of the official vernacular for ventures sponsored by the Crown. However, there were variations of "successful" ranging from extraordinary, via grandiose, to epoch-making. The Bering expedition was called only "extraordinarily successful" and because its titular leader was no longer available to receive frigid honors, Tshirikov was summoned to St. Petersburg, where he arrived in 1745.

Bored naval officers coached the embarrassed ex-skipper for an audience at Court, and mentioned in passing that he should wear a captain commander's insignia, a promotion actually overdue on the basis of seniority.

Tshirikov appeared before Empress Elizabeth, the fifth ruler of Russia since the death of Peter the Great. Elizabeth was one of the daughters born to the first Peter by Catherine, and her views of the sanctity of Peter's eastern designs differed from those of her mother. She did not conceal her impatience when Tshirikov labored through the reading of a script drafted by Admiralty scribes, and dismissed him with curt words of acknowledgment of some merit or other.

The thus-promoted Captain Commander returned to the Admiralty to inquire about a new assignment, and was told to wait. The lords of the Russian Navy had to struggle for appropriations for every single craft and they would not divert funds on exploration. Should the government want further voyages in the east, it should take better care of the Navy's financial requirements. When, several months later, the Captain Commander called again, he heard unflattering remarks about his past performance and his present lack of discretion. Soon thereafter Tshirikov died, solving a problem for the naval brass.

Steller too died unexpectedly, in 1746. He could not have revised the passages of his journals dealing with Bering even had he wanted. The papers were still under study in St. Petersburg. Eventually their publication was authorized without changes. It was the never avowed, but carefully pursued, policy of the Russian authorities to claim all credit for achievements, real or imaginary, and to strip individuals of their title to glory.

Papers dealing with America, gathered in bulky files, were passed on to the Foreign Service. The career diplomats conducted surveys on possible effects and likely implications of discoveries in America upon relations with England, France, and Spain. It had taken almost one decade to prepare Bering's third voyage, but it took almost three decades until another official naval expedition set sail from the mouth of the Kamchatka River to America. Private expeditions, however, began as early as 1745.

Empress Elizabeth was busy with European politics and family affairs. The power of the Russian Army was at a peak, and the never quite workable pattern of European stability was upset by the decline of Turkey and the rise of an aggressive Prussia. Russia could hold the key to the balance of power, and the daughter of a foreign-born baggage-train whore watched, keen-eyed, for the right moment to make Russia the dominant power on the continent. She was spinning threads to Empress Maria Theresa of Austria for an alliance against King Frederick II of Prussia, which could expand the Russian sphere of interest across doomed Poland, far into Central Europe. Another leap like that would make Russia a factor in Atlantic policies. But Elizabeth could not hope to live to direct the second phase of expansion; and her nephew and heir presumptive to the throne was a half-witted weakling, and a domineering wife might keep that wretch from wrecking her policies; Elizabeth was more concerned with finding the right spouse for nitwit Peter than with discoveries in America. Hardly did she realize that her choice, the German-born Catherine "the Great" would frustrate her designs by making a separate peace with Frederick of Prussia when the rapacious King's armies were on the verge of collapse; and that she would rid herself of Peter by instigating a rebellion of the guards, and become the sole ruler of Russia.

Only in 1755 did Elizabeth show passing interest in her Far Eastern domain. She then requested that six Kamchadal virgins be sent to St. Petersburg so that she might get acquainted with her distant subjects. Soon, however, she seemed to have forgotten the matter, very much to the relief of the agency in charge, who had just learned that the six had meantime become visibly pregnant.

In the earlier part of Elizabeth's rule eastern-minded St. Petersburg was mainly concerned with the China trade, from which, they opined, immense profits could derive after some flaws and irregularities were eliminated. Flaws and irregularities, however, had always been, and would always remain, the essential features of Russian official ventures.

Back in 1727, Tsar Peter II had dispatched a special envoy to restore relations with China. Russian diplomats were neither smooth nor ingenious, but St. Petersburg had a suitable candidate for the tricky mission; or rather, the ladies of the Tsar's court had an idol to whom they would entrust everything in the world, including themselves.

Count Sava Vladislavitch Ragusinsky was the most colorful, bombastic swaggerer ever to trick his way to the Russian Court, where foreign quacks, Quixotes, and phonies in the disguise of experts and counselors were crowding out native professionals. His name, probably adopted like his title, came from Ragusa on the Adriatic Sea, where unusually handsome people can be found. Ragusinsky was a handsome man. Enraptured ladies insisted that his profile was that of a prince out of a fairy tale, but the gaudily attired gentleman insisted modestly that he was only a count, and was accepted as such.

Ragusinsky told wondrous stories of distant lands he had visited, of hair-raising hazards he had overcome; and since nobody had ever seen him reading a book, even male detractors trusted that he had traveled extensively. China was one topic of Ragusinsky's tales; Russian officers drew most of their information on the eastern empire from the Count. Several Germans who held top commissions in the Army came under his magic spell. Talking about another Amur campaign, however, they were opposed by Princes Golizyn and Dolgoruki, who warned the Tsar against military adventures on the Chinese border. But the princes voiced no objection against sending Ragusinsky to Peking.

The irresistible Count had various grandiose projects he proposed to carry out on the spot; but, for an immediate program, he accepted instructions to settle all existing controversies between Russia and China, to redraft boundary lines so that communications between Lena River and Kamchatka would be secure—which implied Chinese renunciation to lands north of the fifty-fifth parallel—and to find a new basis for Russo-Chinese trade.

Hardly anybody in St. Petersburg doubted that the Count would charm Chinese Emperor Yund-shin into granting Russia whatever he asked for.

The Chinese Emperor, however, did not even admit the envoy into his presence.

Upon reaching the Bura region the Russian delegation was told by border guards to wait for Chinese plenipotentiaries. Only weeks later negotiators arrived, neither as high in rank nor as splendid in appearance as the delegates to Nerchinsk had been. They responded to Ragusinsky's tirades with clear-cut statements that they would not sanction Russian territorial aspirations, which Ragusinsky couched in a demand that China renounce claims to suzerainty over tribes living north of traditional Manchu territory. However, they did not demand that Russian establishments east of the Lena be withdrawn, and they were amenable to a resumption of commerce and communications between the two countries.

On June 14, 1729, a treaty was signed at the site of Kiakhta. Once every three years a Russian trade caravan, of no more than 200 persons, equipped and supplied by the Russian Government, was permitted to proceed to Peking, along a route determined by China, and under Chinese guard. Russian traders would have to put up in a specially built caravansary; their movements within the capital were subject to restrictive controls.

Permission was granted to build a Russian church adjacent to the caravansary. Four Russian priests obtained permanent residential privileges.

A number of Russian scholars would be admitted to Peking to study the customs and language of the land and act as interpreters.

Russian private merchants were barred from Chinese territory, and so were privately owned wares. But private traders would have an opportunity to deal with Chinese merchants in border places.

Future negotiations between Russia and China should be conducted between the Tribunal for Foreign Affairs in Peking and the Board of Foreign Affairs in St. Petersburg. This reaffirmed the determination of the Emperor of China not to deal with the Tsar.

Back home the envoy explained cheerfully that he had suggested the ignominious provision, because it would facilitate official exchanges. He was lionized and showered with attentions, but his diplomatic career had come to an end.

In Peking church and caravansary were built by sons of former Russian prisoners of war, who had refused repatriation, married Chinese women, acquired Chinese citizenship, and forgone Christendom.

Russian scholars translated the Chinese code of law, Chinese books on history, geography, and fiscal accounting. They had little opportunity to serve as interpreters since trade between China and Russia on government level remained extremely slow. St. Petersburg never chose the right wares and could not find proper commercial experts. Operations were discontinued in 1755, after ten Russian caravans had arrived in Peking and invariably wound up in the red.

A considerable amount of business was transacted at the border, however. A new town sprang up in the romantic valley of the Kiakhta brook, 1025 miles from Peking, and 4335 miles from St. Petersburg, surrounded by high mountains with densely wooded slopes and wild, rocky summits.

The Account of the Russian Discoveries between Asia and America, by William Coxe, describes this city of trade:

"The Russian section, called Kiakhta, consists of a fortress, and a small suburb. The fortress, built on a gentle rise, forms a square enclosed by palisades with wooden bastions. There are three guarded gates facing south, and east respectively. The principal public buildings within the fortress are a wooden church, the governor's house, the magazine of provisions, and the guard house. The fortress also contains a range of shops, a church, warehouses, barracks, and residential houses belonging to the Crown, and inhabited by the principal merchants. The suburb is surrounded by a wooden wall, reinforced by barbed wire entanglements; it consists of some 120 buildings, including a store house for rhubarb.

"Roads leading into town are fenced in by barbed wire to prevent the smuggling of cattle, on the export of which the Crown levies a substantial duty.

"The Russian garrison of Kiakhta, one company of regulars and a few Cossacks, is better armed, and looks more impressive than Chinese border guards. There have been no border clashes. The only dispute that arose—about who should occupy a dominating hill—was solved in a conference in favor of the Chinese."

The Chinese called their part of the town Maimatchin (Fortress of Commerce). It was encircled by a wooden wall, at spots only 140 yards away from the Russian citadel. It was much cleaner than Kiakhta; the houses were spacious, one-story buildings, plastered, whitewashed, and built around neat, graveled courtyards. Every house had a living room in which merchandise was put on display, a chamber, a kitchen, and a storeroom. Furniture was simple, but niches were covered with silk curtains, and artificial flowers stood on small lacquered tables. Heating installations were superior to those of the Russian town, and so was the water supply system.

Maimatchin had four public buildings; a governor's palace, two pagodas, and one theater. The theater was but a shed accommodating only the stage; audiences watched the show from the street outside. The larger of the two pagodas, next door to the theater, was the most elaborate building in town; it was surrounded by flower-adorned colonnades, resplendent with columns, and lacquered and gilded carvings, small bells, and numerous paintings. The temple contained five idols, the largest of which, four times the size of a tall man, represented Loo-ye, the First and Most Ancient God. Flanked by female figures, Loo-ye sat cross-legged on a pedestal, wearing a crown and a garment of rich silk. He held a tablet from which he seemed to read. To his left lay a bow; to his right seven golden arrows. On prayer days the Chinese presented the First and Most Ancient God—and promoter of their business—with cakes, pastry, dried fruit, and meats.

Foreigners were admitted to the temple but were not allowed to make offerings.

On solemn occasions the theater gave special performances in honor of the idol. The shows were usually satires, ridiculing corrupt officials and magistrates.

The governors did not mind the topic even though their appointments were punitive: only mandarins guilty of misconduct in office would be assigned to the poorly remunerative post. But the undaunted governors of Maimatchin augmented their meager earnings by collecting bribes from merchants who wanted special favors.

In his palace the Governor administered justice. In court he wore a crystal button and a peacock's feather as insignia of rank on his cap. Persons submitting applications, complaints, or petitions had to bend their knees and wait, kneeling, for his reaction. The Governor was also chief of the local police—ragged Manchu ruffians armed with clubs—and commander of the sloppy garrison.

Maimatchin (pop. 1200) was a city of men. No Chinese woman was permitted to stay in a place swarming with Russians. Men displayed amazing talents as housekeepers, but they did not enjoy celibacy. They all had business partners with whom they took turns of duty, up to one year. A relieved partner would take Russian merchandise to China, and when his relief term expired, he would return to the all-male city with Chinese goods. Caravans usually took fifty days for the trip.

The trade was on a strict barter basis. The Russian Government barred export of its coins, and the Chinese had no use for them. Their currency was bullion: mostly silver and rarely gold dust. Merchants carried adjusted scales to weigh the metal.

William Coxe describes the exchange of commodities: "After the Chinese factor [broker] has examined Russian merchandise in warehouses, the price is adjusted over a dish of tea, drunk from saucers. Then, both parties go to the warehouse; the goods are carefully sealed in the presence of the merchants, after which they repair to Maimatchin. The Russian chooses Chinese commodities, and leaves a person behind to assure that there is no fraudulent exchange; and, after delivery is made, he returns to Kiakhta with the merchandise.

"Various Chinese merchants learned to speak Russian, but even though they acquired a formidable dictionary, the Russians could never quite understand them. The Chinese accent was soft; they could not pronounce "R" and said "L" instead, and they interposed sequences of two consonants by a vowel."

The average Russian made no attempt at learning Chinese, and Russian interpreters preferred to converse with the foreigners in Mongolian, which was simpler and harsher in sound. Most Chinese merchants spoke Mongolian.

Even after a second barter town was established in Zurukaitu, the major part of Russo-Chinese trade concentrated in Kiakhta-Maimatchin.

In the mid-eighteenth century the annual turnover averaged four million rubles. According to statistics for the year 1772, one ruble purchased thirty pounds of beef or forty pounds of lamb in Kiakhta.

The Russians sold furs, cloths, hides, cattle, glassware, hardware, provisions, hounds, and even camels. Camels were supplied by intermediaries from Bokhara, which was not Russian territory then. The coarse cloths were made in Russia; finer materials came from England, France, and Prussia. Many furs originated in Siberia and the Aleutian Islands, but others came from Canada. Canadian skins, mostly beaver and otter, were sent to England and from there to St. Petersburg, and after touring most of the globe were bartered to customers at Maimatchin for approximately three times the price they would have fetched in London.

The Chinese prohibited export of raw silk, but encouraged export of the finished material. However, smugglers took care of the former, which went to Kiakhta in volume. Among the most profitable Chinese items of trade was tea. European connoisseurs found that tea leaves lost much of their flavor in sea transport, but that flavor was well conserved during caravan transportation. Chinese tea delivered in Kiakhta, and dubbed Russian tea, was consumed throughout the Western world.

The Chinese also delivered porcelain, fans, toys, tobacco, rice, rhubarb, dainty furniture, and boxes inlaid with mother-of-pearl, the latter of Japanese provenience. Porcelains were painted with Grecian and Roman deities to please Western customers whose taste, so the Chinese thought, had changed as little as their own during the past 1500 or 2000 years.

Some Chinese exports were not listed on Russian customs reports. They included a variety of choice poisons that could kill a person without leaving evidence a coroner could detect. It is said that Russian demand exceeded Chinese supplies.

Rhubarb had become a favorite drug in Europe. The Chinese Government objected to export of Cantonese rhubarb, the finest of its kind. But Bokharan merchants devised a procedure that made Canton rhubarb look like one of inferior quality. Russia, as always, lagged behind in European crazes, but the international rhubarb business was so remunerative that the government of St. Petersburg established a rhubarb monopoly. At Kiakhta rhubarb sold at 16 rubles a pood; in St. Petersburg it brought 65 rubles. Of 1360 poods imported in 1765, 1350 went abroad.

The Russian Government realized that monopolies and the collection of duties, the latter averaging almost 30 per cent, were infinitely more profitable than dilettantic trade ventures. In 1762, seven years after the last official caravan had arrived at Peking, Empress Catherine decreed that no more trade caravans should go to China. With the consent of China the privilege passed on to Russian private enterprise.

With the exception of one brief interruption in 1780, Kiakhta-Maimatchin remained the principal Russo-Chinese trading center until Russia regained its hold on the Amur and Ussuri rivers, concluded the first trade pact with Japan, and revised its trade policy toward the enfeebled Chinese Empire.

As the Mongolian language gradually became the main business idiom, Russian merchants hired Siberian Mongols as handy men, carriers, and interpreters. These Mongols were poorly paid and arbitrarily taxed. Meeting their kin from across the border, they learned that life under Chinese suzerainty was much better and easier than under the Tsar. Mongolian princes could collect only limited taxes; owners of twenty heads of cattle paid no more than one ram a year: owners of forty heads two rams. This was the ceiling beyond which taxation of cattle breeders could not go. Draft calls issued by Mongolian princes were subject to revision by the Chinese Governor General. Veterans were entitled to allotments of cattle and grazing land. Mongolian citizens could appeal to Chinese authorities against decisions by local authorities. Officials who transgressed their authority were subject to stiff penalties. The Chinese Governor General supervised the administration of law. No defendant could be forced to testify under oath on his own behalf, but such testimony was accepted from his superior or an older relative. Nobody got rich or all-powerful in Chinese-supervised Mongolia, but there was little destitution and no persecution. It would have been difficult for China to control a territory of one million square miles upon which less than one million people roamed, but equity worked miracles.

As Siberian Mongols got a glimpse of life under Chinese suzerainty, the trade road to the border turned into a sally port for refugees from Siberia.

Mongolia was the only land in which these fugitives could expect to make a living. They had neither the skills nor the linguistic capacities required in other regions of Southern Asia. They could not go north, where they would have starved in the tundra, or turn east, where Russian spearheads barred the path of migration once trod by mammoths and hunters; while turning west they would have run into the heart lands of their Iasak-collecting taskmasters.

Mongols flocked south from the Siberian districts of Tomsk, Yeniseisk, and budding Irkutsk in desperate defiance of Russian decrees. Governors organized posses, paid premiums for every migrant's head. The Russian administration asserted that the total number of refugees was trifling, a statement which may have been correct in so far as the total number of Mongols was small, but which does not reflect the anxiousness of Siberian natives to escape Russian domination.

The Peking government did not interfere with the migration, nor did the Chinese Governor General take any action. However, the Russians devised a retaliatory policy.

Agents, some under orders from the Board of Foreign Affairs in St. Petersburg, others directed by Siberian governors, and yet others acting on behalf of unknown wirepullers, went to Kiakhta, where they mingled with Mongols from Chinese-controlled territory. They told of paradisiacal conditions prevailing in Siberia, of justice, peace, and prosperity for all, and of the Tsar's particular care for his Asiatic subjects. They derided the corruption of the Chinese who bribed the princes, and emphasized the alleged iniquities common people suffered under Chinese tyranny. Only by rebellion against Mongolian princely pensioners, by overthrow of Chinese occupation authorities, and through incorporation of Mongolia into Siberia could the Mongols hope to enjoy the blessings of the Tsar's rule. The agents sang the praise of Russian domination while, practically within sight of their listeners, a thin trickle of its desperate victims defied barbed wire and rifle bullets to cross the border.

Absurd as it seemed, the propaganda was not entirely ineffective. There were fools who trusted glib, deceptive words rather than what their own eyes had beheld; there were mental perverts who either blamed their own troubles and shortcomings upon general circumstances, or expected personal profit from defection that spelled disaster for their fellow-men. Never throughout more than one and a half centuries of anti-Chinese propaganda did the Russians run out of Mongolian apostates. At first the Chinese discounted the matter, and when the Peking government eventually became alarmed it was no longer strong enough to stop it. But only in 1912, when the Chinese monarchy collapsed, did Russia establish control of Mongolian territory.

CHAPTER FORTY-FOUR

Chinese demand for furs stimulated Russian expeditions into the Bering Sea. They started in Kamchatka, about 3000 miles from the city of trade.

Shares of co-operatives were in rising demand. It did not affect the popularity of the investment that canvassing swindlers fleeced little people of their savings by selling them stock in non-existing companies. Authorities wormed their way into the promising business by charging fees for anything, ranging from cutting timber for ship construction to general licenses to land and hunt on territories which, as they claimed, came under their jurisdiction by the mere fact that Russian expeditions had set foot upon them.

Neither fraud nor coercion nor high risks could deter the Siberian adventurers from engaging in a trade that promised to be superlatively remunerative. How profitable the fur trade to Kiakhta actually was is difficult to ascertain; most of the co-operatives' records were destroyed.

One balance sheet, however, found its way into the *Journal of St. Petersburg*. It concerned the expedition of a boat, registered in the name of one Ivan Popov, which returned to Kamchatka on June 2, 1772. The venture had been financed by 55 shareholders, with an investment of 400 rubles per capita. After deduction of 10 per cent for customs duties each shareholder received 20 sea otters, 16 black or brown foxes, and 3 sea-otter tails, with a combined retail value of 800 to 1000 rubles. In addition they kept their share on a boat which was still seaworthy.

The "brown foxes" were, in fact, blue foxes, which change their coats with age and season.

An eighteenth-century report on Aleutian sea otters tells: "These animals are taken by striking them with harpoons as they sleep on their backs in the sea, by hunting them down in row boats, by surprising them in caverns, or by catching them in nets. The finest sort of fur is thick and long haired, of dark color with a delicate glossy hue."

Around 1790 sea-otter prices ranged as high as 400 rubles; sables fetched 20 rubles; ermine and fiery red foxes 15; wolves 12; and even the pariahs of the fur market, the black foxes from Bering Island, found buyers at 30 kopeks apiece.

At the turn of the century gems of Aleutian furs found their way to European Russia; Greek and Armenian traders delivered them to furriers who supplied a new mercantile aristocracy and knights of the stock exchange who paid the pelts' weights in gold to drape them around the bare shoulders of the most expensive women of a lavish period.

The first hunting ship to leave the mouth of the Kamchatka River was the *Eudokia,* commanded by Captain Michael Novodsikov of Tobolsk, Western Siberia. The *Eudokia* sailed on September 19, 1745, and returned on July 21, 1747. The proceeds of the trip were 320 sea-otter furs, cartographic sketches of Aleutian islands, and one captured native who had been duly baptized, and christened Paul.

The term Aleutian Islands was introduced by the Russians. It had never been used by the natives, who were split into several tribes. The Russians had trouble remembering the odd-sounding names, and called all natives Aleyuts, after one particular island.

Captain Novodsikov reported that he had collected almost a thousand furs, but that much of it had been lost in a storm that swept most of the equipment and cargo overboard. He had been forced to put to sea in threatening weather by a vicious attack by savage natives, who, he said, were brutal and treacherous people who had murdered twelve of his men without provocation; and not even the prisoner should be trusted, despite his conversion.

Paul was sent to Okhotsk for training as an interpreter. He learned Russian and gave his own version of Novodsikov's expedition:

A Russian landing party had visited the island to barter sewing needles against fowl, and tobacco against carved sticks; and when the natives wanted to detain them by seizing the rope fastened to the boat, the Russians fired muskets, killing two and injuring one. Next day the Russians assaulted a group of fifteen islanders. The natives fought back with bone spears, but they were routed, and two captives were taken. One of them, an old woman, was released, and returned to the Russian camp with a group of young girls who performed dances to the beat of a drum and slept with seamen. There weren't enough girls for the sex-starved crew and so a group of ten made for the natives' village to requisition more matable women. Husbands and fathers defended their womenfolk with spears, but Russian muskets scored another victory, fifteen men were killed and twenty women seized.

One Russian, the shareholders' trustee, wanted to have all natives poisoned with corrosive sublimate, but the people refused to swallow the concoction and the plan was eventually abandoned. After bartering two crude shirts against a canoe and all the furs the islanders possessed the Russians left, taking their prisoner along.

On the way to new hunting grounds the *Eudokia* ran into a violent storm. Several sailors drowned in the surf, most of the tackle and much cargo was lost, and eventually the boat cast anchor off a rocky island. Friendly inhabitants supplied survivors with food and shelter, and helpted patch up the vessel.

The Russians requested payment of tribute, and the islanders readily delivered furs. But when a sailor assaulted the chieftain's wife, the outraged population took up arms, and even though superior armament prevailed again, the Russians suffered some casualties.

The trustee, questioned about Paul's testimony, claimed that the extermination of natives by poison would have been justified by the islanders' refusal to surrender an iron belt.

It was the old, boringly repetitious story of Russian conquest, no different in the eastern seas from what it had been in Siberia. To the people affected, however, it was always new, always horrible, a new aspect of brutality even to men and women whose tradition was struggle for survival with no quarter asked or given.

In Siberia murder was a capital crime only if the victim was an official or the killer's superior. It was still a serious offense when the killed was a useful person or a citizen either of Russia or of a nation whose government granted protection to its traveling subjects, such as England or China. Murder became only a misdemeanor when it affected a useless man or a person of not respectable nationality. The Russian code of law did not explicitly say so, but this was the practice ruthlessly established by a Siberian administration pledged to adhere to the Russian law.

More ships sailed from Kamchatka into the Bering Sea, more atrocities were committed, more furs went to Kiakhta. Ships were lost, but they were not always destroyed by the elements. Mutinous crews and fraudulent skippers would take ships and cargo right into Chinese and possibly even into Japanese ports, sell them for whatever they would fetch, and never return to Russia.

In 1749, Emilian Yugof, a merchant from Yakutsk, applied for the monopoly of sea-otter hunting in the eastern seas. He claimed to own four large ships and sufficient funds to operate them efficiently. Concentration of business in his hands, he said, would give the authorities rigid control over the trade, assure collection of duties and fees, and keep unreliable elements and black-marketeers from interfering.

The chancery of Bolsheretsk, district capital in Kamchakta, charged 25 per cent of future earnings for passing the matter on, with recommendations, to the central administration in Irkutsk. The myriapod of Siberian administration stretched out hosts of paws for greasing, and Yugof tried promises. Officials wanted cash rather than bills due in a nebulous future. The applicant had excellent contacts in St. Petersburg. The subject came up in the Russian Senate, and the monopoly bill was passed without consultation with Irkutsk. Yugof had to pay a fee of $33\frac{1}{3}$ per cent, which included customs and all local levies.

A copy of the decree went to the Admiralty because the monopoly had something to do with shipping. A clerk put it into the file in which the account on Bering's voyage rested. Somehow an officer became interested in the affair.

Department heads were alerted, dust rose, and eventually the dormant document "Bering-Tshirikov" was resuscitated.

An express courier followed the Senate messenger, carrying an amendment to the monopoly decree: Yugof was ordered to take one Russian naval officer aboard each of his vessels; the officers would arrive in Kamchatka in due time.

Innocuous as it sounded, the amendment threw Yugof into panic. His flotilla consisted only of one sloop in need of repair, with a crew of thirty-one, most of them Kamchatkans. The mendacious claim of owning four big ships had been made to bolster his request for a monopoly; nobody in Siberia owned and operated such a flotilla. Siberian officials would not have bothered about such incongruities, but the Admiralty might take it amiss and all efforts might have been in vain.

A meeting of shareholders decided to gamble. "In due time," according to official terminology, could mean several years. The sloop *John* would sail at once; if they were lucky, the trip might yield sufficient furs to build the flotilla and construction could be completed before the officers arrived.

But on October 16, 1750, after only ten days of navigation, the rickety *John* ignominiously ran aground near Novi Kamchatskoi Ostrog. It took one year of wrangling with antagonistic local authorities who interfered with money raising and repair work until she left port again. The naval officers had not yet arrived.

They reached Kamchatka in the closing days of 1752, and were met by sneering local officials who told them that the Yugof project was a hoax, perpetrated upon Their High Excellencies in the capital, who would be well advised to leave decisions on Eastern affairs to competent Siberian experts. Nobody in Kamchatka, the officials said, had been deceived by Yugof's glib talk and extravagant statements. And the Crown had suffered previous loss; for the Yugof monopoly had upset regular hunting operations, and deprived the treasury of income from duties.

In fact the Yugof monopoly had not interfered with other sailings, and duties collected in Kamchatka never reached the coffers of the Crown. But Siberian authorities seized the opportunity to kill several birds with one stone: not only would they discourage further Senate intervention in lucrative Siberian affairs; they would also build the Yugof incident into a major corruption case. Discovery of Siberian scandals was long overdue. Yugof's monopoly provided a God-sent opportunity to expose an outrage out of which Siberian governors and *tshinovnitzi* would emerge pure as angels.

The navy men relayed the matter to St. Petersburg. Senators were dismayed; admirals insisted that with an adequate naval budget traffic in Far Eastern waters would have been purged of unreliable elements; civilian cabinet ministers noted proudly that the Siberian administration itself was sound. At Court ladies and gentlemen talked about the scandal and it could well be that Empress Elizabeth's interest in her subjects from Kamchatka was caused by the "Yugof affair."

The swindler was at sea, hoping for high profits, when he became the topic of conversation at Court. He died at sea, and was buried on Copper Island without ever learning what would have been in store for him in Siberia. The *John* returned in July 1754. Authorities ordered ship and cargo confiscated as a fine "for general misconduct of, and misstatements made by, its owner." The cargo was a rich prize: 755 old sea otters, 35 sea-otter cubs, 417 cubs of sea bears, and 7044 arctic foxes. Two substantial vessels could have been built from the proceeds. Yugof's business associates disclaimed knowledge of his fraud, and after much bickering and bargaining obtained a 40 per cent settlement of their claims. St. Petersburg received $33\frac{1}{3}$ per cent, in accordance with the voided monopoly contract; the rest went to the gentlemen in Irkutsk, who, with the blessings of the government, decreed that hunting trips to the eastern seas would have to be licensed henceforth. Siberian officials made handsome profits by issuing, or withholding, hunting charters.

Some officers of the Russian Navy, however, did not consider the case closed. After the passing of Peter the Great the Navy had turned into a stepchild of the Russian Crown, an object of slight to other powers. Trifling as Yugof and his monopoly had been, it showed the way toward a worthy objective of frustrated naval ambitions: the Bering Sea.

Even if the government of St. Petersburg could not compete, financially and technically, with other seafaring nations, in the waters of the east, it held an edge over Westerners which neither a hoard of gold nor technical skill could counterbalance.

Only Russia had naval bases on the coast of the Bering Sea; only Russia had a hinterland under its sovereign control; no other country had such resources on the spot as the Russians had in Siberia; St. Petersburg could turn the waters between Asia and America into a Russian lake, and the Aleutian Islands into a bridge linking Russian Asia and a new Russian America, and make Russia the ruler of the Eastern world.

The architects of the biggest castles in the air ever built showed no concern over the precariousness of communications between the capital and the Far Eastern realm, over the inadequate development of Siberian resources, the shortage of manpower, the primitivity of naval installations, and the Siberian mentality that would have sold St. Petersburg's world domination for one black fox from Bering Island. Ambitious admirals and foreign adventurers raved about opportunities; and because raving in Russia kept the captivated too strongly under its spell to allow them to do anything practical, nothing was done in St. Petersburg for the decade that followed the Yugof scandal.

Empress Catherine II had established herself on the Russian throne. The Seven Years War, which coincided with the French and Indian War, had come to an end, with Prussia emerging as a major power instead of being destroyed; and Poland, prostrate by the *liberum veto,* was on the verge of its first partition among Russia, Prussia, and Austria, to be followed by two more partitions that would temporarily wipe the country off the map. The *liberum veto* gave each member of the Polish Diet the power to prevent promulgation of any law; Russian agents had been bribing deputies into vetoing military appropriations and every vital administrative measure.

Catherine the Great was mainly concerned with grasping the lion's share of the spoils, but her Germanic imperialism being global, she would not disdain expansion in the East.

The heads of the Admiralty advocated continued exploration in the Bering Sea, and of the American continent. During the past decade many merchants had sailed the waters, explored islands, charted routes, and carried out measurements, but the top brass had taken no cognizance of such "amateurish findings." To the Admiralty, Steller's *Journals* were the most recent report on these areas, and any new expedition would have to start from where the Bering party had left off.

Four decades after the first Catherine signed her orders to Vitus Bering the second Catherine directed Captain Krenitzin to explore the eastern waters, islands and continents, and the people who lived there.

In July 1768 a new expedition left Kamchatka, the galiot *St. Catherine* and the hooker *St. Paul;* Lieutenant Levashev was Krenitzin's next in command.

The officers found that the "distant islands," as they summarized, were located farther to the south than Admiralty charts indicated, and that merchants' accounts of Copper Island were no tall tales; copper, washed up by the surf, littered the northeastern shores in such abundance that several large boats could be loaded without mining operations. Siberian fur hunters, however, would not waste cargo space on copper. An entry in the expedition journals reads: "Some trader might make a profitable voyage from the Copper Islands to China, where this metal is in demand."

The trip, hampered by poor visibility, continued toward the Fox Islands. Clear spells of three or four days were rare, while seas would be veiled in dense fog for weeks. The *St. Catherine* spent an uncomfortable winter in the straits of Unimak; the *St. Paul* wintered at Unalaska.

Navy specialists surveyed the islands of Alaxa, Unimak, Unalaska, rediscovering, for the benefit of the archives of St. Petersburg, what was known to every Siberian seaman.

The journals of the expedition tell of the natives and their dealing with the Russians:

"The natives are of middle stature; they have a brownish complexion and black hair. In the summer, the men wear *parki* (blouselike shirts) made of bird skins, over which, in foul weather, they throw *kamli,* cloaks made of whale's intestines. Their headgear consists of wooden caps adorned with vari-colored beads, small figures of bone or stone, duck feathers, and also ears of the animal *seivutcha* (sea lion). Through the gristle of their noses they put a bone four inches long or the stalk of a dark plant. On festive occasions, strings of beads are attached to bones or stalks. They thrust beads and bits of pebble into holes made in their lower lips; beads and pieces of amber adorn their ears. Their foreheads are covered by hair, cut just above the eyes. Some have the crown of their heads shaven like monks.

"The women's hairdo differs from that of man only in one respect: instead of letting their hair fall freely over their backs, as men do, women have it tied up in a knot. They dress like men, but their *parki* are made of fish skin.

"Natives paint their cheeks blue and red, they wear nose pins, and earrings, and strings around their necks and arms.

"However, their total neglect of cleanliness is utterly disgusting. Their bodies are covered with vermin, which they eat . . ." (Further details of their sanitary habits defy reproduction.)

"These people are extremely rude and savage . . . They engage in frequent bloody quarrels, and commit murder without inhibitions. In war, the victors carry off the women of the defeated. The people of Unimak constantly invade other islands. These islanders have neither religion, nor a rudimentary notion of God. They listen to fortune tellers, who claim to be inspired by *kugans* (demons). The fortune tellers wear wooden masks, and perform turbulent dances.

"Men have up to four wives who live in different huts. It is common usage to exchange wives or to sell them for a bladder filled with fat.

"They all hate the Russians, whom they consider ruthless invaders."

The *St. Catherine* and the *St. Paul* sailed back to Siberia in 1769 without making new discoveries.

The officers did not investigate Russian business procedures in the Aleutian Islands, but other records tell the story.

Merchants visiting the islands opened their operations by raiding villages and seizing children as hostages. Only afterward they displayed their wares: fox traps, beads, goads, wool, copper kettles, and hatches, and luxuries such as tobacco and brandy. The natives, in turn, brought furs for barter. They received but half the goods to which they were entitled under the deal; for the balance the Russians would hand them sheets of papers as receipts for a head tax, the meaning of which the islanders did not always understand. Objections were to no avail since the Russians held hostages. Russian gross profits averaged 10,000 per cent. The people of the Aleutians succumbed to the lure of hard drink and smoking. They went otter hunting instead of gathering food, and famine became the number-one killer on islands where fish, fowl, and edible roots abounded.

One Russian merchant reported famine in the Aleutians, but claimed that he and his countrymen were combating, not fostering, the tribulation. Actually Andrew Tolstyk from Selenginsk was more important as an explorer than official appointees. After making huge profits as a shareholder in various expeditions he formed a co-operative to exploit information received from dubious, but apparently well-informed, characters.

One Tunulgassen, they told him, ruled over wealthy lands between the Bering and Fox islands; he who could coerce Tunulgassen into submission could collect all the riches of his realm.

Tolstyk's ship, the *St. Andrew,* reached Attu in August 1761. Attu was part of Tunulgassen's domain, or, rather, it had been, for Tunulgassen was dead and his successor was Chieftain Bakuntun.

The Russians sent Bakuntun a few trifling presents and requested his visit aboard. But he pleaded poor health and delegated a substitute. The native spoke a halting Russian. He did not object when told that the island was under the suzerainty of the Empress and that tribute would be collected. He offered voluntarily, according to Tolstyk's journals, to supply the *St. Andrew* with food and canoes, and he told of fine fur-hunting grounds farther to the east. According to the journals, he volunteered to stay aboard until all deliveries were completed. But the Russians did not release him after their vessel was loaded.

The trip continued past Amchitka Pass to an archipelago that the skipper named after his vessel, Andrew Islands—Andreiovskie Ostrova. Six islands are specifically mentioned in the logbook: Kanaga, Ayagh, Tsetshina, Agalak, Amlak, and Atshu. "The inhabitants of these islands are tributary to Russia," it was recorded. "They dwell in subterranean cabins, and are so negligent storing food that they are often visited by famine. We taught them to catch codfish and turbot with bone hooks."

The journals are not consistent. The Russians never used hooks of bone. Such fishing implements were native-made, and had been used for time immemorial. Yet another paragraph blithely tells of dried salmon found in the subterranean cabins.

But Tolstyk gave a few trinkets to the natives, and admonished them to behave in a friendly manner toward all Russians, and to tell other tribes that friendliness toward Russians was everybody's duty.

The vaunted fur-hunting grounds were not as rich as the skipper had expected. The journals did not say what happened to the delegate of Chieftain Bakuntun, but the vessel never returned to Attu, and the Russian-speaking delegate hardly ever returned home.

The Andrew Islands—better known as Andreanof Islands—linked the Near and the Far Aleutians into one giant arc. Krenitzin later included Tolstyk's findings in his own report.

As often before in the history of Siberia, of which the Aleutian Islands had become an annex, the vanquished did not record history, and the epic of resistance against impossible odds would have remained untold had it not been for an occasional Russian protocol or foreigner's account that afforded a furtive glimpse of the struggle against invasion. Godless, aggressive, and immoral as the islanders may have been, they possessed a fundamental dignity bestowed by the Lord upon all human creatures, a dignity that revolts against extreme outrage.

In Siberia, where outrage had prevailed on and off for thousands of years, and where it had ruled in permanence since Mongolized Russian conquerors had come "as a cloud to cover the land," it was legal, if not decorous, to tread people of lower station underfoot. The abased could always vindicate himself by rising to a rank that would in turn enable him to brutalize fellow-men. The ship's officers belonged to a modest class and sailors were at the bottom of vulgarity. In the distant islands, however, they all were aristocrats, and natives were pariahs who had to atone for all iniquities the Russians had suffered at home. Retribution upon the innocent satisfied Russian vindictiveness, flattered the Russian's pride, and fanned Russian lasciviousness into murderous sadism.

Edicts, carrying the imperial seal, forbade the maltreatment of His or Her Majesty's new subjects, but such ukases were generally considered theoretical treatises by do-gooders in high office, who had no business interests in Siberia. However, Siberian governors showed some concern when maltreatment of natives resulted in a rebellion that injured Russian prestige.

In 1764 a Russian crew had been disgracefully chased away from an island, and authorities in Kamchatka took captain and sailors to answer.

The defendants included several Kamchadals. With obvious pride skipper and sailors told that they had not only seized all the children they could find, but also a score of women, two men, and three older boys. The hostages were treated in a manner designed to teach them respect of their captors. Fourteen women leapt into the sea in a futile attempt to escape. This indicated collusion and therefore the remaining natives, except one boy who was considered useful, were roped and thrown overboard. Islanders had been called to watch the execution; but instead of taking it as a warning against unruliness, the savages took up arms and staged a sneak attack that forced the Russians to leave with some loss of life and total loss of collected goods.

All defendants were acquitted.

Russian seizure of child hostages was frequently followed by killings. Yet another skipper's journal tells that the islanders themselves slaughtered their infants, drank their blood, or used it as glue to fix sharp points on their darts. One decade later an Englishman who ventured into the Aleutians branded this story as an invention by criminals bent on painting the islanders in the most hideous colors to hide their own infamy. He said that the blood found on darts was that of the men themselves, who struck their noses until they bled, to obtain cement for their weapons.

The closer the Russians came to the American mainland, the more the natives' resistance stiffened.

A Russian party descended upon an island near Unalaska, seized hostages, furs, food, and canoes. The natives indicated by gestures that they expected something in return. The invaders thereupon pulled out "tax receipts" and proceeded to force them down the savages' throats. One of the islanders struck a sailor, and the other sailors fired their muskets—"fiery arrows," the islanders called them—killing the offender and several other men. The victors built a winter hut and from there raided the island. Natives learned to use their knives and darts so quickly that the Russians had little opportunity to use their firearms. In a series of ambushes all Russians but one who had managed to hide were wiped out. Their muskets were captured by the natives, who apparently did not learn to use the fiery arrows. The lone survivor was later rescued by another Russian ship.

The journals of yet another boat, the *St. Vlodimir,* charge natives with murder and arson. Two Russian sailors who attempted to seduce girls were killed; "seducing a girl" was the Siberian term for rape. The natives burned down Russian huts. Their ambush of sailors who went to bathe in a hot spring was repulsed by alert musketeers, and in retaliation seven child hostages were put to death. "Finding ourselves in constant danger, we weighed anchor and sailed off," the journal stated.

Islanders in the vicinity of Alaska lived in communities of between 50 and 300, headed by *taigons* (magistrates) selected for their hunting and fishing skills and the large size of their families. The taigons organized resistance, but they would not attack without provocation. At first the landing itself was not considered as such; only if the parties committed outrage did the natives go into action. The island warriors had bows and bone-pointed arrows, spears, and darts, which they threw with great accuracy and at a fairly long range. They used *kuryaks,* wooden shields which offered no protection against Russian bullets. In close-quarter fighting, however, the natives gave a good account of themselves.

The inhabitants of Unimak and Unalaska, early Russian visitors related, "had no religion, but held soothsayers in high esteem. They had no regard for filial duties, and no respect for the aged; they followed all calls of nature in public without inhibition. But they were loyal to each other, cheerful, and lively. They met guests with friendly ceremonies, men beating drums and women performing dances. Visitors were treated to the finest food: wild lilies were the preferred delicacies. The islanders never fought for the sake of booty, but they were determined to avenge insult. Once visitors from Alaska came to a village at Unimak. They were well received by the taigon, whose son had a crippled hand; a boisterous Alaskan fastened a drum upon the boy's arm, and wanted him to dance like a woman. A bloody brawl ensued, and resulted in a prolonged feud between Alaska and Unimak."

The Russian invaders collected tribute, bartered corals for furs, and once requested that all taigons let their first-born attend classes in Russian. The magistrates brought their children to the assigned place, but instead of teaching them right on the spot the Russians carried them aboard ship. Desperate taigons waved "receipts" to prove that they did not owe taxes, offered ransom, pleaded, implored, but the children were not returned.

The ire of the natives knew no bounds. In rickety one-man canoes they rowed toward the cannon-equipped Russian craft to board the vessel. The naval battle resulted in the destruction of the canoes, but fury stirred ingenuity. The islanders used darts against sails and tackle with telling effect, threw missiles at landing parties before they could disembark, destroyed Russian supply dumps, and set grassland afire to smoke out entrenched enemies.

The ship whose commander had kidnaped the first-born of the taigons eventually got away with a greatly reduced crew, badly damaged rigging, and the victims still aboard. Several of its successors fared worse. Boats never returned to their bases; crews were decimated in battle or by starvation.

The islanders learned to build bigger canoes; men were trained for sneak boardings under cover of darkness. Russian firearms were captured, and, unlike the people of Aleutian Islands closer to Siberia, the natives did learn to use them.

Yet, more Russians kept coming, hunting hostages, extorting whatever they could get, and occasionally even bartering, for the natives' desire for corals was insatiable.

The Russians trained captured boys as saboteurs and traitors. They would release the indoctrinated youths somewhere along the coast, where they would pose as runaway hostages, spy upon their countrymen, and communicate their findings to the Russians by prearranged signals. The alleged runaways would set fire to native arsenals and damage canoes. When caught they were put to death by their countrymen, but they invariably trusted that they would be freed by the Russians before they could be executed.

Russian crews who landed in Unimak, Unalaska, and adjoining islands invariably reported having found remains of other seamen, some in grass-, earth-, or log-covered mass graves, others rotting in the open, near springs, or on hunters' tracks.

Resistance continued during the lifetime of a generation which had been of age when the Russians first came. But a new generation, decimated by casualties, enfeebled by starvation, plagued by diseases, accepted humiliation as a prize for precarious survival.

When the first Russians reached Unalaska the population numbered about 2500. Krenitzin put the figure at roughly 1000; it was down to less than 500 when resistance faded out.

The invaders suffered higher material losses in the Aleutians than they had while subjugating all of Siberia, and casualties were substantial. Yet as long as the price of otter was rising on continental markets, and as long as fur animals and forced hunters abounded on the islands, losses did not discourage the freebooters. In Siberia a human life never rated as high as an otter fur.

As the natives resigned themselves to their fate, they came to take the Russians for granted. People on neighboring islands vegetated under similar conditions. There seemed to be nothing worth hoping for.

Morbid people were of little use as hunters. As the yield of furs declined, the Russians moved on east to the Far West of the North American continent, to Alaska's more auspicious hunting grounds, abandoning the Aleutians to perpetual misery, which not even the end of their rule could remedy. Today the combined population of all Aleutian Islands is about 2000; less than that of Unalaska alone 200 years ago.

CHAPTER FORTY-FIVE Siberian Chutskis who rowed their canoes from the northeastern promontory of Asia eastward had called the continent beyond the straits Alakshak, meaning the "wide land." The first Russians who met the fierce aborigines may have thought that, since there could be no land wider than Siberia, the Chutskis were using their small craft for coastwise traffic only. As time went by, however, it must have become obvious to the invaders that Alakshak was located beyond the sea. But there are no records indicating whether and when Cossacks or *promyshleniki* visited the "wide land" prior to Deshnev's, or even Bering's voyages.

The Russian Government obtained its first official information on Alakshak by one Michael Gvodzev, a geodesist who was sent to Siberia to survey the regions of which Bering had told in a report on his first two voyages. Gvodzev claimed to have sighted Alakshak and to have established that it was part of America; but otherwise he was rather vague about his discovery, which occurred in 1730 or soon thereafter.

Officials were never too accurate in recording foreign names; somewhere on its way to the Russian state archives "Alakshak" became "Alaska."

The name remained unfamiliar even to Americans for several generations. When the U. S. Senate debated the purchase of Alaska, a survey disclosed that people thought of the territory in terms such as Walrussia, Zero Islands, American Siberia, and Icebergia, to name only a few.

The acquisition of the 586,400 square miles of Alaska on March 30, 1867, was the largest real estate transaction in history, dwarfing the Louisiana Purchase, which had involved only 48,506 square miles. The price of $7,200,000, roughly 2 cents per acre, was considered high by objectors to the bill, and three years later Karl Marx sneered that Alaska was not worth one penny economically. This appraisal turned out to be as unsound as most other estimates and prophecies made by the co-author of the *Communist Manifesto*. Between 1880 and 1922, Alaskan mineral production was valued at $486,-725,813, while between 1868 and 1921 fisheries and fur hunting accounted for a gross income of $540,000,000,

A last-minute snag caused by fussiness almost kept the deal from materializing. When the cable company presented its bill for telegrams exchanged in the course of negotiations, the Russian Government insisted that it would not pay for it, and angry Americans objected to their treasury footing the bill. Eventually the cable company granted a discount, and the United States paid the reduced charges. The formal surrender of the territory took place in Sitka, on October 18, 1867, and with the lowering of the Russian flag and the hoisting of the Stars and Stripes, "American Siberia" had passed out of existence.

Had it not been for the discount on the cable bill Alaska might have remained Russian. After the misplacement of the Deshnev file in Yakutsk this trifling incident again interfered with Russia establishing herself permanently on the American continent.

The Russians have a valid claim to priority in Alaska over other European nations and American settlers, but the aborigines of Eastern Siberia have known the "wide land" for time immemorial and are in all likelihood the distant ancestors of Alaskans.

English, Spanish, and French explorers sailed in Alaskan waters in the eighteenth century and Captain James Cook's expedition to find a northwest passage linking the Atlantic and Pacific oceans produced more information on the American west coast than any single Russian voyage on record.

Lord Sandwich, head of the British Admiralty, secured the assignment for Captain Cook in 1776. The record of the then forty-eight-year-old Cook, a native of Marton Village in Yorkshire, included voyages to Tahiti, New Holland (Australia), and New Zealand, the rounding of Cape Horn and the Cape of Good Hope, a distinguished survey of the coasts of Newfoundland and Labrador. Cook left England on June 25, 1776, with two ships, the *Resolution* and the *Discovery*. He reached the Cape of Good Hope on November 30, and in the following February found the Hawaiian Islands, which he called Sandwich Islands to honor his patron. This was not a new discovery, however. The Spaniard Gaetano is said to have sighted Hawaii as early as 1555, but his report had not been released by the Spanish Government.

Continuing his voyage, Cook reached the American west coast at a latitude of 44°55′ N, still within the present area of the U.S.A. He sailed north as far as the Icy Cape, latitude 70°41′. His records and maps were not yet completed when he made another voyage to the Sandwich Islands, where he met violent death at the hand of natives in February 1779.

His findings were considered authoritative in St. Petersburg despite a few influential quacks still holding out for the long-disproved theory that Siberia extended thirty degrees farther to the east than it actually did. Cook was the first to measure the width of the Bering Strait.

Cook touched Kiska. He found and named Cross Sound, Cape Fairweather, Controller Bay. He landed on Kayak Island and continued to Nutshek Bay (Port Etches), Cape Hinchinbrook, and Montague Island in Prince William Sound. Rounding Cape Yelizaveta, he explored an inlet—Cook Inlet—of which he first believed that it was the gateway to the Northeast Passage. Next he followed the shore line of Alaska Peninsula, touched Unalaska and Dutch Harbor, turned north through Bristol Bay and Norton Sound, and eventually to Bering Strait. His trip farther north was stopped by heavy ice floes twelve feet high, which looked like a frozen continent. Sailing west, he reached the Siberian coast on a promontory which he called Cape North.

Not everybody in England was pleased with Cook's statement that there was no navigable link between the Atlantic and the Pacific oceans. Eventually George Vancouver was assigned to check Cook's report, and to investigate whether a shipping lane between the two oceans did exist south of the Bering Strait. Vancouver left home in 1791, reached Portland Canal in 1793, surveyed Alaskan coastal waters, made a number of additions to, and a very few slight changes on, Cook's maps, and reiterated that a passage between the Atlantic and Pacific did not exist.

Vancouver's and Cook's trips, as well as Alexander Mackenzie's crossing of the North American continent in 1793, were considered a basis for English claims to all of Northwestern America. However, no attempt was made to enforce this claim when the Hudson's Bay Company extended its trade zones, and the Russian-American Company, chartered in 1799 in Russia, broadened its sphere of interests toward the interior of Alaska.

The United States, emerging from the struggle with England as a new, ambitious nation, did not interfere in the early race for the northwestern part of the continent, which was more difficult to reach than Europe and Africa. The only indications of possible early U.S.-Alaskan traffic were two Massachusetts coins which an explorer found worn as earrings by an Alaskan in 1791. American whalers were the first ships known to have carried the Stars and Stripes to Alaskan waters. In 1821 the Russian Government issued a decree banning foreign shipping from the Bering Sea. Washington joined London in a sharp protest, and the decree was abrogated. This controversy did not result in an increase of U.S. shipping in the Bering Sea, but it led to the establishment of boundaries not previously fixed between Russian America and Canada by a convention signed in 1825.

France, unable to keep its hold on Canada after 1763, and desperately short of funds, waited until 1785 to dispatch an expedition to explore the new territories. In August of that year Captain La Pérouse left Brest under instructions to visit the Aleutian Islands. Ten months later he arrived on the Alaskan coast, near Mt. St. Elias. Instead of surveying the Aleutians he searched for a passage to Hudson Bay, failed to find it, and returned to France with a batch of costly furs. Another Frenchman, Etienne Marchand, followed La Pérouse, his main concern being China trade. Louis XVI, unfortunate King of France, did not attempt to annex territory on or off the American Northwest.

Spaniards from Mexico had had a head start over James Cook. Juan Pérez sailed in 1774, touched the Alaskan coast near Prince of Wales Island, and in 1775, another Spanish ship, commanded by Juan Francisco de Bodega y Cuadra, sighted land near Mt. Edgecumbe and visited various points of Alexander Archipelago, which Cuadra pronounced annexed in the name of the King. Four years later he returned as second-in-command of a larger boat and annexed the southern section of Kenai Peninsula. In 1788 two Spanish expeditions visited Kodiak, found it settled by Russians, continued to Unalaska, and took possession of the island on behalf of the Spanish Crown.

But the Spanish Crown did not confirm the annexations, and the Spanish Viceroy of Mexico limited himself to a vague approval of exploring activities. Spanish settlers refused to pioneer in the rough north, and merchants showed no intention of operating from bases not under Spanish sovereignty. Eventually the Viceroy announced that there would be no further voyages. This was the end of Spanish infiltration of Alaska and the Aleutians.

English, Spanish, and French expeditions stirred Russian official interest in Alaska, and eventually the habitual pattern of individual, overlapping irruption changed into a centralized, authorized, but no less rapacious scheme of conquest.

In the fall of 1763, when a boat from Kamchatka opened the procession of Russian expeditions investing Alaska and outlying islands, procedures were still according to tradition. Stephen Glotov, the skipper who became notorious as one of the worst tormentors of the people of the Fox Islands, requested that the natives of Kodiak produce boy hostages and pay tribute. Kodiakans refused to comply. Russian landing parties went ashore, where they treated islanders turning up in groups from five to thirty, with "kindliness, but also with proper circumspection." The captain's journals tell of finding summer huts covered with high grass, in which only men were found; women and children had been evacuated.

Russian demands, and what was labeled "circumspection," obviously infuriated the men of Kodiak, and on October 1 a flotilla of canoes attacked the Russian ship. The canoes were repulsed by musket fire, and several bundles of hay, stuffed with sulphur and dried birch tree bark, found outside the Russian accommodations ashore were not set aflame in time to smoke the invaders out.

Four days later the islanders showered the Russians with a hail of arrows, but retreated under Russian musket fire.

On October 26, the journals say, the alarm bell aroused the crewmen, who slept with their muskets within reach. Seventeen large and several small canoes were seen ashore, and groups of natives cautiously advancing toward the craft. The groups were covered by mobile breastworks made of three rows of stakes "placed perpendicularly, tied together with seaweed, and with osiers twelve feet wide and about half a yard thick." Each screen shielded between thirty and forty men armed with bone lances. Archers flanked the groups. As Russian sailors raced to their stations, arrows hit the deck, and from the rear a solid formation of warriors came up, wielding wooden shields, and swords made of the jawbones of whales. Russian bullets failed to pierce the screens. However, the journals boast of signal victory, that of repulsing the natives and preventing them from embarking and carrying the attack to the Russian ship.

The Kodiakans refused trade throughout the winter. On April 4, 1764, however, to believe Glotov, four islanders called at the Russian winter hut. They displayed large fox skins, and inquired what they might get in return. The natives disdained shirts and nankeen, but could not restrain their enthusiasm at the sight of glass beads, and eventually the Russians did a thriving business bartering foxes and sea otters against beads. Except for one sentence Glotov's journals would indicate an idyl of trade. This sentence, however, discloses that "some natives were persuaded to pay a tribute of skins, for which receipts were issued."

The natives told of people who lived on the continent of which the skipper saw the wooded coast line, but he did not continue his voyage beyond Kodiak.

Glotov's description of the people of Kodiak indicates that they were outwardly not much different from those of the Aleutians; they sported the same adornments of lips and noses, but they wore stockings of reindeer skin, unknown to Aleutian tribes. They called their wooden shields *kuryaks,* a Greenlandish term for small canoes. The large Kodiak canoes were reminiscent of similar craft used in Greenland. The natives called themselves *Kanagists,* the word bearing resemblance to *Karalits,* as Greenlanders and Eskimos on the coast of Labrador had been named. (The Russians soon mangled Kanagist into Konaghi.)

The Kodiakans produced small carpets interwoven with beaver wool; they sheared otter skins with sharp stones, which made them look like velvet. The ornaments of their caps were highly artistic and they used a red hair dye that the Russians could but admire.

The fauna of Kodiak included ermines, martens, beavers, river otters, wild boars, wolves, and, to judge from tracks, also large bears.

Records kept by Russian hunters, traders, and buccaneers who roamed the approaches to the American continent were scientifically inconclusive, and sordid in their profligate descriptions of dealings with natives.

The combined information they produced in half a century was less abundant than James Cook's fragmentary report on the American northwest coast. Captain Billing, a Russian navy man who had joined the English expedition, warned Russian authorities about the possible consequences of Cook's account. Since Canada had been incorporated in the realm of the King, England might occupy neighboring Alaska before the Russians could establish control of the wide land.

St. Petersburg studied the matter; again files piled up ceilingward and begot other files dealing with projects that had no immediate bearing upon Alaska. In Irkutsk, however, reaction was faster and more to the point. The Governor General of Siberia, Lieutenant General Jacobi, did not want to see the wide land lost to efficient foreigners. He realized that makeshift operations, such as were under way in the Bering Sea, could subdue and exploit savages, but that only well-organized action could protect the Russians against being outmaneuvered by more civilized rivals. Jacobi was an enterprising man with strong business acumen, and he knew the right people. The "right people" were people who had money and were secretive about their dealings with authorities.

In 1782 the American company was constituted in Siberia, with funds adequate to build three galiots, arm them with cannon, hire and equip 190 officers and able-bodied seamen, and cover operating expenses for several years. Nothing was disclosed about the personal benefits the Governor General derived from the operations, but Jacobi issued a charter granting the company extensive privileges of trade, and administration of discovered territory. The term monopoly was purposely avoided.

The Governor General's first written orders to the company's trustee Shelekov and chief factor Delatov were to sail along the coast of America, to explore new islands, to bring the natives "under Russian domination, and to secure the newly discovered part of America to the Russian Empire by creating, and using, tokens with the Russian Coat of Arms, and proper inscriptions."

The tokens were copper plates with a relief of the coat of arms, which the explorers were directed to bury in the ground, erecting crosses at the spot, with the inscription "Russian Imperial Territory."

Village elders and chieftains were to be notified that the Sovereign of All the Russians solemnly pledged herself to protect the inhabitants of her distant lands, and that in grateful recognition of Her Majesty's pledge and as a token of loyalty they would have to wear replicas of the coat of arms on their outer garments. No stranger would be permitted to injure Her Majesty's people.

But Russians were no strangers in the Empress's realm and felt free to injure Her Majesty's compulsory new subjects.

Governor General Jacobi's initiative was well timed. In 1785 a British brig carrying twelve guns and a crew of seventy-seven arrived in Avacha. Captain William Peters presented a letter from the British East India Company to Baron Stengel, Governor of Kamchatka, expressing the company's intention to do business in the Bering Sea. But by then the chartered American Company was already operating, and Captain William Peters was not encouraged in his endeavors.

Dutch vessels also appeared off Alaska, but left without doing noticeable business.

The first expedition of the American Company arrived at Kodiak in August 1784. Natives went aboard the galiots, behaved in a friendly manner, and offered furs for barter, but their attitude changed abruptly when Shelekov's Aleutian interpreter explained that the Russians had come to settle on their island. The Konaghis expressed determination to resist invasion, and their spokesman indignantly refused to accept a bribe.

That night the interpreter swam ashore to reconnoiter, and logbooks tell that he found inhabitants from neighboring islands gathered to assist the people of Kodiak, and that they were set to attack the Russians, to massacre those who resisted, to reduce the others to slavery, and to share the spoils.

It was unusual for islanders to come to each other's assistance, and slavery was an unknown institution in Kodiak, but Shelekov claimed that the natives' conspiracy warranted an action of which the logbooks tell:

"In order to strike the Konaghi with extreme terror, I ordered the gunnery to aim at dwelling places. Broadsides of Russian two-pounders smashed huts and killed inhabitants; darts thrown by natives fell short of the ships. We captured the rock, and took more than 1000 prisoners.

"To impress the captives with our superiority, and to spread the fame of what they called our 'fiery arrows,' I had a hole drilled in a big boulder, charged it with gun powder, had a match cord laid and kindled, and as the explosion scattered the boulder, a general discharge of artillery and musketry added to the commotion."

The dejected natives were submitted to "education" on the spot. The interpreter declared that protection by the gracious Empress would henceforth bring them peace and security; that Russia was great, strong, and serene; and that enlightened Russian science could explain phenomena which they, in their crude ignorance, had considered of a divine nature.

"I used every means to assure them that they would be blissfully happy if they obeyed our gracious Empress, but that they would be severely punished if they were recalcitrant," Shelekov recorded.

The captive men, women, and children were guarded by Russian sailors and by natives who turned collaborators and informers. Men were put to work for their captors, women were utilized in the usual way, and whenever adults escaped, children were disposed of as hostages. Never had the natives worked as hard for themselves as they were forced to work for the Russians; hardly ever had they been so poorly fed; and they experienced confinement for the first time in their history.

The modern vernacular would call the stockades of Kodiak concentration camps. Prison stockades were spreading all over Siberia, and the Russians considered it only natural to establish them in new territory.

Americans were the first foreigners to suffer the horror of that Siberian institution.

From a fortified encampment on Kodiak, Russian settlers controlled all areas in which the ominous copper tokens had been buried. A steadily growing staff of informers told the Russian commander of every gathering on islands, of every manifestation of discontent, of every indication of conspiracy. Suspects were questioned, and Shelekov noted that "most of them confessed their guilt."

In 1787, Shelekov left Kodiak for Okhotsk, but the Russian settlement on the island remained, and nothing changed in the treatment of the Konaghis. His report does not tell when and where he visited the American mainland, but it mentions observations made among natives of interior districts:

"They have no notion of deity, and even though they claim that there are two spirits in the world, the spirits of good and evil, they do not make likenesses of them and they do not adore them. Sorcery and divination, however, are held in high esteem. They have no code of law, they are extremely choleric, particularly the women; they are enterprising, malicious, and resentful of injury, even though they may appear gentle and meek. Due to the brief period of observation, no final opinion could be formed as to their veracity and integrity. They are lively and thoughtless, careless and riotous, negligent of economic matters, which often causes them to suffer from hunger and nakedness."

The Russian tendency to insult those upon whom they have inflicted injury is the mainspring of this characterization. Other contemporary accounts on the Konaghis tell of their habit to lift their faces skyward when making solemn pledges, indicating that the Alaskans did have a deity: the sky, like the Mongols.

On May 10, 1788, the Russian galiot *Three Holy Fathers* anchored at a latitude of 60°8'50", at Prince William Sound. A party went ashore to bury the portentous copper plate and erect the cross with the inscription "Russian Imperial Territory."

This was the first recorded official act of annexation on the American mainland. Later Russian scouts found an inscription carved into a tree: "John Etches of the Prince of Wales, May 9th, 1788, and John Hutchins." An English boat had visited the spot, but the skipper did not claim land in the name of the King.

The skipper of the *Three Holy Fathers* buried copper plates on various unpopulated islands, and on May 28 returned to the site of his first landing, where he found six natives who had furs for barter, and whose leader, a grave-looking middle-aged man who gave his name as Atasha, accepted the fateful badge. "Atasha's brother is Taigon of a place called Tshitik," the logbook recorded, "and he will deliver the badge to his brother."

The Russians called the shore Tshugatsk, and the Empress's new subjects the Tshugasks.

One Tshugask was held in custody, but escaped later, when the vessel anchored near Montague Island. The local *taigon* (magistrate) was called upon to help hunt the fugitive, but refused to comply, and even "treacherously assaulted" the landing party—six men armed with muskets—with a concealed spear. The logbook tells that the taigon was killed in the ensuing struggle.

In June the galiot entered Yakutat Bay. Large wooden canoes, each manned by fifteen natives, met the ship. Some natives wore furs of the sea otter, sable, marmot, and glutton; others were clad in "European garments." They were affable and prone to barter, but their mercantile practices shocked the Russians. "They had no settled rules of trade," the journals complain. "They were extremely covetous, and wanted special gifts for every regular exchange. Clothing, objects of iron, kettles, and stills were in demand; they did not care for beads even though they did like earrings of coral. The natives were accompanied by their wives and children; they offered to sell skins and tails of otters and beavers, garments made of fur, woollen clothes of their own manufacture, and also purses of grass and filaments of roots."

The Russians were not the first foreigners to enter Yakutat Bay. An English trader had been there only a short time before and more foreigners would keep coming, English, Spaniards, and other people of Caucasian race. They were not inhibited by decency, morality, and honesty; they too would seize hostages, cheat and brutalize natives, but cruelty to them was not an objective in itself. They would just try to get as much as possible in return for as little as possible, and leave for good afterwards.

Ilshak, taigon of the Koliuskis, as the people of the bay were called, was taken aboard the *Three Holy Fathers*. He was shown portraits of the Empress and the successor to the Russian throne, and was subjected to a lecture on the importance of the two illustrious personalities, the number of their subjects, upon whom their all-powerful masters lavished their blessings, and how fortunate the Koliuskis were to partake of these blessings and live in peace and security ever after.

It would have been well nigh impossible to translate the grandiloquent address into the natives' idiom, but the Russians were satisfied that Taigon Ilshak understood it all. When he called again, he was handed an engraving of the heir to the throne, with an inscription in German and Russian.

Thus read this first document of Russian annexation in America:

"His Imperial Highness Paul Petrovitch, successor to the throne of All the Russians, Sovereign of the Duchy of Holstein.

"In June 1788, the factor of the Company of Golikov and Shelekov, the pilots Gerassim Ismaelov and Dimitry Betsharov of the galiot *Three Holy Fathers,* with a crew of 40 men have engaged in considerable traffic with Taigon Iltshak and his subjects, the Koliusky, and have received them under the protection of the Russian Empire. In memory of this event, said taigon had received a Russian Coat-of-Arms, and the engraving of His Imperial Highness, successor to the Russian throne. All Russian and foreign ships sailing to this place are hereby ordered to treat this Taigon with cordiality, without, however, omitting necessary precautions. Said factor, pilots and crewmen, while at anchor here from June 11 to June 21, experienced nothing but friendly behavior."

The taigon behaved in a friendly manner when he offered the Russians an iron image of a crow's head. The crow was the sacred animal of the Koliuskis.

To believe the logbooks, the natives claim to have descended from the crow. They invoked the bird in magic incantations, and told of having been assisted by crows when in distress.

But even though the annexation document emphasizes Koliuski friendly behavior, the logbooks note that "these people have crude manners and are addicted to stealing."

Other entries tell of the natives' dwellings, garb, and habits:

"The outside of their scattered habitations is made of earth, the inside of wood. The top is covered with the bark of fir; a square opening serves as a chimney. The buildings are supported by four poles 4 feet 8 inches high, and by cross beams. Instead of a door, they have apertures covered with mats.

"The Koliusky resemble the Konaghi. Their complexion is brown, but some of them are fair. The men tie their hair in knots, dye it red, and adorn it with feathers. They cut their beards, and paint their faces with varicolored stripes. They perforate their ears but not their lips. Some wear caps adorned with brass ornaments, apparently purchased from Europeans. The way they carry their headgear reminds of European grenadiers. Their necks are covered with cloth, woven from filaments of roots; the backparts are ornamented with eagle's feathers. Their upper garments are thrown over their shoulders, and they occasionally wear aprons, like the Siberian Tunguses. Their arms are bows, arrows, and darts with points of stone. Beaks of birds of prey, mostly eagles, are used to harpoon seals and sea-otters, and occasionally also to catch fish. The Koliusky women part their hair with wooden combs, slit their lower lips and insert pieces of wood 2 inches long and shaped like spoons. They make five and six holes in their ears, and some also tattoo their chins. Natives carry iron heads of crows as charms. They burn their dead, put the ashes in a chest, and suspend it on poles."

Landing parties of the *Three Holy Fathers* went inland, erecting annexation crosses and burying copper plates as they proceeded. They distributed badges among elders and collected good-will presents in the name of the Empress. Had it not been for an outbreak of scurvy aboard ship the expedition would have continued for a long time. But the dreaded epidemics forced the skipper to sail to Okhotsk. Hardly was the galiot in port when merchants kept arriving to inspect the American merchandise. Siberian officials also showed a more than formal interest in the imports. Not even the charter granted by the Governor General would prevent subalterns' preying upon the proceeds of company trade, which, to judge from the samples collected by the men of the *Three Holy Fathers,* would be lucrative enough to take care of many greedy hands.

In the summer of 1789, shortly after the return of the explorers' galiot, a mission from St. Petersburg headed by Captain Billing arrived in the east, to supplement Captain Cook's findings.

Billing paid no attention to the mercantile excitement in Siberia, but made his ships, the *Glory of Russia* and the *Good Intent,* ready for sail, and left port before the year drew to a close, very much to the relief of all concerned. His expedition produced no important results, and its journals do not deal with furs, copper plates, and glass beads.

The American Company had been successful in recruiting settlers for the Aleutians and Alaska. The fabulous resources of Siberia were hardly tapped in two centuries of Russian exploitation, and yet the fertile vastness could not fully support the relatively small number of immigrants who all wanted to harvest, but who either did not know how to sow or were given no proper opportunity to do it. Since the 1740s recurrent famines raked Eastern Siberian promyshleniki, Cossacks, and adventurers. Government storehouses were looted and looters, in turn, ambushed by lawless late-comers, and more supplies were lost in riots than reached the needy. Peasants joined the outlaws; they would abandon their farms rather than see them plundered and burned down by marauders.

The American Company offered land beyond the seas. The former peasants enlisted eagerly, as did promyshleniki, who would go wherever industrious people went, to live on refuse and spoils. Agents told of fabulously rich territories to be sold for a share in the net proceeds. Applicants had to own basic equipment. The applicants were destitute, but company agents delivered anything on credit from boots to guns, payable out of future income.

Contract forms mentioned many dues deductable from the farmers' income, such as navigators' fees, church dues, special payments to foremen, and contributions of a variety of funds. The figures were presented in fractions too complicated to conceive, even by people who might still be able to solve simple arithmetical problems with the abacus. Applicants asked no questions, but put three crosses under the document, said *"Boze pomoshtsh"* (Gold helps), as they were told, and never got out of the red in the company books.

The company was the only agency that could buy and sell commodities, and it cheated settlers at every turn. Nevertheless the new territory was Lubberland for the Russians. The promyshleniki set the tune, and the peasants quickly understood that, even as slaves of their creditors, they were still masters of the natives. Natives built accommodations for their new taskmasters; native men were put to work and hunt, native women served as housemaids. This was a life to the Siberian heart, and those who were not all too indolent could even do some business stealing trinkets from company storehouses and bartering them against furs. In periods of famine among the natives they could sell at fabulous prices some of the food the natives had been forced to gather for the Siberians.

However, this state of affairs seemed threatened by Englishmen doing business with Russian America, regardless of the inimical attitude of Siberian governors.

Grigory Ivanovitsh Shelekov, of the American Company, noticed the threat at an early stage. Shelekov was illiterate. He seems to have started as a promyshlenik, but he was a genius in his own right. He did not propose to remedy Russian abuses, but he intended to undersell foreign competitors on regular markets. The English, he told the Governor General, would get American furs and ship them to Canton, China, the East India Company would have a hand in the trade, and the French might also interfere. The American Company would be free to supply China by sea. Trade via Kiakhta was burdened by prohibitive overhead and agents' profits.

At first the Governor General did not believe in foreign infiltration in the business.

However, the traffic which Shelekov had predicted started as early as 1785, when Captain Hanna, an Englishman, acquired 500 American sea-otter furs and sold them in Canton. In the following year two English vessels from Bombay sailed to Alaska; they too did business with Canton, with a then fabulous net return of $24,000. In 1788, 6643 sea otters from America reached Canton by sea. The English were agents of the East India Company, but when some skipper felt short-changed, he would simply hoist another flag and deal on his own account. They introduced new, tempting items in the barter: vessels of tin and copper, a great variety of hardware, flashy clothing, and even firearms. Etienne Marchand, the Frenchman who saw the weapons, contends that most of them were not in working order, but this the natives did not seem to mind. Trying to outdo the English, Marchand offered the Alaskans French sailors' uniforms in exchange for furs. When he left Alaska, he was acclaimed by an enthusiastic crowd of natives dressed up as French navy men, waving at the crew, which, deprived of their uniforms, wore Alaskan garb, including eagles' feathers.

One circumstance in the early 1790s, which not even Shelekov could have foreseen, caused the Peking government to ban the import of fur to Chinese ports. An avalanche of skins, mostly seal, poured into Canton from South America: Chile, the Falkland Islands, and Tierra del Fuego. This caused a drain on China's bullion too strong even for a financially sound economy. For some time Kiakhta remained the only major place of entry for furs.

However, Shelekov did not wait for unforeseeable events to help his business. In 1788 he suggested to the Governor General that the company charter be amended to include a trade monopoly in Alaska, and that company trustees receive delegated sovereign powers to maintain the monopoly against everybody regardless of nationality.

Jacobi no longer thought that Shelekov's various misgivings were unjustified, but he had misgivings of his own: only the Empress could delegate sovereign powers; once the matter was referred to the Crown, it was out of his hands forever, and the clever company manager might discontinue bribes. The Governor General contended that regulations prohibited his taking the initiative. Only should the Empress request a report on the matter would he submit the charter to Her Majesty.

Jacobi trusted that the crude and ugly man would never find a way to interest St. Petersburg in his affairs.

But Shelekov's partner, Ivan L. Golikov, was a presentable-looking man who knew his way around offices in the capital. He would go to Europe and present Her Majesty with an account of Shelekov's travels and the noble doings of the company.

A scribe from Irkutsk drafted the document, a compilation of wild exaggerations, dubious claims, and extravagant self-praise, couched in terms of patriotic servility: "Without the approval of our Monarch," one passage read, "my labors could not satisfy me, nor would they be of any importance to the world. The object of all my undertakings remains to add to the glory of our wise Empress, and to secure profits for Her. Natives of newly discovered lands and islands were awe-stricken on being duly told of Her Majesty's kindness, greatness, wisdom, and magnanimity by Her unworthy, though fanatically devoted, servants. They wooed to express their loyalty to the gracious ruler whose picture has a magical effect upon them. The number of new subjects is legion; up to 50,000 live on a single island; explorers have found scores of islands, not to speak of the American mainland. The Company is incorporating territories into the Empress' realm before other powers can invade them, and it trades for the benefit of the Treasury. But it would not be in the spirit of Her Majesty to pursue such aims without also taking care of the spiritual advancement and the promotion of civic virtues of people previously deprived of the blessings of law and religion."

Supplements to the epistle quoted directives allegedly issued to members of the staff of the company, such as: "You should explain to the natives the benefits derived from our laws and institutions; you must tell them that the faithful will be protected, but that the wicked shall feel the strength of our Empress' arm. . . . You must teach them to build houses, to be economically-minded and industrious. Schools shall teach native children to read and write. The sacred scriptures of our Church shall be translated into their language. . . . Meticulous order and discipline must be maintained among our officers and men; we cannot ask natives to adhere to rules which we do not, ourselves, obey. . . . All traffic must be carried out honestly; disputes shall be settled by arbitration; hostages and native workers must be well treated. Native women shall never be compelled to enter houses in which Russian men live."

Thirty years after this document was drafted a Russian captain denounced it for its barbarous style, for its stupidity and falsehoods. But the captain did not take the mentality of the late Empress into account. Such style and stupidity appealed to Catherine the Great, who, through a lifetime of intrigue, treachery, violence, and debauchery, had conserved a taste for phony dime-novel virtue.

When Golikov arrived in St. Petersburg, Catherine was on an inspection trip arranged by her favorite, Prince Potemkin, the legendary trickster who had thriving villages painted on stage props to make the Empress believe in the prosperity of her land. The visitor from Siberia was advised to present his papers to Catherine while she was en route. He caught up with the imperial party at Kursk, Southern Russia. Catherine liked both the script and the handsome man who prostrated himself while presenting it. She told Golikov to call his partner to the capital for introduction at Court, and ordered the Imperial College of Commerce to investigate the activities of the American Company.

The Governor General was shocked at the college's request, but tried to make the best of the new situation. Politely he asked Shelekov for a copy of his script, wished him the best of success in the capital, and settled down to draft an "opinion" that would satisfy and oblige all concerned. He explained that there could be no doubt of the veracity of Golikov's and Shelekov's report; it would be just recognition of the company's achievements to grant exclusive rights of hunting and trading; it would be advisable to entrust administration of the new territories to a man who put the interests of humanity above personal advantage. He did not say, however, who this paragon of duty was; if the College of Commerce selected Shelekov, Jacobi would keep his finger in the pie, by suggesting that a strong naval squadron be dispatched to the Pacific to protect Russian navigation. As a governor general of Siberia, he was in control of navy units operating from Siberian bases.

He resented Shelekov's claim that business was conducted to profit the treasury. The treasury had not yet drawn one ruble from the operations; if that part of the script were read by a fiscal expert, a *revisor* might come to Irkutsk and find evidence of fraud.

The Governor General had a brain storm. Much good could be accomplished, he wound up his letter, if the savages were permitted to express their gratitude for the Empress's tender care by voluntary contributions. No revisor could ever check such contributions by people who kept no records.

CHAPTER FORTY-SIX The Governor General's couriers traveled fast, and officials set speed marks to woo the Empress's favor. When Shelekov arrived in the capital, the College of Commerce and the Admiralty had already made their recommendations.

The college suggested granting the company exclusive hunting and trading privileges, in addition to a 200,000-ruble loan without interest. The Admiralty counseled the dispatch of two squadrons from the Baltic to the Pacific, one to the Kurile Islands, the other to the American coast. The Empress already had accepted these suggestions.

Shelekov's and Golikov's audience at Court turned into a travesty of virtue, one that would have made officers, sailors, and agents of the American Company roar with laughter.

Catherine delivered a speech: "As a reward for the services you have rendered the fatherland by discovering unknown countries and nations, and by establishing commerce and industry there, we most graciously confer upon you swords, and gold medals with our portrait on the face, and an inscription on the reverse. The medals shall be worn on ribbons around your necks, so that everybody can read that they have been conferred upon you for services rendered to humanity, and for other bold and noble deeds."

The thus honored performed well-rehearsed antics of gratitude and obedience, and, after a courtier read out the privileges the company was granted, Shelekov suggested that the Kurile naval squadron be used to bring Japan into the Russian orbit, and to secure a trade monopoly with that island empire.

However, the bemedaled merchants left the palace with a feeling of disappointment. The decree did not give the company delegated sovereign powers, and their hunting and trading privileges applied only to regions under actual company control. Rival traders, foreign and Siberian, could establish themselves in adjoining parts of American territory.

And there was yet another bewildering aspect: The Empress had also ordered that her American subjects be exempt from duties. This could, of course, be by-passed in various ways; but did Catherine expect to receive personal gifts, and how would her officials interpret "tax exemption"?

The loan was never paid out, and the Kurile naval squadron did not sail to Japan. No paragon of virtue was nominated to administer the new territories. Satisfied that neither Shelekov nor Golikov had been appointed, Jacobi now looked for someone to take care of his interests in the company.

His candidate was one Aleksei Baranov, a bald, smallish man of forty, who looked like a timid dullard.

These looks had been Baranov's main asset in his early career, which had started in a Moscow retail store. The storekeeper had been looking for a clerk not sufficiently smart to be a crook. When he found out at last that Baranov was quite smart, the latter had already left him and opened a business of his own, but the storekeeper could not prove that Baranov had done so on embezzled funds. Baranov found a number of suppliers who trusted his looks and gave him merchandise on credit. He went bankrupt, and his creditors empty-handed; and he hastened to take himself and his ill-gotten profit to a safe distance from the prosecutor's offices. In Irkutsk a glass manufacturer hired him as a manager.

By the time Baranov attracted the attention of the Governor General, he had already cheated the manufacturer out of his plant, and was also doing a brisk moonshiner's business with Northeastern Siberia. In Irkutsk everybody gossiped about Baranov's shrewdness and sneered at an Englishman who had called him a licentious, lazy, godless drunkard. Only a poor loser could pass such a judgment, and having defrauded an Englishman gave the moonshiner-glass manufacturer an aura of glory.

An appreciative Governor General appointed him a member of the Civil Economic Society, the Siberian association of manufacturers. Jacobi realized well enough that Baranov was a perfectly ruthless man, but he also believed in a weird kind of gratitude that would prompt him to use his dangerous talents for his sponsor's benefit. He notified Baranov of his promotion to chairmanship of the Economic Society, and mentioned in passing that he was being considered for appointment to the board of the American Company, as a trustee of the administration.

But Baranov, looking perfectly ludicrous with a black wig tied to his scalp with an untidy handkerchief, apologized: he did not want to spend long periods overseas as such an assignment might require.

The Governor General told him that Shelekov was in poor health, had no sons, and that his presumptive widow was a primitive backwoods character; Baranov might soon become Shelekov's successor. But to Jacobi's indignant surprise Baranov reminded the Governor General that he had encouraged him to establish trade posts as far away as Anadyr, and that it would be well nigh impossible to take care of affairs in Irkutsk, in the land of the Chutskis, and in America.

Jacobi did not know that Baranov was simultaneously negotiating with an agent of Shelekov.

Shelekov and Golikov, worried at aspects of competition in America, wanted a hard-hitting man to consolidate their overseas business. They agreed that Baranov could handle the matter; and Baranov, playing both ends against the middle, told the company agent that he could not accept an assignment at the moment but might consider it later on.

While Baranov engaged in double dealings, Jacobi turned to multiple dealings. He had had no word from Shelekov and Golikov, which seemed to indicate that these two fellows were thinking that, with medals and swords, they could short-change the Governor General. But the Governor General could still issue charters to people familiar with "free" regions of America. And he had his contacts with other people who could well harass the company.

The partnership of Lebedev-Lastoshkin, for example, as unscrupulous an outfit as could be found in the Russian East, held islands off the American coast. Another firm, that of Panov and Kisselev, did unsavory business in the Aleutians; and there were other operators of this kind. Jacobi bickered and bargained with all of them, issuing charters in return for unspecified benefits; and as time went by, and Shelekov and Golikov showed no indications of meekness, he devised a system of petty chicanery to impede operations of the American Company. The company's Siberian boats were subject to inspection, which invariably resulted in detainment in home ports. Settlers at Kodiak ran short of ammunition, and ill-processed furs rotted in storehouses.

More English ships and U.S. whalers sailed through the dangerous channels of Alexander Archipelago. The objects they offered the natives for barter were far more attractive than anything the Russians produced. The turnover of the American Company declined. Baranov and Shelekov were not quite aware of how much of the recession was caused by Russian competitors and the scheming Jacobi, but they decided that the man in charge of operations in and around Kodiak, a Greek, was not up to his task. Baranov would have to take the place of the Greek, and if he did not accept the job on their terms, they had ways and means to deal with tough customers.

Baranov had just refused to consider another offer by Shelekov's agent, saying that he was deeply involved in an important commercial venture. It was always dangerous to tell the truth in Siberia, and this time Baranov had been telling the truth.

He had invested almost all of his funds, and substantial amounts of borrowed money, in the biggest caravan ever to carry contraband to the land of the Chutskis. But then a short distance away from the trade post it was ambushed by superbly equipped and well-directed Chutski highwaymen who captured every piece of goods, every cart, every animal, and vanished into the wilderness.

Baranov was notified of the disaster by an unsmiling Shelekov, who visited him in his Irkutsk offices and presented himself as the holder of all of Baranov's bills payable on sight. In 1791 a chastened Baranov signed up as Kodiak manager of the American Company, leaving Jacobi out in the cold.

His first action was to purchase the merchandise the English carried to Alaska. Next he established a company shipyard. A former English naval officer, wanted by the polices of many lands, assisted Baranov, while other English navy men mockingly watched the construction of a thing from which, they contended, nothing that floated could ever come.

In August 1794, however, the first full-sized vessel built in that part of America was ready to sail. It was a one-hundred-ton affair, seventy-three feet long, with two decks and three masts, neither as big nor as neatly built as English craft, yet superior to anything Siberian yards had ever produced.

Shelekov notified the authorities in the capital that his firm now operated a frigate, and that more vessels were nearing completion in the company's American shipyards.

A more difficult problem than naval construction remained to be solved, however. When Baranov came to Kodiak, he found the Lebedev-Lastoshkin forces on the march, and those of the American Company on a precarious defensive. One Konovalev, a mercenary in the services of Lebedev-Lastoshkin, had established headquarters in Port Etches, and from there ruled adjoining mainland regions by means of terror, which paled the exploits of American Company personnel and settlers. He forbade his subjects, under penalty of death, to deal with the American Company; and his bands invested territory under American Company control, overpowering guards wherever they resisted.

Konovalev boasted of having credentials which entitled him to expand his rules at will, but he did not produce the papers when Baranov challenged him to do so.

Natives watched the fratricidal feud. Ill-armed and disorganized as they were, they could become an important factor in the struggle. Baranov realized it well enough, while Konovalev scoffed at native rabble.

Every ruffian under Konovalev's orders established a tyranny of his own in awarded territory. They all had men slaves and harems; they collected tribute and administered justice as a pastime, and as another source of income.

Baranov issued decrees temporarily restraining his own men from excessive suppression of natives, and he also changed the terms of barter in favor of the Alaskans.

Trusting that this would at least prevent the natives from siding with the enemy, he gathered his forces and staged a moderately successful raid on a rival outpost, followed by an ultimatum in which he asked for surrender of the Lebedev-Lastoshkin band. The ultimatum drew a scornful reply. Baranov worried about drastic counteraction, in which he could not hope to hold his own.

In this emergency he tried bluff. He was positive that Jacobi was backing the other party. If Konovalev believed that they were forsaken by the Governor General, he might still capitulate. Baranov sent a letter to his opponent, announcing that he had been directed by His High Excellency, the Governor General of Siberia, to restore order in America. Konovalev promptly surrendered.

"Had I had his strength and his strategic position," Baranov noted, "I would have conquered all of Alaska."

A bewildered Konovalev was sent to Okhotsk in chains. A mock trial staged by Jacobi, who wanted to save his own face, resulted in the prisoner's acquittal from charges of violence.

With peace restored, and Lebedev-Lastoshkin territory incorporated into the American Company's realm, Baranov rescinded restrictive orders and repealed the new barter terms. He hired Konovalev's bandits; they and American Company personnel co-operated to subject the Americans to ruthless "foremen rule."

Every clerk, every mercenary, every leader of settler groups was a foreman, a *peredovshik*. The peredovshiki ruled districts, lived in crude comfort, wore more objects of clothing and more barbaric trinkets than non-foremen Russians, consumed food in gargantuan quantities, had the strongest drinks and the stoutest women, imposed contributions, collected shares in all profits allegedly made by natives, and drew substantial income from administering local justice. There were price tags on acquittals, but one crime was always punished: an offense against the dignity of the peredovshik. Litigation between natives was decided in favor of the higher bidder. Litigation between Russians and natives was hopeless for the latter, but the Russian had to share the spoils with the judge. There was no appeal against a sentence.

But whatever foremen collected, business was again prosperous for the company. A dark shadow, however, seemed to loom over the lands and islands of Russian plenty: the English, whom Baranov dreaded.

Baranov's Intelligence reported that England would invade the Cook inlet no later than 1796, and exploit the natives' despair to turn them against the Russians.

In an attempt to mislead the English about the mood of the Alaskans, Baranov had Siberian clerks pose as natives and tell an occasional English merchant or captain that everybody in the "wide land" was reasonably happy.

He did not expect such masquerade to have a lasting effect, but English Intelligence had been poor in the early stages of Russian conquest, and it had not improved since.

No lesser man than Vancouver had reported in 1787: "Had the natives been oppressed by the Russians, had they been treated as conquered people, some uneasiness among them would have been perceived; some desire for emancipation would have been discovered. But no such disposition has been noticed. They seemed to be held in no restraint, nor did they seem to wish to elude the vigilance of their directors."

London did not feel that the Americans were being wronged by the Russians. Contemptuous reports on the smallness of Russian ships, drunken crews, stupid hunter-traders, and shoddy merchandise were not taken too seriously in England. Not being English, these Russians were considered inferior shipbuilders, manufacturers, and colonizers, yet good enough for Alaska.

The year 1796 went by, and all was quiet in Alaskan waters. Baranov sent an exuberant report to Shelekov, but the addressee had died in the preceding year.

The "primitive backwoods character," Natalia Shelekova, had inherited her husband's shares in the company.

Natalia was primitive and came from regions to which the term backwoods well applied, but she was a woman of indomitable energy, not ready to part with anything that she could possibly hold. She even had social ambitions, and combined them with an iron determination to exploit social advancement for commercial purposes.

She had married off their sickly only daughter to a nobleman from St. Petersburg, Nikolai Rezanov, who had come to live in Irkutsk. Rezanov looked askance at Siberian ways and manners, and talked about converting the American Company into a European-Russian affair with an imperial charter. Business people and officers at Irkutsk detested the "son-in-law from St. Petersburg" and his glib talk. He was said to have been in the good graces of the Empress, but Catherine had extended her good graces to more men than she possibly could have remembered, and she happened to die at about the time that Shelekov closed his watchful eyes. Everybody in Irkutsk agreed that Rezanov was a good-for-nothing, a dead weight that would impede old Natalia in her hopeless task of keeping control of the company.

Irkutsk was convinced of the hopelessness of that task. Several women had been able to run empires, but no woman could run a big business.

If Baranov had particular ideas about the future of the company, he did not disclose them, and kept aloof of the controversy.

Jacobi maintained the appearances of neutrality, but it seems as if he had a hand in the establishment of competitive companies that sprang up after Shelekov's death.

Natalia Shelekova spectacularly mourned her husband. Sentimentalists in Irkutsk pitied the poor woman who had been bereft and would soon be despoiled. An unsentimental merchant, Mr. Milnikov, raised 129,000 rubles for a company to trade with American furs. Two smaller companies formed for similar purposes.

Milnikov was the man of the year in Irkutsk in 1797; he rode the crest of his popularity as the heir apparent to Alaska in the early part of 1798. People praised his generosity when he called on Natalia Shelekova instead of snatching whatever assets the American Company held overseas.

He had a contract drafted before he visited the widow. It provided for an exchange of Shelekov's shares against a minority of the shares in Milnikov's company. But the aging woman did not put her three crosses under the text. No merger, she contended, could serve a useful purpose unless the other two companies came into the fold. When Milnikov contacted the other parties, he found to his dismay that Natalia had already acquired the majority of their stock.

On August 3, 1798, Milnikov sold his business to the American Company, renamed United American Company, in which Natalia held the majority of 724 shares, of 1000 rubles each. He lost the greater part of his investment. The "son-in-law from St. Petersburg" scored in the capital, smugly flattering the vain, slow-witted Tsar Paul into granting him privileges that Catherine had withheld from Shelekov and Golikov.

On August 11, 1799, the Russian American Company, as Natalia's enterprise now was renamed, received the exclusive privilege of using all hunting grounds and existing establishments, making discoveries of new territories, and occupying them in all regions of Western America north of the fifty-fifth parallel for a period of twenty years, subject to extension. Similar privileges were granted for the chains of islands extending from Kamchatka to America and Japan, including the Kuriles, the Aleutians, and other islands that could be found in the northeastern ocean, and even in regions south of the fifty-fifth parallel not yet occupied by other powers. The Russian American Company was exclusively entitled to use, and to profit from, new discoveries, to establish settlements, fortify them, expand navigation, do business with other nations, and hire for navigation, hunting, and all other activities under the charter "free and unsuspect people, having no illegal aims or intentions." Only shareholders or their trustees could hold office in the administration of territory, and judicial powers were officially vested in the administration. Company headquarters were transferred to St. Petersburg. So auspicious seemed the prospects of the Russian American Company that the Tsar and members of the imperial family acquired sixty shares.

Viewed from St. Petersburg, it was a sound investment. Even though imperial shareholders paid little for their stock, their partnership was profitable for everybody else; the government had to make every possible concession to a company whose dividends went into such exalted wallets.

In 1795 the American Company had netted 22,000 rubles; in 1853, with the capital increased to 13,600,000 rubles, 10,210,000 rubles were disbursed to stockholders. Had it not been for the Crimean War, which convinced St. Petersburg that overseas territories could not be held against superior naval powers, Alaska might not have been sold, and the company's privileges might not have expired for a long time.

The mercenaries in Alaska were pleased with the transfer of the administration. They feared neither God, who was high above, nor the Tsar, who was far away, and now the board of directors, also, would be far away.

In Irkutsk people shook their heads. Maybe they should have shown more respect to Natalia. It might have been better to keep Siberian business in Siberia. But on the other hand it might be easier to do illicit business with America if the people in charge had moved a few thousand miles away.

When Baranov received the news, in the spring of 1800, he did not think that company shares were a desirable investment. Had he had an opportunity to find a profitable assignment in Siberia, he would have resigned his post.

After having escaped trouble with the English he expected perplexing difficulties with the Americans. "The American republic," he recorded in his papers, "is greatly in need of Chinese goods, such as tea and silk. These objects have been formerly purchased by coin, but since the discovery of these shores with their abundance of furs, the Americans no longer need to pay cash. They can load their vessels with European goods, and produce of their own manufacture, barter them against Alaskan furs, and with these furs pay for purchases in Canton. One shipload of furs should be worth 90,000 rubles, six boats a year would mean a business of 540,000, compared with an annual 150,000 sold by the old American Company."

The Chinese ban on fur imports by sea alleviated his fears of American competition in that field.

But there were persistent rumors of a Spanish fleet sailing to Alaska. Baranov's frigate could not keep intruders away, and he trusted that the Spaniards came to conquer. The Spanish vessels did not arrive.

Another predicament, however, was real. Baranov's settlers were no builders, and he was in great need of useful people to consolidate the company's hold on America and keep the natives in check. He had begun to expand and consolidate the company's holdings, fortifying a settlement at Sitka, establishing a garrison at Yakutat, and landing on the shores of the Gulf of Konai. He would have to establish an agrarian colony near Cape Suckling, on a western point of Controller Bay. But he had no farmers to operate the colony. The people from Siberia were spoiled; they would let natives do the work, and Baranov worried about an American rebellion. He transgressed his authority by applying to the Governor General's offices at Irkutsk for colonists instead of waiting for dubious human deliveries made by the company.

In 1800 the first colonists, courtesy of the Governor General, arrived in Alaska; they emerged from dark, stinking holes of vessels in which they had been crowded under despicable conditions; they crawled over the decaying bodies of fellow colonists who had succumbed to starvation, suffocation, or disease. The survivors were emaciated, lice-ridden, struggling in the sudden brightness, but with few exceptions they were hardened beyond belief, and capable of doing harder work than they had been performing before.

It turned out that the colonists were convicts, former inmates of forced-labor camps. Irkutsk labeled the men agrarian workers; the officials felt that anybody could do farm work.

Baranov did not think so, but the forced laborers turned out to be more manageable than his own settlers. With the assistance of experts they could be turned into useful colonists.

Without the help of an aristocratic great landowner in Siberia with idealistic notions about the patriotic virtue of colonization, the company could hardly have expanded agrarian operations. But the Siberian Count arranged the migration of picked peasants and reasonably skilled mechanics to Russian America.

In 1802, Sitka was the center of gravity of Russian operations and the headquarters of Baranov's administration.

A cluster of Russian dwellings was protected by Fort Sv. (St.) Mikhail, a citadel armed with cannon and surrounded by palisades. Warehouses, cattle sheds, and barracks sprang up; sentries watched the approaches of Sitka, where several dozen settlers lived in reasonable prosperity with their more or less wedded native wives and many children. The women were of Kolosh origin. The Koloshes were a warlike tribe, but leaders of the colony asserted that they were on friendly terms with the Koloshes, who enjoyed bartering; and even if it were true that the natives had been buying ammunition from English traders, they would hoard the weapons as valuable merchandise rather than use them in action. Nobody in Sitka would have thought that the Kolosh women who placidly satisfied their Russian mates' desires and raised their children would ever turn against their keepers.

And yet these cowlike females urged their male kin to expel the invaders, and they supplied information on weak spots in the Russian establishment and the habits of Russian sentries. No professional spy could have done better than the women of Sitka.

Even Baranov, who saw specters of lurking danger where they did not actually exist, trusted the womenfolk of Sitka.

Came June 24, 1802.

Witnesses of the events of that day were not at first quite positive about the date, so thoroughly was their memory blurred by the horrible experience. Because of some celebration sentries had been withdrawn; men stayed indoors or lounged within the palisades. Nobody watched the edge of the dense forests lining the settlement's pastures. Silent Kolosh warriors emerged from the woods. They carried guns, spears, and daggers, their faces were covered with masks of teeth-gnashing monsters and smeared with red paint, their hair was tied in knots and covered with eagle down. Closer and closer the warriors crept, without a sound. The air was still; not even a blade of grass moved on the pastures.

A lazy Russian rose from the ground on which he had been sitting and saw the ghastly procession. He uttered a shout of horror; a present-minded soldier sounded the alarm; a few bewildered men staggered to stations, and the crew of two cannon reached their weapons; but there was no organized defense. The aggressors broke into wild yells and battle cries, fired their guns at windows, and stormed forward, scaling walls, and climbing roofs with incredible speed and agility, and breaking through palisades as if they were made of cardboard.

A few cannon balls fired at close range only increased the fury of the attack. The Koloshes thrust lances and daggers into Russians, dragged the wounded over stairs to worsen their agony. Heads were severed. Kolosh women set buildings afire, unconcerned with the fate of their own children, many of whom perished. A brisk wind suddenly sprang up and fanned the blaze; Russian stores caught fire before the natives could seize them; from windows leapt fear-crazed men who made for the beaches. Light-footed Kolosh warriors set after them, spearing whomever they overtook.

An English vessel anchored in the bay. Survivors of the Sitka massacre swam to the ship. Baranov was among those who survived. Other sources claim that he had not been there when the debacle occurred.

No Russian ashore was spared. When the Koloshes had no more men to kill, their bloodthirstiness turned against Russian cattle.

Sitka was lost. The skipper of the English vessel took survivors to Kodiak, but he would not release them until he received compensation for his expenses in the mercy mission. Captain Barber charged 50,000 rubles for an operation that normally could have netted him not even 100. A furious company agent refused to consider the request, but the gentleman from England insisted that he had lost time reserved for sea-otter business; and when this did not mollify the agent, he had decks cleared for action and twenty guns trained at the Russian post. After some negotiations carried out in an extremely unfriendly spirit Captain Barber settled for 10,000 rubles cash.

No amount of bluff or deceit could erase the impression that the news of the disaster created among the peoples of Russian America. Wholesale murder of native hostages, as suggested by mercenaries, could but stimulate this American aggressiveness. The Russians had been defeated, so they in turn would have to defeat the natives.

Baranov had no illusions. His old-timers were demoralized and he did not trust the soldierly qualities of the new specialists; he did not believe that deportees would sacrifice their lives for the greater glory of the company and fatherland. He would have to wait, and hope that no further disaster would occur until help arrived. Help would have to come from the Russian Army and Navy, he thought as he sat down to prepare the most tricky document of his career: the report to St. Petersburg.

He insinuated that Captain Barber, the blackmailer, had had a hand in the matter; and that so puny a man could not have indulged in conspiracy had he not had at least tacit support by higher authorities. But the heroic stand of the Russian garrison had foiled Barber's intention to establish himself in the Russian colony. And, being in the line of heroic storytelling, Baranov went on to rave about immense Kolosh casualties, relatively small Russian loss, and the marvelous strength of Fort Sv. Mikhail.

Baranov's tales outdid those of the fabulous Hanoverian Baron Muenchhausen who had died six years prior to the Sitka massacre, but they would not have placated the Russian Government had not Rezanov talked disaster into boon.

A derogatory account of the state of Alaska had just been presented to the Russian Admiralty by Lieutenant Krusenstern, who had taken a leave of absence from the Tsar's navy to enlist on an English merchantman and study navigation in Chinese waters and operations in and around Alaska.

Lieutenant Krusenstern found neither churches nor schools in Russian America; he called Russian trade establishments inadequate, commercial practices intolerable, shipping facilities less than primitive, and he estimated, conservatively enough, that company reports on population figures were 1000 per cent exaggerated.

The Admiralty informed Natalia's son-in-law of Krusenstern's findings. Formerly it would have required substantial bribes and a great deal of persuasion to have the paper filed, but after the Sitka disaster no official, however corrupt, would assume responsibility for concealing facts. Rezanov was advised to break the bad news to the Tsar, as a member of the board informing a stockholder.

Dull-witted Tsar Paul was dead. Alexander I, his successor, fancied himself a man of destiny; he had an indomitable urge to accomplish great things for his own people, for any other people—for mankind. His urge lacked intelligible objectives, but the words "progress" and "reform" sent the Tsar raving with unspecified delight. Admirals, generals, and cabinet ministers spelled the cue and waited in respectful silence for the youthful ruler to run out of emotional superlatives.

Rezanov had done better than the camarilla. In his first audience, when Alexander was not yet Tsar, he had not only given the watchword "progress," but had carried on from where an exhausted Crown Prince left off, to amplify the words of His Imperial Highness so well that the Crown Prince could but admire his own genius.

Rezanov, now a widower, protested that he would never have withheld the truth from the Tsar. But he would study Krusenstern's complete report before informing His Majesty.

Graying Lieutenant Krusenstern was a staunch believer in English excellence. He advocated reforms of Russian procedures to emulate England. An attentive Rezanov found a point fit to demonstrate the neglect of company commitments: The Russians had to rely on profits to educate natives. Profits had been curtailed by the shortsightedness of Siberian authorities. Had not Governor General Jacobi prevented the expansion of company navigation through his insistence that all trade between the newly discovered lands and China go via Siberia?

Krusenstern stated that, while it took only a few months to ship English merchandise to Canton, it took two years to bring goods from Alaska to Kiakhta. This burdened Russian goods with prohibitive transportation costs, and it increased the danger of spoilage. With excess money spent on transportation the company could have built more churches and schools than all Americans could attend.

This was the lead of Rezanov's comment on the Krusenstern report. The lieutenant had mentioned the necessity of establishing a new shipyard in America, with all modern facilities and operated by the best specialists available. Had not the old company done better in this field than the people in Kamchatka, Okhotsk, and Anadyr? And would not the reorganized company have done much better had it received official encouragement?

Rezanov became convinced that the Krusenstern papers were a godsend rather than a calamity, and much to the lieutenant's surprise he received an exuberant letter of praise from the company executive.

Rezanov's final report to the Tsar was a masterpiece of elocution and verbiage. Peter the Great, it said, had opened Russia's window to the West, yet it was a small window for as big a house as Russia and it opened into the small, almost completely landlocked Baltic; Alexander I, by his wisdom, was about to give Russia the greatest of all windows; unlimited access to the largest of the Seven Seas, the Pacific. The title "the Great" would be inadequate to commemorate such an achievement. By championing Russian navigation in the eastern seas, the Tsar would extend his salutary influence to many lands and people. As the report proceeded, Japan emerged as the immediate object of Alexander's charitableness. Japan should be opened to Russian traffic and trade, Japan should come into the Russian orbit; and the Russian American Company would take care of commercial operations.

Even though the Tsar had an unabridged copy of Krusenstern's paper, Alexander did not seem to notice that Rezanov lightly passed over false Alaskan population figures, intolerable commercial practices, and similar issues. He was enraptured by prospects in Japan; he would do anything to make the project a success.

Two fine vessels were built for the voyage to Japan; they should carry the Russian flag around the world for the first time, an event "which, after a century of progress in Russia, was reserved for the reign of Alexander I."

The ships *Nadeshda* (Hope) and *Neva* were ordered in London, but they got another coat of paint in the Kronstadt Navy Yard, outside of St. Petersburg, and were therefore considered practically of Russian manufacture.

Krusenstern, promoted for the occasion, commanded the expedition; Captain Lisiansky, who had served aboard an English ship in the War of Independence, was next in command.

The ships sailed in 1803. They carried, as the most important passenger, Mr. Rezanov, His Majesty's Ambassador Extraordinary to the Emperor of Japan; and as most important cargo, the Tsar's presents to the Emperor, Russian industrial goods, most of them made in England.

Alexander saw the expedition off. It consisted of 139 persons, including career diplomats, scientists, and two sons of Counselor von Kotzebue, a German in the Tsar's personal service.

It is claimed that a trade agreement between Russia and Japan had been signed eleven years before Rezanov's mission, and that, like other documents, it had been misfiled. The agreement allegedly permitted one Russian vessel a year to visit Nagasaki, but no such vessel had ever come there, and if Rezanov had ever heard of the compact, he did not say so.

Late in the fall of 1803 the expedition reached Japan. The *Nadeshda* stayed there, while Lisiansky with the *Neva* continued to Alaska. During the trip Rezanov made himself extremely disliked for his conceit, but even antagonists were mortified by the treatment the Ambassador received from Japanese local authorities. He was neither admitted ashore nor would the provincial governor relay his credentials to the Imperial Court. It took almost five months to persuade the Governor to accept the papers. Another month went by before an imperial plenipotentiary notified the weary Ambassador that an audience was granted, but that he would have to comply with the ceremonial. Rezanov would have to appear without sword and shoes, and squat on the floor, feet tucked under his body. After a few protests, which the imperial plenipotentiary chose to ignore, and some humiliating squatting exercises, Rezanov agreed to respect the ceremonial.

On April 4, 1804, an ornate barge took him to the palace grounds. The first audience consisted of the presentation of a personal letter of Alexander to the Emperor of Japan, and the Tsar's gifts, a few circumstantially translated greetings, insignificant questions, and answers. Another audience was as dull as the first, and when it was ended, Rezanov received an artfully drawn rescript:

The Tsar's letter was therewith returned, unopened, and the Tsar's presents were rejected. The Russian ship was ordered to leave Japanese waters at once, and to keep out for good.

Rezanov had not even seen the Emperor of Japan. According to Krusenstern's diary, the man before whom he had crouched, swordless and shoeless, was the Shogun, Crown Captain of the realm, Commander in Chief of the Army.

CHAPTER FORTY-SEVEN In Alaska, Captain Lisiansky was welcomed by Baranov, who told him that the *Neva* had arrived not one minute too soon. The ghosts of Sitka, still unavenged, harassed the company. The natives had built the disaster into a legend that inflamed the spirits of American tribes even in areas which the Russians had considered perfectly safe. Already the hold on Yakutat loosened. In many regions not even armed Russians could venture beyond the range of blockhouses and forts. Nothing short of a spectacular recapture of Sitka could prevent further deterioration of company affairs and of the morale of its personnel.

This morale was at an all-time low, Lisiansky learned from the company manager, whose tongue was loosened by despair.

With the exception of the foremen the company staff was dangerously dissatisfied with its contracts. Terms provided that, in addition to nominal wages, the men receive shares in hunting proceeds, credited against purchases in company stores. Total annual earnings averaged 200 rubles, more than a clerk made in a Siberian city, but the employees were running up bills twice as high; and when notified of their debts and of future curtailment of deliveries, they charged that accountants were cheats, and the percentages of their shares frauds; and the fewer drinks they received, the more restive they became.

There were no other stores in Alaska, and no moonshiners to satisfy the demand for booze. If a man made much money, he used it up during the bleak winter; and if a man had no money, he needed alcohol even more. If the company would not restrict deliveries to debtors, it would see all its earnings go down the throats of its staff.

As long as the company expanded, the personnel had plenty of illicit earnings at the natives' expense, but since the Sitka massacre, these sources had dried up. The establishment of which the Tsar was a stockholder faced mutiny.

Baranov did not mention that prices charged by company stores were six or seven times as high as those for similar goods in Siberian cities, and Lisiansky did not inquire about such details. All that mattered, he heard, was to win another battle of Sitka.

The Russian American Company had several warships, all homemade and officered by former navy men of dubious efficiency and ill-repute. If the *Neva* were to join operations, however, the reinvasion of Sitka could be carried out.

Captain Lisiansky was ready to co-operate and did not object to Baranov assuming command. The company manager had no military training, but he knew the enemy as well as his own men, and he had an indomitable determination to win.

Landing parties would consist of hunters who had been promised the free run of captured native settlements, cancellation of their debts in company stores, and one year's free supply of drink. The hunters were an undisciplined lot, and insisted on taking their wenches on the expedition; Baranov had no choice.

Late in the fall of 1804 the armada arrived off Sitka. Lisiansky cursed company skippers whose clumsy maneuvers delayed the opening of fire from the *Neva's* batteries.

When the first Russian balls hit the shore, the Koloshes evacuated the beaches. Landing parties, still accompanied by women, reached the shore unopposed, set up a comfortable camp, and asked for supplies, meaning many items other than ammunition.

At dusk a Kolosh came to negotiate. He was told that the Russians would talk to a chieftain only, and that hostages would have to be delivered prior to negotiations. The man returned on the following morning accompanied by another native whom he offered as a hostage. This was called unsatisfactory. By that time the Russian hunters were making merry, with heavy traffic going on between warships and the gay landing party.

Baranov interfered with unbridled energy. He had the camp broken up, tents removed, women chased into canoes and rowed away; and his vehement oratory whipped the hunters into a fighting force. A frenzied midget, his crazy black wig warped under the handkerchief that seemed not to have been laundered since he had worn it in Jacobi's office, circled the big hunters like a fox terrier shepherding bulls. Suddenly he pointed at the edge of the forests; the men had not noticed anything there but trees and bushes, but now they perceived a fort, so well adapted to the surroundings that only an eagle-eyed observer could have detected it from a point within gun range.

Baranov's oratory continued when a party of thirty Koloshes offered to stage a palaver. "We want hostages, and we want the fort," he shrieked. The natives turned about and silently made for the woods.

Baranov would not take the chance of seeing the martial spirit of his troop give way to jollification again. Upon his orders Russian ships opened fire on the fort; the hunters advanced, firing muskets and roaring abuse in the direction of the silent stronghold. Any professional noncom would have been shocked at the disorderliness of the Russian ranks, but Baranov was not even a noncom.

They approached the edge of the forest. The fort, still silent, could be theirs in a matter of minutes. Field cannon dragged ashore by Aleutian conscripts who served as the company's pack animals might not be needed at all.

Then suddenly native warriors debouched from the dusky cover. Not even Baranov had noticed them before. Solid formations, maneuvering with a smartness and precision that no European regulars could have excelled, fired muskets at the hunters, who staggered, broke, and ran as the Aleutian conscripts kept pushing the cannon toward the advancing enemy.

Baranov had a notion that the Aleutian natives were co-operating with the Alaskans, the Aleutians delivering cannon and ammunition to the Koloshes, who probably could operate artillery. A disaster infinitely worse than the Sitka massacre was looming, should the Koloshes turn the cannon against the Russian ships and destroy the landing forces. The puny company manager threw himself in the way of the fleeing hunters, hitting them with fists, yelling orders, curses, and entreaties. The big men shoved him aside. Already he stood alone between Russians and Koloshes. A bullet pierced his arm. He staggered with shock and pain, but recovered, his intact arm conjuringly pointing at the cannon. From aboard the *Neva,* Lisiansky had watched the rout of the hunters and the ghastly advance of the field pieces. When Baranov was wounded, sailors and cannoneers from the *Neva* arrived at the beaches, caught up with the Aleutians, secured the cannon, and opened fire. Big gaps were torn in the closed ranks of the Koloshes. A suicide attack by their vanguards collapsed in withering fire. Ship's artillery joined the charging sailors. Defeat turned into victory. The Koloshes fell back to the cover of the woods, leaving scores of dead behind. Artillery kept raking the edge of the forest and the fort.

Baranov had his injury dressed and mustered his forces. They had lost thirty-six men and were in no shape to attack beyond the range of the ships' artillery. But the manager expected the natives to make overtures and to concede defeat.

As he had predicted, a Kolosh negotiator appeared on the following morning. He was a very old man whose dignity of bearing impressed even Baranov. But only after members of the highest-ranking native families were surrendered as hostages, would the manager state his terms. The old man listened, nodded, left, and returned later with a number of ranking Koloshes, whom he rowed in his own large canoe to the *Neva,* where Captain Lisiansky took them into custody. The terms were now stated: cessation of resistance, surrender of the fort, unconditional acceptance of Russian "protection."

"At high tide," the old man replied cryptically.

High tide came. Native canoes left the beaches for the Russian ships. An observer aboard the *Neva* reported columns moving through the woods toward the Russian beachhead. The fleet opened up with every piece. Most canoes were shattered, the rest rowed back. The observer signaled that the columns had vanished.

Again the old man returned. He implored Lisiansky and Baranov to cease fire. He asserted that the fort was being evacuated, and completion of the operation would be announced by shouts *"oo," "oo," "oo." Oo* meant end.

Darkness fell as the shouts were heard. They were followed by a rhythmic chant as the Russians had never heard before, a sustained sound which grew louder with every phrase. "They sing with joy because they no longer have to fight," a Russian sailor scoffed, but his comrades did not feel at ease.

In the early morning sailor patrols entered the fort. Only dead were found, twoscore bodies. The ammunition chamber was empty. The Koloshes had used up all their bullets and powder. Scouts found the neighboring woods deserted. Baranov, weakened from loss of blood, inspected the fort. Together with the sailors and some hunters he then walked into the forest. A few hundred yards away, they found, piled up behind a broad screen of underbrush, many small bodies: the corpses of children these Americans had killed to the tune of the rhythmic chant lest they turn slaves under the Russian yoke.

This act of antique savagery impressed the Russians as illegal interference with their title to booty. Children were future chattels, of whom they must not be deprived. In retaliation they put the torch to all native buildings they found nearby.

The backbone of Alaskan resistance was broken.

A new Russian fortified settlement sprang up at the site of Sitka. It was called Novo-Arkhangelsk. A strong square stockade, with blockhouses on every corner, protected dwellings, barracks, and warehouses. In the winter of 1804–05, Novo-Arkhangelsk received its first inhabitants: hunters, their female accessaries, and their retinue of slave laborers imported from other parts of Russian America.

Russian overseers from Siberia were assigned to all American settlements. Men who had scruples against whipping a person to death did not qualify. Their rule of terror fostered hatred, yet it also discouraged rebellion.

The *Nadeshda* joined the *Neva* in Alaskan waters after the mass infanticide. Ambassador Rezanov, still smarting under the Japanese insult, received the news of Kolosh humiliation and of victory with immense relief. His account to Tsar Alexander, drafted in various versions, none of which he considered satisfactory, would take yet another shape. To the glory of Sitka-Novo-Arkhangelsk should be added the glory of coming victory over Japan.

Rezanov would admit failure, but he would also suggest swift retaliation. The Ambassador, who had learned to think along the Tsar's line, but straighter and faster, realized that Alexander's version of beneficence did not preclude violence if morally justified by the other party's maliciousness. The final version of his account added fictitious injury to actual insult, by telling that the Japanese had brazenly established themselves on Russian territory in the Kuriles.

"I hope that Your Majesty will not consider it criminal aggression," it wound up, "if, after having the ships repaired and their armament improved, I shall return to the coast of Japan, destroy the place called Matsmai, and proceed to drive the Japanese from Sakhalin Island and their Kurile establishment, and break up their fisheries. This would deprive 200,000 people of their livelihood, and force the Japanese to open their ports."

Rezanov, chairman of the Russian American Company, showed no less expansionist tendencies in his report to Alexander the stockholder than Ambassador Rezanov had expressed in his account to Alexander Tsar:

"As Your Imperial Majesty's faithful servant, I take the liberty to state that the development of our American colonies requires that bread, the staple food, be available in quantity. Bread is now being brought to Alaska from Okhotsk. It would be advisable to purchase bread and grain also in the Philippines and in Chile, under trade agreements with the government of Spain."

Those trade agreements would give Russia a dominant position in commerce between those territories and the other great powers.

Baranov had slightly worried over Rezanov's reaction to his dealings with Irkutsk concerning settlers for America. But the chairman of the board approved of this arbitrariness. He proclaimed that convicts were a danger to society at home, but an asset in the colonies, and he even decreed that deportees should get top priority for overseers' assignments. And because this contradicted the wording of the charter that "only free and unsuspect people" should be employed, he petitioned that the Crown approve of his decree.

The petition was favorably acted upon, and it was ordered that Alaska receive an annual contingent of Siberian convicts.

But St. Petersburg did not agree to Rezanov's proposal of shooting his way into Japanese ports, nor did it authorize him to expand company operations into Spanish colonies.

The Tsar was busy with his ill-fated campaign against Napoleon I, which in the fall of 1805 led to the disastrous Battle of Austerlitz, in which the Emperor of the French shattered the allied Russo-Austrian armies. Alexander probably learned all the details of his ambassador's vexations in Japan, but not even in the period between the conclusion of his pact of friendship with Napoleon in 1807 and the French invasion of Russia in 1812 did Alexander consider retaliation against Japan. He accepted the setback which would be followed by other pitfalls, all signposts on a road to frustration that would eventually turn a befuddled reformer into a somber tyrant.

Meanwhile Rezanov ordered the *Neva* on a trading trip to Canton. Lisiansky's ship carried furs valued at 400,000 rubles. It was rightly assumed that Chinese restrictions would not apply to the cargo. However, the pelts were not properly prepared for transportation in scorching heat and the stench of rotting skins eventually forced the crew to throw the greater part of them overboard. Chinese importers offered poor prices for the salvaged furs and overcharged for tea and silk. Lisiansky's schedule did not permit a prolonged stay in Canton. When the bargain was completed, the new cargo was worth less than 150,000 rubles.

Rezanov pinned the blame for the deficit upon "the Bostonians," as he and Baranov called the people of the United States. To them "the Bostonians" were ruining the China trade; "the Bostonians" were plotting against Russia; "the Bostonians" were the number-one enemy.

Lisiansky hailed his superior's attitude, and Captain Krusenstern joined chorus. The two navy men conserved the spirit which had existed among English officers on the eve of the Boston Tea Party. The people of America should be put in their place. And if the English had failed to do so, the Russians would succeed. Already they had chastened the American Westerners; now it would be the Easterners' turn.

Another account to the Tsar mentioned fifteen to twenty "Bostonian" ships turning up in the Russian colonies each year. "If we don't keep them out, we shall go empty-handed. The Company should use heavily armed ships, so that they can never again interfere with our own China trade."

In hectic sessions aboard ship Rezanov, now "Commander of America," Krusenstern, and Lisiansky rattled swords; and minutes of their meetings indicate that they considered starting a Russo-United States war right then and there. They would not be content with sweeping "the Bostonians" from Pacific waters; they also wanted to establish company posts in India and Burma.

The Russians talked but did not shoot. Baranov may have cautioned the debaters. He had to realize that Eastern Americans would be more difficult to defeat than the Koloshes. Eventually the Russian flotilla reconnoitered the American west coast south of the fifty-fifth parallel, deep into California waters.

"The name of Baranov," the Ambassador told company personnel in a farewell address, "is now known all over the American West Coast, as far south as San Francisco. The Bostonians respect him, the savages dread him, and natives from distant regions surrender to him and woo for his amity."

Rezanov would not stay aboard ship, but would use land transportation from Okhotsk, through Siberia.

In August 1806 the *Neva* and the *Nadeshda* anchored at Kronstadt. They were triumphantly received by the Tsar in person, who said that the crewmen looked extremely well, and that this was obviously owing to the quality of Russian salted beef, as it was served to Alexander at a party aboard. "It tastes much better than English beef," His Majesty said smiling. He did not know that the meat had been purchased at Falmouth on the return trip.

The Order of St. Vladimir was bestowed upon Captains Krusenstern and Lisiansky, who were also awarded pensions of 3000 rubles. Everybody aboard the *Nadeshda* and the *Neva* received a pension ranging from 1000 for ranking officers to 50 for sailors.

Rezanov's expansionist proposals were not mentioned at the reception. The topic may have come up after the return of the Commander of America, but the voyager never reached St. Petersburg. He died of pneumonia, in Krasnojarsk, Siberia.

Baranov established new offices at Novo-Arkhangelsk. Hardly had he resumed routine operations when alarming news reached him: Insurgent deportee settlers, led by two exiles from Poland, had hatched a plot to seize power in Alaska; one of the conspirators gave away his accomplices on the very eve of the putsch that would have caught the management unprepared. Baranov had the ringleaders arrested and sent to Siberia for trial. Blueprints of the conspiracy, as revealed in court, included distribution of company property among the ringleaders. No benefits were to be granted to the Russian rank and file, and the lot of the natives would remain as unhappy as before.

Yet another attempt to wrest control of Russian America from the company was later attributed to John Jacob Astor.

The man who charged the kingly American merchant with conspiracy was Captain Golovin, who visited Alaska in the summer of 1810 as the skipper of the Russian sloop of war *Diana.*

Captain Golovin was plainly angered by the attitude of Baranov, who treated him like an unwelcome subordinate. Golovin's account bristled with righteous indignation about the wrongs he found in Russian America. "Just as the huckster on the market makes the sign of the Cross and calls God to witness in order to cheat a customer out of a few coppers," he wrote, "the management of the Company uses the name of Christ and the fundamentals of our faith to deceive the Tsar's government and to lure unfortunate families to the savage shores of America, where they succumb to the infamy and avarice of the Company manager."

Baranov was pictured as having sunk below the level of a savage, as being responsible for the neglect of religion, and for usurious practices that had destroyed whatever decency the settlers had conserved.

Such charges would have been filed away by the authorities in the Russian capital had they not been accompanied by more sensational accusations.

His own linguistic skills, Golovin related proudly, had been instrumental in uncovering a dangerous plot. When the *Diana* arrived at Novo-Arkhangelsk, the *Enterprise,* an American vessel, was lying at anchor there. Captain Ebbet of the *Enterprise* carried a credential letter to Baranov, drawn up in French. Golovin was the only person in Novo-Arkhangelsk who knew French, and he was called upon to translate.

In this letter John Jacob Astor explained that he had been established in business in New York, and had been trading with the Canadian Company, as well as with Europe and China, for the previous twenty-five years. Mr. Astor had a trading outpost at the mouth of the Columbia River, and he was now sending his ship, the *Enterprise,* to the northwest coast of America, with a cargo of salable commodities; Captain Ebbet was empowered to make long-term arrangements.

This letter could hardly be called suspect, nor could Baranov's reaction be considered conspiratory. The manager purchased the American goods, sold Ebbet a load of furs, and promised to consider offers of Chinese wares. He did not sign long-term contracts.

Yet Golovin insisted that he had had a premonition of evil, that he would keep watching developments.

The Americans were better salesmen and more efficient buyers than the Russians. Baranov grew ever more amenable to their suggestions. In another letter Astor addressed the manager as "Governor," "Your Excellency," and

"Count," and in separate instructions to Captain Ebbet the kingly trader from New York ordered the skipper to obtain detailed information on general conditions in the Russian colonies, on military strength, on the powers vested in Baranov, and on the manager's relations with his government.

Captain Golovin did not disclose how he managed to intercept these instructions, but he charged that they were part of preparations for a coup in Alaska, and that Baranov was conniving with Astor's skipper.

The Admiralty opened an investigation. Captain Golovin's deposition was highly emotional, but the only fact emerging from it was the captain's furious animosity against Baranov. Conspiracy charges became less credible with every presentation. The Golovin testimony was eventually shelved.

If Astor ever had considered a coup, and Baranov was in collusion, nothing resulted from their conspiracy. In 1812 the war forced the American to abandon his Columbia River post, and Baranov showed blithe disregard of company liabilities to J. J. Astor.

Correspondence between the house of Astor and the Russian American Company deteriorated into a monotonous succession of unanswered admonitions for payment of overdue bills.

Eventually Russel Farnum, one of Astor's agents, undertook the precarious trip to Novo-Arkhangelsk to collect, and when he did not receive payment went to Siberia, crossing the Bering Strait in an open boat and proceeding to Kamchatka by dog sleigh. Unable to get cash in Kamchatka, he continued to Okhotsk, to Irkutsk, and eventually, in a three-year odyssey, to St. Petersburg, where he obtained a draft on the London branch of a Russian bank. By the time the draft was honored Baranov had died.

The company manager had felt weary already at the time of his dealings with Ebbet. His assignment was practically completed. Alaska was reasonably secure for the Crown and the company; and further developments depended on world politics rather than on business practices. The revamped board of directors did not include anyone Baranov knew; he felt isolated and wanted to retire.

However, his letter of resignation to the board remained unanswered. The executives in St. Petersburg first wanted to choose a successor.

No successor could be found at Novo-Arkhangelsk. Baranov, the autocrat, had not trained another man to assume responsibilities. There was little chance to find the right man in Siberia, either. Persons with sound administrative and trading background were scarce, and the smarter a Siberian was, the less he could be trusted. St. Petersburg officials offered theoretical suggestions, but when asked to accept the job, they would plead poor health or other circumstances that prevented their going to America. Civil servants' salaries were small, but a clever man could always make an extra ruble to make life in the capital comfortable enough. Only adventurers would want to go to America; and Russian adventurers usually were itinerant thieves.

Board members and officials agreed that a foreigner, or at least a man of foreign ancestry, would be the best choice.

In 1816, at last, the board found a suitable candidate, one Hagemeister, who had served on the *Neva* under Lisiansky. Naval authorities approved of the German, and courtiers called him an outstanding personality.

Hagemeister left for Novo-Arkhangelsk with instructions to be careful lest Baranov embezzle all company funds before his successor could take the reins.

The German promised to outsmart his predecessor all the way. When he arrived in Alaska in November 1817 he introduced himself as a visitor, and courted the aged manager's favor, giving lavish praise to his host's drinks, his concubines, and their offspring; and he even had one of his companions marry one of Baranov's daughters in the church of Novo-Arkhangelsk.

The company capital now had a church. The manager developed an almost maniacal religious fervor, strangely contrasting with his earlier libertinism.

For several months Hagemeister stayed in Baranov's house, listening to the old man's lectures on the blessings of religiosity.

After winning his unflinching confidence the German notified him briskly that he was deposed by orders from St. Petersburg, and would have to surrender company property at once.

The shock overwhelmed Baranov. He was unable to decipher the letter his host presented; it took Hagemeister three readings before the old man began to understand what the document said. Ashen, his head shaking, Baranov fumbled for the keys to storehouses and strongboxes. This Hagemeister took as an indication of guilt.

But he did not find evidence of fraud.

Assets on hand in Novo-Arkhangelsk alone were in excess of 2,500,000 rubles, almost four times the company capital after Natalia Shelekova's triumph. Cash on hand and practically all stocks were found to be in accordance with available records. The only discrepancy existed in the liquor account. Baranov had also kept elaborate entries on territorial assets: regions scouted and occupied by company hunters and settlers expanded about as far as the boundaries of Alaska, fixed some seven years afterwards.

Hagemeister would not acknowledge the surprising honesty of Baranov's management. His Teutonic conception of excellence required a background of another man's wickedness. Baranov had to be disgraced so that Hagemeister could shine.

A blustering, wildly acting new manager stormed into the deposed man's bedroom and shook him up, roaring that his fraud was uncovered, that he had embezzled the company's immensely valuable liquor assets, that he would have to answer for the crime before a special tribunal. The Baranov who led the charge of the hunters of Sitka would have made short work of the German; but the Baranov who staggered out of bed was not even a shadow of his former self. Blubbering, his chin drooping ridiculously, he did not seem to understand Hagemeister, who shouted that a comedy of imbecility would be of no avail.

Baranov spent ten months in semi-confinement, between spells of dull despair, loud prayers, and babbling imbecility.

Then he was taken aboard a company vessel for trial in St. Petersburg. Also with that vessel traveled a voluminous bill of indictment, in which the captive's untold crimes in the field of liquor distribution were told against the background of newly introduced reforms that would prevent similar misdeeds forever.

On the way the company vessel anchored in Batavia, on April 16, 1819. Dutch colonists saw a crude coffin carried ashore. Russian sailors were not secretive about the identity of the dead man: one Alexander Baranov, formerly a manager, but last seen as a befuddled oldster.

To the residents of Batavia, however, as to most other Europeans in that part of the world, Baranov was a dramatic figure, the man who but recently had been instrumental in a fantastic comic-opera coup that almost resulted in Russian control of the Central Pacific. Many Dutchmen attended the funeral.

In fact this coup, staged while the company was already considering Hagemeister as a new manager, had marked either the last flare-up of Baranov's indomitable energy or, possibly, his first surrender to the initiative of other people.

CHAPTER FORTY-EIGHT In 1815 a government-owned Russian ship discharged three "authorized passengers" in Novoarkhangelsk: one was Mr. Kotzebue, who had been with Rezanov; the second was Kotzebue's younger brother, and the third, who had a big frog's mouth and sputtered Russian with an ironclad German accent, introduced himself as Dr. Schaeffer.

Schaeffer seemed startled to learn that Baranov had not heard of him before: neither of Dr. Schaeffer the engineer, the physician, nor of Schaeffer the explorer, the botanist, and the expert on scientific colonization.

The manager had lost much of his astuteness, but he still fancied himself of knowing a quack and an impostor when he saw one, and he first considered the doctor a malodorous blending of both species. The captain of the boat that had brought him to Alaska was a notorious cheat, and he suspected doctor and captain of working hand in glove on some crooked scheme. But Schaeffer's credentials were weighty and looked genuine, and the Kotzebues talked of their companion as a man of integrity and genius.

The threesome was on an exploring mission. "Exploring" could be a cloak word for poking noses into managerial affairs, but Schaeffer, the leader of the team, confined himself to brief trips inland, from where he returned with piles of notes on plants and herbs—"routine matters," as he called them. There was still room for improvement, he said cryptically. Opportunities in Alaska were limited and would remain so—but not forever.

This could be a tactless reference to Baranov's resignation, but Dr. Schaeffer soon got specific: The glorious future of Russian America depended upon Russian control of the Pacific. The manager had heard such talk before, and he knew about Russian governmental inertia on the subject. But the versatile visitor pulled a plan of action out of his hat: He would seize the Sandwich Islands.

The Sandwich Islands, he lectured, were the hub of Pacific navigation, the strategic key to the ocean. They were, politically speaking, no man's land, which, to Schaeffer as to Baranov, referred to all territories in which natives still had their own sovereign institutions. The English and the Americans had trade posts there; the two held each other in check, but might gang up against the Russian American Company if it were to seize the islands by a coup.

No coup was required, Dr. Schaeffer insisted; the conquest would be strictly legal; he would travel to the islands and negotiate the establishment of a model agrarian settlement. The settlers would be picked mercenaries, and their tools would be ammunition. The people of the Sandwich Islands were an easygoing lot. One year after the establishment of the Russian foothold the islands would be under Russian protection, and their remunerative trade a company monopoly. The English and "the Bostonians" would accept the facts. They might fight at sea, but they would never fight on land. The Tsar would be forever grateful to the pioneers who raised his flag in the Sandwich Islands.

To Baranov this sounded as a bugle sounds to an old cavalry horse. It stimulated his energy, made him forget retirement. However, easygoing as the islanders were, there might be trouble with their kings. The company had had an unpleasant experience of late. One of its boats had carried a load of junk merchandise to the island of Kauai; Tomari, King of Kauai, had it confiscated and refused to pay damages. And King Kamehameha, most powerful of the Sandwich Island monarchs, and Tomari's sovereign, had answered Baranov's complaint with nice generalities. Couldn't it be that English and Bostonians inspired Kamehameha's policies, and that they would intrigue against the settlers' project?

But Schaeffer claimed to have it from reliable sources that the King was fed up with English-American meddling in his affairs. The more they intrigued, the sooner he would apply for Russian protection.

In October 1815 a plan was adopted in Novo-Arkhangelsk. In the following month Schaeffer left for the islands as the sole passenger on a Spanish tramp ship. In the spring of 1816, Russian American Company craft would follow with settlers and implements.

King Kamehameha enjoyed interesting company and the doctor was as interesting a man as had ever visited the archipelago.

Kamehameha resided in a palace of straw, which, like other native dwellings, was open to the cooling draft of land and sea breezes, cross-ventilation, which Occidental architecture had yet to adopt. The most striking features of royal furniture were neatly made European chairs, and a big mahogany table.

His Majesty wore a white shirt, tight-fitting blue trousers, a red waistcoat, and a gaily colored neckcloth. His courtiers sported black frocks from which protruded bare bellies. Sentinels carried muskets and belts with cartridge boxes and two pistols; these were their only garments.

Several English and Americans lived nearby. They dressed and behaved like comfortable colonial settlers, and did a thriving export-and-import business. Life was easy and opulent, and affairs of state were simple. Out of courtesy rather than need the King occasionally consulted with the foreigners.

Through the idyllic settings of a munificent nature and lighthearted people walked Dr. Schaeffer, somber in gait and garb, a symbol of cantankerous dignity.

Kamehameha respected the doctor highly, and listened to his talk with a vague feeling of guilt. The doctor criticized the natives' playful frivolity, the government's lack of strictness, and the greed of foreign traders who wanted nothing but profits for themselves and would never invest in educating the people and improving agriculture. Schaeffer would not confine himself to studying the island's curative herbs, as had been his original intention. In grateful recognition of His Majesty's friendship he would establish a model colony of Russian scientific peasants to teach the natives efficient farming; and he would also improve trade.

The English and Americans, who had never quite believed in the doctor's scientific mission, were becoming positive that his intentions were fiendish.

They warned Kamehameha that the Russian model colony was a sham. If the Russians were such efficient farmers, why did they not improve agriculture in Alaska? And, speaking of trade, there was nothing Russia could produce that England or America did not manufacture in better quality and at lower cost. Did Schaeffer consider importing Siberian or Alaskan furs? They would be in short demand in the tropics.

Kamehameha did not want to hear evil. True, the foreigner was not always pleasant, but why should he doubt his honesty? Schaeffer should have an opportunity to show what he could do. He would be free to select a fitting plot of land for a model settlement. But the interests of the old, established traders would be safeguarded, and the King would not sign contracts with the Russian American Company unless the doctor's plan were established in detail.

Schaeffer informed Kamehameha that he would go to Kauai Island to look for suitable land. The King gave him his blessings and told him to pick any domain he wanted. Kauai's king had to take his orders.

Schaeffer knew all about it, and his knowledge had produced a modification of his original plan to establish the foothold at Kamehameha's front door. He had come to doubt that the irksome resident traders would look on inactively while he completed his sinister arrangements. He would rather move the theater of operations to another island. It was most convenient that King Tomari, once Kamehameha's rival, had become his vassal. He could be used as a tool against his sovereign.

A fretful Tomari had expected Schaeffer to come as a stern collector of compensation, but the doctor mentioned the cargo affair only in passing, as an inconsequential misunderstanding, and claimed to be visiting the territory as an agronomist and a physician. Tomari was a hypochondriac. He told the doctor of the aches and pains that beset him and his queen. Schaeffer listened with imperturbable patience, and spent the rest of the day checking ailing royalty, and explaining that he was the Tsar's secret medical adviser, specialized in diagnosing the most complicated diseases. By nightfall he pronounced his findings: it was dropsy for the King, and consumption fever for the Queen, both fatal had not science lately devised new medicines; and wasn't it fortunate that he happened to carry samples of it in his luggage?

One week later both King and Queen said that they were feeling better. A grateful Tomari offered to settle the cargo affair; and his delight knew no bounds when Schaeffer suggested that he return to the company goods he did not want to keep, and pay for the rest in sandalwood, which Kauai produced in quantity.

In his exuberance Tomari granted the company exclusive purchasing rights for the sandalwood and taro roots of the island, but then retracted. Curtailment of his royal prerogatives did not permit him to grant monopolies.

Schaeffer had a panacea against prerogative trouble, too: Russian support. Tomari should overthrow Kamehameha, the tyrannical impostor, turn out the English and American usurers, and establish peace and order under Russia's unselfish protection.

"Kamehameha is a powerful man," the dropsy patient sighed. "And think of all these English and American ships!"

But Schaeffer revealed that he was as outstanding a military and naval expert as he was a physician; he claimed to have 500 specially trained and equipped professional soldiers under his orders. This army was on its way to the Sandwich Islands. And as to Anglo-American naval strength, Russia had all the ships needed for the purpose, and the Russian American Company was so wealthy it could buy everything afloat in the Pacific. The company had supplied him with fabulous funds. As a proof of his means he would right then and there buy an American ship.

A schooner flying the Stars and Stripes was at anchor off Kauai. Its skipper worried that the decrepit craft might break up at the first rough sea. He considered it a stroke of luck when the pompous doctor paid $5000 for the contraption.

Nothing stood in the way of a contract between Schaeffer and King Tomari. The doctor was appointed commander in chief of all armed forces. The campaign against Kamehameha would start immediately after the Russian landing in Kauai. After victory Tomari would be proclaimed King of all Sandwich Islands; would in turn place his realm under Russian protection; and grant the Russian American Company a long-term monopoly for sandalwood and other national produce.

But as time went by, and the Russian armed forces were not yet sighted, a restive Tomari again wondered whether the Russians really had enough shipping space to transport so strong a force. He asked the commander in chief to purchase yet another American ship, a more seaworthy affair that had just cast anchor in the bay.

The American captain charged $40,000 in hard cash. He sneered at the frantic doctor's offer of a bill payable in furs and at his assertion that his word was better than gold. The deal fell through.

The skipper informed his countrymen at Kamehameha's court of his experience. Already rumors told of a conspiracy between Tomari and the doctor. The English and Americans urged Kamehameha to have Schaeffer arrested and to keep all Russians out for good. The King no longer quite trusted the doctor, but he disliked drastic action. He would do no more than warn vassal Tomari not to engage in rebellious activities, and to restrain Schaeffer from overstepping his assignment, which was to select a plot of land for a model farm.

The gently worded warning arrived at Kauai just as the Russian "settlers" were, at last, disembarking: not quite a hundred strong, half Aleutian chattels, half roughshod hunters.

They established themselves in Tomari's straw-hut capital and feasted on whatever they could lay hands upon.

The islanders despised Aleutians as crude savages, and came to hate the hunters as voracious, abusive rapists.

King Tomari was incensed. This expeditionary force could never conquer other islands, but it would arouse his people to depose him even before Kamehameha could enforce his abdication. He wanted Schaeffer to leave and take his bandits and savages along. But Schaeffer took his "army" to strategic spots and had native forced labor build fortifications. Yet another group of Russians arrived: a score of tough characters, whom the doctor called his mechanics. They had considerable trouble getting ashore, faced with a hostile population and an angry king.

Schaeffer dispatched a message to Baranov. Without substantial reinforcements his action, most auspiciously begun but temporarily stalled, would not produce the desired results.

Throughout the Pacific area news spread of a coup staged by the Russian American Company in the Sandwich Islands. People had never heard of Dr. Schaeffer, but they knew Baranov. Manager Baranov was reported to be seizing the islands, defying England and the United States, waging his own war. . . .

But Baranov would not assume responsibility for a real war, and asked for orders from St. Petersburg. St. Petersburg was already dealing with Hagemeister, and directed him to shun further trouble in the Pacific.

The English and Americans in the islands did not wait for the reaction of their respective governments. The English threatened to attack Schaeffer's fortifications, and American sailors did attack a Russian station and wrought havoc in the barracks of hunters who had no stomach to fight the crew of a merchantman. Natives, enthused by the damage suffered by the Russians, seized a fort and trained its gun at the only Russian ship in the bay. Fortunately for the Russians they were not trained artillerymen. Fear-stricken Russian hunters huddled in a remaining fort and watched the natives dancing their triumph.

Schaeffer was not wanting in personal courage. He eventually gathered a few dozen hunters for an invasion of Oahu. The natives checked the advance, but only after the Russians had destroyed the famous Morai Sanctuary.

The doctor and his men stayed ashore, encircled by spiteful natives, waiting for their doom.

However, the adventure had a happy ending.

Hagemeister received a supplementary directive to liquidate the matter amicably. The assigned company manager picked the brothers Kotzebue as messengers of Russian good will.

The two German Russians called at Kamehameha's court and notified the ruler of the Sandwich Islands that the Tsar disapproved of the coup, that Schaeffer was an impostor, and would have to answer for his misdeeds.

Kamehameha was in a forgiving mood, toward Tomari and everybody else. A drinking party closed the incident with a toast to the Tsar. Schaeffer and his hordes were allowed to leave with bag and baggage.

The men returned to Alaska. Schaeffer boarded a Canton-bound American vessel.

But he did not die in China, a forgotten, penniless vagabond, as had been claimed. The doctor continued through Siberia to St. Petersburg, perfectly undaunted and as venturesome as ever.

He appeared before his sponsors in the Russian capital, not to answer for his misdeeds, but to request redress and vindication.

He charged the management of the Russian American Company with double-dealings and deceit, with abandoning the drive to seize the Sandwich Islands when it was on the verge of success. Schaeffer did not humbly appeal to the dignitaries who attended the session. He reproved them for failure to back him in time, and asked that adequate means for another expedition be provided at once. He would complete his task, and if the English and Americans, emboldened by Russia's humiliated attitude, were to interfere, he would deal with their fleet as he had dealt with Napoleon's Grande Armée.

This was a reminder of Schaeffer's alleged achievements, which had netted him the sponsorship of persons of consequence. The doctor was said to have devised an epoch-making system of serial reconnaissance in 1812, when the enemy marched to Moscow. Every move of the advancing army was observed from balloons. This was said in the final victory report to the Tsar, in one of many paragraphs dealing with unusual performances, but it did not elaborate on the details of the system, nor on its practical effects. Had it not been for nationalist pride in Russia's being the first country to introduce reconnaissance from the air, the paragraph would have been overlooked, if not distrusted altogether.

The doctor's boast prompted the sponsors to try to enlist other forces-that-were in a new Pacific venture.

They approached the Admiralty. The Excellencies of the Fleet told the hackneyed story of Russia having no navy to meet a major challenge. And the board of directors of the Russian American Company regretted injury inflicted upon Dr. Schaeffer, but it could not divert manpower to the mid-Pacific. They would rather expand along the American continent to San Francisco and beyond. The company, they wrote, was responsible to its stockholders; and expenses involved in an operation in the Sandwich Islands would curtail dividends for a long time to come.

Impeded by such opinions, no proposal to resume the Pacific adventure could be submitted to Tsar Alexander, commander in chief of the Navy and stockholder of the Russian American Company.

An angry, resentful Dr. Schaeffer left St. Petersburg in 1819. A dignified, versatile aristocratic globe-trotter, Count Frankenthal, turned up at the court of Dom Pedro I of Brazil a few years later. Frankenthal became the ruler's favorite, and his oracle. Much as other courtiers disliked the frog-mouthed Count, who sputtered Portuguese with an ironclad German accent, they were powerless against his influence. Frankenthal was scornful of everything Brazilian, in particular its soldiery. He suggested that the monarch get himself a smart German bodyguard, and offered to go to Germany to recruit the tallest and best-drilled specimens for the purpose. Dom Pedro liked the idea, and Frankenthal, abundantly supplied with gold coins to take care of all expenses, sailed off—never to return.

Count Frankenthal, who called himself Dr. Schaeffer now, lived happily to a ripe old age in his true homeland, on funds earmarked as recruiting fees and transportation expenses for Brazilian bodyguards.

CHAPTER FORTY-NINE Nobody admitted having given the word, but suddenly flags sprang up on isolated buildings of Irkutsk and spread with the speed of grapevine until the Siberian capital was bedecked with the banners of the Tsar—to welcome the Tsar's conqueror. It had been learned that Napoleon was in Moscow, and the people of Irkutsk expected the Emperor of the French to march into Siberia and bring freedom. Not until the allied armies of Russia, Austria, Prussia, and Sweden had occupied Paris were the flags lowered, and a dream of freedom shelved.

But the freedom which the Governor General and his minions, officials and officers, operators and usufructaries of illicit businesses, and fly-by-night characters who catered to their whims had in mind was not the rise of the individual from bondage. They wanted permanent immunity from restrictive laws and abolition of the institution of the *revisor*.

There had been *revisors* in Siberia before. Every now and then a ranking dignitary had been taken to task, and some had had to atone for their misdeeds with their lives. More often exposed evildoers had to pay exorbitant bribes to obtain exoneration. But these were occupational hazards, caused not so much by unusual wickedness of the culprits as by recurrent paroxysms of a tsar's spite against his appointees.

Disastrous as such occurrences were for the affected, the machine of corruption continued to operate to the advantage of those who could get their hands on one of its variformed levers.

But ever since ominous tidings had first told of the young Tsar's addiction to reform, a shadow had been lingering over Irkutsk: the shadow of another revisor, quite different from his predecessors: an uncorruptible, righteous man who would weigh the officials' deeds against the law and collect the balance in penitence.

Irkutsk would much rather see the Tsar go down and the alien conqueror raise his Eagle over Siberia than account for traditional misdeeds and carry a crushing burden of morality into a chastened future.

The city of 14,000 was the showcase of Siberian corruption, the mecca of those who wanted to enjoy and augment ill-gotten affluence in an atmosphere in which law, represented by sheets of yellowing paper, gathered dust in backroom files, and in which power, parading in brutish splendor, ruled supreme.

Irkutsk had not been reclaimed from the wilderness. It had been planted upon the grandiose expanse, a cluster of barbaric ugliness, with indomitable dark earth protruding between artless constructions of stone and timber, which ranged from an oversized gubernatorial mansion to ramshackle booths. Over the unpaved ground bumped pompous carriages of generals, prelates, and racketeers.

Irkutsk was not only the seat of the administration of Siberia; it was also the residence of the Orthodox archbishop. Twelve churches had been built by wealthy patrons: ten Orthodox, and one Catholic and Lutheran respectively. The latter served a parish of fourteen women and one man: Governor General Jacobi. The clergy of Irkutsk did not censure the citizens' immorality, but accepted it as an established institution. Irkutsk was also the city of entertainment.

Booze was being superseded by champagne. In a country in which transportation could not handle vital supplies horse-drawn carts carried cases of French wines over thousands of miles to satisfy the gourmets of the Siberian East. Eight bottles of champagne cost as much as one good horse, but consumption rose almost two hundredfold in the first twoscore of years of the nineteenth century.

Untidy native wenches and veterans from soldiers' brothels in European Russia were crowded out by silk-and-lace-clad perfumed demimondaines, who initiated overdressed but unkempt customers into an art of love-making which became imbued with a local tinge of excessiveness. Sadism and masochism were its main features, and the orgies of Irkutsk paled the revelries in ancient centers of voluptuousness. No longer would Siberian parvenus go west. They went to Irkutsk, where nobody expected them to behave like civilized men, and where nobody asked indiscreet questions. In Irkutsk everybody behaved as he liked, and nobody inquired about other people's business, presuming that it was no more legal than his own.

In Irkutsk you did not even have to fear the smoldering wrath of the poor. The small townspeople lived on crumbs from banquet tables, and had no greater desire than to join the horde of crouching, purloining servants.

Governor generals were the overlords and patrons of corruption who levied private taxes, sold government property, rented Crown monopolies, and transferred public funds to their private accounts. General Gagarin built a mansion, the biggest and most hideous structure in Siberia, at a cost of well above a hundred governor generals' annual salaries. The ceiling of its main hall consisted of a giant aquarium. General Tchitcherin, who did not like the rugged looks of Russian regulars, maintained a private palace guard of Haiducks, pedigreed specimens of pure Magyar descent garbed in a gala that not even the Tsar could have afforded for his bodyguard.

General Jacobi hired an elite of German ruffians, and had them built up to regimental strength; he also had a private orchestra of forty virtuosos whose individual pay exceeded that of the Assistant Governor General.

Governor generals arranged festivities that everybody who lived within the province had to attend. Absenteeism was checked and punished. Destitute cattle breeders feasted on roast oxen, which the Governor General's myrmidons had driven away from their depleted herds; bread-starved mushiks were swilled with spirits distilled from illegally confiscated bread grain. Drunkards mated on festival grounds while from windows and balconies guests of honor watched their doings, disgusted and stimulated, repeating time and again that people were worse than beasts and ought to be treated accordingly.

Resident governor generals claimed to know best what was good for Siberia. They styled themselves regents and aspired at viceroyship as a transition to regal powers. They reported to the capital at lengthening intervals, confined their accounts to formalities, and began to ignore summonses.

Siberia remained too large a domain to be ruled by any single man of their caliber, but tyrants based their rule upon the support of a hard core of accomplices. Governor generals authorized abuse of office and transgression of law, regionwise, and beneficiaries acted as the governor generals' trustees, the mainstays of his control, and his unflinchingly perjurous witnesses. They acted as his executive organs against rebels who claimed their rights under the Tsar's law.

This law provided that people could convene in an orderly manner to review their affairs, but the governor generals' trustees delegated their organs to "maintain order" and meetings stopped at once.

As the eighteenth century drew to a close, the only means to present grievances was the filing of a written complaint, and since Siberian authorities summarily arrested complainants, disgruntled men would have to write to the Senate of St. Petersburg, nominally the highest court of appeal in Siberian affairs.

The St. Petersburg term for complaints was "denunciation"; in Siberia, they were called "rabulistics," manifestations of a spirit of calumny, which pervaded the common people—and distinguished them from the animals.

Most complainants were illiterate and had to confide their grievances to scribes, who more often than not would inform the police. If a letter of complaint were intercepted, the sender was likely to disappear without a trace. Some "denunciations," however, did reach the Senate. But since grievances reflected unfavorably upon senatorial efficiency, if not integrity, it could happen that the Senate would refer a denunciation right back to Siberian authorities.

Had it not been for disgruntled petty clerks in Siberian offices who, envious of the wealth of their superiors, managed to get complaints into the proper hands, the practice could not have continued.

After the reformer Tsar ascended the throne, exasperated officials tried to stop all complaints. Newly appointed Governor General Pestel, a senator himself, opened a furious campaign against the "white collar people" (petty officials wore uniforms with white collars), charging them with fostering rabulistics. His investigation of irregularities in the district of Viatka resulted in mass arrests of white-collar people and was followed by similar disciplinary actions in other Siberian provinces. The very name of Pestel scared the small fry and his scornful nasal laughter sent a chill through their bent spines. "Denunciations" stopped, but resumed again when Pestel returned to Russia on a prolonged leave, leaving a favorite in charge of official business in Irkutsk.

And the shadow of the supreme *revisor* lengthened.

In St. Petersburg parlors it had become fashionable to talk social progress, to engage in soul-searching and high-minded criticism of the state of affairs. Noblemen adopted the young Tsar's lofty vocabulary, and ladies his charitable sentimentality. Siberia became a topic of high-society conversation. Reforms in Siberia, drastic as they might be, would not necessarily affect life in the capital, and Siberia was big enough to warrant humanitarian concern.

Statistics as of 1800 gave its area as 4,815,000 square miles, 34 per cent of it arable land, 25 per cent forests, and the population approximately 1,800,000. And because figures alone were no incentive to reform, archives were opened to disclose facts about two centuries of Russian administration of Siberia.

Records were incomplete and occasionally equivocal. It took serious historians a lifetime of research to analyze the situation in Siberia. Only in 1845 did the chronicler Gersevanov sum up his findings in this sentence: "Siberia will never grow strong; it will always sap the strength of its foster land."

Three years later Shtshapov, a man of considerable erudition, reasoned: "In Siberia, men never were the masters of nature, but nature dominated and overwhelmed men. Discoveries were made incidentally and at random. The wealth of Siberian nature stimulated the Russians' urge to explore and exploit it, but it also revealed the intellectual impotence of the Russian people."

Soul-searching society, however, would not talk about intellectual impotence and, least of all, blame the people, represented by the picturesque mushik, whom it temporarily adopted as an untouchable pet. And socialites devoted less time to research than to gossip. Everybody gossiped about the wickedness of Siberian governor generals. Parlors featured the story of the replica to the Russian throne, which was set up in the gubernatorial mansion in Irkutsk; during inauguration ceremonies the Governor General was supposed to stand on its lowest step. Since 1782, however, incumbents had walked right up the stairs and sat down. Next thing they would wear crowns! Only by removal of the replica, parlor reformists insisted, could the outrage be stopped.

One report, written as early as 1736, told of "Regent" Shobolov; his trial became the *cause célèbre* in St. Petersburg seventy years after his execution. Shobolov had shown complete disregard for the Tsar's ukases. He had not only refused to carry out a rescript ordering him to assign land to peasant petitioners, but he had the courier who carried the order mutilated and put to death. His military organs had engaged in confiscations, arrests, and executions without due process of law. He had ruled by corporal punishment, jail, and extortion. The verdict had found him guilty of "having acquired huge property by deceit and acceptance of bribes." He had coerced wealthy burghers into surrendering their gold and furs, and made lesser fry pay for his "tolerance" in money and commodities ranging from textiles to eggs. The first revisor who had visited him in Irkutsk was given the free run of the city, where he collected the fabulous sum of 150,000 rubles from the townsfolk before reporting that Governor General Shobolov was a man of outstanding virtue. Another revisor, however, had sealed Shobolov's doom; the Governor

General went to the gallows, a merciful death compared with procedures he had applied to his own antagonists.

Alexander knew the sordid story of Shobolov. His courtiers kept elaborating on the wickedness of governor generals who, by mistreating the people of Siberia, committed *lèse-majesté*. For was not the Tsar the father of his humble subjects? The Tsar was embarrassed. He could depose a guilty party, but he could not abolish the office of Governor General. And he also realized that by adding more virtuous and resounding words to admonitions by his predecessors he could not remedy abuses. Alexander wanted more information and specific suggestions.

The country was said to be wealthy beyond belief? What had happened to its riches?

Siberia's abundance of fur animals had been squandered. The migration of sables had taught hunters no lesson. They had continued slaughtering precious animals, and, provided Russian America did not make up for the deficit, European and Asiatic Russia would soon have to import furs.

Siberia's soil had produced crops twice as large as those of similar European Russian areas, and at first the virgin land had not even required manure. But the farmers had never given the land its due; whenever a tract showed indications of fatigue, it had been abandoned by the shiftless peasantry.

Siberian transportation was a calamity. It took 125 years to build a dirt road connecting two cities, a project originally scheduled to take two years; and the eventual costs exceeded the original appropriation by thousands per cent.

In 1754 the Russian paper *Monthly Treatises* had printed an officially inspired editorial, which predicted that Siberia's budding industry would soon supply domestic and foreign markets with textiles, glass, hardware, and leather. But fifty years after the auspicious forecast Siberian industry stagnated. Workers were in short supply and their skills low, and they were shiftless. And industrialists had no patience to build up production in a country where you could collect 200 per cent annual interest for loans.

Siberia's mineral deposits and forests were property of the Crown, but no benefits had been drawn from iron, coal, precious metals, and timber. The Crown was an inanimate object, and those acting under its symbolic authority had none of the qualities that boosted industry elsewhere. Russian administrators would lease forests and mines to suspicious characters who would make a fast ruble, split with the officials, and get out of business rather than make an investment; or they would just order deportees and conscripts to dig the treasure, and jailers to supervise diggers; and if their orders produced more human fatalities than material profit, they would file charges against alleged saboteurs.

Under the rule of the second Catherine, when commercial agreements with Bokhara were signed, this was hailed as the inauguration of a golden age of Siberian trade. And outbursts of patriotic conceit had greeted the exchange of goods with China. The expansion of Russian control in the southern steppes unleashed similar explosions; and eventually all resulted in disillusionment and weird bitterness.

Confronted with a record that made reforms appear absurdly hopeless, Alexander might have switched his attention toward less frustrating objectives, and courtiers would have gladly followed their monarch's lead toward greener pastures of charitableness had it not been for one man who worked relentlessly for drastic exposure and effective reconstruction of Siberia. This man kept Alexander's interest in Siberia alive and took care that investigations continued in war and peace, and through the vicissitudes of the Tsar's life and his own.

Ukases dating back to Ermak's day were unearthed. They directed officials to question natives about places where gold, silver, iron, and precious stones could be found, to keep records on useful plants and animals, and to see that every sable fur be forwarded to the Tsar. After eighty years the ukases produced a joint petition of Siberian district governors to the Tsar, to let heralds, complete with mantle and tabard, summon everybody who knew of gold, silver, copper, and glimmering mountains, to report to the authorities. Yet another fifteen years later, almost one century after the first orders had been issued, only pranksters, fools, and cheats had responded to the challenge.

The administration, more prolific in putting the blame for failures on unofficials than in devising remedies, complained about the Russian's innate aversion to stability. The population, they said, refused to be "fixed." As one report from Siberia specified: "The Russian enjoys nothing better than a life free of control and tutelage; he dreams of fabulous treasures in mythical lands, either somewhere in the Arctic or beyond the steppes." St. Petersburg reacted to this psychological treatise by another ukase, directing Siberian governors to forbid peasants to sleep outside the house. The ukase did not indicate how the governors should check its abidance.

Other decrees dealt with the "fixation" of craftsmen. They ordered that guilds and co-operatives be formed, that every craftsman join them and remain tied to his trade. Whoever changed profession without authorization would be considered a vagabond, liable to forced labor and corporal punishment. However, the greater part of the professional population of Siberia belonged to that category at one time or other.

Mounted patrols roamed large areas, hunting runaways; and since nobody trusted Cossacks, the authorities used dragoons for the purpose. But the soldiers were not smart enough to deal with vagabonds whose habits were not much different from those of wild creatures. Considering that it required a mushik to handle a mushik, the government of Siberia organized auxiliaries to assist the dragoons, shiftless peasants who would gladly turn torturers of their own kin. The auxiliaries were named *Ssermjaga* bands, after *ssermjaga*, the coarse cloth of which the peasants' caftans were made. The Ssermjaga men knew how to find vagabonds. Every man caught dead or alive netted a bounty. And because dead men were easier to handle the deliveries consisted almost entirely of corpses.

Once, however, a large Ssermjaga band was ambushed by an even larger band of vagabonds: the entire population of a community who had abandoned their assigned land and had trekked south, well armed and reasonably well supplied with food. Peasant butchered peasant in a savage orgy of piled-up hatred.

It had happened that groups of shiftless peasants crossed into China. The wanderers hardly knew of "Ki-tai," but, trudging south, they encountered guards in a garb they did not know, and then learned that they were on a territory where they would be free to settle, liable to nominal taxes payable every other year, and with no statutory labor to perform. To their surprise the wayward peasants found that this was true. They became loyal subjects of the emperors of China, and remained free until Russian invaders caught up with them.

An indignant administration of Siberia considered border crossing tantamount to desertion. A decree of 1743 stipulated that persons found without a valid passport in the vicinity of the border were subject to the whip and stick if under forty, to the knout if they were older.

The files disclosed that nobility of birth and dignity of station were defiled by holders of offices in Siberia, and that ranking officials sent there on inspection often violated their oaths and misused their powers to force their way into rings which traded in spirits, contraband, prostitutes, and food set aside for emergencies.

The Siberian clergy was no better than Siberian officialdom. Ukases issued during the eighteenth century ordered secular authorities to prevent ministers from engaging in profane trade in the disguise of pastoral activities. But secular authorities and clergy agreed upon mutual tolerance and division of illicit interests. Monasteries acquired land by nominal purchase and actual robbery; they sold seeds, food, and other wares against labor, at rates which could cause a professional usurer to blush, and which kept the debtor permanently enslaved. Archpriest Jergunov of Beresov obtained a spirit monopoly and made an average profit of 700 per cent annually. Parish priests ran local stores and kept competitors away by sheer violence. Abbots established themselves in the transportation industry by renting debtor workers as relay whenever horses were in short supply.

Transportation was another Siberian woe. The first road linking Tobolsk and Verkhoturie had been completed in 1593; it was a track rather than a road, but the Russians had thought that it was good enough. Later the jamstshiki coachmen entrusted with official transportation duties were ordered to build more roads, but they were not industrious men, and they did not believe in the necessity of transportation arteries. A cart and a horse could always tread a flat expanse. Most of Siberia was flat expanse, they thought, and did not see why they should bother with construction.

It took until 1637 to complete another track linking Tobolsk and Tara; this record of slowness crumbled, as the next overland route took 125 years to be completed in a fashion no less haphazard than earlier communications. In the mid-eighteenth century 6724 jamstshiki had been counted in Siberia, one to more than 700 square miles; and even if these highhanded, insolent, blackmailing men had been the most zealous lot, they could not have turned Siberia into a land with adequate communications.

Health counselors who visited Siberia told that the country had a higher percentage of misfits, idiots, and incurable drunkards than any other territory of which records were kept. Most natives had syphilis, and in some Russian settlements the entire population suffered from the disease. Goiter was spreading, and with it went further physical and mental deterioration.

Decrees promoted education in Siberia. But only eighteen elementary schools were said to exist—one to 100,000 people; how many of them actually were in operation no archive would tell.

The peasantry was supposed to defray expenses of elementary schools, but the mushiks shirked that obligation, and authorities were lax in enforcing it. The peasants would not send their children to school and thus waste the children's working hours. Officials and merchants were expected to give their sons a higher education; officials wanted them to meet civil-service standards, and businessmen would have them learn to deal with arithmetic problems which could not be solved on the abacus. Girls were not expected to go to school. But early in the nineteenth century the urge for higher learning had not produced noticeable results. Only two "gymnasiums"—a type of school midway between high school and junior college—existed in Siberia, and the combined attendance was seventy. Records of 1803 indicate the existence of two universities, complete with imperial statute, privileges, and a private endowment of 100,000 rubles. However, not until 1811 did these dormant institutions merge into one operating university—Tomsk. The Iasak, the bane of Siberia, was no longer levied. Intercourse between Russians and autochthonous Siberians had reduced "pure natives" to a figure that made collection unlucrative. Yet vagabonds and soldiers raided villages and imposed arbitrary head taxes, payable mostly in food supplies or children. In times of famine parents would sell their offspring for a crust of bread to vagrants, who operated itinerant begging businesses. Boys and girls were organized into hordes of aggressive beggars, collecting alms and delivering them to their bosses. Occasionally itinerant entrepreneurs sold their inventory to established city begging businesses. Escaped little beggars formed gangs of thieves, notorious for their ability to squeeze through the smallest apertures in walls and fences.

Usurers accepted children in lieu of cash. Usury was big business in Siberia, but not even its victims would call it a transgression. It was an established practice, and circumstances rather than disposition determined who would exploit whom. Usury had its seasons; the best was tax-collecting time. Taxes were not preassessed. Collectors determined what was due. He who couldn't pay in full might be lucky and get away with a penalty—usually two lashes with the knout for every missing ruble—or he might have to borrow, to escape arrest. Lenders accompanied collectors. Interests were charged in labor. No mushik would have understood the meaning of principal, interests, and their interrelation even had it been explained to him. Entire families might toil for many months to pay a few rubles interest, and then still owe the principal. Lenders who owned the labor of many able-bodied mushiks would acquire land, put them to work there, and use the proceeds to lend more money, get more chattels, still more estates, and ever more chattels. Such usurer-landowners were called kulaks. Local authorities and kulaks co-operated in matters of recruitment. The kulak determined who should join the Army. He drafted reasonably well-off youths and exacted bribes for deferment, which he split with officials, and eventually he inducted paupers. Kulaks controlled the village trade as agents of city merchants who dumped junk upon the yokels. Holding monopolies, the kulaks always managed to sell. Their monopolies were sustained by administrators, in return for fees for tolerance and protection.

Administrators were in charge of emergency stores: food set aside for recurrent famines. Sporadical reports on Siberian famines reached St. Petersburg, where they usually caused a mild stir of pious regret, and a zealous and unavailing interoffice correspondence. In Siberia emergency storehouses were thrown open to contractors who sold the contents to the needy for labor.

The latest reports on famine reaching St. Petersburg after the Napoleonic invasion concerned the district of Turukhansk on the lower Yenisei River. Socialites did not enjoy having the event mentioned in their drawing rooms. The description was too drastic for their taste.

But the man who kept alive the Tsar's interest in Siberia managed to get the facts before the ruler, in 1815, when the disaster of Turukhansk was at its peak. Alexander learned that Russians and natives alike had no other food than the bark of fir trees, and the flesh of carcasses. Corpses of the starved littered the tundra, and the outskirts of Turukhansk City. Limbs were torn from the dead; cannibalism was rampant. One mother first devoured her starved daughter, then ordered her sons to kill one from among them, and for a while the family feasted on his remains; then it was another boy's turn. Two sons remained. The mother insisted that they repeat the fratricide, and when they hesitated, she grasped a knife and hurled herself against the younger. The boys joined, slaughtered the woman, lived on her flesh, and when it gave out, walked away to the tundra.

The administrator of Turukhansk, who had sought refuge in better-supplied areas, eventually returned to his district. He found the population almost extinct, and beasts of prey roaming the town. He did not report, however, what had become of the emergency supplies he should have distributed among the sufferers free of charge. The victims obviously had not paid the price charged by corruptionists. A St. Petersburg cynic quipped: "It's better to be a forced laborer than a dead cannibal."

Conversationalists reasoned philosophically that Siberia was a country of extremes, and that all extremes were breeding violence. The story of the Raskolniki was revived. These people, who had abandoned their ancestral homes and followed the conquerors of Siberia rather than accept changes of religious doctrine, these ardent believers in their version of the unadulterated word of the Redeemer, had turned into rabid fools. Whenever their unfathomable anger was stirred, they protested by stripping themselves, and putting the torch to their dwellings. In one single year, 1760, 3000 Raskolniki committed suicide at the stake of their flaming settlements.

Then there were also the Kamenshtshiki, sectarians of mixed Russo-Mongolian-Tunguse ancestry, said to have incited rebellions of serfs since 1685. And the common people in Siberia accepted without objection what the regular clergy told them about these and all other sectarians, namely that these heretics were to blame for practically every evil, be it cattle disease or banditry.

In St. Petersburg it was considered a blessing that the pyromaniacal Raskolniki were moving to Russian America; Siberia could replace their number soon enough. Hadn't the population figure increased prodigally since 1709, when it had not yet passed the quarter-million mark, and since 1622, when it had been estimated at 70,000 including 10,000 deportees?

Parlor statisticians did not take into account that the 1622 figure covered only a fraction of the total area, that it did not include natives, and that the one-quarter-million figure had been based upon the accounts of tax collectors, who listed only settled populations.

But even so, mankind was not marked for extinction in Siberia. The Lord's sun shone over that land, and its light would dispel the darkness of minds. The decent, though temporarily dominated by the wicked, would prevail. With proper assistance this could be achieved within Tsar Alexander's lifetime, to the reformer's everlasting glory.

The man who believed this looked like a debonair *bon vivant,* and more like a highborn drawing-room habitué than most scions of ancient boyar families. And yet, Mikhail Speranski, who was forty when the Grande Armée evacuated blazing Moscow, was a humble man by origin and background.

Son of a nondescript village priest, he had studied in an ecclesiastic seminary. His professors had thought that the soft-spoken young man would do better as a teacher of mathematics and physics than as a parish priest, and gave him a tuition assignment. Mikhail Speranski dutifully funneled as much science into the minds of his pupils as they were ready to absorb. Continuing his own studies, he became fascinated with what seemed to him a relationship between the phenomena of nature and the social organization of men. These highly theoretical observations would have had no practical effects had not

Prince Kurakin, a Russian statesman looking for an original and brilliant secretary, learned of Speranski's wisdom.

Kurakin talked to the mathematician-physicist-philosopher, and hired him on the spot. Catapulted from the Spartan dimness of the seminary into the limelight of the household of a ranking courtier, the ex-teacher gave such an extraordinary account of his originality that his master introduced him to the young Tsar whose demand for stimulating minds was insatiable. From being a prince's secretary Speranski was promoted to the Tsar's spiritual mentor. He did not attempt to outrun Alexander's mind on its twisted track, but tried to guide it toward greater efficiency.

Even though the Tsar could rarely follow his mentor's reasonings, he appointed him court counselor, and in 1806, when Alexander went to Erfurt, Germany, for a first meeting with Napoleon, Speranski became a member of the Tsar's staff. "This man seems to have the only clear head in Russia," the Emperor of the French is quoted as having said about Speranski, who was promoted Minister of State, much to the dismay of established diplomats who wanted to deal with new international problems the good old Russian way and disliked the upstart's attitude at the conference table.

Speranski talked reform at the conference table. The Tsar did not seem to mind it, and did not object to Speranski mentioning Siberian affairs in the presence of foreigners.

The Erfurt Conference paved the way for another meeting between the Tsar and the Emperor, one year later, in Tilsit, which resulted in the first short-lived Franco-Russian pact of friendship.

During the six years that followed the Erfurt Conference, Speranski—now titled—wielded more influence than all other cabinet members combined. His words, carefully memorized by courtiers, determined political fashions.

Siberia remained his pet topic. His ministerial colleagues and senators would have wished to see him appointed Governor General of Siberia. But the Tsar was not yet willing to see his favorite prompter leave for the wilderness.

Came March 1812. Vanguards of the Grande Armée gathered along the banks of the Niemen River, among them Polish cavalrymen, rebels against the Tsar's rule. Napoleon was about to attack, and already he had subverted nations that were under Russia's sway. Erfurt was a failure, and so was Tilsit. Soon there would be war.

Alexander was desperately looking for a top military expert to counter French strategy better than his own generals. He had offered supreme command to a former Napoleonic marshal, Jean Baptiste Bernadotte, who had started out as a stable boy in Pau, France, and in a comic opera career had been kicked upstairs to the rank of Crown Prince of Sweden. But Bernadotte was stalling and bickering, obviously afraid of meeting Napoleon in battle. Courtiers insinuated that the Tsar should leave Marshal Kutuzov in charge of the Russian Army, and rather look for a scapegoat to be blamed for whatever happened to Russia.

A corpulent grand duchess, a Swedish-born general, and a few bold dignitaries charged Speranski with conspiring against the Tsar, with having plotted with Napoleon, with wanting to turn Russia into a testing ground for revolutionary experiments reminiscent of the Terror in France. There was no evidence against the Minister of State, but the accusers said that it would be found later—after the parvenu had been put out of the way of honest investigations by being sent to Siberia as an exile.

Alexander did not believe in Speranski's disloyalty, but he was not ready to shoulder full responsibility for the war and everything that had led up to it. Fretting and vacillating, he discharged his minister of state. He did not send him into exile, but requested that he move to the provincial town of Pensa, and, on a pension, wait there until further notice.

The waiting period lasted until 1816, but Speranski kept informing the Tsar on Siberian affairs. Meantime the greatest wars in European history were won and the greatest opportunities for a lasting peace lost because statesmen tried to establish an animated order upon dead issues. And Alexander saw the Holy Alliance, his pet brainchild, come to naught, when the Congress of Vienna did not embrace his pattern of merging the peoples of Russia, Prussia, and Austria into a nebulous Christian nation, and to grant them title to free movement as a panacea.

Failure of this project was the turning point in Alexander's life. From then on he would impose his will upon his subjects with more benevolent fundamental intentions perhaps than his predecessors, but with even greater ruthlessness.

He would start by reforming Siberia. Speranski should show what he could do there. The pensioner from Pensa was summoned to St. Petersburg and nominated acting Governor General of Siberia, in charge of revision and purification.

"One dozen years without the visit of an incorruptible revisor would debase every Russian administration," Speranski had once told the Tsar. "Revisions in Siberia have always been farcical. Revision requires a clean sweep, followed by lasting reforms."

Alexander reminded him of his words. Speranski would have the power to make a clean sweep; to use his powers to the best of all concerned.

The revisor had no delusions about difficulties ahead. He had two herculean labors to perform: cleaning the stables of Siberian maladministration and slaying the hydra of Siberian corruption. But while King Augeas's legendary stables had not been cleaned for thirty years, the filth of Siberian administration had kept accumulating for more than two centuries. And while the multi-headed water serpent of the saga grew only two heads for every one severed, the corruption of Siberia could grow one thousand heads for every one destroyed. And the ten other labors of the mythical Greek demigod looked like child's play compared with Speranski's mission to establish lawfulness where men believed in violence only, and trust where deceit ruled supreme.

But in the hour of impending trial the ex-Minister of State and Governor General reverted to the simple philosophy his naïve father had once taught him: that to trust in the righteousness of one's own doings was better than to ponder over clever ways of reaching one's goal.

CHAPTER FIFTY

Speranski's mission opened with a hearing in Russia.

Former Governor General Pestel, who had resigned one step ahead of Speranski's appointment and remained a member of the Senate, testified about the administration of Siberia.

With haughty grandeur of attitude and terminology he insisted that he had no knowledge of irregularities in Siberia; that his assistant, who had conducted affairs in his absence, was a faithful servant of the Tsar and a man of unflinching honesty; that accounts of rampant corruption were so much gossip, devised by malicious, idle minds; and that whatever petty fraud may have occurred in remote districts had been attributable to white-collar misconduct, practically wiped out during his term of office. Pestel introduced testimony by high-placed officials and senators, to the effect that all recent charges of misuse of office in Siberia had been proved wrong.

Speranski had a bitter foretaste of things to come: the phalanx of liars in office, standing like a wall in the way of investigation; scared small fry, who would choose the better part of valor and not stick their necks out as witnesses; the prospect of a one-man struggle on a thousand fronts, and a thousand travesties of justice standing up against one truth, which he had yet to establish.

Pestel's testimony wound up with an emphatic declaration of his personal integrity and impecuniousness. However, for more than one decade he had been drawing two salaries, that of a governor general and that of a senator, and Russian civil-service regulations forbade acceptance of multiple salaries. Speranski mentioned it dryly, just in passing.

The retired Governor General left Pensa, determined to encourage all forces in Siberia to sabotage the investigation.

Siberian officialdom was in bad need of encouragement.

Speranski was the incarnation of their nightmare, the man whose possible appointment had been haunting all the ranks but the lowest. Now that he was appointed, nothing short of a fatal accident might prevent disaster. So great was the shock of Speranski's assignment that not even uninhibited killers were able to organize an accident.

Pestel's secret couriers offered comfort. Whatever reports Speranski would make, the Senate, still the highest resort in Siberian affairs, would not accept one man's word against that of many others. Even if the Revisor-Governor General were to communicate directly with the Tsar, there were sensible people in Alexander's entourage to counsel the Tsar against rash action. There would also be means to delay Speranski's departure. Time would work against the reformer; the Tsar might abandon certain ideas and Speranski himself might become open to traditional Siberian arguments. . . .

In Siberia, Lieutenant Governor General Treskin, his wife, and their associates girded for the struggle. Treskin had once worked as a postal clerk in Russia, where Senator Pestel discovered him and made him his assistant, his creature, his henchman, and eventually his lieutenant. Treskin, the plebeian, worshiped Pestel, the patrician. He despised the common people, and after having been installed in office in Siberia he pledged himself to root out plebeian white-collar rabulists (quibblers).

"Treskin never abides by the law and pays no attention whatsoever to Ministerial decrees," a letter by a distinguished personality informed Speranski, but the writer did not want to be quoted and did not specify particular instances of Treskin's illegality.

"Treskin was quite clever," another contemporary wrote about the Lieutenant Governor General, "but his intelligence and efficiency never outgrew that of a postal clerk. Given proper guidance, he would have made a reasonably good subaltern. As the acting head of the Siberian administration, he turned into a vile despot."

In fact his despotism had aspects of burlesque. He would tour households of Irkutsk burghers at mealtime, sample dishes, and decree punishment for poor cooking. He would regulate hours in which tea could be consumed, or he would rule whose vegetable garden should be converted into a tobacco plantation. He would also interfere in matters of greater bearing, ordering sections of the city to be torn down because they annoyed him, or decreeing that the course of a river be altered because it was "altogether wrong," and inflict draconic punishment upon engineers who did not succeed in making a river flow the "proper way."

His assumption of office was highlighted by a good-will present threateningly solicited from the citizenry: a large estate outside Irkutsk. Anija Fjodorovna—Madame Treskin—was the guiding spirit behind her husband's demand for the gift, and she took charge of general business affairs.

Anija was a homely woman of loose morals. Her personal lackey was her number-one lover and keeper of her accounts. Whoever wanted a favor, be it an office or a commercial concession, had to register with the lackey, who charged a stiff tip for an appointment with his mistress. Anija received applicants in her bedroom, claiming that she wanted to know a man thoroughly before acting upon his request. She collected a price for the bedroom check, higher than local demimondaine's fees. The delights did not warrant the expense, but nobody could hope to achieve his aims without passing the horizontal check point, as a sneering lackey would say.

Every office had a price: Anija and her lackey collected, her husband signed appointments.

Mrs. Treskin also handled licenses for retail trade in major cities. She would invent variations of collecting procedures, such as making the applicant buy a fur coat worth 50 rubles at 5000. Newcomers to Irkutsk were advised to pay courtesy calls on Madame Lieutenant Governor General. No caller was admitted empty-handed; nothing less valuable than a case of tea was deemed acceptable by the lackey. To be invited to a card game was a dreaded distinction. Stakes were extravagant, and he who did not lose to the hostess faced grievous inconveniences.

Mr. Treskin was represented at his wife's parties by his secretary, Mr. Beljavsky, and his counsel, Mr. Hedenstrom, who also were the lady's permanent lovers number two and three respectively. Anija shared her husband's predilection for patricians and called the two men genuine thoroughbreds even though the only known fact about Beljavsky and Hedenstrom was that they were thieves. The lackey apparently did not resent his mistress's nonprofessional infidelity, and the Lieutenant Governor General benignly tolerated her doings and enjoyed being called a fine family man.

There was one field of business activities that Treskin reserved for himself: the administration of government granaries and emergency supplies. He charged huge sums for keeping government larders bulging with food, and his reports never failed to mention the establishment of grain reserves. But when famine struck, warehouses were empty, reserves had disappeared, and Treskin produced witnesses who had seen bandits looting the stores.

Such testimonies were kept in the files. After Speranski's assignment special protocols concerning the disaster of Turukhansk were fabricated.

In Pensa, meantime, Speranski waited for completion of official preparations for his trip. He needed a staff of civil servants, military escort, and compilations of files and records. There were constant delays, and even a man of lesser experience would have realized that he was faced with organized sabotage. Speranski sent a few memoranda to the Tsar, but Alexander was not in the mood to interfere, and even the Tsar would have had difficulties disentangling the labyrinth of red tape.

Speranski's intimate friends urged him to cheer up. Eventually he would leave for Siberia; once there, he would fulfill his mission against all odds. But the friends, too, had to admit that malevolent glee spread among his antagonists.

Two years after his nomination Speranski was still in Pensa, consulting with one Mr. Zeyer, a conscientious civil servant of German ancestry, an honest "ink soul," who would be the Governor General's chief investigating agent. Zeyer had to study thousands of documents relating to Siberia, of which he knew only that it was big and, evidently, rotten.

In the early spring of 1819, at long last, Speranski left at the head of a staff not large enough to handle the affairs of one single province, and escorted by a military force not strong enough to have dealt with Siberian Praetorian guards.

Immediately after crossing the Ural Mountains, Speranski improvised a revision of the accounts of a district commissioner. The little man had defrauded a paltry 50 rubles, allotted for building a small bridge over a river that did not really exist. The culprit was dishonorably discharged. Speranski intended to show all concerned that he would not condone the smallest fraud. But administrators and magistrates from all over Siberia, who maintained a network of informers to watch his actions, breathed with relief: Speranski, they thought, did not really go after the big fish, but turned against the small fry instead. Next he would join the anti-white-collar drive, and might wind up, with bulging pockets, as an apologist for the administration.

But, at Speranski's next stopover, prospects for corruptionists dimmed again. The local governor, who had pocketed every copper of public revenue, was arrested. Peasants from all over the district, even soldiers and a few burghers, made damaging depositions against their former tyrant. However, Speranski's choice for a successor to the arrested man was every bit as fraudulent as his predecessor and observers agreed that, come what may, the Revisor could not leave the country without an administration. Having no other trained experts available than old Siberian hands, he might change names and faces; but the system would stand, reform-proof.

Hardly had Speranski left the district when the new administrator turned against the witnesses. They were forced by the knout to revoke their charges; eventually Speranski would have to reinstate the deposed man.

Tobolsk was the first major Siberian city on the itinerary. At the gate a delegation of citizens and officials offered Speranski bread and salt, as it was an ancient custom throughout the Tsar's realm, and put the offering on a platter of massive gold, as it was the custom in Siberia to placate a revisor. The Governor General did not accept the platter, but, assisted by Mr. Zeyer, checked files and accounts.

"Had I tried all these felons in court," he wrote a friend, "they would have gone to the gallows." But Tobolsk was but one district, and whatever frauds had been committed there were but a foretaste of things to come in Irkutsk. With almost three years lost in Pensa, Speranski could not afford to stage major trials in every district capital and wait for their outcome before continuing East.

"The farther I proceed into the interior of Siberia," another of Speranski's letters read, "the more evil I find; and already, the evil is almost unbearable."

The Governor General did not lack the faculty of impressive writing, but what he found at every turn had to be seen to be believed. It was the absolute evil, the perversion of established truth, the reversal of every concept of decency, a Sodom and Gomorrah, where not one single righteous man seemed to dwell.

There were some veiled innuendoes that he did not aim at righting the wrong, but at settling scores, old animosities nursed by his friends against Siberian personalities. This was perfectly stupid, but nothing seemed to be more difficult to combat by logic than stupidity. Speranski's powers were unlimited. However, he applied for the Tsar's special authorization to arrest the Governor of Tomsk, and also Lieutenant Governor Treskin. Alexander granted it in a note which breathed skepticism. Other tsars had had governors arrested and nothing good had resulted from it; did Speranski know of no better remedy than arrest?

Even though the note did not literally say so, Speranski read this between the lines.

He sent express riders ahead of his fast-traveling party, to announce that the Tsar's own delegate was coming to accept complaints, and to bring remedy and justice to all of the Tsar's subjects. The delegate's mighty arm, riders shouted, would protect all honest men who appeared before him against retaliation.

But people were scared. Few presented grievances, and of them who did most did so outside of settlements, throwing letters at the party as it drove past, and running away without answering the challenge to stay and speak up. Questions formed in Speranski's mind, haunted him in his sleep, harassed his days: What could administrative reforms achieve that would but redistribute responsibilities? What good would directives and regulations produce unless the written word were animated by the good will of those in charge to carry them out? How could good will be created where it had not existed before?

Similar questions seemed reflected in the faces of local dignitaries who continued to present bread and salt on costly trays. They were omnipresent in the surprised and hurt expressions of officials, whom he berated for their criminal highhandedness. They glared at him whenever he investigated aspects of Siberian administration and human relations.

What he saw and read was mortifying, and mortification begot indulgence, as only hopelessness can create. Speranski appointed local commissions to investigate local administrations. Appointees worked hand in glove with administrators. . . .

Eastward the Governor General rode, through the serene beauty of Central Siberia, the perplexing gayness of flowering prairies, the reverie of pine forests, the lush fecundity of fat soil. And in the settings of felicity men lived in misery, sin, and shame.

In Irkutsk, District Leader (Ispravnik) Leskutov took charge of counter-revisor strategy.

The name of Leskutov, practically unknown in St. Petersburg, had figured prominently in Siberian letters of complaint. The Ispravnik was a myth in Siberia, the most brutal, cynical, and dishonest person in office.

As Speranski approached the district of Irkutsk, complaints and petitions stopped. Leskutov had made it known that he would learn of any complaint, and deal with the complainant later. Speranski, he insisted, would not challenge his authority. The Siberians did not doubt this. Nobody could defy Leskutov.

The Governor General sent another express courier ahead to ask Treskin whether it was true that he or Leskutov was suppressing petitions. The answer was not yet ready, when it was learned that Speranski was *ante portas*. Meantime two defensive moves had been under way. The first was carried out and the "citadel" was ready. The other, to clean up the archives, was not yet completed. Derogatory evidence listed under L, Leskutov, or C, complaints, was removed and destroyed, but afterwards, it occurred to the culprits that derogatory evidence might exist in other files, which could not all be checked prior to Speranski's arrival.

For a few days Irkutsk had turned into a ghost town. Amusement places were deserted; patrons stayed at home, and only smoke pouring from many chimneys despite the summerly weather indicated that they were busy burning evidence. Burning papers even interfered with preparations for a solemn reception of the Revisor. But undaunted amazon Anija chased members of the reception committee back to their jobs. "Keep denying charges," she advised committee members, her husband, and her illegitimate associates. Leskutov did not need any coaching. He was a determined man. Madame Treskin admired him greatly.

The District Leader in person headed the advance welcome party that waited for Speranski, several miles west of Irkutsk. Small groups of curious peasants and burghers roamed the place.

At last Speranski's carriage drove up, dust-covered and slightly battered. The Governor General looked tense when a man in full office regalia stepped forth. "Ispravnik Leskutov," he introduced himself, smiling, and began to read an address of welcome. But he had not had an opportunity to recite the meaningful words that the district's, nay, all of Siberia's, wealth, was the Crown's when Speranski shouted: "Have that felon arrested at once." One of the Governor General's officers tore the sword from Leskutov's belt. Another tied his hands.

A flabbergasted audience could not trust their eyes. "But it's Leskutov—Leskutov," peasants shouted. The Governor General could not really dare to arrest the all-powerful man. But Speranski did not seem to fear even Leskutov, who was bundled up on a cart and taken away. Peasants followed the cart at a safe distance, wondering what other earth-shaking events were ahead. Would Leskutov be hanged right away or later?

But Leskutov was not hanged. His property, 138,243 rubles in cash, and gold, silver, and furs of much greater value, was sequestrated; but then an investigation commission took over, and red tape soothed, protracted, and trivialized the case. . . .

At the city gates stood a group of dignitaries headed by Treskin. A band played, and fireworks had started even though it was not yet dark. Treskin and his companions, including Beljavsky and Hedenstrom, were flushed with excitement and champagne. They were rather comforted by Leskutov's prolonged absence. He probably rode in the Governor General's carriage, and talked to him.

But when the column at last approached they were mystified to see a shabby cart heading it, and two officers escorting the battered conveyance.

The cart stopped in front of the dignitaries. "What's on that cart?" a bewildered official inquired. "The felon Leskutov," an officer shouted through the thunderous brass of the band.

Treskin staggered.

"The outpost has fallen," Hedenstrom ventured, "but the citadel still stands."

Anija's number-three lover thrust the "citadel," a bag of money, into her husband's hand. The citadel had been Anija's idea; she had collected the cash, the highest bribe ever to be offered to a revisor, without investing any of the family funds.

Music blared. Fireworks cracked. A bewildered Treskin held the canvas bag, wondering how to hand it over to the Revisor in an unobtrusive manner. Maybe he shouldn't have listened to Anija, who said that money should always precede courtesies.

But he did not know how to alter the procedure. Already the crowd cheered dutifully . . . and here was Speranski's carriage, and the Governor General himself. He had been said to look jovial, but Speranski's expression was scornful curiosity as he glared at the Lieutenant Governor General, who looked like a paltry, overdressed scarecrow.

"As the head of the administration," Treskin began to stammer his prepared address, but the scornful glare made him lose track of the script. "I'm Treskin," he grunted sheepishly, and held the canvas bag in the direction of the carriage. "Treskin . . . That's me."

"Welcome, Your High Excellency," the chorus of officials shouted their line. "Welcome, Your High Excellency."

Mutely Speranski reached for the bag. The chorus fell silent. A trumpeter blew a wrong note. The bandleader forgot to conduct and the martial tune broke off. There were a few lone firecrackers—then that too stopped. Hundreds of pairs of eyes stared at Speranski's hands.

These hands firmly and quickly pulled the cord of the bag. Bills poured out, neatly bundled, gold coins in between. Speranski counted, carefully, deliberately, slowly—one bundle, another bundle, and yet another, and many coins . . . His expression indicated neither disgust nor amusement, not even surprise. It seemed inscrutable. Speranski was beset by curiosity to find out what the Irkutskers had estimated to be his price.

As he sat and counted, spirits rose. The band struck up. Treskin was still too weary to resume his speech, but Anija seemed to have been right. His High

Excellency was counting. He was human. There was no place like Irkutsk to cater to humanness.

Suddenly Speranski sighed, dropped the canvas bags, precious contents spilled out. He rose, and his high boot with the tinkling spurs kicked the scattered treasures. Treskin noted, with panic, that the Governor General had not pocketed one single bill or coin.

"You are discharged," Speranski said casually, and it took the flabbergasted Treskin several seconds to notice that he meant him.

The thunderbolt had struck. And so strong was its dramatic impact that neither the audience nor Treskin realized once that it had been sound and fury but not really devastating.

Speranski now was determined not to fight criminal arbitrariness by summary procedure. No error, however slight, should mar the prosecution of a criminal, however mean. He would not arrest Treskin. An investigating commission should study the record of his administration. Its findings would determine the charges against the ex-postal clerk and his unsavory associates.

A despondent Treskin drove back to his mansion to await his doom. But Anija was as optimistic and imaginative as ever and determined to fight to the finish. The files would hardly suffice for an airtight indictment. Speranski would have to rely on witnesses. Witnesses could be dealt with. His commission would have to include members from Siberia. Not even the best legal minds on Speranski's staff were familiar with the particularities of the case. Anija could handle Siberians.

The commission the Governor General appointed had a majority of Siberian members. Chief investigator, Mr. Zeyer, would have to rely on their opinions.

Zeyer appealed to the townsfolk and peasants to present complaints against the deposed Lieutenant Governor General, emphasizing that Treskin's discharge was irrevocable.

Anija sent her husband riding in his pompous carriage with his liveried coachman through the city and its suburbs, so that everybody should see that he was free and might someday return to office. Treskin had not yet resumed his air of cockiness, but peasants and burghers did not search his expression and only noticed that nothing had happened to the despot.

People were reluctant to make complaints, and when the first letters were received at last, a member of the commission claimed that they could not be acted upon. The letters were written on unstamped stationery, and an ancient district ordinance required that petitions, memorials, and similar documents had to be written on stamped paper obtainable at the tax collector's office. The office claimed to be out of forms, and that it would take a very long time to produce new supplies.

Zeyer was raging, but the commission adopted a motion to adjourn, pending a ruling on either different stationery or on the production of new supplies. Anija started rumors that it would never reconvene.

However, sessions were resumed after Speranski ruled that petitions would be acceptable regardless of paper. But then other issues hampered the investigation. The Siberian members of the commission kept bringing them up. Was this a criminal investigation or a checking of accounts? Speranski ruled that it was both.

But were not crimes involving financial issues necessarily civilian issues? Zeyer thundered that fraud, embezzlement and thievery were necessarily criminal even though money was involved. Yet truisms did not impress Siberian members of the commission. And whatever decision the Governor General would make, they queried, did the commission have actual powers beyond those of investigation and recommendations? And if the cases were brought up in a court of justice, would not recommendation constitute interference with the prerogatives of the court?

Speranski made a decision based upon expediency rather than revenge. He decreed that the principal objective of the procedures was reparation of damages caused by illegality. The commission should investigate and prepare the cases. They would not be brought up before a Siberian court, but be referred to a special committee in St. Petersburg.

Already the Great Revision dissolved into a maze of suits for damages, and the number of actual complaints was still discouragingly low.

It required strongly worded appeals to break the dam of caution. Finally more letters began pouring in.

People who had been deprived of their property and impressed into forced-labor gangs without due process of law, the next of kin of persons put to death in violation of the basic principles of justice gave hair-raising accounts of untold crimes. But there were also complaints that did not sound convincing, even though they were forcefully worded. It was established that they emanated from minor officials who were hoping for a promotion and by unsuccessful businessmen who wanted to succeed. The incongruousness of their charges reflected upon rightful complaints. Members of the commission ventured that the very nature of denunciations required that they be taken with a grain of salt. They would even use the term rabulistics, and speak of perjury of the malcontents.

When the irate Mr. Zeyer became convinced that the most dastardly crimes would go virtually unpunished, he turned into a brooding misanthrope. Pondering over how to unblock the straight road to justice, he showed signs of mental disturbance, which members of the commission gleefully reported to Speranski.

Speranski interrogated Treskin. "He is the most incompetent person, the worst blockhead, I have ever met," he would say. This was not quite correct, but it fitted into Anija's design. The more stupid her husband was found to be, the less responsible would he be held for "errors in office."

In St. Petersburg, Pestel came to the assistance of his creature by stating that Treskin was perhaps not really bright, but otherwise good and loyal.

Hardly anybody in the capital doubted that Pestel had been a partner in the proceeds of Treskin's frauds, but Senator Pestel had many powerful friends. Only Speranski could give the signal to investigate him.

No such signal came, however, and the Tsar made a caustic remark about soft-pedaling certain issues.

Speranski was more than skeptical about his achievements. "If they were measured in terms of abuses I have discovered," he wrote, "the result would be gratifying. But there can be little merit in persecuting minor officials seduced and corrupted by the evil example of their ranking superiors. The conduct of top officials is outrageous."

But, outrageous as it was, the expedient leniency toward its perpetrators was not satisfactory either.

"I could not even attempt to establish an administration of Siberia under the prevailing conditions," a defeatist Speranski confided to a friend. "Nobody could do it, nobody in his right mind would even try it."

He had not found one decent man in office. The man who had pocketed the 50 rubles allotted for the bridge over the non-existing river was the least dishonest official encountered thus far. Speranski called him to Irkutsk to work in the district administration. Offices were understaffed. Literate Siberians normally found free professions more remunerative than civil service. Officials from the West shunned Siberian assignments as ostracism. And there were not enough men on official pay rolls in European Russia to restaff the Siberian offices if malefactors were discharged.

Gradually all officials Speranski had suspended, demoted, and discharged along the road from the Urals to Irkutsk were reinstated.

Probably inspired by Anija, letters of complaint poured into the offices of the St. Petersburg Senate. They denounced Speranski's arbitrariness and brutality toward meritorious functionaries, whom he was now forced to restore to their offices but who had yet to be exonerated. The Senate did not act upon such complaints; yet in Irkutsk sympathies turned toward Treskin and even Leskutov. Had not Treskin always been a fine host, and was not Leskutov a man of prodigal energy? Leskutov's order to have vagabonds skinned alive was rather drastic, but weren't vagabonds a dangerous nuisance? Speranski may have been brilliant in St. Petersburg, but in Irkutsk he was a scholarly nonentity.

People scoffed at his alleged infatuation with the humble man, with those roaming mushiks, those good-for-nothings whom not even the knout could turn useful, and whom this former Minister of State expected to charm with highbrow words that not even educated Irkutskers could have understood.

Speranski had never expected to charm unsteady wanderers, never had expressed infatuation with the humble man, but he had not expected Siberia to be quite as rotten from top to bottom as it was. Almost everybody was both exploiter and exploited. Governors extorted from vice-governors, vice-governors from department heads, officers from enlisted men, enlisted men from the convicts they guarded. The stronger extorted from the weaker at all levels. Nobody was unimpeachable and Siberia, gem of the Crown, offered opportunities for every shade of viciousness.

He regretted having accepted the title of Governor General. So he was responsible for the iniquitous mess during his term of office. As a mere revisor he would have been free from such burden. Every day spent in Siberia sapped his strength; only faith and pride kept Speranski from committing suicide. He would drain the cup to the dregs, return to St. Petersburg, and tell the truth.

Investigating commissions worked in Irkutsk and in practically all Siberian cities. The final results of their labors were disheartening.

Of ten thousand criminals who had defrauded Crown and citizens by many hundred millions of rubles, 681 were sued for total damages of 2,847,000 rubles. All but forty-three were restored to office, some after paying nominal amounts; the rest went off lightly. Treskin was not reinstated, but he did not have to pay much either. Anija managed to recover the "citadel," and but a fraction of its contents went into the fine. On the witness stand an emboldened Treskin ranted about his own blamelessness, and the stupid, lazy plebeians who kept frustrating the sincere efforts of benevolent authorities.

Mr. and Mrs. Treskin spent the rest of their lives, both to a ripe old age, at their mansion and none of their victims, or their victims' descendants, ever made an attempt on their lives.

Speranski did not try to palliate his failure as a revisor. However, he had yet another task to perform: to rewrite the laws of Siberia.

He stayed in Irkutsk for more than one year, no longer dreaded and hardly respected. He did not partake in the roisterous life of the city, which resumed as fears subsided. He was not a fine host, but spent most of his time in seclusion.

The Governor General drafted plans: he wanted a constitution for Siberia, but would rather call it statute. The very mentioning of the word constitution could still send a person into exile.

Two books served him as sources of inspiration: a long memorandum on Siberia, by His Excellency Kosodavlov, Russian Minister of the Interior; and De Pradt's *Des colonies et de la révolution d'Amérique*.

Kosodavlov was a holdover from Alexander's own utopian period. In his enthusiasm for Siberian opportunities the Minister called Siberia "Our Mexico and Peru." He advocated popular participation in the conduct of local affairs, representative advisory boards, and similar institutions as close to democracy as a member of the Russian Government could dare to venture.

De Pradt's work, frowned upon by the Russian censor, even quoted the Constitution of the United States.

Speranski laid down basic rules for a reform: Part of the personal powers of the Governor General should be transferred to an institute, whose sessions would be open to the public and whose decisions and actions were publicized.

Supervisory boards should be established, and where they already existed in fact or name their functions should be so expanded that all local administrations would be under constant supervision.

Representatives of local boards should constitute an All-Siberian Institute, to act as an adviser to, and represent, the central government as well as the people.

Prerogatives of existing branches of the administration should be revised and more clearly defined.

Administrative branches should be co-ordinated and made to co-operate.

The administration should be adapted to the specific requirements of the thinly populated vast areas.

All procedures should be simplified to promote efficiency.

Another draft dealt with the establishment of a general administration, presided over by the Governor General. The general administration would also act as a supreme court. It was to be advised by boards of local officials and officials of the ministries, whose advice, however, would be binding only above the signature of the Governor General. In case of dissent between advisers and Governor General the latter was entitled to decide the issue, but advisory boards could introduce corrective motions to the central government.

Speranski composed multitudes of directives, rescripts, and regulations to foster "fixation," to promote better education, to improve the lot of the downtrodden, to champion clean local government, to develop communications, abolish usury, boost honest trade, and concentrate production on consumer goods other than spirits.

He stormed, pen drawn, over sheets of paper, to assault strongholds of evil, and wondered if this could shake a single wall.

Speranski considered his assignment completed with the draft. He arrived in the capital in 1821 to present his opus to a distinguished forum of cabinet members and senators.

"The history of Siberia will be divided into two periods, before and after Speranski's reform. 1821 is the crucial year." The man who so exulted was Kosodavlov, who found his own ideas expressed in the papers.

But Speranski did not seem to consider 1821 a crucial year. Weary and worn, he appeared before the officials, and with a tired, scarcely audible voice gave curt answers to courteous queries.

There was some mild criticism couched in rhetorical questions.

How could boards composed of men of questionable virtue be trustworthy? Would not bills aiming at the control of monopolies produce but further reductions of the already unsatisfactory volume of trade. Did he really think that "Meetings of the Steppes," made up by villagers, could impress officials whom they should supervise, and could villagers act as justices of the peace? Would stabilization of the populace be promoted by settling deportees and ordering them to till the soil?

The Meetings of the Steppes, and settlement of deportees had been drafted on Speranski's return trip through steppes enlivened by mirages. He did not speak of mirages now, but asked for amendments.

No such proposals were forthcoming. Objectors asserted that their queries were just passing thoughts spoken out aloud. Did not Mr. Speranski, greatest of all experts, have additional suggestions?

The greatest of experts shrugged his shoulders, and then whispered that members of the boards should be selected from people not previously linked with the authorities. It would be difficult to find the proper men. Siberian nobility could not supply them; neither could Siberian economy or Siberian educational institutions. Something ought to be improvised. Later, much later, after conditions had improved, boards could be restaffed.

After several sessions in which every conferee put himself on the record with some futile phrase or other, Speranski's draft was approved and the majority of senators and cabinet ministers signed a memorandum to the Tsar saying that after 250 years of tremor, the tremendous edifice of Siberia was now underpinned.

Alexander I accepted all recommendations and appointed Speranski a member of the Imperial Diet. This was a consolation prize. Alexander had no delusions about the practicability of the reforms. He no longer believed in reform based upon popular consent.

Speranski never delivered a speech in the Diet. He no longer believed in reform, either, even if dictated by the Crown. In 1835, Alexander's successor, Nicholas I, appointed him to codify the Russian book of law, and a few years later he created him a count.

The new Count is said to have winced when he read the decree, which also mentioned his Siberian accomplishments. Neither he nor the members of his family had mentioned the name of Siberia for years.

He had outlived even the dimmest hopes that his ordeal in Siberia might have beneficial effects. Already in 1827, Senate-appointed "Revisors of Western Siberia" found that maladministration and abuses had reached a new peak of grievousness. The governor general who had succeeded Speranski vied with lesser administrators in sabotaging Speranski's regulations; local boards were either powerless or collaborated with corrupt authorities and shared the spoils. Meetings of the Steppes were dissolved by gendarmes, and, more often than not, never convened again. . . .

After studying reports Speranski wrote his daughter: "And yet, Siberia is a blessed land. Some of its regions, such as the district of Tomsk, could be Russia's treasury chest. Nature has made that land for vigorous, strong-minded, industrious men. Such people would prosper. They would develop natural resources, of which ores and mineral deposits are only a minor part. Siberia is well worth the most strenuous efforts by everybody—even by statesmen. But Siberia being Siberia . . ."

The sentence remained uncompleted. And this would be the last Speranski wrote about Siberia. He died several months after his elevation to Count.

CHAPTER FIFTY-ONE When the census of 1800 disclosed that the Siberian population was about one third of the American, Russian enthusiasts freely predicted that before the end of the century Siberia would have at least as many inhabitants as the United States.

And when the American lead steadily lengthened, some experts attributed this to mass immigration—ten million in sixty years—while immigration to Siberia was negligible. However, small immigration figures alone could not account for slow developments in Siberia, whose population reached five million in the 1880s, when that of the U.S.A. was more than ten times as high.

The nineteenth century was an era of enlightenment despite the political buccaneers and social quacks it begot. Stimulated by studies of Siberia under the early rule of the first Alexander, Russian scientists scrutinized the anthropological problems of Siberia.

So vast and involved was the field of research that even the findings of resourceful and conscientious men appeared erratic and controversial.

Rovinsky and Shtshapov called the Siberians a race in which remarkable physical and intellectual qualities could be found, but which also produced many morons and misfits. Microcephalia, cretinism, dwarfishness were rampant practically everywhere. The goiter still spread in Eastern and Southern Siberia. Fools, prophets, and soothsayers infested the cities. Peasants of Western Siberia were afflicted by a nervous condition which turned them into "bewitched sobbers."

"The breeding of idiots and misfits," Shtshapov wrote, "is caused by poor selectivity and irregular sexual intercourse, due to general demoralization, numerical disproportion between sexes, prostitution and excessive drunkenness."

Other anthropologists attributed many troubles to unhealthful bread. Bread, the main item on the Russo-Siberian popular diet, was often made of spoiled wheat and caused chronic intestinal troubles. Physical affliction produced mental disorders, drunkenness, and addiction to narcotics.

The deterioration of the health of aborigines was said to be caused by their ancestors' departure from traditional roaming grounds to evade the Iasak. Wanderings resulted in poor diet and general destitution.

Earlier reports on Siberian health conditions were supplemented by accounts of a typhoid epidemic in 1825, which decimated the Tunguses in the Lena River valley, of smallpox devastating Russians and natives alike in the districts of Tobolsk, Tomsk, and Yeniseisk; of disastrous reduction of the Samojed by leprosy and elephantiasis.

Syphilis raged beyond control and was not even considered a disease. The

1867 records of the Russian Archives of Legal Medicine disclosed that afflicted persons covered their sores with bark of birch and continued to live as usual until they succumbed.

A medical inspector who had visited Northern Siberia in 1835 called syphilis, scurvy, and rheumatism the scourge of the population. Another inspector found Western Siberia haunted by eye diseases, intestinal worms, and skin troubles caused by filth. In Western Siberia one fifth of the population died of dysentery.

Single physicians were in charge of areas of up to 100,000 square miles. One inspector urged the Russian Army Medical Corps to prevent extinction of threatened tribes. The Army Medical Corps reacted fifty years later with the statement that the tribes whom the meritorious late inspector had called threatened could now be considered extinct.

Other tribes shrank to the level of ethnic curiosities. However, the Russians did not commit premeditated genocide. They would not deprive themselves of the commodity that was native labor. "Poor selectivity" was a highbrow term for the mating of Russians and aborigines. The male Russian immigrants had temporarily outnumbered the females by ten to one, and Russians claimed that Siberian women were "hotter" than their own.

It was as difficult to cope with Russian mating habits as with Siberian mentality.

N. Jadrinzev, an outstanding scholar of Siberian affairs, calls the Siberian man submissive to the point of servility when dealing with people more powerful than himself, but otherwise coarse and insolent.

And yet another scholar wrote: "Siberian mentality concentrates on enrichment; the Siberian is possessed by an urge for things material, he ignores idealistic or social notions. Community spirit is practically nonexistent except among sectarians."

Whatever fine traditions were found in immigrants to Siberia became deadwood in the new country. Attachment to the soil no longer existed in the second generation.

Religion was all but forgotten. The ikons were left in dark corners and the sign of the Cross was still made, but the Siberian turned to the shamans for advice.

And yet, despite disease, filth, and degeneration, another finding tells of a new and sturdy Siberian type of man that emerged in the early nineteenth century: "The Siberian is rather tall and robust. He has a brownish complexion. In the eastern parts of the country, he has slit-eyes, and prominent cheek bones. His endurance is remarkable, and so are his recuperative powers."

The same source indicated that the Siberians shaped their aesthetics in accordance with their new type. They sneered at the milk-and-blood complexion and flaxen hair glorified in Russian folklore. An olive skin and black hair were considered the highest assets of attractiveness. Siberians were fond of finery and loved luxury items. The peasant disdained the shoes of bast that his Russian ancestors had worn. He wanted high boots and preferred urban clothing to traditional costumes. Women considered the Russian *sarafan,* a wide, sleeveless upper garment, a smock frock, and would do anything to obtain blouses, wool dresses, lace frills, stockings, and laced boots. Village merchants sold chignons and crinolines many decades after they had been in vogue in Europe; they displayed bead-adorned coats, spectacular chains, mirrors, and the like, which could not be found in any contemporary Russian village. Pictures of allegedly aristocratic fashions caused Siberian mushiks to crave objects for which they had no practical use. The most coveted things were "novelties"—it did not matter what the "novelty" was.

Siberians had no sense for economy. He who had cash would squander it. Kulaks bought carriages with gold-lacquered wheels, paid premium prices for champagne, and threw parties attended by district officials, in which they would spend in one night the proceeds of their wiping out a dozen peasant families.

There were no qualms and no regrets. People had to fall so that others would rise. Those who rose today might fall tomorrow. Changes were "novelties."

Changes of occupation also were "novelties." The urge for changes was ubiquitous; it turned peasants into treasure diggers, hunters, and robbers, hunters into mineworkers, coachmen into craftsmen, kulaks into manufacturers, and everybody into speculators. It promoted rebellion against established institutions, regardless of value.

Some observers claimed that the Siberian peasant was cleverer than the Russian mushik; however, others said that the Siberian's mind was quicker but less thorough than that of the Russian.

Social distinctions were not as deeply rooted in Siberia as they were in the West. A small stratum of higher nobility remained disdainfully aloof from other people, except for a few "stimulating exiles"; but in general money was the supreme social regulator; it promoted its winner, and demoted its loser. As long as money changed owners, social conditions were fluid.

"Brutality and impudence, knavery and degradation, typical of chattels, are the characteristics of the new Siberian species," a pessimist lamented. "These traits emerge under terrific pressure, in a struggle for survival, under persecution, and exploitation, in a world without spiritual values, without dignity, and no other honor than wealth and power can bestow."

And while every day people perished in Siberia from causes which effective reform might have eliminated, well-meaning anthropologists, physicians, educators, and clergymen drafted a variety of programs to advance the Siberian Man. They advocated conservation of the aborigines, health improvement, betterment of morals, higher education. Government experts studied the programs, added recommendations, and submitted bulky documents to agencies, which made more recommendations, which in turn begot more ukases forwarded to Siberian governors for implementation.

The implementation decrees ordered natives who had been driven from their home grounds to discontinue their wandering forthwith, but then did not restore the land to the evicted. Cattle breeders, who could feed their herds only by roaming, had the choice of seeing the beasts die or be tracked down themselves. If their cattle died, they would starve, if they were tracked down, they would be slain. Either way their problem would be "solved."

St. Petersburg ordered special medical care to be given to afflicted districts. Governors recalled personnel from other regions to operate in the assigned areas. The pathetic improvement of medical services did not eliminate diseases in emergency regions, but it turned the neglected districts into centers of epidemics.

The highest authorities of the Russian Church drafted sermons that priests in Siberia read for the edification of the faithful. The attendance did not understand the meaning, and consulted with shamans, whose juggleries appealed to them.

Governors were ordered to build schools and directed local administrators to draft peasants into their construction. Local administrators collected deferment fees and reported that the work was under way. And all the time fresh blood from Russia was fed to Siberia, by a slow and haphazard process of migration. The fostering of the Siberian Man was not carried out in accordance with scientific selection or controversial racist principles, but it increased the number of population despite waste and abuse.

The people of Siberia, of which nineteenth-century Russians still spoke as Magog, had not yet accomplished its Biblical task, and none of the tsars had revealed himself as King Gog.

Enlightened observers turned a deaf ear to Biblical allusions, and reasoned that perseverance, justice, and incorruptibility by the government could stir up noble instincts slumbering under the foul enclosure and rescue the Siberian Man and his soul.

Old Siberian petitions were said to show a fine longing for justice, and even a sense of chivalry. Even later reports by revisors told not only of grievances, but also of an urge for redress.

Travelers told of Siberian exploits. Was not courage a manifestation of highmindedness? Siberian rangers engaged bears with clubs, and fought hair-raising duels with the formidable beasts. Armed with a rifle they could not hope to reload, they would track tigers; and if the first shot were not fatal, they would use knives or their bare hands against the angry giants. Mountaineers from the Altais, descendants of runaway peasants, and roaming natives were considered the most daring men anywhere. Their acts might have enthused supermen-addicts of a later generation, but they embarrassed nineteenth-century humanitarians.

The men from the Altais hunted natives, single hunters ambushing entire families. They tracked "hunchbacks," as escaped captives and vagrants were called, butchering their prey, and collecting bounties afterwards. The proceeds of three heads of hunchbacks bought a pair of high boots; six heads bought a blouse. . . .

And yet the Siberian souls should not be lost. The more the studies progressed, the more Russians compared Siberia with the United States. Even if the birth pangs of Siberia were more violent, and lasted longer, Siberia would emerge as an Eden. A new generation of statisticians established that if the most fertile farm lands of Siberia were settled by peasants at the ratio prevalent in the regions of Ukrainian black earth, they would have a population of fifty million.

Whatever holdings officials, soldiers, kulaks, mundane and ecclesiastic institutions carved out for themselves, whatever allotments governors signed legally, the land of Siberia was Crown property, and allotments by the Crown invalidated other property claims.

During the nineteenth century the Russian Government decided to distribute Crown domains in Siberia among qualified settlers in lots of between 80 to 100 acres of cultivated soil and twice that area of good virgin land. No cash price was charged, no mortgage had to be paid off. There was not even a rental fee, only an annual tax of six rubles per member of the family.

No other government anywhere had distributed land on such terms and on a comparable scale. It sounded utopian, but the government was ready to back its decree by deeds.

Such readiness, however, was confined to the top echelons of the European Russian administration, who left the implementation of reform to the lesser bureaucracy.

The government did not pay for travel expenses. Transportation costs per family were believed to run between 75 and 175 rubles provided the migrants traveled frugally, as befitted mushiks.

But even 75 rubles was more than any non-prosperous peasant held in cash, and prosperous peasants did not emigrate. So, in the nineteenth century, as before, migrants had to sell at least part of their belongings. The battered implements of a mushik's household were not in demand by neighbors, whose inventory consisted of similar objects. Prospective emigrants had to deal with buyers from district towns, oddly clad, strangely talking, characters who offered small sums and quickly said that this was a take-it-or-leave-it proposition. The peasants usually took it, and if they were still short of cash, they would sell livestock for nominal prices.

Only after producing a certain amount of money for local authorities could they apply for allotment of land and authorization of departure. There was a fifteen-ruble charge for release from one community and admission into another. Local magistrates and village elders, however, would ask from thirty to fifty rubles. A mushik could refuse to pay the overcharge, but few mushiks were familiar with the law, and those who did object would never get to

Siberia. The next step was the filing of a petition proving their qualifications as farmers. Not even the most educated mushik could write such a document, for one single mistake disqualified the applicant forever. He had to hire a scribe; scribes worked hand in glove with the municipality and would insert "mistakes" into applications by people who had refused to pay extra charges for release and admission.

A rejected applicant could still appeal to the district governor. For such purpose he would have to travel to the district capital, and there office clerks would hand him over to some shyster who would strip him of his last kopek. One mushik was known to have struggled for documents for a full eleven years, and he might have struggled even longer had he not meantime died of starvation.

Families who obtained clearance usually gathered in caravans. They walked all the way, except the frail and sickly who rode in telegas, crude, four-wheeled carts pulled by single horses. Covered with straw mats, the telega also served as night quarters.

Only in the greatest emergency would the head of the emigrating family part with any of his possessions. Emigrants tried to live on begging in the name of Christ. The womenfolk and the children shouted the incantation formula; the men did the collecting.

Peasants who lived along the road were not opulent, but the emigrant's begging was considered legitimate. Nobody knew whether one day he would be on the road himself. Some villages acquired the reputation of generosity, others that of stinginess. Caravans made long detours to reach the former and by-pass the latter.

A weary horse falling by the wayside spelled disaster to its owner. Better-off families in the caravan never helped him. Local peasants charged between 100 and 300 rubles for a horse. Unable to buy a horse, an emigrant would wind up selling himself and his family as laborers. Loss of a member of the family was not as heavy a blow as loss of an animal; however, it was a serious inconvenience, because taxes were assessed according to the number of the members of the family who left their Russian domicile; and only after a long procedure were cases of disease accepted as deductable items. Once a family group was still assessed twenty-five people, while its number had come down to eight.

The deeper the columns penetrated into Siberia, the scarcer begging opportunities became. Emigrating peasants considered it a stroke of luck if they found a gang of forced laborers with whom they could mingle to cheat dull guards out of a meal.

Emigration, like many other aspects of Siberian life, was organized chaos, and it took a Russian to survive it.

After a journey lasting between one and three years survivors would reach their destinations, and find plots waiting for them, large and fertile.

But the very size of a plot was a source of calamity. Between three and five horses would be required to work the land, and not even the luckiest settlers had more than one or two. Vast tracts of soil required more and better tools than the few rickety objects emigrants still owned. The mushiks might have started operations on a small scale, but no peasant would ever abandon one square foot of land. There was plenty of timber on hand to build log cabins, but mushiks did not want log cabins; they wanted mud huts, and mud was not always available.

Families stranded on their "estates" camped under the straw mats of the telega. Usually city slickers—the Siberian type compared to whom a European Russian shyster was a timid soul—turned up when hapless settlers were at the lowest ebb of morale. The gentlemen from the city had everything to sell: horses, cattle, implements, at three to five times the European market price.

A record shows that one family was charged 2097 rubles for basic equipment.

Desperate peasants would be told that there was another plot of land available nearby, gratis, of course, and complete with buildings, implements, and livestock. Its titular owner, a church, an official, or an officer, only expected compensation for his cash investment, payable on the installment plan. The installment-plan payment turned the new owner into a perpetual debtor.

Zeal and frugality could not solve a debtor's problems and even a succession of bumper crops would hardly free him from bondage. Markets were few and far away, and they were controlled by monopolists. Peasants had to deal with agents, who called at farms, inspected crops, and dictated prices.

In accordance with an ancient Russian custom peasants formed co-operatives called *arteljs*. But agents were stronger than *arteljs*. If members of a co-operative managed to get into a town with loaded carts they would find every booth, every patch of ground on the market place, occupied; and if they tried to sell outside the market they were chased away by gendarmes or goons. Persistent co-operatives faced boycott by purchasing agents. Tax arrears of 100 rubles or more resulted in foreclosure, and usually it took no more than two years to bring a boycotted co-operative at bay. Together with the beadle a "reorganizer" turned up, offering to pay the arrears if he were put in charge of the co-operative. The peasants remained members of their *artelj,* but the manager was omnipotent and the mushiks never got more cash than they needed for taxes. There was no legal way of quitting the co-operative; working places were marked in passports, and authorities refused to change entries for members of a "captive co-operative."

Some members of captive co-operatives, however, did get away, defying gendarmes, hunchback hunters, bears, and tigers; occasionally they would wind up as kulaks and employ agents to "reorganize" *arteljs*.

In the later eighteen thirties gold fields became the goal of runaways, investors, and adventurers. After an earlier brief tumult, stimulated by misleading stories of tremendous deposits of precious metal, the great Siberian gold rush started in 1836. As usual it opened with rumors carried by grapevine.

People all over Siberia heard that somewhere in the mountains bold and lawless men had gathered fabulous riches from gold fields, and that Jewish black-market operators, the most cunning lot the world had ever known, had spirited the gold beyond the reach of authorities. Nobody had ever laid eyes upon the bold outlaws, but almost everybody claimed to have met somebody who had seen them. A small number of Jews were as obvious as exclamation marks with their outlandish looks and strange cloaks. They were frantically chasing after shreds of trade and moneylending, and their appearance did not indicate prosperity. But people whispered that they carried fortunes under their queer hats, and in the shafts of their boots, and that treasures had been found on the bodies of slain Jews.

An ever-increasing number of prospectors, burrowing parties, and geological expeditions streamed to areas which seemed to fit the description of gold fields. Geologists were at a premium, but phony experts abounded; and with Siberians trusting quackery rather than science, they had a field day. Shamans staged conjuring rides to the very attics of heaven and produced divine hints about the locations of fields.

Nobody knew, nobody cared, how many prospectors fell victim to beasts of prey or to their own even more murderous kind; how many died in the wilderness of exposure and starvation. But the gold was at last located. A party equipped by the merchant Jakim Rezanov found what was described as "rich alluviates of gold, 5200 feet up in the Sayan Mountains," about halfway between Krasnojarsk and Irkutsk; almost simultaneously another party in the pay of merchant Tolkatchev found gold not far from the Birussa River. More gold was detected in brooks emptying into the Birussa. These fields constituted the first "system," which was named after the Birussa River. Two more systems were found on the northern and southern Yenisei River.

According to the law, the gold was Crown property. But the Tsar's treasury had already gathered experience with mine operations in Siberia. Since 1825 platinum was produced in the district of Nizhni Tagil under the auspices of the administration. Annual production of crude platinum rose from 5 poods to 117 poods, but even though convict labor worked the mines, and one pood of crude platinum brought an average of about $870, operations did not produce a profit. The Treasury considered offering private operators' licenses for platinum when applications for gold mining licenses came in.

The Ministry of Finance took charge of the applications. Everybody could obtain a license except men with prison records, officials on the active list, and Jews. Jews were not permitted to work in the mines and barred from visiting them. "The Jews are smuggling gold," an official comment explained, "most of these people have been deported to Siberia under charges of illicit operations." If the Jews did engage in smuggling gold they must have done it with extreme cleverness, for the record does not indicate that any of them were caught red-handed. Promyshleniki, familiar with smuggler paths, carried undisclosed quantities of gold to China.

Despite the exorbitant costs of black-marketeering shipping gold to China was more remunerative than selling it to the newly established governmental agency in Barnaul in the Altai district. Three times a year officials in this city accepted deliveries in a wearisome procedure of weighing, checking, measuring, casting, and stamping. One pood of pure gold brought 12,300 rubles (quotation as of 1845). License fees were deducted, and the deliverer received a treasury note for the balance, payable in St. Petersburg after the procedure of weighing and checking had been repeated and discrepancies cleared with Barnaul. This could take any number of years. Operators needed cash. Treasury notes did not provide for interest; Siberian financiers charged the usual 200 per cent and asked for the license as collateral. On an improvised exchange at Barnaul notes were negotiated with a discount of 60 to 70 per cent. In St. Petersburg one bank charged only 40 per cent discount, but it took one year to get the money.

Regulations required that applicants for licenses minutely specify the location of their claim. A mistake in marking the location voided the license even if the mistake was caused by the inaccuracy of official maps. The maximum size of a claim was 5600 by 220 yards. License fees were 15 per cent of the produce, plus 4 to 8 rubles per pound of gold for administration expenses. The first licenses were valid for the duration of continued operations; later, however, validity was restricted to twelve years, and license holders pledged themselves to sell the gold exclusively to the government.

The actual working season lasted only four to five months owing to climatic conditions. The first year was lost in preparations. Nobody would make a big investment before holding the license. Then he would have to order simple mining equipment from foundries in the Ural Mountains, and more complicated machinery from England or Germany. He would have to bring in food supplies for his laborers from markets up to a thousand miles away. And, last but not least, he would have to recruit labor under trying conditions.

When the gold rush began, a merchant-prospector needed 3000 rubles to start operations. Three years later investments would run close to 100,000 rubles, and one man spent 260,000 before hitting gold.

Wages and living costs skyrocketed. Back in 1771, when Krasnojarsk had been a somnolent little place, 1 pood of rye flour cost 3 kopeks, and 1 pood of beef 25; in the boom town of Krasnojarsk of 1843 the same items cost 1.25 rubles and 12.50 respectively. Literate clerks, who were in shorter supply than they had been in 1771, now earned 6000 to 8000 rubles annually, plus maintenance, an increase of some 5000 per cent.

Despite inflation, which brought the value of bank notes down to one third of that of silver coins, actual wages and salaries were at their highest peak.

For a brief period Krasnojarsk outdid Irkutsk in high living and Tomsk rivaled both cities. Some of the wealthiest mineowners, the most successful usurers and smugglers' ringleaders lived in Krasnojarsk, and their demand for house servants was as urgent as that for diggers and laborers.

The new rich wanted "civilized" servants; well-bred lackeys, and cooks who could do a Kiev cutlet of minced chicken. It did not matter that such servants talked back, and worked only when they felt like it. It was an indication of success to have "civilized personnel."

Ernst Hofmann, a German mine expert whom the Russian Government commissioned to inspect the mines and gold-washing establishments in Siberia, saw Krasnojarsk in 1843. He found new mansions, which had sprung up at sites on which mud huts had once stood, many houses of stone, and many more under construction. Solid sidewalks of wooden planks lined unpaved streets. Freshly painted old-fashioned log houses were taken up by fashion shops, displaying the latest creations of *couture* and millinery. Other stores carried furniture, glassware, bric-a-brac, and all sorts of fancy merchandise at even fancier prices. Storekeepers reported that their sales figures were up 500 per cent since 1838.

Handsome carriages drawn by thoroughbreds, with liveried coachmen in the drivers' seats, carried ladies on shopping trips. The ladies rummaged expensive wares with finely gloved hands. They almost never took off their gloves, because despite treatments their hands looked distinctly unaristocratic.

Krasnojarsk itself reminded Hofmann of an upstart washerwoman, and yet the natural setting of the city seemed to justify its name (*krasnij*—beautiful). Nestled between the majestic Yenisei River and a romantic brook, flanked by undulating wooded mountains crowned with delicately shaped rocks, Krasnojarsk could have been a charming city had it been properly planned and allowed to grow organically. However, in Siberia, nothing man-made was allowed to grow organically.

The ladies of Krasnojarsk, and also those of Tomsk and Irkutsk, engaged in social activities: sponsoring, promoting culture and refinement, or rather romantic men who stood for culture. Deportees with thrilling backgrounds were in high social demand, in particular if they could play the piano and speak an idiom that could be taken for French. Some sponsored gentlemen were not really deportees, but their accounts were never checked. Millionaire miner husbands showed little interest in their wives' social activities. They went to the entertainment places of the cities instead, and staged orgies as wild and uninhibited as their physiques could stand.

However, Mr. Hofmann thought that the upper class of Irkutsk was much more refined than such debauchees, and that they kept aloof of brutish upstarts. He was quartered in a two-story stone house, with large, well-furnished rooms, and even flowerpots. "Trade with China," he was told, "has created a new class of wealthy merchants and comfortable burghers, whose favorite entertainment is to ride in carriages to the nearby countryside."

"I became acquainted with all members of educated society in Irkutsk,"

Hofmann wrote. "The governor general lavished hospitality upon me; at a birthday party, I met the cream of Siberian society, and I had an opportunity to speak my native tongue in distinguished company. Listening to the military band, and looking at fashionably dressed ladies promenading through finely decorated salons, one could hardly believe himself to be 4000 miles east of the capital. There was hardly a bonnet or a gown that did not seem to have come from St. Petersburg, faster even than it could have been shipped had railroads and steamboats linked Irkutsk and the capital. Mechlin lace, and ostrich feathers abounded. Elegant couples waltzed to the tunes of Johann Strauss.[1] Fancy goods are imported, but Irkutsk has a great deal to offer in return. Throughout the Russian Empire, people warm themselves on tea distributed from Irkutsk, and a cape of sable is an object of envy all over the world."

Mr. Hofmann stayed in Irkutsk for only one week. He did not seem to have noticed its corruption and depravity. His mention of steamboats could have referred to the construction, at nearby Baikal, of the first paddle-wheel steamer in Siberia to replace some of the antiquated, collapsible crafts in which fishermen caught *omuls,* the salmonlike fish that was a Siberian delicacy.

The mine inspector had entered the gold district east of Tomsk. Mr. Van Astashev—who through the good graces of Fedot Popov, the most successful of pioneering prospectors, had become a "big shot" in the mining industry—helped him to continue his voyage as comfortably as possible. Astashev lived in a palatial mansion and directed the social and economic life of Tomsk. Anyone who was not in the good graces of the big man would have had trouble proceeding eastward over desolate tracks which the ancient Mongolian dispatch riders would not have considered communication lanes. The mining industrialists and officials with whom they collaborated knew how to keep unwelcome intruders away.

The land between Tomsk and Krasnojarsk is flat, part steppe, part mire, and in spots covered by the wild taiga, the swampy virgin forests, in which bulks of trees and underbrush seem to wander on the slippery, unsteady ground. Countless water lanes change their courses, swell and recede, as if according to the unfathomable moods of sylvan gods. The taiga never dried; Siberians who spent the night there went to the trouble of kindling a fire to burn all night.

The saying went that the carnivorous bears of the swampy wilderness extinguished fires before attacking and the sounds warned prospective victims. Steppe dwellers would kindle the immense pasturages of their home grounds, claiming that fire fertilized the steppes. Conflagrations of the steppes devoured the vegetation of areas as large as European kingdoms and darkened the skies for hundreds of miles around. When the face of the land was ablaze, men could not bring the fires under control. But the fire eventually

---

[1] Johann Strauss, Sr., the father of the Waltz King.

devoured itself. A clear sky again vaulted over a baked steppe, and the land, mocking man's mania, would again grow flowers and grass.

When Hofmann traveled east, gold-washing parties worked deep in the taiga, in regions that even nomads had hardly visited before, far beyond cart tracks, and near clearings where the ground seemed sufficiently solid to bear a camp.

In the most productive gold districts men and horses would often sink in, and suffocate in the swamp. The atmosphere was so saturated with humidity that men got soaked even between the vehement downpours that seemed to emanate from high trees rather than from a sky hidden by thicket and vapor. Downpours were nature's contribution to mining. They loosened tons of auriferous mud, earth, and gravel. It was hard toil to dig a burrow. Even at the driest spots subsoil water stood only a few feet below ground. One group of the workers operated pumps; the others dug, watching the water level that receded slowly when the pumpers worked full blast, and burst forth upward like a charging beast of prey when their work slowed down. Pumps were small and primitive. Pack animals could not carry the load of heavy implements, and operators contended that efficient tools were out of place because gangs were too dumb to operate complicated mechanism. Standing waist deep in pits and knee deep in morass, the men kept digging until they struck solid rock; every layer of scree would be searched for nuggets.

Rivulets and rivers, the ponds and lakes of the taiga would be here today and elsewhere tomorrow. The mass of water and scree was inexhaustible. Had all the people of Siberia worked for a thousand years, they could not have finished exploring it. Parties penetrating into the depth of the taiga may have walked and staggered over masses of gold that defied human imagination. But not even the ruthlessness of all the tyrants Siberia ever produced could have stripped the wilderness of its hoard; and if ever a man-shaped ogre could put all mankind to work to obtain all the riches, the quantity of gold produced would make the metal worthless.

Workers could rarely set up permanent camps. They had to roam with the roaming waters. Nothing edible grew in the taiga, and the laborers had to carry provisions for several months. Food that did not rot grew moldy and had a nauseating taste.

Wages were high, but did not really compensate a man for privation and toil. And nobody knew if he would enjoy the money. When frosts made digging temporarily impossible, gangs would often be reduced to half their original number. Almost every man tried to hide some nuggets as a premium when he passed the controls.

Thievery was punishable by death. But a man, if caught, would not necessarily suffer the extreme penalty. Gendarmes and comptrollers, working hand in glove with smugglers, stripped him and reported his arrest to his employer, who would more often than not ransom the thief, because replacements were hard to get.

Operators even conspired with guards and wardens of Crown mines to obtain labor from convict gangs, who produced platinum, salt, or coal. Convicts toiled on small rations, and in leg irons, which grated through sore flesh and diseased bones. Authorities justified small rations with poor output, and fetters with the violent character of the men. Mine inspectors confirmed the low level of production, and uniformly brutal treatment which turned even fundamentally gentle persons into mad desperadoes. During the gold rush almost 50 per cent of the convict laborers ran away, assisted by their bribed guards, who actually passed them on to private operators.

It was easy to conceal such "losses." A convict who entered the stockade of a Crown mine lost the last vestige of his identity. He lost his name and turned into a number. Numbers passed on from the dead to the quick, numbers never escaped, and numbers would keep answering the roll call as long as fresh supplies of creatures kept pouring into stockades.

Mr. Hofmann did not see mineworkers in the cities. The men never went to Krasnojarsk, Tomsk, or Irkutsk. In the rough season and during brief layoffs they invested their paper money in high-priced fancy wares, which peddlers carried to the vicinity of the gold fields, or spent it on itinerant whores who ventured to the rim of the taiga and catered to between thirty and fifty customers a day. Miners who wanted social entertainment would find it in wayside pothouses, where depraved characters who pretended to have been the Tsar's servants offered enlighteningly sentimental conversation for a few cups of brandy.

The mine inspector describes one of these wretches: "He was emaciated, almost skeletonized; his garments consisted of two mats of linden bast, stitched together and pulled over his shoulder like the sleeveless mantle of a herald in a penny gaff. The fellow was incredibly filthy and so disfigured that he hardly looked like a human being. He stretched out his bare arm and croaked: 'You wouldn't refuse a discharged man of rank ten kopeks for a drink.'" No trace of dignity was left in the beggar. In Siberia apparent dignity was a by-product of power, and true dignity was as lacking as its noblest manifestation: compassion.

Hofmann talked to ex-convict laborers, and called them hypocritical criminals. "When asked for the reason of their exile, they will turn tearful eyes skyward and say: 'It happened by the Lord's will.' They also tell sob stories about their far-away home to arouse the traveller's sympathy. Their sweet talk and mild looks may make you believe that they are repentant sinners or altogether innocent, but as you stay among the rabble, you will notice nothing but savage boozing, bald-faced lies, brazen fraud, thievery, and murder. The district of Tomsk harbors the most hardened criminal elements. Decent citizens told me of many instances of burglary and manslaughter by malefactors to whom lashes with the knout are but a moderate inconvenience."

Similar information was conveyed to the inspector in the most distinguished establishment of Tomsk. This hostelry was run by a Pole, a former circus clown, put in business by mine executives who appreciated his talents as a procurer, and who patronized certain rooms of his hotel where they found entertainment which neither the plushy brothels of old Russia nor even the *lupanars* of Paris could have provided.

Agents traveled through Siberia to recruit workers. They went to the most secluded regions, occasionally discovering settlements not marked on maps. A hundred, even two hundred years before, mushiks had gone into hiding in regions beyond the reach of tyrants. They had built their mud huts, cultivated the soil, and left holdings to their children, and their children's children. Generations had been "fixed" without knowing ukases to such effect, eventually forgetting what had led their ancestors to found the communities. The last of these settlements was discovered in the late 1860s. Nobody could tell when it had been founded or if this was really the last to be relinked with a barbaric civilization. Curious villagers signed with the recruiters; so did aborigines, and "hunchbacks," putting three crosses under a form.

Signing on a worker was not a safe operation. Hiring fees were paid to recruits who pledged their passports as security. But the illiterate yokels developed an amazing cheating acumen. They stole other fellows' papers, and signed up with several agents. Multiple signing and multiple collecting went unpunished, because the operator with whom the cheat eventually stayed paid bribes to prevent his arrest.

Physical requirements were high. A wheelbarrow man had to be able to pull loads of up to 120 pounds over a combined distance of twelve miles a day. Basic wages were between twelve and fifty rubles a month, but production premiums boosted the amount by several hundred per cent. One gang of workers set an all-time high by netting 105 rubles per capita on a single Sunday. The system of incentive produced high individual earnings, collective loafing, and general inefficiency. Whenever it looked as if a worker were about to set a mark, gangs stopped digging to watch him as they would watch a wrestling bout. And because premiums were paid per pound of nuggets, washers left tons of moderately rich rock untouched, and concentrated on the richest sands.

Management did not mind that the workers invested their money in booze during the period of layoff, but they struggled against drunkenness during the working season.

Eventually drinking places were banished from the perimeter of gold fields within a radius of forty miles. Heavy guards were set up to prevent alcohol traffic within the area. The effect was practically nil.

Gold production reached its peak in 1847. During the five years that followed it declined by 40 per cent, and by 1860 privately operated gold fields were practically abandoned. The Crown retained its monopoly, nameless numbers continued to dig for the murderous metal, the weight of their decaying bodies far exceeded that of the nuggets produced, and nobody profited from it.

Usurers sifted the remains of a deceptive prosperity: mansions, brothel furniture, carriages, horses, and fineries, for which there was no further use. They did not search the taiga for abandoned equipment and did not find the "beautiful wares" which peddlers and hucksters in their employ had carried. The workers had taken it all, before walking off to the vastness to turn vagabonds again or return to their villages if they had once been peasants.

But often returning villagers found their old homes in ruins, and their fields unattended. Nobody wanted farm hands. The closure of gold fields produced a general recession. Bands of robbers formed, and starved for lack of loot.

Gold-mining operators who had salvaged some of their assets had gone to St. Petersburg, to collect treasury notes, leaving their Siberian creditors high and dry. In Siberia even usurers became destitute, villages were deserted, cities went bankrupt, and with a scornful gurgle the moss and swamp of the taiga closed over the remnants of the great gold rush.

CHAPTER FIFTY-TWO For twelvescore years deportees had been marched across the Ural Mountains: hapless wretches, diehard criminals, unidentified victims of administrative mistakes or of the spite of some underling, mingling with personalities stripped of exalted rank. Fjodor Romanov was followed by Ukrainian princes who, in shackles, held court in ditches. Imperial ex-favorites had trudged the long track. Generals, including a Russian Von Bismarck, who had held their own on battlefields but had met disaster in parlors, staggered across the mountain range. Several counts and one field marshal went this way; one prima ballerina, daughter-in-law of a chancellor, tripped it; two authors of note walked the Russian calvary; one of them had once extolled Russia as the best-governed land on earth, but then an unappreciative tsar gave him an opportunity to study Russia's murderous back yard. Another author reached the crest of the Urals when Tsar Paul saw one of his plays and had him returned to the capital. One thousand Polish prisoners of war who had volunteered with Napoleon wound up in Siberia. Yet the most popular exile of them all was one Korevev, champion of bandit-coiners, credited with eighteen felonious assaults and the production of the best fake coins ever made.

In European Russia deportation was a shadow that loomed over the powerless and darkened the shine of prominence. In Siberia it was an industry and a labor pool. But outside of the one sixth of the earth that constituted the Russian Empire it might not have become a familiar topic of conversation for more scores of years had it not been for the Freemasons.

Freemasonry became an issue in the Dekabrist rebellion, and after over a hundred men involved went to Siberia, lodges and intellectuals in many countries put deportation high on their agenda of the world's woes and injustices.

Freemasonry had become fashionable in Russia in the later eighteenth century. Persons of noble birth and social prominence joined lodges. Count Tshernitshev, I. W. Lopuchin, Novikov, and other notables of Freemasonry were pillars of law and order, but after the French Revolution turned into the Terror, the aging Catherine II began to look upon Freemasons as clandestine Jacobins. Had it not been for the high rank of Russian Freemasons, drastic action might have been taken against lodges. Actually there were only superficial investigations resulting in vaguely worded warnings that increased the attraction of Freemasonry for romantically united noblemen with plenty of spare time. Catherine admonished her son and successor to beware the evil schemers. The Crown Prince, smarting under the edifying talks of his domineering mother, resolved to champion Freemasonry as soon as he could free himself from her tutelage. Dull Paul hardly understood the implications of the movement, and his reign was too short to give him an opportunity to boost Freemasonry. But he passed his feelings on to his son Alexander, who might have preferred the title of Grand Master of a lodge to that of Grand Duke of Finland, the country he acquired as a price for his understanding with the Emperor of the French.

Russian lodges were still favored by nobility and intelligentsia after Russian occupation forces were stationed in post-Napoleonic France.

Young officers of the Guards, reared in the oppressive monotony of dull home garrisons, breathed the high culture of the West. They became infatuated with French institutions, as they saw them: civil rights, personal freedom, and a law to protect the individual rather than to uphold regimentation.

The officers studied such institutions with almost religious zeal and resolved to introduce them to Russia, to make their glum, stagnant country a citadel of progress. They ignored the deep gulf that divided Western and Russian popular mentalities, and trusted that Tsar Alexander would always want to lead the world in social reform.

It was said that the Tsar still considered Freemasonry the finest instrument of reform. Guards officers on occupation duty joined lodges and, back in Russia, lodges formed in every Guards regiment.

And because lodges did not completely satisfy the officers' urge for progress, secret societies were created to promote the latest versions of human rights. Secret societies also flourished in restive Poland. Guards officers established ties with Polish patriots. The Polish Patriotic Society assigned Prince Jablonsky to meet with Russian delegates: Colonel Pestel, son of the ex-Governor General of Siberia, and Prince Volkonsky. Jablonsky asked for assurances that reforms would restore Poland's independence; Pestel wanted that the future government of Poland establish a constitution strictly in accordance with the Russian pattern of reform.

This the Poles would not guarantee, and they also refused to join a Russian-controlled confederation of Finland, the Baltic States, and the Ukraine, which Pestel and Volkonsky considered forming. "Nothing will turn the Pole into a Russian, or the Russian into a Pole," Jablonsky declared; "they are different in faith, language, and tradition." Eventually it was agreed that Poles and Russians should consider mutual assistance in case reforms in Russia encountered armed opposition. It was believed that opposition could come only from a conservative clique but not from the Tsar.

Russian reformers considered yet another pattern of brotherly federalization: the United Slavonians, a league of Southern and Northern Russians, later to be joined by the Poles, Czechs, Slovaks, Serbo-Croats, and Slovenes, to form a Pan-Slavist superstate.

In 1821, many secret organizations existed in Russia, all of them respectable and highly patriotic: the Literary Society of Arsamas, which had two cabinet ministers among its members; the Promoters of Enlightenment and Benefaction; the Political Society, sponsored by Colonels Prince Trubetzkoy and A. N. Muraviev; the Union of Public Weal; the Worthy Sons of the Fatherland; the Russian Knights, whose list of functionaries included Nikolai Turgenev, and Count Maranov; and the Union for National Prosperity, to name only a few.

Secret organizations engaged in open debates on betterment of the world in general, and Russia in particular; they extolled their Tsar as the guiding spirit of world improvements. They read the teachings of the *Carbonari*, French revolutionary thesis, the statutes of the German League of Virtue, the Declaration of Independence and the Constitution of the United States, and recent Russian *pronunciamentos* of virtuous generalities.

Late in 1821 and early in 1822 indications were that such activities were no longer viewed with favor in high quarters. Officers and officials whose applications for membership in lodges and societies had been granted used subterfuges to postpone their actual joining. Rumors said that the Tsar no longer was a champion of progress; heads of the secret organizations disclaimed such stories; Alexander would never abandon them; his taciturnity on progress was a clever move to placate frightened ultraconservatives.

But on April 13, 1822, lightning struck. An ukase ordered officers and civil servants to pledge themselves never to belong to secret organizations, and all Masonic lodges were ordered closed.

Fellow-travelers jumped off the band wagon at once, relishing their legality and relief from intellectual burdens. The faithful who remained were bewildered but determined to pursue their aims.

The forty-eight-year-old Tsar Alexander was on an inspection tour in Southern Russia, and apparently in good health, when he suddenly died in the town of Taganrog on November 27, 1825. Peasants whispered that the Little Father had become tired of ruling and entered a monastery.

Members of secret organizations did not believe that Alexander had become a monk, but they thought that he had been murdered, a martyr of progress. Guards officers alerted their regiments, certain that the time to act had come, but waiting for inspiration on what course to take.

Grand Duke Constantine, Alexander's brother, was next in line to the throne. Constantine, a mild-mannered, almost timid man, resided in Warsaw as Governor General of Poland. The highest-ranking member of the ruling house in St. Petersburg was his younger brother, Grand Duke Nicholas. When news from Taganrog arrived, Nicholas took the oath of allegiance to Tsar Constantine, and ordered that all garrisons and officials pledge loyalty to the new Tsar.

His express couriers galloped through the palace gates when the Governor of St. Petersburg, General Count Miloradovitch, and Prince A. N. Golizyn, drove up to convey a crucial message.

Three years before, Alexander had deposited a sealed letter in the Senate archives; the envelope was marked: "No action shall be taken after my death, until this letter is opened."

Miloradovitch and Golizyn presented the letter to a shuddering Grand Duke: It was the late Tsar's will that Nicholas succeed him to the throne.

"But nobody loves me, nobody wants me," Nicholas burst out. He ventured desperately that his brother must have written the will in a passing mood and forgotten to void it. He was not fit to rule, he kept saying, and he did not want to rule. Nobody loved him. . . .

The people at large hardly knew him, and few courtiers only had lavished well-calculated affections upon a grand duke whose peculiar station seemed to bar him from absolute power. As a sidetracked prince, Nicholas had developed romantic ideas on what a tsar should be to his subjects and now he doubted that he could ever live up to his own standards.

The visitors were persistent. Alexander's will was the law. Orders to administer the oath to Constantine had to be revoked at once. Russia could have but one legal ruler: Nicholas. There should be no interregnum lest the country be thrown into turmoil as in the days of the false Dmitri.

"Whoever refuses to swear allegiance to my older brother," Nicholas shouted, "is the country's enemy, and mine."

Senators and members of the Holy Synod were called to the palace. Mundane dignitaries and prelates shook bearded heads. The wording of the letter was clear; Nicholas would have to accept the Crown.

From Warsaw, Constantine announced his formal resignation, and released all concerned from their oath and, after thirteen days of vacillation, Nicholas resigned himself to unwanted dignity. But as the troubled waters in the palace calmed, a storm was brewing in garrisons.

Persistent rumors told of a sinister conflict in the house of Romanov, a feud between a false tsar and a hapless pretender. It would spell disaster to Russia unless the right men took matters into their hands.

On December 12 members of secret societies gathered in the house of Prince Obolensky in St. Petersburg. Radicalism, fostered by perplexity, produced a pattern for revolt. Regiments of the Guards, and whatever other units could be induced to follow suit, were to refuse the oath to Nicholas, pretending to defend the rights of Constantine. They should seize the Winter Palace, all government buildings, post offices, and banks. After the putsch had succeeded, the throne would be declared vacant. Next a provisional government should be established. Government and Senate should convoke an assembly to adopt a constitution.

Somebody raised the question whether the enlisted men of the Guards would obey orders to riot; he was told that soldiers could not tell rioting orders from any other command. Another officer wanted to know whether there should not be putsch drills; time was running short, he was told, and drills might be impractical. Time was also running short for the drafting of a constitution, but nobody raised this question.

Prince Trubetzkoy, a gallantly loquacious officer, was appointed commander in chief. His orders were to strike at the earliest opportunity, and to carry out a strategic retreat to Novgorod should the putsch fail.

Detailed directives were not issued. The meeting coined a slogan to substitute for all shortcomings: "There must be a beginning."

Trubetzkoy hailed the slogan, but as he struggled for a conception of a beginning, nothing but words came to his mind.

Colonel Pestel had not been present at Obolensky's house. He was in the country, enlisting supporters for the United Slavonians. Learning of Trubetzkoy's appointment to a post he had expected to obtain himself, he grew frantic and behaved so conspicuously that the conservative commander of the Second Army District had him arrested.

In St. Petersburg's palaces members of secret societies kept repeating: "There must be a beginning."

In barracks officers had soldiers memorize the word "constitution" without explaining what it meant.

An inauguration parade would be held on December 14. The entire St. Petersburg Corps would participate. Such were the orders received by brigade and division commanders. The general officers also learned of the strange exercises in the barracks, and wondered if Nicholas would really grant a constitution.

During the night of December 13 a captain of the Guards, torn between conflicting allegiances to his tsar and to his lodge, committed suicide. Still, low-echelon generals were not disquieted. Regrettable as suicides were, they had happened before and would happen as long as there were card games and love affairs.

Officers' suicides had to be reported to Court. Nicholas was worried, and his worries reflected upon courtiers and ranking military. There were consultations and conferences.

On the morning of December 14 the conspirators learned of it and became panicky. Prince Trubetzkoy would have to order "the beginning." But Trubetzkoy could nowhere be found. In fact he was trying to locate Pestel. Prince Obolensky was roused from his sleep and asked to take over. Obolensky was a military dilettante, but, being a cavalier, he could not refuse.

He decreed that the parade be turned into the putsch. But when messengers reached the conspirators' barracks, many units had already marched out. The messengers raced after marching units to convey the order, adding that everybody concerned should use his own judgment as to time and place of action. Battalion and company commanders led their units in confused marches and countermarches. The only artillery regiment in the mutineers' camp returned to the barracks, marched out again, and left half its cannon behind. Soldiers were weary and footsore, and did not understand what it was all about. When officers met troops in the streets, they could not always tell conspiring friend from loyal foe.

One cavalry officer, believing that his squadron was being encircled, wanted to disentangle his unit. Cavalry charged into an infantry company. There were casualties. When the dust settled, it turned out that the infantrymen had also been conspirators.

The corps commander realized that his military machinery was out of gear, if not out of control, but the parade had to proceed, and he could do no better than remind regimental commanders of its itinerary.

Through the maze of troops and milling crowds rode the new Tsar on horseback. Behind him, on a pony, came his seven-year-old son, followed by a selected retinue. Nicholas looked calm, if not haughty. The boy seemed to enjoy the confusion. The retinue was tense. Crowds cheered. So did enlisted men from both camps.

The imperial party rode to Senate Square, where infantry and cavalry of the Guards deployed. The officers did not salute the Tsar.

This *was* mutiny, but not necessarily rebellion of the rank and file. Behind the ranks huge masses of civilians gathered.

The Tsar motioned a general. The general addressed the Guards, admonishing the men not to offend their tsar. Several companies left the rank of mutiny. Their officers stayed behind in hapless stubbornness. Still rebels outnumbered loyalists.

It was silent rebellion by implication, an uncomformity in the military structure, suddenly revealed and difficult to understand.

An artillery regiment drove up in good order. Officers saluted, cannoneers cheered. Nicholas smiled. These men were loyal.

The rebels' growing perplexity found vent in an urge for self-martyrization. They dared the artillerymen to fire. In the presence of the Supreme War Lord only he could issue such orders. A battery commander imploringly looked at

Nicholas. The Tsar ignored him, attracted by the sight of two mounted men forcing their way into the packed square from opposite directions. One of the two, Prince Obolensky, had come to reorganize the putsch; the other, Grand Duke Michael, roared at the mutineers to surrender. A shot rang out. A bullet whizzed past the Grand Duke. A civilian brandished a pistol.

Count Miloradovitch was in the Tsar's retinue. The General was a veteran of many battles, a hero of 1812, his men called him bulletproof, and loved him. He rode forth; Obolensky blocked his way, and seized the bridle of his mount. The horse pranced, the irate Prince stuck a bayonet into its hind quarters. Another shot rang out. Miloradovitch collapsed, mortally wounded. A rebel officer had fired, one Lieutenant Kashovsky, who was anxious to make up by ardency what he lacked in social background.

A dismayed colonel of the Guards, a conspirator, now roared at his regiment to hail His Majesty. Kashovsky shot him at once.

The soldiers wavered, rallied, then wavered again. . . .

Metropolitan Seraphim, head of the Church, appeared in the square garbed in the full vestments of his office and lifted his golden, jewel-studded Cross.

The masses fell silent. From afar came sounds of fusillades. Confused skirmishes went on in various quarters of the town. "Surrender . . . surrender for the love of Christ! Return to your barracks," the prelate's voice boomed. "In the name of the Tsar, I pledge full pardon to all of you but the ringleaders."

Nicholas nodded. There was unrest in his retinue. Things seemed to have gone too far to warrant leniency.

The soldiers did not know who the ringleaders were, or what it was all about. But they, too, seemed to feel that things had gone too far. "Pray for us, Father. . . ." men shouted, and did not move.

Dusk fell early in St. Petersburg that time of year. Already the sun had disappeared behind the city walls. But the crowd still grew. Civilians infiltrated the ranks of the Preobrashensky Regiment; soldiers fraternized with civilians.

Count Toll, another member of the Tsar's retinue, was seen talking with Nicholas. The Tsar looked stern, the Count seemed insistent. The din on Senate Square suddenly subsided, thousands heard the fateful sentence: "Sire, you must either have the Square swept by cannon, or resign the throne."

The battery commander whom the Tsar had previously ignored stepped forth, saluted. Nicholas made a gesture of desperate acknowledgment.

Cannoneers jumped to their stations—"*Urra* [Hurrah]," shouted a Preobrashensky officer.

The first cannon fired, but there was no sound of a missile. A blank cartridge . . .

So the artillerists did not dare use balls. Or maybe they too were mutineers. "*Urra! Urra! Urra!*" The Preobrashensky ranks stood firm, civilians were immured in the military rock. "*Urra.*"

Two more shots. Two balls humming over the heads of the mutineers hit the Senate building.

So the artillerists were poor marksmen. "*Urra!*" civilians joined in. The affair turned into a show of heroism, in which everybody wanted to play his part. "*Urra!*"

The Tsar, very erect in the saddle, called the battery commander. "Grapeshot. Sweep the square!" he ordered. The captain crossed himself.

"Boom, boom . . ." Six booms at few-seconds intervals. The square resounded with shouts of the dying. Mutineers broke formations, civilians struggled to reach the safety of side streets.

Nicholas rode off in silence. His horse, his son's pony, and the mounts of his retinue tramped through puddles of human blood.

The battery kept shooting. Other batteries joined action, mowing down guilty and innocent, mutineer soldiers, civilian conspirators, and casual spectators as well.

One irate rebel officer gathered his battalion to storm the St. Peter and St. Paul Fortress. His pathetic and fundamentally senseless exploit resulted in another carnage.

From other quarters of the town rebel officers led small units to a hopeless retreat toward Novgorod.

By midnight of December 14, 1825, the absurd, pompous, and yet gallant rebellion was quelled.

Two weeks later all surviving culprits had been rounded up. They were now called the Dekabrists, the "Men of December."

The Tsar did not retract the promise made by the Metropolitan. The rank and file received full pardon.

Special commissions interrogated officers, and the one arrested civilian, a college teacher. The commissions were directed to avoid rudeness. Generals and grand dukes intervened in favor of the Dekabrists and the Tsar himself had a mutineer, Captain Bestushev, brought into his presence. "You know that I can pardon you," Nicholas is quoted saying, "and I shall do so, if you promise to serve me faithfully in the future."

"Your Majesty," Bestushev allegedly replied. "It is unfortunate indeed that you are above the law. It was our design to make all men subject to the law, instead of to your whims."

Similar noble phrases were said to have been exchanged between defendants and investigators.

From abroad came appeals for clemency. Reports on Dekabrist aims all sounded inconclusive, but this was attributed to vicious Russian censorship. Practically everybody in the West abhorred tyranny, and a glimpse at the Russians during the Napoleonic Wars had made Westerners view Russia as the symbol of tyranny. Foreign observers tended to identify the objectives of the Russian rebels with their own ideas. French radicals extolled the Guards officers as standard bearers of a revised Jacobinism; intellectuals from Scotland to Naples saw Russian secret societies as protagonists of each and every reform advocated in recent literature; progressive-minded burghers hailed the Dekabrists as champions of liberation of the Third Estate from official chicanery; English and French grandees praised Russian nobles for standing up against the vulgarity of oppression; and Freemasons everywhere joined in praise of their martyrized brethren. Even the kings of France and England sympathized with revolution in Russia. They instructed their respective representatives at Nicholas' coronation, Marshal Mortier, and Field Marshal the Duke of Wellington, to put in a word for the Dekabrists.

"Europe will be amazed at my leniency," the Tsar told the Duke.

However, Europe was amazed at the harshness of Russian procedures. The defendants did not have their day in court. The Supreme Criminal Court divided the 121 offenders into eleven categories, and pronounced sentences categorywise. Five men, including Pestel and Kashovsky, were to be quartered; thirty-one, including Trubetzkoy and Obolensky, were to be beheaded; seventeen others, Bestushev among them, should put their heads upon the scaffold as a symbol of civilian death, and then perform forced labor in Siberia for the rest of their lives; sixteen men should serve fifteen years at hard labor in Siberia; and punishment for lesser categories ranged from ten-year, hard-labor terms to forced settlement east of the Urals, and loss of rank and title.

The highest court commuted the sentence for the first category into death by hanging. Beheadings were commuted to life imprisonment. Prison terms were shortened, and deportation statuses eased. But there were no acquittals.

The deportees left in groups of four, shackled and under heavy guard. Gendarmes were instructed to protect their wards against spontaneous outbursts of indignation by Siberian patriots. Local governors had reported that the people of their districts were saying prayers of thanks for the Tsar's deliverance from danger, and implorations for the Lord's continued protection of their new Little Father.

In fact the glory of the Dekabrists spread all over Siberia, where people had no use for enlightenment but acclaimed violence regardless of objective. To have rioted in the heart of the capital was supreme achievement. Lavish receptions were prepared, and the very governors who had reported on the peoples' prayers joined reception committees for the Dekabrists.

The only persons threatened by popular wrath in Siberia were the escorting gendarmes, who, however, quickly unshackled the exiles and joined in parties thrown in their honor. Guards collected donations for the prisoners and tips for their good treatment.

The division of the exiles, however, required so many repetitions of celebrations that Siberians grew tired of the expense involved. The last parties did not receive much attention.

The worst offenders went to the Crown mines of Nerchinsk, where they found a sympathetic commander, a former cavalry colonel, who appreciated the company of distinguished people even in prisoner's garb.

Men under less heavy sentences were sent to towns and fortresses; local authorities granted various mitigations, including the right to read books and newspapers. Governors took pride in opening their libraries to the erudite newcomers. There one of the Dekabrists, Lieutenant Baron Andreas Rosen, found novels by Walter Scott, the *Voyages of Cook,* the *History of Abbé Laporte,* and Russian newspapers half a century old, one of which contained an editorial calling General Washington a "disgraceful rebel."

The fate of the Dekabrists remained hard despite mitigations, and they suffered it in flawless attitude. No Dekabrist succumbed to depravity and corruption, and, even separated, they formed a group of gentlemen in a land of perniciousness.

Siberian revolutionary enthusiasm turned toward Polish deportees.

During his philanthropic period Alexander had granted a Diet, a national administration, and a national army to the territories he had grabbed in the partitions of Poland. The Tsar was King of Poland, and the Governor General acted as his viceroy. This satisfied neither Polish nationalists nor social reformers, but the people at large were assuaged. Yet in 1830, Tsar Nicholas had Polish territory east of the rivers Bug and Niemen severed from autonomous Poland and incorporated into Russia. The Poles turned against the Russian hereditary enemy with furious indignation. Those were the same territories east of the Bug and the Niemen that 119 years later would be awarded to Soviet Russia when Hitler and Stalin agreed to share the spoils of Poland; and they would remain the apple of discord after the Moscow pact of friendship and non-aggression went up in the smoke of the German-Russian war.

Late in 1830 revolution broke out in Poland. In a dramatic sequence of events Russian occupation forces were forced to evacuate the country; the Governor General fled; the Polish Diet deposed the Tsar as King of Poland; Prince Adam Czartoryski formed a national government; and Russian relief forces suffered reverses at Grochow and Ostroleka. But new Russian armies invaded Poland, forced the passage of the Vistula River, took Warsaw, and after ten months of struggle Poland was prostrate.

The national army had been granted free conduct out of the fallen capital. Most of its personnel crossed into Prussia. The rest chose to remain in a fatherland stripped of its autonomous privileges and purged by a tyrannical military governor. Large numbers of Polish patriots went to Siberia. Not even soldiers who had sought asylum in Prussia were secure; the Prussian police was a secret but active contributor to the pool of deportees to Siberia.

Patriotic Poles hated all things Russian, but they accepted gifts and protestations of friendship with which they were showered on their way into exile. The stream of Polish deportees to Siberia never quite subsided, and during a temporary ebb droves of Ukrainian nationalists were marched across the Urals.

Russian governments of the seventeenth and eighteenth centuries had kept only sketchy records of deportations to Siberia. However, figures of 1622 indicated a deportee population of roughly 15 per cent of the total of Russian nationality in Siberia. Two hundred fifty years later, the percentage was 5.2, and this proportion did not essentially change until the outbreak of World War I.

In 1807, the first year in which deportation figures were included in Russian annual statistics, 2035 exiles crossed the Ural Mountains.

A. P. Velitshko, Counselor in the Ministry of the Interior, gave a breakdown of deportation figures for the decade of 1823–33, complete with the reasons for banishment.

REASON FOR DEPORTATION	PEOPLE AFFECTED	
	MEN	WOMEN
Heresy, church robbery, apostasy, blasphemy, desecration	1427	385
Rebellion against, and disobedience to, the authorities	865	25
Illegal attempts at border crossing	136	6
Defalcation and misappropriation of public funds	96	—
Manslaughter	5435	1150
Homicide	74	23
Self-mutilation to evade the draft	388	3[?]
Disobedience to the master	827	204
Desertion	1208	—
Receiving of stolen goods	551	212
Forgery, counterfeiting stamps and passports	2610	268
Infringement of paternal power	23	2
Rape and adultery	258	59
Pederasty	11	—
Robbery and predatory attack	2497	126
Arson	418	325
Theft and fraud	20755	2451
Perjury	157	19
Vagrancy	30703	4605
Debauchery and disorderly conduct	2798	519
Poor standing with the authorities	716	20
Serfs against whom landlords lodged complaints	951	332

These figures include deportees supplied by courtesy of the Prussian police.

No other foreign police is known to have handed over persons within its jurisdiction to the Russian authorities.

In Russia not only courts pronounced deportation sentences. Local administrations down to mayoralty offices issued deportation orders; draft boards shipped suspected dodgers to Asia; the Army made its contribution by clearing fortress dungeons and barrack jails of their inmates; lords of manors shipped recalcitrant servants and mushiks to deportation centers; and communities dumped petty lawbreakers and public charges on Siberia.

Codification of deportation established four groups of exiles: the *katorshnije*, punitive laborers who were cantoned in prisons and put to work in chains; the *ssyljno-posselenzy*, compulsory settlers who after ten years at forced labor could apply for reclassification as plain settlers; the *wodworenje*, compulsory settlers exempt from involuntary labor; and the *shytje*, who had freedom of movement within a limited area and who were eligible for pardon and return to Russia.

Political exiles who had not actively partaken in uprisings usually belonged to the last category.

An all-Siberian table of statistics for the decade ending in 1876 gave new arrivals of *katorshnije* as 18,582, of *ssyljno-posselenzy* as 28,382, of *wodworenje* as 23,382, and *shytje* as 2551. However, 78,686 more deportees had entered Siberia during this decade, and statistics did not disclose their status.

Under the deportation code husbands could join exiled wives, and wives husbands. Couples were permitted to take their children to Siberia. Companions were not liable to forced labor, but could not return to Russia unless their deported kin had been pardoned or had died. Mates who chose to stay behind could obtain divorces without much formality.

A survey made in 1884 among 11,905 male and 829 female deportees disclosed that only three husbands had joined their wives, while 1752 wives chose to go with their deportee men; and 3631 children were taken to Siberia by their parents.

Mortality among children was appallingly high. The complete absence of medical care, and the exertion of long marches turned relatively harmless diseases into mass killers. In 1874 measles wiped out half of the children en route.

Official accounts claimed that women deportees were "of generally bad character and altogether unfit for matrimony." Most women turned prostitutes. This, however, was not caused by "generally bad character," but by the fact that they were forced to submit to every guard and to pay with their favors for every morsel of extra food. Wives who accompanied deported husbands found it practically impossible to remain faithful. Actual temptation was not strong, but if a woman wanted to help her man and children, there was but one way for her to do it.

Age was no bar to sexual intercourse. Siberians thought that intercourse with old women, the more haggish the better, turned a man immune against disease.

An average of 15 per cent of the deportees escaped en route; almost half of the *ssyljno-posselenzy* vanished from assigned domiciles; and about 10 per cent of the members of chain gangs were estimated as missing in normal years. But during the gold rush, when forced laborers were turned over to mine operators, the percentage was much higher.

Within a fifty-year period a total of 100,000 male and a few daredevil female deportees disappeared in the wilderness, where they joined outlaws in recklessly savage bands of robbers. At times some 30,000 bandits plagued the countryside. The settled peasantry organized battues and collected bounties, where they outnumbered the raiders; but in regions where the raiders were superior in strength peasants would offer them shelter and food, and their farms would turn into bases from where the bandits raided more densely populated regions.

Rape, arson, manslaughter, and robbery were routine, but the bandits would also resort to peaceful cheating. Some peasants were liable to accept polished uniform buttons for coins, and sheets of colored paper for bank notes.

According to judicial statistics, 62 per cent of all murders and 23 per cent of other felonies tried in Siberia in 1872 and 1873 were committed by outlaws. However, the methods of investigation do not make these figures reliable. Not only the suspects were put to the rack; members of their families, including babies, were tortured in their presence to exact confessions.

Banditry was exploited by dignified townspeople to screen their own crimes. In 1874 a lawyer from Irkutsk acted as a defense counsel to a teen-age bandit charged with the murder of a wealthy widow. The attorney had, in fact, assisted the police in solving the crime, and he made his client put three crosses under a voluntary confession, which netted the lawyer high praise and the defendant the company of a priest to the place of execution. Quite accidentally it was learned later that the lawyer himself had killed the widow and used his powers to help himself to her property. He too went to the gallows, but the citizenry of Irkutsk had no regret for the bandit-victim. The consensus was that they should all be hanged without trial.

The peasantry abided by this rule. The bandits they captured were dispatched in "lynching parties" of obscene cruelty, and their corpses were produced to collect bounties, of three rubles apiece. Village children adopted "lynching" as their favorite game.

Everybody could exploit or kill a runaway, but even exiles who did not run away were often helpless. Reclassified *ssyljno-posselenzy* who worked for farmers would, more often than not, receive abuse instead of wages. Courts invariably accepted the employer's word that he owed nothing. When it came to deal with the *posselenzy,* mushiks, kulaks, and lords of the mansion acted alike.

Official accounts claimed that some *posselenzy* had turned landowners and would have become wealthy had it not been for their deplorable tendency to spend large sums on booze and whoring. Eyewitnesses called the *posselenzy* landowners' houses warped, lice-infested huts, and their land pathetically neglected for lack of seeds and tools.

Siberian fly-by-night operators had jobs for skilled deportees, and they would even assist the escape of persons who qualified. In demand were coiners, forgers, horse thieves, and "tea cutters."

The profession of tea cutter was a Siberian specialty. Its performers joined tea caravans. During the march they clipped bales from the loads of pack animals, leaving assistants to pick up the "cut tea" for delivery to the ringleader.

The Russian Government devoted much paper work to the deportee problem. But most investigations were pigeonholed or died in commissions and committees. The main achievement was an expansion of the deportation to Sakhalin. Seven hundred families were shipped to the island to work the soil and the coal mines; they were granted more personal freedom than they would have had in Siberia. However, observers agreed that conditions in Sakhalin remained unsatisfactory.

A memorandum on Siberia signed by Russian Minister of the Interior Possjet had nothing kindly to say about the deportees:

"This grandiose territory, 2½ times the size of European Russia, a land whose riches are hardly tapped, is doomed to be the domicile of the refuse of a population of 70 millions. Such a colonization made sense when Siberia was a wasteland, bound by the wild Pacific, and sparsely inhabited by savage nomads. But now that the Pacific has become a link between civilized countries, it is high time to purge Siberia from the stigma of "land of criminals." We are being faced with a serious shortage of trustworthy and useful elements. Siberia is falling behind its neighbor states in the East. The progress, nay, the very existence of Siberia was neglected for the sake of deportation."

The neighbor states, China and Japan, knew all about Siberian deportation. Fugitives had reached China since the seventeenth century and the Sakhalin experiment resulted in runaways crossing the narrow straits to Hokkaido.

Possjet's appeal had no practical effect. There was no other territory under the Russian Crown to substitute for Siberia as a deportation land.

The Siberian administration gave little thought to such memoranda. Deportation was part and parcel of the domain, and it even had bright aspects. Political exiles with intellectual backgrounds still satisfied the Siberian intelligentsia's craving for refined conversation. Siberian upper-tens knew their neighbors to the point of nausea; they had told each other a hundred times over all there was to say, and they had paraded their talents a hundredfold, but rebels brought fresh thoughts and topics into a dull atmosphere. Rebellion remained a fad in Siberian society. People who stood to lose everything from rebellion and who applied the knout to their own chattels were eager to associate with exiled mutineers.

Snobbish kulaks bribed clerks into issuing servants' permits to exiles. Such distinguished "domestics" were well fed, grotesquely overliveried, and never overworked. They could even steal or sleep with their master's wife. But when they transgressed unfathomable limits, and the master used knout or gun, their death would be ascribed to "natural causes."

However, the number of deportees who benefited from snobbishness remained a small fraction of the total.

Thrift rather than humaneness caused new Siberian investigations in the late 1870s.

Two hundred thousand persons were listed as public charges in the "grandiose territory." The number of deportees available for compulsory labor and descendants of deportees who could be usefully employed was lower than expected. During the half century preceding the new investigation 393,914 deportations were recorded, but little more than half that number was listed in the latest census. The average life expectancy of a deportee was about ten years. This had been attributed to the "advanced age of the exiles," but actually the average age of deportees was thirty. Investigators found that the exile's reproductivity was unsatisfactory, owing to poor health, marriage restrictions for deportees, the free Siberian's aversion to marrying exiles, the vagabonds' apparent dislike for family ties, and also syphilis and prostitution.

The government's investment in deportation could not pay dividends unless the deportees reproduced properly. Officials took exception to this conclusion. Files gave shipping expenses as 50 rubles per capita, which was an evidence of Russian efficiency, as compared to England, which spent £180, roughly 1700 rubles, to bring one exile to Australia.

But then the 50-ruble figure came up for investigation. Before the survey started, statisticians acknowledged that it might be outdated, and that expenses would run anywhere near 140 rubles. But the investigation took its course, and the results were devastating.

Substantial expenses had never been charged to the deportation account. Transit prisons had been built to house the prisoners on the road. Yakutsk alone had collected for sixteen such institutions. Districts had been paid for recapture of escapees; the capture of one and the same man had been billed a dozen times. Covering forces of 14,867 officers and men were on the general pay roll; "extra transportation" costs were charged to the treasury with Yeniseisk leading the collectors with payment obtained for 5296 carts and 5202 men. Districts had also charged extra expenses for security and huge sums allegedly paid out for relief of *posselenzy*.

Practically every Russian governmental agency, military and civilian, had contributed to prisoner expenses, under different titles. Most bills had been fraudulent; there could be no sixteen transit jails in one district, and not even a hundred carts could be engaged in the transportation of deportees who, with the exception of boat rides, almost invariably walked.

Three months after the investigation had started in earnest, the estimated deportation costs stood at 300 rubles per head. Another three months later the 500-ruble mark was reached, and faultfinders began to wonder whether the deficit of the Crown mines, owing to the workers' failure to earn their upkeep, should not be added to deportation expenses.

Optimists, however, insisted that deportation was a paying proposition. It cost 74.37 rubles annually to maintain one man in a Russian jail. A deportee lasted ten years, and unless it would cost 743.70 to bring him to Siberia, the procedure was still in the black. But less than a year later the estimated expenses passed the 743.70 mark, and then the matter was shelved.

In Siberia two thirds of the administration staff kept working on deportation files. Governors kept collecting extra deportation bills from whatever governmental agency was ready to pay, and the population was assessed more taxes for handling exiles.

And exiles kept trudging the fatal road east.

> For Christ's sake
> Have mercy, O little fathers;
> Don't forsake the forced wanderers,
> Don't abandon those who languish in the prisons,
> Keep us, support us, little fathers.
> Give alms to help the wretched and afflicted.

Thus the wretched and the afflicted chanted in the settlements through which they wandered. It was a beggar's song, little different from the incantations that could be heard throughout the Russian realm.

CHAPTER FIFTY-THREE Chroniclers of Siberian woes listed narcotic addiction as a minor woe. Smugglers carried quantities of opium across the Chinese border.

The Chinese did not grow opium, but they had been importing it in small quantities for almost a thousand years as a medicine against dysentery. Only when European merchants interfered with Asiatic trade did the consumption of opium rise and addiction spread in China.

Opium was grown in India, Persia, and Turkey. Portuguese traders brought the superior Persian and Turkish product to Macao, their English counterparts carried inferior Indian opium to Canton, and both Portuguese and English used illicit channels to bring their goods into Chinese ports, which were closed to foreign trade.

European demand for Chinese goods was growing, but China's imports from the Western world barely kept level. Ingenious merchants' minds conceived the dumping of opium on Chinese markets as a means to improve the balance of trade.

Not until the late eighteenth century did the Chinese Government awaken to the damages caused by opium imports. Before that no restrictions were imposed on the narcotic trade, and only nominal customs duties were levied.

Eventually the English took a long lead over their Portuguese competitors in the field. The Chinese called these bickering, haggling, fastidious traders, these boisterous, hard-drinking sailors, these gaudily garbed skippers "red-haired barbarians."

In 1717, Emperor Kang-hsi already had warned that "precautions should be taken to prevent these men from endangering our Empire." But the wise monarch thought that it would take many hundred, if not a thousand, years until the danger would materialize, and no precautions were taken against the "red-haired barbarians."

In Emperor Kang-hsi's day the Manchu dynasty ruled the lands from the Amur River to Eastern Turkestan. Burma, Mongolia, Tibet, and Nepal were vassal states, and even parts of India were under the Manchu-Chinese sway. Three hundred million people lived in the realm, far more than the combined populations of all European countries and Siberia. China was at peace; but peace did not benefit the people. Domestic production did not keep up with the rise of the population, but more rapid even than the latter was the growth of the administration. Public expenditures skyrocketed; civil services spent more on sumptuous office buildings and elaborate costumes than it would have cost to maintain a powerful army. And because the defense establishment seemed useless, the government retired most officers, sapping its strength without reducing expenditures, as retired officers continued to draw their salaries as pensions. Instead of prosperity the average Chinese experienced creeping depression.

In the 1770s various secret leagues formed in China. Their programs had one point in common: the inept and wasteful Peking government should cede most of its powers to regional administrations. This would have been tantamount to political dismemberment, but the Chinese common man, whose allegiances were clannish rather than national, did not mind the implication.

The Society of the Divine Law was the most influential secret league. In 1813 its members staged a coup in Peking. The uprising was put down, but the imperial prestige suffered a telling blow. Next Turkestan rebelled. The Chinese hold on vassal-neighbors loosened; and provincial governors ignored orders from the capital.

When this happened British India was still under the rule of the East India Company, but the company's policy was at least as imperialistic as that of any empire. From Indian bases British troops struck out in all directions, to turn the subcontinent and adjoining territories into British dominions. This was not done in the name of conquest, but under such pious pretexts as restoration of law and order, enforcement of existing treaties, retaliation for alleged ill-treatment of English merchants, abuse of Royal Navy personnel, and, last but not least, in the name of legitimate trade.

The weaker China became the more retaliation-minded turned the agents of the East India Company, and the more vociferous were their complaints about their neighbor's lawlessness.

In 1824 "the red-haired barbarians" charged Burmese nationals with encroachment upon Indian territory. English troops seized two Burmese provinces, utterly unconcerned over Chinese rights in the region.

China did not strike back. The Emperor could do no more than draft pompous enunciations—not to aggressive foreigners, but to his own unappreciative governors; and because six years before the invasion of Burma a decree had been issued, there was not even paper action in 1824.

The document of 1818 said: "Our Empire used to tame barbarians by laws and directives for decent behavior. Those who abided by the law received our favors; the disobedient and the rebels were subdued. Laws and directives concerning English trade in Canton and English commercial shipping have been issued long ago. It should be sufficient to remind the barbarians of our orders to restrain their greed. Should the barbarians dare to defy our law, they will have to face our ire, and tremble before the thunder of our guns. However, you are directed to apply reason to the limit, and not to resort to force unless peaceful means are exhausted."

The "barbarians" were undaunted by the threat of thunder and ire, and the governors remained non-violent beyond the limit, doing nothing.

Already in 1767, Chinese medical authorities had found that smoking and drinking of opium had detrimental effects upon public health. The government prohibited sales of narcotics. Chinese merchants in good standing obeyed the ordinance, but illicit operators kept buying opium from foreign importers who paid no heed to "laws and directives concerning trade and shipping."

Chinese addicts craved the dope. Go-betweens, who supplied the afflicted, propagated the use of opium. Demand rose at a staggering rate, and with the demand the prices rose—100 per cent during the 1820s.

The East India Company established new opium plantations in India, and hired experts to improve the product.

When the Europeans started dumping opium on China, annual deliveries had amounted to 1200 cases; by 1834 they reached 34,000 cases of 80 pounds each.

April 1834 was a crucial month in the history of the East India Company. Its Chinese trade monopoly expired, and all English subjects were henceforth authorized to do business with China. Lord Napier was appointed as the English Government's trustee for the China trade.

Lord Napier wrote to the provincial governors of Kuangtung and Kuangsi, insisting that, as a ranking official, he would not deal with socially inferior people like Chinese merchants, and that henceforth correspondence with his offices would have to be conducted by the Chinese Government.

Chinese officials were ready to take political humiliation, but they would not stand for personal discourtesy. They resealed the letter and returned it to Lord Napier, whom they addressed as "Overseer of foreigners," together with an accompanying note: "The statutes of our land are unalterable. We are familiar with the barbarians' habit of making arbitrary changes and unjustified demands. The wisdom of our Empire does not tolerate wanton fickleness. It has been learned that the East India Company's men have been replaced by the King's men. This is none of our concern. Every state is the master of its internal affairs, and regardless of replacements our civilized Empire will uphold established procedures. We are not anxious to know the terms under which the English Government authorizes its subjects to engage in business. The government of China is utterly disinterested in your communication."

The Chinese did not snub the Portuguese. Portugal at least did not use its foothold in Macao for aggressive purposes, while the English seemed to consider their Canton factory as a stronghold for expansion.

The London government had not expected such a reaction. Neither had Lord Napier. And when the Governor's note was followed by acts of chicanery against the English, the lord was recalled. The opium trade, however, continued despite the deceptive triumph of the Chinese over English arrogance.

A survey made by the Chinese Ministry of Cult in 1836 concluded: "Stringent laws have stimulated rather than restricted the smuggling of opium. Opium addicts cannot abandon the vice, even though it spells destruction. Prohibition encourages mischief. It should be considered lifting the ban on opium traffic and collect opium taxes instead."

The Office of Censorship took exception, insisting that the evil ought to be rooted out. Eventually a man was appointed to organize a nationwide campaign against the plague.

Lin-tse-siu, the appointee, had formerly been a department head in the War Office and district Governor. He was a man of humble birth and modest means, reputedly a paragon of sagacity, honesty, and steadfastness. He proclaimed that bygones should be bygones. Chinese charged with smuggling opium into the country were summarily pardoned. Smugglers who carried the narcotic to Siberia were not indicted; they were, in fact, unwittingly combating addiction in China.

Lin-tse-siu launched an appeal to foreign merchants. He reminded them of the high profits they had made by legitimate trade, and went on: "But why do you bring opium to our country, a drug that is barred in your own lands, because it spreads death and destruction? Why do you enrich yourself dishonestly by corrupting our people? Don't you understand that the law of our land applies to everybody who lives within its borders? As long as you stay on our territory, you too must abide by our laws. I understand that there are thousands of cases of opium in the holds of your ships moored in our waters. I request that you surrender this cargo to the government, and sign pledges never again to import opium. In the future, opium will be subject to seizure, and its importers regardless of nationality liable to punishment. It is said that you attach great importance to the term 'decency.' You should show yourself worthy of so fine a word, so that past iniquities may be forgotten, and you may enjoy your opportunity to acquire riches in a decent manner. But, should you persist in your folly, you will have to suffer penalties provided under the law."

The English would not yield to bluff. And, knowing of China's troubles, they discounted the possibility of law enforcement. But then Chinese soldiers deployed at the outskirts of Canton. Panicky Chinese operators refused to buy contraband, and the English, who were worried at the prospects of business recession, offered to negotiate.

Launcellot Dent, dean of opium dealers, explained that 1056 cases of opium had been stored in the holds of English ships. These boxes would be delivered against a compensation, but Chinese authorities would have to guarantee the safety of English nationals. And there remained a controversy to be settled: the case of an English subject who allegedly had been detained somewhere in China eighty years before.

With such an issue being raised parleys would drag on endlessly, and Lin also doubted the authenticity of the figure of opium cases.

Upon his orders the Englishmen in Canton were virtually isolated, cut off from services and supplies. Charles Elliot, Lord Napier's successor and Superintendent General of English trade in China, intervened; he notified Lin that stores of opium would be rechecked and reasonable regulations were considered.

The number of cases turned out to be 20,283. China purchased the contraband and had it destroyed. But the English stalled when Lin requested that they never again ship opium to China. And all the time new loads of opium kept arriving, and Lin's scheme to combat addiction became unworkable.

He appealed to Charles Elliot to force English opium runners to return to their country. The Superintendent General refused to be a party to the "exposure of the foreign merchants' life and property to Chinese arbitrariness," but he ordered all English subjects to leave Canton. Chinese junks did not interfere with the English exodus to Macao and Hong Kong. Hong Kong was Chinese territory, but it was considered beyond the range of the pathetic Chinese Navy.

Not until English men-of-war turned up in Chinese waters did Peking realize that London was set to teach China a lesson on English power and on English conception of Far Eastern trade.

On November 3, 1839, ships of young Queen Victoria's navy engaged twenty-nine Chinese war junks, poorly maneuverable vessels with little fire power. Six junks were sunk with their crews of 1000; the English suffered neither damage nor casualties.

The government of China, anxious to be spared a loss of face that could speed its own downfall, did not inform its people of the disaster, but instead it barred all Englishmen and English products from the country, including Macao. The U. S. Consul in that city was asked to see that no English goods be imported under the American flag. The Consul warned the Chinese against drastic action and drastic language, as had been used in the decree of banishment, which called the English "outlaws that should be tracked down like wild beasts."

Lin requested that Launcellot Dent be extradited as chief black-marketeer, and he wrote a letter to Queen Victoria, admonishing her to mend her ways, and abide by the law, as her ancestors had done.

In the House of Lords the Duke of Wellington took the floor: "Whatever Mr. Dent may be otherwise, he is an Englishman. This should suffice not only to prevent other Englishmen from extraditing him, but also compel them to defend him to the last."

And while the old hero of the Napoleonic Wars made this pronunciamento, another English armada, including three ships of the line, twelve lesser units and thirty transport craft with 4000 soldiers and artillery aboard, assembled in Singapore. Its commanding Admiral, a namesake of the Superintendent, carried a letter signed by Lord Palmerston, in which the English Government complained about Chinese procedures and asked for reparations.

Still farther to the east Superintendent Elliot compiled fancy figures of damages allegedly suffered by English traders, plus expenses for forcible collection, for, as it was stated, "The dice are cast; force of arms, the last resort of Princes and peoples, shall decide."

And, last resort of opium traders, Admiral Elliot's ships entered the Chinese island port of Tinghai, on July 14, 1840. The local commander of a flotilla of junks was nowhere to be found and neither was the commander of Chinese troops camping on surrounding hills available to receive an ultimatum asking for surrender within six hours.

Inquisitive Chinese crowds swarmed the piers to catch a glimpse of the visitors. Local officials paid courtesy calls and were told that England was at war with China to avenge iniquities inflicted upon Englishmen in Canton. The ultimatum was about to expire when the Chinese flotilla commander rushed aboard Admiral Elliot's flagship.

"You ought to settle scores with the men from Canton," the Chinese implored the Admiral. "We never wronged you. It would be sheer madness to fight against your superior strength, and yet, we shall have to resist attack."

Elliot extended the ultimatum until the following afternoon, but he insisted upon capitulation, which to the Chinese meant a complete loss of face. Had the English invited them to desert, many officers and officials would have run over; but the Admiral hardly understood, and certainly did not care about

Chinese psychology. He opened fire at the very moment his ultimatum expired. The Chinese tried to reply, but all but one of their cannon blew up, and the only piece left had been cast in 1601 and was not effective.

The guns of the battleships caused severe damage in the city. The cries of the wounded were still heard when English landing parties marched into the town. They were met by survivors who kowtowed and asked for mercy.

The commander of the junks had been fatally wounded during the bombardment, and the First Mandarin of Chusan committed suicide by drowning himself in a pond.

The invaders were amazed by the beauty of Chusan Island and the magnificence of its temples and mansions—evidence of an ancient culture infinitely more refined than anything they had ever seen before. Officers searched abandoned arsenals and found muskets, pikes, and incendiary rockets alongside bows and arrows. Army manuals indicated that the Chinese had effectives of 1,000,000 men, including 160,000 Manchu elite troops. But the manuals were outdated, and the strength of the Chinese Army was barely 10 per cent of the figure.

Admiral Elliot took the bulk of his ships to Tientsin, where he expected to dictate his terms to the Chinese Government. Faster than his craft traveled the news of English naval superiority. Millions of Chinese camped along the mainland coast to see the barbarians' steamers ride past in an ominous procession.

An imperial plenipotentiary, third-ranking man in the Chinese hierarchy, met Admiral Elliot with protestations of good will, and of admiration for his vessels. He announced that the Emperor of China wanted all foreigners to be treated with kindness and consideration, the imperial government had had no knowledge of the unfortunate controversy in Canton, but if the Admiral would sail to that city, he would find an imperial delegation waiting for him with full powers to accept every equitable demand the honorable English nation might make.

Elliot set course for Canton, where he found the imperial delegation. However, the chief Chinese delegate concentrated on courtesies, evading English demands. Parleys dragged on. Elliot became the laughingstock of his own men, who resented being held in suspense by the Chinese.

Almost six months after action at Chusan a Chinese fleet came in sight of Canton, a maze of junks more numerous but no more battleworthy than the flotilla of Chusan. Admiral Elliot ordered destruction of the Chinese fleet, and also of the land fortifications surrounding Canton.

English Congreve rockets wrought havoc among the highly inflammable junks, and English shells shattered Chinese forts.

The imperial delegation stood by as their emperor's ships and fortifications went up in smoke and dust, and their emperor's subjects were being killed. When it was over, they suggested that, with the English military objectives apparently achieved, a preliminary armistice should be signed.

Admiral Elliot agreed. Peking, however, refused to ratify the armistice. After sheer endless, unavailing palavers, the Admiral and Sir Hugh Gough, commander of the landing forces, decided to seize the hinterland of Canton and its Four Castles.

A small force of Manchu soldiers manned the castles, but the Chinese provincial Governor issued a draft call which swelled their ranks to 40,000. Twelve hundred cannon were gathered, hazards to their crews rather than to the enemy. Fortunately for the gunners there was no powder available. Draftees quarreled with veterans and settled old family and village scores in violent spats.

When the English opened the attack on May 24, 1841, Chinese recruits made for their homes, and the Manchus had no stomach to fight. Three days later the Chinese ratified the armistice, and paid £1,419,663,7s. 6d. "for destruction of property and other damages incurred by Her Majesty's subjects, and armed forces, in and around Canton, and also as indemnity to other European nationals." Other European nationals collected not quite 1 per cent of the sum.

English public opinion, however, had been violently aroused by previous events. It was obnoxious to see the Queen's invincible navy and her glorious land forces bamboozled by tricky natives. The Queen's government, sensitive to patriotic clamor, relieved Admiral Elliot from command and replaced him by Admiral Sir William Parker. Simultaneously Sir Henry Pottinger was appointed Plenipotentiary for China.

Sir William and Sir Henry arrived in the East sixty-seven days after the armistice had been ratified and indemnities collected, but they resumed hostilities at once.

The Peking government appealed to its subjects to battle the invaders. The British countered by claiming that they were, in fact, the friends of the Chinese people and opposed only to its despotic rulers. Sir Henry appealed to collaborators, encouraged defection of provinces and cities, and the setting up of local puppet governments. However, as in the case of Ningpo (Ninghsien), in October 1841, English patronizing protestations were followed by imposition of exorbitant contributions, and even though the English forces won every battle, there were several instances of Chinese heroism. The defenders of Tshinhai committed suicide rather than surrender; captured fishermen stood up against English investigators who wanted information about Chinese naval forces; and in Tshapu 300 Chinese trapped in a row of burning houses died in the flames, firing their muskets, killing thirteen, and wounding forty-six aggressors.

By the end of 1841, Tshusa and Tshinhai had fallen; Wusong and Shanghai were taken in the first half of 1842. English naval units suffered some damage from Chinese fire ships. In the summer of 1842, English craft patrolled the Yangtse River, and on July 21, English troops of the 1st and 3rd Brigades stormed Chinkiang at a considerable loss: 168 men, 16 of whom had suffered heat strokes. On August 10 the Royal Navy anchored off Nanking, whose population of 1,500,000 was threatened by famine.

Sir Henry issued a proclamation, opening with a moralistic statement on the fraternity of all people under the skies, and the sinfulness of overweening national pride. The epistle denounced Lin-tse-siu as a dishonest person and the Peking government as men who did not keep their word, who mistreated helpless English prisoners, restrained English merchants, and were guilty of many more misdeeds which could but outrage decent men. The English, faithful to their queen's orders, would make the cause of justice prevail.

Emperor Tao-kwang of China wearily countered that the cause of the conflagration was opium, the poison which contaminated the Chinese people. He did not elaborate on English charges, which, in fact, had been made for consumption at home, where even the most hypocritical perversion of the truth would be acclaimed if it identified England with the cause of justice. In one instance, however, the charges were correct. The treatment of the few English prisoners who fell into Chinese hands had been bad indeed.

The Governor of Nanking offered to pay ransom for his city. Sir Henry Pottinger replied that only surrender by the Peking government could prevent the destruction of Nanking.

Despite the haughty tone of their enunciations the English were in dire straits. Their communications were threatened by high water in rivers and canals. There had been several cases of cholera, and it would have been impossible to combat a large-scale epidemic. Another Chinese stand like the one at Chinkiang, another determined raid by Chinese fire ships could have led to military disaster, but the English gambled and won.

Three days later delegates arrived from Peking, meek, submissive, and utterly dispirited.

There was no bargaining or bickering. On August 29, 1842, peace was signed aboard the English flagship *Cornwallis*.

China was made to pay the equivalent of $21,000,000, under a variety of titles, such as compensation for the 20,283 opium cases, for which, in the name of prevailing justice, the English collected for the third time. The Chinese ports of Canton, Amoy, Foochow, Ningpo, and Shanghai were opened to traders of all nations. Foreign consuls were admitted to supervise tariffs and duties. Hong Kong was ceded to the British Crown "for times eternal." British subjects held in Chinese custody were freed. Chinese officials who had collaborated with the English would not be taken to answer, and, in China, English officials would henceforth deal with Chinese officials on equal terms.

The original Chinese version of this instrument of surrender naïvely used the term "barbarians" for English, but the victors had it changed to "English" before it was signed.

After the ceremonies the victors handed a copy of the Bible to each member of the delegation of the vanquished.

Lin-tse-siu was dismissed, not because of wrongdoings, as the Emperor of

China told his people, but because his rash actions had committed the country beyond its strength.

"I hate myself for being unable to protect my subjects against disaster," the Emperor asserted, "and for not having known that the barbarians' ships are so big and powerful, and that there are so many dastardly cowards in our midst. . . ."

The Treaty of Nanking opened Chinese ports to foreigners, but it was not desirable for the rapidly expanding U.S.A. to see its Oriental trade come under English protection. President John Tyler delegated Caleb Cushing to China to make official arrangements for future relations between Washington and Peking.

Mr. Cushing's credentials were composed in flowery language, to meet the Oriental taste. They said that the twenty-six states of the union were as large as China, though not as densely populated; that they extended from ocean to ocean, and the rising sun illuminated the big rivers and high mountains of the U.S.A., and that, after having set over powerful America, the same sun rose over the equally big rivers and high mountains of China. The two mighty nations were practically neighbors, and the heavens wanted them to respect each other, to communicate in a sensible and friendly manner that should be established by laws and norms. The wise and learned Mr. Cushing was directed to proceed to Peking and draft an agreement which, after its acceptance by the plenipotentiaries of China, would be signed by the President of the U.S.A., with the authorization of the Senate, the Great Council of the Nation.

Mr. Cushing arrived in Wanghia, China, where he disappointed the local authorities by carrying only the letter, but no presents, as Oriental custom required from friendly callers. And the American did not ingratiate himself with the governors of Kwangtung and Kwangsi provinces, with whom he dealt; he did not tolerate that in the protocols the names of Chinese negotiators be written in larger characters than those of the American delegates. Mr. Cushing expressed views on intercourse between nations which sounded businesslike, and made no reference to mountains, rivers, and the course of the sun.

The governors wanted to let the visitor cool his heels indefinitely, but the American lectured the Chinese on the theme that foreign envoys symbolized sovereign nations, that they should be free to come and go and call on courts and governments, and that if envoys, the messengers of peace, were refused admission, they might be followed by troops and ships, the instruments of war.

The Chinese did not want another test of strength. In July 1844 an American-Chinese pact of peace, friendship, and trade was signed in Wanghia, granting U.S. citizens all privileges extended to other nationals or to be granted to foreigners in the future. Americans would not be subject to restrictions by monopolies; American envoys would have access to the Emperor; and communications from the government in Washington would be forwarded to the Imperial Court without hindrance.

And while the English continued their opium trade, America obtained a wide-open door to Chinese ports and markets. The material proceeds of the pact of Wanghia, however, fell short of expectations. In the first decade of its validity combined annual imports and exports averaged only about $10,000,000.

American industrial experts suggested that the administration of President James K. Polk obtain another treaty, giving America fishing privileges in Chinese waters, including whale hunting and pearl fishing, the right to build railroads and telegraphs, and to establish ship services in Chinese rivers. This project, promoted by Secretary of the Treasury Robert J. Walker, was never carried out. Neither was Secretary Walker sent to China, as he had hoped, to watch the internal conflicts there and help to organize a new government should the Manchu dynasty be overthrown.

French national pride would not tolerate the English-speaking nations consolidating their positions in China, with France sitting on the fence. And because French dignity required that the nation promote more exalted aims than sales of narcotics or even of regular consumer goods, the government of France styled itself protector of Catholicism in China.

According to Jesuit statistics, 200,000 Catholics lived in China, an infinitesimal fraction of a population risen to 414,000,000 by 1844. The Chinese Government had not committed overt acts of religious intolerance. However, a pompous French delegation arrived at Whampoa and introduced itself as the guardian of humanitarian and religious rights. The French agenda also included several quite materialistic items, and on October 24, 1844, France was granted essentially the same privileges as obtained by the U.S.A., in addition to a pledge that Chinese subjects would always be entitled to join every denomination of the Christian faith. This put Catholics, Protestants, and even the Orthodox on equal footing, which was not strictly to French desire, but the Chinese protested that under the terms of the treaties with England and America they could not discriminate against Protestants, and that other Christian denominations also should be free of restrictions.

Chinese statesmen did not want to give Russia a pretext for intervening for the sake of religion. Russia was the last of the expansionist great powers to impose agreements upon hapless China, but the Russians of Siberia had been on the move long before the English started collecting for their countrymen's contraband.

A contemporary Chinese chronicler noted that "Russia has developed a deplorable habit of grabbing its neighbor's territory without as much as a pretext."

The latest grabbers of territory were jail breakers who had escaped from the *katorgas* and roamed the Chinese border prior to the rebellion of the secret societies in Peking. When Chinese troopers were withdrawn to reinforce the palace guards, these *katorshnije* looted Dawrien settlements, and eventually established a settlement of their own in China, on the far bank of the Amur River. It was a riotous community, levying tribute from neighbors in the name of the Tsar. The ex-convicts were followed by deserters who taxed Chinese subjects for "protection against robbers." *Katorshnije* and deserters sold trade monopolies and opium privileges to Siberian black-marketeers, and kept competitors out at gun point.

The Treaty of Nerchinsk was still in force, but authorities in Irkutsk chose to forget the framing of borders which it contained. The offices of the Governor General marked the farthest points of the intruder's advance as preliminary borders.

Russians also entered Outer Mongolia, and behaved in their usual manner.

Peking wondered if this intrusion would not result in a flare-up of Mongolian aggression. It was rumored that fanatical wizards were stirring a new wave of nationalism in the Djenghiskhanide tradition, and that 274,000 horsemen under the command of three princes were ready to break out from their confines. But the Mongolian princes kept collecting Chinese pensions, the Mongolian herdsmen did not take to horse, and wizards kept selling precipitation at cut-rate fees.

St. Petersburg watched developments along the Siberian border with a mixture of glee and apprehension. The Russian Government considered the Nerchinsk borders a misfit and subsequent changes by misinterpretation had not sufficiently improved the situation. Russia needed control of the Amur River for unlimited access to the Sea of Okhotsk, to Kamchatka, and to America. Russia wanted Outer Mongolian territory to solidify its hold on the far-flung territories between the Upper Yenisei and the Pacific. But Russia also had annexionist aims, thousands of miles to the west where time seemed ripe for another bid for Constantinople and European provinces of the tottering Turkish Empire. Rival great powers took a dim view of St. Petersburg's designs in Europe, and conservative circles warned against provoking another controversy in the Far East, where England, America, and France had vested interests.

Eventually Russian senators, members of the State Council, and Foreign Service experts drafted a novel pattern of action in Siberia.

The Governor General should encourage the land-grabbing drive at the expense of China, but if this produced sharp countermeasures he would be disowned by his government for highhanded activities.

It was hazardous to vest clandestine discretionary powers in a dyed-in-the-wool Siberian official. There was no way of telling what such a corruptionist would eventually do. The Governor General would have to be incorruptible in dealing with his own government, a master of prevarication in dealing with foreigners, a man who wore kid gloves over mailed fists, whose pedigree made him eligible for membership in a swank English club, and who could still outbully Their Lordships in handling Orientals.

St. Petersburg's choice for the difficult job fell upon Nikolai Nikolaevitch Muraviev, Lieutenant General in the Army and acting Governor of Tula. The

Muravievs were an ancient boyar family with a record of distinguished services alternating with rebellion. They had outgrown their rebellious phase and could be relied upon to serve the Tsar and yet to fool foreign progressives.

Nikolai Muraviev was thirty-seven years old in 1846, when he was appointed Governor General of Siberia. His career had been highlighted by unscrupulous love affairs, casino intrigues, and internecine plots out of which he had emerged unscathed and ready for promotion. He was even said to have outwitted and browbeaten a diehard ring of moneylenders.

He was renowned as a "fine dresser" who sported light "English" pantaloons and swallow-tailed coats of Viennese design; his way of wearing watch chains was imitated by carpet knights about town. Plump-shouldered, high-bosomed belles admired Muraviev's attractively masculine figure, his clear features, and smart mustache; and their grudging husbands could but admit that His Excellency had a brilliant mind.

Muraviev was getting bored with St. Petersburg. Society seemed to wear blinkers, and even debauchery was uninspiring. He considered settling in Paris, when his Siberian assignment came through.

He accepted with genuine enthusiasm. His directives were thrilling beyond expectation. Such an opportunity came but once in a lifetime. Paris could wait.

Siberian black-marketeers who learned of Muraviev's nomination told Manchurians, Tunguses, Dawriens, and Mongols in newly invaded territory that a high dignitary would soon inspect their settlements and have pagans thrown to the bears and tigers; only Christians who could identify themselves with brass crosses would be allowed to stay. Frightened natives bought a hundred thousand crosses at fancy prices before Muraviev arrived at Irkutsk.

The personnel of the offices of the Governor General worried lest the new appointee be another reformer and revisor, but at the first reception Muraviev put their minds at rest. Sporting a lieutenant general's uniform with two rows of medals, plenty of tassel, and some lace, the new head of the administration was jovial, and radiating indulgence. His entertaining habits were strictly unascetic.

Siberian experts warned against diplomatic dealings with China. The Chinese would consider overtures as evidence of weakness and might even request that the invaders withdraw behind the Nerchinsk line, which China still regarded as the border.

There should be no renewal of secret talks with Japan, either. Practically unnoticed by other foreigners, a Russian mission had been to Japan to talk the government into collaboration. But the Japanese had replied that "friendship was like a chain; unless all links were of equal strength, weak links would be ground to pieces by the strong ones." Japan's strength was not at par with Russia's. Once Russia was firmly established in the Pacific opposite the Japanese islands, Russia would remain strong forever. There was no need to share spoils with Asiatics.

Muraviev approved of the experts' opinion. He would see that Russia expanded along the Amur and the Pacific. The local agent of the Russian American Company emphasized that only control of the big river could make the company's business really prosperous. Land transportation from Siberian commercial centers to the Pacific required 15,000 horses; river transportation would reduce costs to less than half. It would be easy to fight off Chinese junks should they try to interfere. The Russian American Company had acquired a few gunboats that could take care of junks, but thus far authorities had not given the company a free hand to use the boats.

Muraviev authorized the agent to use his navy as he wished, provided it carried the company flag and not that of the Tsar's navy. His top-secret report to St. Petersburg delighted the authorities. If trouble resulted, the government would not even have to disown its appointee; the blame could be put squarely upon a private company.

One soft spot remained in the government's pattern of non-responsibility. In 1843 the Russian Academy of Sciences had delegated Alexander von Middendorf, a professor of zoology, to explore wild life in Transbaikalia in the district of Okhotsk. The professor, however, had not confined his activities to the animal kingdom, but had taken a bewildering part in conquest. One Vaganov, a Cossack who accompanied the explorer, became notorious for incursions into Chinese territory. Members of the Academy kept asking the Senate to restrain Middendorf and his man. The Senate could not disclaim knowledge of Middendorf's activities, but it did not want to restrain so useful a personality. Muraviev had not been briefed on the Middendorf case, but he obliged the senators by a spontaneous statement that the scientist was working for the offices of the Governor General. The Senate was rid of an embarrassing responsibility. Muraviev acquired the reputation of a genius. But Vaganov vanished from the scene in 1848, and no further gains resulted from Middendorf's incursions.

The Governor General did not need wayward explorers to grab bits of territory. Now working with the Russian American Company, he devised a pattern that would even make the use of forces under the Tsar's flag appear legal. An elaborate report drafted for diplomatic use notified St. Petersburg that Russia was being elbowed out of the Sea of Okhotsk, where English, American, French, and even German ships engaged in illegitimate catching of whales, and that measures should be taken to safeguard Russia's fishing interests. Should such measures be considered hazardous, however, a secret letter explained, Russian men-of-war could be sent to the Far East for "exploration." There were yet many uncharted islands in the Sea of Okhotsk.

The Russian Government was just fretting over the Pacific situation. With international trouble brewing it could not leave the eastern waters unprotected, and it would invite more trouble should Russian warships appear in the Pacific. One small unit, the *Constantine,* was already on its way east, and the authorities had not yet decided how to define its assignment. The genial

Governor General provided the answer before knowing the question: the frigate *Baikal* was dispatched to join the *Constantine*—for exploratory operations.

Muraviev and the Russian American Company did not wait for the ships to arrive. In 1849 company agents established a so-called trading post as a strategic foothold on Chinese territory. In the following spring Lieutenant Orlov, who worked for the company, "borrowed" a ship from the Tsar's navy, hoisted the Russian American Company flag, and entered the mouth of the Amur. Frightened natives showed landing parties brass crosses, but the Russians did not care about Christendom and drafted natives with or without crosses into unpaid labor to build fortified "trade posts" which dominated the lower course of the river. The posts were called Nikolajevsk and Marinsk.

Muraviev prepared a letter to be used in case foreigners should object to the new encroachment: the document blamed Lieutenant Orlov for transgression of his powers and it promised investigation. But the foreigners did not interfere.

Along the Amur natives accepted Russian rule with fatalistic resignation. Even people of Chinese stock, intellectually and culturally superior to Dawriens, Tunguses, Manchus, and Russians alike, made no attempt at revolt. At the sight of the Cossacks who joined naval crews they wondered whether these people were not Yakuts rather than Russians. In fact many Cossacks came from Yakut Province; some had been borne Yakut mothers, and all had the coarseness of Yakut natives.

Despite Russian decrees prohibiting transfer of property many Chinese would have moved to the interior of their country had China not been in turmoil, shaken by a rebellion of would-be reformers.

Leader of the rebels was Hong Siutsinen, who styled himself the "younger brother of Jesus Christ and the Lord's chosen to depose the nefarious imposting Manchu dynasty."

Lack of wisdom, Hong preached, was the cause of China's prostration. "What are scholars doing nowadays?" he thundered; "they fawn before the mighty, they flatter their vanity, they are quacks; they pretend to know all about heavens and hell and to have found mysterious panaceas. But, in fact, they cheat the common people, they line their pockets, and they suppress the prudent. As Lao-tse has said: 'It has become a rule not to enlighten the people, but to make it dull. An intelligent people is difficult to rule. He who rules the Empire through sagacity destroys the realm, but, he who rules in stupidity is its conserver.' There is no Emperor saved by the multitude of his host; a mighty man is not delivered by much strength. A horse is a vain thing for safety; neither shall he deliver any by his great strength."

The Chinese did not recognize the quotation from the Thirty-third Psalm, but they came to wonder whether it hadn't been stupid to keep them unaware of the foreign threat.

Hong's adepts proclaimed their master legitimate Emperor of China. They called themselves Taiping, the "Peaceful Ones," and in 1851 set out to battle the Manchus. Two years after the rebellion started, the fanatics conquered Nanking.

"Be pure at heart," the fighters were instructed; "don't smoke opium, don't drink wine, always be righteous, straightforward, and conciliatory, never be overly lenient toward subordinates or refractory toward superiors. Do not let the armies of men mingle with the armies of women. . . ."

Chinese women were no amazons, but the Peaceful Ones interpreted the rules by staging a gruesome mass massacre of courtesans whose beauty and skill had made them the glory of their profession.

As the Chinese Emperor concentrated his soldiers in Peking, not a single Chinese soldier stood between Muraviev's toughs and the Chinese capital; but the space separating the intruders from the heart lands of China was too big to be occupied.

Taiping atrocities were not confined to courtesans. The followers of Hong raged against men, women, and children, Christians and non-Christians alike. Lord Elgin reported that Taiping campaigns of destruction were comparable to those recorded in the Old Testament, that Taiping ways of living were as repulsive as those of the worst pharisees, that their creed was based upon a few misinterpreted passages from the Scriptures, and upon a vague natural cult. The Taiping were enemies of orderly communities, foes of civilized society, held together by ties of theocratic despotism, polygamy, and robbery. The Chinese Government deserved severe censure for its inadequate and belated measures to stop Taiping outrages.

The virtuous reporter did not concede that the policies of his countrymen and other foreigners accounted for the Chinese Government's impotence and that the Opium War was more to blame for the upheaval than governmental negligence.

Peking took belated action against the followers of Hong. In the course of a counteroffensive imperial troops conducted themselves with no less uninhibited brutality than the Peaceful Ones.

Muraviev's reports gave no space to moral issues, but they radiated optimism about the effect of China's disaster upon Siberian expansion.

The Russian American Company was adding more posts to its holdings, but the Russian merchants lacked the skill to exploit the commercial opportunities. American businessmen from California established themselves in Nikolajevsk, and from there went to the interior of Siberia as far as Nerchinsk and Yakutsk. They did prosperous business with cotton goods, wines, machinery, and supplies for the Russian Navy. American yards built the first steamboats on the Amur River. Mr. P. Collins, American commercial agent for the Amur district, became a better expert on Siberian economic affairs than executives of the Russian American Company. His opinions were included in the Executive Documents of the first and second sessions of the Thirty-sixth Congress. American leadership in the development of Eastern Siberian resources might have turned the Amur basin into one of the most prosperous regions on earth, one that could have absorbed the population surplus of the great South Asiatic nations. For the first time in recorded history Siberian wealth could have benefited man. There would have been frictions, rivalries, and encroachments, yet the ultimate effects would have staggered man's imagination. But the Russians would rather be sole proprietors of a wasteland than partners in a paradise. Neither Muraviev nor the St. Petersburg Senate was willing to let another nation establish itself firmly in Siberia.

Events in the Far East, however, accounted for one unexpected development: Chinese mass migration into the United States. Having no place to go in their own fatherland, unwilling to carry the burden of Russian rule, Chinese from the Amur basin and other stricken areas eventually tried their luck in America.

In 1852, two years after Congress sanctioned the California State Constitution, 20,026 Chinese landed in San Francisco, only 1780 left the port home-bound; in 1854 the respective figures were 16,084 and 2339; but they did not include immigrants smuggled ashore. Twenty-two years later official records indicated that total Chinese arrivals had exceeded departures by 124,137; conservative private estimates put the number of Chinese residents of the United States at more than 150,000.

Chinese immigrants were expendable flotsam from disasters in Asia; most of whom would have perished at home, unrecorded. It was charitable to carry them to American safety, even though this was not done in a charitable fashion. Six shipping lines competed, cutthroat style, to ship the flotsam from Hong Kong to the American west coast under circumstances that beasts would hardly have endured. It was not disclosed who actually paid for the passage. Nobody admitted "importing" Chinese.

The state government of California was alarmed by the influx. In 1856 Governor John Bigler suggested that Chinese immigration be prohibited. Three years later, a state law barred immigrants of Sino-Mongolian race, but the Supreme Court found it unconstitutional.

But neither California nor all other states of the Union combined could have absorbed the stream of immigrants. More political quakes in China caused afflicted people to pour into foreign beachheads established on Chinese territory. Herds of Chinese trooped into Macao, immigrants would eventually make Shanghai the third-largest city of the world, and two generations after the Russian occupation of the Amur they would go to Manchuria after conquering Japan turned Manchukuo into a puppet kingdom, where the laws were stringent and the rulers arrogant, but where there was, at least, stability of oppression.

Muraviev was more concerned about conquering territories than about population policies. His next objective was the Kurile Islands. Russian freebooters had been visiting Urup on the Kuriles for many years. Japan laid claim to sovereignty, but it had no garrison on the islands. In 1852, Muraviev sent a detachment of Russian Marines to Urup to occupy the place permanently.

Latest directives from St. Petersburg advised Muraviev to put speed above caution. Established strongholds should be consolidated, and more strongholds be set up, as fast as circumstances permitted. Naval reinforcements were on their way from Kronstadt. Their commander, Admiral Putjatin, would give Muraviev every support. Siberian garrisons were ordered to divert every man they could spare to guard the Pacific coast against hostile landing attempts.

With the Russians in Europe set to invade Moldavia and Wallachia provinces, England and France urging the Turkish Sultan to resist, and Austria unwilling to join Russia, war seemed inevitable. Unless effective measures were taken, all gains along the Amur might be wiped out by a single stroke of superior Anglo-French naval power.

Siberian district commanders had less than one man to spare for every mile of Pacific coast. Admiral Putjatin had gloomy forebodings about an encounter between his three frigates and capital units of the Western navies. Had it not been for Muraviev's prestige and his indomitable energy there might have been disobedience, but the Governor General prevailed upon Siberian garrison commanders to send a few battalions, squadrons, and batteries to Kamchatka, Okhotsk, and outposts on the lower Amur. Putjatin's ships cruised in Far Eastern coastal waters, depending upon American deliveries for supplies.

The year 1853 went by without a major war. Muraviev established posts in Castries Bay, Port Imperial, and Aniva Gulf on Sakhalin. A detachment of Russian Marines went to Dui, on Sakhalin, to secure the coal mines. Late in the year one of Putjatin's auxiliary craft, the *Vostok,* entered the mouth of the Amur. The *Vostok* was the most modern Russian ship in the East. It had been purchased only one year before in Southampton, England. Muraviev concentrated 1000 infantrymen, several field cannon, and hastily constructed river barges near Shilinsk. Still, he tried to maintain some semblance of peacefulness. By adding members of the Russian Geographical Society to his staff he could always claim that his actions were taken for scientific purposes.

But when, on March 28, 1854, the Crimean War broke out, no further disguise was required. Muraviev could not challenge either France or England, but he turned against China.

CHAPTER FIFTY-FOUR   Muraviev applied his diplomatic talent to the drafting of notes to the Viceroy of Urga and the Governor of Kiakhta. In a style of solemn brashness he summoned the Chinese dignitaries to recognize Russia's title to control of the Amur River. The Chinese replied in officious terms that such requests would have to be made to the Imperial Court, whereupon the Governor General of Siberia invoked the "law of necessity," and assumed command of a Russian army set to move into Manchuria Province.

The size of the army did not warrant a commander of Muraviev's rank. Normally a captain could have taken charge of the outfit. But Muraviev wanted the operation to be altogether different from past invasions staged by Siberian ruffians in office or out of jail. It should be an elaborate affair; conquest by consent of the conquered.

On July 7, 1854, the Russians entered the first Manchu village and summoned all inhabitants for a parley. Three men appeared; the rest, except for a few bedridden, had fled to Aigun on the right bank of the Amur, which had been overlooked by previous intruders. Muraviev did not confer with the trio, but went ashore near Aigun with all the pomp he could stage.

The Chinese district Governor had made impressive arrangements for the occasion. A tent was pitched close to the riverbank and an honor guard drawn up. In the tent refreshments would be served, and an enlightening conversation should take place.

The honor guards were armed with everything that could pass as weapons: matchlocks with and without barrels, poles blackened on top to make them look like lances; bows, empty quivers, and medieval swords. There were even a few cannon, none under 200 years old, protected against rain by red marquees.

After a brief exchange of courtesies outside the tent Muraviev announced that his own men would take up position opposite the Manchu guards. The Chinese official expressed both delight and regret. It would be a privilege, he smiled, to have Russian soldiers join the array, but—and the smile vanished—without imperial consent no foreign army was admitted to Chinese territory. If His Excellency, the Governor General, wanted to file an application for admission, he would forward it to the Court and mark it as urgent, so that a reply could be expected no later than in the following year.

Muraviev thought that the Chinese wanted to keep face before the guards and milling crowds and that inside the tent he would be amenable to Russian suggestions. However, the district Governor remained stubborn after the parleys were transferred. He did not yield to Muraviev's demand that he invoke Russian protection; he did not confess to misdemeanors when faced with vague accusations; he even pretended not to know that a war was on and that emergency measures were required.

To make the matter even more vexatious, the townspeople of Aigun pressed into the tent to catch a glimpse of the historical meeting. They saw their own official unruffled and the Governor General of Siberia profusely sweating from hot tea and even hotter embarrassment.

Muraviev could have seized Aigun. Neither the barrelless matchlocks nor sheltered cannon nor the thirty-five rickety junks marooned in the river port could have stopped the Russians. But there was one serious hazard involved in aggression: should the Allies learn of a "Battle of Aigun," they might send naval forces up the Amur and wipe out all Russian gains by one stroke.

At last a resentful Muraviev settled for a promise, the one and only he could obtain from the Chinese official: Aigun would not be used as a base of anti-Russian operations.

The Russian position on the Amur was even weaker than Muraviev had expected. The Russian American Company was unco-operative, if not more. Five of the six company river gunboats had had their guns dismounted, and the sixth, a cannon brig, was laid off for repairs. The agent claimed that the company was autonomous and not at war with any European power; also it had an agreement with the Hudson's Bay Company that made the borders between Alaska and Canada inviolable.

Muraviev snarled that the English would certainly not respect interbusiness arrangements, but the agent remained adamant. The company was not at war.

The English did respect the interbusiness agreement, to the annoyance of the French Rear Admiral in command of Napoleon III's warships. The French intended to establish a bridgehead in Russian America. However, the English, who had more and larger naval units in the Pacific, cautioned the French Government against arousing U.S. touchiness by flagrant disregard of the Monroe Doctrine. London did not say that it did not want the French to establish themselves in the neighborhood of Canada.

Eventually the Allies staged a substitute for war in American waters by seizing a handful of Russian American Company personnel at sea and shipping them to Tahiti as prisoners of war.

The first loss of Russian eastern territory occurred in Sakhalin. Shortage of men and supplies forced Muraviev to evacuate Aniva Gulf; and quietly the Japanese moved into the abandoned camp.

Already at the time of the Aigun palaver Muraviev knew that the English and French would attack Kamchatka.

Russian Intelligence had found out that an Allied fleet of eight powerful units, armed with 200 cannon and combined crews of 2000, was gathering in Hawaii, to attack Petropavlovsk, Russian fortress city on Avacha Bay.

The Russian Intelligence drew its information from English newspapers whose elucidating comments on the conduct of the war were more reliable than accounts by spies. Admiral David Price, commander of the combined fleet, expected Petropavlovsk to surrender during the opening bombardment. Muraviev expected the place to fall after a siege of two to four weeks. The city of 1500 civilians had a garrison of 1000 and four batteries of medium caliber.

The Allied cannonade opened on August 30, 1854. When the city did not surrender, Allied landing parties went ashore, where they ran into an ambush, suffered 100 casualties, and evacuated the beachhead.

The despondent British Admiral committed suicide. His successor took the English ships to Vancouver. French Admiral de Pointes with his units sailed to San Francisco.

The people of Petropavlovsk first believed that the evacuation was a feint. Nobody thought that the Allies would break up operations because of so small a loss. The Anglo-French ships had not been hit, while damage to the city was considerable.

But after a few days of suspense, when the Allies did not return, a hurricane of optimism raked Petropavlovsk. Tall tales magnified the ambush into a major victory. Several versions of the action credited different persons with devising the plan. One of the alleged masterminds was a naturalized-American resident of Petropavlovsk, a native of France. The entire American colony, consisting of three businessmen, cautioned the fortress commander against underestimating naval power and predicted that the Allies would soon return. Admiral Putjatin, whose fleet went to Avacha Bay after the English and French were safely in America, shared the American view.

Through the English journals it was established that another Allied fleet would assemble in Hawaii in the spring of 1855. Howling snowstorms blanketed Kamchatka when a messenger from Governor General Muraviev straggled to the fortress, carrying evacuation orders.

Admiral Putjatin said that he would have left Petropavlovsk anyway. An elusive fleet in being was better than a daring fleet at the bottom of the seas. The commander of the land forces bragged that he would hold the place to the last.

On April 17, 1855, Russian sailors cut lanes through the thinning ice of the harbor, and the fleet left. A few days and another fighting statement later the army retreated 200 miles inland. In the wake of the soldiers rode officials with their families, and in the wake of officials trudged the populace, with bag, baggage, cattle, and horses—with anything that could be eaten or sold.

The three Americans stayed behind and hoisted the Stars and Stripes on their roof tops.

With the Americans stayed the mongrel dogs of Petropavlovsk.

In June an Allied fleet entered the bay, fired an opening broadside, and waited for Russian counterfire. When no such fire came, landing parties went ashore. They were met by the Americans, who claimed that every object in town was American property, that Petropavlovsk was under U.S. sovereignty, and that no Russians were anywhere near the place.

And while the three talked to the bewildered navy men, swarms of hungry dogs sniffed at the intruders, barked, and snarled.

Aboard the Allied flagship strategy parleys continued deep into the night, while sounds of barking rang through the bay.

Allied naval officers fancied themselves knowing all about canine habits. Dogs invariably stayed with their masters, so the Russians were around preparing another ambush. On the following morning demolition squads used torches and explosives to wreck harbor installations, heavy naval guns hammered away at fortifications, and then the fleet lifted anchor. The English and French would not walk into another trap.

The savage mongrels had saved for the Russians Petropavlovsk, all of Kamchatka, and possibly even large sections of Siberia without violating the code of canine behavior: wild dogs, having no masters, do not follow men, but stay at their roaming grounds.

The Allied Intelligence did not immediately learn of the Petropavlovsk misunderstanding. Censorship kept the Russian press from being as informative as English newspapers.

The French did not like the overweening attitude of English naval officers. One French squadron took independent action, and put landing parties ashore in the Kurile Islands. This was not mentioned in press reports, and the Russians learned of the invasion only after the cessation of hostilities. Muraviev had left no soldiers in the archipelago; and the French did not lay claim to making their conquest permanent.

A British squadron under Commodore Elliot, on its way from Hong Kong to Japan, detected Putjatin's ships in an inlet south of the Amur estuary, protected by a passage so narrow that attacking units could enter only single file. Commodore Elliot did not want to take dangerous chances, and the Russians did not give battle.

Putjatin made a few sorties, however. He called on Chinese ports and summoned Chinese local governors to grant Russia whatever privileges were held by the French and the English. The governors brushed him off and were not impressed by his statement: "I shall report this affront to His Majesty the Tsar, and his orders will be executed."

The first winter of the war found Muraviev greatly worrying over an Allied attack in the Amur Valley. One glance at the map should convince the Allied general staffs that control of the Amur basin was of crucial importance. With the Western powers established along the Amur the Russians could not hope to hold onto the Pacific.

The most difficult problem of defense was transportation. Despite a hinterland of fertile vastness the small band of Russian troops along the Amur would be short of food, while the Allies, thousands of miles away from their home bases, would be well supplied. The Allies had all the shipping facilities, and Russian transportation was woefully inadequate.

Muraviev devised a pattern of supply by forming mobile peasant units to follow the army and to work the soil whenever and wherever circumstances permitted, to abandon the crop if the soldiers left, to harvest it if they stayed long enough.

Five hundred peasants, with their families, cattle, horses, and implements, were drafted. Every person was subject to military discipline. Who would run away was a deserter and his family would be held as hostages until the fugitive was tracked down. Peasants had no share in their produce, except for small personal rations. Withholding of food was punishable as theft. There was no discharge from farm service, nor did the draft end with the death of the head of the family. The status continued for survivors, and the survivors' offspring, a sinister bequest of bondage.

The pattern survived the war, and other wars yet to come. It outlasted the regime of the Tsar, and Muraviev could not have foreseen that thirty-six years after his death a new tyranny would adopt it for its purposes, which were but a gruesomely efficient version of Siberia's age-old striving for universal rule: the tyranny of the Soviets, which turned Siberia into a colossal springboard of expansion. Fifteen million deportees, five million compulsory workers, and more than twelve million peasants, corralled into state-dominated collective farms and supervised by one million uniformed jailers would spend themselves to supply the means for subjugating many more millions of different races to a regime which made their own lives miserable.

During the Crimean War, when Muraviev traveled to St. Petersburg to apply for more help in Siberia, he mentioned the peasant draft as an improvised expedient. He gave a somber picture of conditions in the Amur basin. Only Nikolajevsk and Marinsk remained Russian strongholds on the lower course of the river. Port Imperial, manned only by a bunch of hard-drinking semi-invalids, was considered untenable. Castries Bay was evacuated; and in Fortune Bay the local Governor had embezzled funds earmarked for fortification, and had left for an undisclosed destination.

Authorities in the capital would do no more than allot a small number of field batteries of recent design and some funds for the construction of river barges to bolster defenses along the Amur. Muraviev returned to his seat of office with premonitions of evil. Chinese military men, constantly defeated on the battlefield, were still sufficiently acute to evaluate the strategic situation. They, too, considered an invasion of the Amur basin as imminent. Besides Chinese fishermen reported that an Allied fleet was concentrating in the Sea of Okhotsk.

The Chinese Government did not intend to participate in hostilities, but governors of northern border provinces were given a free hand to roll the Russians back from the central Amur Valley.

An ominous silence settled along the Russo-Chinese border, while Muraviev had barges built and artillery concentrated, and Chinese provincial governors deliberated with the circumstantial grandezza befitting dignitaries of their rank.

News from Europe took about two months to reach Chinese seaports. It would take another month or two until it reached Peking through the usual channels, and from there it would travel three more months to the northern border.

In June 1856 four elaborately adorned junks carried a party of mandarins to Nikolajevsk. Credentials introduced the mandarins as high dignitaries assigned to discuss boundary questions which had arisen from erroneous interpretations of existing treaties, as exemplified by Russian intrusion into Chinese territory.

Muraviev was not available, and the commander of Nikolajevsk had the mandarins in their elaborate silken gala paraded through military encampments, past modern batteries, and through rows of jeering soldiers. The soldiery tore precious adornments from the junks before permitting them to leave.

The stunned mandarins did not know that on March 30 of that year peace had been signed between England, France, and Russia.

The Russians no longer saw any reason to treat the Chinese with consideration. Muraviev was directed to liquidate the onerous treaty of Nerchinsk and to expand Russian territory in the East.

The Governor General still had a score to settle with the Russian American Company. Already during his sojourn in St. Petersburg he had had a few unflattering things to say about the company; now he reported that Russian control of the Amur basin could bring results only if natural riches were developed by a new enterprise which would serve the country unconditionally and with unflinching efficiency.

With the Russian authorities determined to rid themselves of an American territory they could not hope to defend, and shareholders of the Russian American Company equally determined to dump their stock for whatever it would fetch, Muraviev's suggestion was accepted. In 1858 the Amur Company, founded with a capital equivalent to £150,000, received an imperial charter to develop commerce and industry in the Amur basin. Muraviev undertook to supervise the company's activities, for an annual fee of £300,–,–, in addition to £675,–,– for "table money," traveling expenses, and "entertainment of Manchus."

The first transaction of the Amur Company was the purchase of river steamboats. One 60-h.p. craft was ordered in Belgium, two craft of similar type in England, and a fourth boat in the United States. The English-built craft were lost en route to the river; the Belgian boat did not function satisfactorily; but the *Amerika* stood up against the fury of Siberian elements and engineers, and became the most useful boat along the 1890-mile-long course of the Amur.

Not until May 28, 1858, did Muraviev sign a border agreement with the Governor of Aigun, the highest-ranking Chinese official available for the purpose. The Treaty of Aigun superseded that of Nerchinsk. Chinese ceded the left bank of the Amur to the junction of the Ussuri River, and both banks from there to the Pacific. This opened the Sungari and Ussuri rivers to Russian navigation, which was tantamount to Russian annexation of the basins of both rivers.

The document, hastily drawn up, left several questions unanswered; but an irate Muraviev, being engaged in a race for a treaty against Admiral Putjatin, could not afford to bargain for any length of time.

The inglorious naval commander of the Crimean War had resumed his calls to Chinese ports as soon as the seas were safe. His threats to use the guns of his fleet against Chinese cities now had telling effect. Muraviev's protests against this interference with his prerogatives were to no avail. Putjatin continued his highhanded action, and in St. Petersburg influential circles seemed to enjoy playing the Governor General against the Admiral.

Muraviev won the race by a trifling sixteen days, but Putjatin made up for the lead by including in his treaty of Tientsin, of June 13, items not covered by the compact of Aigun.

The document of Tientsin included a declaration of peace, friendship, and equality between the contracting parties, which neither side took seriously; it opened nine Chinese ports to Russian commerce, introduced mail and passenger services between Peking and Kiakhta, and stipulated that delimitation of borders would be subject to a survey by delegates from both sides.

This stipulation contradicted the terms of Aigun. Putjatin had not been aware of it, but St. Petersburg did not object. Both Muraviev and Putjatin were created Counts. Muraviev, who adopted the predicate Amursky, considered this a gross injustice.

Russia emerged from defeat in the Crimean War with a territorial aggrandizement of 361,000 square miles in Siberia, in addition to formal recognition of previous land-grabs. This gain more than outweighed losses in the West: renunciation of the Russian protectorate over Wallachia and Moldavia provinces, evacuation of the Danube estuary, and of Kars in the Caucasus Mountains.

Putjatin also signed an agreement with Japan, another step on the road out of Japan's isolation.

In fact isolation was not the traditional Japanese way of life, but only a relatively brief phase in the more than 3000-year-old history of the country, which opened when several tribes of the savage Ainus came under the mollifying influence of Chinese civilization.

The civilized Ainu—the Japanese—lived on the Eight Islands of the Rising Sun and collected tribute from their savage kin who roamed the island chains from the Ryukyus to the Aleutians. They traded with Hindustan, Arabia, Persia, and other continental Asiatic countries. From Korea, Buddhism came to Japan in or about A.D. 552.

Not until 1542 did the Japanese lay eyes upon Europeans: Portuguese seamen driven ashore by adverse winds. The islanders first mistook the crew for people from India, land of religious sages; but the newcomers' behavior soon made them aware of their mistake. Curiosity and business-mindedness, however, made the Japanese treat the crude visitors with great friendliness.

Seven years later Catholic missionaries visited Japan. By then the Portuguese had made themselves thoroughly disliked. The missionaries received a less than lukewarm reception, and their activities were viewed with suspicion.

It was said that Christian neophytes were being alienated from their fatherland. This did not, at first, prevent expansion of Japanese trade with European nations. The Portuguese were joined by the Dutch and the English; the Japanese Government issued privileges, but grew ever more suspicious as uneasy decades went by. In 1637 a rumor circulated that European padres were smuggling Japanese converts abroad to train them as saboteurs and traitors. Then another rumor, fostered by extreme nationalists, told of a Portuguese army gathering somewhere in the Pacific and of adherents of the "Religion of Jesus" in Japan set to spearhead Portuguese invaders. No Portuguese army was assembled, and small Christian communities in Japan were peaceable and scared. Yet on April 12, 1638, the government struck a savage blow. In one single day about 37,000 Japanese Christians were put to death in mass auto-da-fés; a decree forbade the utterance of the name of Christ, the celebration of Sundays or Christian holy days, the erection of crosses, and ordered that crosses already raised be publicly trampled underfoot. The law applied to Japanese citizens and foreigners alike.

Japanese Christendom was wiped out, but with the exception of the Portuguese, who were dubbed the archfoes of Japan, the foreigners did not leave.

In 1673 an English party was expelled from Nagasaki, and all English citizens were barred from entering Japan on the grounds that the King of England had joined Japan's hereditary enemies by marrying a Portuguese princess.

No degree of mortification, however, could induce the Dutch to give up business in Japan. The Dutch East India Company had obtained trade privileges in 1611. Its agents became the targets of sadistic decrees by Japanese governments.

Dutch traders were ordered out of their factory at Firando, and assigned quarters in a jail-like building in De-shima. They were not permitted to live with their families, and they were not allowed to associate with Japanese women other than prostitutes selected from the lowliest brothels. They had to deliver presents to the Crown, and a special procedure was devised for the occasion: the merchants, led by their superintendent, had to crawl on hands and feet, heads lowered to the ground, to the steps of the throne, and then backward like crayfish, to the entrance. From there they were taken to a hall, where notables, their families, and even servants, made them perform ignominious clowneries, sing parodistic chants, fight among themselves, and stand on their heads. The corpulent, bearded men obeyed, short of breath with effort.

During the two centuries following the Christian auto-da-fé the average Japanese developed a feeling of absolute superiority over the foreigners. The spineless Dutch were Japan's window to the outside world; the government of Japan knew more of Europe than Europe knew of Japan. The Dutch told of powerful European fighting ships, and Japanese fishermen who had met vessels carrying foreign flags asserted that they were bigger than anything domestic shipyards could produce.

580

However, the government did not quite believe in strength, unless applied. Foreign victims of disasters at sea who reached the coast of Japan were considered spies; and Japanese survivors of shipwrecks who were rescued by foreign craft and returned to their homeland fared no better. But the Opium War in China showed Japan that aliens did apply strength with telling effect.

In 1844, King William II of Holland wrote a letter suggesting that Japanese alien laws "promulgated by the Serene Ancestors of His Majesty, the High and Mighty Emperor of Japan" be mitigated to permit the establishment of closer ties between Japan and other countries.

In the following year the Dutch traders in De-shima received a note from the State and Government Council of Japan, addressed to the "Grandees of the Netherlands," saying that recent events in China had strengthened Japan's determination to uphold the ban of aliens. Had the English not been admitted to Canton, China would not be prostrate. The grandees should notify their king and all foreigners of this "unalterable decision."

This was, in fact, a rear-guard action, the swan song of Japanese isolationism.

In 1851 the Dutch superintendent at De-shima, who had been permitted to move into comfortable quarters in town, was handed another *pronunciamento*. The Shogun of Japan wanted all foreign governments to know that for several years every possible assistance was being extended to foreign vessels and crews in distress. This attitude was prompted by the purest motives and should not be considered an abrogation of alien laws.

In 1846, already, French Admiral Cécille had sailed into Nagasaki harbor, to request that shipwrecked Frenchmen be treated with kindness and consideration, and permitted to leave aboard Dutch ships, but the Japanese refused to make promises. Soon thereafter, Commodore James Biddle, U. S. Navy, went to Yedo (Tokyo) Bay and inquired about Japan's intentions about opening the country's ports. He was told that Japan's attitude toward foreigners was determined by the country's tradition, and that he ought to leave at once, never to return.

Contrary to their own traditions, the Russians did not use strong-arm tactics in Japan. Their offer of collaboration, however, was not favorably received. The parable of the chain with unequal links pictured Japan's worries about dealings with foreigners. In 1852, Russian Chancellor Count Nesselrode wrote to the government of Japan, in the name of Nicholas I: "For the last twenty-seven years, our country enjoys the blessings of a wise government, and peace at home and abroad. The Russian army and navy are shielding the realm against attack."

In contrast to this happy state of Russian affairs the Chancellor pictured Japan as being threatened by determined aggressors. Their prosperous cities, rich rice fields and bustling workshops, and the large fishing fleet might be destroyed unless Japan granted Russia military bases for defense. The government of Japan ignored Nesselrode's epistle.

During the Crimean War, however, Admiral Putjatin paid a fleeting call to Japan to lay the groundwork for an agreement between the two countries. Signed late in 1856, the agreement was a far cry from Nesselrode's ambitious proposition. Russian ships obtained limited port facilities, Russian merchants were admitted as buyers and sellers, the Kurile archipelago north of Urup Island was recognized as Russian territory, the Kurile Islands south of Urup remained under Japanese sovereignty. The status of Sakhalin (Karafuto) was not defined, which led the Russians to claim it as their territory.

The priority of forcing Japan out of its isolation belongs to the United States.

On July 14, 1853, four American war sloops anchored in Yedo Bay; their commander, Commodore Matthew Calbraith Perry, carried a message from President Millard Fillmore to the Emperor of Japan.

The Governor of Uruga, city of 10,000 on the shore of Yedo Bay, did not request that Perry leave, never to return. The sight of 65 cannon and 300 well-armed Marines who went ashore induced the officials to use niceties rather than rudeness. However, he did not immediately forward the letter of Mr. Fillmore, of whom he spoke as "His Majesty, the President of the Glorious American Republic," but insisted that a special commission appointed by the Shogun take the exalted document to the capital.

The Japanese had their ways of stalling, but the fifty-nine-year-old Commodore had a grouchy diplomacy of his own. The Shogun's commission went to Uruga sooner than the government in Yedo had planned. Perry lectured the commission that the Americans had the power to take anything they wanted, but they were prompted by humanitarian considerations and would treat the Japanese fairly, and as equals.

One of the Japanese delegates is quoted as having said: "We shall emerge from our isolation; we too shall build steamships, travel to foreign lands, and learn of their achievements." But the reply to President Fillmore's letter was circumstantially negative.

The young Emperor, it said, was pledged to uphold the laws of the realm. The laws conflicted with American wishes to have access to Japan; a similar request made by Russia had gone unanswered.

The Japanese would not cling to formalities, but would "grant some of the President's solicitations, regarding delivery of food, water, and wood for American ships, and kindly treatment of shipwrecked crews. Even coal would be available in Nagasaki in the following year, and within another five years a port would be ready to receive American ships."

Perry was impressed neither by the antics of Japanese style nor by being addressed as "Your Excellency." He wanted a treaty.

The members of the commission pretended not to understand what kind of treaty His Excellency had in mind, but Perry had a memorandum ready, specifying in English, Japanese, and Chinese what he wanted.

The Japanese were stunned. Then they explained that the memorandum would have to be submitted to the Emperor, who in turn would consult with his Council of Ministers, and the State Council. This would take time.

Commodore Perry would not permit the Japanese to stall indefinitely, but he left Yedo Bay announcing that he would be back in the following year.

During Perry's absence Japanese conservatives struggled with progressives. The conservatives, including the samurai warrior caste, called relations with foreigners indecorous, and the lowest depth of national humiliation, if imposed by force. Modernization was a sacrilege, and altogether unnecessary; for, conservative spokesmen contended, foreign technical advantages were outweighed by Japanese superior valor.

The progressives insisted that modernization would make the Japanese the most powerful nation on earth.

Power was also the conservatives' supreme target. However, the controversy was not a struggle about procedure, but the conflict between two systems of government: Shogunate and imperial rule.

The Shogunate was essentially a dictatorship of the Army through its commander, the Shogun. Since 1603 the Shogunate had been hereditary in the Tokugawa family. Anti-foreigner laws had been promulgated under the Shogunate. The progressives expected that, with the anti-foreigner laws, the Shogunate would fall and the Emperor would re-emerge from figurehead obscurity.

In fact the Shogunate survived Perry's first call for another fourteen years only. The change of regime did not prevent champions of modernization and samurais from co-operating until Japan was strong enough to make its almost successful bid to reduce Asia into a "co-prosperity sphere."

Neither Commodore Perry nor the government in Washington could have foreseen such developments on February 11, 1854, when the American squadron, reinforced to ten units, again cast anchor in Yedo Bay, this time off Yokohama, 10 miles from the capital.

The Americans displayed gifts, including a small railroad train complete with engine and 100 yards of circular track, a telegraph, a printing press, and small arms for the Emperor; a telescope, a lorgnette, and loads of cosmetics for the Empress.

Japanese delegates who arrived at the scene vied for train rides at 9 m.p.h. They found that American drinks could stand up against sake, and even though the first reaction to the American proposals was evasive, signature of a treaty was not delayed beyond March 31, 1854.

U.S. ships were granted the use of ports in Shimoda and Hakodate. They would be supplied with all necessities. American craft in distress would receive unlimited assistance. Unrestricted trade between America and Japan was to be established, and privileges extended to other nations would automatically apply to U.S. citizens. The treaty was not yet ratified when the bark *Edward Koppich*, the first American ship to trade with Japan, left its home port in Salem, Massachusetts.

Old sea dog Perry, however, did not share American public enthusiasm about achievements in the Far East. "England," he wrote, "holds the most important points in the Chinese and Indian Oceans. Singapore dominates the northwestern, Hong Kong the northeastern, and Labuan the central approaches to those waters. The English could cut off American commercial shipping, valued at £15,000,000 a year. We shall have to establish strong points of our own."

But America was reluctant to take a strategic approach to commercial affairs.

England did not want the U.S. to retain the lead in Japan. Five months after the U.S.-Japanese treaty was signed an English squadron from Hong Kong entered Nagasaki. Its commander, Admiral Sterling, aboard the fifty-gun flagship *Winchester,* made it known that Her Majesty's Government wanted her subjects to enjoy all privileges granted to other nationals.

The Japanese had expected the demand. However, the manner in which it was presented enraged even the progressives, and the conservatives had reason to shout about national humiliation. The Queen's admiral had a studied way of offending the Japanese, and his men behaved no better than their commander. The citizens of Nagasaki refused delivery of food and water to the abusive visitors, and the Admiral's letter to the government was not delivered. Admiral Sterling threatened to proceed to Yedo. On October 14, 1854, the government yielded and signed a treaty that contained a few carefully worded passages which reduced concessions slightly below the level of those made to the U.S.A. Sterling was not up to Japanese verbal artifices, but his government detected the shortcomings and in 1855 Japan had to sign a protocol giving the English all that had been withheld.

Three years later, Lord Elgin went to Yedo, put up in a magnificent Buddhist temple, and browbeat the government into more concessions. English ships were admitted to the ports of Hakodate, Kanagawa, Nagasaki, Nagata, and Hiogo (Kobe); English citizens obtained the right to own land in Japan; litigation between English and Japanese citizens was to be decided by English authorities in accordance with English laws; there should be no restrictions to English trade, and an English ambassador was admitted to Yedo.

Compared with such capitulations, concessions obtained by France were rather minor. The Dutch eventually obtained a status about equal to that of France.

CHAPTER FIFTY-FIVE Count Putjatin returned to Western Russia to enjoy his promotion and the privileges that went with it.

Count Muraviev-Amursky, however, graying but still a stylish dresser, stayed East to consolidate and organize the land-grab.

People in St. Petersburg considered this a cavalier's fancy. But Muraviev, who had come under the strange fascination that Siberia can spell, abandoned all designs of voluptuous living in Paris, and dedicated himself to the cause of the Tsar's Eastern realm.

He did not think in humanitarian terms; people were tools to him to be used in working the Russian domain, but his affection for this domain was genuine.

He had denounced Putjatin's treaty of Tientsin as a dangerous instrument because of the clause providing for border surveys. He had predicted that the Chinese would use it to contest the annexation of certain territories. First, the St. Petersburg cabinet gave little attention to criticism which appeared to have been prompted by personal antagonism. However, Peking soon sent notes urging that a border commission be organized. Muraviev asked for more soldiers to "bring China to its senses." The government of Russia was just involved in expansion in the regions of Turkestan, Bokhara, and other Central Asiatic areas, and chose to ignore China's notes; enunciations from a weak government were not worth while answering.

But St. Petersburg's reaction to Muraviev's administrative suggestions was swift and affirmative.

Muraviev reported that Eastern Siberia had grown too large to be centrally administered. Under the existing system every local measure was subject to approval from Irkutsk, which caused delays rendering even well-conceived steps ineffective. More and better administrators were needed, but those available in Siberia were still notorious for their corruption, and officials from the capital would be equally fraudulent and lacking in basic knowledge of Siberian affairs. The Governor General wanted to establish regional military governments. Soldiers might be less corrupt and better adaptable to new environments.

A ukase of December 31, 1858, divided territories of Eastern Siberia into the "Maritime Province," including the districts of Gishigin, Nikolajevsk, Petropavlovsk, Petrovsk, the Kuriles, Northern Sakhalin, Sofisk, and Udsk; and "Amur Province," which comprised all the territories along the Amur as far as the Ussuri junction. The provinces were to be administered by military governors who were responsible to the Governor General and his Council of Administration. The military governors would nominate regional administrators, soldiers preferred. No more than twenty civilians should hold office in either province, and their salaries should not exceed the equivalent of $950 per annum.

But Muraviev was not yet satisfied, contending that with an improved administration the new territories were a hollow shell unless Manchuria were incorporated into Siberia. Russian observers told of densely populated villages and cities on the far side of the Manchurian border, of bustling traffic, and apparent prosperity, while a provisional census established that no more than 24,000 natives lived in the annexed provinces. Russia needed people, and if people were tied to their domiciles, Russia wanted their land.

But St. Petersburg warned Muraviev not to go too far, too fast. He should solve the population problem with whatever settlers he could find within the realm. Annexation of Manchuria would be kept on the agenda for a later time, possibly even for a later generation.

The newest Russian subjects were mostly Gilaeks and Ainus, the latter of the uncivilized type. The Gilaeks had Mongoloid features, bushy eyebrows, and profuse beards. Men and women wore their black hair tied into either one thick pigtail or several tresses. The Russians claimed that Gilaek girls were repulsive despite their stoutness, which, however, did not keep Cossacks from mating with the high-booted females. The natives lived in rickety, rat-infested cabins, together with their rat-hunting pets. Only the wealthiest Gilaeks owned tomcats; the average family could afford only ermines, which were fierce rat killers and of which one got two dozen for the price of one cat. Long before the Russians arrived, Manchus and visitors from not yet isolated Japan had introduced rice, but rice, like cats, was too expensive for most Gilaeks, whose staple food consisted of fish prepared with herbs, roots, and train oil. Fish of up to 1000 pounds were caught in the Ussuri River. Gilaeks were shamanites, but their shamans were destitute. Only at family funerals would parishioners show some generosity, provided the defunct had not been killed by a tiger. In such cases the remains were buried on the spot without ceremony to prevent more calamities for the next of kin. However, the number of tiger victims was small compared to victims of murder, which was not considered a crime. It was a capital crime, however, to carry burning objects out of a dwelling, for the Gilaeks believed that the fire would return and destroy the building. So, when a Gilaek left a house smoking a pipe, he was liable to capital punishment.

Insular Ainus made their livelihood by hunting, fishing, and selling "surplus population." Orphans, widows, old maids, and fools were considered salable. Manchu traffickers paid three to seven gold coins apiece, and even though the coins were generously clipped, the Ainus considered this to be a fair price. In times of old the Manchus resold surplus Ainus to dig Sakhalin coal. The Russians considered mining to be convict labor and later imported deportee miners. Meantime they put the Orokes, a tribe of reindeer-breeding natives, to work the mines of Sakhalin. The Orokes were ruffians who did not fear violent people but were deadly afraid of dogs. The invaders exploited this fear to good advantage.

Early in 1859, 7776 Russian officers and men garrisoned the new territory. Two battalions were on the march and marine infantry was expected from Kronstadt. This would raise the military forces to about 10,000, a formidable army, yet a poor host of settlers. Soldiers were quick with the knout to get mushiks or natives busy, but they were refractory when asked to do manual work themselves. Muraviev offered Siberian soldiers a settler's statute which would turn them into great landowners, provided they found help.

The woods were swarming with outlaws; the soldiers staged man hunts, and within a few months caught almost 20,000—"souls of both sexes," as records called them.

This figure dwarfed the number of draftee peasants that Muraviev could produce. The Ministry of War promised to send another 18,000 men, not first-line soldiers, but able-bodied individuals released from army jails. Three thousand women went with them, all dubious characters, but considered good enough for the Amur Valley. The main trouble with the reinforcements was that almost half of its effectives deserted.

The Governor General called upon deportation authorities to supply peasants. In 1859 and 1860 some 10,000 deportees were routed to the Amur basin; 60 per cent of them escaped.

Army and navy personnel and their dependents settled in newly founded cities, but soldiers and sailors had no useful skills, and Muraviev needed craftsmen and transportation workers. *Kartorga* wardens and deportation officials sent to the new provinces all they had on hand.

Late in 1859 the population of Nikolajevsk numbered almost 4000. A naval station was established in Olga Bay, pending completion of a settlement in Victoria Bay, which eventually became the port city of Vladivostok.

Military stations all along the coast and on strategic spots inland sprang up—nineteenth-century versions of the early ostrogs.

Muraviev had the fortifications of Nikolajevsk armed with the strongest coast artillery ever assembled in that part of the world. Eight 18-pounders, forty 24-pounders, twelve 36-pounders, and twelve 100-pound mortars could deal with any attempt to force a way up the Amur. In 1860 the Russian Pacific fleet included 19 steamers with a combined engine power of 5150 h.p., and an armament of 380 guns. This force could not challenge the great Western navies at sea, but it could help protect the Amur estuary.

In 1861, twenty-one years after Morse received his patent, the Russian Government authorized construction of telegraph lines in the Siberian southeast.

Muraviev's colonizing achievement excelled anything in past Siberian history; yet when the telegraph lines were authorized, only 70,000 people lived in the 260,000-square-mile area on which the Governor General concentrated his effort.

The Amur Company turned out to be a total flop. The capital had been trebled, the board of directors issued verbose communiqués on successful operations, but the St. Petersburg stock market reflected the true state of affairs. Shares with a nominal value of 250 rubles went begging at 85. Mismanagement and dishonesty had brought the company to the verge of ruin. Settlements complained about company stores carrying only few badly needed items and these in dismal quality and at outrageous prices. Company vessels were deliberately wrecked. Officials purchased cargoes at nominal prices and with the help of black-marketeers resold them at a 1000 per cent profit. No responsible foreign merchant would do business with the Amur Company; shipyards asked for deposits before starting to repair company craft.

Almost £1000 a year were at stake for the Governor General if the Amur Company folded up. Company executives trusted that nobody would want to lose such a sinecure, but Muraviev urged the Russian Government to have the company liquidated, and with no exalted personal interest involved the Amur Company vanished from the Siberian scene.

Muraviev championed the development of competitive private trade. In 1859 eleven companies operated in Nikolajevsk, six American, one Prussian, and four agencies of Russian mercantile establishments. Local officials were directed to co-operate with the merchants, but instead of assisting the trade, the administrators' creative stupidity hampered it by a maze of paper work. However, imports from places such as Boston, San Francisco, Honolulu, Hong Kong, Antwerp, and Altona kept Eastern Siberia supplied, and there were indications that foreigners intended to create new industries. Muraviev decided to encourage such a development; his successors, however, would look askance at any foreign-operated plant strategically more important than a brewery, and many industrial projects were shelved.

Looking for more and better settlers, Muraviev tried foreign colonists from European Russia.

Some 16,000 Mennonites of German stock, thrifty, hard-working sectarians, lived in Southern Russia. The Mennonites shunned the baptism of infants, all acts of revenge, divorce, and the oath, but they invariably gave Caesar what he claimed as his due.

They would never have left their homes of their own free will, but when the government of St. Petersburg decreed that one hundred families from Taurida be sent to Siberia, they accepted it without grumbling. The district administrator of Taurida, however, kept his scribes busy bombarding the provincial Governor with petitions to prevent an exodus bound to wreck the district's economy. The provincial Governor lodged respectful protests with the Ministry of the Interior, but the order was not rescinded.

One hundred families gathered their belongings. They took every dismantlable object from homesteads which their elders had built fifty years before. They built new carts that would last throughout the long track, on a schedule they prepared with the thoroughness of experts on logistics. They would not use ships on any leg of their voyage, because this, according to their creed, was a sin; and they eventually left the land on which they had grown such rare items as tobacco and mulberry, to start from scratch on virgin soil thousands of miles away.

One year later they settled near Aigun, built houses, stables, and granges exactly like the ones they had abandoned. They planted wheat, barley, oats, potatoes, and, of course, tobacco and mulberry trees, to establish a new Taurida on the Amur, as it had been Caesar's will. They did not protest when the Army requisitioned much of their produce. Muraviev clamored for another shipment of Teutonic settlers, but St. Petersburg had no more Mennonites to spare and refused to draw on its reserves of Volga Germans.

Prussian-born Captain von Bries, who operated a steamboat on the Amur, undertook to bring Germans from California to Siberia, and the Governor General put aside settling land for them on the Bureya River. But the forty families the captain imported as a first installment turned out to be flotsam from the gold rush, and, despite their industriousness, altogether unfit as agricultural settlers. Muraviev halted further influx from America.

The Governor General was an ardent student of American westward expansion and thought that railroad construction in the New World was a crucial factor in the speedy development of new territories. It occurred to him that a trans-Siberian railroad would produce amazing results in the development of Siberia.

The Russian Government still considered the "Siberian Track" adequate for all transportation purposes. In the late 1850s and the earlier 1860s the track was still a road in name only. For stretches hundreds of miles long it led over steppes; and merchants who carried "express" goods from the famous Fair of Nizhni Novgorod to Irkutsk covered the distance in four months, at a daily average of thirty miles.

In St. Petersburg, Muraviev's suggestion to build a railroad from Moscow to Irkutsk was considered plain extravagance. The Governor General tried to stimulate official interest in Siberian transportation by reporting that he would extend the Siberian track another thousand miles, to the Pacific coast, and that the work had already begun. St. Petersburg reacted by saying that its public construction funds were inadequate to meet the most urgent requirements in European Russia, and that the Governor General was on his own. Actually the work begun by Muraviev did not proceed beyond construction of a triumphal arch in the outskirts of Irkutsk, bearing the inscription "Road to the Pacific Ocean."

And yet Siberia should have a railroad; this the Governor General emphasized in a letter to his brother in April 1858, and he kept discussing the project with foreigners.

An Englishman offered to build a 5000-mile tramway from Nizhni Novgorod to the Pacific, a horse-drawn affair, since there was little coal available in Siberia, but between three and four million horses.

An American expressed interest in building a trunk line from Irkutsk to Chita, as a first step to a trans-Siberian steam railroad to be financed by Siberian capital. Muraviev referred the matter to the government, which reacted with a curt no.

Late in 1858, Morrison, Horn & Sleigh submitted a project to link Moscow with the Pacific at no cost to the Russian Government, and without raising funds in Russia, but they asked for trade privileges that Russia would not grant.

Meantime Siberian river flotillas received new steamboats at the rate of three to eight a year. Elderly excellencies in St. Petersburg thought that this was progress; transportation specialists sighed that it was less than a drop in the bucket; and Muraviev kept clamoring for his railroad. Russia's link with the Amur became a favorite topic of conversation. "Oh, really, someday you will all lose your wits over the Amur," the Tsar was quoted as having said.

The Governor General did not lose his wits, but he grew ulcers and had to travel halfway around the globe to Marienbad, an Austrian spa, to nurse his stomach. Marienbad was a fashionable resort, popular among ranking Russian nobility. At the colonnades the Governor made a nuisance of himself by buttonholing his countrymen and talking railroad. He was told that Russia would have to take care of the needs of her civilized European realm before considering luxury transportation for tramps, savages, rebels and similar characters populating Siberia. There were several brisk arguments followed by suggestions that Muraviev's assignment be terminated.

On March 3, 1861, a ukase abolished all vestiges of serfdom in Russia. Twenty-three million mushiks were free to acquire land on a government-financed installment plan.

Muraviev tried to direct the flow of emancipated peasants to Siberia. He offered free plots of land averaging forty acres per family, and tax exemption for twenty years. But the peasants would rather buy a plot from their former feudal lords. The mushik did not understand the meaning of the debt he incurred. Had he been told to pay one ruble, or perhaps ten, no later than after the next harvest, he might have worried: this meant less vodka, and no new boots or fur caps or a kerchief for his wife, but a debt of 1000 rubles, payable in terms he could not understand, meant nothing to him. The landowners did not worry either. The Treasury advanced 100 per cent of what was coming to them under the contract, and the Minister of Finance should try to collect installments from a score of million mushik families.

During the twenty years following the emancipation ukase only 110,000 peasants voluntarily moved to Siberia, an annual average of one man for every 1000 square miles. And Western mushiks who lost their new estates through foreclosure preferred European factory jobs to a Siberian farm.

Another source of manpower for Eastern Siberia was eventually found in Korea, where recurring disasters and upheavals caused refugees to cross the mountainous border into the Maritime Province, and to accept poor wages and harsh treatment for work on farms, wharves, and in shops.

Had Muraviev still been Governor General of Siberia at the time of the Korean immigration, he might have tried to expand his domain into Korea. But Muraviev had been recalled in 1862, almost ten years prior to the event, and his successors would do no more than scout the Korean coast for naval bases, and shelve the matter in favor of a deal with Japan.

Japan officially acknowledged Russian sovereignty over all of Sakhalin in exchange for the return of the Kurile Islands. St. Petersburg made Korea another item on its agenda for another generation.

In 1876, Japan forced an impotent Korean Government to open its ports to Japanese shipping, in a manner reminiscent of the actions which had terminated Japan's isolation. The Russian Government showed little concern about a possible establishment of the Island Empire on the Asiatic mainland, but trusted that it would control the entire coast opposite Japan long before Japan could become a great power. The Western nations did not see the handwriting on the wall, and either ignored or acclaimed the islanders' teachability.

Count Muraviev-Amursky was still living in 1876—the grand old man of Asiatic politics, and, like other grand old men, a symbol whose words were constantly praised, rarely quoted, and never heeded.

Muraviev had no official dealings with Japan, but he was strangely involved in imbroglios in China that started during the Crimean War and continued until the end of his term in office.

The Chinese tried to delay the actual opening of Canton to foreigners. The government asserted that Westerners entering the town would be threatened by public wrath and produced posters as evidence of the danger.

"We shall rise like one man," the posters said, "as soon as the barbarians befoul our fair city; we shall defy official orders, and chop off the heads of the plotting Englishmen. We know them well enough. Indomitable they are like wild horses, voracious like vultures and silkworms; they have more crimes upon their consciences than hairs on their heads. They were born far beyond the realm of civilization, in a poisonously vicious land. Their beast-like features reveal their wolf's nature. If we let them stay in our town, they will prey on us and eventually turn into our masters."

The posters were leftovers from the Taiping insurrection. The English knew it well enough, but with the Crimean War on their hands they first let the Chinese bid for time.

But England would never let China tamper with business. Chinese officials in Canton charged that English consular agents were aiding smugglers who carried contraband from Hong Kong to Chinese inland ports, and that the English flag was being used to cover up illegal operations. Such charges were considered brazen defiance. And when the Governor of Canton had twelve Chinese sailors from a Hong Kong smuggler's craft arrested, British Consul Parkes issued an ultimatum requesting their immediate release and formal apologies.

The Governor of Canton refused to comply. English warships shelled the castles on the approach to the town. In London, Parliament put the Canton affair on the order of the day. The debate produced rhetorical fireworks which resulted in the resignation of Lord Palmerston's Whig government and in the nomination of Lord Derby's Tory cabinet. Lord Derby had hostilities stepped up. Admiral Seymour took his powerful squadron from Canton to Whampoa and to coastal areas adjoining Hong Kong. Wherever the English warships went Chinese furor rose to a pitch, and the Chinese people did not distinguish among foreigners of various origins.

An American cutter en route from Whampoa to Canton was fired upon; an American request for reparations remained unanswered and subsequent retaliation put the castles of Hong Kong temporarily into American hands. Washington, however, did not feel that the incident warranted further action.

Next it was learned that earlier in 1856 a French Catholic missionary, Father Chapdelaine, had been arrested in Northern Kwangsi Province, charged with conspiracy, tortured, and beheaded.

French units joined English men-of-war in an action in which the Chinese did not have a "Chinaman's chance." It was by no means a gentlemen's war.

In a letter to the editor of the Hong Kong *Register* an Englishman describing the capture of Canton by Anglo-French forces claimed that his countrymen had, without distinction, displayed great thieving skill, and that the French contingent had made a reputation of being a band of ruthless brigands. On the other hand, Chinese civic committees put a price of $130 on every English head delivered to their offices.

The fall of Tientsin in May 1858 ended hostilities, or rather established an uneasy armistice. Canton was unconditionally opened; so were eleven more ports on the Chinese mainland; and on Formosa foreigners were granted all privileges enjoyed by the members of the highest Chinese social strata. Litigation involving Westerners was taken out of the hands of Chinese judges and assigned to foreigners' courts. China paid an indemnity of $4,000,000. The legality of opium imports was again confirmed and, most annoying to the Chinese, the use of the term "barbarians" for the English was forbidden. Lord Elgin, Plenipotentiary of Her Majesty's Government, threatened to seize Peking if the Chinese stalled on this particular issue.

America signed another advantageous arrangement with Peking, which was put into effect without much ado. President Buchanan called the Chinese official attitude friendly and honorable.

However, the American Envoy Extraordinary to China, John Ward, was not received in special audience by the Emperor, as he had requested. Chinese traditional etiquette remained the Court's basic policy even in defeat. Etiquette called all the lands whose ambassadors called at the palace "tributary countries." Tributary countries, according to the code of ceremonial, "shall file obedient applications to the Tribunal of Decency to ask for the terms under which they might be admitted." The code also required that credentials be drawn up as humble applications made by the ambassador's sovereign, and that the personnel of an embassy should not exceed 100, only twenty of whom would be admitted to the palace. Mr. Buchanan did not feel like filing a humble application, but neither did the President and his ambassador want to hurt Chinese feelings by insisting on a procedure that would have violated the venerable code.

The English, however, would not permit Orientals to restrain Her Majesty's Ambassador. Lord Palmerston's axiom that the customary Christian laws of justice should not apply to dealings with Oriental people was again applied. When Peking requested an English mission headed by Ambassador Bruce, a brother of Lord Elgin, to travel with a small staff and light baggage, and escorting men-of-war not to proceed beyond the mouth of the Pai River, an English squadron under Admiral Hope was ordered out to Tientsin. The English wanted to force their way into the Imperial Palace on their own terms at the point of naval guns.

Chinese warnings that force would be met by force were discounted as bluff and bluster. English gunboats and transport craft carrying a thousand soldiers invaded Chinese inland waters and were joined by light French units.

To the surprise of the Europeans, Russian armed vessels were sighted. The government in St. Petersburg asserted that the Russian naval officers were directed to refrain from any move that could arouse French and British suspicion, and that similar orders had been issued to Governor General Count Muraviev.

When Allied ships approached Tientsin in the early summer of 1859, they were met by blistering artillery fire. Not only had the fortifications of the town been completely rebuilt; they had been rearmed with modern rifled cannon. Several gunboats were sunk, others were beached, and the English lost 89 dead and 345 wounded. Admiral Hope was among the latter, and the remnants of his armada beat a hasty retreat.

The fortress guns were not Chinese-made; some were of American design, others apparently Russian, and to the embarrassment of the London government, English cannon too had had a share in defeating English ships. Indications were that Hong Kong smugglers had had a hand in supplying China with arms, but some of the equipment undoubtedly had come from or via Siberia.

London issued another ultimatum to China. It denounced Chinese unwarranted aggression, asked for apologies and the return of all British craft and ammunition left behind, for safe-conduct for the British embassy to Tientsin, and arrangement of transportation from there to Peking. China should also reimburse England for expenses incurred in preparing another campaign.

Emperor Hienfong was granted thirty days to "meet his obligations." This was an unusually long term for an ultimatum, but England needed time to reorganize its battered naval forces.

The Chinese Government issued a formal statement on the "incident," emphasizing that China had committed no act of aggression, but careful not to denounce the English or the French. Peking hoped that either the U.S.A. or other neutrals would offer to mediate. But no such offer was forthcoming.

The English quietly let their ultimatum expire. They were still assembling strong forces that would wipe out the blot of defeat. Not until April 1860 were preparations completed, and they were on an unprecedented scale. A huge fleet armed with a combined total of 3000 guns was ready to sail. Twenty-five thousand men, English, Bengals, Sikhs, and Gurkhas, concentrated. France contributed several ships and 9000 soldiers, partly from Cochin China. On April 14, 1860, another ultimatum, milder in tone but no less harsh in terms, preceded the opening of hostilities.

China also had an army, but it had a strange complexion. Remnants of Taiping bands who had been living in remote parts of the land emerged, officered by individuals who did not look Chinese and spoke Russian. Mongolian cavalry turned up near Peking. Its commanding general, one Sankolinsin, ordered his horsemen to submit French and English captives to degrading corporal ordeals; yet otherwise did not act as independently as Mongolian conquerors of yore, but seemed to take orders from superiors. The identity of these superiors was not revealed, but they did not seem to reside in Peking.

Lord Elgin, reporting on the matter to Lord John Russell, refused to believe that Sankolinsin would dare challenge Allied military might, and attributed the Mongolian chieftain's attitude to "the conventional blending of stupidity and suspicion, conceit and roguishness, that characterizes the conduct of business in China."

After the Allied operations opened, it was said that roaming ex-Taiping bands were set to sack Shanghai. The Taiping attack did not materialize, however. Instead French soldiery ordered to protect the city burned down the eastern suburbs so that they might not be used as hideouts by bandits. In August 1860 almost 80,000 Chinese inhabitants of Shanghai were homeless, and the trade of the city was paralyzed, to the benefit of Japan, whose exports rose sharply. The "Shanghai transaction," as the French action was called, was described in a letter to Mr. William Bryant as "one of the most atrocious and diabolical transactions that has disgraced history in modern times."

It took the main Allied forces ten days and 400 casualties to fight their way into Tientsin. Civilians suffered heinous misery through indiscriminate bombardment, requisitioning, and acts of brutality, in which the French far outdid the English.

The Mongols obeyed Sankolinsin's orders on the treatment of prisoners. Among the victims were a British newspaperman, who had ventured far beyond the Allied lines in quest of news, and truce officers whom Lord Elgin had sent to Chinese headquarters in September. Several foreigners succumbed to maltreatment.

Had it not been for the seizure of the truce officers, the war would have ended in September 1860. But Peking, requested to produce the missing men within three days, had no control over Sankolinsin.

On October 5, 1860, Mongolian cavalry and some Chinese infantry barred the approaches to the imperial capital. Their array was reminiscent of Djenghiskhanide pattern, but Sankolinsin was no Subotai. The Allies pierced the lines and advanced along the Imperial Canal over the magnificent Imperial

Highway. At dusk cavalry vanguards sighted the Summer Palace and the mighty tower dominating the northeastern gates of Peking.

The invaders reached their goal as darkness fell. Hundreds of eunuch servants rambled about the courtyards and halls of the imperial residence, screaming with fear. Forty imperial guardsmen threw away their heavy ornate bows and took to their heels. The French and English engaged in a violent looting spree. They did not understand the beauty of delicate forms and colors, but reached for the most shining objects. There were more shining things than they could carry and they threw away what they had already gathered, picked new objects, and junked them again as they saw things even more attractive. Floors were littered with treasures and trifles, soldiers trampled upon them in fierce haste to snatch more, only to throw it away later. The looting continued throughout the night. Fires flared up. The uniformed mob raced through clouds of smoke, trampling on burning objects, pushing their way through singed tapestries, damaged furniture, and heaps of rubble, which included fragments of delicate vessels of jade and nephrite and sheets of magnificently embroidered silk, in search for yet other booty. Somebody roared that they ought to help themselves to the Emperor's females, but the wives and concubines of the Emperor had fled, and the intruders found only jewelry and lap dogs. They killed the animals and pocketed the jewels. Officers joined their men in the orgy of pillage. Their tastes were not quite as primitive, but they too were not really selective.

On the morning of October 6, Lord Elgin and the commanders of the French and English expeditionary forces, Generals Montauban and Sir Hope Grand, arrived on the scene. Savage pillaging by the rank and file was superseded by more dignified procedures that were certainly not in accordance with Christian laws of justice. A joint commission was set up to select "gifts" for Queen Victoria, Emperor Napoleon III, and the most venerable institutions of their realms. A priceless marshal's baton of jade inlaid with gold was the Queen's share, and a duplicate found among the Chinese Emperor's personal belongings was set aside for Napoleon. A unique selection of bibliographical rarities went to the British Museum. And while grandees and generals sedately stole for Queen, Emperor, and fatherland, tumult again raked the approaches to the palace.

The soldiers were fighting over their spoils, and drove tumultuous bargains with native receivers of stolen goods. Sir Hope interfered and decreed that all English officers and men surrender their booty for orderly sale at public auction, proceeds of which would be distributed among all troops.

French and British, Chinese and ubiquitous Indians participated in the bidding, which netted only $100,000, about $4.00 per man. The actual value of the stolen goods cannot be estimated.

After the auction the English summoned Prince Kung Jesin, highest-ranking member of the government present in the capital, to arrange for an orderly entry of all Allied troops and for a worthy reception of Allied embassies.

Lord Elgin was determined to mortify Chinese pride. For several days he held court in a requisitioned palace, while Prince Kung Jesin and his mandarins were kept waiting on the stairs of the Court of Decency. At last the lord chose to proceed to the Court building for a conference. Bands played "God Save the Queen" as Lord Elgin strode past the despondent young prince, with theatrical bearing and an icy glare. At the conference table, he had his chair put on a raised platform and, the left side being the place of honor, he motioned the Prince to sit on a low chair to his right. The conference consisted of a reading of English terms and affixing of Chinese signatures.

China regretted, and apologized for, iniquities inflicted upon Her Majesty's subjects. The British Ambassador received the freedom of the city of Peking; China ceded Kowloon Peninsula; Tientsin was opened to English trade; the Chinese Government undertook not to interfere with the immigration of its subjects to British colonies and the enlistment of Chinese personnel into English service. In addition China had to pay another $88,000,000.

On the following day, October 25, French Plenipotentiary Baron Gros had himself carried up the steps of the Court of Decency in a palanquin, and Prince Kung Jesin signed another treaty giving France $8,000,000 in cash, and authorizing Chinese citizens to board French ships for immigration overseas.

Both France and England needed industrious, frugal coolies for their colonies. They would keep drawing upon China's inexhaustible resources of manpower, unconcerned over ethical, social, and economic implications.

Prince Kung Jesin was congratulated for having obtained peace with England and France "at so cheap a price" by Russian Ambassador General Nikolai Ignatiev, who announced that he had good news for China: Governor General Muraviev was willing to settle all remaining border problems in an equitable manner. Settling all border problems meant unconditional Chinese assent to the Russian version of boundary lines, which not only followed the line of farthest Russian penetration but even snatched a strip of coastal area west of the Ussuri, and of the surroundings of Vladivostok, from mutilated China. Chinese immigration into Siberia was not mentioned in the Treaty of Peking of November 2, 1860.

The Chinese Government never presented its side of the story of Chinese-Russian relations during the latest Anglo-French aggression, but a few documents the Allies found in Peking indicated that St. Petersburg's earlier claim to an offhand policy was not in accordance with the facts. The documentation was incomplete, and neither London nor Paris seemed overly anxious to unearth all the facts.

Only shreds of information are still available. But it appears as if Governor General Muraviev, probably with the connivance of his government, had conceived a cabal of conquest by trickery which seemed naïve under the circumstances but, in a way, set the pattern for the communist seizure of power in China more than sixty years after Muraviev's death.

The Russian squadron the Allies encountered in Chinese inland waters had gone there by orders from St. Petersburg to watch events and to take action at the appropriate moment.

The appropriate moment would have come had the English and French been in grievous trouble, if not in full retreat, before a counterattack by Chinese ground forces. But these ground forces were imperial in name only. Regular units were outnumbered by Taiping and Mongolian contingents, which treated the regulars like the Mongols of the past had treated newly enlisted auxiliaries.

Sankolinsin had been to Siberia shortly before the Allies reopened their attack. There can be little doubt that he met Count Muraviev; and it has been established that he remained in close contact with the Russian Ambassador to China during the war and even afterwards. Ambassador Ignatiev also is known to have maintained relations with Russian-speaking officers who led the Taiping remnants.

Old Siberian hands would long reminisce on the prosperous days when rifled cannon went to China. Siberia supplied Chinese fortresses and Russian-controlled Chinese troops with modern artillery. Had the Allies been defeated on land, it can be presumed that a military government would have superseded the Chinese Emperor's cabinet, and that the military would have either reduced the Emperor to a figurehead or established a new dynasty. The military were Russian puppets, and they would have turned China into a Russian satellite.

The directives Muraviev received at the time of his appointment did not preclude so fantastic a concept, and it was consonant with these directives that St. Petersburg claimed that the Governor General was ordered to abstain from moves that could raise Allied suspicion.

Official Russia wanted to wait and see how far these suspicions would go. It might never have acknowledged complicity in the cabal had it led to the desired result. St. Petersburg might have called it a matter of Chinese national politics. But this, of course, is conjecture.

Russia's Ambassador Ignatiev remained at his post after Muraviev's assignment had come to an end. He was on friendly terms with the British and French embassies and never got tired of emphasizing that in 1860 he had been working for a speedy acceptance of Allied terms.

CHAPTER FIFTY-SIX More than one decade had passed since Muraviev had left the gubernatorial mansion in Irkutsk, and there had been no more clamor for extravagant Siberian innovations such as railroads. Officials in St. Petersburg breathed with relief.

But in 1873 there emerged other champions of reform. Executives of mines and forges in the Ural Mountains insisted that their rising output required more effective transportation than old-fashioned river barges and wagons on the Siberian track; and they introduced statistics showing that no more than 1600 wagons traveled over the track every year.

The Russian Government, anxious to occupy a distinguished place among the great powers of the world, realized most uncomfortably that industrial potential was becoming a major factor in determining the rank of a nation. Several foreigners of consequence, mostly Englishmen, held stock in Ural industries and could not be snubbed.

European Russian industry included 17,000 plants and shops, in which upward of 1,000,000 workers produced about 1,250,000,000 rubles' (one ruble being approximately 50 cents) worth of goods. Ural industry, even though situated partly on Asiatic territory, was included in the European statistics. Siberia was listed with only 600 establishments, 10,000 non-compulsory workers, and an output worth 10,000,000 rubles.

In 1875 the Russian Government adopted a plan to link river traffic on the European Volga and the Siberian Ob by a trunk line.

It took three years to link Perm (now Molotov) with Ekaterinburg (now Sverdlovsk), and twice that long to extend the line to Tumen. This first Siberian railroad was a modest achievement and nobody thought that it would affect immigration. But to the surprise of officials the influx of peasants to the eastern parts of the empire rose sharply.

It seemed incredible that mushiks, who would walk alongside their carts rather than ride in them, would use a railroad. Immigrating peasants offered no plausible explanation either. "We just came . . ." they would answer questions by Siberian authorities.

News of immigration and industrial progress, magnified to suit patriotic pride, unleashed a new tempest of enthusiasm for Siberia. The Russian intelligentsia almost "lost its wits because of the Amur."

It was freely predicted that *ssi tshass* (within the hour) immigration to Siberia would catch up with that to the U.S.A. The average Russian did not know that immigration to the U.S. had reached a staggering 788,992 in 1882, 3000 per cent above the corresponding figure for Siberia; and experts who knew it did not seem to mind. Russians considered theirs a country of miracles, and there were no limits to what miracles could do.

Generals who had been studying maps of Turkey and Persia bent bearded heads over maps of Siberia and adjoining territories, and announced that a railroad line crossing Siberia and branching out into Manchuria, Korea, and China would upset all advantages held by the naval powers and give Russia a dominating position throughout Eastern Asia.

Planners from the Ministry of Transportation expressed vociferous approval of the strategic thesis; and suddenly they saw little, if any, difficulty in building a line, close to 5000 miles long, at a time in which the total Russian railroad net was still under 15,000 miles. *"Nitshevo,"* they replied to cautious objectors. "Doesn't matter."

There would not be sufficient labor available? *Nitshevo!* It should be possible to train a monkey for track work, so why couldn't a mushik be trained? And some way or other you could always get mushiks.

There would be no food for the laborers if the mushiks abandoned the plow and took up the shovel? *Nitshevo!* Russia never had enough of anything, and yet Russia always managed to subsist.

Expenses would be forbidding? A figure of 350,000,000 rubles had been mentioned and Russia's finances were not strictly sound. *Nitshevo!* Russian finances had a tradition of unsoundness, and yet the country was not bankrupt.

Russia ranted, jubilated, joked, and philosophized. It produced billions of words and not one yard of railroad. But in 1884 even the most sanguine generals had to realize that the time they had spent with braggadocio had been used by Japan for a sounder purpose. The Japanese were entrenched in Korea, and Tokyo was set to blackmail China into concessions which the Russian military had considered within their own grasp. Intelligence reports from Vladivostok, Sakhalin, Korea, and Manchuria indicated that unless something effective were done *ssi tshass,* in the literal meaning of the word, Russia would lose the race for Eastern Asia.

No amount of optimism could relegate the emergency to the dustbin. The Russian Government appointed surveyors to check Siberian resources and map plans for their exploitation, so that expenses of the railroad could be met.

The surveyors divided the area of Siberia into three zones: the agricultural, the forest, and the arctic, covering 25 per cent, 43 per cent, and 32 per cent of the total respectively. The agricultural zone included only the most fertile regions with average temperatures of 57°F. and up. Its annual produce per acre was only 3 per cent of that of similar regions in the U.S.A., but surveyors added comfortingly that the less these areas now produced, the higher the rise would be.

The forest zone, they reported, was a treasure chest of century-old cedars and pines, of game and fur animals. And the arctic zone was not plain, arid tundra. Wheat and oats could be grown in many parts of it; some of its steppes could provide grazing land; and fishing in the northern streams should bring amazing returns.

Copper, silver, lead, and iron were found in the Amur Province. Kamchatka produced sulphur, copper, iron ore, amber, and mica. The Baikal region was a source of gold, silver, tin, lead, copper, iron, hard coal, graphite, rock salt, sulphur, and naphtha. Vast deposits of silver and lead existed in the Stanovoi Mountains, the coldest range on earth. The Maritime Province had deposits of amethyst, jasper, agate, and topaz. No less than 500 varieties of stones were found throughout Siberia.

Russia's total fiscal revenue was about one billion rubles, but surveyors, none of whom earned more than 1500 rubles a year, predicted freely that Siberia could easily double, nay, treble the Treasury's intake.

Not only Russians were elated by the very size of Siberia. George Kennan, an American explorer, wrote: "You could take the whole U.S.A. from Maine to California, and from Lake Superior to the Gulf of Mexico, and set it down in the middle of Siberia without touching anywhere the boundaries of the latter territory. You could then take Alaska, and all the states of Europe with the single exception of Russia, and fit them into the remaining margin, like pieces of a dissected map; and after having thus accommodated all of the U.S., including Alaska, and all of Europe except Russia, you would still have more than 300,000 square miles of Siberian territory to spare. . . ."

But manpower shortage could not be eliminated by enthusiasm, and *nitshevo* did not solve the problem either. The annual rise of peasant immigration to Siberia during the early 1880s was only 15,000. In European Russia the annual birth rate exceeded the death rate by 1,000,000, and a short-lived slogan predicted that 25 per cent of the excess population would go to Siberia. But actually even the Western part of the empire was short of manpower.

Soon a gruesome provider of population for Siberia raised its medusa head: famine plagued European Russia. Starving mushiks who had neither seeds nor cattle left were ready to go anywhere food could be had.

The government relied on nature to stop the famine in the west and ordered surveyors and the Governor General of Siberia to make practical suggestions about more effective settlement in the east.

European surveyors suggested that voluntary immigrants be sent only to the agrarian zone and the settlement of other areas left to deportation authorities. At the prevailing rate of voluntary immigration this would have added one settler in thirty years to every square mile of the best land.

The Governor General of Siberia opined that allotments of land should be increased in newly acquired areas, and that voluntary immigrants be granted draft and tax exemptions. But not until 1889 did the Russian Government embody this opinion in a decree that granted settlers of the Amur and Maritime provinces 270 acres of land per family and a twenty-year tax and draft exemption. In other regions of Siberia allotments of "Crown land" remained at forty acres, and exemptions were limited to three years.

The effects of the decree were not as strong as had been expected, and the administration of Siberia was urged to make more proposals. The Governor General appointed commissions of surveyors and land agents who produced statistics and comments.

The aboriginal population, it appeared, was now a minor element in Siberia. Ninety per cent of the people of the agricultural Western parts were of Russian stock, and corresponding figures for the central zones and the Transbaikal region were 84 per cent and 70 per cent respectively. Only in the extreme north and in the Kirghiz steppes did the aborigines retain a majority estimated at 75 per cent. But the Samojeds of the tundra, according to a booklet published by the Chancery of the Committee of Ministers, "played no part whatsoever in the cultural and social life of Siberia."

Samojeds were not considered worth the shipment to areas of railroad construction. A census taken in the southern steppes, however, indicated that approximately two and one half million Kirghizes and Tatar Mongols roamed the 908,000-square-mile flatlands. The Committee of Ministers did not examine what part these people were playing in the cultural and social life of Siberia, but decided to draw on these reserves.

Scholars of ethnography found that many nationalities survived in Siberia—Mingrelians, Talyshins, Aphasians, Samurzakanes, and Pshaves among them. But they were collectors' items rather than labor pools.

The last decade of the nineteenth century dawned. The Trans-Siberian railroad was in the talking and planning stage, and the tone of intelligence reports from the East was getting shrill.

Generals consulted economists. Economists ventured that as soon as work got under way, German-English-American competition would result in a boon for Siberia. Politicians launched a campaign of slogans.

Rambling patriots shouted that Russia was the biggest country of the world, had the longest telegraph line, the greatest navigable mileage of rivers and canals.[1] The eternal glory of the fatherland required that it also get the biggest railroad of the world.

On March 17, 1891, a rescript entrusted the heir to the Russian throne with the task of laying the cornerstone to "the uninterrupted line of railway across the whole of Siberia to the Russian coast of the Pacific."

When the rescript was publicized the future Nicholas II was aboard ship off Vladivostok. Two days later he performed the ceremony, pale and distraught, haunted by fear of *attentats* and bewildered at the settings of a ramshackle city surrounded by ugly clay hills and with many foreign vessels in its port, most of them German.

The heir to the throne returned to the capital across Siberia. His itinerary included Irkutsk and several district capitals where governors arranged patriotic demonstrations and noisy festivities. It also led through Ekaterinburg, where little more than one quarter of a century later ex-Tsar Nicholas II and his family would fall victim to the bullets of a Bolshevik murder squad.

Committees were appointed to supervise construction, to organize auxiliary undertakings, and to promote Siberia's colonization and industrial development.

The Siberian Railway Committee, under Nicholas's chairmanship, topped

---

[1] In fact Russia was second in the field of waterways with 20,079 miles as compared to Brazil's 20,433.

the new office pyramid which was linked to the Committee of Ministers and to the Ministries of the Imperial Household, of Foreign Affairs, of the Interior, of Justice, Agriculture, War, and Navy.

Among the members of the Railway Committee were General Aleksei N. Kuropatkin, who was to lead the Russian armies to defeat in the war against Japan; Sergej (later Count) Witte, who was to head the first Russian Government under a new constitution in 1905; and two Muravievs, who were listed as representatives of the Ministries of Foreign Affairs and of Justice. Glowing official eulogies did not mention Count Muraviev-Amursky.

This fate of oblivion the former Governor General shared with the engineers who designed the alignment, with supervisors, organizers, and the drab host of men who toiled, suffered, and died so that the longest railroad in the world would come into existence.

Their epic has remained unsung by eager chroniclers who extolled the "shining band of iron" as a crowning achievement of peaceful conquest, a glorious route to expansion of the white race, the open-sesame of the Siberian hoard, and a tie uniting nations from the Atlantic to the Pacific. Not even the vanguards of realism in literature chose to deal with the individuals who drafted, carted, and blasted the "shining band," men who did not meet the pharisaical standards of primer heroes, and most of whom did not even know the word "dedication."

The public was made to believe that the laying of the foundation stone would be immediately followed by the start of construction work. Official agencies issued flowery reports on erections of triumphal arches and protestations of solicitude for the welfare of the country. However, the Railway Committee was beset by conflicting requests from important quarters about the tracing of the line.

Ural mining executives clamored for it to run through their districts. Fuel experts warned that it had to be kept close to coal and naphtha fields. Generals shouted that there should be no detour, and that a straight line to Transbaikalia, and from there to Peking, was the only acceptable solution. Admirals proclaimed that the railroad's true objective was the establishment of a land link between Kronstadt and Nikolajevsk, Vladivostok, and Petropavlovsk. A harassed committee accepted a compromise, worked out by Mr. Ostrovsky, which was not deemed satisfactory by the interested groups and denounced by topographers who wanted to by-pass some of the areas through which the Ostrovsky line ran.

The track went from Cheljabinsk roughly east in the vicinity of the fifty-fifth parallel to Chita, from where it would be continued south, as far as political conditions in China would permit, and also branch out along the Amur and Ussuri rivers to Vladivostok. It was subdivided into six sections: the Western Siberian Railway, from Cheljabinsk to the Ob (879 miles); the Central Siberian Railway, from the Ob to Irkutsk (1115 miles); the Irkutsk Baikal Railroad, only 42 miles long; the Baikal Circular Line (141 miles);

the Transbaikal Railway from Lake Baikal to Sretensk (685 miles); and the Eastern Chinese Railway, from Chita to Nikolsk Ussurijsk (1271 miles). The Eastern Chinese Railway had been traced mostly on yet-to-be conquered Manchurian territory, and it was to be linked with another railroad which would lead from Khabarovsk to Vladivostok, a distance of about 477 miles. The western terminal of Cheljabinsk was to be linked with the European Russian net by a railroad to Samara; and a trunk line was to connect the Trans-Siberian with Ekaterinburg.

The Railway Committee had pledged itself to give Siberian firms priority in the award of labor contracts. But many Siberian contractors collected advances and made no pretense of starting work. German business agents beleaguered the offices of the committee; they declared that unless the entire construction were entrusted to reliable German industrialists the railroad would never be built; and they whispered that their Western competitors were spies.

The Russian military was convinced that all foreigners were spies. Treasury officials warned of the effects that the dealing with foreigners would have on the Russian currency, and everybody agreed that Russian patriots would resent foreign construction. The Railway Committee was on the side of military, financial, and plain patriots. Generals and officials had no industrial experience, but they knew bankers who in turn knew people in the construction business.

And while wild animals still roamed over Siberian soil marked as railroad track, busy pens in the capital drew up and signed construction contracts. Later it was claimed that corruption had ruled supreme in the operation. Investigators found that some of the construction firms had been novices in the field, that vital material had been purchased with complete disregard to requirements, and anti-Semites sneeringly pointed at Jewish names on the list of business agents and contractors.

There had been a great deal of corruption, but in fact confusion ruled supreme.

Professional Russian railroad builders were bewildered by the scope and implications of the undertaking, and when semi-amateurs were put in charge in various parts of the line, the result could be but a maze of blunders and total absence of co-ordination. Even Russian professionals were able to deal with certain problems only after long and costly trials and errors. A procedure that had sped up American railroad construction was applied: provisional tracks were laid to carry heavy material to the spots where it was needed. But the Russians did not have the American "know-how," and the method was not really effective in Siberia.

In the spring of 1892 work had not yet begun. Not even in the easily accessible Western sector was there a trace of the "shining band of iron." The Railway Committee, showered by suggestions, applications, protests, and unsolicited advice, decreed that regardless of the contractor situation and the state of supplies, construction had to start at once, and in all sectors. The Railroad Committee eventually built 72 per cent of the line under its own management.

Committee and contractors' agents competed in recruiting labor. Natives were rounded up in the southern steppes; destitute Korean refugees, runaway peasants, stranded immigrants, tax delinquents, draft dodgers, men without passports, and victims of the Russian famine were enlisted. *Katorga* governors shipped their wards to recruiting centers, and, as in the days of the gold rush, deportation authorities made many a dishonest ruble by reclassifying deportees and making them eligible for chain gangs.

Wages were high. But the men were charged for lodging, food, and clothing at exorbitant rates determined by the employers, and they would never keep more than a few kopeks for a full day's work.

Few laborers had a clear notion of what a railroad actually was. Track tests almost invariably resulted in casualties when men were crushed to death trying to stop the snorting steaming monsters. More men were smothered in swamps or lost in snowstorms. Siberian tigers claimed many victims. The sick and the injured were left without medical care. Foremen did not report casualties; they split the missing men's wages with the paymasters.

Committee and contractors complained that the men were a lazy lot and that their output was but half of that of European railroad workers.

Conditions in Siberia were different from those in the West, however. Given proper care, tools, and training, the workers might have fulfilled the construction quota of a combined total of two and one half miles a day in all sectors. Under the circumstances the pace of construction temporarily fell below the one-mile-a-day mark.

The topographers' objections against the Ostrovsky line were justified. Part of the projected line ran over marshlands and stretches of rocky ground covered only by a deceptive thin layer of earth. And there were many more watercourses to cross than had been marked on the maps the planners had used; 265 bridges would have to be built in the western section and 815 in the eastern part.

A dam twenty-five inches high had to be built along 1000 miles of track on treacherous ground, and contractors would not start the work unless the Railroad Committee made additional allotments for the purpose. And the excess number of bridges also would have to be paid for. The Railroad Committee violated accepted international-security standards by ordering that wooden constructions be used instead of steel-and-stone spans. But not even Siberian constructors would use timber to span rivers more than 400 feet wide, of which there were twenty-one in the central sector. Next, operators of river boats protested that bridges hampered river traffic, and while protests were still under consideration contractors reported that the unvarnished wooden structures were beginning to rot.

The committee appointed subcommittees to study the thorny problem. The subcommittees threw out the protest of the river boatmen and established rules for bridge construction. The new bridges should have a substructure of stones and superstructures of varnished timber. Decaying timber structures should be replaced by steel. The solution was not really efficacious, but much time was lost reaching it.

And even more time was lost through the use of inadequate rails. Specifications of construction contracts were not very strict about the type of rails to be laid, and unscrupulous contractors purchased the lightest and cheapest type of rails, hoping that it would last through test runs and utterly unconcerned over accidents bound to happen later. However, the rails broke down under the tests and had to be replaced by heavier material, which in turn led to prolonged controversies between the contractors and the committee.

But no defective rails and no number of rivers to cross could pose as startling a problem as Lake Baikal.

Maps of the region indicated that foothills of the Mongolian mountains were sloping down to the lake, and the men who delineated the road in St. Petersburg presumed blithely that there would be sufficient level ground along the shore to lay at least a single track. But when work on the Baikal sector opened, flabbergasted technicians realized that there was no level ground at all. They reported to the committee; the committee considered construction of three or four tunnels, none over one mile long.

But the first tunnel, just outside Baikal village, would have had to be two and one half miles long, and from then on hill after hill descended precipitously into the lake, like folds of a gigantic curtain of rock. Surveyors took to boats and counted the number of folds. More than thirty would have to be tunneled, which would take years of labor and expenses hard to estimate. Russian railway constructors had little experience with tunnels, and financial experts asked for time to make estimates.

Generals were up in verbal arms against delay. Already Japan had attacked China; Eastern Asia was in foment; men and guns had to get through. General Kuropatkin spoke of blundering civilians. Upon his insistence the Railway Committee decreed that the sector had to be completed, hills or no hills.

Technicians tried patchwork. The Central Siberian line would temporarily end at Baikal village, and the Transbaikal sector at Mysovaya, a ramshackle cluster of huts forty-three and one half miles across the lake. Over this expanse of water or ice freight and passengers would have to be moved until the tortuous work of tunneling was completed.

But the indomitable lake did not easily permit such operations.

Lake Baikal has a surface of 13,180 square miles. It is 405 miles long, up to 56 miles wide, and 5765 feet deep. Its bed is formed by a volcanic crater whose outbursts before the dawn of mankind shook an area thousands of miles in circumference. The volcano was flooded in the diluvium, when cascades of melting continents of ice burst down upon Siberia. It is buried alive in the lake, into which some 300 rivers and torrents still empty. The tremors that once marked the titanic struggle between fire and water have never subsided. The bottom of the lake is still shaken by convulsions. Occasionally shocks are accompanied by windstorms that make the waves of the lake rise higher than those of stormy seas.

The climate of the lake region is as intemperate as the volcano. Sudden temperature rises and drops by 50° to 55°F. are not infrequent. Visibility may change from excellent to zero in a matter of minutes as dense fogs tumble down like avalanches of opaque moisture. From early December to mid-April the lake is covered by a layer of ice three and one half to six and one half feet thick, which can carry any man-made weight; but late in the winter when the ice turns brittle, sudden convulsions may crack the heavy layer, swallow several square miles of it, or pile them into towering obstacles. During the summer hurricanes and driving but not dispersing fogs may smash ships against sharp cliffs of granite, syenite, slate, and porphyry that stagger the shore line.

During the winter shuttle service across the lake was carried out by sleigh. Three thousand horses were used. But no more than 22,000 persons and 168,000 tons of goods were shipped within three months, at a cost of 1,100,000 rubles.

Water traffic was cheaper and boats had a greater carrying capacity than the fleet of sleighs. Total shipping costs were about 900,000 rubles for a seven-month season.

Icebreakers were required to prolong the period of water traffic. The Russians bragged that their icebreakers were superior to anything other nations could build, but when specifications for an icebreaker ferry were announced, Russian wharves were reluctant to enter bids and the contract went to Armstrong of England. The English-built *Baikal* had a hull of steel, an over-all length of 290 feet, and a top speed of 20.6 knots. It could carry a train of 25 cars and break through a block of solid ice 150 feet long and 3 feet thick. But the period of water transportation still could not be extended beyond eight months, and despite the *Baikal's* high top speed, ice and fog held it down to three trips every 48 hours. The Railroad Committee commissioned another icebreaker from a Russian yard; the terms of the contract were not as strict as those of the order to Armstrong, and the Russian product was greatly inferior to the British.

But the Lake Baikal predicament was temporarily overshadowed by startling developments across the Siberian border. The Sino-Japanese War turned into a disastrous walkover for Japan, and the peace of Shimonoseki, signed on April 17, 1895, established Japanese hegemony in Korea and, for all practical purposes, Manchuria, and gave Japan Formosa; worst of all, the Empire of the Rising Sun gained a foothold on Liaotung Peninsula, in and around the city of Port Arthur. Liaotung Peninsula was a key to the Chinese coast and could become an ideal springboard for an attack on Siberia.

Consternation gripped St. Petersburg. From Irkutsk came telegrams which told of Japanese-equipped irregulars raiding labor camps and supply dumps on Siberian territory, in vital sectors of railroad construction. The Siberian generals' Cassandrean prophecies visualized an impending Japanese drive to roll back the border to the onerous delimitations of Nerchinsk, and they insinuated that even if St. Petersburg now had the will to fight, the odds were all in Japan's favor.

St. Petersburg then intended to avoid war, but the government could not afford to pay a price for peace. Any territorial concession made to Japan would doom the eastern section of the railroad, and along with the railroad, Siberia would be doomed. Russia had to try its hand at diplomacy; and in a game of diplomacy the cards were stacked against Japan.

France had recently signed a treaty of alliance with Russia; France could not idly stand by when her ally was threatened. England was flirting with Japan; but not even England would want to see Japan become as strong as it would be after Russia's elimination as a major rival in the East. And there was ambitious Germany; a pact of mutual guarantee between Berlin and St. Petersburg had just expired and would not be renewed. German officers had helped train the new Japanese Army; Germany considered Russia a potential enemy; but Germany had global ambitions which turned all overly powerful nations into potential enemies, and Berlin might pull the brakes on Japan. Kaiser Wilhelm II's foreign office was not averse to double dealings.

France supported its eastern ally, and Germany eagerly took the initiative in settling the Russo-Japanese dispute in a matter that would leave the East a smoldering witches' caldron.

Eventually Tokyo agreed to evacuate Port Arthur and its hinterland. Hardly had the Japanese troops been withdrawn when Berlin claimed Chinese outrages committed against German missionaries, and extorted from Peking a lease of the port of Tsingtao and adjoining territories on the Bay of Kiaochow. The lease of Tsingtao to Germany gave St. Petersburg a pretext to request that Peking lease Port Arthur to Russia, and even though this treaty was not signed until March 28, 1898, Russian army and navy units entered the place without delay. China was not in a position to refuse any demand.

St. Petersburg's diplomats scored, not only on the coast of China, but also in Manchuria and Korea, where the Japanese abandoned some ground, leaving Russian soldiers free to move in without firing a shot. Not even the Tsar's most exuberant officials and officers thought that Japan would weakly forgo further aggressive intentions. But time had been gained to build the railway.

In 1896 the Chinese Government officially accepted Russia's plan to link Chita with Port Arthur. A concession was granted to the Eastern Chinese Railroad Company, a subsidiary of the new Russian-controlled Russo-Chinese bank. But then disaster struck at a sector of the Trans-Siberian Railroad that had caused no trouble before. In 1897 floodwaters of the Amur destroyed every yard of railroad in the river basin and caused temporary abandonment of construction in the Nerchinsk-Khabarovsk sector. Water transportation should have substituted for railroad transport, but river boats could not even temporarily link Khabarovsk with Vladivostok. The line along the Ussuri River, also badly damaged by inundation, had to be completed, and Vladivostok would also be linked with the Eastern Chinese Railroad, which would run from Manchouli on the Siberian border via Tsitsihar to Harbin, and from there branch out to Vladivostok, and also to Mukden and Port Arthur. The distance from Manchouli to Port Arthur was 1602 track miles, that from Manchouli to Vladivostok 1501 miles.

Construction on the Eastern Chinese Railroad had begun immediately after full-scale operations on the Western Siberian sector had been opened on October 3, 1896. The line Cheljabinsk-Vladivostok was 1400 miles longer than that of the Union Pacific, and 1855 miles longer than the Canadian Pacific. Russian patriots, computing mileages of connecting lines as far west as the Prusso-Russian border, calculated triumphantly that their railroad had a total length of 6200 miles.

But the line was single-tracked throughout; and as the patriots praised its length, it was far from being completed. Also unmentioned by the patriots was the fact that the engines were of foreign design, most of them American, purchased by the Railroad Committee against German competitive bids. The average speed of Siberian express trains was only twenty-one miles an hour, half that of American crack long-distance trains. The Siberian track did not permit fast runs. Engines had to operate on whatever fuel was on hand: coal, wood, or naphtha. The watering system was appalling; watering stations were few and far between, and run by semi-nomadic natives of colorful inefficiency. There were no established schedules for freight trains, and passenger trains would gather delays of one day or more in one sector.

On the Siberian run hazards were limited to accidents, but along the Manchurian tracks train rides turned into military ventures. Bands of highwaymen, armed with new German Mauser carbines, old Chinese muskets, and ancient Mongolian bows, raided transportation and were in turn engaged in running battles by Russian army personnel.

And if it was difficult to protect the line against bandits, it was impossible to guard it against sabotage. Chinese laborers seemed involved in plots which left Russian surveyors helpless. Sections of track built in daytime disappeared at night. Infuriated Russian officers retaliated by mass executions of workers; but not even firing squads could restrain sabotage.

A suggestion to discharge all Chinese and Korean laborers was impractical; these men could not be replaced. Soldiers could not be assigned to construction duty; they were needed to fight bandits. There was an ever-growing shortage of convict laborers, who staged mass escapes despite their chains while the guards fought raiders; the number of mushiks at hand was reduced during the floods, when destitute peasants joined outlaws; and even outlaws were at a premium.

In 1899 an outbreak of bubonic plague wrought havoc among construction gangs. Managers ordered that no manpower be wasted on burials, and even though unburied corpses aggravated the danger of contagion, they would scare bandits away. The effects of the order were said to have been satisfactory.

Next the Baikal section turned again into a vexatious trouble spot. In 1900 the Boxer Rebellion in China required mass transportation along and across the Lake. Russian generals had hoped to impress Westerners and Japanese alike by the performance of the ferry system. However, during one month of unusually fair summer weather, only 40,052 officers and men, 10,125 horses, and 2227 light carts could be moved across the lake.

This was highly inadequate. The generals insisted that the patchwork would have to come to an end. A gap of 161 miles remained between the Central Siberian and the Baikal sectors, including the crucial track along the lake shore.

The Railroad Committee set itself a limit of five years to complete the task. There would be no ceiling to expenses. Already the original budget was overdrawn, and it did not seem to matter whether the excess would be 25 per cent or 50 per cent. Actually total construction costs were some 700,000,000 rubles, more than 100 per cent above the preliminary estimates.

In the Baikal sector expenses ran at roughly $175,000 per single-track mile; however, the work was completed ahead of time.

Russian reports did not credit foreigners with any share in this achievement. However, foreign technicians, including at least one American, did most of the planning.

Thirty-three tunnels were blasted, removing ten million cubic yards of rock; 210 culverts, spans, and bridges up to 240 feet long were built; earthwork on 161 miles of track equaled that on 2000 miles in other sectors.

The labor battle of Lake Baikal turned into a massacre. Between November 1901 and April 1904 an average of 20,000 men were on the pay roll. Almost 14,000 cases of death, injury, and sickness were recorded. Five men were killed and 257 wounded in brawls, 225 fell victims to dynamite blasts, 15 died under the debris of collapsing barracks. Poor food caused 2900 cases of intestinal disease, 160 of them fatal.

A wage dispute was settled by a pay rise of 150 per cent, promptly followed by a 125 per cent increase in charges for food and shelter.

Traffic in the Baikal sector opened on September 25, 1904. Capacity had been calculated at fourteen pairs of trains a day. Engineers were provided with bulky books of rules, but the men were no eager readers, and they were confused by the sight of shunt points, and even more confused when clouds of fog made shunts invisible. They did not pull brakes on descents they could not see a long distance ahead; and they would often race their engines at twice the regulation speed. Their record of collisions, derailments, and trains plunging into the water cut capacity in half, and eventually accounted in part at least for Russia's defeat in the war against Japan.

This defeat stimulated the powers of revolution in Russia. It might well be that thirty-three tunnels, halfway between the zones of ancient European and new American civilizations, were instrumental in the advent of the latest struggle between a weary civilization and unreformative barbarianism.

CHAPTER FIFTY-SEVEN In each year that passed after Commodore Perry unlocked the gates of their country the Japanese made up for at least seven years of the Western lead in technical prowess and military skill. The younger generation of the warrior caste read Western military and naval textbooks and armament manuals, and studied the patterns of the latest conflagrations in the technicalized world; budding Japanese industry gave weapons top priority in its blueprints.

In the wake of foreign naval intruders came business agents who offered the Japanese many objects that had accounted for Western superiority. The business agents were followed by foreign experts who offered to train the rejuvenated military forces of Japan. The Japanese may have been wondering about the attitude of Westerners who sold the keys to conquest as if they were merchandise. But they did not express their amazement, and accepted training and tuition with such politeness and circumstantial display of gratitude that the men from abroad trusted that their disciples would always be docile tools.

Germany, looking for short cuts to colonial expansion, dispatched instructors to Japanese military academies. Italy, not yet in the race for overseas dominions, sent artillery experts. Austrian arms manufacturers sponsored a cannon factory in Osaka, and in 1875 a new 90-mm. bronze-barreled field cannon was introduced in the Austro-Hungarian and the Japanese armies simultaneously.

English, French, and German industrialists sold Armstrong, Hotchkiss, Canet, and Krupp products to Tokyo, including rapid-fire pieces and siege equipment of up to 320 mm. caliber.

Before the turn of the century, when certain conservative officers of the West still called Hiram Maxim's invention "circus equipment," machine guns became standard weapons in the Japanese Army and Navy.

In 1872 compulsory military service had been introduced. Medical examiners applied extremely rigid standards. As long as Japan's industrial potential was not fully developed, available arms were to be distributed only among the fittest men. By 1880, Japan had a standing army of 64,000, reserves of 91,000, and 106,000 territorials.

Within thirty years an efficient Japanese Navy had risen from a tattered fleet of rickety junks. It included torpedo boats and high-speed armored cruisers, most of them purchased abroad; but already Japanese labor was building formidable warships in domestic navy yards.

China too had learned a lesson from Western superiority. Western ammunition makers and fortress constructors did thriving business with Peking. Chinese acquisitions included two 7430-ton battleships with main batteries of twelve-inch caliber, but China did not turn toward arms production and establishment of national navy yards. The ancient industry of the empire still concentrated on silk-weaving mills and artcraft shops.

Reprinted Chinese army manuals listed eight banners of Manchus, Mongols, and Chinese, totaling 296,872 officers and men; Chinese Green Standard troops with effectives of 599,019; in addition to 96,750 Braves. Manchurian garrisons were said to number 175,000.

But Japanese intelligence services estimated the garrisons at 13,500. They claimed that Peking could muster no more than 30,000 soldiers worthy of this designation, and that the rest was rabble, dangerous only to their own officers and civilians. No Chinese instrument of mobilization was said to exist, and a spy's check of Chinese arsenals disclosed that they contained only one modern rifle to every fifteen men listed in the manuals.

Against this background of Chinese wretchedness, and watchful of developments in Siberia, Japan prepared to establish itself on the Asiatic mainland. The first goal was Korea, but Korea was but a steppingstone toward more ambitious objectives.

The "opening" of Korean ports was followed by small-scale landings on the Korean coast and the establishment of Japanese garrisons in the southern part of the country.

Under the terms of an ancient compact the King of Korea was the vassal of the Chinese Emperor. The Korean Government, torn by upheavals, rediscovered Chinese suzerainty and asked Peking to restore law and order. Peking wearily shifted small Manchurian garrisons into Korea.

Japan countered by recognizing a puppet government of Korea, headed by a refugee of dubious repute, and, upon this "government's" request, reinforced its own troops in Korea for the sake of law and order.

But Japanese preparations were yet inadequate, and China was bent on appeasement. In 1884 the two governments agreed to notify each other before sending additional troops into Korea.

Ten years later Japan was ready for a fresh test. The Japanese Ambassador to Korea organized riots in Asan and, through an agent planted in the Chinese-sponsored government of Korea, arranged that Peking be asked to quell the rebellion. Peking ordered a few battalions from Manchuria to restore order and informed Japan of its step. Tokyo claimed that marching orders had been issued prior to the notification, and that this constituted a flagrant violation of sacred treaties. China wearily denied the sequence; the battalions from Manchuria advanced at slow motion and halted on the northern bank of the Yalu River.

Meantime 5000 infantrymen joined the Japanese garrison of Seoul. Tokyo did not care to notify Peking of this operation, but requested that negotiations open on granting Korea full sovereignty, provided the country introduce certain reforms. Full sovereignty meant relinquishment of Chinese rights, while the vaguely specified reforms aimed at turning the country into a Japanese dominion. China asked for additional information; Tokyo charged Peking with an unreasonable attitude toward a generous proposal. The deceptive cat-and-mouse play began in June 1894, but by late July there had been no act of aggression.

Chinese General Ma-yun-kun's Manchurian troops crossed the Yalu, careful to keep out of range and sight of the Japanese. The general concentrated the bulk of his battalions and of local Chinese garrisons, altogether 13,000 men, in fortified Pyongyang. Only a small number of soldiers went to Asan.

A Chinese fleet operated off the Yalu estuary, but did not sail to the southern tip of the Korean Peninsula, where Japanese transport ships unloaded crack troops, artillery, and vehicles at Pusan harbor.

On August 1, 1894, without previous warning, the Japanese hurled themselves against Asan, cutting the Chinese garrison to ribbons. On the same day a Japanese torpedo boat sank a Chinese troop ship with 1200 aboard. And also on August 1, 1894, Japan declared war on China.

The army of Seoul, 17,000 strong, raced on to Pyongyang, took its fortifications in a one-day battle, killed and captured 2600 Chinese at a loss of 633 casualties. The victors, under General Oshima, were joined by new and larger forces under Field Marshal Yamagate, who led the advance toward the Yalu. Japanese fast vessels under Admiral Ito attacked the Chinese fleet halfway between the Yalu and Port Arthur.

Foreign observers raved about Ito's tactics. His whippet ships circled the solid enemy formation, showering it with close-range rapid-fire and giving the battle wagons little opportunity to use their fire power, which was superior to that of the Japanese squadron. After five hours only the battleships were left of Admiral Ting's Chinese armada; four of the other units were sunk, and one beached. Japan had lost one ship and two others had suffered damage, including the flagship of Admiral Ito, who was lionized by countrymen and foreigners alike.

Japan now controlled the sea lanes. Three brigades were rushed to Liaotung Peninsula for an assault on Port Arthur. Field Marshal Yamagate's army, built up to 80,000, crossed the Yalu near Liaoyang and, regrouping as it went, formed one arm of a pincer aimed at Peking; the other arm would be formed by three brigades from Liaotung after they had reached their immediate objective.

"On to Peking," became the Japanese's battle cry. "Those who did not live to see Peking," they eulogized their dead.

But Peking was far away, and winter was at hand. The Chinese Government mustered new armies to block Yamagate's drive, but these armies, one of which had more than 2000 combatants, were whirled away like dust. Subzero temperatures in Manchuria could not stop the Japanese.

The world was swamped with epics of Japanese indomitableness. Newspaper readers on all continents had several hundred lines on heroism added to their daily breakfast diet: wondrous tales of tiny yellow fellows who, their pockets bulging with hard-to-spell explosives, hurled themselves against fortifications held by fellows of similar size and complexion but considerably less boldness.

The human-bomb saga referred to the capture of Port Arthur. But the Japanese did not have to resort to human-bomb attacks to seize the rich prize. German engineers had built the ancient Chinese port into a modern fortress equipped with 300 guns of up to 240 mm. caliber, and German instructors had supplied Marshal Oyama, commander of the attacking brigades, with detailed maps. The Japanese broke through the main defenses even before their siege equipment had been unloaded. A French expert had predicted that the capture of Port Arthur would result in 20,000 casualties; but Oyama reported eighteen killed—and Japanese figures were generally reliable.

The Chinese battle wagons, however, were not part of the booty, as Tokyo had hoped. Admiral Ting had gone to Wei-hai-wei to join a yet intact flotilla of torpedo boats and a few larger units.

Admiral Ito blockaded Wei-hai-wei. Oyama seized the forts overlooking the harbor. Then the Japanese staged a naval surprise raid that was to set the pattern for an assault on the Russian fleet ten years later and, under changed circumstances, on Pearl Harbor, another thirty-seven years thereafter. Foreign observers applauded the tactics, but they did not seem to think that Ito's pattern might be used against their own navies.

A pot shot from a captured fort sank one Chinese battleship. Ito sent Ting a case of champagne and a courteous letter asking for surrender. Ting returned case and letter with elaborate thanks and regrets: there would be no surrender. Caught in a bowl with guns pointing at his ships from every direction, the Admiral ordered that the fleet be scuttled. The crews refused to comply and on February 12, 1895, Ting drafted an explanatory telegram to Peking, sent another note to Ito, saying that his demand would now be met, and swallowed a large dose of Indian opium which put an end to his ordeal.

And because he presumed that the Chinese Government would deny posthumous honors to the Admiral, Ito arranged for an elaborate funeral which was attended by all ranking Japanese officers and delegates from foreign naval units in Chinese waters.

The surrender of the Chinese fleet yielded one battleship, six torpedo boats, and three cruisers, worth $15,000,000.

Japanese authorities kept meticulous accounts on the war. The balance sheet showed a substantial profit. An enlisted man's pay was less than one dollar a month, his frugal meals were supplied from requisitioned stock. Also requisitioned were most of the draft animals, and captured ammunition dumps provided many times the Japanese consumption. However, Tokyo was not satisfied with having made one war a paying proposition unless the surplus would finance another.

And there would be another war soon. Already the Germans were interfering, preaching moderation. The friendly English showed no sign of coming out of a neutrality which, under the circumstances, could only benefit Russia, Japan's foremost rival. France was clearly on the Russian side. Japanese statesmen close to the Emperor warned against overstraining the country's resources. Soldiers flushed with victory wanted to drive on to Peking, and on to Irkutsk; naval officers, no less triumphant but more cautious, pleaded for limited objectives; and industrialists made estimates of their potential, which revealed that Japan could not sustain a protracted campaign. The people staged patriotic celebrations and ignored the basic issues. But neither army nor navy men, neither industrialists nor, least of all, the common man, would challenge the Emperor's authority to decide all matters at will.

The partisans of moderation won out, but what the Japanese called moderation was still an outrage to the Chinese.

Preliminary peace parleys started in Hiroshima and were subsequently transferred to Shimonoseki. The first Japanese draft called for a war indemnity of 300,000,000 taels (approximately $225,000,000) for cession of Formosa, the Pescadores, parts of Sinkiang Province, Liaotung Peninsula, Kwantung, and a slice of Manchuria; it asked for abandonment of all Chinese rights and privileges in Korea and, pending fulfillment of all Chinese obligations, for Japanese occupation of Mukden and Wei-hai-wei.

"In this clause," Chinese delegates told their opposite numbers, "China hears Japan saying: 'I am going to be your ever-threatening, perennial foe; my army and my navy will pounce upon your capital, whenever I deem fit; I shall humiliate your Emperor by taking from him his ancestral home.'" And, more soberly, the Chinese explained that money for an indemnity would have to be raised by foreign loans. Financiers charged between 7 and $8\frac{1}{2}$ per cent interest, in addition to heavy discounts on the nominal value of Chinese government bonds. In order to pay Japan 300,000,000 now China would have to repay nearly 700,000,000 over a twenty-year period.

Tokyo reduced its financial claim to 200,000,000 taels and curtailed territorial demands in Manchuria and Kwantung, and with Yamagate's and Oyama's forces poised for attack the Chinese signed.

But then stunned Japanese masses learned that some of the fruits of their victory had been given away, that the Russians would get Liaotung and Port Arthur, that their German friends were taking Chinese Tsingtao and the Bay of Kiaochow, that the English were "leasing" Wei-hai-wei, and that France was about to snatch Kwang Tshou-wang. The neutrals were feasting on pounds of Chinese flesh denied the victors.

An immense wave of resentment against Russia rose. After China had been forced to finance material armaments to fight Russia, Japanese propagandists freely provided emotional equipment. The hatred of Russia grew even further as Siberian agents moved into the vacuum created by China's expulsion from Korea. Japanese ships ruled the coastal waters, Japanese soldiers policed much of the countryside, Japanese trade dominated Korean markets, but Japanese agents could not handle Korean political factions, and Russian intriguers, carrying huge amounts of cash, seemed familiar with the subtleties of Korean political feuds and Korean corruption.

Some Russian agents were Korean-born and told their countrymen glowing tales of opportunities under Russian rule. They profited from every Japanese mistake. The men from Tokyo made many blunders and their cruel doltishness increased as the Russians gained ground. The Queen of Korea was assassinated; Russian agents insisted that the crime could not have occurred without connivance of a ranking Japanese official, and when the weak-minded King sought refuge in the Russian Legation, the prestige of the Japanese in Korea fell to an all-time low.

Japan countered by staging its own campaign of rebellion along the Eastern Chinese Railroad, which, in turn, left the Russians helpless.

And Tokyo watched gleefully as the Russian "burglary of Port Arthur" boomeranged upon its perpetrators. Japanese officers had dismantled fortress equipment and harbor installations, and instead of obtaining a first-class fortress harbor intact the Russians found themselves with yet another construction problem on hand. Naval authorities in St. Petersburg had been urging to abandon Vladivostok as a major Far Eastern strong point, and work on this base had been neglected. Pending the completion of construction in Port Arthur, however, Vladivostok would have to be used and put in shape, which required not only diversion of skilled labor but also of icebreakers needed on Lake Baikal.

Russia now bragged of its skyrocketing industrial output. Statistics showed that steel production had risen from 307,000 tons in 1880 to 897,000 tons in 1895, and coal from 3,289,000 tons in 1880 to 9,314,000 in 1896. This was not sensational, and Tokyo knew that the increase was caused by Western Russian production, and that Siberian industry remained incapable of supplying modest local needs. As long as the Siberian railroad was not completed, European Russian products could not reach the Far East in quantities adequate to supply a big army. Also Russia was still far from being self-supporting industrially.

In 1896 the value of Germany's exports to Russia was 190,170,000 rubles; England was second with 111,309,000, and the U.S.A. third with 65,671,000.

Even had it not been for statistics, American, German, English, and Austrian manufacturers, who offered rolling stock to the Railroad Committee in St. Petersburg, also had agents who dealt with importers and authorities in Tokyo. From these men the Japanese learned that Russian railroad officials had refused to divert any of their European material to Siberia, and that it would take a long time until foreign supplies could bring the Trans-Siberian up to reasonable capacity.

The Railroad Committee, which had learned the technique of propaganda much faster than that of construction, announced that the Trans-Siberian line had carried 1,075,000 passengers and 657,000 tons of freight in 1899, as compared to 417,000 passengers and 184,000 tons three years before. And it also issued statements on equipment and fares which should startle foreigners: Express trains would carry library cars, bathing cars, and similar luxuries which could not even be found in the West's crack trains; tickets from Moscow to Vladivostok would cost only 100 rubles in first-class, sixty in second, and forty in third-class accommodations.

But when the Railroad Committee made this announcement, no ticket would take anybody all the way through Siberia, as the track did not yet run through, and advertised luxuries existed only in the propagandists' imagination. The Japanese realized that transportation figures applied essentially to the westernmost sections of the railroad, 2000 miles away from the potential theater of war. Besides they doubted their accuracy. The Trans-Siberian's rolling stock consisted of 26 imported modern locomotives; 127 thoroughly obsolete engines, useful only for construction and checking; 54 new and 8 old passenger cars; 13 luggage, 13 mail, 2 service cars, in addition to 1773 trucks, which were in an incredible state of dilapidation. The next delivery of rolling stock would include 13 special cars for the transportation of convicts, and one new "church car," for religious services. It was doubtful that such stock could carry upward of a million passengers, and equally doubtful that there were enough people in Siberia to make so many rides.

St. Petersburg also released stories on a sensational rise of immigration to Siberia. In the mid-1890s, it was said, the annual influx averaged 142,000, and an all-time mark of 225,000 had been set. The population of Russia had grown to 130,000,000; this staggering figure should have provided a grandiose pool of settlers, soldiers, and workers. And yet Japanese spies who checked the Eastern Siberian military establishment with pedantical accuracy put its strength at slightly above 20,000. Russia could not seize the initiative unless it had 200,000 men in line and monthly reinforcements of 40,000 available.

The bulk of such armies would have to come from the West. Most recent immigrants into Siberia had been settled in the districts of Tomsk and Tobolsk, where they would be of little use to the Far Eastern forces even if their draft exemptions were disregarded. And whatever Russian propagandists insinuated, their own statistics showed that the new population did not constitute a formidable labor resource. Mushiks were hard to train for industrial purposes, and 87 per cent of Russia's population lived in villages. In the U.S.A., the classical country of colonists, 29.2 per cent resided in towns of 8000 and up; and the percentage of urban population in industrial England, Germany, and France were 71.7, 49.9, and 37.4 respectively.

Japan was confident that it could turn its nationals into modern industrial producers at a much faster rate and in greater number than Russia could build an industrial army. Japanese students of Russian statistics also found that data provided by the Administration of Russian Domains was not consistent with claims by immigration authorities. Of 25,000,000 acres of Crown land set aside in Tomsk and Tobolsk only 17,500,000 had been distributed. Had the immigration figure been correct, not one square foot of Crown land would have been available. And the administrators of the Crown domains did not seem to think that Siberia should be industrialized; otherwise they would not have suggested that the government sponsor a project to irrigate dry Siberian steppes for the benefit of indigenous nomads.

The Japanese party of moderation that prevailed at the end of the Chinese war seemed borne out by developments. Yet some military men championed preventive war against Russia, claiming that Germany would join such a war and that the Germans, satisfied with gains in Europe, would let Japan gobble up whatever was available in Asia.

But the project of preventive war was shelved. As the twentieth century dawned the smoldering Boxer Rebellion in China flared into a fierce blaze, and attention the world over focused on Peking.

The Boxers called themselves I-Ho-Tuan, which meant League for Justice and Mercy. Another version translated it into Righteous Harmonious Fists, or Band, and bowdlerization eventually turned Band into Boxers. The I-Ho-Tuan had been founded in 1770 as a secret religious society, and was later reorganized into a fraternity with changing mundane objectives. More than one century after its foundation the I-Ho-Tuan emerged from obscurity by adopting the motto: "Protect the country—Destroy the foreigners."

Violent mottoes in China were not always indicative of violent designs, or of the intentions of the leaders of the I-Ho-Tuan—Boxers first had no real intention to go to extremes. However, the violently anti-foreign popular trend provided an impulse to Boxer radicalism.

Christians became its principal target. Converted Chinese were dubbed "secondary foreign devils." Missionaries had an age-old distinguished record, but Boxer demagogues proclaimed that these men were symbols of oppression, for they enjoyed the protection of the same foreign soldiery that had humiliated, despoiled, and devastated the country.

For a while the leadership of the Boxers, which included ranking officials and dignitaries of the realm, still kept aloof from abuse of missionaries, but made no attempt to restrain a rank and file that was swelled by backwoods ruffians, outright bandits, and madmen. And as the tempest could not be controlled, some highly placed leaders preferred to have it grind their mills to being engulfed by its squalls. Among the dignitaries who thought so was the Governor of Shantung Province, whose attitude prompted foreign embassies to lodge formal protests with the Peking government. The Governor was discharged, but his successor was an even more radical champion of Boxer extremism. But the great powers were busy dividing China into spheres of interest, which seemed more important than a lengthy controversy over a mere provincial governor.

Conservative members of the Boxer high command took the foreigners' unusual indulgence as an indication that the Boxer movement was stronger than they had realized. Rabble-rousers harangued the rank and file; they told the violent men that the foreigners wanted to break up China and that the devils were in a desperate hurry to do so lest they be swept away by the invincible Boxers. Quacks joined the rabble-rousers, staging crazy rites after which the masses trusted that they were now bulletproof. Late in 1899 an English missionary was murdered. "Secondary foreign devils" were rounded up and subjected to the most gruesome tortures Oriental henchmen's ingenuity could devise.

Prince Tuan, a member of the imperial family, joined the Boxers' ultraradical wing. Dowager Empress Tsu Hsi, back in power eleven years after her formal abdication, sympathized with the torturers.

In early June of 1900 the Boxers laid siege to foreign embassies in Peking. The cathedral grounds, precarious haven of Chinese Christians, were encircled and the German envoy was killed.

The Empress's Privy Council assembled to formulate Crown policies. Tsu Hsi would not let its members debate circumstantially and draft pompous, long-winded statements. Her orders were to kill all foreigners. This was her Crown policy and whoever would try to oppose it would be subject to cruel retaliation. The aging woman raved with delight at the Boxers' violence. It satisfied her gluttonous appetite for revenge of all the iniquities she had had to suffer in the past and which she attributed to the foreigners. It stimulated her craving for exhibitionistic brutality. Her right-hand man, Li-lien-ying, chief of palace eunuchs, would see that those who annoyed the Empress would be subject to methods of execution such as even ancient China had not applied.

But a few weeks after the siege began, military and naval detachments of many nations closed in on Peking, seized its outer fortifications, and forged an iron ring around the besiegers turned besieged.

This should have been the proper moment for a Russian display of strength. St. Petersburg had several divisions ready. Irkutsk clamored that they be supplied with the most spectacular pieces the Putilov artillery plant could produce. Optimists trusted the carrying capacity of the railroad and the Baikal ferry. But the railroad and the ferry were disappointments; and sabotage in Manchuria grew, as Japanese-trained bands were joined by Boxers, and wrecked 540 miles of track.

Russia was no dominant factor in the campaign; and it was little short of insult to Russia that German General Count Waldersee was appointed commander of all international contingents.

The Count had been the spokesman of the German military faction advocating preventive war against Russia, and, like other German champions of aggression, he might alter his projected procedure but never his fundamental objective. He gave participants in the campaign an object lesson in cold-blooded efficiency, which resulted in the capture of Peking on August 14.

The harmony of joint action did not outlast the battle. Legations, hardly freed from the nightmare of lurking murder, officers who had marched, fought, and pillaged side by side soon quarreled over issues that had nothing to do with the protection of their respective nationals or liquidation of the rebellion. Cabinets in distant capitals exchanged angry notes that insinuated that the other party's greedy scheming jeopardized co-operation in Eastern Asia.

In fact everybody had designs on Chinese territory, economic concessions, and whatever privileges could be had, and only the foreigners' rivalry prevented China from losing the last vestige of sovereignty. But even so China had to pay an indemnity of 450,000,000 taels, secured by the revenue from maritime customs. China had to grant foreigners title to maintain and safeguard land communications in its own territory. A two-year embargo was placed on imports of ammunition. China was insolvent, disarmed, and the days of the Manchu dynasty were numbered. But no mighty barbarian conqueror with a subconscious longing for Sinofication, not even a colorful Chinese usurper, would make a bid for the tottering throne.

Constitutional, judicial, and educational reforms could neither save the Manchus nor uphold the monarchy as an institution. A decade later China was a republic. However, the *res publica* was alien to Chinese tradition and Chinese social structure. Still the people could not conceive self-rule beyond clan level. To them a republic meant an illegitimate empire, with the reins passing on to whoever could hold them; to a demagogue, a dictator, or, in the absence of both, to anarchy in a vacuum. Prolonged ordeal had not purified China. Being persistently wronged does not turn men, nations, or governments righteous.

Thirteen months passed after the capture of Peking before the bickering and fidgeting great powers made China sign the latest instrument of surrender; by the time of the signature Russia had won a signal victory that wiped out the failure of transportation.

Manchuria was Russia's.

While other foreign diplomats used threadbare arguments and pettish tricks to have the text of the treaty with China worded in terms which lent themselves to advantageous interpretation, the men from St. Petersburg carried on clandestine negotiations with Peking. On November 1, 1900, they obtained a secret treaty giving them, not only the right to guard and police the Eastern Chinese Railway, but also a free hand in all military, and almost all civilian, matters of Manchuria. China undertook to supply Russian occupation forces there; and while Western contingents waited for shipment to their respective home countries, a total of 41,000 men from Siberia—27 battalions of infantry, 26 *sotnias* (squadrons) of cavalry, and eight batteries of field artillery—established themselves in Manchuria along the railroad and in the main cities.

For more than two months the secret did not leak. An emboldened Russian Government asked for, and received, another concession. But this time the

English learned of it, for the Sankhaiwan–Taku railroad, which Russia had been authorized to police, was on Chinese territory that London considered part of its sphere of interest.

A violent English protest drew a caustic Russian reply. The matter of this railroad, according to St. Petersburg, was not connected with the Boxer Rebellion and not subject to joint action. But eventually Russia abandoned the concession in return for a foothold in Chinese-controlled Tibet. Great-power politics wanted to subject China to an "open-door policy" which would give everybody the free economic run of the empire. Russia could not compete with Western industry and commerce, and Secretary of the Treasury Witte, a member of the Siberian Railroad Committee, negotiated yet another agreement with Peking, which gave Russia a virtual trade monopoly in Northern China.

Japanese intelligence services learned of it immediately after the signature. Tokyo's fierce *démarche* in March 1901 was followed by protests from the U.S.A., Great Britain, Germany, Austria-Hungary, and Italy. And, as in the case of the Sankhaiwan–Taku railway, Russia displayed sweet reasonableness, and, while denying that the agreement violated the "open-door" principle, agreed to have it canceled. Full control of Manchuria should give Russia opportunity to interfere with foreign competition.

Tokyo did not trust Russian reasonableness and reinforced its garrisons in Southern Korea. St. Petersburg made no countermove. On January 30, 1902, England and Japan signed a five-year treaty of alliance, subject to automatic extension if not expressly denounced. The spheres of interest of the contracting parties were respecified: England recognized Japan's special interests in Korea; should one party be involved in war with a third power, the other was bound to a policy of friendly neutrality, and would have to render active assistance should the third power be joined by another ally.

Russia stated that the terms of its alliance with France applied also to the Far East.

France was uneasy. England was its trusted friend in the West, a potential supporter against German aggression. It would be disastrous if a Far Eastern war turned England into a foe, and it would be almost equally disastrous to antagonize Russia, the other bulwark against Germany, by ambiguous statements.

Eventually Russia promised to evacuate Manchuria. By October 8, 1902, Mukden should be freed; on April 8, 1903, Russian troops would abandon all railroad lines that were not part of the Eastern Chinese system, and also on that day, the Russian garrison would leave Heilungkiang (Tsitsihar).

However, this pledge was not made to any great power but to prostrate China; and it contained two clauses that made the document hardly worth the paper upon which it was written: Russia would keep protecting the Eastern Chinese Railroad; and no withdrawals of troops would take place should actions by other powers make such step inadvisable.

The Russian Government at once claimed that bands organized and equipped by Japan jeopardized the security of Manchuria.

October 8, 1902, came and went. Russia had a few towns evacuated with much display, and reoccupied immediately afterward without ado. Russia moved a few regiments from Manchuria to Port Arthur. A temporary reduction of the Manchurian garrisons to about 30,000 was made up by reinforcements from Siberia. Japan wrote angry notes, which did not impress Russia.

Tokyo wanted London to press Russia to move out and stay out of Manchuria. England, however, did not want to antagonize Russia needlessly. In 1902 the English and Americans were anxious to have economic barriers lifted in Manchuria.

Russian generals scorned the English as hucksters, and betrayers of the white race, and they considered Americans to be no better than Britishers. Progressive statesmen in Russia cautioned old-fashioned swashbucklers by explaining that in view of Russia's economic plight investment-minded Westerners should not be discouraged by belligerent abuse.

But official St. Petersburg displayed studied coolness toward English and American businessmen in Manchuria, and expelled all Japanese operators, contending that they were spies.

Japan took the insult in silence, but there was a presage of revenge in Tokyo's attitude. The English-speaking nations seemed awed by Russia's defiance.

Early in 1903, St. Petersburg announced that unless China offered effective guarantees for the security of the railroad Manchuria would not be evacuated. And since China had no guarantee to offer, the Russian unilateral announcement legalized the *de facto* occupation of Manchuria. Japan still restrained itself. But it signed a new commercial agreement with China, including trade concessions in the Manchurian districts of Mukden and Antung, as a token of its non-recognition of the Russian status there. The United States followed suit, optimistically assuming that Mukden and Antung would eventually be restored to China.

The Manchurian powder keg, filled to the brim, was neither removed nor covered, but suddenly the shower of sparks drove in a different direction. The high-explosive danger spot was Northern Korea and the Yalu River.

Throughout the Boxer Rebellion and the international diplomatic antics that had followed both Russia and Japan had remained in Korea, the Russians in the north, the Japanese in the south. Now Japanese industrialists acquired timber concessions in the Yalu basin and moved into this Russian-occupied territory. The Russians produced another concession dating back seven years, which gave a Russian company exclusive title to exploitation of Yalu forests. The Japanese disputed the authenticity of the Russian document, whereupon the occupiers, charging that the alleged timber industrialists were working for the Tokyo General Staff, asked them to leave. In fact the Russian document was a fabrication and the Japanese were spies, just as the Japanese "businessmen" in Manchuria had been.

Radical military men in Tokyo stormed that the moderates' opposition to preventive war had put the country in a mortifying position and that further stalling would be treasonable. They did not want to see the machinery of alliances in motion; Japan should fight, conquer, and rule, alone.

The Japanese Government, swayed by the radicals but not quite determined to attack before the highest state of preparedness had been reached, filed notes of protest, the tone of which grew shriller with every delivery.

The war party in St. Petersburg asked for an even higher pitch of diplomatic language; and the government, having learned that one ounce of forceful language could substitute for one pound of material strength, answered protests in kind.

Russian intelligence service knew that the Japanese *ordre de bataille* was ready and that only a few more army and navy units had to be set up before it became fully operable. The Russian general staff, however, did not yet know whether to fight a fundamentally offensive or defensive war. The Transbaikal line was still an enigma, and in the seclusion of pompously furnished offices in St. Petersburg, generals, admirals, diplomats, and governors exchanged vituperous charges of incompetence and seemed more anxious to destroy one another than to defeat Japan.

The official Russian news agency again struck up the theme of Siberian wealth and colonization. All Siberian gold mines combined actually produced only sixty-six pounds of gold annually at undisclosed costs, but undeveloped gold-bearing districts were said to exist on the Lena, the Yenisei, and the Amur, and on the northwest coast of the Sea of Okhotsk; diligent geologists even discovered gold in Port Arthur. Fifteen-year leases were offered, but companies who started operating new deposits were dissatisfied and no further serious bids were made. People abroad learned that thirty stations had been opened in the western sector of the Trans-Siberian Railroad, where immigrants could obtain medical help and food at low prices, and that three orphanages, one hundred churches, and seventy-three schools had been added to Siberia's institutions.

But only martial news would satisfy the appetite of an international audience thrilled by tales of Korean treasures for which two spectacular gladiators were set to cross swords. Korea made headlines.

Yet Korean timber concessions involved capital investments of no more than $3,000,000 and a labor force of a few thousand men. Every substantial operation on a Western stock exchange was more important than the Korean timber affair, and yet many people believed that peace or war depended solely on timber from the Yalu.

Later in the year 1903 the controversy became less stringent. Champions of peace here and there began to trust that Russia and Japan could eventually be reconciled and that, with the Korean issue out of the way, nothing could stop the march of the millennium.

CHAPTER FIFTY-EIGHT War was inevitable. Willful men in Tokyo and in St. Petersburg had so decided.

Had they wanted to justify their sinister decision, they might have claimed that the other side had aggressive intentions and that no part of China's realm should be permitted to fall into hostile hands. But the men in the two capitals would no longer tailor legal cloaks for an action that to them had become a functional necessity. Whatever they still did short of opening hostilities was exclusively designed at improving odds.

The Japanese Army was built up into a force of 115 battalions, 55 squadrons, and 114 batteries; a total of 200,000, with 320,000 trained reserves available. Most important, it would take no more than two weeks to land huge invasion forces on the Asiatic mainland.

The Japanese Navy had come a long way since the Chinese war. Japan had 8 battleships, 4 of them 15,000-ton wagons of latest design, 6 modern 9000-ton heavy cruisers, 14 cruisers of lesser displacement, 22 gunboats, 15 destroyers, and 65 torpedo boats. A large fleet of troop ships was ready to sail; and more men-of-war were under construction.

Russia had the largest standing army in the world. About 1,000,000 men were under arms. A general mobilization would bring the number to three million, and drafting of untrained men between the ages of twenty and forty could carry numerical strength to figures which almost defied imagination, and certainly defied the capacity of Russian arms production.

The Russian Navy of the Far East had a tonnage of 183,000, 63,000 less than the Japanese fleet, and Russian sources claimed that a balance of power would be established by sending another twenty-six units to the Pacific. The Tsar's battleships were neither as large nor as fast as the Japanese, and their armament was not quite up to Japanese standards. However, the Russian Admiralty trusted that Japan would have to use most of its potent units to protect troop transports, while Russia would carry its troops by land and have all its ships ready for mobile warfare.

In the late spring of 1903 sixteen Russian infantry battalions and six batteries went east. The transportation schedule was not kept despite fair weather in the Baikal region; this did not augur well for large-scale troop transfers.

Ranking generals from European military districts argued against indiscriminate shipments to Siberia. They had no artillerists, engineers, and railroad troops to spare, and agreed only reluctantly to having a small number of hand-picked officers and drill sergeants from these services transferred to Siberia.

Compulsory military service was introduced in the Russian East, and draft exemptions were disregarded. The average recruits were illiterate and completely unfamiliar with modern mechanical tools. Drill sergeants used knouts to whip savage yokels into cannoneers, sappers, and communication soldiers, but Japanese spies reported that target practice with new 76-mm. cannon outside of Irkutsk had shown the Siberians as poor marksmen.

Observers wondered about the Siberians' soldierly morale. Recruits were trained to shout *urra!* at the top of their lungs, and they shouted just as they would execute right or left turns. But the men were also indoctrinated with two fears: that of torture by the enemy if they surrendered, and of equally colorful maltreatment by field gendarmes behind their own lines if they ran away. This indoctrination was more effective than outsiders had thought. Drill compressed the men into a strait jacket of coherence and manikin-like maneuvering. Devotion above and beyond the call of duty was not expected.

Late in 1903, Russia's main Eastern forces consisted of 62 battalions, 36 squadrons, 19 field batteries, 17 companies of fortress artillery, 44 companies of railroad troops, engineers and sappers, and a lone machine-gun company. Half of the total was garrisoned in Transbaikalia, the rest in Manchuria and Port Arthur. In addition 4 mixed brigades policed the Eastern Chinese Railway and 2 brigades were stationed in Vladivostok. The combined number was 140,000; 20,000 infantry were on their way through Siberia; 40,000 more were gathered in Europe for transportation east. A Siberian mobilization would produce 80,000 trained reservists.

Derogatory reports on lack of co-operation among Siberian authorities had caused the establishment of a viceroyship in the Far East by a ukase of August 13, 1903.

The Viceroy was in full charge of Transbaikalia, the Maritime Province, and all recently acquired Chinese and Korean territories. He would act as joint commander of all land and sea forces. Admiral Jevgeni Alekseiev was appointed to the office.

The fifty-eight-year-old Admiral had been commander of Port Arthur, where he had collected so many kickbacks from construction firms and purveyors of supplies that his estate ran into millions. However, this was investigated only after Alekseiev's dishonorable discharge following Russian defeats.

The Viceroy was not assigned to negotiate with Japan. This task of temporizing fell upon General Kuropatkin, member of the Siberian Railroad Committee, Minister of War, Designate Commander of Russian Far Eastern land forces, and, as known only to himself and one other person, the highest-bribed general in the Tsar's army. That other person, who, after discussing delivery of English-made ammunition, had "forgotten" a wallet containing the record bribe in Kuropatkin's office, was the legendary Sir Basil Zaharoff.

After inspecting Siberian and Manchurian establishments and finding them not up to requirements Kuropatkin proceeded to Tokyo, where he told politely unresponsive Japanese statesmen that, in principle, Russia did not object to the admission of Japanese businessmen to Manchuria, but that this matter was for the Chinese to decide, since Russia might eventually evacuate the region.

From Tokyo, Kuropatkin returned to Manchuria to establish provisional field headquarters. He informed St. Petersburg that Dalny, another port on "leased" Chinese territory, would have to be built up at top speed, that a six-months supply of food and ammunition for 300,000 men would have to be stored in Eastern Siberia, and that he needed two crack infantry brigades with mountain artillery for a Korean campaign.

In the fall of 1903, Russian naval units massed in the waters of Port Arthur, Japanese battle wagons maneuvered in the Straits of Tshushima, and Japanese troop ships entered Pusan harbor. The troops they carried established themselves on outlying islands, and the Russians countered by occupying remote areas of Northern Korea.

Less than three months after Kuropatkin's travel to Japan, Viceroy Alekseiev proclaimed that the evacuation of Manchuria was an internal Russian affair with which no outsider would be permitted to meddle, and he said, ominously, that banditry along the railroad was more rampant than ever. And yet it was still peace as the year of 1903 came to a close and exchanges between the governments of Russia and Japan continued.

The topic of abortive diplomatic parleys was again Korea.

Russian notes were tuned to reasonableness. The Japanese, however, dropped the last vestiges of Oriental courtesy and threatened to establish themselves on the Yalu estuary. The Russians suggested mildly that Japan confine herself to territory south of Seoul. Tokyo countered vitriolically that Japanese moves in Korea were none of Russia's business, and in turn suggested that Russian troops withdraw behind the legal border of Siberia, evacuating both Korea and Manchuria; Korea should become a Japanese protectorate.

St. Petersburg experts on foreign policy were positive that the establishment of a Japanese protectorate would antagonize other nations interested in Asia, and bar all economic aid that might otherwise be extended to Tokyo by England and the United States.

The Tsar received a confidential report from a member of his suite, Admiral Abasa, to the effect that Japan's economy was weak and that lack of foreign support soon would bring the country to bay. "The Japanese are neither merchants nor colonizers," the Admiral said. "They would gain no advantage by occupying all of Korea." Nicholas II also read that recent Japanese impudence was largely caused by Tokyo's erroneous belief that Russia was afraid of war. Abasa suggested making one last moderate and reasonable-sounding proposal and, after Tokyo had rejected it, to force Japan's hand by suspending parleys. Japan would have to go to war penniless, or beat a disorderly diplomatic retreat, or challenge the world by proclaiming the protectorate, followed by the landing of large invasion forces.

Korea would turn into a deathtrap of the Japanese Army, the graveyard of the Island Empire's continental ambitions. On January 14, 1904, the Tsar sent a personal note to Viceroy Alekseiev, stating that it was desirable to have Japan open aggression. "Don't interfere with their landings in South Korea," the note concluded. "But should their forces cross the 38th parallel, you are authorized to attack without waiting for them to fire the first shot. I rely on you. May God help you."

A whimsical, nagging, and melodramatic Viceroy passed the order on to the designated commanders of land and sea forces, General Kuropatkin and Admiral Stark, who tersely commented that the Tsar's will would be carried out to the letter.

In fact the Tsar's will was a strategic absurdity. It gave the enemy time to array its armies along the thirty-eighth parallel without Russian interference and to attack at the most propitious moment.

Kuropatkin assembled his forces far north of the crucial parallel, well beyond the Yalu, inside Manchuria. The General disguised his desire to gain time by a display of perfectionism. He bombarded St. Petersburg with requests that everything be improved: recruiting, transportation, and supply.

Russian Admiral Stark concentrated his main units in Port Arthur and had a small squadron proceed to Vladivostok.

Japan presented its demands on Russia in ultimatum form. When they were rejected, Japan severed diplomatic relations, on February 5, 1904.

Kuropatkin did not consider this a danger signal, but Stark pondered over taking the fleet to sea. Alekseiev was in no mood to take such a risk; having set up his own headquarters in Port Arthur, he would not bare the fortress of its naval arm. Stark was replaced by Admiral Makarov. On February 8 the Japanese main fleet under Admiral Heihachiro Togo steamed north through the Yellow Sea. Later that day Togo detached his torpedo boats as vanguard, headed for Port Arthur.

A single cruiser could work havoc with a torpedo-boat flotilla. But no Russian warships were sighted. Night had long fallen when the blacked-out boats approached the port. Searchlights, poorly operated by drowsy fortress crews, did not graze the units. Japanese commanders carried sketches drawn by Japanese spies marking the berth of every Russian ship.

These spies had also reported that the entrance of the port was not mined. Japanese naval officers could hardly believe that this was true, but orders were not to slow down until the torpedo boats were within range and the Japanese furrowed the breakwaters at top speed. There was no shock, no sound, as the greyhounds of the sea entered the inner harbor and, outlined against the nocturnal skies, the Russian warships became visible on the moorings marked in the sketches.

A minute later the torpedoes struck home.

Flashes lit up the harbor, terrific explosions rocked the silence, columns of water sprayed over the torpedo boats as they effected masterful turns. Then the forts opened up, erratic beams of searchlights tapped the foaming waters. The torpedo boats made their way out of the pandemonium to the outer bay without loss, their skippers trusting that they had destroyed the entire Russian fleet.

But while the wires carried the news of Russian annihilation all over the world, Togo's main fleet arrived off Port Arthur and was met by withering fire, not only from land, but also from battleships inside the harbor.

The Russian Navy had suffered grievous loss, and had ceased to be a major offensive weapon, but it was still in being and formidable enough to force the Japanese Navy to blockade Port Arthur.

The morning after the attack Viceroy Alekseiev left the fortress for Kuropatkin's headquarters. As if by the touch of the magic wand the neighborhood of Port Arthur was infested by aggressive, copiously armed, and organized Chunchuse bands which also swarmed out over Southern Manchuria.

Alekseiev told Kuropatkin that the fortifications of Port Arthur were far from perfect, that the morale of the 37,000-men garrison was low, and that General Stoessel, the commander, was restless.

Kuropatkin visualized the Japanese Army under General Nogi, whom he knew to be assigned to attack Port Arthur, seizing the fortress by a coup and dashing north to join other Japanese forces in a drive that would destroy his own army. But except for Nogi's assignment Kuropatkin knew little about Japanese plans.

The Russian intelligence service, well informed about political trends and intrigues, had been unable to pierce the last screen of secrecy guarding the Japanese *ordre de bataille*. However, rumors in the General's headquarters had it that the location of every single Russian company was marked on the maps in Japanese General Staff offices.

Admiral Makarov ordered the Vladivostok squadron to intercept Japanese troop ships in Southern Korean waters. But when the Russian ships approached the Straits of Tshushima, they did not sight transports bound for Pusan.

The Japanese General Staff had chosen Inchon as a disembarkation point. One Russian cruiser eventually ventured to Inchon and was promptly sunk by Japanese covering forces. No Russian soldier interfered with the landings, no unit from Manchuria moved into the rear of General Nogi's siege army under deployment.

Kuropatkin now wanted to concentrate his armies deep inside Manchuria, as far north as Harbin, new railroad town, bustling with pubs, brothels, and honky-tonks. The General thought of nothing but retreat, a Far Eastern version of the strategy of 1812. But retreat from Harbin would have abandoned the link between Manchuria and the Maritime Province, and so had to be ruled out. Next the General considered concentration around Mukden, but Mukden was allegedly honeycombed with Japanese agents.

Fear of spies eventually drove Kuropatkin to a spot only 100 miles north of the Yalu. He established headquarters near Liaoyang, and ordered the Third Siberian Corps under General Sassulitsh to detail one brigade to reconnoiter the Yalu Valley and fight a delaying action should the enemy cross the river. Sassulitsh had had no previous opportunity to gain laurels, but he held the Order of St. George and his *gasconnade* that the knights of that order never retreated was duly recorded as an expression of traditional Russian valor, implanted in a Siberian corps.

Russian gloom gave way to optimism because the approaching spring would change Korean roads into quagmires over which Japanese transport columns might be unable to advance. It was freely predicted that later in the season, when the mire would turn into dust, ten Russian army corps would sweep down upon the Japanese First Army, burst through all of Korea, and down to Port Arthur. Fundamental transportation problems were said to have been solved already.

In Liaoyang officers toasted the magnificent achievement at Lake Baikal. Against the advice of construction engineers who predicted untold disaster the military had a double track of rails laid across the frozen lake. The operation took only 18 days. On March 1 trains started running on the unique short cut.

But on March 27 the angry volcano caused fissures in the forty-five-inch-thick ice. Traffic had to be discontinued after some casualties had been suffered and several locomotives lost. Altogether 16,067 soldiers, some 3000 horses, and 24,570 long tons of supplies had been transported over the lake track. These were not really impressive figures, but the few officers who realized this fact did not dampen the general enthusiasm. Should there be another winter campaign, they said, soldiers would be trained to be less indolent than they had been in March 1904, when they had installed stoves in their cattle cars, reducing their carrying capacity from forty-two to twenty men. Transportation from Western to Eastern Siberia took four to five weeks; but the men were not supposed to enjoy such extravagant comfort as space-consuming heating accommodations.

Between February 8 and December 29, 1904, the Trans-Siberian carried 10,800 officers, 537,000 men, 118,000 horses, and 245,700 long tons of military freight. These figures covered trips both ways. The effects of the strain on the railroad were little short of disastrous. Almost all the rails had to be changed, the rolling stock was in complete disrepair, and the Siberian fuel situation chaotic. Timber prices rose 2000 per cent, and the equipment of Siberian coal mines was practically ruined by inexpert round-the-clock operation. Rehabilitation of the railroad consumed funds which had been allotted for the construction of a second track on the eve of the war. This second track from the Urals to Vladivostok figured in several later budgets of the Russian Empire. Allotments were invariably used up, but the Trans-Siberian remained essentially a single-track line. The feature was carried over to Bolshevik accounts, and yet, with the entire population of Russia turning into a forced-labor pool, completion of the second track remained a phantom until the Red Russian Government solved the problem by stating that the second track did exist, discounting whatever claims to the contrary a handful of foreign travelers who trusted their eyes rather than their ears might make.

The spring of 1905 came to Manchuria and no major land action had yet occurred. Viceroy Alekseiev now called Port Arthur's preparedness exemplary and advised Kuropatkin to attack and crush the forces of General Nogi between the fortress and the Russian mobile army. But Kuropatkin waited, and the angry Viceroy communicated with the Tsar's military advisers, painting the over-all situation in bright colors and asking that it be exploited by a drive on Port Arthur.

General Sassulitsh reported that his advanced brigade had not found a single Japanese soldier on either bank of the Yalu. The Russians confined themselves to watching the south bank through binoculars. They overlooked superb camouflages covering the large number of Japanese troops that concentrated for the first battle.

Sassulitsh's detailed brigade of 7000 camped in poorly camouflaged positions, when Kuroki's army, 40,000 strong, debouched from its take-off points and crossed the river at sunrise, May 1.

The Russians' actions were primitive, but they did fight. The Siberian soldier had no stake in the war and no loyalty to the men who made him fight it, but, thinking that flight or surrender would be equally fatal, he clung to the ground on which he stood.

But General Sassulitsh, suddenly oblivious of the Knighthood of St. George, ordered retreat at a time when the brigade was intact. The command resulted in panic. Before order was restored the brigade had lost more than one third of its effectives. Japanese losses totaled 1100.

General Sassulitsh brought the evil tidings to headquarters. Depressing as they were, strategic implications should not have shaken the commander in chief. The brigade had not been supposed to fight more than a rear-guard action. But General Kuropatkin called his corps commanders to discuss immediate retreat from Liaoyang. The meeting was joined by an irate Viceroy, who had become the object of dislike by everybody in headquarters. Ashen-faced, Kuropatkin paced the map room, stopping occasionally to point at rear areas in which the Army might concentrate, but changed his mind about locations before the other officers could check the areas. He spoke with a low voice, repeating the ominous word "retreat" over and over again.

A German observer with the Japanese armies, Colonel Geadke, wrote later that the Russians lost crucial battles, not because they were beaten, but because their commander lacked the will to win. Kuropatkin wrote a book about the war, which was published in English in 1909. He admitted having made mistakes. Nowhere, however, did he explain the strange metamorphosis of his spirit. As a young officer, he had seen action in the Balkans and in Turkestan, where he gained the reputation of a daredevil and promotion to generalcy at thirty-four. The Kuropatkin of the Japanese war certainly was not even a shadow of the brigadier general a score of years before. Sensation-minded reporters have insinuated that the Russian commander had been bribed by the Japanese. But whatever bribe Kuropatkin accepted for buying excellent English cannon, it can be ruled out that he sold his country to its enemy.

He never faced a tribunal for either fraud or treason. Still on the active list in 1914, he was subsequently appointed Governor General of Turkestan and remained in office until the Bolshevik seizure of power. Not even the Bolsheviks arrested him. He became a village teacher, and died in inconspicuous poverty in 1921. One explanation of his failure would be psychic rather than psychological. It could be that the prowling ghosts of destruction and futility of human effort which pervaded Siberia had incapacitated Kuropatkin. Siberia was stronger than any one man.

The meeting in Liaoyang was still in session when a courier arrived at headquarters with an order signed by the Tsar. The Army should relieve Port Arthur at once.

Kuropatkin shook his head after reading the note and passing it on to the Viceroy. Alekseiev declaimed that the Tsar's words were sacred commands; he raged that the General would be held responsible for the fate of the fortress, and, in the same breath, reminded him that he, Viceroy Alekseiev, was the highest military and naval authority in the East. But he did not actually assume command. General Stakelberg, commander of the First Siberian Corps, Siberian-born Linevitsh, whose Ussuri army had not yet crossed from Maritime Province into Manchuria, and Sassulitsh, who was regaining his loquacity, argued against relief of Port Arthur, against retreat, but also against advance. The wrangle produced no workable solution.

The Army remained in the Liaoyang area, waiting for the enemy to attack, and Kuropatkin was not recalled.

The Japanese General Staff learned of the unavailing conference at Russian headquarters. Kuroki's First Army was joined by Oku's Second, and Nozu's Fourth, and Marshal Oyama led the group in one of the most pedantically organized and slowest advances in military history. The troops covered an average of little more than a mile a day, but the egotism of the Japanese generals, inflated by intelligence reports, made them certain that the Russians would not even try to take the initiative.

On August 26, Marshal Oyama opened the assault on the Russian echelon, which was hinged on Liaoyang. Four days after the fighting started the attackers had gained practically no ground and Kuropatkin had not yet committed substantial reserves. Then Russian cavalry patrols reported that a gap had opened between Kuroki's and Nozu's armies. A few hours later infantry confirmed the existence of a gap which seemed to be widening by the hour.

The moment had come for a counteroffensive with ambitious objectives. Kuropatkin seemed to realize it; the men in the western sector of the line knew it. But the commander in chief first wanted to build up his mobile reserves to the limit by shortening his line.

Shortening the line implied local withdrawals and concentrations to the rear. Startled regimental commanders, brigadiers, and generals of divisions received orders to retreat instead of the signal to advance. They made inquiries and waited for clarification; and as they waited, marching schedules worked out by Kuropatkin's staff went out of gear. When eventually the moves went under way, the timetables were in confusion. One brigade crashed into another marching unit. Russian soldiers fired at each other. The brigade broke into panic, clogging the roads. Most of the day was lost by regrouping, and the gap in the Japanese lines had closed. Yet it was covered but by a thin screen of infantry and an immediate attack still would have resulted in a break-through. In a calculated risk Oyama pressed his attack on Russian positions in other sectors. The Russians hurled the Japanese back south of Liaoyang, but lost the Yentai Mines; one Russian cavalry charge collapsed. The Yentai Mines were not really important, and Kuropatkin still had plenty of cavalry.

However, Kuropatkin, who had summoned his corps commanders, seemed to have eyes and ears only for adverse reports, and kept talking about nothing but adversity. The corps commanders exchanged charges of incompetence, and blamed each other for setbacks.

At dawn, at last, Kuropatkin disposed of his reserves but not for attack. He ordered that all uncommitted divisions move into line at once to cover a general retreat toward Mukden.

The general did not have the will power to win a battle that still could have been won. Russian losses of 19,000 were more than outbalanced by 23,000 Japanese casualties. Kuropatkin's forces outnumbered the foe by five to four.

And while the Japanese advanced into Manchuria, trusting that there were no limits to what they could do, more clouds gathered on Port Arthur.

Admiral Makarov had tried a few sorties from the blockaded harbor, but what remained of his fleet could not challenge Togo's 15,000-tonners. On April 13, Makarov's flagship and another Russian battle wagon had struck mines. Makarov went down with his craft. The other ship was permanently disabled.

Togo also had lost two capital ships to mines, but new and even better units were coming from Japanese shipyards.

On August 10 a huge Japanese transport fleet began to unload fresh divisions and 280-mm. siege howitzers near the fortress. The elusive Russian squadron from Vladivostok was ordered out for a surprise attack on Togo's fleet, while the squadron from Port Arthur made an all-out sally. The units from Vladivostok were intercepted by fast Japanese cruisers, and only scattered remnants joined the Russian ships from Port Arthur as they limped back into the blockaded harbor, battered by Togo's unscathed battle wagons.

The garrison had suffered few losses, but ammunition supplies were not as formidable as they had seemed to be when the struggle opened. Leftovers from Chinese dumps, which the Japanese had not destroyed prior to the evacuation, turned out to be composed of duds and missiles that damaged the barrels of their own guns. There was plenty of food, but storage accommodations were poor; gastric diseases spread and hospital installations were inadequate.

Fortress commander Stoessel was both uninspiring and uninspirable. As Nogi's troops tightened the siege ring, news from St. Petersburg reached Stoessel that a huge armada assembled in the Baltic was ready to sail to Port Arthur. He was reminded of his duty to hold the place at all cost.

General Nogi had the Russian message decoded. He would not temporize and let the new fleet take shelter in the fortress harbor.

Soon after the Battle of Liaoyang, waves of *banzai*-shouting Japanese infantrymen hurled themselves against the forts; the garrisons stood up in the carnage until they were engulfed by hand-grenade-throwing suicide squads.

Staggering losses could not dampen the fury of the assault. The Japanese were in a frenzy to kill and get killed. Death became a goal no less coveted, and more decorous even, than conquest. Fort after fort fell, their escarpments filled to the brim with dead Japanese. In November Nogi's fanatics invested the Russian key position on 203 Meter Hill (618 ft. hill). Staunch Siberians tenaciously clung to every inch of the blood-drenched slope. Inch by inch the attackers, crawling and stamping over corpses, pressed on, and on December 15 they reached the crest.

Draft animals could hardly have carried the huge howitzers to the top of 203 Meter Hill, but small, groaning cannoneers pushed the guns into positions commanding the port, and the northern and northwestern sectors of the land defenses, where Russian battalions still stood and died lethargically.

On January 2, 1905, General Stoessel surrendered.

The victors took 23,491 prisoners. They captured 546 guns with about 150 rounds of ammunition apiece, and whatever remained of Russian naval units; floating junk rather than fighting ships. Japanese combat losses were between 55,000 and 65,000, in addition to several thousand victims of the beriberi disease.

In St. Petersburg the surrender was denounced as one individual's act of depravity. General Stoessel was said to have capitulated while in Manchuria Russian forces were irresistibly advancing, and in the Indian Ocean a mighty Russian fleet was on its way to sway the tide of naval war in the Far East. He was blamed for having jeopardized victory on land and on sea.

After his return from Japanese captivity, the general was tried by a military tribunal. He insisted, wearily, that the garrison had been decimated by loss of 31,306 dead and wounded. The figure contained many duplications, as a great number of men had been wounded more than once, and the court also paid no heed to the general's plea that Port Arthur's plight had warranted nothing but surrender. The sentence was demotion and ten years' detention.

The fate of Stoessel neither satisfied nor shocked the average Russian. By the time of his trial every phase of the Japanese war was already considered *nitshevo*. Russians do not brood about defeats.

But the charge that the fall of Port Arthur prevented victory was not justified. No fleet could have entered the blockaded port without previously defeating the Japanese Navy. Later events have proved that the Russian squadron was not up to this task. And the course of the war in Manchuria was another evidence of Russian inability to vanquish.

The "irresistible advance of the Russian forces" in Manchuria was said to have started late in October, with Kuropatkin's forces, reorganized into a group of three armies under Generals Linevitsh, Grippenberg, and Kaulbars steam-rolling south with 300,000 men and powerful artillery.

In his field headquarters, however, a melancholy commander in chief, surrounded by a swaggering, quarreling staff, harassed by tempestuous but altogether incongruous orders from the Tsar's military cabinet, parroted the motto "offensive" and did not know how to carry it out.

Nobody who kept in contact with the commander in chief could have had delusions about his state of mind. But his subordinates preferred a game of intrigues, which could bring dividends later, to assuming responsibility which might bring disaster now, and the Tsar's advisers not only refrained from amending buoyant generalities on attack into an elaborate order, but did not even make suggestions as to who should replace Kuropatkin. And as Russian communiqués featured advances, the main Russian forces waited south of Mukden. Drafted Siberian mushiks, accustomed to spending most of the cold season indoors, believed that they were living in winter quarters.

There were no winter quarters for the victors of Port Arthur. General Nogi's soldiers enjoyed only a brief rest before marching north to join Oku's forces on the left wing of the Japanese array. Tokyo was not only Spartan-minded; it was impatient, as extended communication lines and thinning reserves made it imperative to seek a quick decision.

General Grippenberg's seven Russian divisions faced two divisions from Oku's army. On January 26, Oku ordered probing attacks against Russian outposts to keep Grippenberg off balance until the junction with Nogi's army was completed. The attacks were easily repulsed, and local pursuits of driven-off Japanese set Grippenberg's numerical superiority in motion.

A terrific storm broke as the Russians moved. Blinding masses of snow, whipped into hails of ice shrapnel by hurricanes from the distant Baikal region, turned the battlefield of Sandepu into a subzero witches' caldron in which the roar of artillery and the death cries of men were drowned out by infernal howl.

In the opaqueness of snow soldier butchered soldier, and the weight of numbers was telling. Oku faced annihilation and Marshal Oyama could do no more than order diversionary attacks on the Russian center, none of which gained ground.

Kuropatkin considered Oyama's diversionary attacks to herald an all-out assault on positions the strength of which he did not trust. He used the cover of storm to disengage all his three armies, and to fall back to a forty-seven-mile-long line anchored upon Mukden.

Japanese tactical defeat of Sandepu paved the way to the Japanese victory of Mukden.

The battle for Mukden began on February 25, 1905, and lasted through March 10. Some 600,000 soldiers were engaged on both sides. Russian losses were 96,500. The Japanese reported 41,000 casualties.

At Mukden, as at Liaoyang, Kuropatkin did not fight to the finish. But the situation of his armies, which had not been properly deployed when Oyama struck, was worse than it had been in the first great battle of the war. Kuropatkin was relieved from command and replaced by Linevitsh. The Russian armies would have to stay on the defensive until adequate reinforcements reached Manchuria.

Field Marshal Oyama, a student of German Field Marshal von Moltke's victory over the French at Sedan, had hoped to achieve a similar success. But Mukden was not another Sedan. The Russian Army was not destroyed. And should the Russian fleet reach Vladivostok and raid Japanese transportation, Japanese supplies might fall below the minimum volume and Manchuria would yet have to be abandoned. Oyama knew it well, and so did the Admiralty and the government of Japan.

The Russian fleet under Admiral Rozhestvensky had started out from the Baltic in October 1904. It consisted of a colorful assortment of recent battleships and cruisers; of armored antiques which were floating batteries at best; of a few modern destroyers alongside river gunboats that under normal conditions no skipper would have taken out to sea. This array was joined by a ramshackle fleet of colliers and supply ships, that slowed the pace to a crawl.

On October 26 the Russian fleet reached the Dogger Bank, sixty miles off the coast of Northumberland. Dense fog blanketed the shallow waters; jittery captains pondered over rumors that Japanese torpedo boats operating from secret bases in England were infesting the North Sea. One Russian observer reported ominous low contours behind wavering vapors of fog. The skipper of his craft ordered his gun crews to open up. The Russians scored several hits on the ghost flotilla, which turned out to consist of English trawlers. Two subjects of His Britannic Majesty were killed.

There were violent outbursts of English indignation and talk of war. The English Government sent stern notes of protest. St. Petersburg hastened to agree to arbitration by an internal commission which met at Vigo, Spain, termed the incident an unprovoked act of aggression, and awarded £65,000 to the victims.

Rozhestvensky proceeded, circling Western Europe and Africa. He was barred from English ports, not particularly welcome in French colonies, and forced to take supplies wherever and at whatever price they could be obtained from tough Germans, shrewd Portuguese, and cosmopolitan brokers.

In Madagascar he learned of the fall of Port Arthur. A few days later news reached the fleet of the Bloody Sunday in St. Petersburg, of crowds led by the priest Gapon petitioning the Tsar, of soldiers firing at them at the gates of the Winter Palace. The news had a tinge of revolution. Russian sailors were less disciplined than Russian soldiers, but there was no outbreak of mutiny. But there was some unrest in a fleet of cruisers that, under the command of Vice-Admiral Nebogatov, was on its way to join Rozhestvensky via the Suez Canal.

From the Mediterranean to the Indian Ocean globe-trotters of various nationalities made it a hobby to look out for the Russian cavalcades of ships and to cable observations to the Admiralty in Tokyo. Tokyo had its own intelligence men stationed along the route, but it gathered data supplied by amateurs, acknowledged their receipt, and even mailed fees which, however, rarely covered telegram expenses.

Meantime Togo's ships were refitted at their home bases, and gunners received new instructions on fire concentration. Early in May the Japanese Navy reached a new peak of strength.

Early in May, also, Rozhestvensky and Nebogatov had been scheduled to join forces, but not until May 14 did their squadrons meet off Cochin China.

One crucial strategic question remained yet unanswered. Would the Russians take the shortest route to Siberia through the Straits of Tshushima, or would they sail out into the Pacific, by-passing the straits and keeping far away from Japan? When they joined forces, the Russian admirals had not decided which route to take. Eventually they decided to take the shortest route.

Admiral Togo guessed correctly when he took his fleet—4 battleships, 8 heavy and 22 light cruisers, 21 destroyers, and 42 torpedo boats—to the Straits of Tshushima.

The Russians had 8 battleships, 2 heavy and 7 light cruisers, 2 armored coastal units, 9 destroyers, and 7 torpedo boats. Only four of the Russian battle wagons were really battleworthy. All ships were heavily overloaded and their draft increased beyond the safety limit.

On May 27, Japanese torpedo boats sighted the enemy. A signal was hoisted on Togo's flagship: "This battle will decide the future of our empire. May everybody do his best."

Rozhestvensky had not disentangled his best ships from the dead weight of obsolete armed claptraps and slow supply craft when the first Japanese shells whined through the clear morning air. The Japanese would concentrate the fire of their heaviest batteries upon the strongest Russian ship within range and switch to another target only after the first was crippled. They were hitting the backbone of the Russian fleet, while Russian batteries directed erratic fire at the weakest enemy ships. Five hours after the battle opened the two best Russian battleships had been sunk.

Rozhestvensky went down with his ship; Nebogatov succeeded him in a command that was no longer effective. Every Russian skipper tried to get away. Three cargo ships escaped to Shanghai, three light cruisers fled to Manila for internment, one light cruiser and two torpedo boats slipped past Togo's fleet and eventually made their way to Vladivostok. As May 28 dawned, Nebogatov found his forces reduced to four badly damaged fighting ships and four auxiliaries; the rest had either fled or gone down. He surrendered his eight ships, with crews of 6000. In addition the Russians lost 4000 killed.

The Japanese had lost 700 men, mostly from three torpedo boats sunk in the earlier phases of the battle.

For the time being Russia had ceased to be a naval power. Japanese sea transportation could no longer be challenged. There was talk of impending Japanese attack on Vladivostok, of a river campaign up the Amur, and of an offensive against the Baikal region.

But in Tokyo generals and admirals who had kept their heads reasonably cool talked moderation; and financiers and industrialists spoke of peace. Japanese extremist patriotic societies raged against peace and moderation, but they could not silence the champions of either.

The Army had stepped up its training program to the limit, but reservists were not up to the standards of veterans, and even inadequate in number to replenish communication guards; the number of effectives of Oyama's army was no longer rising; and, should the Trans-Siberian function properly, Linevitsh could have outnumbered his opponents before the end of the fair season.

Japan had already spent two billion yen. More cash would have to come from foreign loans. But England, thus far Japan's most generous creditor, did not seem happy at the thought of Japan's continued advance on the Asiatic mainland, and English bankers were tightening purse strings. America, not yet England's equal as a world banker but already a great financial power, wanted peace.

Peace could be more remunerative than war. This was also the prevailing opinion in St. Petersburg.

Russia's ranking expert on Far Eastern affairs, Baron Rosen, scion of the family of the Dekabrist, went to Washington to discuss matters with President Theodore Roosevelt.

A ranking member of the British Embassy staff in Tokyo, Cecil Spring-Rice, stayed in the American capital at the time of Tshushima. He too explored avenues to peace.

On June 8, 1905, Theodore Roosevelt sent identical notes to Tokyo and St. Petersburg. ". . . While the President does not feel that any intermediary should be called in in respect to peace negotiations themselves, he is entirely willing to do what he properly can if the two powers concerned feel that his services will be of aid in arranging the preliminaries as to the time and place of the meeting. . . ."

On August 9, 1905, the conference opened at Portsmouth, N.H., and two weeks later the treaty of peace was signed.

Russia returned the southern part of Sakhalin to Japan. Russia recognized Japan's predominant military and economic interests in Korea and pledged herself not to interfere with Japanese actions there. Russia ceded to Japan the lease of Port Arthur and adjacent territories. Both signatories agreed to evacuate Manchuria and to operate their respective railroads there exclusively for commercial and industrial purposes. Both parties, however, were entitled to have their properties protected by armed guards. This ambiguous clause practically voided the evacuation agreement. Russian guards were limited to fifteen men per kilometer (0.62 miles); numerical limitations for Japanese guards were approximately the same.

Large territories legally still under Chinese sovereignty changed hands without China having a word in the deal. Japan had not built one yard of railroad track in any part of China, including Manchuria, but it forced the government of China to grant it railroad privileges in Southern Manchuria and in Kwantung Territory in which Port Arthur was situated. Japanese railroad guards turned into garrisons centered on Mukden.

Four years after the Peace of Portsmouth, the United States made a suggestion to free Manchuria from foreign occupation by presenting a "neutralization plan" for all sectors of the Manchurian railroads. But neither Russia nor Japan wanted neutralization. In 1910 they signed the Motono-Isvolsky Pact, pledging mutual consultation if the *status quo* in Manchuria were menaced.

The recognition of predominant Japanese interests in Korea paved the way to its annexation, which took place in two arbitrary steps: first, the establishment of a Japanese protectorate on July 27, 1907, and next, formal incorporation into Japan on July 22, 1910.

The only Russian territory ceded to Japan, the southern part of Sakhalin, was not considered a grievous loss. It had a population of slightly above 10,000, and was neither economically nor strategically valuable. The losing of the foothold in Manchuria was a bitter pill to swallow for champions of Siberian expansion into China, but the Russians were not completely ousted from "Ki-tai," as they kept calling all of China. The loss of Port Arthur was shrugged off; so was expulsion from Korea.

The real loser in the conflict was England, who could no longer move into China at will without challenging both Russia and Japan, the self-styled heir-apparents of the decaying empire in the forefield of India. Diplomatically His Majesty's Government was on the defensive, and this was already demonstrated by its eagerness to sign a second treaty of alliance with Japan on August 12, 1905.

Article IV of that treaty read: "Great Britain, having a special interest in all that concerns the security of the Indian frontier, Japan recognizes her right to take such measures in the proximity of that frontier as she may find necessary for safeguarding her Indian possessions."

Half a century after "opening" Japan to its conquering commerce Great Britain allied with Japan to have this upstart great power recognize her right to defend India.

Peace, as embodied in the instrument of Portsmouth, was but an intermission. There would be some changes of strategic settings and the show would go on.

CHAPTER FIFTY-NINE During the Japanese war immigration to Siberia sank to a mere 40,000. But it recovered quickly, reached 220,000 in 1906, 577,000 in 1907, and an all-time high of 759,000 in 1908. In 1910, Siberia's population figure passed the 10,000,000 mark, which was still less than two per square mile. The event was not celebrated by a government bewildered by a sudden decline of new immigration to 353,000 and 226,000 respectively in 1909 and 1910. Russian authorities thought that official planning could work miracles and that social and economic trends that determined movements of population in other parts of the world had no bearing on Russia. There had been a great deal of planning lately, and the Duma, since 1905 Russia's Parliament and sole lawmaking body, had contributed by eloquent intercessions.

The latest colonization plan had failed. It had been called benevolent, efficient, in accordance with Russian popular tradition, and yet its workings had been no different from those of authoritarian schemes. In fact the pattern was not new, nor had the methods of execution improved.

It had started with another investigation of settling opportunities. Experts contended that settlers of Russian stock would hold their own only in the temperate zones of Central and Western Siberia and in the Amur Valley, and that settlement elsewhere would be a waste of manpower and money. They told of large tracts of land in colder regions that had been abandoned by mushiks who had joined outlaws, and of other mushiks in the icy Kolyma district turning pagans, nomads, and barbarians, no better than members of "alien races," which was the latest scientific term for aborigines.

The government decided to confine future land allotment to a broad belt astride the railroad, covering approximately one fifth of Siberia's territory. Prospective settlers had to form co-operatives and to elect a manager. The manager appointed a "land scout" who would have free transportation to Siberia to select the plot he considered most suitable. The land would then be granted to the manager, as a trustee of the co-operative, and he would in turn assign individual plots to member families, no less than forty acres per male, regardless of age. Assignments were subject to periodical revisions with the consent of the majority, to reward the industrious and punish the loafers. Shares in the proceeds of the co-operative were in proportion to the size of the allotted land.

But the government was faced with the problem as to which areas were available for distribution. Legally all of Siberia remained the Crown's, and all grants were subject to revocation. However, the remainder of Crown land previously set aside for new farmers was not sufficient to meet an expected growing demand, and it appeared as if some co-operatives would have to be settled in areas to which other people laid claim.

Long-established Siberian squires and farmers considered themselves rightful owners of the land on which they lived, and were determined to rise in arms if their ownership were challenged. Siberian authorities sided with squires and farmers, stating that their particular grants had been irrevocable. And since documents pertaining to ancient allotments were either lost or destroyed, or apparently had never been properly filed, the government did not persist in checking established holdings and confined new colonization to uncontested and not always suitable territory.

The land scouts were crude men. They could tell fertile from barren land, but they could neither evaluate local construction facilities nor the amount of clear water required, and, least of all, required investments and the time it would take to make the venture self-supporting.

Their selections, however, were binding, and many a collective faced a hopeless task from the outset because of poor selection.

The government granted loans of 165 rubles per family, payable in the district town closest to the settlement. There were many opportunities to invest the money in things other than farming appliances. Many peasants had nothing left but a colossal hangover and a load of cheap trinkets when they arrived at the site of the collective.

A revised policy directed Siberian administrators to grant loans only in kind. Applicants received seeds, tools, building material, even garments, but no cash. Outside of official buildings operators bought the objects at half their assessed value. They sold booze and trinkets to the mushiks, and they would also sell young gypsy boys, whom peasants acquired to boost the number of male family members and to obtain larger plots. The wares that had constituted the loan in kind were redelivered to the government agency, with agents and operators splitting the profit; 27,000,000 rubles a year were charged to the Treasury for settlers' loans. The expenses were substantiated by bales of vouchers, almost all of them signed with three crosses. The Treasury accepted the vouchers and did not ask further questions. Fraud was *nitshevo*.

A destitute, demoralized, brawling lot of collectivists would eventually take possession of the land their scouts had selected. Less than half of the collectives would ever operate. Co-operatives that had not failed before they started mostly vegetated, their members living in miserable mud cottages and tilling small plots virtually by hand, while large patches of virgin steppe remained unattended.

"We found ragged, hungry people listlessly wandering about," members of the Duma told after returning from an inspection trip.

"The bleaching bones of victims of hunger and disease litter the grounds of ruined farms where these people had stayed to the end," wrote a German traveler.

There were but few industries that would hire unskilled help and they were usually far away from ruined co-operatives. Most mushiks did not even know where and how to apply for an industrial job. Well-to-do landowners were averse to hiring ex-collective farmers, whom they considered vagabonds.

Benevolent government planners could but rarely salvage the human remains of farm catastrophes. In one single year 82,000 persons emigrated *from* Siberia. These were the privileged among the victims of failure. Others just "stayed on to the end."

German experts made suggestions for another colonization pattern, based upon a booklet by one A. Stirne. Stirne spoke of "Blitz colonization" long before "blitz" became part and parcel of the German lingo of military conquest. He advised the Russian Government to grant privileges to competent foreigners (viz., Germans), who would gather shiftless Siberians and put them to useful work, such as road construction, irrigation, woods clearance, and draining of swamps. Official appropriations for such works should be doubled. New settlers would have to be picked from "free colonization elements," such as Volga Germans and German peasants from the Crimean Peninsula. They would receive loans of 2500 rubles per family and permanent grants of land in Siberia.

The Russian authorities, however, had little use for German blitz operations, and, after the shock of colonization failure subsided, prophets of doom were silenced by glowing accounts of Siberian prosperity bursting forth from the debris of inevitable calamity.

Despite settlers' tragedies, widespread corruption, and official incompetence many Siberians were doing well in the nine years of peace that followed the Treaty of Portsmouth. Nostalgic observers later called it a period of opulence, and occasionally also the Age of the Tshaldones.

The *tshaldones* were descendants of early settlers who had been lucky enough to establish themselves in regions where cities later would be built. As the cities grew, the farmers grew wealthy; the value of their produce and of their holdings skyrocketed despite the dubiousness of their title to property. The Russo-Japanese War had been a windfall to all purveyors of the

Army, and to the tshaldones it was a rain of gold which they enjoyed in their own uproarious way.

The revelries of these brutish men became the talk of all Siberian towns. Tshaldone carousers made Parisian roués appear like timid provincials on guided tours through stiffish dance halls. The tshaldones were of humble origin, but they were not satisfied to live like boyars; they wanted to *pass* as boyars. Panders and waiters freely addressed them as Highnesses and Excellencies, but Siberian squires of titled ancestry expressed disgust at the upstarts' lack of humility toward the socially superior. This, however, would not keep the real boyars from patronizing the establishments in which the tshaldones had their savage fun, and the women who taught the wealthy plebeians the art of riotous love-making.

Cossacks too went to the cities, drank vodka rather than champagne, and spent their evenings in brothels rather than in boyar-tshaldone night spots.

Only a handful of Cossack families remained in the dreary tundra, where they had adopted the habits, if not the features, of "alien races."

About 115,000 offspring of the conquering vanguards had comfortable estates in the fertile Irtysh Valley, near the lakes of Southern Siberia and along the borders of the Kirghiz steppe. Long before, most of these families had been awarded 130 acres of land per male member. As time went by, they had, by bickering and bargaining with generations of military commanders, obtained grants of "army reserve land," ten, twenty, and even fifty times the size of their original holdings.

Cossack holdings of Crown land were neither checked nor challenged. Officially the Cossacks were still considered the mainstay of Russian military power in Siberia, but in fact the percentage of draft dodgers was highest among great Cossack landowners. They were bold only in their business operations. After statutory labor had been abolished, they had granted wages to their native labor, but found ways and means of withholding most of the pay. Natives, afraid of their influential masters' wrath, kept tilling their soil and raising their cattle, which the Cossacks sold to traveling buyers and the milk of which went to mushrooming dairies, from where butter went to countries as distant as England. Cossacks controlled local traffic in contraband, invested in black-marketeering, held partnership in moonshiners' businesses. Had it not been for their innate thrift they would have been as boisterous as squires.

The Army, however, boasted of keeping a pool of Cossacks with legendary fighting spirit; 181,000 of this vaunted breed lived in Transbaikalia, 20,000 on the lower Amur, and 7000 along the Ussuri River. All able-bodied men were pledged to serve four years as regulars, and another five years in the reserve. These Cossacks held allotments of 100 acres of army reserve land per family. In case of war they were expected to muster 30,000 mounted men. But throughout the fighting in Manchuria only 9090 of these warriors joined the Army. The alleged military elite also dodged the draft, and not even the most eager researchers could find material for modern Cossack hero tales. The Eastern Cossacks also cheated natives out of wages and, policing the countryside, they subjected Russian peasants to profitable chicaneries. They blackmailed Chinese smugglers who refused to co-operate with Cossacks, whom the Chinese held in deep contempt. The military elite had turned into a middle class with the ethics of highwaymen.

Scattered groups of model farmers kept aloof from Cossacks, tshaldones, and gentry alike. They husbanded their property, shunned sinful entertainment, and never withheld earned wages, of eight to twenty rubles a month, from hired help. They lived in well-kept communities, intermarried, and developed particular, often very attractive, features. No more handsome people could be found in any part of the Tsar's realm than among the "Poles," in the southern foothills of the Altai Mountains. The "Poles" were usually tall, superbly built, with classically clear features, sleeping-beauty complexions, and jet-black hair; they were, in fact, of Muscovite stock, descendants of people who in protest against religious reforms had left Moscow for Poland two centuries before, but had been overtaken by Russian expansion into Poland and exiled to Siberia.

Other model farmers were sectarians: Duchoborians, Molokanes, Sabbathists, and Skopzi, less attractive, fanatically unbending people, intolerant toward any creed other than their own and toward any mundane innovation that would not increase the yield of their farms. At country fairs sectarians would contemptuously walk past displays of stylish finery, but they were good customers for agricultural machines.

Fairs had become as important an institution in Siberia as they were in the Russian heart lands. Most fairs were held in the relatively populous West. Fashion dealers had no reason to be dissatisfied with their sales. Wives, daughters, and mistresses of moneyed men were eager customers, and so were the Kirghiz cattle millionaires and their kin. The Kirghizes loved anything that was brightly colored, sweet-smelling, and soft to touch, and they would unhesitatingly pay the proceeds of a calf for a scarf of bright red silk.

The cattle breeders lived in clans apart. Herds were owned by individuals who, as the most substantial clansmen, were leaders of their folk. But even clan members who did not have one lean sheep to their name were not destitute unless the clan itself was ruined. They worked as shepherds and received all the milk, cheese, millet, gruel, and meat they could eat, and even a gulp of kumiss, which the Kirghizes still preferred to any other beverage.

In the rough season, when the steppe was buried under snow, the community stayed in villages called *auls*. When spring lifted the white sheet from a reposed, blooming land, the women took the *yurtas* (tents) apart, loaded roofs, awnings, poles, and carpets on carts and pack camels, while the young men gathered cattle, sheep, horses, and camels, and the older men, dressed up for the occasion in their finest garb, supervised the operations. Departure from winter quarters was a day of promise on which everybody rejoiced and made merry.

Every *aul* had its own grazing grounds; varying from 10 to almost 250 miles in diameter. Grounds were not staked out or marked on maps, but the invisible boundaries were not violated.

Some cattlemen owned tens of thousands of beasts, and with horses rating 150 rubles, cows 70, and sheep 6 rubles in the prosperous year of 1908 some Kirghizes were genuine millionaires. But few Kirghizes remained rich, and most of the millionaires of 1908 were paupers three years later.

There were no means of checking cattle diseases or of coping with pyromaniacal excesses that transformed succulent grasslands into wastes of smoldering stalks. Such calamities would always strike certain areas and reduce a number of clans to destitution; but in 1911 disaster spared almost no region. During the preceding winter diseases decimated many herds, and after a short breathing spell in a fairly dry spring a mass outbreak of pyromania ruined the pastures. Clans drove their animals to distant markets to sell them for whatever they would fetch. A horse brought six rubles, a cow four; and it required an investment to bring the starved animals into a shape acceptable to buyers. At the end cattle millionaires had neither beasts nor money left.

The stocky, curve-legged men had a reputation of sober tenacity, and army records indicate that their wounds healed faster than those suffered by other men. Ruined Kirghizes became workers and soldiers, but they hardly ever acquired their own shops, and never obtained commissions. A few ex-millionaires turned farmers; government agents settled clans on smallish plots. When the harvest was abundant, they invested every kopek into breeding cattle and returned to their abandoned *auls* to start again on the only road to prosperity they knew.

The eastern neighbors of the Kirghizes were descendants of ancient Tatars who had intermarried with Russians and now considered themselves aristocrats among Siberian aborigines. They were fair-haired, slit-eyed individuals, of whom an enthusiastic traveler once wrote that they were "supple and graceful, had dark, shining eyes, under long lashes, faces shaped like birch leaves, and a delicate brownish complexion, through which glimmered a mysterious crimson." The beauteous aristocrats were Mohammedans and they had developed mercantile instincts that made them more than a match for curio dealers in Oriental bazaars. They were contrabandists, speculators, middlemen in every disreputable trade, and haughtily averse to physical labor.

Still farther to the east, in the border lands of ancient Mongolia, Buryaets had settled down. Statisticians estimated their number at 250,000, and a government anxious to give magisterial care to every nationality directed local Russian authorities to promote Buryaet traditions and blend them with modern Russian culture. The authorities subsidized Buryaet-Lamaist priests who in turn exhorted the believers to be faithful and obedient to their mundane lords, and as a profitable side line established market stalls which sold a produce of Russian culture—methylated vodka at outrageous prices. Travelers visiting Buryaet regions became fascinated spectators of duels between a man armed with a knife and a ferocious bear, in the true Buryaet tradition. Accounts on the state of Buryaet economical affairs were not conclusive, but it appears that they held their own.

The Yakuts, however, said to number 230,000, remained poor but for a few exceptions.

The government suggested that they resume breeding of reindeer. Wild reindeer still roamed the wide territory, but if the Yakuts ever learned of the government's suggestion they did not heed it. It was extremely hazardous to ambush the huge animals. Only when swimming through rivers could they be set upon; and the strong-teethed reindeer would furiously snap at intruders, occasionally inflicting fatal wounds. It also required a great deal of patience to domesticate captured animals, and the Yakuts did not seem to believe that the modern Russians would refrain from decimating their herds as the ancient invaders had done. Fur animals had long been exterminated. However, smart Yakuts became agents of Russian fur buyers in Chutski territory.

The massacre of the sables and their migration kept Siberia forever from leading in the export of that precious fur. In 1911, Siberia supplied 70,000 sables of a total of 215,000 sables sold. However, Siberia had a dominant share in other fur items. It supplied the world market with 15,000,000 of a total of 15,500,000 squirrels; 5,000,000 of 5,250,000 rabbits; 820,000 of 1,300,000 martens; 150,000 of 300,000 polecats; and 6000 out of 8000 bearskins.

The Chutskis preferred ambushing and robbing Russian traders to wearisome bargaining, but they did deal with Yakut agents who visited them in sleighs drawn by horses sturdy enough to exist in a climate of extremes varying between 90° above and 85° below. Yakut agents faced skillful competition: Americans from Alaska, who also had their way with the fierce Chutskis. However, returns were better than fair, and well-to-do Yakut fur agents became the sponsors of the Orthodox Church in their homeland. They considered the popes as shamans whose deities controlled the fur business, and they contributed generously to keep their good will. The long-established shamans did not go quite empty-handed, since they were still believed to regulate the weather.

The average Yakut looked at his prosperous kin in wonder, and so did a few Russians whose families had settled in the north several generations ago, and who now vegetated—apathetic, dull-witted, repulsive pictures of degeneration.

Remnants of Ostjak reindeer breeders survived on the lower Ob and Yenisei rivers. They were not even advised to re-form their herds. There were still some sables and plenty of fine fish in their territories. But the Ostjaks had no business acumen; they sold a sable, which would bring a hundred rubles at auction, for five, and spend ten rubles on a bottle of booze hardly worth one ruble in the nearest town. Fishermen collected half a kopek for a pound of fine fish and had not enough money left for material to repair their leaking canoes. Destitute fishermen were hired by newly established Russian fisheries and earned just enough to turn dipsomaniacs.

The general squalidness of Northern Siberian natives became the object of yet another governmental investigation. Investigators found that syphilis had not reduced in scope and that outbreaks of smallpox were still recurrent.

Narrow, calm river valleys with muddy soil were breeding grounds of the goiter.

Leprosy was rampant in the Lena district. There, around Lake Nedsheli, the lepers existed, singly or in small colonies, subsisting on rotting fish and spoiled milk which native wardens deposited at marked spots, several miles away from the sick people's tents. Spoiled food and brackish water caused fever, which shortened the agony of the afflicted. And when food had been left untouched for more than one week, the wardens knew that it was time to burn the tents and whatever else remained of the victims.

Diphtheria, scarlet fever, trachoma, all imported from Russia, raged throughout the period of Siberian prosperity, and so did Siberian mental diseases.

Medical explorers wrote more treatises about *menrier* and *emirjashestvo*. *Menrier* was a woman's disease, which made the afflicted scream, vociferate, and rant oddities until, shaken by terrific convulsions, they ran headlong into walls or trees and collapsed. Spells of *emirjashestvo,* which mostly affected men, began with ferocious outcries at the sight of certain objects, or at hearing certain sounds. Then the victim repeated the name of the object or imitated the sound, ever faster, ever louder, in a growing frenzy, foaming-mouthed, and eventually succumbed. The frenzy could be diverted to other sounds. Villagers of the Lena district enjoyed prompting obscene words to the maniacs. Medical men experimented by shouting Latin phrases, which the maniacs repeated correctly and without soothing effect.

The Russian Army eventually assigned several scores of surgeons and medics to take care of sick people in the wilderness. A few hospitals were built in cities. A number of physicians established themselves in Siberian centers, but the average state of health did not improve.

Champions of purification decried governmental inertia toward the depravation of Siberians by Russian liquor dealers. The government pointed at a rapid-fire succession of temperance ukases, but with the laudable exception of Tunguse districts the temperance drive had had no effect. The Tunguses had introduced their own version of anti-alcoholism through public derision of drunkards; the system first produced remarkable results, but as the novelty wore off deriders turned toward other objectives and drunkards again stumbled along unmolested. A hard-pressed government contended that depravation was not caused only by Russians. The Americans, it was said, were perverting the Chutskis by inducing them to consume whiskey in sinister quantities. Whiskey reached Siberia via Alaska, but Chutski addiction was not quite as ruinous as that of other tribes. Americans added less methyl alcohol than Russian moonshiners.

Americans also were charged with resorting to unethical business practices in Siberia. In 1910 a group of Russian collective settlers went to the Maritime Province, where they discovered that their domain consisted of virgin forests. Having neither tools nor time to clear the forests, they sold their title to property to a Russian operator for 500 rubles. The operator passed it on for 2500 to a contractor who in turn sold it for 10,000 to the representative of an American firm that eventually hired help to cut the timber, the value of which was close to 1,500,000 rubles.

The "timber case," however, was dropped as an unproductive topic of debate, and St. Petersburg concentrated on its achievement of having introduced local self-government to backward Siberians.

Tribal elders and starostas were in charge of local affairs, responsible to their constituents and to regional Russian administrators. They had been "freely elected"; but only administrators were entitled to nominate candidates.

The administrators were directed to respect ancient tribal tradition, but since there were no records of popular self-government, they established local tyrannies, with their nominees acting as tyrants.

These petty dictators were familiar with every trick and mimicry natives used to shirk abuse. They considered themselves superior to the common herd and their feelings found vent in ill-treatment and blackmail, but they would slavishly serve the administrator as the only person who could protect them against the lurking threat of assassination.

Conditions in Siberian rural communities at the eve of World War I set the pattern for later Bolshevik administrations, in which magistrates, appointed under a travesty of democratic procedure, exercised absolute power over the community and in turn unconditionally submitted to superiors who kicked subordinates and cringed before individuals in higher echelons of a governmental structure cemented by fear.

Starostas of pre-Bolshevik Siberia appropriated themselves women, beasts, and objects, according to their greedy whims. They staged mock trials in which they acted as prosecutors, judges, and principal witnesses. They assessed taxes, reintroduced the long-extinct Iasak for people they disliked, collected "voluntary gifts" for His Excellency the District Governor: cash, handicraft, even garments. Starostas also took a hand in temperance drives, collecting bribes from moonshiners.

Their Excellencies the District Governors, who were legally neither excellencies nor even governors, resided in large huts surrounded by clusters of miserable hovels called office buildings. There they received the starostas' reports and accountings, and checked every item of Iasak and bribes in which they had shares of more than 50 per cent.

People in Siberian cities were too sophisticated to be subjected to such treatment, but city magistrates had no reason to complain about lack of illicit earnings. As long as Siberian cities had the highest percentage of prostitutes in the world, as long as moonshining prospered and magistrates had the power to regiment all trades, they would be as prosperous as squires.

Russian officials now refused to return to Europe even after retiring. They claimed that Siberia was the freest country on earth, the only place where a man could live. In fact nowhere else had violence, perversion, roguishness, and fraud as free a run of so large a territory; nowhere was a ravisher who knew his way around as safe from prosecution as he was in Siberia. Had anybody objected that this was the ruinous antithesis of freedom, officials might have replied that Siberia prospered on such freedom.

By 1908 the annual value of Siberian industrial produce, exclusive of mining, passed the 120,000,000-ruble mark. Fifty thousand workers were permanently employed in mills, distilleries, dairies, and other light industries.

The Crown mines were still worked by convicts with complete disregard of safety and efficiency. The annual output of gold mines in Western Siberia was only thirty poods. Production of iron, silver, and salt for the government was equally unsatisfactory, but licensed private mining companies prospered.

The mines of the Lena Company, partly owned by English industrialists, produced 784 poods of gold-bearing ore in 1910. English concessionaires operated productive copper mines near Akmolinsk. Other foreigners developed coal mines of Central and Eastern Siberia.

On the eve of World War I, Siberia had fourteen cities. Omsk, with 150,000 inhabitants, was the most populous. Its rapid growth was the result of business with cattle breeders and the establishment of a meat-packing industry. The pioneers of industry in Omsk were Germans who later sold their investments to Englishmen.

Omsk's industrial rival was Kurgan, which its town counselors dubbed "Siberia's Chicago." The mayor had bribed census takers into giving the population figure as 80,000, almost double the actual number. Kurgan had stockyards, more filthy than any Western slaughterhouse, and two model canning factories, the tasty produce of which made citizens predict that *ssi tshass* their town would be the center of the world's meat-packing industry.

Tomsk, population 105,000, was the center of Siberian learning, with two universities, one commercial high school, and several junior colleges. Well-to-do Siberians sent their children to Tomsk to give them an education, and would realize only belatedly that Tomsk's colleges were hotbeds of revolution. German immigrants taught in universities and controlled libraries; other Germans established breweries, glass and match factories; and much as the political views of the two groups differed, they agreed that Tomsk was a German outpost in Siberia, a springboard for future German expansion.

Irkutsk, with 100,000 inhabitants, looked down upon Omsk, Kurgan, and Tomsk as upstarts which sooner or later would decline to unimportance, while Irkutsk would always remain the citadel of Siberian civilization. In fact the citadel of civilization still held a few leads over other Siberian cities: a very precarious lead in the per-capita consumption of champagne and the per-capita number of brothels, and a more comfortable one in general housing shortage and high prices of essential commodities.

Irkutsk was no longer a center of commerce, and the entertainment trade had spread all over Siberia. Even in village hostels procurers offered travelers "superbly skilled wenches, aged 8 to 12," and practically everywhere brothels outnumbered schools and churches combined.

Tumen, town of 40,000 people, nearly all of whom smelled of fish, raw hides, and other odoriferous sources of local opulence, was another mecca of carousers. So was Barnaul, with 46,000 inhabitants, where people coined gold from corn trade and the manufacture of sheepskin coats.

There was a late gold rush in Krasnojarsk, fourth largest Siberian city, site of mills and soap works. In 1911 a man announced in the public square that, promenading at night, he had found large nuggets of gold in furrows dug by cart wheels in the mud-soaked main street. The man was not a substantial citizen, but the nuggets were genuine. Within a few hours business was at a standstill. Thousands of people started staking, buying, and selling claims, with the lucky finder acting as the principal claim holder and broker. Tens of thousands of prospectors from the surrounding countryside invaded Krasnojarsk and dug in the streets. Houses collapsed as foundations were hollowed out. In the general craze it was not immediately noticed that the gold-finding hero had vanished; only a few days later was it learned that he had made off with the fastest million ever made in local history and that there was not one ounce of gold in the soil of Krasnojarsk.

A new railroad-hub town sprang up in Semipalatinsk, where 40,000 settled to wait for the construction of blueprinted transportation. And on the Manchurian border, in Chita, some 60,000 railroad men, contractors, officials, and soldiers gathered in accommodations that would have been inadequate for half their number.

In the east, Blagoveshchensk and Khabarovsk, river ports on the Amur, boasted populations of 60,000 and 50,000 respectively, and Novo Nikolajevsk had 53,000.

But these cities were being outdistanced by Vladivostok, the only important Russian Pacific base left after the cession of Port Arthur. The Russians called it the "Queen of the Far East," built a huge, ungainly Admiralty Palace atop one of the city's ugly bare hills, had the main street cobbled, and established a trolley line. From hillside villas foreign consular agents watched the unkempt "Queen" grow into a major fortress. Washington and Tokyo, Berlin and London had day-by-day reports on the expansion of land and sea fortifications and on naval traffic in the wide bay and the narrow inlets which ranged into the heart of the town.

Last on the list of Siberian cities was Yakutsk. A clumsy wooden tower remained of the ancient ostrog; 12,000 people lived in wooden shacks, log houses, and tents, but even Yakutsk had night spots where Russian fur dealers crowned the success of their Yakut buyers with savage celebrations.

"Siberia is developing American style," Russians would tell globe-trotters on the Trans-Siberian Express. The trains were now running regularly, even though never quite on schedule, except for the Ussuri line, where regular operations opened only in 1914.

Foreigners did not think that the term "American style" applied to anything they saw.

Cities in newly colonized countries everywhere else retained a touch of incompletion until a period of normalized inhabitance gave them the appearance of solid novelty. In Siberia even the most recent developments showed signs of dilapidation, which seemed to grow with inhabitance. And at stations most people looked like immigrants, even if they were said to be regular travelers. Nowhere did foreigners see indications of fixity as they characterized American settlements.

There was an element of strangeness in the Trans-Siberian Express, in the musty plushiness of its first-class compartments, in the servility of the bearded porters who were constantly at the voyagers' beck and call but never dusted the accommodations, and also in the diners, which gave the impression of backwoods night clubs. The bathing facilities and libraries of which propaganda told were still missing. Russian officers and officials, who traveled first-class free, tried to be genial, but their demeanor strengthened the foreigners' impressions that Siberia was a country where one could make money and see wonders of nature, but where one could not live.

The foreigners hardly ever contacted average Siberians. Except for the very wealthy, these people invariably traveled third-class. They did not ride trains like Westerners; they lived in trains, and transformed the interior of cars into a mixture of gypsy camp and village shacks, in which all phases of community life, including the most intimate conjugal relations, went on undisturbed.

No statistics, no description could convey the vastness of Siberia. But a ride on the Trans-Siberian made men feel the breath of immensity, dwarfing even that of the ocean and making man-traced borders appear absurd.

Seven years after the Treaty of Portsmouth, however, the Asiatic borders of Russia expanded again. The Japanese had recognized Outer Mongolia as part of the Russian sphere of interest. Legally the territory was Chinese, but the government of the Republic of China, constituted in 1911, discontinued payment of pensions to Mongolian princes and princelings. Pensioners rebelled, Siberian troops occupied strategic positions, and St. Petersburg assumed "protection" of the territory with the approval of a Russian-subsidized Mongolian princes' cabinet. China had no means to enforce its right, and eventually became a party to the Russo-Chinese-Mongolian Treaty of Kiakhta of 1915, which created an "autonomous" Outer Mongolia under Chinese nominal suzerainty and actual Russian occupation.

A prolonged period of prosperous stability might have normalized Siberian life and Siberian thinking, but in Siberia nothing seemed permanent but foment.

A faint social quake had struck Siberia early in 1905. In Krasnojarsk railroad workers went on strike and mill workers shouted slogans that the police called revolutionary. The Governor filed a laconic report to the Governor General, who supplemented it with a statement that order had been restored and troop transportation to the Far East continued. The Ministry of the Interior, haunted by the specter of Bloody Sunday, ordered an investigation but warned against drastic action.

The investigators found that socialist students and Jewish demagogues had incited the disorders, but that the number of socialists in Siberia was trifling, hardly one tenth of 1 per cent of the population, not including political deportees. It was added that those deportees had played no appreciable part in events at Krasnojarsk. The report alleviated misgivings about the activities of socialist deportees in Siberia.

Forty-five thousand were on their way into banishment and more were yet to be rounded up, some prominent, some obscure. Some were considered to be criminals rather than politicians, such as one Iosif Vissarionovitsh Dshugashvili, later to be known as Josef Stalin, and one Vladimir Ilitsh Uljanov, a petty nobleman who had inherited his alias of Lenin from a relative exiled to the Lena district. There were even officers among the deportees; they had not participated in revolutionary action, but had joined secret Marxist societies.

Karl Marx had died in 1883, but he had lived to see *Das Kapital* published in Russia. The bard of international revolution had sneered at the snobbish curiosity of Russian intellectuals and predicted that revolution would come to Russia last.

But, like the Dekabrists, the modern Russian military intelligentsia carried the germs of rebellious reform.

The socialist students in Siberia despised their *tshaldone* and businessmen fathers, the crude officials, and the boisterous soldiery. But education instigated their own thirst for power. They had no affinity, no love, and no respect for laborers and shiftless peasants, but they would use the keenness of their intellects to gain control of those people's muscular ruthlessness to establish dictatorship based upon a philosophy that its chief promoter had considered incompatible with Russian reality. Students buttonholed workers, addressed small gatherings, roamed factory grounds and railroad stations where the shiftless waited.

The objects of their shrill agitation hardly understood the slogans they were taught to shout. They did not like the prompters who promised to lead them to power. They wanted power, and it did not seem to matter who showed them the way; it could even be a Jew.

The first Jews had been sent to Siberia by deportation authorities who either ignored or disregarded the general ban on Jewish immigration. After the statute of banishment was no longer on the books, small numbers of Jews settled in Siberian cities and large rural communities to transact any business that did not require long-term investments. Jews lived as segregated as they could. They never dressed like local people, and avoided every token of assimilation. They would not even use tricks that Siberian gentiles applied in business. But while the average Siberian took the established businessmen's malodorous practices for granted, he cursed Jewish machinations as infidel deceit and hated their perpetrators.

The number of Jews remained small, but their different looks made them stand out everywhere. Despised by the people, snubbed and blackmailed by police agents, government clerks, and court attendants, Jewish immigrants to Siberia ducked, shirked, and shuffled; and even though they never controlled major lines of business, they did reasonably well for themselves. They had no affection for the authorities, but, being zealots of their own law, older Jews never indulged in rebellion that violated their general duties toward authorities, however malevolent.

But there might be fundamental changes of conception within one generation. Young Jews whom ambitious parents sent to non-religious institutions of learning ceased to adhere to the precepts of their religion. Stripped of the support of its tremendous moral power, incapable of overcoming the handicap of dissimilitude, many fell victim to frustration, and adopted Marx's prophecy of destruction as a guiding star and promise of their vindictiveness.

Siberian revolutionary masterminds welcomed the neophytes of socialist-communist extremism with guarded obligingness. They were useful as fanatics, but also a burden through their conspicuousness, unpopularity, hysteria, and imperviousness. Jews held only a fraction of important extremist assignments in Siberia. Leon Trotsky probably never lived there, and Lev Kamenev, most prominent among Siberia's Jewish revolutionaries, made a real career only after his return to European Russia.

During the Bolshevik Revolution, Siberian Jewish renegades treated "bourgeois" co-religionaries no better than "bourgeois" gentiles. The majority of young Jews did not join the Red forces in the early days of Bolshevism; a Siberian Jewish battalion even formed in Northern Manchuria to combat the Reds.

But in May 1914, when the first Siberian military contingents were transported to a Europe still at peace, revolution in Siberia seemed to be no more than a fleeting bogy, vacillating in eternal space.

CHAPTER SIXTY The wrathful Lord was unfathomably high above and a scared Tsar was stupendously far away when mobilization orders and war manifestoes, invoking the Lord and signed by the Tsar, reached Siberia. But the Army was omnipresent, and through its thousand polyp's arms drained the country of its manpower.

Elders and starostas, regional administrators, city magistrates, and hordes of nondescript ink souls turned procurers for the Army. They also did thriving business selling deferments to parties who could afford to pay handsome bribes, and they substituted for dodgers by rounding up individuals without papers. White-haired vagabonds and adolescent gypsy boys were enlisted under the names of bribers.

From the tundra to the steppes elected functionaries shepherded drafted constituents, their kinfolk, and hapless substitutes to induction centers, from where gendarmes and policemen escorted the men to the nearest railroad station, which might be hundreds of miles away. The forces of order did not permit their wards to mingle with relatives, but civilians trailed the troop within shouting distance all along the trek, and when the station was eventually reached, they stayed on until long trains of vans swallowed the men to take them to an unknown destination.

In waiting rooms from Vladivostok to the Ural Mountains, and all the way to the war zone, candles burned in front of ikons. The Siberian draftees had little opportunity to say prayers, as their guards would not let them wander about. But their folks crossed themselves before the saints' images, murmuring supplications, fearful that a soldier's fate was not within the province of a peaceable holy man; and after returning to their domiciles they would haggle with shamans for a deal with some demon versed in military affairs.

In Siberian cities manifestoes and mobilization orders were posted on walls and fences. Teachers read out the officious and bombastic words for the benefit of illiterates.

People listened to the teachers, and they listened also to strange demagogues haranguing them to revolt for deferment and better pay. Among the demagogues were new arrivals in exile, well versed in the techniques of rabble-rousing, comtemptful of the home-grown orators' Marxist speeches. The crowds responded with shouts, rock throwing, and similar rudimentaries of rioting, all quickly quelled.

Seven hundred thousand soldiers from Siberia joined the Tsar's army of twelve million, 73.6 per cent of which were killed, wounded, or captured even before Mower Death donned the red star to reap the Bolshevik dragon seed.

Not even in the day of the legendary conquerors had so large a Siberian host gone to war; never before had a Siberian army suffered comparable casualties; and never in three thousand years of recurring aggression had Siberian soldiers had less to gain from the issues on which they staked their lives.

What the issues actually were those Kirghiz shepherds, sectarian farmers, Ostjak fishermen, dairy workers, railroad men, miners, and even *tshaldones,* did not understand. They knew little about the *attentat* of Sarajevo that had prompted the outbreak of the conflagration, and practically nothing about the fateful system of international pacts in which the government of a far-away Tsar was a party, about the ententes and alliances hailed as safeguards of peace when they were signed and turning into mechanics of global war when put to test.

Siberian teachers and elders were directed to tell rural people that the war was sacred, for it combated the Germans, who were devils incarnate, complete with hoofs and horns. The hoof-and-horn version was eliminated for urban consumption, but the townspeople were told that the Germans were responsible for every pitfall on the Siberian record. In order not to complicate the matter propagandists usually did not refer to other nations at war with Russia.

The presence of Siberian riflemen and cavalry in Russian Poland and Austria's Galicia Province in August 1914 indicated that they had left their home garrisons no later than in May of that year, several weeks before the *attentat* of Sarajevo. German sources interpreted this as a conclusive evidence of Russia's determination to start the war in 1914 regardless of international developments. However, it is more likely that the early shift of Siberian units to the west was part of a program of dislocation of garrisons, devised in 1913, when several uprisings had occurred in European Russian towns and soldiers from local regiments showed reluctance to fire at their fellow citizens. Government and military authorities decided to transfer regiments to places where the men had no affinity with the populace.

In the victorious opening battles of the war Siberian soldiers gave a good fighting account of themselves. Their later combat weariness was caused by lack of supplies and heavy losses rather than by mutinous tendencies.

Never before had a war produced a comparable number of prisoners on both sides. The Russians lost 2,804,529 men captured, and in turn took a total of 2,322,778 prisoners; 2,104,146 from Austria-Hungary, 167,082 Germans, the rest Turks and some Bulgarians.

The greatest part of Russian-held prisoners went to twenty-seven camps in Siberia. Approximately 600,000 foreign officers and men died there. The camps survived. They were used, enlarged, but never improved, by the Soviet Government, to hold legions of deportees, who eventually became a major factor in trebling the population between 1914 and the present, and in turning Siberia into the only land on earth in which more than half the inhabitants are deprived of their freedom of movement.

Between 1914 and 1917 prisoners of war and civilian internees formed the nucleus of a new immigration into Siberia, the largest influx of foreigners the country had ever experienced. At times more than one third of the male population of Siberia consisted of foreigners.

Internment of prisoners of war in Siberia was in the Russian tradition, yet to the people of the Central Powers and of many other nations news of the establishment of Siberian prisoner camps came as a shock. The Western mind still pictured Siberia as an icebound inferno, and so deeply rooted was this legend that no assertion to the contrary would have been believed. The Russian Government, however, did not take the trouble to explain the virtues of Siberia, and The Hague Convention only said that prisoners of war should be accommodated in "cities, fortresses, or camps," but did not bar any regions because of their bad reputation.

In August 1914 the U. S. Government assumed protection of German and Austro-Hungarian interests in Russia. Miss Elsa Brändström, a Swedish philanthropist, whose self-sacrificing devotion to the welfare of prisoners of war earned her the glorious epithet "The Angel of Siberia," has no praise for the activities of the American Embassy in Russia on behalf of Austro-Hungarian and German prisoners. According to her book *Among Prisoners of War in Russia and Siberia, 1914-1920*, the U. S. Ambassador's antipathy against Germans prejudiced his relief work. America's passive attitude changed in the spring of 1916, when another ambassador came to St. Petersburg, then called Petrograd, but little could be accomplished in the short span of time that remained before the severance of diplomatic relations between the United States and the Central Powers. Miss Brändström, however, gives warm praise to the humanitarian endeavors of the American Consul General in Moscow and the Consul in Odessa.

There is no greater authority on prisoners of war in Russia and Siberia than this gallant woman, whose clear-cut, serenely beautiful features would deserve to figure prominently on a memorial honoring those who served mankind in global war. Undaunted by hardship, she traveled on relief missions to infection-ridden camps, through hotbeds of violence, to regions of starvation, obsessed by the passion of helping, spending herself with an ardor rivaling the feats of the boldest men. Her one-woman fight against destruction did not save the lives of the 600,000, but it probably saved many other lives and won her countless affections, perhaps the purest and deepest any heroine ever enjoyed.

Elsa Brändström dealt with Russian officials, high and low. She knew how to deal with malice, incompetence, and corruption, yet was unable to cope with one element that prevented Russian authorities from treating the prisoners with reasonable consideration. Fear is the mainspring of brutality, and not since Ivan the Formidable's frying pans and his Stroganoff-supplied savage bears had such fear gripped the hearts of highly placed Russians as in and after the fateful ides of August 1914.

A nightmare haunted cabinet ministers, governors, and counselors: the vision of millions of Russian soldiers turning into a host of avengers of all iniquity they and their forebears had suffered. Prior to the general mobilization peasants and townspeople lived virtually segregated. The workers' problems were alien to the mushik, and vice versa, and when one group revolted the other group could still be used to suppress the revolt. Cities and country were worlds apart in their mentalities and grievances. Now men from both camps were herded together, beset by the same frustrations and grievances, stirred to a uniform anger that could but grow into a cataclysmic outbreak against the government unless channeled in the only direction in which it could serve the government's purposes.

Hatred of the enemy was preached with cultic fervor: the enemy was the devil incarnate, and authorities would have disowned themselves had they treated the alleged creatures from the underworld with consideration.

The war party at Court, and the Russian generals who put chances of promotion above the hazards of war, insisted that the enemy would be defeated before an outbreak could occur, and that a victorious army never rebelled. Russian intelligence services had laid the unshakable groundwork to triumph: Alfred Redl, Austrian General Staff colonel, a homosexual, and the most sinister spy in military history, had twice, in 1901 and 1910, sold his country's *ordre de bataille* to the Russian military attachés in Vienna. After the sale of the first war plan was discovered, Redl, in his capacity as military prosecutor, had had another officer convicted for his own crime; and in 1913, when, at last, irrevocable evidence of his treacherous activities was discovered, his superiors had Redl commit suicide before the scope of his betrayal was established. The Austro-Hungarian Army seemed doomed; it would run headlong into Russian pincers.

The pincers closed. Austria-Hungary suffered staggering loss of men and material, but it remained in the war, and the former optimists in St. Petersburg now worried about rebellions in the hinterland spreading to the front lines, and insisted on tightening dealings with prisoners of war, and stepping up hate propaganda.

Russian soldiers were told of tortures inflicted upon their captured comrades, and when letters from Russian captives indicated that their lot was bearable, officers were ordered to keep such news from their men. (On December 24, 1914, the commander of the Russian XIIth Corps warned his officers against letting epistles from prisoners of war circulate among their men. Similar orders from the 41st Russian Infantry Division, dated June 12, 1915, were captured.)

Russian newspapers, which had enjoyed reasonable freedom during the nine years preceding the war, became subject to editorial control. They featured stories about untold atrocities committed by enemy soldiers on Russian territory.

Actually the German soldiers were arrogant, imperious, and often brutal; the Austro-Hungarian soldiery included highly immoderate elements. Both armies requisitioned with equal ruthlessness. But never did the armies of the Central Powers in World War I sink to the level of depravity of the German Wehrmacht in World War II.

The enemy armies were not the sole target of propagandists, however. Russian citizens of German stock were dubbed enemies. German settlements on the Volga, established under the rule of Catherine II, had a population of almost 700,000 in 1914. The people had conserved their ancestral language and traditions, and kept apart from the Russian mushiks.

Between 1,300,000 and 1,500,000 more people of German ancestry lived in other parts of the empire, not as isolated as the Volga colonists but greatly distinct from their Russian fellow-citizens and displaying notions of superiority.

The average German Russian was a better farmer than his Slavic-Russian counterpart, a more successful clerk and businessman, a more skillful worker, better educated, thriftier, and an odds-on favorite in any race for promotion. Russian governments had appointed them to high offices. Russian industrialists and bankers preferred them to other applicants for jobs.

However, the German Russians' uninhibited methods of competition, their obvious disdain for people of different origin, and, last but not least, their success turned them into objectives of intense popular dislike. There had been quite a few trumped-up denunciations of German Russians, but until August 1914 the authorities turned a deaf ear to such charges. After the outbreak of the war this attitude was abruptly reversed. A dark shadow of suspicion fell over 2,000,000 Russian citizens of German ancestry. Virtually overnight the former pillars of society turned into alleged spies and saboteurs.

There were no specific charges against individuals, and due process of law in Russia was not yet based on collective suspicions, but synthetic popular indignation substituted for legality. Local police officers co-operating with rabble-rousers supplied violent mobs with lists of German-Russian-owned plants, shops, stores, and homes. Policemen stood by as the crowds destroyed property and gave vent to patriotic zeal by manhandling its owners.

Police masters drafted suggestions to deport the objects of popular indignation. The government had already decided to take such action.

It started with a "resettlement" of part of the Volga Germans. Large numbers of model farmers were driven from their homesteads and marched to areas of Western Siberia, long abandoned by Russian settlers. The forced emigrants from the Volga Valley did better than their predecessors in these not particularly fertile regions, but their success was curtailed by lack of ardor and shortage of equipment. Abandoned Volga farms were transferred to Russians who made the highest bids to resettlement officials. Volga Germans were followed by German-Russian businessmen whose assets were taken over by competitors greasing the right palms.

No foreign government took charge of the interests of Germans who were Russian citizens, and whatever the allegiances of German Russians actually were, the Kaiser's Reich considered them enemy aliens.

Deportees from Poland joined the stream of forced immigrants. "My loved Poles," Nicholas II's manifesto had addressed them when the first shots were fired, but before enemy siege rifles battered the forts of Warsaw, Russian military authorities removed droves of Poles from the zone of war, and the last stop on their long road was Siberia.

The Balts also became objectives of Russian governmental mania for displacements. Estonians, Latvians, Lithuanians, stepchildren of a long succession of Russian rulers, had not rebelled during the mobilization. They had no nationalist-revolutionary organizations, and apathy caused by dulling tradition of suppression kept them from rallying for resistance. A fear-ridden government, however, pictured these people as plotting with the enemy, whose vanguards invested the northern route of invasion. And while Baltic regiments fought Germans, Austrians, and Turks, their next of kin were summoned to police headquarters, and, after a head count and an agonizing period of suspense, transported to "new domiciles" in Siberia.

And as they perished on marches, suffocated and starved in cattle cars, or vegetated in exile, their sons in the Army began to recite these lines:

> *"We sing no tune*
> *We speak no poem*
> *We clench our fists*
> *We march on along the bitter road,*
> *We, men without a country."*

After Poles and Balts, Ukrainians went to Siberia. How many went the bitter road official statistics do not disclose. Estimates run at one and one half to two million departures, and about half that number of arrivals.

The trek of tribulation started with marches escorted by mounted Cossacks, professional soldiers from Eastern Siberia who were dodging the battlefield and who unleashed their martial instincts upon the deportees, using their knouts against the exhausted who fell by the wayside. Survivors who reached railroad hubs soon learned that transportation by train could also be a nightmare. Cattle cars were kept tightly closed through most of the trip of several months. The stench was agonizing; foul air bred epidemics against which there was no medical help. The few physicians along the road had no time to attend deportees who did not even fit into established categories of exiles. Poor organization, fraud, and negligence often left the forced travelers without food for days and reduced them to human wreckage.

In Siberia the no-longer-loved subjects of the Tsar were not even interned. There were no appropriations for their upkeep, and governors had deportees dumped, left to rot or to sprout. Three years later the same governors wondered about new disorderly elements turning up in their districts. This was the flotsam and jetsam of deportation who had survived and were whirled up by rebellion. Each individual was sheer nothingness, but, combined, they gathered into a devastating storm. Bolsheviks controlled the force of destruction and used it to telling effect. It not only promoted their rebellion, it taught the new tyrants a lesson which they later applied with total ruthlessness: that no potentially hostile elements, however prostrate, should be allowed to survive and that only the dead were harmless.

Enemy aliens trapped by war in Russia were also liable to deportation.

Police masters in charge of the operation levied fees for postponement, and, after the means of the parties were exhausted, charged upkeep and shipment expenses to a fund of 20,000,000 rubles contributed by the German and Austro-Hungarian governments for the relief of their subjects. The aliens received hardly half the food allotment billed to the trustees of the fund, and while police officers charged for conveyances, the aliens were made to march over distances of hundreds of miles. Almost 300,000 persons were held as enemy aliens; how many of them eventually reached Siberia has not been established.

Even from East Prussia and Galicia deportees went east. During their occupation of part of these German and Austrian provinces Russian commanders had some 11,000 Germans and 30,000 to 50,000 Austrians exiled, in blatant disregard of international law. The Russian Supreme Command disclaimed responsibility for these measures, but once the mills of deportation had begun to grind there seemed to be no way of stopping them. And there also seemed no way of controlling excesses of savagery, committed by Russians of all ranks in occupied territory, and occasionally followed by weird spells of sentimentality. A Russian enlisted man would smash the skull of an "enemy" child with his rifle butt and burst into tears over the body of the victim. And officers who had enemy civilians deported would make protestations of regret over their alleged mistake when the afflicted already were crowding cattle cars rolling east; and they would keep on rolling for a long time, since district officials did their utmost to keep the shipment of misery from being unloaded in their territory. Half of this deportee problem was eventually solved by typhoid fever, and the other half disposed of by turning the remnants loose somewhere in Siberia.

Berlin, Vienna, and Budapest continued relief payments even after defeat, well into 1920. Little of the money benefited those people, who scattered over the Siberian vastness and had no more desire to contact local authorities than the authorities had to use allotments for the support of "contrabandist vagabonds, molesting the country with their presence," as they called them. There was a grain of truth in the insulting description. Some of the shiftless joined Siberian smugglers, moonshiners, and black-marketeers, and, sharpened by misery, their wits might turn them into ringleaders.

Not before October 7, 1914, did commanding officers of Russian military districts receive directives about treatment of military POWs. Commanding generals were directed not to violate the principles established by The Hague Convention; but an accompanying secret memorandum authorized them to make such adaptations as they deemed fit. Many adaptations were laid down in orders to camp commanders who also received directives from St. Petersburg and district capitals. Hundreds of draft-deferred clerks turned out thousands of regulations and amendments. Eventually camp commanders drafted their own laws, which usually were the antithesis of the fundamentals of The Hague.

Article 4, Paragraph 2, of the Convention requires that prisoners be treated with humaneness. Humaneness has different meanings in different countries. The Russian version accounted for the death of about one prisoner out of four.

Article 6 permits the captor state to put prisoners to work commensurate with their qualifications, provided that work was neither excessively strenuous nor serving the war effort. Working captives were to be compensated at established rates or in accordance with the general practices. Officers were deferred from work.

The Russian Government decreed that 50 per cent of the wages for farm labor be withheld for costs of guards and transportation, and that the balance, minus the equivalent of roughly $1.00 per month, be deductible for "maintenance." Prisoners detailed to work on Crown property would also receive "net wages" of about $1.00 per month; earnings of prisoners laboring in industry were about the same.

The Governor of Saratov amended decrees to the effect that "prisoners should be treated in such manner that they should be harmless, yet still profitable."

The commander of Irkutsk, whose jurisdiction extended over several large camps, proclaimed: "It is the prisoner's duty to perform the work to which he is detailed regardless of the difficulties involved. Offenders shall be subject to penal confinement for the duration."

Prisoners charged with substandard performances were subject to twenty-five to fifty strokes with the lash or the rifle butt. Throughout Siberia prisoners of war were detailed to mines and projects serving the war effort.

In manpower distribution centers industrialists and farmers applied for laborers; they had to pay the full wages to officials and hand out bribes to get competent, strong men. Yet, acting with despotic stupidity, clerks assigned metalworkers to glass factories and peasants to mines, insisting all industries were alike and that mining in rural districts was agricultural work.

Industrial managers remonstrated against the assignment of men who did not seem to know the trade. Clerks said that the men were saboteurs and ordered them flogged and put on starvation diets. Mistreated prisoners struggled desperately to acquire professional skills that might save them from punishment. They learned much faster than average Siberians, but the better they did, the more Russians trusted that prisoners were saboteurs, and still holding back.

Recalcitrant authorities put almost insurmountable obstacles in the way of neutral observers assigned by the Red Cross to check Russian treatment of prisoners of war. Only the most determined, the boldest, and cleverest of them ever reached a prison camp or the site of labor projects on which the prisoners toiled. Unfavorable reports on their findings drew indignant Russian denials. It seemed impossible to obtain improvements; about the only neutral who occasionally achieved the impossible was Elsa Brändström.

Horrors were not confined to Siberia; 70,000 prisoners lost their lives toiling on the Murmansk Railroad, which linked the Baltic and the Barents seas. The Russian Government first denied using prisoners of war on the project, and later amended the denial by stating that only 25,000 of them had died.

In December 1916 the Russian Government released figures on working prisoners of war: 496,917 were said to be working on farms, 293,968 in mines and factories, 168,614 on railroad and canal construction, and 151,054 on unspecified projects.

Never before had Siberia had a comparative labor force. And even though official corruption, brutality, and incompetence wasted this hoard of manpower no less stupidly than other Russian governments had squandered their human resources, the prisoners became a major factor in Siberian economy.

According to The Hague Convention, captured soldiers should be stripped of weapons, military documents, and horses, and marched off to the nearest place of shipment. Russian commanders had prisoners despoiled of practically all valuables, and because of prevailing bottlenecks in transportation, the march to the nearest place of shipment could take several weeks, at a rate of fifteen miles a day.

Severely injured captives were entitled to cart rides; lighter cases had to walk. Food, or food money, was to be distributed at halting places. Enlisted men were entitled to the equivalent of twelve cents a day, officers to thirty-seven cents. Commanders at halting places usually sold the food and withheld food money.

Mushiks who lined the dirt roads over which the prisoners were marched exclaimed: "Why, they look just like ourselves!" They crossed themselves, fed the marchers, and taught them their first Russian words: *vojno plenni* (prisoner of war).

Charitable as the mushiks were, the authorities gave the *plennis* vicious treatment. They would keep them overnight in filthy, lice-ridden local jails; they would not part the sick from the healthy; they would never see that dressings were changed. Wounds festered and blood poisoning claimed many victims. The infantrymen who escorted the *plennis* were not as brutal as Cossacks, but they were indifferent to human sufferings.

When the prisoners eventually arrived at shipment places, enlisted men were jammed into cattle cars, thirty-five to forty-five men per car. Officers were given fourth- or third-class passenger accommodations. Generals went first- or second-class. Three central depots for *plennis* were established in St. Petersburg, Kiev, and Moscow.

Moscow, most conveniently located for continued transportation to Siberia, had by far the largest "depot." But in Moscow, like everywhere else, no adequate provisions had been made to accommodate the staggering number of prisoners. Barracks were overcrowded; sanitary conditions deteriorated by the hour. Cases of smallpox, typhoid, diphtheria, scarlet fever, and cholera went to isolation wards; to the same wards went sick men whose ailment had not been diagnosed. *Plennis* with mere colds often caught cholera.

The wounded went to barracks with one bed to ten men, where three or four surgeons, not all of whom had yet completed their medical studies, worked to the limit of their capacities. Whenever an injury startled the medics, they amputated the affected limb, occasionally interrupting their work to look up textbooks on veins and muscles. Anesthetics were rarely available, and almost never applied.

On paved corridors and stairways the infirm lay on couches of rotting straw or on the bare floor. Windows remained closed, and the stench of unwashed bodies and festering wounds polluted the air.

In December 1914, Tsar Nicholas went to Moscow to inspect prisoner-of-war depots. The news of his impending visit reached commanding officers twelve hours before his scheduled arrival. Not within twelve days, not even in twelve weeks could herculean power have cleaned the stables. The Tsar had German relatives. Officers, worried lest they be taken to answer for dereliction of duty, moved the worst offenses out of sight. Batches of sick and wounded plennis were evacuated to cellars, open lots, and similar localities the imperial party was not expected to visit.

Nicholas visited one ward, the best kept of all. But even so, the Tsar was nauseated by the stench, and discontinued his inspection tour. But not until the imperial train had left were the evacuees removed from their hiding places. By then hundreds of them had frozen to death.

Patients who were pronounced fit for transportation joined their uninjured fellow-plennis for shipment to camps.

Trains of forty to fifty cattle cars, luggage vans, and one or two passenger cars took an average of 2000 plennis to their destinations. The trip from Moscow to the most distant internment places took about four months.

Two rows of planks were established in cars for enlisted men. There they slept, tightly crowded together. During the cold season small stoves were set up in the centers of the cars. Near the stoves the heat was oppressive, but a few feet away icy air penetrating through hatches and crevices reduced the temperature to subfreezing level.

Transport commanders were in charge of buying provisions for the men en route. Allotments were the equivalent of six cents per man per day. This was inadequate when food prices in Siberia were still low, and it became a travesty when they skyrocketed later in the war. However, few transport commanders could resist temptation of withholding at least a fraction of the pittance. The combined allotments for a trainload of men traveling to Transbaikalia or the Maritime Province was about $15,000; a lieutenant who clipped this amount by 20 per cent made five times his annual salary during a four-month trip.

Siberians along the railroad got accustomed to the sight of transports, and of the *Germanskis,* who had neither hoofs nor horns, and they gave them food, cigarettes, even pieces of clothing. Donors were mostly peasant women who had come to believe that to be captured was a drafted man's ultimate design, and who hoped that the kinfolk of the Germanskis would requite in kind when Siberian captives were shipped across Germany.

The plennis stared at women dressed in diapered cotton skirts, sheepskin jackets, felt boots, and colorful kerchiefs, who did not look as gruff as they had thought and wondered if they were not only kindhearted but even acceptable as females. Most prisoners were in their twenties and even though recent hardships had made them look older, their recuperative powers were strong. The sight of their benefactresses stimulated their salutary curiosity, and with it the desire to adapt themselves to conditions that, hard as they were, still held the promise of a future.

Narrow hatches of cars crawling through the endlessness of Siberia, at speeds varying between those of an oxcart and of a runner, were crowded with faces marveling at the sights that unfolded before them. With the exception of herdsmen from the Puszta in the Hungarian lowlands, they had never before seen a land that spread like a board under the transparent bell of a sky that seemed higher-vaulted, and spanning a larger area, than the skies of their native lands. The magic of the steppe, its mysterious will-o'-the-wisp and siren song got hold of incarcerated strangers.

During the winter there was little to see except vastness animated by fantastic shades of light and darkness. But when spring came and the steppe burst into bloom, even the most callous men were stunned by the triumphant symphony of form and color.

The trip through the steppes lasted about six weeks. For six weeks they traveled through a divine nosegay of azaleas, tulips, lilies, carnations, wild orchids, and edelweiss, the sight of which created the delusion of sweet perfume inside stench-ridden cars.

Beyond the Yenisei River the scenery changed to forests, larger than the prisoners' countries of origin, with trees taller than rural church steeples, impenetrable underbrush, and clearings with savagely variegated vegetation. Still farther to the east, the plennis entered the taiga, the monstrous grandeur of which seemed to indicate that it had fed on man in the past and was still covetous of human flesh. The men grew sullen in the twilight of dripping sylvan solitude. They were surfeited with impressions which lost their soothing effect as they accumulated, and caused giddy bewilderment.

The human types at stations changed like a slow-motion kaleidoscope: Russians, Kirghizes, Buryaets, slit-eyed, primitive hunters, farmers of Siberian stock, Mongols, Manchus, Chinese, and Koreans. The plennis were hungry and yearned for a smoke, but it became increasingly difficult to collect alms. The Easterners were not as generous as the Western Siberians. Plennis no longer thronged at hatches. They saw little of Lake Baikal, of the Amur, and the roaming ground of the tigers.

Journey's end usually found them an apathetic lot, trotting or dragging themselves meekly to the camp, between a thin screen of equally apathetic guards.

Officers traveled segregated from the enlisted men, but even though their passenger cars had windows, they were not permitted to open them; the smells in officers' cars were no better than in vans, and neither were sanitary conditions. In one respect the commissioned soldiers were even worse off. The peasant women of Western Siberia shied away from epaulets and spangled stars, and hardly ever fed their holders.

The largest camps were located near Beresovka and Chita, with respective capacities of 27,500 and 32,500. They had occupancies of twice these numbers.

Stockades were occasionally set up around vacant buildings, such as abandoned factories, fair halls, evacuated barracks, stables, and prisons, the latter including the Krepost of Omsk, which gained notoriety through Fjodor Dostojevsky's book *The House of Death*. The most general type of accommodation, however, was the "earth barrack," a semi-subterranean structure, where most enlisted men and some officers dwelled. The "earth barrack" is still the main feature of Soviet Siberian concentration camps. The crudely boarded floor of earth barracks was five to seven feet underground. Joists ten feet high planked earthen walls and propped pointed roofs slated with earth and mud. The barracks had no partitions, and only a few small windows at ground level. Slanted doorways led into the interior, which contained three or four rows of boards which served as mass berths, a stove, and two petroleum lamps. There were neither blankets nor mattresses; Russian army regulations did not provide for such commodities; Russian inductees brought their own bedding; but the plennis had nothing to put on the planks but their rag-clad bodies. There was hardly ever sufficient firewood. "Stoves are means of ventilation," the commander of Srjetensk Camp told complainants on Christmas 1915, when the temperature outside was 52° below. "If you want to keep comfortable, just try to maintain the natural warmth of your bodies." And there was never enough petroleum to keep the lamps burning while snow piled up high above the windows.

Enlisted men and noncoms were entitled to a Russian soldier's daily food ration: 11 ounces of meat or fish, 2 pounds 10 ounces of bread, and generous servings of buckwheat, potatoes, cabbage, beets, fat, sugar, and tea. In May 1915 meat and bread rations for prisoners were reduced to 4 ounces and 1 pound 12 ounces respectively. The quality of the food was poor, often despicable: cow heads and hoofs figured as meat, the buckwheat was fusty, potatoes frozen, and fat rancid. The prisoners did not learn to what rations they were entitled and scales were withheld from them. The only means to right wrongs were complaints, but commanders considered complaints infractions of discipline, in which they were upheld by their superiors. In 1916 an Austrian major who presented an inspecting Russian general with a list of grievances was shouted down. "Prisoners are not entitled to voice criticism."

This was in conformity with Siberian club law, and it was also in accordance with such law that, when the same general returned to the camp for another inspection, mutinous guards tore him to pieces.

Poor food caused mass outbreaks of scurvy and nyctalopia. During the second year of the war the U. S. Embassy suggested an increase in POW rations, but a self-righteous Russian Government replied that the rations were adequate.

Camp commanders charged the administration the price of adequate rations, but part of the payments went into the pockets of the commanders, their assistants, and dodgers entrenched in commissariats. Officers had to purchase their own food from camp commissariats. Clerks there had inscrutable ways of keeping accounts, which kept their customers in the red even though they paid cash for every item.

Plenni enlisted men were supposed to draw a Russian soldier's pay, subaltern officers to 50, field ranking officers to 75 and generals to 125 rubles a month. On the eve of payday, however, camp commanders would present orders for mass transfers and assert that the transferred would collect in the new camp. The transfers hardly ever took place and the soldiers never got their full wages. Desperate, penniless officers would often sign receipts for 50 rubles against payment of 25.

Countless parcels and some twenty-two million rubles in cash were sent to plennis from home through the good offices of the Red Cross. Camp scribes changed the names of addressees into their own and shared money and objects with their superiors. Information discovered later put the camp commander of Omsk atop the list of despoilers. This worthy gentleman robbed his 14,000 charges of 500,000 rubles. His colleague of Samarkand "earned" only 100,000, and the commander of Tobolsk contented himself with 70,000.

Investigators had no way of compiling figures of "dues" levied upon plennis; prisoners had to pay for permission to take a bath, to carry water, to get a shave, and for transfer to "clean accommodations."

After a few months of occupation earth barracks crawled with vermin. Catching lice became an occupation as time-absorbing as it was futile. Men could not catch the pests as fast as they multiplied, and unless they escaped these carriers of infections, they had little hope to survive. Spotted typhus killed 4500 out of 8400 inmates at Novo Nikolajevsk, and 4300 out of 8000 in Krasnojarsk. Vans commuting between town and camp carried food on one trip and corpses on the other.

Dead prisoners provided camp personnel with yet another source of income: they remained on the pay roll even after their demise.

The attitude of Russian guards was determined by that of their commander. If the commander called the plennis German swine, the guards would do the same; and if the commander defrauded his wards, his enlisted men would steal or confiscate whatever they could lay hands upon. If the commander were decent, so would the guards be. But decent commanders became ever rarer after the tide of war turned against the Russians in May 1915. It was not a spirit of vengefulness that motivated Russian behavior, but a premonition that opportunities for illicit gains and brutish self-assertion would vanish with military disaster, and that there was no time to lose for a man who wanted to satisfy such desires.

Russian officers were frequently beset by feelings of inferiority toward the better-learned and higher-cultured foreigners, which caused them to victimize captive officers and men alike.

The men were taken on "training marches" of twenty miles and more, round and round barbed wire enclosures, with Russian noncoms bullying marchers into attitudes warranting treatment with the *nagaika*, the cat-o'-nine-tails. Plennis who remained mute throughout the "training" might be found guilty of collective rebelliousness and be forced to run the gauntlet groupwise.

Plenni officers were vexed by inspections in which their trifling personal belongings and their cherished letters were seized. The officers were entitled to accommodations in "lodgings." Some lived in crowded buildings, without plumbing and adequate heat, others in earth barracks, which they called cemeteries.

Being crowded together indefinitely begot exasperation. Soldiers came to know each other's stories, jokes, wisecracks, obscenities, and sentimentalities to the point of nausea. What had made them smile or sympathize when they had first heard it stirred them to furious hatred when it was told for the hundredth time. Few new topics of thought or conversation came up to alleviate the nerve-racking monotony.

Elsa Brändström told of detention psychosis. It started with a feeling of poignant unrest, ill-humor, and disgust. Afflicted men left their barracks, walked through the camp in odd planimetrical patterns, then called upon some group of prisoners, abused them, ran out, dashed back to their own barracks to pick fights with fellow-inmates because one man's laughter was shrill or the other had an annoying way of talking, a third coughed, a fourth was silent, and yet others snored. Controversies about a spoon produced challenges to duels to be fought "after the war." Garrulousness was not taken as an indication of mental disturbance, however, and the countrymen of Professor Sigmund Freud did not apply psychology. Detention psychosis occasionally defied rehabilitation after the prisoner's return. Many broken homes in Central Europe during the 1920s and 1930s could be traced to Siberian camp experiences.

Prisoners whose moodiness suddenly exploded into frenzy were removed to hovels, set aside to let the insane die in isolation. Also if restive plennis refused to take orders, commanders had them sent to the dungeon; and there, in dark solitary confinement, many perished in raving madness.

For almost one year only Orthodox clergymen were admitted to the camps. The Russian Government distrusted priests of denominations over which it had no control. Only after a diplomatic démarche by the Holy See were Catholic, Protestant, and Jewish chaplains permitted to see plennis.

But the first ray of hope which stimulated the plennis came from a source that was certainly not spiritual. Successful fakery brought comfort to earth barracks and barbed wire enclosures; fakery of "documents" convinced the prisoners that they could outwit their keepers.

Illiterate Russian soldiers had a superstitious awe for *boomagas*. A boomaga was a document, in fact any piece of writing; and the more stamps, pictures, and ornaments it carried, the more inviolable and important it was. Siberians were familiar with a great variety of lawlessness, but they had never thought that anybody could venture to fake a boomaga.

Now boomagas were being fabricated in clandestine shops in every camp. They were adorned with stamps, odd markings, and fantastic characters.

If a man wanted to leave the camp and was stopped, he drew a boomaga and read out loud that its bearer was entitled to move about at his discretion. If he wanted to buy and sell contraband he presented the same boomaga and read out that it licensed its bearer to do business.

The guards listened and believed. The plennis knew basic Russian well enough to sound convincing.

If shops ran short of paper or printing supplies, boomaga-carrying plennis made their way to nearby settlements and stole menu cards from which convincing boomagas could be made.

Russian officers did not tell their men that boomagas were not infallible, for this might have put the ax on the foundations of discipline. Their plight was even more difficult as genuine boomagas were being issued to identify prisoners assigned to extracurricular duties. Irate commanders staged raids but hardly ever found the hidden shops. Many prisoners made bids for freedom, equipped with nothing but a patched-up menu card.

Army regulations in Germany and Austria-Hungary required that officers vindicate their capture; this was occasionally interpreted to the effect that prisoners were duty-bound to escape. The desolation of camp life induced even men who did not agree with this interpretation to try escape. Fences and entanglements were not overly strong, and guards lingering on small square platforms of pyramid-shaped wooden watchtowers were not really alert. Boomagas helped holders who were challenged. Enlisted men too made bids for freedom, and showed more resourcefulness than their superiors in rank.

Thousands of plennis crossed the Eastern Siberian border into China and the border of Western Siberia into Persia. Until 1917 the road home from China led via the Pacific to the United States, across the American continent and to neutral Holland. The British held a close lookout for escapees; a few men who had come all the way to within sight of the Dutch coast were taken from their boats by naval patrols and interned in England. One Austrian explenni, whom the British had captured one hour before the boat on which he worked as a stoker would have made port in Rotterdam, went on a hunger strike, on the Isle of Man, and was eventually exchanged, a jittery skeleton. In Austria he recovered sufficiently to serve in the closing battles of the war, remained in the Army afterwards, and in 1938 was impressed in the German Wehrmacht as a colonel, served at Stalingrad, and after the surrender of the German army group there was shipped to Siberia, where he died thirty years after his original escape.

Men who had left the stockades tried boomagas to fool patrolling Russian gendarmes, but this did not always work since some gendarmes could read; and there was never sufficient time to try the "document" on plenni-hunters who would shoot on sight rather than lose a substantial premium. Siberian authorities paid 100 rubles for each officer, and 50 rubles per enlisted man, captured dead or alive. Buryaets, Cossacks, and other border people made plenni-hunting a profession.

Plennis who escaped the hunters had to deal with Manchurian smugglers who charged stiff fees for guidance across the Siberian border. But even those who could pay were not safe. Smugglers might lead them right back into Siberia and collect head money.

And there were the Siberian tigers, more alert than camp guards. An undisclosed number of plennis fell victim to the huge man-eaters. "Our finest guards," Russian camp commanders called them; and the Bolsheviks still consider the tigers the most efficient jailers in Eastern Siberia.

Russian penalties for attempts at escape were harsh, and camp commanders jailed barrack mates of successful escapees for failure to report. Siberian authorities, then as now, consider denunciation a civic duty.

Improvement of plenni morale boosted the men's urge to work. Officers set up co-operative workshops, directed by men who had once learned a trade as a hobby rather than a potential source of income. Professional soldiers and former white-collar workers, civil servants, students, lawyers, and teachers, drafted as reserve officers, were trained as craftsmen; their products were marketed by fellow officers and enlisted men who developed an amazing ingenuity to keep the business going without surrendering proceeds to camp commanders.

New ties were established between officers and men. The officers were better educated, the men cleverer in most practical matters. Joining forces, they won many a silent struggle against their keepers.

Profits made in plenni trade often bridged the gap between starvation and survival. Even skeleton health services were established, and disinfection of barracks and filtering of water reduced epidemics to a less than catastrophic level.

Officers founded mutual-assistance societies and clandestine committees to explore avenues of escape. Experts in various fields delivered lectures to fellow-plennis desirous of broadening their education, and, as Russian commanders always suspected and could never prove, taught international law, with emphasis on the rights of POWs.

Camp shops became a new and successful branch of Siberian industry, and an even greater stimulant to Siberian economy was the broadening stream of working plennis who, as time went by, learned to by-pass distribution centers and to find employment in trades really commensurate with their abilities.

Many Siberian plants and shops were poorly equipped, but plennis were handy even with obsolete equipment, and manufacturers paid premiums to their employees whose performance increased after they were no longer assigned by Russian clerks. Several small industrialists offered partnerships in return for reorganization of their businesses.

Farm hands were in even higher demand than industrial labor. Plennis who had slipped out of the camp could almost invariably find work and shelter with peasants. They would not have to take chances by presenting a boomaga to gendarmes searching for hidden fugitives. The peasants, hating the gendarmes as corrupt autocrats, led the searchers off the track.

With able-bodied farmers mostly in the Army the oldest man or woman of the family selected helpers. They would feel the applicant's muscles, inspect his teeth, and they preferred handsome men to please their womenfolk. Thin men were least in demand. Siberians believed that thin persons were fundamentally wicked.

"Our men," the peasant folk would call their workers. "My farm," plenni peasants would soon come to say. The plenni planned the farm's economy, tilled the soil, tended the animals, and begot new Siberian citizens with every younger woman in the household.

Siberian women were not worried about illegitimate offspring, but one aspect frightened some of them: would the child ever learn Russian, or would it speak only the father's native tongue?

Returning Siberian husbands did not mind finding their families increased. If houses, fields, and animals were found in good shape, the mushiks would even praise the babies.

Among the plennis were men who back home had not been paragons of legality. In Siberia they found employ in illicit trades and competed with shiftless civilian countrymen for ringleadership. The black market enjoyed a new prosperity as regular transportation was almost at a standstill. The Trans-Siberian Railroad, clogged by military trains, its rolling stock reduced far below requirements, no longer played an appreciable part in the supply of Siberia. Only the most inventive and the most uninhibited minds could think up means of satisfying demands for vital commodities. The men from Central Europe did better than the Siberians. They became both bloodsuckers and providers of the country. Plenni racketeers moved into cities, bribing the police and scornful of local toughs who could not deal with the intrusion. These plennis helped marketing camp products as a token of comradeship, but this was but a side line of their business.

Siberia to them was a hooligan's world. There was money in smuggling, cheating, stealing, and violence. And the late-comers in such rackets could still go into politics. Plenni-hooligans who knew hideouts and secret meeting places listened to conspirator addresses. Their seismographical senses registered faint tremors and their keen minds analyzed the essentials of rebellion in their large beats.

Heterogeneous as the people of Siberia were, varied as were their sentiments and resentments, one element animated all of them: hatred; violent, diffuse, burning, aggressive hatred.

Mushiks hated big landowners; officials hated their superiors; civilians hated the military, nomads the settled, workers their managers, the managers merchants, merchants black-marketeers. Tribesmen hated their elders, elders their constituents, aborigines the Russians. Everybody out of office hated everybody in office. There were countless varieties of hatred, but hatred was the common denominator of Siberian feelings, and this much European-born racketeers realized: he who would channel labyrinthical hatreds into one stream would rule the obsessed and their land.

Plennis tried their skills at rabble-rousing and fared better than accent-free demagogues. Siberian authorities, always ready to throw wretched victims into dungeons, could cope with neither rackets nor sedition. But still, as the third year of war dawned, no unifier of Siberian hatred was in sight.

CHAPTER SIXTY-ONE In the summer of 1915 a youthful attaché from the British Embassy in Petrograd (St. Petersburg) arrived in London. He besieged lesser luminaries of the War Office, imploring and pestering them to arrange for an interview with the Secretary in person. Field Marshal Earl Horatio Herbert Kitchener of Khartoum, stuffishly venerable symbol of Victorian soldierdom, usually had no time to spare for small-fry outsiders. The attaché insisted that he had information to convey, so secret and portentous, that no lesser man than the Field Marshal should receive it, firsthand. Eventually he was granted ten minutes to report. He spent one night putting his observations into the sequacious terminology that the sixty-five-year-old legendary soldier was said to prefer to more dramatic presentations, and training his speech to underemphatic *mezza voce* required for the occasion. But when he stood before the great man he forgot script and timbre; he blushed, and blurted, "There is going to be revolution in Russia—soon."

"Kind of hot outside," the Field Marshal snarled. "Some fresh air in a park might do you good."

Other responsible Western statesmen assumed similar attitudes toward reports on the impending collapse of the Russian Government. This was caused not so much by political purblindness as by wishful thinking.

Japan, however, who had joined the Allies in August 1914, did not even wish to see the Tsar's empire survive. Tokyo had not gone to war to assist Britain, France, Belgium, Serbia, or, least of all, Russia, but to establish its own hegemony in Asia. With German-leased Tsingtao in China's Shantung Province seized on November 7, 1914, after a three-month siege and German island strongholds in the Pacific eliminated by Allied action, Japan reverted to other objectives.

The Japanese Government continued the time-dishonored procedure of usurpation and encroachment in China. In the spring of 1916, when the republican government of China tried to stall, Tokyo issued an ultimatum and collected another ninety-nine-year-lease on Port Arthur, Dairen, the South Manchurian and the Mukden-Antung railroads, the right for Japanese subjects to lease land in Southern Manchuria for periods up to thirty years, and to "travel, reside, and carry on business therein at liberty." Japanese citizens were granted extraterritorial status in all parts of China; Inner Mongolia was opened to the Japanese; "joint undertakings" were established in that territory. Japan obtained a preferential status in the selection of political, financial, and military advisers to the Chinese Government; a priority in granting loans, which China would solicit, and a list of lesser concessions, that, combined, lengthened Japan's lead over her rivals in China.

Washington protested against Japan's ultimatum to China, but the protest was not followed up by action, even though it was taken for granted that the U. S. Government would intervene should Japan proceed to squeeze American enterprise out of China.

Since 1913 the Standard Oil Company had held title to exploit oil fields in Shansi and Chihli (Hopeh) provinces; in 1914 the Chinese Navy Department signed a contract with the Bethlehem Steel Company, awarding the Americans a contract for construction of dockyards near Foochow; in 1916, Lee, Higginson & Company granted a loan to China. American corporations prepared restoration of the Great Canal and blueprinted highway projects and development of telephone and telegraph communications.

Russia had little to show in the race for China. In March 1916 the Russo-Asiatic Bank obtained title to construction of another railroad linking Harbin with the right bank of the Amur; the project was to be financed by a loan of fifty million rubles in gold. But Russia had no funds to spare, the Western European Allies would not lend Petrograd money not strictly required for the conduct of the war, and America viewed further Russian penetration into China with strict though not hard-hitting disfavor.

Had Japan continued to concentrate on China, a crisis in Japanese-American relations might have been precipitated. But early in 1916, Tokyo planned to take possession of the Asiatic heritage of a soon to be defunct Russian Empire.

Russia and Japan were co-belligerents, but not legally allies. Japan, having learned a lesson of synthetic legality justifying unlawful international action, wanted an agreement that would be interpreted to warrant intervention in Russian affairs.

On July 3, 1916, Petrograd and Tokyo signed a secret pact. Both countries pledged themselves not to become parties to any agreement or political combination directed against the other signatory; to consult each other should one party be menaced; and to take fitting measures to prevent China from falling under political domination by a third power.

The Central Powers, with whom both parties were still at war, were, at the time, not candidates for domination of China. Excepting Russia, Japan's only rivals in China were Great Britain and possibly the United States. The secret pact could have resulted in a united Russo-Japanese front against Britain.

Tokyo doubted that Great Britain could emerge victorious. After Great Britain had helped Japan to eliminate Germany as an Eastern competitor, Germany might give tacit approval to the elimination of Great Britain as an aspirant for domination of China.

One month after the signature of the pact the Japanese press opened a vitriolic campaign for breaking away from the Entente, and making up with the Central Powers, who, as government-inspired editorials claimed, were obviously winning the war. Pro-German neutrals carried messages back and forth between Berlin and Tokyo; German prisoners from fallen Tsingtao enjoyed almost complete freedom and, praising Japanese chivalry during and after the siege, they contributed to renascent good will between their country and its former military pupils.

London did not yet know of the pact of July 3, but worried British diplomats inquired about terms under which the press campaign would be called off. Tokyo requested that the Entente and its associated powers recognize Japan's title to all former German establishments in China and former German islands in the Pacific, and that Japanese representatives be given a decisive word on these matters at a future peace conference. This was reinsurance in case the Central Powers did not win.

London was amenable, and in return requested Japan's consent to incorporation of Tibet into Britain's sphere of interest. Such infringement a prostrate Peking government could not hope to prevent, even under its status as an "ally," and Tokyo agreed condescendingly. In an Asia under Japanese hegemony Tibet was of little importance.

Japanese diplomacy had acquired a new touch of Machiavellianism, but Japanese Intelligence still relied upon sober facts and figures rather than on psychological analyses.

To Tokyo the Trans-Siberian Railroad remained the seismograph of Siberian tranquility and stability. As long as the railroad functioned, the Russian regime would function; if transportation were undermined, the regime would be undermined and a standstill along the track was considered tantamount to a standstill of the administration of Siberia.

Three thousand alleged Japanese businessmen crowded Vladivostok; another thousand or fifteen hundred Japanese civilians went after their mysterious business between Vladivostok and Irkutsk. They all worked for the Central

Intelligence Agency and predicted that the crucial standstill would occur no later than the winter of 1916. Japanese goods, a great part of it ammunition with the highest percentage of duds on record, littered yards all along the eastern section of the Trans-Siberian. No less than 600,000 tons of freight from Japan remained unguarded and unprotected on the piers of Vladivostok. Along the Transbaikal and Maritime Province sectors Siberian draftees camped, waiting for trains to take them to assembly areas. They had to wait for months, as the number of military trains was down to 10 per cent of normal. Civilian transportation was down to 5 per cent of normal. Russian engines seemed fit for the scrap heap. New American locomotives were unloaded on Vladivostok piers without means of getting them to the tracks; and even had they been put before a train, there would have been no fuel to keep them rolling.

During the German-Japanese wartime flirtation Berlin forwarded reports by its wizards on logistics to Tokyo. The Germans estimated that the usefulness of the Trans-Siberian had come to an end in December 1915. Trunk lines between Transbaikalia and Vladivostok via Khabarovsk were said to be out of operation and signal installations all along the track no longer operable.

Russian experts made somber predictions about the Trans-Siberian but suggested no remedies. The government assumed a fatalistic attitude. Everything was in the lap of the gods—the railroad, the war, and even a revolution. *Nitshevo . . .*

But 1915 passed, 1916 hobbled by, 1917 came, and transportation in Siberia continued, chaotic but full of the strange vitality which Russo-Siberian chaos can beget.

There were still no highways, not even through dirt roads; but there were river shipping and the traditional carters and wagoners who knew how to drive over roadless territory. Siberian transportation was not all geared to railroads. Most Siberian adults remembered the time when there had been no tracks and yet goods had kept moving. If the railroad ceased operating, *nitshevo,* goods would move. And yet the Trans-Siberian continued to operate. Racketeers did what no Russian railroad wizards could have done. They organized a patchwork of traffic; scrap locomotives kept crawling thousands of miles on the oddest combustibles. There were no schedules, no operating signal installations, nothing of the essentials of regular transportation. There were countless accidents, yet makeshift transportation continued and some plenni operators, who made fortunes on chaotic traffic, insisted that the Trans-Siberian carried three to four times the loads it had carried during the Russo-Japanese War.

Japan did not discontinue deliveries of goods while unpaid-for merchandise was rotting on Siberian piers and yards. Tokyo kept shipping wares to Siberia and requested that the Russian Government grant Japan the right to have them guarded by its own organs. Tokyo also suggested that its guards assume protection of Japanese citizens in Eastern Siberia, giving their figure as a staggering 10,000.

But Petrograd wearily declined to discuss the issue, convinced that if Japan ever got the boots of its soldiery into the Siberian door, it could never be dislodged.

Tokyo did not press such demands in 1916. Its agents still watched the railroad, fascinated by the antics of its operators.

There was yet another issue the Japanese military viewed with keen interest, though not with as many delusions and as grave concern as it was viewed by the Western Allies: the issue of the plennis.

The boon of Russia's taking more than two million prisoners seemed to have produced a catastrophic emergency: one hundred potential Austro-Hungarian, German, and Turkish divisions were encamped on the approaches of China and of strategic areas in Western Central Asia. Twice as many enemy soldiers were inside Siberia as Siberian soldiers served in the Tsar's army. Captives outnumbered their local guards thirty if not fifty to one. Mobilizing foreign prisoners for military action had become part and parcel of Allied warfare. If the Central Powers were to gather their own captive men and arm and reorganize them, results might be devastating. Such prisoner armies could establish fronts in the heart of Asia, move into Mongolia, China, and Afghanistan, invade India, seize Persia, deploy in the rear of English forces in Mesopotamia, which had suffered severe defeat at the hands of the Turks at Kut-el-Amara in April 1916. German agents were reported swarming all over Asia; they were intriguing and boasting of impending invasion of Kashmir.

London and Paris looked upon Japan as the only protector against the hundred phantom divisions. Japan was ready to exploit Allied nightmares, but Japan was not really sacred. The captured soldiers would hardly take orders to rally and fight. There were not enough arms available to equip even a small fraction of them. The intermezzo of friendliness with Berlin had convinced Tokyo that the Kaiser's general staff discounted the "hundred divisions," and that the Austro-Hungarian Supreme Command distrusted its plennis as a deserter-ridden lot.

The mass of the captives in Siberia never heard the tale of the ghost divisions. They carried on, as their urge of self-preservation directed them. They endured Siberian tribulations, exploited Siberian opportunities, begot one half of the crop of Siberian babies, and more often than not turned into Siberian conservatives, believing that once they had found ways and means of continued existence, a change could be but detrimental. The number of plenni racketeers who worked for, and gambled on, revolution was small and had little contact with their former camp mates.

The people of Siberia were not aware of crucial events in the making. Siberian army corps kept on fighting, no better and no worse than other Russian units surviving under a battering that no other army could have endured. Siberian soldiers wrote only few letters and mail services delivered only a fraction of the total; censors too indolent to read the communications deleted entire pages at random, and what remained did not convey the impression that the Army was disintegrating.

Russian propagandists had built one Siberian general into a national hero, but the people of Siberia did not react by spontaneous outbursts of patriotism. Not even the population of the Altai District talked much about Lavr Georgievitch Kornilov, scion of a local Cossack family.

When the war broke out, Kornilov was a division commander. In the battle of Grodek (Radkow) he was under orders to stay on the defensive while adjoining divisions carried the brunt of attack. Kornilov, however, had his unit attack; the division ran headlong into strong Austrian positions, and lost half of its effectives and most of its artillery, almost turning Russian victory into defeat. In 1915, after the Russian disaster in the sector between Tarnow and Gorlice, he refused to join the general retreat. This time he lost all of his reformed division and fell into Austrian captivity. One year later he escaped and returned to Russia, where, much to his surprise, he was given a hero's welcome, and was promoted to corps commander for "extraordinary valor," by Tsar Nicholas II in person.

Kornilov's temerity and his rough talk against administrative stupidity boosted his legend-fostered popularity in European Russia, but nobody in Siberia would have considered him a leader in a dawning new era.

Was a new era dawning? Siberian orators contended that it was right around the corner. But, like their idol Karl Marx, Siberian youthful intellectuals had been foretelling revolution at every turn, and while their master idol had predicted public clamor for his leadership in all quarters of the industrialized world, Siberian students peddled their own revolutionary services to unconvinced clandestine gatherings. Political exiles also talked revolution, and nothing but revolution, in Siberia while preparing their own return to Russia. The aging professional revolutionaries did not really think that Siberia was a fertile ground for socialism. Plenni rabble-rousers went after their newly adopted business as usual, distrusting native rivals, and in turn being distrusted and disliked by Russo-Siberian rebels.

Authorities occasionally arrested student demagogues, investigated deportees, and rounded up misbehaving outlandish characters. But there were no trials and few charges.

Otherwise officials misbehaved, as they had done for more than three hundred years; the people suffered and harbored feelings of vengefulness, as it had for more than three thousand years; foreigners were under a process of Siberianization; and nature followed its cycles, benign and indifferent. On March 1, 1917, it did not look as if Siberia were on the eve of a fundamental change.

During the following night some men were seen carrying papers, brushes, and pots, and busying themselves on fences and walls. Drowsy policemen were not keenly interested in nuisances that neither drew blood nor audibly disparaged the authorities, and non-officials did not give it a thought.

On the morning of March 2 (old style) unobtrusively printed posters were displayed outside of barracks, on office buildings, public squares, and market places, all along the Trans-Siberian, and even in settlements far away from the railroad. "Prikas One," the posters were titled. *Prikas*—reminiscent of the ancient administration of Siberia—meant ordinance. Number One indicated that this was the first decree issued by new Russian authorities, of whom practically nobody in Siberia knew.

This time no teachers were assigned to reading the posters to gatherings. Policemen stood by, stunned, while students and strange newcomers read the prikas out loud: All soldiers were requested to refuse taking orders from their military superiors, and to accept committees of soldiers and workers as the sole legal authorities.

The populace hardly understood what this meant. Older men remembered that similar appeals had been launched by scattered rioters twelve years before. But then the soldiers had still obeyed their officers, and it was considered likely that they would always do so. In the early hours of March 2 there were not even scattered riots.

Students, however, talked riot. They told audiences that rioting was a civic duty. But Siberians had no use for additional civic duties, and their response was disappointing.

Frightened officials stayed at home that morning. Policemen kept ignoring prikas and commentators. Nothing had happened by noon. Officials went to their offices, policemen tore posters down, and the small crowds dispersed. Siberia returned to normalcy.

Then news kept arriving from the capital by wire. Tsar Nicholas II had abdicated in favor of Grand Duke Mikhail Aleksandrovitsh, who, in turn, had abdicated at once; a provisional government had formed; the Duma (Parliament) had set up one executive committee, and another executive committee had been constituted by a Petrograd Soviet (Council) of Workers and Soldiers. These committees had been instrumental in the establishment of the Provisional Government. The Provisional Government would carry out urgent democratic reforms, pending the convocation of a constituent assembly.

Provisional Government—Constituent Assembly—Executive Committee—Soviet of Workers and Soldiers—even to relatively educated Siberians these were puzzling terms without concrete meaning. Names were mentioned in telegrams. Prince Lvov presided over the Provisional Government. In Russia princes were not necessarily conservatives; this seemed to indicate that the mysterious affair was reminiscent of the Dekabrist revolt, and that nobility would survive the Tsar. But who were Messrs. Kerensky and Tshaidse, who headed the Soviet? Comments called them "moderate Social Revolutionaries." The term "moderate" did not comfort officials trained to consider the very word "social" anathema and all revolutionaries noisome candidates for execution.

From governor general to trooper no Siberian functionary knew whether or not he was still in office, and almost everybody was haunted by visions of social and revolutionary *revisors,* who would check office records and draft criminal charges.

Carloads of files went up in flames. This done, officials played possum.

Siberia was temporarily without an administration. Even mail service was at a standstill. Anything could happen.

Nothing did happen. Siberia had been without an authority before. Siberia waited for further developments, or at least for Prikas Two.

No such prikas came.

The posters of March 2, 1917, were not, as it had first seemed, the work of leftist radicals, even though the Maximalists (Bolsheviks) were anxious to exploit their effect. The Maximalists were the smallest of all groups who had opposed the Tsarist regime, but they were tightly disciplined, and had their agents planted in all other groups. Authorship of the prikas was attributed to three less than extremist men—Tshaidse, Tseretelli, and Sokolov, all practically unknown in Siberia.

The organization responsible for posting Prikas One included militant workers and rebellious students, but also aristocratic youths who worried that officers would prevent enactment of wholesome reforms. They would hardly have agreed among themselves as to what made a reform wholesome, but they were fundamentally sincere and courageous, even though for many the posting of Prikas One remained the one and only revolutionary feat.

By the end of March 1917, Siberian towns again recovered their usual appearance. In Irkutsk the offices of the Governor General were at work on routine matters. Merchants and manufacturers were busy marking up prices and dealing with black-marketeers upon whom they depended. Plennis roamed the muddy streets; ornate troikas, the sleds of big landowners, stopped in front of amusement places, where entertainment hit new heights of frantic lasciviousness.

In Petrograd the Tsar's Guards remained on duty at the Winter Palace grounds, after the crowned occupant had lost both his crown and his abode. The Guards drilled, changed, and paraded under the command of their sergeants, since most officers had donned civilian clothes. Strange crowds watched the Guards, entered the palace, proceeded unchallenged to the innermost sanctums of Catherine Hall and the Hall of the Lost Steps. The pompous settings discouraged roughness, but orators, mostly youthful intelligentsia, shrill and skinny girls among them, delivered speeches to rugged attendances in and out of uniform.

Workers from Petrograd factories and drafted mushiks from all parts of the empire without a Tsar did not understand the quotations from socialist writings, which orators recited enthusiastically, dryly, buoyantly, or shyly, according to temper. They listened to the sound of the speaker's voice, watched the speaker's antics, and expressed delight or disapproval.

Millions of words were shouted, ranted, croaked, and shrieked. Speakers who drew applause were accosted by unobtrusive-looking characters who offered to provide new outlets for the demagogue's talents. The Bolsheviks had their talent scouts all over urban gathering places, and enlisted everybody they considered useful. They did not pay cash, but they promised power.

Even officers were among the new talent; men who would not have dared to show their epaulets, but in mufti denounced the regime of a fallen Tsar, to the service of whom they had sworn to devote their lives. The ex-officers who now pledged themselves to the task of reforming and "rejuvenating" Russia included older, high-ranking men. "For forty years," a graying general in a business suit told an exasperated French observer, "I have been waiting for the dawn of a new era. I praise the Lord for having let me live to see it rise. . . ."

Aristocrats, wealthy burghers, and high-minded ladies rubbed shoulders with unkempt mushiks and hard-fisted workers, to discover the much-exalted people's soul.

Had but half of the blind enthusiasm, the limbless urge for noble deeds, and the elementary power of emotion that seemed to pour forth from unfathomable sources found worthy objectives, a new light, arisen from stale Russian darkness, could have brightened the entire world. But the only leadership-minded group in Russia was the Bolsheviks, and they had but one design: to harness all sources of power to boost their own.

What Friedrich Nietzsche, the sick German champion of Superman, had said in *Menschliches-Allzu Menschliches* (Human-All too Human) well applied to the Russian Revolution: "Every revolution resuscitates the wildest energies; long-buried dreadfulness, and the recklessness of a long past is reborn. A revolution can be a source of power to a mankind grown weary, but it will never be an organizer and a perfectioner of human nature."

The rabble-rousers in Petrograd styled themselves true and only representatives of all workers, peasants, and soldiers from all parts and nationalities of Russia. They would pretend to recognize local delegates from the remotest regions, and introduce them as partisans to make the crowds believe that Russia already had a new social edifice and that the Maximalists held the key to it.

A goodly number of Siberian soldiers were among the audiences in palaces and street corners of European Russia. They listened to orations in bewilderment. Prikas One had reduced the power of the officers, and with no officers to keep them in the Army, they wanted to go home, but the orators said nothing about transportation or severance pay. Some mushiks from the steppes believed that they were not smart enough to understand verbose city slickers and sought advice from a civilian "representative of Siberia," who was, in fact, no less bewildered than his drafted countrymen.

He had come to Petrograd from Yakutsk to look for an investor who would finance operations of a gold mine he had discovered. When he arrived he found Prikas One posted, the Tsar deposed, and nobody wanting to talk business. Most people spent business hours in assembly places.

The gold-mine prospector went to Catherine Hall to look for financiers and buttonhole demagogues. The demagogues told him that mining was being socialized and that socialization implied expropriation. The man from Yakutsk loathed the thought of expropriation and called it bad revolution. The demagogues were not impressed by his protest, but they were impressed by his colorful appearance. The anti-expropriator was tall and wore a spectacular reindeer coat. They dubbed him Representative of Siberia, and he did as he was told, hanging around Catherine Hall, posing as a representative, and hoping that this would eventually net him operating capital.

And there was yet another Siberian prominent in Petrograd: General Kornilov, now commander of the military district, who had arrested Nicholas II and his family. But Kornilov refused to co-operate with the Bolsheviks, and the Provisional Government had the General removed from the sensitive district, and appointed commander of the Russian Eighth Army, replacing General Brusilov, the finest brain in the armed forces.

Brusilov had treated revolutionary organizations with subtle persuasion, making the men feel duty-bound toward their country regardless of form of government. He had welded the Eighth Army into an accomplished striking force and scored upset victories. This soldier-diplomat had never tried to assume leadership in non-military fields, while Kornilov wanted his Eighth Army to be an organ of both national defense and national government.

Kornilov mounted the soapbox, addressed mushiks as a country doctor would scold recalcitrant yokels. He styled himself chief spokesman of all Russian soldiers, and the boss of committees, councils, and similar bodies set up to "democratize" the Army. Prior to Kornilov's assumption of command revolutionary orators had been unsuccessful with the Eighth Army; discipline had been maintained despite Prikas One, and nothing changed after the Provisional Government cautiously remanded the Prikas. But with Kornilov in charge the rabble-rousers had their day. They called the commander a would-be dictator who would wantonly sacrifice the lives of his soldiers to set up a rule of his own. They shouted that Kornilov was responsible for amendments to Prikas One. The new commander had not been consulted on the subject, but the Provisional Government, staggering the tightrope between the need for military discipline and the necessity of championing liberties, its commitments to the Allies, and its pledges for reforms, did not come to his assistance. Mass desertions shook the structure of the Eighth Army, soldiers fraternized with the enemy, the Provisional Government's pledge to fight on seemed to turn into a mockery.

Kornilov's military conceptions were as crude and turbulent as his ideas of national leadership. They were typically Siberian, based on, and inspired by, animosities. He hoped to destroy the enemy by steam-roller tactics, and to direct national policies to satisfy his resentments. He was infuriated by fraternization and desertions, but did not cope with mutiny. If the average enlisted man were unreliable, he, Kornilov, would create an elite of officers, noncoms, and stalwart soldiers. Stores were depleted, but they were still adequate to equip the elite units.

In June 1917 a Kornilov Regiment, almost entirely composed of officers, was ready for combat duty. So was the Savage Division, a cross-selection of the most reckless mobilized individuals.

Had Kornilov led these toughs straight on to Petrograd, he would have seized control of the government. But the Kornilov Regiment and the Savage Division did not march on the capital. The Siberian general probably had no conception of how to hold the reins after seizing them, and, temporizing and gambling, he lashed out in another direction. In addition to his elite outfit he still had one army corps, the Twelfth, in tolerable fighting shape. He did not consult the government as the highest instance in all military matters, but ordered an attack against the Austro-Hungarian lines. The enemy was caught napping, and the furious Russian assault resulted in a local breakthrough, capture of many prisoners and much booty. But then the enemy rallied, and counterattacked. Outgunned and outnumbered, the Russians reeled back with staggering losses.

It had been a fundamentally stupid battle. After the dust settled military experts wondered what caused Kornilov to chance his irreplaceable elite in an attack that had to be futile because of shortage of men and communication. One explanation offered was that the General wanted to avenge the humiliation of his capture two years before. This would seem absurd for almost any other military man, but not for a Siberian Cossack.

When the break-through occurred, the Provisional Government promoted the highhanded General to Commander in Chief of the Army; the Allies, sympathizing with the Russian Revolution even though it undermined the foundations of a state with whom they had been associated, momentarily wondered whether the Russian Republic would not be a better fighter than the Russia of the Tsar.

But all the new Commander in Chief had left were decimated shock troops and disintegrating bands of stragglers who lived on the poverty-stricken homeland and its disorganized production. The war against the external enemy was irretrievably lost.

In August 1917 the Provisional Government had not yet taken root. Only speeches sprouted. Theoretical reformers catapulted on rostrums elaborated on seclusion-born ideals, but one hundred resolutions could not substitute for one practicable suggestion, and one ton of emotion was less effective than one ounce of determination. Passionate enthusiasm, most volatile of all elements, evaporated without leaving traces other than seedy disappointment.

The shadow of determined Bolshevism lengthened. The Maximalist apparatus was highly selective. The number of activists was less than one per thousand of the population of European Russia, but it became apparent that a thousand well-organized men in strategic key positions could terrorize several million of leaderless fellow-citizens.

Bolshevik power could be checked only by military power, but no soldiers' councils, no ensigns substituting for field marshals, no amateur politicians running offices of war and navy could substitute for experienced professional soldiers.

A number of the Tsar's generals scowled at the Provisional Government; others were distrustful of and unpopular with the soldiers; and career-minded turncoats flirted with Maximalist extremism even before the Bolshevik coup.

Kornilov was a swashbuckler, a daredevil, and altogether unpredictable. He had gathered what remained of his elite, and indications were that he wanted to turn against the Bolsheviks. But the Provisional Government did not enlist the Siberian General's services against the threat from within. Fearful of civil war and military dictatorship, it relieved Kornilov from his command in September 1917, which did not eliminate him as a contender for supreme power but paved the way for a Bolshevik coup.

Kornilov did not surrender his command. Bolshevik fellow-travelers in the government obtained orders for his arrest, but the warrant was never carried out.

Remnants of his Savage Division stayed with him. Kornilov was a soldier of fortune, but fortune deserted him. He needed more men and his recruiting drive led to infiltration of the Savage Division by ruthless Bolshevik partisans. He wanted to seize the capital ahead of the Bolsheviks, and he arrived at its gates only after the successful Red putsch. On November 12 (old style), 1917, he made a bid that might have nipped Bolshevism rule in the bud, but Bolshevik infiltration broke the backbone of the Savage Division.

Kornilov did not throw in the towel. He wandered south, at the head of a small band of stalwarts, toward the Ukraine, where his ancestors had lived when Siberia received its name. Defeated by Bolshevik insurgents at Christmas near Kharkov, he enlisted with Ukrainian usurper-atamans, Czech legionnaires, and wayward lansquenets. The last photo of Kornilov, taken in 1918, shows him without insignia of rank in a shapeless fur coat with a high Cossack's cap and a coarse shirt instead of the Russian officer's blouse.

The man who took the picture quoted the Cossack Kornilov as saying: "Tell General Janin that my men and myself are the representatives of the Russian Army, of its noble tradition, its *esprit de corps,* and its conceptions of honor. Tell him that the day will come when all patriots will join us, and that all good Russians will realize that our country has been betrayed, sold down the river. Until then we shall persevere. This is our design. We shall stand fast and carry on to the end."

When the message was spoken, Allied intervention in Siberia was taking its frustrating course.

Kornilov and his men did not live up to the resounding words. Extreme trials and utter distress might have purified and enlightened the bewildered General and his diehards, but they could not stand fast long enough. Kornilov died in 1919, a beaten man.

There had been one enemy against whom the Cossack General was powerless: the watchword "Peace."

Next to the nascent Red Army the most powerful Bolshevik weapon was that word, which paralyzed their opponents' will to fight.

Ranks of anti-Bolshevik Russians who might have stood up under artillery barrage broke under the hammering of the word Peace. Kornilov lacked the inspirational capacity to fight off its impact, and his soapbox oratory could not convince villagers and small-towners that Bolshevik peace was a deception; that the meek would be cudgeled into "peaceful" inertia, and eventually forced to grind the mills of a war that would not end until Bolshevism had achieved all its belligerent goals. Peace to the Russians was leave from dying, and they were weary of death, ready to pay any price for survival.

And when Kornilov fought his losing battle, it did not occur to him that the Maximalists might be able to enlist formidable soldiers.

But the Man without a Fatherland formed the nucleus and the elite of the Red Army. No demagogic persuasiveness, and certainly not Leon Trotsky's much-vaunted genius for military improvisation, could have built a hard-hitting army from deserters of the Tsar's defeated forces. The legend of workers from Petrograd who changed from undernourished, dejected proletarians into invincibly spirited Red warriors is a fairy tale. Hardly would the Bolsheviks have been able to scatter the "Kornilovites," and less even the forces of Denikin, Wrangel, and other officers who attempted to untie the Red knot, had it not been for the Latvians and their Captain Bangersky.

Bangersky's brief and strange career opened in 1915, when Latvian soldiers whispered the conspiratory poem and Latvian parents perished on transports. The captain's ancestors had suffered oppression from landowners of German stock, and he was brought up in a hatred of Germans more intense even than hatred of Russians. He offered the Russian War Office to form special Latvian shock troops to fight the Kaiser's men in return for liberation of their families from exile.

He obtained promises and provided Latvian irregulars who fought like demons. In the summer of 1916, Bangersky had eight battalions in line, but Latvian deportees had not returned. One year later the Provisional Government promised Latvia local self-government, autonomous schools, special church privileges, and other gifts from its horn of democratic plenty, but did not release the country from Russian sovereignty.

In his Petrograd quarters Bangersky brooded about a noble cause lost, when he received the visit of a glib-talking individual in a leather jacket, who told him that the Maximalists were the true champions of small nations and that the gallant Latvians would be granted full and permanent independence once the Maximalists were in power. The unidentified wearer of the leather jacket mentioned in passing that nothing was asked in return except the fighting abilities of Latvian shock troops to speed up Maximalist seizure of power.

And thus it happened that Leon Trotsky, Marxist theoretician, chess player, draft-dodging man-about-coffeehouses, and subversive agent from New York to Paris, found his incoherent Red Army bolstered by eight elite battalions, and that these hard-hitting units were joined by a steady stream of recruits from Latvia, which was occupied by the Germans until after the end of World War I. Kaiser Wilhelm's soldiers were overbearing and brutal, his administrators were word-twisters and tyrants, and they all scoffed at any nationalism except their own. The youngsters from Latvia detested the Germans as heartily as Bangersky had been taught to do; they knew less about Russian infamy than their elders and did not distrust Bolshevik pledges. The peasant boys from the Baltic were staunch believers in the inviolability of private property, which, however, did not prevent them from butchering property-minded "counterrevolutionaries" in Russia. Bangersky's men not only fought in European Russia; they were also sent to Siberia to help plant the Red banner over a land in which their parents had perished for no purpose. Few of them lived to return to their country, to which the Bolsheviks, after evasion, trickery, and attempts at subversion, had granted independence. And some of these veterans lived to see Red Russia renege on its pledges less than a score of years later, re-establish itself in Latvia, and rage against its people with a savagery paling all outrages committed by the eight battalions against non-Bolshevik Russians.

The Latvians were not the first and not the only legionnaires to serve Russia in World War I.

Already in August 1914 the Russians opened a drive for volunteers of Slavic nationalities. Pan-Slavism, siren song to kindred nations not yet under Petrograd-St. Petersburg's strait-jacket sway, hit a new pitch. Czechs, Slovaks, Croats, Slovenes, Ruthenians, Huzules, and others were urged to desert their Austrian and Hungarian regiments and join their Russian "brethren" by enlisting in the *druzina,* a Czech regiment in the Tsar's army.

Prisoners were screened for volunteers. Austrian subjects of Slavic nationality who lived in Russia were also subject to the recruiting drive. Among those who enlisted was one Jan Sirovy, who lost one eye in Galicia Province, and subsequently rose to domineering position in the Czechoslovak Legion, as the druzina was renamed later, became Inspector General and designate Commander in Chief of the Czechoslovak Army, was appointed Prime Minister in the somber days of Munich, and wound up sentenced to ten years at hard labor and loss of his rank for collaborating with Hitler's Germany.

Russian agents infiltrated Austrian garrison towns with large Slavic populations. Their ardent though technically primitive propaganda resulted in mass desertions. The Austrian Infantry Regiment 28 from Prague ran over, men forcing officers to join. The Infantry Regiments 36 and 88 followed suit.

Slavs were parted from other prisoners of war, sent to model camps in

Europe, where they were comfortably housed and well fed, where picked commanders were under rigid instruction not to despoil and not to abuse them, where they were permitted to visit nearby cities, and their only duty consisted in sitting through indoctrination courses in which they were harangued to fight against the Austro-Hungarian monarchy. Unresponsive Slavs faced punitive transfer to Siberia. Allied consuls visited model camps, brought presents, and delivered pep talks; Czech political exiles delivered frantic appeals to their countrymen to fight for the Allies.

The men who eventually joined fighting units of the druzina made themselves heartily disliked by their new comrades in arms. Russian section commanders reported that the volunteers were good soldiers, but overbearing, constantly clamoring for privileges, and altogether contemptuous of mushiks and poorly educated Russian subaltern officers.

The Russian administration had pictures circulated in model camps, showing mutilated corpses of volunteers who had been caught by the Austrians. Almost every country in the world would have ordered the summary execution of its subjects fighting in the enemy ranks, but the Austrians used truly gruesome methods of putting traitors to death. The Austrian command trusted that the procedure would have deterring effects; the Russian administration thought that the pictures would spur vengeful determination to fight.

Even though the Russians were infinitely superior to their enemy in the essentials of psychological warfare, the Austrians were right in this respect. The volunteers were anxious not to fight, even though their number was swelled by more Slavic brethren, longing for the plennis' Lubberland.

In April 1917 the Russian Cadet Party (Constitutional Democrats), faithful supporters of the Provisional Government, demanded a reorganization of the *druzina* into an effective fighting machine. In May a Czechoslovak Congress convened in Kiev. Delegates from model camps and Czech battalions heard eloquent appeals to their Slav nationalism, harangues to show themselves worthy of honors, privileges, and rewards that a not yet constituted independent Czechoslovak Republic would grant them. Orators raved about democratic Russia's indomitable power and its determination to win the war.

The front was not too far away and steadily moving closer to Kiev; and the Central Powers' divisions advanced toward other Russian cities in which legionnaires led an easy life.

Delegates asked that their men be moved to safety. Representatives of the Cadet Party and of the Provisional Government turned a deaf ear to insinuations that safety was to be found only outside of Russia, but promised to move the men to comfortable training centers beyond the range of enemy attack.

This promise made the Kiev Congress a success. More than 100,000 Austro-Hungarian Slavs expressed willingness to get trained and reorganized. Even Austrians and Hungarians of Italian and Rumanian nationality volunteered for enrollment in legions.

The new armies required twoscore of generals, but Austro-Hungarian generals shunned the legion and ranking officers were appointed without adequate checking and screening, almost at random. One Rudolph Gajdl, a drugstore clerk from Moravia Province who lacked all basic requirements for a commission but had successfully posed as an Austrian lieutenant, was eventually made a general. General Radola Gajda, as he then called himself, became a division and group commander in Siberia and, after his return to Czechoslovakia, a self-styled fascist leader, putschist, and eventually a stool pigeon of the German Gestapo.

When the Bolsheviks gained power in the capital and large parts of European Russia, they proclaimed all plennis to be free men. Allied generals, and the newly constituted Czechoslovak National Council, under the chairmanship of Professor Tomáš G. Masaryk, assisted by Eduard Beneš and Milan Stefanik, worried that the legion would be cut off from supplies and dissolve.

General Pierre Janin, the former French Military Attaché in Petrograd, returned to Paris in November 1917. With him the National Council discussed the issue of getting the legion to the Western front.

The only European Russian ports accessible to Allied shipping were Murmansk and Arkhangelsk. But the railroad link to the former was controlled by unfriendly Reds. The capacity of Arkhangelsk was inadequate and the port icebound 190 days a year. The only practicable route led via Siberia to Vladivostok, and from there west to French home ports, circling three quarters of the globe. Never before in history had any army traveled a comparable distance.

But before the transports could start, the Trans-Siberian would have to be cleared of wreckage, signal installations would have to be restored, engines and cars would have to be requisitioned from dilapidated European Russian rolling stock. Also fuel constituted a major problem. And the legion might have to draw its food supplies from Siberia.

But Janin visualized Allied intervention to bar the Bolsheviks from Siberia, and expected the legion to help hold anti-Bolshevik lines until Allied regular forces could arrive. The slow, tortuous Czechoslovak anabasis through Siberia began at once and in April 1918 small legion vanguards camped in and around Vladivostok.

Assistance to the Czechoslovak Legion became one of the watchwords of Western statesmen and politicians, who viewed intervention in Siberia with uneasiness even after it was under way.

CHAPTER SIXTY-TWO The remote Siberian tundra, where not even Russian fishing companies maintained establishments, was the only region where people did not learn of Prikas One. The depressed aborigines would not have understood its meaning, but elders, trustees, and accomplices of rapacious Russian gendarmes were alarmed by the absence of those organs of law, who had ceased to patrol their beats. The elders had a premonition of rebellion, and, convinced that their security could be upheld only by pressure, tightened their petty tyrannical regimes. "Constituents" knuckled under, and did not consider it a noticeable change.

The average Siberian farmers knew of the prikas, and itinerant demagogues told them that Russia had become a republic. No mushik knew what a republic was, but since demagogues said it would improve their lot, they interpreted it to mean that henceforth everybody would be free to deal with his problems in his own way.

Most farmers were not familiar with the contradictory intricacy of Siberian land laws, but were aware of the insecurity of their title to property. They wanted it secure and they all wanted more land. Mushiks tend to save up land, to hold onto it as a miser would hold onto his treasures, regardless of need or faculty for exploitation.

The Siberians' version of farm revolution was the very antithesis of socialist interpretation. The mushiks resented public ownership, be it by the Crown, the Army, the Church, or even by big landowners, whom they considered dummies of the government.

The Siberian farmers wanted all such domains to be transferred to farmers' committees, MIRs, (*mir* meaning peace), in which every member-family held unrestricted permanent title to allotted property, but implements were shared, and labor could be drafted for community purposes.

With most able-bodied farmers away women and old folks consulted plennis on how to achieve this aim. The plennis were bewildered. In their respective homelands farmers were uncontested owners of their land, but so were public institutions and authorities, and they could not visualize how the mushiks could lay claim to such estates.

Peasant women and old folks eventually formed delegations, which went to neighboring towns to discuss their requests with local authorities.

Administrators were surprisingly guarded and they did not call upon *nagaika*-carrying guards to maintain the traditional version of Siberian discipline. The officials explained, with weary politeness, that decisions on MIRs and related subjects would be made by their superiors *"ssi tshass."*

Ssi tshass had the familiar ring, and applicants took it as an indication that all changes were essentially superficial.

Outside of office buildings demagogues urged peasants not to let themselves be fed on vague hopes, but to keep pressing for action. They insisted that the revolution had hardly begun, that the right men were not yet in office, but that all grievances would be redressed as soon as the right party were in power: the party of the peasants, the men who stood for the peasants' biggest claims; the Bolsheviks; *bolshoj* meaning big (Maximal).

The bewildered mushiks did not know how to press for action, except by petition. Petitions had to be submitted to the same officials who had always been in charge, and to the collaborating local representatives they had been told to elect more than one decade before. But the rabble-rousers knew of a panacea. The peasants should form *zemstvos,* citizens' authorities, to make short work of derelict representatives and deal with the authorities of the state on better than equal terms. And should holdovers from a fallen corrupt government try sabotage, weren't there still able-bodied men in Siberia to enforce the people's rightful demands? The mushik women and oldsters wondered: the seventeen- and eighteen-year-olds were not yet drafted; would they be willing to fight, and wasn't it madness to chance their lives after so many of the older men had gone? The demagogues expressed sympathetic interest and promised that practical assistance would be forthcoming—*ssi tshass.*

Officials turned a deaf ear to warnings that rail yards and factories were swarming with strange, restive elements, and they ignored rabble-rousers lingering outside their buildings. When higher authorities inquired about security conditions in their districts, they replied that no suspect persons were known to be at large. No governor operated intelligent intelligence services. They depended on informers' reports, concentrating on personal denunciation.

Siberian officials were swamped by decrees from Petrograd. Political exiles streamed back to the capital where deportation had become a major asset for job applicants. They told of fraud and violence in Siberia. The Provisional Government poured out huge stacks of well-meant and occasionally superbly worded ordinances to establish decency in Siberia and punish wrongdoing. Hundreds of officials were discharged, but not all of them vacated their offices. All authorities were directed to treat people with consideration, to avoid friction, and to wait for excitement to abate. But in Siberia decency was the antithesis of power; power asserted itself by abusively exhibitionistic display; and without power nobody would govern.

In the spring and summer of 1917 power waited for a claimant, not the most decent but the most ruthless of all aspirants. Officials saw power slipping from their hands and realized that it would never be concentrated in those of the Provisional Government, whose ministers seemed to believe that you could create beneficent energy by destroying the malicious one. The Provisional Government was as far away as the Tsar had been; but while the Tsar had obtained lip service in his eastern realm, his immediate successors did not even get that much.

The Provisional Government ordered that the Siberian gendarmery be disbanded. The gendarmes' record justified the move on moral grounds, but moral grounds were not recognized in Siberia and the gendarmes were the only organs to enforce governmental orders.

Gendarmes were dropped from the pay rolls. Omnipresent rabble-rousers conferred with the deposed despots, and had remunerative suggestions to make.

Replacing gendarmes, militiamen were assigned to guard duty in *plenni* camps. They were briefed to treat their wards gently. The elderly mushiks, who looked funny in their tattered uniforms, grinned, greeted and said *charasho* (good, fine) to everything the plennis did. Later, however, the militiamen were instructed to be tough. Instead of grinning and greeting, they threatened the foreigners with rifle butts, and instead of *charasho* they said *psiakrev na cholera* (may you catch the cholera, you son of a bitch). The plennis abused friendliness and outwitted harshness. Many militiamen could have dealt with angry steers, but none could handle *boomaga*-toting slyboots.

Several hundred thousand prisoners of war vacated their stockades, determined to get home. The route via China and the United States was no longer practicable, since China had joined the Allied and Associated Powers and America had entered the war. It seemed well nigh hopeless to wait for a ride on the Trans-Siberian; the safest means to reach Europe was to hike. The hiking season in Siberia lasted six months. It would take at least that long to cover the distance from Transbaikalia to the Urals afoot, and this would require no less than a dozen pairs of boots of Siberian make.

Nobody had so many boots; very few had enough money to buy them at once. Hundreds of thousands of prisoners needed cash or opportunities to earn it.

Smart and ruthless men did not lack opportunities. Siberia's racketeers, quacks and fakers, bandits, and a modern version of *promyshleniki* were looking for help. Strange organizers recruited, armed, and promised pay to men with combat records. The organizers talked of home-guard duty and partisan formations. They were not specific, nor were the plennis inquisitive. They wanted to make boot money.

Plennis who shunned both jobs and enlistment formed freebooters' groups. But whatever they collected, they never seemed to have enough money to equip themselves, and their enlisted fellow-plennis, who ran away as soon as their wallets began to bulge, faced the same predicament. Siberia was torn by inflation. An object that would cost one ruble today might cost ten rubles tomorrow, and a hundred one week later. Plennis were unfamiliar with the mechanics of devaluation, but they tried to convert money into valuables such as furs or jewelry. These objects could be had on the black market only, and black-marketeers' goons made waylaying of "wealthy plennis" a new line of business.

Destitute plennis joined gangs and accepted strange duties.

In the summer of 1917 the combined number of partisans, home guards, plenni bands, and similar Siberian institutions was estimated at upward of 125,000, and their military equipment included field cannon. They did not consider themselves members of one army. They did not acknowledge loyalties. They would serve as long as they were paid, or as long as they did not receive a better offer by another employer.

The plennis gave no thought to their original soldier's oath. They hardly cared about the fact that the Czechoslovak legionnaires were traitors to the traditional fatherland, but they disliked the legions nevertheless. Legionnaires were much better clad and fed. They received transportation and were generously supplied with luxuries by foreign sponsors.

The plennis had little inclination to battle the Czechoslovaks. It was less hazardous to participate in "punitive actions" instigated by zemstvo secretaries against "recalcitrant villages" than to take the field.

The organizers who had offered home-guard assignments sent groups of plennis to zemstvos of Western Siberia. These popular municipal and district councils were rarely run by their simple members, but mostly by secretaries who neither looked nor spoke like mushiks. These secretaries showed little concern about the property of the people they were hired to serve, and which the plennis had been hired to protect, but they issued tyrannical orders to whom it may concern, and they decreed draconian punishment of communities they found guilty of recalcitrance.

Home-guard commanders occasionally used their men as praetorian guards, and set up short-lived petty dictatorships. Russian ex-soldiers and officers rivaled plennis as guards, dictators, and partisans.

Allied sponsors of the Czechoslovak Legion also supplied home guards and other units, whom they considered Siberian patriots, bent on making the country safe for a nebulous democracy. Several efforts were made to merge them all into one body, but the alleged patriots were split among themselves, each faction more savagely determined to destroy rival "patriots" than the Bolsheviks.

At least five major anti-Bolshevik factions existed in Western Siberia early in 1918. Allied experts thought that they were split only on questions of procedure, and would unite if the Red flood were to spill over the dam of the Urals. But Russian General Staff Colonel Kamenev and former Tsarist generals Khorim, Dutov, and others considered setting up their personal military dictatorships in a Siberia seceded from Russia.

The Bolshevik Government in Petrograd seemed to exert even less control over Siberia than its predecessor, the Provisional Government. When the first legion transport reached Vladivostok and several thousand legionnaires gathered in the vicinity of Lake Baikal, four "independent" administrations of Siberia laid title to legitimacy. A new body had been set up at Omsk; the offices of the Governor General in Irkutsk were still functioning. Ufa, west of the Ural divide, had become a center of usurped authority of an expanded Siberia, and a strange government existed in Harbin, Manchuria, under the leadership of the manager of the Eastern Chinese Railway, retired Tsarist General Horvath.

Siberian officials, anxious to transfer their ill-gotten property to areas not usually visited by *revisors,* supported General Horvath.

Numerous deals to supply Siberian soldiery were concluded in Harbin. Millions of rounds of rifle ammunition, stolen from Siberian dumps, were purchased there by Allied agents for distribution among legionnaires; large stocks of Japanese small arms changed hands; uniforms were imported, but only a small fraction of the goods ever reached the soldiers. Siberian black-marketeers knew how to replenish their depleted stores, and eventually they resold stolen supplies to indignant Allied missions. Inter-Allied heckling resulted in everybody putting the blame for every fraud upon corrupt Russian officials in Irkutsk, and thievish personnel of the resurging Trans-Siberian.

General Dutov was high up on the Allies' early list of "patriotic" recipients of deliveries. He had asked for 20,000 winter coats for his freezing men; 40,000 coats and material for another 30,000 coats were shipped to him since he had hinted that the number of his men was rising. But when the shipment eventually reached the Urals, not even half of the General's actual force of 5000 were supplied. The goods had been pilfered by black-marketeers who sold them to the Bolsheviks.

In the early phases of Bolshevik expansion only black-marketeers had a notion of Bolshevik strength, and the location of Bolshevik establishments in and at the approaches of Siberia. But not even black-marketeers knew of the Siberian Agency, which functioned well west of the Ural divide, in the town of Samara on the Volga River. Samara, renamed Kuibyshev, would be in the international news only in 1941, when Josef Stalin moved his government there under the pressure of the German advance on Moscow.

In 1917 there lived in Samara a petty bourgeois called Smirnov, a quiet man, whom his neighbors considered dullish, and who was said to own some small business out of town. During the revolution Smirnov behaved like most people of his station, a little frightened, somewhat clumsy, and obviously concerned about his own skin rather than the great change. He had only few visitors, the local police never investigated him, and nobody bothered with him when the "Whites" temporarily seized Samara.

But actually quiet, dullish Smirnov was the head of the Siberian Agency, a branch of the Communist Central Committee in Petrograd, later renamed Leningrad. The Siberian Agency was the communists' organ of subversion and eventual conquest, the wirepuller of various fronts set up to deceive Siberians and Allies, in particular the latter. Smirnov's two aides, Karakhanov and Skliandsky, managed a skeleton Bolshevik administration of Siberia, set up in Samara. They directed sixty permanent liaison officers who shuttled back and forth between Siberia and European Russia, unhampered by anti-Bolshevik controls that were temporarily established along the Urals. If challenged, they could identify themselves as ranking officers in the ancient Army; their *boomagas* were genuine, for the sixty were all former general-staff men. The Siberian Agency used a host of informers to spy upon its associates in Siberia, while stool pigeons from Leningrad preyed upon Smirnov, *et al*, on behalf of the Communist Central Committee.

General-staff officers in the agency's pay contacted officers who operated as anti-Bolshevik aspirants for dictatorship in Western Asia. They conveyed dubious information, mongered pernicious rumors, and stirred rivalries. When the struggle for Siberia reached its peak, they would acknowledge relationship with Red partisans, and boldly offer to arrange for partisan support of one contender against the other; they even provided such support, tipping the scales and eventually destroying both victor and vanquished.

The rabble-rousers who addressed farmers' delegations in district towns were directed by Karakhanov. The secretaries who ran the affairs of zemstvos were Skliandsky's selectees. Skliandsky used his talent of deception to make secretaries appear radical reformers rather than Bolsheviks, and he was also in charge of liaison between the Bolshevik high command and leftist-front parties in Siberia, whom democratic-minded Westerners often preferred to Siberian reactionary officers.

Red cells were planted in the anti-Bolshevik formations recruited from war-weary Tsarist inductees who had no more urgent desire than to go home, but who could not find transportation. Again the watchword "peace" proved irresistible. The Red cells told anti-Red fellow-soldiers of impending restoration of railroad traffic, and many soldiers ran away on the eve of battle to seek transportation to peace.

In Omsk, Siberian students of both sexes followed the Red party line with emphatic enthusiasm and unlimited loyalty. They trained popular speakers for rural communities where the intellectuals' lingo was not understood. They taught them many tricks that failed to turn land-hungry peasants into protagonists of state-controlled collectives but deceived mushiks long enough to permit Bolshevik seizure of their areas.

The railroad eventually resumed operations, with American and Japanese technical assistance, and with the co-operation of plennis and legionnaires, of black-marketeers who wanted to ship their goods, and of ambitious Russian generals who needed it for strategic purposes. Railroad foremen, signal operators, yard laborers were responsive objects of Red propaganda drives.

The Reds relied on infiltration. Their treasury was depleted, their partisans lived on the land, but superspies could earn exorbitant fees for finding jobs in the entourage of leading anti-Bolsheviks.

Anti-Red Russian officers engaged in spy hunts. Many people were arrested. To be held as a Red spy was tantamount to execution, but only small fry suffered this fate.

Allied military personnel shunned spy hunts, like anything that might be interpreted as political persecution or interference. Captured Red soldiers and partisans were often hired, and continued as propagandists among Western personnel.

Allied intervention was never popular with the people of Siberia, and Bolsheviks exploited anti-Allied feelings to the limit, claiming that Allied supplies reaching Siberia were but a meager and usurious compensation for Siberian blood already shed and yet to be shed for the benefit of foreigners.

In a book published in 1933 General Janin admitted sadly that communists had infiltrated Allied committees in Siberia. A telegram from Omsk, which he received in June 1919, quoted crew members of a Y.M.C.A. relief train, American citizens born in Russia, as telling Czechoslovak legionnaires: "You are being deceived by your own leaders. You have no business to be in Siberia." Such tirades fostered mutiny, already rampant among non-repatriated Czechs.

On June 1, 1919, General Budberg, then Minister of War in Admiral Kolchak's short-lived Siberian Government, told Janin that the people of Siberia were equally disgusted with Bolshevik and anti-Bolshevik regimes, both characterized by outrages committed by rapacious soldiers and corrupt authorities. The common people of Siberia were divided from the cultured class by an abyss of distrust and disdain. Patriotism was virtually nonexistent. The common men were crude; the higher class was vitiated by laxity and intellectuals who promoted absurdity. Left to themselves, Budberg said, the Siberians, like all other Russians, would never establish a competent regime, and would always be split among themselves; however, if the Allies would unite to establish themselves as guardians and take over the administration, wise and honest Siberians would be available to work for them, forming the nucleus of a popularly accepted government of the future.

When this was said, it was a necrology rather than a prophecy. The cause of Siberia was already lost. So was that of a wise and honest government, and so were hopes that true idealists had pinned on intervention.

Confusion and dissension, ignorance and vicious ambitiousness fostered the exuberant growth of Bolshevik weeds suffocating the organism of human society.

The eventual Red conquest of Siberia makes Smirnov and his henchmen appear as consummate masters of politics and organization. But the petty bourgeois from Samara and his associates were no supermen. The Communist Central Committee frequently issued acid notes of censure, charging the Siberian Agency with poor planning, duplication of work, and factional strife.

Yet the Siberian Agency never lost sight of its goal. And when Allied intervention seemed to turn the tables against Bolshevism, the Siberian Agency carried on. There was nothing else that Smirnov and his associates could have done.

The Entente powers had promptly recognized the Russian Provisional Government, extended their fervent good wishes, and admonished the new cabinet to stay in the war. In April 1917, Washington followed suit by exhorting the Provisional Government to keep on fighting. But nobody offered more than verbal or, at best, financial support to the mediocre theoreticians in Petrograd bent on carrying out a design that would have overtaxed the abilities of mental giants. It was absurd to believe that in a country with a tradition of absolutism, where parliamentarism was unfledged and local self-government medieval, modern democracy could be introduced in four easy steps: abdication of the Tsar, establishment of a caretaking Provisional Government, free elections, and the activity of a Constituent Assembly, all without violence and without radicals' bidding for power.

Georges Clemenceau, Prime Minister of France, had had personal experiences with transition from monarchy to republic. He had been a member of the French National Assembly in 1871, after the downfall of Napoleon III, and he had seen the Paris Commune establishing a brief regime of terror. President Woodrow Wilson was aged fourteen when this happened, but later, as a historian, he should have known that it would take more than good wishes and admonitions to keep the Provisional Government in office and Russia in the war.

Reports from Allied ambassadors and military attachés in Petrograd were alarming. The new government needed reliable troops. Two French or English divisions might have guarded the Provisional Government against overthrow from within, and such military investment could have brought magnificent returns: one hundred Russian divisions might have stayed in action at the front.

The West was short of trained reserves. Transportation via the arctic route would have been extremely difficult, and Western analysts warned of countermeasures by the Central Powers. But the goal warranted every effort.

However, Western statesmen shuddered at the thought of public reaction to interference in Russia. There might be pandemonium in parliaments. Leftists and liberals of all shades, the former with violent energy, the latter with pompous pathos, might charge that Western reactionaries were strangling Russian progress, while conservative deputies would sit by, worried about elections.

Perplexity precluded Western action for several crucial months.

Tokyo, however, had no kindred feelings for the Russian Provisional Government, whose members the Japanese statesmen considered plain rebels. Tokyo gave little thought to leftist oratory and did not even feel tied by compacts signed with Russia. Nevertheless there was perplexity in the Japanese capital. For years experts had planned and prepared for a collapse of

Russia, but when it came, suddenly and unceremoniously, the prepared blueprints did not seem to fit. Improvisation was needed, but the Japanese were no expert improvisers and two extremely difficult requirements would have to be met: no great Allied power should stand in Japan's way, and airtight unity would have to rule at home.

Japanese leaders trusted that France would not protest against Japanese interference. England might write notes but would not put a single boat or man in the way of Japanese advance. Italy was a nonentity in that part of the world. But where did America stand?

America had interests in the Pacific, at Japan's very doorstep. America had shown concern about China. America's war program excluded annexations. America might not stand idly by while Japanese divisions poured into Siberia. America might not let itself be talked out of its program, but might let itself be involved in a Siberian venture, accept partnership or trusteeship. And if other Allies joined, Tokyo would have to outsmart them all, at every turn of the long road.

There remained the problem of unanimity at home. Two forces dominated Japanese policies: the legal government, and the secret societies. But while governments came and went, the powers of the secret societies had been concentrated in the Black Dragon since 1901. The Black Dragon had no titular head, kept no records of membership or financial operations, did not abide by the Japanese code for associations. It was a matter of conjecture how the Black Dragon Council was appointed, but the council, composed of the most powerful men of the realm, had domineering influence on religious and cultural societies; it had trustees in leading business concerns, informers in all branches of the administration, the armed forces, and the police; it obtained assignments and discharges, and whoever opposed its intentions virtually committed suicide. "Unimpeachable channels" conveyed orders, and through these unimpeachable channels officials and military communicated with the Black Dragon Council.

The Black Dragon Council stood for aggressive patriotism at home and expansion abroad. The Black Dragon had approved of the seizure of the German bridgehead in China, and after the German flag had been lowered it had proclaimed that the moment had come to solve the "Chinese Question," and that it was Japan's "divine duty to act at once, for such an opportunity would not recur in centuries."

Unimpeachable channels subsequently carried the council's guarded approval of step-by-step action.

But in March 1917 the Black Dragon requested prompt all-out intervention in China and Siberia. Prime Minister General Count Terauchi was in favor of drastic action, but he had misgivings about charging like an angry bull and whispered his thoughts into the channels.

The price of rice was 100 per cent above the prewar level. There was labor trouble; strikes were outlawed, but not even the toughest police could prevent wildcat walkouts. Essential raw materials were in short supply. Japan depended upon American deliveries to maintain its war potential. And a new Diet should be given an opportunity to debate issues. The Black Dragon commanded all the pistols and daggers needed to cope with stalling, but again it did not press for immediate action.

The Diet debated, and eventually adopted a resolution calling for a better understanding between Japan and the United States. In June the Cabinet appointed Viscount Kikujiro Ishii special envoy to the United States; Ishii arrived in Washington on September 1, 1917.

The Black Dragon had had a hand in the drafting of the envoy's instructions: the only topic on the agenda should be China, Ishii should lull America into complacency by reminding Secretary of State Robert Lansing of a statement made by Marquis Okuma, Japanese Prime Minister at the outbreak of the war, to the effect that his country had no design of depriving China, or any other nation, of its possessions.

In view of later Japanese actions this protestation had a hollow sound. The visitor, however, was treated with marked distinction and taken to Long Island to see the U. S. Atlantic Fleet concentrating for action. Neither Lord Balfour nor André Viviani, recent distinguished guests from England and France respectively, had seen much of the U. S. Navy. Ishii expressed congratulatory admiration for American naval strength and produced another virtuous statement of Japanese intentions:

"We Japanese have taken up arms against Germany because, to us, agreements are not just scraps of paper. We did not enter the war to promote selfish interests and carry out sinister plans."

American negotiators, however, did not want to hear of zones of influence in China, and Ishii requested additional instructions from his government.

Count Terauchi was out of office. New elections had returned his party with a majority in the Diet, but the Prime Minister had to resign and a new cabinet was headed by Takashi Hara, first Japanese commoner to hold the exalted position. Such apparent democratization could but enhance American good will, and Hara also had the good will of the Black Dragon. The unimpeachable channels had "suggested" the change of government. Patience was not among the traditional qualities of the Black Dragon Council, and the Great Plan, upon which the masters of Japan pinned extravagant hopes, had to be put into operation.

Ishii was directed to change the term "zones of interest" into something palatable to the Americans, something that could be interpreted as meaning Open Door policy, but would not interfere with the Great Plan.

The Lansing-Ishii agreement was signed on November 2, 1917. The United States acknowledged "that territorial propinquity creates special relations between countries, and consequently, the Government of the United States recognizes that Japan has special interests in China, particularly in the part to which her possessions are contiguous." And Japan pledged itself not to "take advantage of present conditions to seek special rights and privileges in China which would abridge the rights of the citizens or subjects of other friendly states," and expressed opposition "to the acquisition by any other government of any special rights or privileges that would affect the independence and territorial integrity of China."

Gullible Americans were satisfied with apparent acceptance of Open Door policy by the Japanese. The U. S. Minister to Peking, Paul S. Reinsch, however, was not gullible. He had reliable sources of information and a remarkable capacity for putting it together logically. And while Mr. Ishii was still at sea on his return trip, the fiendish scheme of the Great Plan evolved in the U. S. Embassy.

China, already split, was to be conquered by its own manpower for the benefit of Japan, and China would have to act as Japan's stooge conquering Siberia.

Two rival governments existed in China: one in Peking, the other in Canton. Japan subsidized Peking, and proposed to use it for its designs, yet it made minor contributions to Canton to keep the administration there in being as a means of pressure against Peking.

The Peking government, headed by Prime Minister Tuan, his War Participation Board and the omnipotent Anfu Club, promoted remilitarization to protect China against Bolshevik infiltration. Canton professed economy-mindedness and guarded anti-Bolshevism. Peking appointed General Meng to muster a force of 200,000, for action within or beyond the boundaries of China. Already several Chinese battalions were trained and equipped. Japanese "advisers" swarmed over assembly areas.

Other Japanese officers were stationed in strategic Manchurian districts to direct the actions of Marshal Chang Tso-lin, a local war lord who voiced violent anti-Bolshevik feelings and ranted about dangerous armed *plennis* who might assist Bolshevik infiltration. Chang Tso-lin would never acknowledge that Japanese agents were touring Eastern Siberian prisoner-of-war camps, promoting enlistment of remaining plennis with mercenary leaders, popping up in Transbaikalia, Yakut Province, and the Maritime Province.

The Japanese blueprint of action called for "unification" of China under the Tuan government, for local invasions of Siberian border areas to repel alleged plenni-Bolshevik invasions, and eventually a general advance into Siberia by Meng, Chang Tso-lin, and suitable Russian atamans. Meng would have a Japanese chief of staff; all positions from brigade commander up would be occupied by Japanese; Japanese would direct logistics, Japanese agents would "reorganize" Siberian local administrations.

No existing pacts seemed to commit the Chinese Government to refrain from aggression, and to respect other countries' boundaries. And Japan would not accept responsibility. Tokyo would formally discharge its officers with the Meng army, as soon as the campaign got under way, and pose as a neutral while China invaded Siberia.

So secret was the plan that information was withheld even from the government's strongest supporters in the Diet and the most loyal newspaper publishers. One push on a button should send the avalanche rolling—the signature of a secret Sino-Japanese pact, which would give Japanese stooges control of all Chinese armed forces.

Reinsch stormed against the signature. He exhorted Tuan not to yield to Japanese coercion and he used his persuasiveness to have Washington promote a joint Allied guarantee of Chinese sovereignty, and the grant of economic assistance to make China forever independent of Tokyo's handouts.

Tuan was reluctant. Not only would acceptance of economic assistance be contrary to the treaty that granted Tokyo a priority in matters of loans to China, but acceptance of the guarantee might be interpreted by Japan as Chinese violation of its commitment to give Japanese advisers a word in China's affairs.

Washington was not quick to respond to the minister's plea.

But a fight against the Great Plan started in the most unexpected quarters: in the Japanese Diet and the Japanese press.

News of the plan had filtered out. An undaunted Diet debated the issue, making it obvious for the first time that the Japanese governmental structure was not monolithic. M.P.s used powerful language to denounce an invasion of Siberia and to censure the latest China policy; editorials in Japanese dailies expressed disgust with governmental irresponsibility.

Deputies and newspapermen were more courageous than Black Dragon tyrants and army and navy officers who seemed to have been in enthusiastic agreement with the Great Plan. Greater courage prevailed. The vendetta did not interfere. The Great Plan, though never officially disowned, was wrecked beyond repair.

A great number of Meng's 200,000 coolies were shipped as laborers to manpower-starved France. Another Sino-Japanese agreement, signed to keep face, was but a pale shadow of the Great Plan. However, the Chinese battalions already assembled saw action, even though not on a decisive scale. The Black Dragon kept no minutes of its meetings. But it has been claimed that an all-Japanese invasion of Siberia under some pretext or other had been under discussion, and eventually it was decided that if Siberia could not be conquered by proxy, this should be done by first co-operating with the Allies, and then tricking them out of their designs and their share.

Essential features of the Great Plan survived, however. They were embodied in Stalin's master scheme of Red conquest of Asia, as it evolved after the Japanese surrender aboard the USS *Missouri* in Tokyo Bay in September 1945. Red usurpation of Chinese armies for Russian designs eventually achieved conquests more important even than those for which the Black Dragon and Takashi Hara had plotted in vain.

Still in the closing weeks of 1917, Japanese diplomats in Western capitals peddled stories designed to promote intervention. They spread exaggerated figures of the value of Japanese property dumped on Vladivostok piers, and rotting along the Trans-Siberian, and about Japanese claims for earlier deliveries to Siberian recipients. They told of 10,000 Japanese residents of Vladivostok being threatened by the local zemstvo's arbitrariness, of hundreds of Japanese citizens having allegedly disappeared in Siberia. Japanese attachés produced reports from unidentified informers on huge plenni armies forming on behalf of the Central Powers; and Japan also professed sympathetic interest in Allied investments in Siberia that would be lost unless adequately protected.

In France, General Janin had proposed to use the Czechoslovak Legion to establish an independent Siberia free from Bolshevism, and he had opined that the "government of Ufa," which claimed to have 150,000 fine soldiers, should be the nucleus of supreme authority. Prime Minister Georges Clemenceau was in favor of an independent Siberia, but Professor Tomáš G. Masaryk was reluctant to give his blessings to the plan. His National Council wanted to keep the legion intact as the sole executive organ on which a future government of Czechoslovakia could rely. It doubted that Washington would approve of Czech interference in Russo-Siberian affairs. The bogy army of plennis frightened the council, and since the Bolsheviks had pledged the release of all prisoners of war, but were demanding disarmament of the legions, the council wanted its troops to get west via east as fast as possible.

The bugbear of Central Power aggression in Siberia bowed in the House of Commons on March 14, 1918. Foreign Secretary Lord Arthur Balfour told Parliament of the necessity to forestall German domination of Siberia. The political climate in England was in favor of intervention.

Washington was aware of the hazards of an intervention in which Japan would be a principal. But the United States did believe that plennis might harm the legion and, having not recognized the Bolshevik Government, it was anxious to see a government installed in Siberia that would be friendly, and not Red.

Early in 1918, Admiral Austin M. Knight, commander of American naval forces off Vladivostok, suggested that the various factions and leaders operating in Eastern Siberia be merged into an Allied-sponsored coalition, which should, in due time, constitute a Siberian Government. Later the Admiral made a second report, endorsed by Roland S. Morris, U. S. Ambassador to Japan.

President Wilson called it a "most convincing document." But even though the Knight-Morris papers served as another argument in favor of intervention in Siberia, an Allied-sponsored coalition did never quite materialize.

The storm in the Japanese Diet and press blew over. In December 1917 a Japanese cruiser entered Vladivostok Bay, guns trained on the city's clay hills, on the slopes of which dilapidated houses nestled uncomfortably. The skipper extended no courtesies to local authorities, and showed marked disdain for the zemstvo. He threatened to shell port and town if his government's anger or his own were aroused. Shore installations of Vladivostok were no match for the cruiser's main batteries. The zemstvo was careful not to provoke the heavier caliber. Ice was forming in the inlets of Vladivostok harbor and in the bay where the Japanese cruiser sat, a mailed fist.

A message from Tokyo went to the Western capitals. Japan would no longer tolerate that the lives of its citizens in Siberia be threatened and their possessions despoiled.

America also had citizens in Siberia who were not destitute. Great Britain had interests worth defending, and London did not intend to concede Japan precedence.

In January 1918, U.S. and British men-of-war sailed to Vladivostok Bay. But ice prevented them from penetrating as far as the Japanese cruiser. This had been part and parcel of Japanese timing.

Allied intervention in Siberia, though not yet officially agreed upon, was under way, and Japan held the lead.

"Intervention" as a term was still tabu when the West decided to take a hand in restoring the Trans-Siberian, for the benefit of their own investments and that of the legionnaires, and of such Siberian organizations as would co-operate. Again Japan took the lead by selecting organs to work for a *Pax Japonica*.

At Christmas 1917 a smallish gentleman alighted from a sled in front of the offices of the Eastern Chinese Railway in Harbin. He was wrapped in a heavy coat, the collar put up so high that his features were undistinguishable. Not even the coachman knew that he had driven a Japanese.

The fare brought fateful tidings to General Horvath.

The retired Russian officer, railroad executive, and hapless leader of a so-called Siberian Government, who looked like a basso from the operatic stage, was a pompously naïve, pathetically honest creature with the mind of a conscientious accountant assigned to check the files of an enterprise operated by vicious crooks.

To Horvath figures were the principal denotation of human achievement, and insignia of rank the only reliable indication of a man's value. Prior to his transfer to Harbin he had never left Russia, and he believed that Tsarist Russia had been the best-governed land on earth.

In Harbin he trusted that corruption on the railroad was un-Russian, and would vanish as soon as Russia would regain a firm hold in Manchuria and replace unreliable foreigners in the transportation system by Russian patriots. He relished the atmosphere of discipline in his offices and the martial appearance of the cavalrymen on guard duty outside.

The March revolution had staggered Horvath's mind and grieved his heart. Mindful of regulations, he had never made decisions without prior consultation with his superiors. The highest superiors were deposed, and the elderly general resolved to legalize his future decisions by establishing himself as a temporary authority, but not as an usurper. He would be a faithful caretaker and surrender his assumed powers to the rightful Tsar. As a staunch monarchist, he could not conceive of a rightful ruler of Russia other than a Tsar.

After deliberations with his staff and ranking recent arrivals from Siberia, he set up an interim government and issued a proclamation to that effect.

The proclamation was worded in the lingo of Russian military academies and posted along the Eastern Chinese line, like a notice to passengers.

For a few uncomfortable days the white-haired gentleman was worried about the righteousness of his action. But then people in Harbin and from there up to Siberia and down to Changchun, where the Japanese-operated railroad began, acknowledged that there was a new lawful government under General Horvath, but they knew as little as the head of the regime where its sway began and ended.

From Siberia and Manchuria arrived aspirants for ministers' portfolios, alleged experts in a variety of fields, would-be liaison men with many foreign governments, financiers, industrialists, and plain mystery men. They crowded Horvath's reception room, lounged along walls adorned with timetables and copies of the proclamation; they submitted petitions, applications, and plans for activities of which the soldier had never heard before.

He picked petitioners according to their appearance and conversational gifts, appointed cabinet members, and had them pass upon matters that puzzled him.

Horvath needed an executive, but the smart cavalry guards were not to be reckoned with, even along the Eastern Chinese Railroad, of which he remained the manager. Disorder ruled supreme along the track. Bandits operated everywhere, and the General did not doubt that they were all Reds. His cabinet ministers said that Bolsheviks were swarming over Manchuria and Siberia.

The General learned to his dismay that some of his cavalrymen had gone over to the bandits because banditry was more remunerative than guard duty. He racked his already harassed brain on how to pay regular salaries. His meager personal savings had been consumed during the first week of his rule, to cover the deficit of his administration. He could not raise salaries to compete with bandits.

He had no money to buy arms or to hire demagogues who, much as he distrusted them, might counteract Red rabble-rousers. Horvath felt that, even though a faithful servant of His Majesty should be above pecuniary considerations, money was a vital commodity for all governments, even for caretakers.

He would not deal with local bankers and moneyed speculators, but hoped to find some support by sympathetic governments. The West was wealthy. At the beginning of the war Britain had boasted of winning the fight by using silver bullets. British General Knox was a rabid anti-Bolshevik who wanted to weed out the Reds, but he was also an unhappy man, outraged at the dawdling, self-deluding West that refused to give him the means to do so. He could not solve Horvath's financial problems.

Horvath would have welcomed French assistance, but Paris was just considering the Siberian mission of General Janin. As long as the matter was not settled, the French Cabinet would not deal with Horvath, and, besides, Janin would still rather put his eggs in the Ufa basket than negotiate with the General in Harbin.

There remained America. A corps of 200 picked American railroad specialists had been assigned to reorganize communications in Siberia and Northern Manchuria. They were still cooling their heels in Nagasaki, Japan, when Horvath issued his proclamation. Colonel John Stevens and his U.S. railroad specialists reached Harbin in March 1918, when Horvath had already established other ties.

No sooner had the proclamation been posted than Bolshevik-infested bodies sprang up north of Harbin, terrorizing Manchurian settlements for a hundred miles around. And across the Manchurian border a Bolshevik organization established itself in Blagoveshchensk on the Amur. Red partisans from Khabarovsk raided Northeastern Manchuria, sacked the Maritime Province of Siberia, and bludgeoned the moderate zemstvo of Vladivostok into a temporary coalition with rabid Bolsheviks.

Highwaymen turned political enigmas. Every brigand who had a few hundred ruffians dubbed himself ataman or Cossack leader, and staked out a domain for his operations, like a prospector would stake out a claim. They usually called themselves anti-Red, but they were no less brutish than Red terrorists.

Horvath loathed them with the desperate power of his law-abiding heart, but they scoffed at him. Unless he found support, robbers and rebels would rule supreme. Rather than see this happen, the General would accept support from almost any quarter, and if he could get no money, he would accept soldiers.

The smallish gentleman in the big fur, who called at Horvath's office, offered Chinese soldiers under the command of Japanese officers to sweep Reds and robbers out of Manchuria and Siberia.

The General was startled. Wasn't Japan Russia's most dangerous rival? Horvath requested that he be granted full control of operations.

The visitor was polite but strict. Japan, he said, had the deepest respect for General Horvath and would always be mindful of his prestige, but Japan could not let a foreigner, however respectable, control Japanese-organized armed forces.

This was a stumbling block, but Horvath's cabinet members, whom the General called into a meeting, did not seem to think so. They were all in favor of accepting help, any kind of help. Even Harbin was Red-infested, and unless the Horvath government asserted itself by shooting now, it would fold up in no time.

There are no minutes on Horvath's decisive talks with the important Japanese visitor, but on December 28, 1917, 3000 Chinese, under the command of a Japanese brigadier general, equipped with Japanese rifles and one battery of horse artillery, attacked Bolshevik partisans in Northern Manchuria, killing many, and disarming 2600. The 3000 were part of Meng's ghost army of coolies. Japanese newspapermen and members of the Diet must have known it, but no new storm broke. The host did not continue into Siberia, and Horvath's appeal for further action was conspicuously ignored by the negotiator, who had stayed in Harbin as a liaison man. Also ignored was Horvath's first draft call to the people of Harbin.

Harbin was a strange place.

"Only an imbecile wouldn't make money nowadays" was the citizens' watchword.

To judge from appearances, there were many non-imbeciles in the sprawling Babel that had not even been a village a score of years before. Impecunious Harbiners were crowded in slums, in which 200,000 undistinguished Chinese dwelled. But in the commercial and residential sections lived some 50,000 distinguished Chinese and an equal number of prosperous Russians and other foreigners in the ugliest and most expensive houses makeshift architecture could have built.

Adventurers and refugees kept arriving in Harbin, attracted by rumors that operations that would send their performer straight to jail everywhere else were not objectionable in this city. Coiners went to Harbin, to print Romanov rubles, Kerensky rubles, and not otherwise defined Russian currencies, on paper supplied by a toilet-paper mill in Irkutsk. White-slavers from many lands and dowagers from Siberia brought colorful flocks, entertainers from Siberian establishments, and lush socialites, to establish the biggest brothels in that part of Asia. Swindlers, mountebanks, and jugglers were all over town; the hush money they paid enriched the police corps.

Harbin had a stock exchange, the most buoyant, tempestuous, nerve-racking center of currency operations between Moscow and the Aleutians. Even money had its fluctuating quotations. The rate of rubles of various denominations skyrocketed or plummeted for no obvious reasons. The stock exchange could make or break "governments" by floating or depreciating their money or their bonds.

The Presidium of the Stock Exchange Committee was a political factor of far greater magnitude than General Horvath, who made no money. It pretended to be "neutral." Neutral it was in so far as it championed business with all parties who paid fees of 30 to 50 per cent of the nominal of bonds to be floated.

The committee president, a neophyte to Orthodoxy, professed Russian patriotism and deep religiosity. He did not like foreigners. American and Japanese businessmen who had come to Harbin did not share profits with members of the stock exchange. This pious Harbin resident made a donation to the local clergy and this statement was read in all Orthodox churches:

"Americans and Japanese force us to buy their goods. They are out to destroy our domestic trade and to exploit our land. The Americans are the worst of the lot. They are not even democrats as they claim to be; they have nothing but profit in mind. It is untrue that they want to establish order; they are profiting by disorder. We should build our own strength and tell the Americans and all other Allies that we don't want them here, that we don't need them, and that they ought to return from whence they came."

The American railroad team's mission infuriated Harbin's railroad profiteers, who prospered on chaos. While civilian transportation was paralyzed, men who knew the right operator in Harbin could arrange for round trips to Irkutsk, about 3500 miles, for the equivalent of $1000. And while neither the Trans-Siberian nor the Eastern Chinese Railway seemed to have any freight cars left, one could buy cars in Harbin, stolen from Eastern Chinese stocks, at the bargain price of about $5000. The cars would be restolen in Siberia and returned to Manchuria, where the operation started out anew. Almost 1000 cars were on the market.

Many railroad employees were involved in this procedure. Much as it grieved Horvath, he could not prevent fraud. Average employees earned the equivalent of $60 per month. It cost more than twice as much to maintain a family, but if a man wanted to visit the local gambling casino and have some fun, his budget would be at least $500. Only fools did not look for fun.

There were more Chinese than Russians among the growing number of Harbin millionaires; Oriental cunning and criminal ingenuity was more effective than Russian unscrupulousness. All religious denominations and every political complexion could be found among the new rich. Bolsheviks who had made off with party funds rubbed shoulders with ultraconservative generals who had pocketed the cash of their commissaries.

It was not difficult to do prosperous business. One could buy sugar in Harbin for 90 kopeks per kilo and if you managed to ship it to Omsk, Siberia, it would bring 25 rubles there. Communist-dominated areas were out of cigarettes. Cigarettes smuggled in from Harbin would bring a profit of 1000 per cent of the investment. Black-market novices, anxious to deliver goods to communist areas could go to a certain Harbin pharmacy and ask for Mr. Arkoos.

Arkoos was a smallish, restless young man with eyes that looked like polished black shoe buttons, dark curly hair, and a gesticulating eloquence that had an offensive touch. Sophisticated observers called him either a small soul or a blustering nitwit, or, occasionally, an overly fervent idealist.

Arkoos was a busy broker who collected substantial fees. It was claimed that he had been seen in Red-infiltrated areas, clad in a fancy police uniform, collecting "voluntary contributions" for the Bolsheviks from substantial citizens, and threatening to have the unresponsive liquidated.

The Harbin police listed him as the head of a Red spy ring, chief local Bolshevik organizer, and contact man with a new revolutionary committee promoting Bolshevism in China. But Arkoos paid "protection money," and was, at first, not molested.

Speculators in Harbin who championed anti-Semitism emphasized Arkoos's obvious origin. The Jewish community countered by recruiting anti-Bolshevik volunteers from among its coreligionists, which added to General Horvath's vexations. He needed volunteers, but he was afraid of antagonizing the anti-Semites.

One day in 1918, Meng soldiers invaded the certain pharmacy; they shot Arkoos in the street outside, and left. The full extent of his activities was never established.

CHAPTER SIXTY-THREE The Bolsheviks expected an Allied intervention in Siberia, and since the entry of the United States into the great conflagration had marked the turning point of World War I, they thought that the American attitude would also determine the course of events to come in Siberia.

Leon Trotsky, who had been to the United States and had studied its popular psychology with the speculative mind of an investor in rebellion, was convinced that America was infatuated with revolution as such, and would be against suppression of any revolt, even if it bore little resemblance to the American struggle for independence. The American people would loathe the sordid aspects of Bolshevism, but would sympathize with allegedly reformist groups whose leaders denied Red ties, and it would always dislike militant conservatives bent on restoring a governmental system that was anathema to American liberals.

American newspapermen who made the adventurous trip to Manchuria and from there to Siberia were all in favor of the underdog and his champions. They could easily be taken in by Red fronts, and their favorable reports would pay high dividends, politically and economically.

After Arkoos's death deceitful Bolsheviks shifted the center of gravity of their Eastern Siberian activities from Harbin to Khabarovsk.

Only the secretary of the Khabarovsk Zemstvo had been notified of the impending arrival of a mystery man from somewhere in Russia, who wanted to be called Mr. Krasnotshokov, even though the secretary had first heard of him as Comrade Tabelson. It was said that he had been selected from Smirnov's outfit, but there were indications that he was the personal choice of Leon Trotsky. However, he objected to being addressed as Comrade.

The awe-stricken secretary seems to have warned the members of the zemstvo against antagonizing the visitor; otherwise it would be impossible to understand why the people from the city on the Amur bend meekly surrendered leadership of their council to a character who had never been to their district before and who briskly brushed aside their accounts of pertinent grievances and wishes.

Krasnotshokov turned the town and its surroundings into a city republic. Soon more Siberian city republics sprang up in places such as Chita, Verkneudinsk, and Blagoveshchensk.

Most presidents of city republics were newcomers to Siberia. They all denied being Bolsheviks, but they all followed similar political lines toward goals just as totalitarian and violent as those of avowed Bolsheviks; and even though they used every means at their territories' disposal to combat anti-Red organizations, they never took action against Red partisans.

When eventually the Japanese drive into Siberia reached Khabarovsk, and the invaders proclaimed the local republic disbanded, a jittery Krasnotshokov protested cautiously, and offered to negotiate an agreement granting all foreigners safe-conduct throughout the territory. He even suggested the establishment of a non-socialistic buffer state, including the Maritime Province, the coastal regions of Okhotsk, and all of Kamchatka. He did not elaborate on how this should be done.

Krasnotshokov described himself as an anti-radical, and a convert to capitalism, which he had come to consider the only economic system under which true progress could be achieved. He admitted earlier Bolshevik affiliations, but insisted that subsequent experiences had changed his heart and mind.

Japanese officers treated him with marked disrespect. They insisted that the city republic be liquidated, and questioned him about his ties to Red hit-and-run raiders. Krasnotshokov asserted cringingly and crouchingly that he had never associated with partisans.

Had he been less servile, he might have met Arkoos's fate; but the Japanese, who believed in the self-assertion of power, considered him a person of no consequence, and spared him.

Later, when partisans disrupted Allied communications, and Allied establishments in Eastern Siberia folded up, Krasnotshokov was quite arrogant in his dealings with Allied generals. But even then he would never admit Bolshevik associations. He would claim to be a social revolutionary, a moderate leftist, an adviser to anti-Bolshevik reformers in Eastern Siberia, and he kept talking about the buffer state. Krasnotshokov would even profess desire to see foreigners invest in Eastern Siberia, where, he said, not even socialism could have confiscatory objectives.

When the Allies, frustrated, humiliated, and fooled, eventually abandoned Siberia, Krasnotshokov and other front-men turned into Bolshevik henchmen.

He had always scoffed at General Horvath, but this had not antagonized the Japanese, who, already in the late spring of 1918, had abandoned hope to use the stubborn old purist as an effective tool.

Japanese agents had scouted for a new candidate for figureheadship in Manchuria and Eastern Siberia in Harbin's gambling casinos. The man they found wore a combination of a Russian officer's uniform and a fancy ataman's garb: a fluttering sleeveless sable cape held together by a bast cord, an oblique hat of red fox fur, immense Cossack riding boots, wide breeches, and a coquettishly tight blouse, its breast pockets adorned with rows of pencil clips. He played roulette, admired by skimpily dressed professional belles. He had pitch-dark curly hair, with a pomaded cowlick protruding from under his hat, a straight nose with fleshy nostrils, a sensual, massive chin, deep-set greenish eyes, with the expression of a vicious conqueror; and he was obviously convinced that his charms were an open-sesame to hearts and pocketbooks.

Sophisticated women might have been shocked at the gambler's lank vulgarity, and sophisticated observers of both sexes should have noticed the boundless cruelty of his grinning basilisk's glance. But sophistication was at a premium in Harbin.

Grigory Semenov, at the time of the revolution, had been a Cossask captain, on railroad duty in Manchuria, which was a dodger's assignment secured by his uncle, an old friend of General Horvath. Semenov's assertation that he was an ataman, that his following in Siberia was snowballing, that he was reliably anti-Bolshevik, and that His Excellency Horvath was too unworldly a man to achieve realistic aims won him Japanese favor at first talk.

Japanese consuls and generals interviewed Semenov. They called him candid, co-operative, intelligent, and altogether amenable to practical suggestions. He ranted about chivalrous motives for his actions and sensible notions of problems ahead. Semenov was accepted as ataman, and ordered to serve as Horvath's Man Friday.

Ataman Semenov insisted that he would stamp an elite army out of the Siberian wastelands, given appropriate funds. But Horvath was desperately short of funds. Japanese agents treated the Harbin government with insulting stinginess.

Dressed up in casino attire, Semenov called on Horvath and promised to cover the governmental deficit. The old General sighed that this was too big an amount for any honest person to raise—the equivalent of about $10,000 a month. Irritated at Semenov's looks, he grouchily denounced the fancy uniform and the title of ataman, which he considered to be an archaic surname without practical meaning.

But Semenov produced a big batch of Romanov rubles, bills of high denomination. Horvath was in desperate need of money and accepted it without further comment. Soon the deficit called again, and so did Semenov, well supplied with cash. The General talked about giving him the portfolio of finance; Semenov modestly said that the title of "Financial Adviser to the Government" would be satisfactory, and that he would never wear his ataman's garb in office. Horvath was pleased.

Every first of the month the financial adviser would bring $10,000 to the governmental offices. General Horvath did not seem to know that his appointee collected between $100,000 and $150,000 from the Japanese, and that most of the excess amount was spent in casinos, night spots, and de-luxe

705

lupanars. Horvath apparently did not suspect his friend's nephew of venality. Only when he learned that Semenov, posing as an ataman, hired recruiters, did he admonish him to keep within the bounds of his official duties. Semenov replied that he was doing just that: he had hired men to locate former railroad guards who had not received their dues, and he intended to pay and re-enlist these men. This closed the incident.

In June 1918, Semenov notified his Japanese sponsors that an army of 10,000 was ready in Eastern Siberia to join Japanese regulars in a drive into the interior of the country; 8500, he claimed, were "reservists," subject to call on short notice.

This left a total of 1500 soldiers on active duty. They were remainders of Horvath's cavalry guards, whom Semenov's agents had located and re-enlisted at an expense considerably below the ataman's monthly night-club checks.

Semenov stayed in Harbin until Japanese official invasion forces landed in Siberia. Then he moved to Chita, and while the city republic folded up in discreet haste, the ataman established headquarters and a skeleton government of his own in the railroad station and adjoining buildings.

It was a skeleton government in the true meaning of the first word. The path of Ataman Semenov's men was soon strewn with the bleaching bones of victims, of whom not all were Bolsheviks.

> *Ataman Semenov*
> *Formidable avenger*
> *Unyielding victor*
> *Righteous pacifier*

These were the lines one of his minions had composed and which Semenov kept reciting like a sentimental poem.

Ataman Semenov did not define the scope of his regime. He did not want to embarrass or to encroach upon his Japanese sponsors by calling himself ruler of all of Siberia, but he did not want to settle for anything less than that. A man like him, who had seen a microcosm of a great world in Harbin, who had been granting interviews to Western newspapermen in which he ranted commonplaces while eagerly studying the reporters' reactions, could not fail to realize that the Westerners would abhor his candidacy and prod the Japanese to repudiate him. Conceited as he was, he did understand that Tokyo might use him as an object of barter and write him off in return for any valuable Western concession. He wanted to establish himself in a position of real power and then, leading from strength, make the supreme bid.

At the time Semenov went to Chita, some thirty "atamans" operated in the vicinity of the Siberian-Manchurian border, and their combined bands numbered at least 25,000, possibly even 40,000. They styled themselves overlords over overlapping territories, professed militant anti-Bolshevism, but fought among themselves more bitterly than they would battle Red partisans, and their men marauded the countryside no less viciously than the partisan terrorists.

Ataman lansquenets and Red terrorists were birds of one feather. Both sides included Chinese highwaymen, runaway convicts, *plennis*, and the strange human rubbish defying national or social definition that invariably turns up at scenes of turmoil. Cossacks from the Amur and the Maritime Province returned to the ways of their forefathers, sacking settlements and subjecting peaceful inhabitants to extreme tortures.

Living on the land, and giving vent to primeval ferocity in dealing with its people, they were killers by instinct. They dreaded their rivals and they dreaded their victims. Fear turned them into uninhibited brutes. Fear was the mainspring of their urge for association, fear the reason for wanting to control regions as sanctuaries where no higher authority could take them to task.

Not only atamans, but many other "leaders" claimed districts, provinces, all of Siberia, or just a slice of it. Ludovic Grondijs, a Dutch philosopher, estimated the number of such "governments" in Siberia at nearly one thousand.

One thousand hordes were turned loose upon roughly twelve million people; one thousand hordes shouted slogans to justify what could not be condoned; one thousand hordes were locked in a war in which no quarter was asked or given. Ataman fought ataman; "leader" fought "leader." The Red partisans had neither atamans nor leaders, but they had efficacious commanders, masters in the art of vanishing when faced with superior forces and of re-emerging when the enemy turned careless or left. The partisans never struggled among themselves. They might even come to each other's assistance, which atamans would never do.

Countless outrages were committed by all sides, but the Reds were first to charge the other parties with atrocities. Mr. Krasnotshokov was their unofficial mouthpiece, claiming that White bandits were engaging in bacteriological warfare against the Siberian people. He produced small glass vials allegedly dropped by the Whites, said to contain typhoid bacteria. The claim sounded fantastic, not because either party would have had ethical qualms, but because the robber barons of Siberia were not adequately equipped for such a purpose. Yet the claim was widely believed even after an investigation disclosed that the vials contained nothing at all.

Many foreign newspapermen covering Siberian events interpreted partisan outrages as committed in legitimate self-defense. They were inclined to use the noun "reactionary" for fortune hunters, crooks, tyrants, impostors, and a few rare gentlemen, for anyone fighting the alleged champions of the underdogs. Gentlemen like General Horvath, and later Admiral Kolchak, were poor public-relations men.

Semenov's Japanese supporters provided him with a weapon inaccessible to other pretenders in Eastern Siberia, and that weapon induced many free-lance bandits to climb on Semenov's band wagon or, rather, on his armored trains.

From Southern Manchuria, Japanese armored trains went to Chita, to "secure the Trans-Siberian track."

The ataman moved his personal quarters from a plushy, lice-infested building to a special armored car, and had it decorated according to the taste of an upstart Oriental despot. There were more rugs in the car than in a palatial mansion, more velvet tapestries, and silken bed sheets than in an ancient pasha's harem, folding screens, oversized adornments, displays of weapons, and lush lamps that would have looked extravagant in a provincial Persian bazaar. A thick smell of pomade and tonic pervaded the stagnant air. Semenov preferred to keep windows closed and worried whether they were really bulletproof.

Semenov's armored trains, gloomy symbols of bestiality, rolled a thousand miles east and west along the Trans-Siberian, shunting to sidetracks when Allied conveyances came in sight, but otherwise claiming the right of way. The wheeled fortresses carried rapid-fire cannon and machine guns. Cannoneers and gunners did target practice on people and objects along the line. Every now and then bold men would stage derailments, but more often than not everybody tried to keep out of range. The armored trains stopped at every station, in sight of every settlement, unless Allied forces were in the vicinity—Semenov did not consider the Czechoslovak Legion as an Allied force—and local leaders would be summoned to report.

Formidable, unyielding, and vindictive crews requested accounts of local affairs, of the political attitude of the people, of public and private finances, of partisan activities. The officers invariably found fault with financial dealings and imposed ruinous fines. If the culprits paid up, they were executed because they had apparently defrauded even more than the officers had estimated, and if they did not pay, they were shot as defaulters. All zemstvos were called illegal, and their members were liable to fatal torture and confiscation of property. It was dangerous to tell officers that all had been quiet in the district, for this was interpreted to mean that the people were covering up Bolsheviks; it was equally dangerous to say that there had been partisan raids, for Semenov's men would "investigate." Investigations started with the entire population being lined up along the train. Tolerably attractive women were parted from the rest and pushed into the train to submit first to officers, then to noncoms, and eventually to crewmen. The rapists called that the "Italian Procedure," because one of their officers who had heard of Giovanni Casanova thought that everything lewd had an Italian touch. Other people were beaten and despoiled.

When crews were tired of raping and beating, of pulling triggers and wielding knives, they devised new methods of "Righteous Pacification," such as loading captives on boats and drowning them in Lake Baikal. Ever more perverts and bandits joined Semenov, but neither the ataman nor his closest associates had the talent of organization and conservation required to consolidate mob rule.

Caught between armored trains and bloodthirsty partisans, peasants turned cave dwellers, creeping into drifts of abandoned mines and leaving the weak and the infirm behind. Some able-bodied men even joined atamans or Red partisans, and turned into the most ferocious butchers of the lot.

The carnage continued while within earshot of atrocities soldiers of foreign nations stood by, armed to the teeth, unmindful of their avowed design to establish justice and order. The atrocities survived the intervention. After the Reds eventually established their sole rule, the gruesome routine continued, one-sided, under one-sided slogans.

Accounts of Siberian atrocities had a touch of remoteness as long as they concerned Siberians only, and remoteness made them sound almost unauthentic to foreigners. Late in 1918, however, the world learned of a "mistake" made by Semenov's bandits. In November of that year a Swedish physician on a Red Cross mission in Transbaikalia was lined up, along with the people of a village, outside an armored train where he annoyed the henchmen by addressing them in a language they did not understand, and was shot on the spot. Protests from all quarters of the globe piled up. Semenov was duly denounced and censured by the Japanese. Western officers used rattling language. But eventually the Swedish physician was forgotten, and the incident benefited the Reds, who were believed to be fundamentally righteous as compared with the ataman.

Semenov's terrorism depended upon the operability of the Trans-Siberian. Under the circumstances it seemed more important to keep men and supplies rolling than to immobilize murder trains.

The plennis, professional railroad men among them, had been trying to do just that ever since 1917, and their endeavors had helped bootless stragglers to return to Europe. Municipalities along the track mobilized labor gangs for repairs. Signal stations were restored and manned. Siberian shops and factories mustered specialists to patch up rickety locomotives. A few American engines and cars were put into operation by Western engineers, and even though they essentially served the intervention they added to the depleted rolling stock.

Operations remained hazardous. There were numerous accidents that could be attributed only to sabotage. In 1918 the Czechoslovak Legionnaires organized intelligence services and found that Bolsheviks had infiltrated labor gangs and that foremen were stalwart party members working hand in glove with Red partisans.

Enlightening as the discovery was, it did not harm the Bolshevik network. It was virtually impossible to detect all important individuals involved and to paralyze the organization by their arrest. Most key persons remained unmolested. Some went into hiding. The very few who were caught would be immediately replaced by well-trained stand-bys. Hardly anybody deserted the

Reds. The Bolsheviks were not only stubbornly loyal to their superiors, but also convinced that Bolshevism would eventually prevail. Foremen informed roving Red partisans of every train running through their sector, of every piece of equipment it carried, of strength and morale of covering forces. Partisans planned their raids according to the foremen's information, and disrupted vital transports. The partisans established underground stores and hideouts in rural communities in which Bolsheviks, in the disguise of reformers, secretaries, and advisers, ruled supreme. Siberian governments established in the western and central sections of the country ordered mobilization of the classes of 1917 and 1918, to build up anti-Bolshevik forces. Local secretaries enrolled recruits in partisan bands, and peasant boys joined naïvely, if not eagerly.

In Western Siberia communism adopted a new line. The MIRs, it now said, were the mushiks' only hope. However, authorities who gave lip service to the MIR and tacit approval to the seizure of Crown land were traitors who would use enlisted men to strip the peasants of all land, old holdings and new acquisitions, and turn it into large estates on which mushiks would be serfs. But the partisans would defend the MIR against the big estates. They would take orders from the zemstvos. All power should go to the zemstvos.

Peasants, taken in by the talk, approved of the secretaries' assertation that they owed allegiance to the zemstvos, whatever central authorities established themselves in Siberia. The Bolshevik wirepullers trusted that, with the exception of the Japanese, all of the Allies would sympathize with the zemstvos, and hesitate to dissolve them. In Vladivostok, however, where Czechoslovak Legionnaires kept arriving, the coalition zemstvo was virtually stripped of its power by the soldiers, who felt that the zemstvo was putting obstacles in their way.

Legionnaires were stalled along the railroad line between Irkutsk and the Pacific in the longest traffic jam ever recorded, even though the actual number of waiting men was substantially below 100,000.

The Czechoslovak National Council in Paris issued distress calls that its men were trapped among hostile German and Austro-Hungarian ex-prisoners, that they ought to be rescued, and that they would show their gratitude by securing Allied stores and pacifying vital areas of Siberia.

Tokyo did not think highly of the Czechoslovaks, but it supported the appeal. In early 1918 already Japanese intervention in Siberia had secretly begun. If the West could be induced into a semblance of joint action, it would never protest against it.

Japan had not yet disembarked one single platoon in Vladivostok, where it could have been watched by Allied naval forces. But Japan maintained a military establishment in Southern Manchuria, not subject to Allied control or ceiling. Not only armored trains had gone to Siberia from there; piecemeal, the better part of two Japanese divisions had moved north and northeast, toward undisclosed destinations that could be but the Maritime Province and

Transbaikalia, where they would join "official" invasion forces later to be landed in Vladivostok. This should make the Japanese contingent vastly superior in number to anything other Allies would muster, and equally superior in fighting strength to the legion.

The Czechoslovak distress call started the Allied intervention. On August 5, 1918, the U. S. Government issued a declaration to the effect that, even though any general intervention in Russia was unwise, military action was admissible to "render such protection and help as it is possible to the Czechoslovaks against the armed Austrian and German prisoners who are attacking them, and to steady any efforts at self-government or self-defense in which the Russians may be willing to accept assistance. Whether from Vladivostok or from Murmansk, and Arkhangel, the only present object for which American troops will be employed will be to guard military stores which may subsequently be needed by Russian forces and to render such aid as may be acceptable to the Russians in the organization of their own self-defense."

The declaration carried the assurance that intervention would not interfere with Russia's political sovereignty, its internal affairs, and territorial integrity, and that United States forces would be promptly withdrawn when no longer needed.

Japan followed suit with another declaration, mistakenly predated August 3, asserting that Russian sovereignty and territorial integrity would be respected and that there would be no interference in Russian affairs.

The governments of Japan and the United States agreed that their expeditionary forces should be equal in number: 7500 each. France and England joined the venture.

Disembarkation in Vladivostok started on August 12, 1918, and was practically completed in one day; 7500 American soldiers from Honolulu set foot on Siberian soil, the first military force from the New World to establish itself on Russian territory. The British Empire supplied a token force of 800 Canadians. France could do no better than gather 500, mostly legation guards from Peking.

Japan, however, sent its 12th Division; the effectives of the Japanese division were twice as strong as the combined Anglo-American-French forces.

Japan offered no plausible explanation for this intrusion, and the government was not pressed by Allied inquisitiveness. No Western military man could have had any delusions about the farcical inadequacy of the allied contingents, but they may have hoped that Japan would use its full power to achieve aims upon which all non-Bolshevik elements could agree.

This turned out to be a perfect delusion. In 1918, Japan was determined to go its own conquering ways.

The landings of August 12 boosted Japanese strength in Siberia to roughly 50,000. Subsequent reinforcements brought the number to a peak of some 75,000.

In the ides of August not only Vladivostok saw new Japanese units; Japanese infantry and light artillery went ashore in Nikolajevsk, at the mouth of the Amur River, where they seized the Russian river flotilla to ship their forces upstream. Japanese soldiers also swarmed over the Russian half of Sakhalin.

Japanese battalions from Vladivostok marched north, through the Ussuri Valley, toward a junction with the Amur forces. The Japanese attacked scattered partisans in their way of advance, and invariably prevailed.

Japanese officers coolly ignored the legionnaires whom they encountered on their forced marches. A few thousand legionnaires rushed to Vladivostok after the Allied landings. They shunned battles with partisans, since rumor had it that the Reds took no prisoners but had everybody shot, however high he may have raised his hands in surrender.

Along the winding, unpaved street leading from the piers to the center of the untidy town people gathered to watch the parade of foreigners. Among the spectators were Bolshevik informers who checked, counted, and reported to liaison men who in turn conveyed the number of Allied soldiers, their equipment and deployment to partisan bands hidden in cedar groves and rugged hills nearby. Americans, Canadians, and Frenchmen smiled at onlookers; the doughboys from Honolulu distributed gifts. The onlookers grinned back, confusedly, they grabbed whatever was thrust at them, but they were scared, thinking that these foreigners might turn their city into a battlefield, and that, whatever the outcome, they would be the victims. The people of Vladivostok did not inform the Allies of strange goings-on in the suburbs of their town. Partisans turned up in small groups, obviously gathering for action.

On August 19 two echelons of partisans, about 4000 each, were deployed on the northern approaches of the city, all heavily armed, several women among them. Women were even more furious butchers than men.

The Japanese could have wiped the echelons out, but the partisans evaded Japanese units marching past Krajevsky village, the center of the Red array. But when the British, French, and legionnaires invested the settlement, partisans struck, legionnaires ran, Westerners fell back in disorder, and had not a few Japanese reserves been rushed to the spot Western Allied intervention might have come to an inglorious end one week after it had started. The partisans abandoned the battlefield. The immense plain north of Vladivostok sucked them up, without a trace.

The Japanese command enjoyed the white soldiers' loss of face in the engagement of Krajevsky. Reports to Tokyo emphasized Czechoslovakian cowardice and the altogether undignified conduct of the legionnaires, who were said to set a poor example for the Emperor's monastically devoted fighting men.

American soldiers assumed guard duty at the railroad terminal. The French and Canadians were billeted in the center of the city; legionnaires camped on open lots, in barracks and yards. The Japanese left only rear guards behind.

The bulk of the Japanese 12th Division and the battalions of the Amur advanced into Siberia at a pace surpassed only by the drives of the ancient

Mongols. Meantime the Americans moved up the railroad track, mindful of securing their rear lines, and generally shunned by partisans.

The identity of the Red strategists in Eastern Siberia has not been established, but Krasnotshokov undoubtedly was their boss. His political cunning kept the partisans from battling the Americans. Had there been large-scale fighting, the political temper of the United States might have clamored for large-scale action and elimination of the Reds in Siberia.

The advancing Japanese temporarily outran their supply lines. Japanese columns floated through Maritime Province like small craft in stormy, shark-infested seas. This was a calculated risk, and even though it did not result in setbacks it was a Japanese version of too little and too late.

Had Japan engaged 50,000 men in the East at the time of the Bolshevik coup in the West, they would have swept clean through Siberia; and three additional Japanese regular divisions might have carried the drive all the way to the Urals by the late summer of 1918.

The Japanese General Staff had ten divisions ready for shipment across the Sea of Japan, but the logistic problems involved were startling. The government uneasily watched the reaction of press and Parliament, wondering whether Semenov could not carry the banner of the Rising Sun the long way west.

Japanese detachments went to Chita, to remind the stormy ataman that he was, in fact, Tokyo's tool. Semenov blustered, clowned, and did some inconsequential skirmishing with partisans.

In Chita, as in other places where they went, Japanese behavior was exemplary. The soldiers never molested women; they held yen bills, a precious currency in Siberia, in their outstretched hands when foraging or entering a store; they were so sober that the Siberians thought that they were suffering from some disease; and they did not even ride on horseback on the wooden sidewalks, as Cossacks invariably did. "The presence of the Japanese Army is the best remedy against Siberian ills," read Japanese posters in Chita.

The Japanese loved proclamations and used them lavishly, even in districts with upward of 95 per cent illiteracy. The proclamations were in Russian, and when the Japanese officers noticed that people could not read them, they commandeered local secretaries to read them out loud. Bolshevik secretaries distorted the wording of the posters, but this most Japanese officers failed to realize.

The Japanese were the first foreigners to combat Bolshevism in the propaganda field. In settlements on the lower and middle courses of the Amur a proclamation signed by Colonel Oumeda said: "Some people seem to believe that Bolshevism has freed the country from the burden of Tsarist misrule. However, all the Bolsheviks did was to destroy the foundations of lawful government and to lead people toward the abyss . . . Bolshevism is a grave peril to every nation, its spread must be prevented, and for this reason, the Allies desire that a strong and stable government be quickly established in Russia

". . . We sympathize with your country; we are full of compassion for the crumbling Empire . . . Our soldiers are here to help you restore order . . . The Siberian Bolsheviks do not have an army; they have bands of assassins, which gather as swiftly as they disappear. War against the Bolsheviks is like chasing flies; yet they hold the advantage of being familiar with this country and its people, whereas we have difficulties making ourselves understood and obtaining reliable information. We are working for the benefit of Russia, and yet, a part of the population assists the Bolshevik assassins . . . Maybe people are afraid of the Bolsheviks, thinking that they are superlatively clever. But can't you see that will power and moral principles are stronger than fear, and that by not resisting you are bound to fare infinitely worse than by defending yourself? Siberia is thirty times as large as Japan. Should it be possible that in so vast an area there would not be enough patriots to save the fatherland? The Japanese forces are inspired by high ideals. They will not kill Bolsheviks who did not fight, or who surrender. The Bolsheviks say that we do not behave well. We shall not waste words to answer such charges. You shall judge us according to our actions. Suppose we would evacuate Siberia now? Terrific troubles would arise. Decent people would have to leave, and those staying behind would soon realize that the yoke of Bolshevism is infinitely heavier than Tsarist oppression has ever been, and that God is punishing them for their inertia. Help us to help you, regardless of diversity of race, and nationality, for the sake of your own tranquility and happiness."

In the wake of advancing Japanese partisan bands invaded villages. Bolshevik scribes pointed at people who had assumed a friendly attitude toward the Japanese, and the alleged traitors were slaughtered. Partisan commanders proclaimed themselves supreme local authorities, confiscated everything of value as enemy property, and "restored order." Japanese crews of small steamboats on the Amur trailing the drive on land found evidence of that order: smoldering ruins and mutilated, stripped bodies. Whenever they went ashore to investigate, they found an apparently innocuous character wailing: "If only you'd have come sooner! The Semenovzi did it all—they just left."

The character invariably was the village scribe, and the Semenovzi were Semenov's men. Japanese officers used interpreters to hear the accusers; they took photos and made notes. Investigations were of no avail. Corpses are no sources of information. And pictures of men who were no more than heaps of torpid flesh were not really frightening; broken eyes, if not cut out, conveyed no supreme horror.

Those who saw such pictures in newspapers at breakfast tables in comfortable accommodations, in well-protected distant places, considered them undue infringements on their peace of mind and altogether repetitious. Horror grew stale. Siberians who learned of Japanese proclamations were not impressed by appeals to their will power, moral principles, and that outlandish thing called patriotism. Fear was stronger than idealistic notions. Had the

Japanese truthfully said that they had come to rule Siberia, the natives would have jubilated, for such rule, any organized, powerful rule, meant protection against sudden, gruesome death. Domination by the strong spelled LIFE.

But the Japanese came, posted, and left. And then the assassins would come, and kill—kill. If nobody prevented them from killing, the natives would rather lick the assassins' boots than defend themselves against fiends they could not chase away like flies, whom they could but implore, hoping to their dying breath that they would let them live, if only out of contempt.

Semenov was now denying any part in his men's atrocities, and put all the blame on the Bolsheviks. But foreign observers were present at the railroad station of Chita when men from Semenov's personal armored train sold 348 blood-soaked suits of clothes to the highest bidder. From the window of his special car Semenov watched his men's doings, with a puzzling basilisk's stare.

Semenov became the only formidable ataman in the East. His rise to strength caused thousands of vagabonds, plennis, and legionnaires of many nationalities to join him, to be armed, equipped, and granted a share in the proceeds of terrorism. Semenov's cavalry made forays into Yakut Province, ranging almost to the rim of the tundra. Marauding Mongols joined Semenov. Buryaet tribesmen enlisted in various capacities, that of tax collector preferred.

Semenov's own armored train ceased to "fight." Guns and crews were evacuated to make room for more useful objects and people. The ataman needed treasury vaults to hoard upward of one ton of gold, furs, and other valuables, and he wanted to accommodate a staff of 150 female entertainers.

Semenov, like many other absolutists, was a coward. As his praetorians grew in number, he grew deadly afraid of their inordinate brutishness. He did not dare to restrain them, lest their wrath turn against him. The ataman had no scruples, but the Japanese exerted pressure to have him reform. Western objections against their supporting the tyrant annoyed the Japanese, and even though they did not actually discontinue payment of subsidies, they threatened to do so should the ataman keep massacring civilians. Caught between his sponsor's disfavor and his praetorians' excessiveness, the ataman tried evasion. He protested that his government no longer exercised supreme authority, but that it had been legally superseded by the all-Siberian government of Admiral Aleksandr V. Kolchak. Semenov hoped, temporarily, that the Admiral's prestige would cover up the "Semenovzi's" despicable record. General Horvath, and his withering, tottering, Harbin government, would not shield Semenov.

Kolchak soon learned what a man the ataman was, and detested him no less bitterly than he detested the Reds and his own betrayers. However, Ataman Semenov survived both Kolchak and Horvath. Sometime in 1920 he vanished from the Siberian scene, healthy, prosperous, and obviously pleased to be among the last rats to abandon the sinking ship. He played no important part in the subsequent act of the Siberian drama, the tragedy of honest men like Kolchak and Janin, the travesty of political helplessness, and the apotheosis of infamy.

CHAPTER SIXTY-FOUR Hopelessly hemmed in on an inland sea, the Russian Black Sea Fleet had a less than impressive World War I record. After the March revolution, however, its squadrons of obsolete cruisers and mediocre light craft gained temporary importance beyond their actual fighting power. Three-star Admiral Aleksandr Vassiljevitch Kolchak succeeded in maintaining strict obedience among his crews, while sailors of the Russian Baltic Fleet had joined radical leftist elements.

A few minor relaxations of disciplinary rules, a few words of appreciation had eliminated early signs of unrest. The fleet was loyal to the authorities, and in particular to its commander, who was ready to take orders from the Provisional Government. So outstanding was the morale of the Black Sea Fleet that General Brusilov requested that some of its sailors be sent to his army to address men of faltering loyalty.

Soon the Provisional Government was not entirely happy about the attitude of the navy men in the south. Rumors had it that General Kornilov was sounding out Kolchak for collaboration between land and sea forces in the political field.

And the Bolsheviks, who had included all naval squadrons in their list of assets, were alarmed by the attitude of the Black Sea Fleet. In July 1917, when they were not yet ready to make the decisive bid for power, the Bolshevik wirepullers decided to take action against the Admiral.

Twenty hand-picked Red propagandists went to Sevastopol, where the fleet was at anchor. Kolchak learned of the sinister arrival only several weeks afterward.

Meantime the forty-three-year-old officer indulged in his new favorite activity: addressing crews. The men loved their slightly built admiral, with his neatly cropped dark hair, long, straight nose, well-shaped mouth, and eager, clear eyes. They enjoyed his speeches, which culminated in appeals to be loyal. Loyalty had become a puzzling issue in the year of fundamental changes.

Then, one morning, a group of men who displayed papers with many stamps were admitted to the Admiral's flagship, and when an unsuspecting Kolchak appeared at the bridge to make a speech, they stepped forth toting pistols, and roared at the Admiral to surrender his sword and hand the fleet over to the crews, of whom they claimed to be the legal representatives.

Had Kolchak called upon his sailors the intruders would have been torn to pieces. But the Admiral remained silent, and so remained the sailors who watched the dismal occurrence in disbelief. The ruffians kept shouting defiance, the crew kept watching, the Admiral kept silent, for an endless quarter of an hour. Other sailors lined the decks of nearby units and stared at the flagship. Nobody knew how the news had reached them, but the eyes of thousands of officers and men were fixed on the Admiral who had been their leader, and who would remain their leader if he said the word. But Kolchak did not speak; only his eyes, invisible to most of the crews, pleaded sadly and unconvincingly.

One of the ruffians made for the bridge. Kolchak saw him rush on and reach for his leather-sheathed sword. The Admiral ungirded it and threw it into the waters of the bay. Then he walked down the bridge, past stunned intruders and a shocked crew who snapped at attention, and his barge took him ashore.

He went to Petrograd. The Provisional Government, anxious to rid itself of the man who no longer controlled the fleet but might yet turn into a dangerous myth, offered an assignment in the United States, which the Admiral accepted. He would not wait in the capital for transportation; already Bolshevik and fellow-traveling newspapers featured caricatures deriding his "throw of the saber," and a few superpatriots gave it poetic praise, which annoyed Kolchak no less than derision. He waited in Sweden, but when he eventually reached the United States, the power of the Russian Provisional Government was at a low ebb, and his assignment no longer material. Kolchak continued across the American continent, and eventually went to Japan, where he learned of the Bolshevik seizure of power in his homeland.

He visited the British Embassy and offered to enlist with the Royal Navy. But the Royal Navy had all the admirals it wanted and Kolchak would not accept inferior commissions in the Navy, even though he would be ready to join the British Army regardless of rank. Eventually Kolchak was directed to travel to Mesopotamia via Shanghai.

In Shanghai, Russian Prince Koutashev met the recruit for the British Middle Eastern forces, and took him to Peking, where he was interviewed by various Allied ambassadors who asked about his views on the situation in Eastern Siberia and the possibilities of unifying anti-Bolshevik movements all over Siberia.

The Admiral's sketchy knowledge of Siberia and its affairs dated back to the Russo-Japanese War, when he had served on a cruiser in Port Arthur. He had been close to Siberia as a young ensign on an exploration assignment in the arctic. He stated candidly that the interviewers obviously knew more about Siberia than he, but that the most important matter in Siberia seemed to be the railroad, and that there was no better agglutinant for men and movements anywhere than discipline. Ambassadors insisted that he meet Horvath and Semenov. Kolchak took an immediate dislike to the ataman and had a long talk with General Horvath, who afterward called him a paragon of fine Russian virtues.

The Admiral was relieved to be permitted to leave for Shanghai, where a cable signed by the British War Office reached him and directed him to proceed to Siberia. He had not yet recovered from his surprise when another cable appointed him member of the Board of Directors of the Eastern Chinese Railroad. Kolchak considered himself under orders from London, and went straight to Harbin, where he arrived in May 1918, and learned that he was in charge of railroad guards.

The former Cossack guards were gone. Those who had not enlisted with Semenov served in various bands. There were 3400 Chinese from the Meng army who might be used for guard duty should the Japanese so decide, and there were twenty-two cannon, all Japanese equipment. Horvath suggested that he recruit Russians on the spot, but a few days in Harbin convinced Kolchak that spur-rattling racketeers, gamblers, and pimps in Russian uniform were a disgrace to the fatherland. Horvath insinuated that he try to collaborate with Semenov.

"I shall see that you be named administrator of the Ussuri District," Kolchak told the ataman, and even promised grudgingly to address him "Ataman" in official correspondence.

"I *am* an ataman," Semenov snapped, while his henchmen, grouped around their leader, displayed their scorn for Kolchak by grins and gestures. "My administration—there is no other legal administration in Eastern Siberia—extends far beyond the Ussuri," Semenov continued, "and is steadily expanding. My Cossacks and Tokyo will see to that. And, to us, officers of the Army, an admiral is but a masquerading civilian."

Kolchak called on a general he had known back in European Russia. "Nobody can raise an army around here," the General insisted. "And even if you achieve the impossible, you would have to have at least one foreign officer to every Russian battalion, or else your Russians will quit and sell their equipment to Red agents."

As a last resort Kolchak went to Tokyo. Russian Ambassador Kroupensky, who had turned an independent agent after the Bolshevik coup, warned him against calling at the Foreign Ministry. The man to talk to, he said, was General Baron Güchi Tanaka.

Tanaka, a solemn man in his fifties, listened impassively to Kolchak's account of his odyssey, and said casually, "Never enlist loafers and deserters. Try Cossacks instead—and don't rush. Your time will come. We shall need you—later."

He did not elaborate on the meaning of "we," nor did he suggest how long and where Kolchak should wait. Ambassador Kroupensky told the Admiral to stay in Tokyo.

Kolchak was short of funds. He went to live in a cheap furnished room in a suburb, on short rations.

Baron Tanaka was busy. The man who was to be Prime Minister from 1927 to 1929, author of the infamous memorial that said: "If we want to control China, we must first crush the United States," was stirring a politically embattled Japanese Government into stronger action in Siberia.

The waiting Admiral felt forsaken. The English had sidetracked him; so apparently had the Japanese. He took to studying newspaper accounts of the kaleidoscopic pell-mell of Siberian governments. He did not yet understand the various trends and powers at work.

Time went by; rent was due. A weary Kolchak wrote to Semenov asking for terms of co-operation, and hinting that he was ready to promote the ataman. "I shall promote myself, when I deem fit," Semenov replied; and Tanaka ignored Kolchak's application for an appointment.

The Admiral returned to reading newspapers. In June 1918 the local government of Omsk in Siberia agreed with the assembly at Ufa to set up the framework of an all-Siberian government. Other Siberian rump governments seemed to consider a merger with that agency. Obviously the people of Siberia had not been consulted, but Admiral Kolchak thought that campaigning and electioneering in Russia could but result in destruction.

The all-Siberian Government appointed a five-member directory including three socialists. Kolchak did not think highly of such politicians, who might try snake charmer's tricks in dealing with Bolsheviks instead of battling violence by greater violence. He doubted that the Directory would appoint him an adviser, and yet he visualized military opportunities for an all-Siberian Government and army out west. It occurred to him that the people of Western Siberia would not be as perverted and demoralized as Eastern Siberians. Two classes of recruits could form an army to sweep across the Urals, merge fighting anti-Red forces there, and destroy Bolshevism. The more he thought of it, the more he wanted to enlist with the government of Omsk.

Kroupensky, to whom he confided his wishes, told him to keep waiting. A gloomy Admiral pondered haplessly what to do when Kroupensky visited him with happy tidings: General Tanaka had made distinctly friendly remarks about Kolchak. Tanaka's agents were on their way to Omsk. The General would not disapprove of Kolchak going there too. But Kolchak would have to be endorsed by Western Allies, and his chances for an assignment in Omsk would improve if he could muster some forces, a Cossack brigade or at least one regiment from Eastern Siberia.

Such forces could be gathered only at the expense of that obscene ataman. Kroupensky promised to give the matter careful consideration, but the Admiral would have to try for endorsement himself.

He was told to be careful in dealing with the Americans. The United States was set to intervene in Siberia, but it had apparently very limited objectives. The French seemed to aim at control of all military operations in Siberia. The English were probably Kolchak's safest bet.

The Admiral filed an application for a military assignment at Omsk, and toured embassies, presenting his case to poker-faced diplomats. He underwent polite cross-examinations on the military forces at his disposal, on his plans for enlistment, his funds, and similar embarrassing issues. He answered with dejected truthfulness. Then he was examined about Siberian facts and figures: mineral resources, industrial production, transportation, and farm statistics, of which he knew next to nothing. Had it not been for Kroupensky's prodding, he would have thrown in the towel, but the ex-Ambassador kept repeating that matters were taking a favorable turn for the irate applicant.

In August 1918 reaction came from Omsk: the Directory considered giving Kolchak the portfolio of war. A letter from Chita indicated that one regiment of Cossacks, slightly under strength, stood by to carry Kolchak's standard westward.

British General Knox, at the helm of a military mission, had been to Japan and returned to Vladivostok for a survey of anti-Bolshevik military establishments in Eastern Siberia. And with him traveled Kolchak.

It has been claimed that Kolchak had pledged himself to grant England a long-term monopoly for the exploitation of the riches of Turkestan Province in return for support. This claim, never substantiated, can be traced to Bolshevik sources.

In October 1918, Kolchak arrived in Omsk, followed two days later by his Cossack regiment.

The government already regretted having appointed him Minister of War. Kolchak was a militarist and the Directory was becoming convinced that all military factions aimed at dictatorships of their own; he obviously was Tanaka's favorite, and Tanaka's agents had said a few things indicating that, once established in Siberia, the Japanese would not leave. The government would have preferred to let the Western Allies assume control of all military operations, trusting that the British, French, and Americans would not stay in Siberia longer than absolutely necessary and leave the Omsk government in control.

No propaganda wave had heralded Kolchak's arrival, but he became the object of frenetic jubilation. Suspense, excitement, passion, anxiety, and spite erupted in a thunderbolt of chauvinism of which the Admiral turned into the living symbol. Hundreds of thousands flocked into Omsk to cheer their bewildered hero. They hailed him as a man of their own kind, who had come to put an end to outlandish nuisance and foreign presumption, who would lead them to glory, or to the settlement of scores. Kolchak acknowledged homage from boisterous crowds, exuberant officers and panicky members of the Directory. He did understand that he was being hailed as a leader, but he could not quite see on what merits and toward which immediate goal.

The Directory was too strange an institution to become popular and so were councils and rump governments. The people wanted a man to govern the land so that they might have their MIR and local self-rule; Kolchak was not committed to either, but there was no one else upon whom to pin hopes. The officers wanted jobs and power to make them remunerative. Kolchak seemed to be the only man who could provide it.

Kolchak was not a putschist by education and background, but he was a captive of cheers and shouts, and he certainly had ambitions.

On November 18, 1918, proclamations posted in Western Siberia announced that the Directory was disbanded; so were all councils and assemblies. Admiral Kolchak was the head of a new all-Siberian government, superseding whatever regimes existed throughout Siberia, including that of Semenov.

This was Kolchak's *coup d'état*. It has not been established who masterminded it, and no more is certain about the Admiral's share in it than that he had read the proclamation in galley and approved of text and type.

Through Siberian cities paraded officers in Tsarist uniform, epaulets trimmed in green. Green and white were the colors of the first sovereign Siberia since Kutchum's. A draft call of men aged eighteen to twenty was expected to produce 200,000; arsenals reported 60,000 rifles on hand. Czechoslovak Legionnaires' uniforms also animated the martial picture, but people scoffed at the legion.

Kolchak was the Siberians' Little Father; hardly anybody who wore the uniform of the Tsar gave much thought to another "Little Father," Nicholas II, who, together with his Tsarina and their children had been shot by a Bolshevik murder squad in Ekaterinburg, Siberia, four months before.

Friendly foreign observers wondered whether Kolchak would become a Siberian George Washington. But the Admiral lacked Washington's judgment, wisdom, and good luck.

The chief of state ignored the fundamentals of administration. Experts thrusting themselves at him were discredited old-timers who discredited Kolchak by continuing their bad old ways. The greater part of the Russian bullion was stored in Omsk; Kolchak ordered that it be heavily guarded against thievery. His treasury officials, meantime, ran up a deficit of nineteen billion rubles on a budget of twenty-one billion. Law in Siberia was a chimera: Kolchak signed a decree rescinding emergency regulations and re-establishing prewar statutes. Most courts of law were out of operation, and those that still functioned were sitting on cases of moonshining and crimes committed in drunkenness. An estimated 10,000 moonshiners produced torrents of *somogonka,* a concoction that caused poisoning, blindness, and a sort of intoxication that made the affected commit incredible acts of savagery.

Leaving civilian problems to his staff, Kolchak concentrated on military issues. These issues had looked sensible to the lonely newspaper reader in a Tokyo suburb, but they appeared perplexing on the spot. Kolchak was swamped with reports from local commanders and intelligence officers, but local commanders did not even clearly define their positions and effectives; and intelligence services would claim one day that 250,000 Red soldiers were arrayed east of the Urals, and the next day that 20,000 panicky fugitives, streaming down from the western slopes of the mountains, were all that remained of the Bolshevik forces. There were no credible reports on fighting. The legionnaires styled themselves Kolchak's co-belligerents, but they were a definite nuisance. They requisitioned material and transportation, antagonized the people, and refused to discuss vital problems with the Admiral. Kolchak did not know much about the topography of Siberia and wondered how to deploy whatever armies he had. He made inspection trips on the espionage-ridden railway and returned no wiser than he had left. The curriculum of the Naval Academy, where he had studied, was adequate for future fleet commanders, but not for the commander of a ghost army engaged in a ghost campaign against a ghost enemy. The Admiral suffered mental agonies and, for the first time in his life, he was physically ill.

He needed time to study, to recover, to negotiate with the Allies. But there would be no respite. And the Western Allies were not enthusiastic about Kolchak, who did not seem to fit into their political pattern.

Nine days before Kolchak's "putsch," a man left Japan for Siberia, an honest, well-meaning soldier whose designs were laudable, but who, like the Admiral, became a weak leaf torn from its distant tree and blown away by the Siberian tempest of destiny.

General Pierre Janin's hegira started on July 25, 1918, when he was summoned to the French Ministry of War to receive his nomination as commander in chief of the Czechoslovak Legion in Russia and Siberia, of the forces of the "Siberian Government" of Ufa, and as a "co-ordinator" of whatever Yugoslavs, Poles, Latvians, or other legionnaires he would locate in areas "under his control." He was directed to co-operate with the Japanese in Siberia, and to invite their intervention in the western parts of that country and across the Urals in European Russia, where contact should be established with Allied detachments disembarking at Murmansk and Arkhangelsk, with anti-Bolshevik Russian troops in the south and British forces coming up along the oil-rich Caspian shore. After closing gaps along the Trans-Siberian, a joint drive should roll on to the borders of Poland, Czechoslovakia, and Rumania.

The General did not disclose the full extent of his orders until the 1930s, when Adolf Hitler was already German Chancellor, Josef Stalin wielded supreme power everywhere in Russia, France considered close collaboration with the U.S.S.R., and leftists in the Paris Chamber were handy with the epithet of "fascist" for everybody who did not approve of their policy. Janin's story was occasionally denounced as "hindsight" and reactionary. But the General's book, the spiritual testament of a disappointed, intelligent observer of one of the most portentous phases in recent history, gives a compilation of facts unmatched by any other account.

There was no better expert on Russian military affairs than Janin, who during his assignment as a military attaché to the French Embassy had been a guest lecturer in the Nicholas Military Academy, who spoke a flawless Russian, and was familiar with both the intricate simplicity of the mushik and the chivalresque rascality of the Tsar's officers. Unswerving, persuasive, highly cultured, Janin loved Russia deeply, though critically. His feelings were reciprocated by so many Russian military men that he was the only foreigner who might have been accepted as a reorganizer of the Russian Army. Janin also knew a great deal about the Czechoslovak Legion—more, in fact, than the members of the National Council in Paris.

Ever since his return from Russia, in November 1917, Janin had pleaded with the council members that they abandon the sterile idea of shipping their men around the globe to the West, where there would hardly be a theater of war at the time they arrived, and that they merge them with anti-Bolshevik forces in Russia and overthrow the Bolsheviks.

Professor Tomáš G. Masaryk gave fleeting consideration to this plan when the Bolsheviks ordered disarmament of the legion, but he wrote it off soon thereafter. Dr. Eduard Benes always wanted the legionnaires to go West. The only member of the council in favor of Janin's proposal was General Stefanik, who had been a reserve lieutenant in the French Army, the only Slovak-born officer the Allies had been able to locate. As such, he had been promoted and assigned to the council. But his word carried no decisive weight.

In the spring of 1918 a delegation from Ufa arrived in Paris. The delegates told Premier Georges Clemenceau that, given the proper supplies and full support by the legionnaires, they would unify and pacify Siberia and eventually all of Russia, and that France, as their sponsor, would emerge as the dominant world power. French citizens would receive priority in exploiting the riches of one sixth of the globe.

The agents from Ufa hinted strongly that, unless France seized the grandiose opportunity, Japan might do so, against their will. Clemenceau did not need this intimation to realize Japanese designs in Asia; he also felt that England did not want France to emerge from the war so powerful that she would never again have to woo for support; and he realized that the United States, on whose support the armies of Marshal Foch depended for survival, would view French imperialism with disfavor. But the aging "tiger," the last grandiose patriot of France, wanted everything for his country. He could not afford to antagonize America, England, or even Japan, by an aggressive attitude, but his France, the country of Louis XIV and of Cardinals Richelieu and Mazarin, had always produced men of destiny to carry great designs. Clemenceau was too critical an observer to consider Janin a genius, but fate did not need geniuses as its tools.

Janin's first stop on the fateful trip to Siberia was New York, where he arrived on September 9. He went to Washington to secure support from the U. S. Government, but President Woodrow Wilson stated in a memorandum dated September 27, "It is the unqualified judgment of the military authorities of the U.S. that to attempt military activities west of the Urals is to attempt the impossible. . . . As far as the United States' cooperation is concerned, the government thereof must frankly say that the Czech forces should retire to the eastern side of the Urals to some point at which they will certainly be accessible to supplies sent from the west."

Janin met ex-President Theodore Roosevelt at the Harvard Club and visited him at Oyster Bay. Roosevelt denounced Wilson's Siberian policy and promised to request that General Leonard Wood be sent west of the Urals, with 50,000 cavalry. The ex-President died soon thereafter, before he could have raised the issue.

In Japan, where Janin went next, etiquette required that ranking military men from abroad apply for an audience with the Emperor, and tradition required that the visitor be made to cool his heels. Janin spent his waiting time visiting Western embassies and ranking Japanese soldiers. Diplomats would not yet concede failure in Siberia, but they thought that no inter-Allied harmony could be established and that nothing good would ever come from disjointed improvisation.

Field Marshal Yamagata, Chief of the Imperial General Staff, told Janin that he was tired of writing memoranda on Siberia only to see them shelved.

Baron Tanaka wanted to throw three fresh divisions into the Siberian campaign, and have them go all the way to the Urals. There might be trouble with America, though, he said. The Americans knew nothing about what went on right under their noses in Eastern Siberia, but three additional divisions would take up the better part of the rolling stock of the central and western sections of the Trans-Siberian. American engineers were working there; Washington would learn of the operation, it would lodge protests, the action might be canceled and the sole beneficiaries would be the Bolsheviks. Tanaka produced secret information to the effect that the First Division of the Czechoslovak Legion had refused to fight partisans near Ufa, and that the Second Division, near Ekaterinburg, was honeycombed with Bolshevik agitators. He called General Syrový, acting commander of the legion, an incompetent and unreliable man.

On November 2, when the international cables and wires hummed with reports on the Central Powers' spreading collapse, Janin received a dispatch from Syrový, who tendered his resignation because of physical and mental fatigue. Janin was sufficiently alert not to act upon the resignation. This was a matter to be decided upon at government level.

A parade of strange characters from Siberia added a touch of vaudeville to Janin's experiences. A sheet-sized calling card introduced "Ataman Khalmikov from Ussuri," who claimed to be the ruler of Eastern Siberia. The twenty-two-year-old "ruler" had not heard of Kolchak, but he discounted everybody out West and warned Janin against dealing with the Americans, who were, he said, interfering with executions, and raising hues and cries when they were carried out nonetheless. "No executions—no reorganization," Khalmikov summed up. "All atamans are morons and impostors," one General Ivanov-Rynov told Janin. "I've been an adviser to most of them; they are all alike." The barrel-chested General claimed to have a panacea for Siberia, which he promised to reveal at a party, good old Russian style, complete with dancers and genuine vodka. At the party, however, he had so much of the latter, that he could not remember the panacea. From Vladivostok arrived delegations of "old established Russian political organizations," of which Janin had never heard before. They were verbose and anti-everything that was not their own rule. Free-lance informers introduced themselves, and so did representatives of mysterious "Siberian nations."

Eventually Janin went through the slow motions of a pompous and unavailing audience at the Imperial Palace.

On November 16 he reached Vladivostok, where General Otano, an old-fashioned Samurai, styled himself supreme commander of all Russian and Allied troops in Eastern Siberia, with the exception of the American contingent. Otano, however, was not quite certain that this designation was fitting; he did not know the exact location of all forces under his command, but indicated that he might spare three regiments for Omsk, subject to Tokyo's consent, which would be hard to obtain.

Janin proceeded to Chita. Semenov's henchmen staged a special show for the occasion. "Cossack delegates" in circus regalia elected the ataman "Supreme Ataman and Big Chief of the West." The Frenchman reminded Semenov that Kolchak was his superior now. "Kolchak is an abnormally nervous man," the ataman replied. "Nervousness is a sinister feature for a commander and he also is a bitter man, for no soldier really wants him. Does he think that throwing his sword into the water qualifies him for leadership?" He roared with laughter about this story that the Bolsheviks had made into a joke.

Janin had not seen one simple Siberian man or woman laugh since he had arrived.

On November 24 and 26 identical telegrams from London and Paris notified Janin that he should consider himself commander in chief of all Allied and Russian troops in European Russia and in Siberia west of Lake Baikal. Use of British units would have to be approved by General Knox, and by General Elmsley, in command of the Canadians in Vladivostok. The commander in chief should arrange for organization and training of newly mobilized Russian troops, as well as for procurement of reserves and stores. The British Government would supply ammunition for at least 100,000, but no more than 200,000, men. Some materials should be set aside for contingencies not specified in the order. France and America would take care of supplies for the legion. Janin should set up an inter-Allied general staff and tell all Russian parties concerned that continued support by either Britain or France depended upon unconditional co-operation. He could but feel that Siberian affairs, viewed from the vantage points of Paris and London in the throes of victory, looked different from what they appeared to be in a gloomy, divided Siberia.

On November 30 a heavyhearted but still stalwart Janin departed for Omsk, in a tidy, superbly equipped luxury train. Cars and engine were American-made.

Of twenty trains the Czechs had recently run in the sector only seven had gone through. Janin's trip was smooth but slow. Only on December 13 did he reach Omsk.

On his way Janin studied reports on the military situation. It appeared at first glance as if large sections of European Russia west of the Ural mountains, centered upon Samara, had been wrested from the Reds by anti-Bolshevik Russian generals and their ramshackle armies. A large area of the Urals around Ekaterinburg also seemed securely held by anti-Red forces. Just how far Kolchak's rule in Siberia extended Janin was not even able to guess. But the Admiral had apparently inherited various internecine feuds. Before his putsch Omsk had declared economic war on Samara, Ekaterinburg had battled with Omsk on nebulous issues of provincial federations and local autonomies, and, after its disbandment, the assembly of Ufa called itself Duma of Siberia and defied all other governments. A Japanese general who joined Janin's party between Chita and Irkutsk said that Kolchak depended upon General Anton Denikin in matters of strategy, and that Denikin aimed higher than to be Kolchak's tutor.

In Verkhneudinsk, 7000 Japanese infantry, cavalry, and field artillery had established a fortified camp, allegedly to keep Kolchak's and Semenov's mercenaries apart. All the way to Irkutsk, Japanese pickets guarded the track. A dispatch from Paris told of the Americans wanting the Japanese to reduce their forces in Siberia to 7500.

Near Verkhneudinsk a Russian brigadier general reported that he was in charge of two Polish regiments. Their combined effectives were 600, or perhaps 500, depending upon how many had deserted that day. They had 100 rifles among themselves, and 12 pairs of shoes; the temperature was 20° below.

Krasnojarsk had the most cosmopolite anti-Bolshevik garrison of all. Czechoslovaks, Serbs, Poles, Italians—all ex-*plenni*—and several Russians camped together with a lone Englishman who had been shipped there from Vladivostok by mistake. Austro-Hungarian and German officers also manned Krasnojarsk, doing business with everybody.

A Ukrainian regiment of company strength turned up at Tatarskaja; another group of Poles vegetated in Novo Nikolajevsk.

General Stefanik, who had joined Janin, assigned a legion platoon to guard duty. At stops legionnaires paraded in fine winter uniforms, while tattered international mercenaries tried to pilfer food in the platoon's accommodations.

General Knox also rode in the luxury train. He suggested that Janin induce the Czechs to make a stand as far west as possible, regardless of what Professor Masaryk would say. He warned the Frenchman not to rely on regulars from Western Siberia. Kolchak's recruits, he said, would be swept away at the first blow. But Knox closed his considerations on an optimistic note: there remained a chance of full-scale Western intervention; Allied forces might land in the Crimea, and the British coming up along the Caspian might continue beyond Baku and penetrate into the lower Volga Valley.

Janin did not share Knox's optimism. He recalled the innumerable obstacles that Siberia had always put in the path of honest men and, less abstractly, he recalled President Woodrow Wilson's biting remark about modern proconsuls establishing themselves in Russia; the Chief Executive of the United States was obviously referring to "White" officers. The President now wielded the baton in the inter-Allied orchestra; Clemenceau would not openly defy Wilson, at least not until the peace treaties were signed, and Wilson would certainly disapprove of Knox's designs.

More information reached the train piecemeal. It came from various sources, but never from Kolchak's "Intelligence."

Ekaterinburg was garrisoned by the legion. Legionnaires were said to be established all along the road to Perm, but Perm was still far away from European Russian arctic ports where Allied token forces went ashore. One report said that legionnaires pledged to co-operate with White Russian units were holding a line hinged on Samara. But another report indicated clearly that the Reds were firmly established in Samara, and were expected to advance on Ufa. The legion, entrusted with the defense of both cities, was under Syrovy's command. The legion obviously had no desire to fight, which explained Syrovy's "weariness."

General Dutov, who had been clamoring for overcoats, had a few thousand soldiers near Orenburg. General Stefanik hoped that they would be joined by fighting legionnaires. But actually the Reds were in Orenburg. One dispatch said that the English from the Caspian had reached Tsaritsyn (later Stalingrad) and Bolshevik communications with Siberia were being severed. But this turned out to be false.

Next Stefanik announced that two Red armies of 40,000 were moving across the Urals against legion positions, but that the Czechoslovaks numbered 130,000 and would fight. Actually the legions had only 50,000 in the sector; the Reds had at least that many men, equipped with 200 field cannon and many machine guns, which they cleverly used as road blocks. This was a tactic first applied by the Germans to create the impression of a solidly held front where no continuous line existed. However, the Reds were not led by Germans, as Stefanik insinuated, but by Tsarist officers.

Chief of Staff of the Russian Superior Revolutionary War Committee was Tsarist Colonel Kostiajev. Commander of the 2nd Red Army was Tsarist General Khorine. Another general, whose name was said to be Sunblad, headed the Bureau of Operations. One general-staff colonel and two majors held top assignments in the 1st, 3rd, and 4th Red armies. Only the commander of the 5th was a Bolshevik zealot: one Blumberg, age twenty-three, the only person of his rank the Superior Revolutionary War Committee called "army commander." The others were "technical army commanders." They were tightly supervised by political commissars who, according to a pattern borrowed from the French Revolution, could veto the decisions of technical commanders and all other professional officers on the spot and had no responsibility for delays and confusions caused by a veto. The responsibility always was the technical commander's. The commissar, *politruk*, however, got all credit for every success. If the *politruk* charged an officer with sabotage, a court-martial was held on the spot. No witnesses were called. The charges were accepted as sole evidence; the only penalty was death. Yet few of the officers who served under such harrowing circumstances were Bolsheviks by conviction. Some were turncoats, too frightened to quit; others may have thought of the French Revolution and hoped that there was still a chance for them to turn Napoleon.

Indications were that the Reds managed to keep their soldiers supplied.

Janin trusted that the Czechoslovaks were reasonably well clothed, fed, and armed. But complaints kept coming in. There seemed to be a serious shortage of warm garments, and, worse even, of ammunition. The men were said to have 900,000 rounds of ammunition, all in all not enough for one single engagement. Janin wired to Vladivostok for cartridges. Ten million rounds were under way, the reply read. But one million only got as far as Omsk, and they were of Japanese make and did not fit into the legion's Russian rifles. All the rest had been stolen en route. Meantime supplies on hand were said to have declined further. The legionnaires had the deplorable habit of throwing heavy objects away. Janin admonished legion officers to reform their men and wired for more matériel.

No sector of the Trans-Siberian beyond the Japanese outposts was reasonably safe. Black-marketeers bribed guardsmen into letting them ride the trains; they threw boxes of ammunition and bales of clothes out at places where operators waited with carts and sleighs to ship the objects to their patrons, mostly Reds. To supply the legion via Siberia, as Washington, Paris, and London had considered practicable, seemed impossible.

One of the last messages to reach Janin on his harried trip came from Kolchak. "I insist that Semenov leave Transbaikalia and cede his command to a man whom I shall nominate. If the Japanese keep interfering and preventing me from making such appointment, I will have to interpret this as incompatible with Russian independence." This sounded unrealistic.

By December 13, Kolchak, who was in bed with the flu, had learned of Janin's appointment as commander of Russian troops west of Lake Baikal. He considered it an outrage, a betrayal by the Allies, usurpation of rights that Siberia, as a sovereign state, could not tolerate. His temperature rose as he fretted and fumed; his physician expected a nervous breakdown, but the Admiral held his own.

When he was absent at Janin's arrival, everybody on the train considered his disease to be of a diplomatic nature. A reception committee waited at the station: four cabinet members, one less than scheduled; the missing man had been assassinated by unidentified assailants, hired by the Minister of Finance. A small crowd watched the reception in mute wonder. A few short weeks ago they had hailed Siberian independence and the man who stood for it; and now this same man had delegated ranking executives to salute foreigners, among them a general of the hated legion. . . .

Three days later Kolchak received Janin. His cheeks flushed, his eyes burning, his voice hoarse and pitched, he delivered an emotional harangue: his regime depended upon control of the Army; the people wanted a national army, not Russian soldiers under Allied control. He needed warm shoes, uniforms, and ammunition. "If you won't give them to me, without strings attached, then leave me alone. I shall not trade sovereignty for garments. I shall fight alone and get all I need from captured enemy stores. This is still Russia. This is Russia's war, and not the foreigners'. And Russia will not tolerate Czech presumption. The Czechs are requisitioning, interfering in our domestic affairs; they have pulled wires in zemstvos, some of these zemstvos are Bolshevik-infiltrated."

A French political adviser who accompanied Janin tried to soothe the Admiral by saying that everything would be duly considered, reports would be filed, proposals drafted.

"Disheveled discourses," General Janin called Kolchak's virulent reaction. The sick man shouted and gesticulated, gave the impression of extreme nervousness, monomania, and badly hurt pride. The first meeting between Janin and Kolchak planted the seeds of dissension that were to be blamed upon circumstances rather than upon the principals.

Yet another order arrived from unsuspecting Paris. Janin should form a solid front on the approaches of the Ukraine and the Caucasus. Sane elements of the population from Lake Baikal to this line should be given time to coagulate, and then a general offensive should carry the rest of Russia. Just as a postscript Janin was notified that no French troops would be available for the purpose, but that he had the legion.

Stefanik, who had returned from an inspection tour of legion establishments, sneered, "The legion is like an honest girl that has been confined to a brothel; she is contaminated." And, "Let's not be foolish; this front of ours will collapse."

Stefanik had found many Red fellow-travelers among the legion organizers in the Urals. Ranking officers who owed their commissions to cunning rather than competence addressed the restive rank and file, ranting tirades about civic virtues and freedom. When Stefanik had demanded that they speak of fighting, they had told their men that staying on and fighting was contrary to the wishes of Professor Masaryk, now President of the Czechoslovak Republic.

General Stefanik inquired whether Janin knew of ways and means to move the legion either to Arkhangelsk or to the Caspian. Janin shook his head. Arkhangelsk being icebound until May, no supplies could reach the men there; besides there was no fuel for engines, no food for soldiers to be found in devastated Russia west of the Urals, and the Caspian was more than a thousand miles away.

Together they went to see Kolchak. The Admiral was slightly improved, and less irascible, but still very proud. He offered to appoint General Janin his next in command, and to give him a free hand in matters not affecting basic policies. Janin should at once relieve General Syrovy, whom Kolchak considered the worst of all legion officers. His opinion was shared by Stefanik, but the French General stalled. In Prague, as in Western capitals, Syrovy was being built into a primer hero, without whom apparently not even the most modern republic could do; explosion of a budding myth would result in a storm that might jeopardize Janin's mission.

It was decided to make an inspection trip to Cheljabinsk to recheck the situation in the Urals. As the special train was about to leave Omsk, Kolchak, Janin, and Stefanik heard rifle fire. Three hundred partisans raided the city. The enemy struck at the very heart of Siberia. The enemy was ubiquitous. When the officers requested complete information on the ghostly raid, they learned that the partisans were deserters from Kolchak's new national army, organized into bands by agents who had once served in Syrovy's headquarters. They had been led by a fanatical woman, the former mistress of a legion officer.

The woman was captured, and so were almost 200 raiders. She did not speak up under horrible questioning, and what the less constant men did say confirmed the nightmarish vision the officers had had when the small arms began to sputter: Siberia was not the rock to block Bolshevism in the East; it was a sieve through which the Red torrent poured.

Kolchak, pinning the blame upon Syrovy, claimed that with the removal of the inimical general and his worst cohorts the gap would be stopped. Not only Syrovy's men would have to be evicted, he added, as they drove through the forest-bound flatlands; the legion should be evacuated. "Their role is finished," he raved; "their army is rotten, as ours had been on the eve of the revolution. And this is my prediction: 'Someday, they and their Czechoslovakia will go down, all the way to Bolshevism.' What have they been doing here?" he thundered. "Black-marketeering, seizing 4000 railroad cars, which we needed desperately, gathering riches in an impoverished land. May they take it with them, but they must leave at once. We cannot tolerate their sinister presence. If they stay on, we shall disarm them."

One of Janin's aides took shorthand notes of Kolchak's tirades. They were published only more than a dozen years later, when Czechoslovakia seemed consolidated for democratic survival, eight years prior to the German invasion and more than fifteen years before Czechoslovakia went down to Bolshevism.

Had they met under different circumstances, Janin and Kolchak might have become close friends. Even in the emergency Kolchak trusted the Frenchman, but he suspected all Western governments of trying to appease the unappeasable Bolsheviks, and his suspicions tainted his talk. He had honestly believed that his own forces would soon be adequate to fight the enemy. But what he saw in the Urals made him feel forsaken by God and man.

A new army under the command of General Kappel had been reported ready to take over a vital sector from the legion. The "war commissariat" of General Kappel put 90,000 rations and salaries into account. Kolchak found effectives of 4000, 2500 of them former subaltern officers, too young and inexperienced to deal with common soldiers, whom they treated with aggressive conceit. Angry mushiks delivered some of their most brutal superiors to partisans, who shot the officers and rewarded the mushiks with footwear. Kolchak saw barefooted soldiers, shivering and wrathful wretches, not reminiscent of the enthusiasts he had seen in Omsk in the early days of his regime. Youthful officers voiced patriotism, but they did not want to carry rifles and fight in the ranks. They asked to be transferred to staffs where they could carry sabers, and do gentlemen's work. Kolchak had no need for staff officers, but when he said so, their mien indicated that his no was not accepted as an answer.

Saber enthusiasts formed general staffs of their own. At one time in 1919, 180 corps general staffs existed in Siberia, but not one single anti-Bolshevik army corps.

Kolchak struggled desperately to form an effective army, but did not know how this could be done. He saw Russian soldiers footsore, hungry, and tattered, trailing legionnaires to pick up whatever the hated Czechoslovaks would throw away. The legionnaires kept dumping what they considered cumbersome.

Kolchak visited hospitals to look for dodgers. But the wounded he saw were hardly fit for duty. He did not yet realize that no more than 5 per cent of them were battle casualties, and that the others had mutilated themselves to obtain discharges. The Admiral's advisers suggested that he enlist "converted Reds," who flocked across the Urals. Janin and Knox warned that these men might be Red infiltrators. But Kolchak, blinded by despair, and politically more naïve than the French and the English generals, had many "converted Reds" admitted, and they all faithfully served—the Bolsheviks.

The Red organization of Siberia expanded. All over Kolchak's domain *petiorkas* staged local uprisings. The five-member committees consisted of men and women, centrally directed by a mystery commissar. Kolchak ordered that petiorka members be summarily executed. "They are mostly foreigners," he claimed, meaning members of non-Russian nationalities of the realm, and also Jews. "The few Russians among them are idiots, illiterate dumbbells, seduced by alien viciousness."

He was incensed by the lack of Japanese support and, aware of Tanaka's attitude toward the United States, he hoped that the Americans, "the natural enemies of Japan," would bring their weight to bear in Eastern Siberia to eliminate Ataman Semenov and the partisans, and to counteract Japanese influence.

But soon he exploded. "These Americans are sending representatives whose intentions are just as evil as those of their president are. Their sinister attitude worsens the situation. I am told that they are ill-informed, but they should know as much as other foreigners. The attitude of their chiefs, Graves, Robinson, and Morris, and that of their troops would indicate that they came to Siberia to spread Bolshevism. They are doing incalculable harm, and relations between Russia and America will steadily deteriorate."

General Janin took the Admiral's outbursts in stride, but sent pessimistic reports to Paris, saying that Bolshevik propaganda was spreading and that Red elements had even infiltrated the Y.M.C.A.[1]

Red wireless propaganda called Janin a "sanguinary satrap," and "leader of praetorian hordes, out to choke freedom." Mimeographed sheets advised *petiorkas* to plot *attentats*.

Already the traditional evil of Russia sapped what little strength Kolchak held: fraud, depravation in extremity manifested itself in rapacious spoliation. No member of his cabinet expected the regime to last. They wanted to get over with the interlude and retire as millionaires to some safe haven. They had talked the unsuspecting Admiral into turning over crucial economic matters, including army appropriations, to the Military Industrial Committee in Omsk and appointing one Divarnenko head of the committee.

Divarnenko, a nondescript fly-by-night operator, raided the bullion by organizing a gang of robbers among guards. He and cabinet ministers, his partners in spoliation, used stolen gold ingots to manipulate Kolchak's paper money, and, as a result, commodity prices rose to fantastic heights. Divarnenko set a new mark of organized pilfering. Of 40,000 padded winter coats and 100,000 yards of solid material that arrived in Omsk in the fall of 1919 not one single piece reached the soldiers, while a cold wave sent the thermometer down to minus 70°. Together with the textiles vanished 50,000 rifles, and 300,000 rounds of ammunition. The head of the committee did a thriving business in freight cars. He held enough of them to carry a big army, but the small army suffered from lack of transportation, while the Minister of Supplies collected twenty-nine cars as a dividend for his share in the car business, and sold them to an unidentified buyer 2000 per cent above the prevailing black-market quotation, through the good offices of Divarnenko's assistant. The Minister's ladies indulged in "charities." American relief parcels for families of needy officials were distributed by the charitable ladies to the black market. Generals' wives handled donations for the wounded; no wounded man ever received a gift.

Kolchak received confidential reports on the fraud, but his ministers said that Mr. Divarnenko was a godsend. The Admiral thought that denunciations could be calumnious and ignored letters from old-established madams in Omsk who complained that his officers' ladies were ruining the trade.

He never learned, and even the corrupt executives hardly knew, that

---

[1]See: *Ma Mission en Siberie,* Payot, Paris 1933, p. 109, footnote 2.

Divarnenko's assistant was the elusive chairman of the Omsk *petiorka*. He had stolen goods shipped to the Reds.

Divarnenko cheated even his partners so thoroughly that he left Siberia as one of the wealthiest men in the world. He is said to have spent the long rest of his life under an assumed name in a sumptuous French château, and to have acquired foreign citizenship.

Kolchak was more concerned with the Allied attitude toward his title to sole government than with fraud. On January 23, 1919, the Supreme Allied Council outraged the Admiral by a wireless appeal to whatever government still operated in the Russian Empire, to send delegates to a conference that should establish peace and unity. There remained a good many self-styled governments in Siberia that Kolchak could not liquidate. His pride suffered yet another blow when the partisans staged another raid on Omsk. Bolshevik propaganda was also gaining ground among the Siberian mushiks. The Bolsheviks had despoiled and massacred countless peasants, yet mushiks, yearning for the promised "peace," welcomed advancing Bolsheviks through ikon-carrying deputations, with priests offering bread and salt.

Kolchak enthusiasm had fizzled out. To the people the Admiral had brought neither victory nor independence, nor fulfillment of any pertinent desires: to political groups that had once hoped to achieve some of their aims under the mantle of his government he was a failure, so complete a failure that they were not even afraid of antagonizing him. Social revolutionaries and similar not yet communist controlled leftists looked for American sponsors; conservatives wooed the Japanese; middle-of-the-roaders counted on the French and British; and rightest extremists hoped for a military dictatorship by a man other than the Admiral.

Torn between recurrent spells of grippe and mental depression, Kolchak drew vague comfort from assertations of loyalty by deputations from puzzling political groups, who invariably wound up asking for favors.

The man he had come to like best was his chauffeur Kiselov: a fine, devoted servant, the Admiral called him. Kiselov wanted nothing for himself and promised that he would always stand for the Admiral. He even offered advice as to with whom Kolchak should deal and whom he should not trust. Somebody warned the Admiral that Kiselov was a Bolshevik plant. Kolchak flew into a rage: he would not have this excellent man calumniated; even if the warner produced Kiselov's membership card in the Bolshevik party, he would not consider it as proof. There were many other men by the name of Kiselov. Yet the *piatiletka* had its plants in every camp, and Kiselov was one of its two best agents.

Janin never investigated why his valet, walking his newly acquired Siberian dogs, always took them to a Czech-operated plant near the railroad station of Omsk. In fact the soft-spoken middle-aged valet had important business in the plant. There documents rifled from the General's drawers were photostated. The plant was *petiorka* headquarters.

General Janin traveled extensively to look for soldiers he might enlist in anti-Bolshevik forces, and took notes on his findings. Thus the *petiorka* learned that 1500 Italians, ex-*plennis* from Trieste, were billeted in Krasnojarsk, but would not fight; that two Latvian battalions were in the district, but that Paris had directed Janin not to enlist these men; that 8000 Poles were assembled under General Haller, but that two rival Polish National Committees in Siberia were exchanging charges of imposture, corruption, and treason, and that two officers challenged General Haller's command. In Irkutsk, 4500 Hungarian ex-plennis formed a Rumanian Legion but refused to take orders from that "pomaded gypsy," as they called a Rumanian officer whom Bucharest had dispatched to Siberia to assume command. Serb, Croat, and Slovene units had been formed from plennis not anxious to fight in, or for, Siberia; 200 of them had organized a formidable black-market co-operative; a group of Lithuanians offered to form an anti-Bolshevik battalion, but Janin discounted the offer. Nearly 200,000 German and Austro-Hungarian plennis were at large in Siberia, but Janin had misgivings against enlisting these men, and his misgivings were shared by the French Government, which realized the incompatibility of protecting the legion against an alleged threat by plennis and enlisting them. The Omsk Petiorka drew a good deal of comfort from this information. Thus far only 7000 plennis had joined the Red forces, but now that the others were barred from joining the anti-Bolshevik ranks, they might be ready to enlist with the Red armies.

All Janin had been able to scrape together were 2000 Russians, plus the French expeditionary force of 500, and a battery of field cannon. He had them shifted as far West as Cheljabinsk.

"The Czechs and the Russians must be kept apart. Retreat is inevitable. Lines will crumble and hardly reform. French prestige must suffer from our responsibility for a worm-eaten organization. Treason from all quarters is certain. Czech morale is low; but they have control of some communications, plants, services; they even have ambulances. The Russians have nothing."

Trotsky himself read a photostat of these notes jotted down by Janin.

The Bolshevik wireless issued distress bulletins on the alleged plight of the Red armies in the Ural region. They were said to suffer from privations, their number was small, their equipment inadequate to meet an assault. This invited attack from the east, and this was the Bolshevik design.

The Reds had 62,000 crack troops along the 1500-mile Ural front. This force and troops of lesser fighting efficiency would enable the Bolsheviks to maintain a static defense, but it was not adequate for a victorious campaign unless anti-Bolshevik forces staged an ill-considered attack and lost whatever coherence and fighting spirit they still had.

The wireless ruse worked. Admiral Kolchak, who had just reorganized his general staff to plan retreat, ordered an all-out invasion of European Russia; legion commanders, anxious not to yield the reins to the Admiral, who spoke of them as "Czech dogs," also took the initiative. On March 3 the ramshackle army that carried the green-and-white banner of "Kolchak's Siberia" jumped off, made some progress toward Orenburg, and re-entered Ufa. And then, to the Admiral's embarrassment, General Gajda wired that his legionnaires had overrun Red strongholds in the central Urals and were marching west. In Cheljabinsk a victory bulletin reached the headquarters train: the legionnaires had taken Perm and seized 32,000 Red prisoners.

"On to Moscow!" Kolchak exulted.

"On to Moscow!" it reverberated through the Ural Mountains.

"Easter in Moscow!" the men rejoiced. Good Friday would bring redemption to the mother city of Russia and everybody trusted in the Lord's miracle; the God in whom they believed was created in their own likeness; they would have enjoyed his miracle in their own sanguinary ways. And yet there were tears of emotion and many resolves. Easter was near. Moscow was far away from Ufa, Orenburg, and Perm. But miracles could lend wings to sore, bare feet.

Came another bulletin. The correct number of prisoners was 8000. Then General Kappel reported that the Czechs' prisoners were not Red soldiers but veterans the Czechs had rounded up at random. Next the Czechs claimed that the situation near Ufa and Orenburg was deteriorating, that Kappel's raw recruits, equipped with rifles into which ammunition did not fit, and officered by incompetent adventurers, were on the run. Kolchak refused to believe it, but confirmation came from Dutov, who reported on the train. Dutov no longer had his "army." It had dissolved like melting snow, but he had Cossacks instead, and promised that they would ride on to Moscow. "We'll get there by Easter."

"Sabotage everywhere," he answered the Admiral's anguished questions about his army. "Even the engineer and the stoker of my train were saboteurs. They let the locomotive freeze. But my bodyguards tied the engineer to the locomotive until he too was frozen, and then they heated the engine and boiled the stoker." The bodyguards, all of Mongoloid type, grinned. "*Nitshevo*," Dutov snarled. "Still a few days to Easter. Cossacks ride fast."

Omsk was celebrating the "Easter in Moscow" drive with gala balls when news arrived that the march to the Volga had been postponed because of trouble in the Orenburg sector. Cabinet members who had just been profitably busy boosting the rate of exchange of the Kolchak ruble reversed their trend. The Bolsheviks spent Easter in Moscow, and the city's 1400-odd churches remained closed.

A portentous telegram addressed to General Stefanik, care of General Janin, reached the headquarters train. But General Stefanik already had left for home via the United States and France. He never read the telegram; he never reached home. His plane crashed in sight of his goal: Bratislava.

The telegram, signed by Marshal Ferdinand Foch, said in part: "The Czechoslovak Army in Siberia shall not engage in battle; the armies of the Entente and those of America, to whom they are tied by feelings of solidarity, have abandoned intervention; they will henceforth limit themselves to passive defense and methodical retreat." Concentration for repatriation should proceed in the region of Irkutsk.

"I shall lead my own men in combat," Kolchak stormed when Janin told him of Foch's message. He raged against the legion, against all allies, and in particular against the Americans, whom he charged with befriending the Reds in the Maritime Province. His men would eventually reach Moscow and their faith would prevail over fiendishness.

Kolchak had still one officer whom he trusted unconditionally: General Bielov. Bielov took crazy risks: his flanks exposed, his communications in chaos, he advanced toward the Volga. He reached it on April 23. General Janin congratulated the Admiral, and left for the front to see for himself. Ten days later Kolchak realized that all had been in vain.

CHAPTER SIXTY-FIVE "On to Moscow!" Shouts had ushered in debacle.

First the shouts subsided on the disintegrating front, then they were choked at headquarters trains on their return trip, and they vanished from the Siberian settlements where they had never sounded really convincing. But they continued to animate the perfume-and-alcohol-saturated atmosphere of swank night spots at Omsk. They were uttered by gaudily uniformed young men who posed as members of assault troops, death brigades, and similar heroic units nobody had ever seen in combat. They were echoed by black-marketeers, panders, amateur and professional prostitutes, who joined in orgies while waiters listened soberly to drunken gabble to find cues that might ingratiate the *petiorka*. "On to Moscow!" belched men who had just secured transportation to Harbin, at a price that a few short years before would have bought substantial stock on the Eastern Chinese Railway. On and on to disaster! Disaster was a windfall to the depraved.

"I have increased my property a thousandfold," stammered a drunken man who sprawled on a sofa in Omsk's most expensive night club. "I've won . . ."

The stammering man was Mikhailov, Vice-Premier in Kolchak's cabinet. "Fools," he gabbled. "Only fools would take less! Fools!"

The band struck up, its brassy blare drowning out the Vice-Premier's frantic babble. Mikhailov struggled against the blare. "A thousandfold . . . I've won." Women, their bare breasts protruding from deep *décolletage,* bent over the Vice-Premier, listening lewdly. "He's a man, he made it," they chirped. The night club resounded with cheers, then fell silent. Waiters, bottles in hand, stopped pouring; the bandmaster beat time with clenched fists, but his men did not play. Somebody switched on all the lights. Emaciated, Admiral Kolchak stood in the entrance, like an avenging ghost.

"Come on, join us, here's to the new Tsar and to the Lord who's blessed me a thousandfold!" Mikhailov belched happily.

"You're under arrest!" Kolchak's voice resounded. He reached into his pocket, but in the hurry of his dash to the night club, after learning of Mikhailov's outburst, he had forgotten his gun. Mikhailov escaped a bullet, and he also escaped arrest. Guards bribed by wads of 1000-ruble bills released and safely spirited him across the border. He had not even told the full truth. Mikhailov's assets at the Russo-Asiatic Bank had increased at a rate of 1461 to 1 since he had taken office.

Triumphant Red bulletins told of immense stores seized in the advance, including tens of thousands of tons of food, 30,000 pairs of shoes, and 230,000 rifles. Stores were not really captured, but were delivered in the most shady dealings the world has known.

The Bolsheviks apparently learned of Foch's sinister telegram immediately after it was received. Picked partisans engaged in sabotage along the Trans-Siberian from Omsk to Irkutsk. A new *tsenter* (center) of Bolshevik infiltration was set up in Novo Nikolajevsk (now Novosibirsk). Its star performer was Vara, a primitive-looking, buxom woman who worked in a small shop and supplemented her meager income by sleeping with legionnaires. Vara was a genius at sabotage, a cold-blooded murderess, and a near-to-perfect spy who had two passions: Bolshevism and her ten-year-old daughter.

The daughter also associated with legionnaires and denounced her mother to an anti-Red Czech for a piece of candy. Vara was put on the rack and, delirious in her death agony, she revealed the name of her superior: Pavlov.

One Pavlov was president of several apparently innocuous local clubs, which all turned out to be partisan centers, and he had secret dealings with legion units and allegedly anti-Bolshevik Poles. He was arrested in a grove outside the city, in the company of four more ranking Reds: another Vara, age twenty-two, a student from Kazan; Hilde, twenty-three, Latvian-born socialite from Krasnojarsk; Motia, eighteen, who had made a success as a fashionable milliner at Novo Nikolajevsk; and Polycarp, an illiterate mushik and pyromaniac, whom Pavlov had trained as his right-hand arsonist.

Cossacks took care of a public execution that would have pleased Ivan the Formidable. But the butchery was hardly over when new acts of sabotage were committed. The Bolsheviks never entrusted jobs exclusively to any single man or woman. There were always stand-ins available, and it seemed impossible to destroy the labyrinthine organization.

Kolchak still tried to stem the Red tide. He went to the Ural Mountains. General Kappel had drafted recruits, but they had to be driven into action like frightened sheep and invariably surrendered. The line was breached. "Nothing can be done to stop the gap," the Admiral learned. Soldiers were so feeble they could hardly carry their packs. Hardly ever under the Tsar's regime had the people been treated in such dastardly fashion as now, by men who styled themselves Kolchak's servants. The Admiral asked for advice. A sad general said that the peasants would prefer the Tsar to any other ruler. Unless the Admiral could produce a Tsar, the mushiks would trust that the Bolsheviks could not be worse than the "Whites," and that once the Bolsheviks had arrived, the war, at least, would be over.

Only 30,000 White soldiers staggered about the western approaches to Siberia. The youngest was nine years old; the oldest may have been seventy. They only wanted to make a living, but they would die without having ever received a full ration. Stores were needed, but all stores, as the Admiral now knew, would eventually benefit Reds.

For a while Kolchak hoped that the Red commissar system would antagonize the Tsarist officers; that they might sabotage and join him. However, the Tsar's turncoats would rather suffer at the hands of a victor than cast their lot with a loser.

General Knox received reinforcements: one regiment, the Hampshire. The Canadians, however, were slated to be withdrawn from the Maritime Province. Knox proposed to form a mixed brigade of Hampshires and Russians, push through to Arkhangelsk, join Allied forces there, and stage an offensive into Central European Russia. The British Government, he ventured, might look with favor upon such a venture and even support it. Kolchak did not think that a mixed brigade could conquer Russia.

Legion General Gajda came forth with a surprise proposal. He had just suppressed a rebellion in his division by drastic means and now offered to turn against the Reds, disobey Masaryk's orders of passive withdrawal, ignore whatever directives might still be issued to that effect, conquer Siberia, reorganize its government, and keep on fighting until all of Russia was his.

The Admiral considered Gajda a vain braggart, and was dismayed at the thought of this foreign impostor playing a part in the conquest and reorganization of the land, but he invited him aboard his train for discussions, which continued, unavailing, as the Reds closed in on Ekaterinburg.

Janin would not disobey Foch's orders, but he made inspection trips along the Trans-Siberian, scouting for opportunities to stop the Red advance, and preventing Siberia from being overrun by the Reds, whom Marshal Foch himself called "the wretches." Socialists in the French Chamber, strangely well informed about Janin's travels, denounced him as a "vile reactionary," and a suspect "friend of the late Tsar."

A member of the British mission to Siberia, Mr. Ward, Labor M.P. and onetime commander of the Middlesex Regiment, threatened to expose Janin in the House should he support alien elements against representatives of the people. This referred to a political congress convoked to Irkutsk for June 11. Local anti-Bolshevik authorities, supported by Janin, had prohibited the congress, since they understood that it was Bolshevik-sponsored. The defiant delegates convened, were arrested, but were freed by Czech Legionnaires stationed in the city. The delegates constituted themselves as a diet; their language differed but little from that of the European Bolsheviks, and their session was protected by partisans who brought out artillery from a factory building.

Janin went to Irkutsk. He had three legion companies, the focus of Bolshevik infiltration, disarmed. The Diet was confined to barracks where sessions continued, still guarded by partisans. A Russian general told Janin that governmental authority was nonexistent throughout Transbaikalia, that local administrators acted arbitrarily, and that nobody could say which of them were Bolshevik stooges. But everything would be settled after August, after Kolchak's great offensive to Moscow had reached its goal.

Janin did not say that there would be no offensive.

The Red advance had slowed down when watercourses, swollen by melting snows in the mountains, interfered with supplies. The few White regiments, none of them more than 800 strong, did not attempt to stop the aggressors. "Why don't we go home and try to keep the Bolsheviks out of our villages?" mushik-soldiers reasoned.

Early in July, Red shock troops crossed rivers, and with the shock troops went propagandists to tell the people of peace they would bring to the huts. Kolchak had strange propagandists of his own: Western observers called them Mohammedan sans-culottes. These Mohammedan Bashkirs had experienced Red rule. "The infidels are guided by lies," they said wherever they went. "The Bolsheviks have stolen our horses and our grain, but they shall not steal our faith." The mushiks stared at the strange soldiery in funny woolen blouses, wide pantaloons, and exotic headgear ranging from burnooses to Tyrolean hats, and realized not only that these men's faith was not their own, but also that they were retreating.

On July 25 the Reds were in Cheljabinsk, after advancing sixty miles beyond fallen Ekaterinburg. On July 30, Kolchak ordered the garrison of Krasnojarsk to leave for the front, but the Russians refused to leave. The local legion commander, called upon to crush the mutiny, said that he would guard tracks but not battle insurrection.

Gajda had claimed to have 30,000 men around Ekaterinburg. Kolchak tried to contact the legion General, but Gajda was already on his way to Vladivostok, and the 30,000 legionnaires were only a phantom.

Still Red communiqués told of capturing fabulous stores. The Military Industrial Committee in Omsk washed its hands. Divarnenko insisted piously that he had planfully located depots so that Kolchak's army would have plenty of everything even on a retreat. It was not by his fault, he claimed, that the White generals did not use, or at least evacuate, the stores. The White generals said that they hadn't known of their existence.

And with the Reds advancing non-Bolshevik Siberia lost its source of iron. Only the United States could make up for the lacking metal. Kolchak told Janin that the United States would be paid for its deliveries in gold. But the

French General figured that not only iron but at least $500,000,000 worth of other commodities would have to be purchased in America. The bullion might not suffice to cover all the imports. Besides he suggested that Kolchak have the treasure shipped east on the Czechoslovak armored train *Praha*. The Admiral did not want to part with the gold, which was his sole remaining source of power.

On July 24, 1919, the U. S. Ambassador to Tokyo arrived in Omsk to see conditions for himself and draft a report to Washington. He talked to Frenchmen, Britishers, Japanese, and Russians, but he did not meet Kolchak. He spoke of Kolchak's "movement" instead of Kolchak's government, and mentioned that even though protection of the Trans-Siberian was America's design, American troops would not assume guard duties far out west, where they might be engaged in battle against advancing Reds. British High Commissioner Elliot stated that all the goods his government had already supplied had fallen into the hands of the Bolsheviks, and General Knox added that only a damned fool would suggest more deliveries. Even a solemn-looking Japanese smiled wryly when Kolchak's delegate spoke of his government's sovereignty, and of Russia's ability to put 500,000 men into the field.

A Japanese secret mission called at the Admiral's headquarters. Its members addressed Kolchak as Prime Minister, and they suggested a deal. Several Japanese divisions would be sent to Western Siberia in exchange for cession of Northern Sakhalin, all of Kamchatka, and economic privileges in the Altai Mountains. The secret negotiations failed to produce results.

But the poker-faced Japanese delegates obtained confidential information on the state of Kolchak's affairs: "The Russian front is in the process of liquidation, Russian soldiers are assassinating their officers. Nobody knows where the legion will be."

Janin had a telegram from Paris: the evacuation of the legion should be sped up, and after it was completed the French mission would be reduced in number and French troops recalled. The General replied on August 15 that the morale of French and British soldiers had suffered from their contact with the Russians.

The conscientious officer kept records on the causes of Kolchak's disaster: most soldiers too young, officers inexperienced, no communications, tactics poor, reconnaissance nil, discipline wanting, panics frequent, hospitals in heart-rending conditions, no medicines, no instruments, no laundry, typhoid cases littering floors. In hospital trains corpses are crowded into freight cars and dumped at stations. Incompetence and corruption appalling. Commissariats never delivering goods, soldiers marauding. "We want to live according to God's will," officers said. ("They do not care for the Lord, they only care for their own enrichment," Janin noted.) Officers and soldiers hate each other. Retreats out of control, soldiers and refugees mingling in columns of trudging misery. Generals use special trains. A search of one train produced seven automobiles, nine motorcycles, a score of bicycles, several thousand pairs of ladies' hosiery, gilded chandeliers, Persian rugs, and three pianos.

Janin recorded reports from Red-occupied territory: in Perm constant massacres; prior to the thaws victims thrown into holes hewn into the ice of Kama River; nightly executions, with most grueling procedures reserved for the clergy. The Archbishop and his auxiliary bishops among the killed; 15,000 out of Perm's population of 100,000 murdered; Ufa, Nirsk, Sterlitamak sites of fearful outrages; three bishops, three archimandrites among the victims; former fellow-travelers disappointed, leftist intelligentsia rudely awakening.

New rumors had it that Kolchak was plotting with the defeated Germans. Field Marshal-General Paul von Hindenburg allegedly had offered 80,000 men to fight under the command of White Russian General Denikin. General von Hoffman, who had negotiated the first "peace" between Kaiser Wilhelm's Germany and the Bolsheviks at Brest Litovsk, was said to be somewhere in Siberia. However, Hindenburg had no soldiers, and Hoffman never went to Siberia.

General Diterichs, Syrovy's former chief of staff, stayed in Kolchak's headquarters train. The Admiral took a passing fancy to Diterichs, who seemed to trust in him.

On October 2, 1919, the Bolshevik armies were astride the Tobol River. Diterichs comforted the Admiral, saying that the Red forces consisted of 25,000 weary, ill-supplied stragglers, and that some 32,000 anti-Bolsheviks were ready for action. The former was another version of the bad old underestimate of the enemy; the latter was absurd. But Diterichs sounded convincing to the Admiral, who ordered an all-out counteroffensive.

Diterichs had some 15,000 Russian stragglers and adventurers of various nationalities; the Bolsheviks had 40,000 soldiers, weary but in reasonable fighting shape. For three days Kolchak sat up, waiting for battle reports. Diterichs sent them almost every other hour: advance, morale high, the enemy routed. And yet there had been no battle; anti-Red columns trudged through no-man's-land. On October 6, Red vanguards equipped with machine guns and light artillery opened up against the Whites, who had no such arms. "Situation stationary," Diterichs wired Kolchak, and he sent another wire to his wife, telling her to pack up and go to Chita, where he would join her later. His next communiqué spoke of disengagement, and then he was back in Omsk claiming that winter would dispose of the Reds. Not only winter would tip the scales, he added, seeing Kolchak wince; the legions were still in being and might fight. Syrovy was extremely vain; he might be cajoled into joining the anti-Red struggle, and even President Masaryk was human; the right approach could make him change his mind.

Jointly Kolchak and Diterichs drafted a telegram to the Czechoslovak President, emphasizing friendly feelings and speaking of the "common struggle" against the Bolsheviks. They also sent a message to Syrovy, flattering him and speaking of the salutary effects that his participation in the common struggle would produce.

Masaryk had just issued a statement to the effect that the conflict in Russia was an internal affair. The opposition of the Conservative minority in Parliament did not cause him to reverse his policy, and Kolchak's telegram did not impress him. Syrovy, however, irresolute and scared at the prospect that the Reds might prevent the evacuation of legionnaires who were stranded on overrun territory, wanted to palaver. Janin learned of it, and took the fat General to task. Syrovy, anxious to rid himself of a dangerous responsibility, said that Janin should decide. The French General ordered the evacuation of the legion to continue without a fight.

Japanese Ambassador Kato arrived in Omsk, while the Reds, unimpeded by cold spells, advanced toward the city. Kolchak was now ready to barter fishing concessions, coal mines, and a Siberian timber monopoly for one single Japanese division. The Ambassador listened, promised to report to his government, and left. Tokyo never replied to Kolchak's offer. Whoever spent the late October days of 1919 in Omsk could but realize that everything was lost.

Kolchak ordered labor squads to build trenches. The squads marched off, never to return. The Admiral decreed that every soldier and every rifle be thrown into the defense of the city. There were neither soldiers nor rifles available.

Not a single shot was fired on the approaches of Omsk, but inside the town furious internecine struggles were fought among cabinet members and generals. Everybody clamored for an armored train for his personal evacuation and that of his folks and their belongings. There were not enough armored trains to meet all requests.

Came November 3, Kolchak sat in his special car. Before him were reports on his effectives: 20,000 men were said to be afoot. They had not really fought for many months. Couldn't they be inspired to fight? The Admiral remembered the effect his words had had on the Black Sea crews. He called his chauffeur. "Words will do a great deal to men who trust them," the man said. "I *do* trust your word. They, too, will trust you. Why don't we drive out and you talk to them?"

Generals Knox and Janin saw the automobile leave, and saw it return later in the day.

Kolchak went to his railroad car and refused to see anybody. The chauffeur went to *petiorka* headquarters to report to the "boss" that not one organized platoon stood in the way of continued Red advance.

On November 6 snow was piling up high on the streets. Crowds watched legion and generals' trains pull out. The travelers were comfortable and their freight cars were loaded to the rim. The crowds were tattered, hungry, and incensed. These soldiers had been living on the land, they had enriched themselves, and now they dropped off to let the other despoiler in. Suddenly men brandishing axes made for the train and hacked the invaluable cars to pieces.

Kolchak, huddled in a fur coat, walked past the wreckers. He too would have wanted to use the ax, but already his regime was being cut down.

A nervous twitch distorting his face, he notified Knox and Janin that he had decided to transfer his government east. "How many men have you got to protect the railroad?" he was asked. The Admiral shrugged his shoulders. "One brigade maybe," he ventured. Five brigades had last been reported in areas he had not inspected. "One hundred ninety-four men in all, and they may already have deserted," added a sad officer who trailed Kolchak. He looked and sounded like a ghost. Kolchak did not seem to hear him, and the foreign generals did not remember having seen him before.

The wreckers had disappeared, but people squatted along the rail yards, waiting apathetically. In one single night 320 died of exposure. The *petiorka*, who had moved into more luxurious quarters, enlisted volunteers to prepare flags and streamers to welcome the Red army. And because there was some heat in the shop many people worked for the Reds while the Whites were still in town.

Janin, Knox, and Kolchak left Omsk on November 9.

In the small hours of November 16 soldiers knocked at many doors and windows, shouting that Kolchak had returned. People who expressed joy were massacred on the spot. This was the first experience the citizens of Omsk had with the Red army.

Petiorka members led the victors to stores abandoned by the profiteers and to depots bulging with Allied supplies. Red squads gathered spoils. Other Red squads carried out arrests and executions according to a list prepared by the petiorka. Red agents told gatherings that Kolchak was a thief who had taken away seven trainloads of riches, and also that he had stolen all the gold. The bullion was in the Admiral's train, but he had not taken one coin for himself.

Kolchak's next stop was Novo Nikolajevsk, 330 miles away. The trains covered hardly 100 miles a day. People in Novo Nikolajevsk talked economics. They thought that the front would hold, and besides nobody could overrun Siberia during the winter. There should be time to liquidate stores gathered in the city: 6400 tons of butter, 350,000 sets of men's underwear, 4100 cavalry horses, and many hides. Chinese buyers were expected. Nobody cared whether the goods would eventually go to China or to the Bolsheviks. But everybody was concerned about currency regulations. Would Kolchak rubles still be exchanged against Romanov rubles at par, and would the Japanese continue to give one yen for 3.50 rubles? The black market had different quotations, and a man who knew his way around the exchange jungle could multiply his investment twenty-three-fold in one operation.

No soldiers were in Novo Nikolajevsk, but fourteen regiments were said to be in Tomsk, 150-odd miles to the northeast. Fourteen regiments should be at least 20,000 men. But it turned out that the regiments averaged only 250 men, and this was rather fortunate for the unhappy Admiral. Tomsk was now controlled by a government that professed anti-Bolshevism and called itself the representative of farm co-operatives and labor, but whose phraseology was reminiscent of that of the Bolsheviks.

The "government" of Kolchak could not stay in Novo Nikolajevsk. The next stop was Krasnojarsk.

Between Marinsk and Krasnojarsk tracks were unguarded, signal stations deserted, coal dumps looted. Thirty recently sabotaged locomotives had to be removed. The Admiral was said to be torn between outbursts of blind rage and fits of sobbing depression. Some of his companions did not waste their time and feelings upon a fallen leader. They engaged in boisterous drinking bouts and seedy conceptions of business opportunities to result from Kolchak's downfall. They lit cigarettes with Kolchak rubles, which they considered less valuable than matches.

At Krasnojarsk, where they arrived on December 17, the temperature was down to minus 30°F., and the price of bread up to 25 rubles a pound, which was the equivalent of three days' wages for a railroad worker, but wages had last been paid in September. No fuel was on hand. Kolchak was reported having said that legion transportation ought to be discontinued. "He's cracking up," legionnaires scoffed.

"I shall throw the way to Vladivostok wide open for my soldiers," Syrovy snarled. The legion General felt reasonably safe since he had joined the convoy of Allied trains, which had been pulling ahead of Kolchak's transportation.

At Christmas the Reds entered Novo Nikolajevsk. Two hundred fifty city notables stooped low before Bolshevik officers, *politruks,* and *petiorka* members; they offered to make a contribution of 300 million rubles and 40,000 men as soldiers or workers. The notables were manhandled and kicked out. Bolsheviks needed no contributions; they apropriated for themselves everything they wanted—men, money, and objects.

Also at Christmas, Allied trains pulled into Irkutsk—all trains except that of the Admiral, which had been permitted to fall behind on the nightmarish ride from Krasnojarsk east. General Janin called a session in his car. The list of those present included Ambassador Kato from Japan, whose whereabouts had not been known to Kolchak; also Mr. Harris of the United States, Miles Lampton of Great Britain, Monsieur Maugras of France, and Mr. Glos of Czechoslovakia. Neither European Russia nor Siberia was represented.

Irkutsk had turned hostile toward Kolchak, and blackmailing toward intervening powers. Since the establishment of the Diet, anti-Bolshevik forces had never regained control. The city and adjoining districts were ruled by a "coalition government," called "Political Center," in which the Social Revolutionaries held the majority. The real ruler, however, was one Iakovlev, who styled himself provincial governor, and blandly asserted that even though there had been no elections, the people had given him a clear mandate. He expressed readiness to negotiate with the Allies but would not tolerate any interference, certainly none in Kolchak's favor.

Posters were visible from Janin's train. They announced the imminent arrival of Japanese troops to restore the Admiral's regime. A Japanese colonel, however, who visited Janin, asserted that these posters had been printed on orders of another colonel in transgression of his authority. There would be no assistance for the discredited Admiral.

The meeting in Janin's car emphasized the urgency of fast evacuation and of dealing with non-Bolshevik forces as they were in control along the route. What exactly non-Bolshevik forces were seemed to defy definition, but it became a practice to accept the local leaders' assertions as evidence of their political stand. All along the line of retreat Red fronts, puppets, and stooges asserted that they were non-Bolsheviks. They did so in identical terms; drafted by seasoned Bolshevik political specialists in Europe.

Kolchak was no longer a force in being, but still the custodian of some five hundred million dollars in bullion. In lands where public opinion was a factor to be reckoned with it might be felt that the Allies owed him protection. Janin was inclined to share such feelings. But he did not speak up in the Admiral's favor when the meeting levied charges against Kolchak to vindicate his repudiation.

The main charge was true.

Desperately brooding over means to save what was irretrievably lost, Kolchak had contacted Semenov. His car had a wireless transmitter and all messages were intercepted. The meeting thus learned that the Admiral had suggested that the notorious ataman raid Irkutsk, seize the rail yards, and deny legionnaires transportation through Transbaikalia.

The dispatch had not been followed up by further exchanges, but it was denounced as an overt act of aggression against the legion.

The session resolved to negotiate with the rulers of Irkutsk about neutralizing Allied trains, and an ambiguously worded dispatch was forwarded to the Admiral's train, still some 600 miles away.

Kolchak learned that the Allies were ready to take every possible measure to grant him security, that his application for protection would be favorably received, but that negotiations for his safe-conduct would have to be undertaken with all parties concerned, and that under certain circumstances his problem would be considered an internal Russian affair. Also the bullion and all other valuables on his train would have to be surrendered into Allied custody for eventual transfer to the Russian people.

The Admiral did not learn that General Syrovy, called in to check the draft, had sneered, "We've been protecting him too much already. He *is* an internal Russian affair, and our orders are not to interfere."

But even so Kolchak might have known that the dispatch was his death warrant, and that the "Russian people" to whom it referred were the Bolsheviks.

Kolchak read the dispatch in silence and brushed it aside. He did not speak up when, at Nizhni Udinsk, legionnaires, armed to the teeth, boarded his train "to assume protection of his person and the bullion," as a morose subaltern officer grumbled.

Howling crowds demanded that the Adventurer Kolchak be extradited to them. Crowds gathered at every stop on the five-hundred-mile track to Irkutsk, always asking extradition of the "Adventurer." At Chernikovo the morose subaltern told rioters that Kolchak's extradition had already been decided upon and that the "Political Center" in Irkutsk would receive the Traitor.

The Admiral did not hear the portentous announcement. He was having strange callers. They had been his minions, they had profited from his regime, but now they took leave, ranting noxiously self-righteous phrases about having been faithful to him to the last but seeing no way of remaining with a leader who had not kept faith.

The Admiral did not remonstrate. The train ride from Omsk had taught him more about human nature than all his past experiences combined. But apparently he still believed that men were not necessarily doomed to go down in disgrace without a struggle. He wrote a message to all those who were still loyal, urging them to continue the struggle against Bolshevism to the last, and, since he himself could no longer lead them, to rally around General Denikin. He did not mention Semenov.

Legionnaires aboard the train did a thriving business, the nature of which the lonely Admiral at first did not understand. The number of his companions shrank rapidly. It was safe to get off the train wearing a Czech tunic or blouse. The apparel seemed to secure the most valuable item of all: safe conduct.

Meantime in Irkutsk the Allies were visited by a burly individual who introduced himself as Mr. Kalatshnikov, commander of the social-revolutionary armed forces and the person with whom they would have to deal in all pertinent matters, including transportation and neutralization. The foreigners were scared by a general strike, obviously staged with the connivance of the Irkutsk government and spreading to the rail yards. They were comforted to find Kalatshnikov genial though argumentative. Kalatshnikov protested against the appearance of a Japanese armored train, but seemed satisfied to learn that the train would not interfere in Irkutsk's internal affairs. Kalatshnikov even charged the Allies with abetting Semenov, whose bandits, he contended, were investing Irkutsk. The commander of the social-revolutionary armed forces had not yet finished reciting his list of grievances, interspersed by genial quips, when a lone shell landed several hundred yards away from the trains. The foreigners immediately protested abhorrence of the ataman, and one opined that the only person to know about Semenov's aggression might be the absent Admiral.

Kalatshnikov nodded: the going would be smooth, once the Allies had rid themselves of Adventurer Kolchak, the ataman's accomplice. Kalatshnikov supplied the Allies with local newspapers, which featured atrocities committed by Semenov's torture squads recruited from Cossacks, Hungarian, and German *plennis*. These squads had committed mass drownings in Lake Baikal, and after the lake froze, they had turned to hanging victims over burning stakes and thrusting nails into their skulls. The papers of Irkutsk never mentioned Bolshevik atrocities, but gave much space to reports on Bolshevik gains.

Records on Kalatshnikov's talks with the Allies are sketchy. It appears that he once said that it was up to the central government to decide the fate of Adventurer Kolchak and his henchmen, but that the Political Center would act as their recipient. Since the authorities of Irkutsk did not claim to be a "central government," the phrase could but refer to the Bolshevik government in Europe.

New Year's Eve of 1920 was rather quiet on the rail yards of Irkutsk. There was no strike; Kolchak's train had not yet arrived. However, it was known that it was approaching the town at an average speed of five miles per hour.

Kalatshnikov did not join the Allies' dispirited celebrations, but he called on New Year's Day and invited the foreigners to see for themselves how gently the Political Center treated people in its custody. Allied personnel joined him on a sight-seeing trip of Irkutsk's dungeon, where 183 Mongols, Buryaets, and Manchurians were being held as hostages. Interpreters explained the outcries of the captives as expressions of satisfaction about food, heating, and the kindness of jailers.

Out on the rail yards workers built up a strange array of trains: the twenty-five trains of the Allied missions were so arranged that all shunt rails were jammed but for one in the center, which turned into a trap encased by three walls of cars.

The station building, under huge layers of snow, looked like a casemate. Nobody was admitted to the station, and social-revolutionary guardsmen lined the flat grounds between a suburban street and the adjoining track. Civilians gathered behind guardsmen who kept them off with rifle butts. Darkness fell around 3:00 P.M.; nothing had happened; and the civilians left.

Four hours went by; guardsmen trampled and fidgeted to keep from freezing; nothing moved on the rail yards, nothing moved in the station building. A light breeze sprang up, a few snow squalls. Another two minutes—then a door of the station building was flung open, a column of men emerged, torches in hand. At the same moment a train pulled into the station. The engineer shunted, maneuvered; eventually the train halted—in the trap. The column marched toward the part of the shunt not encased by other trains. Their torches formed a wall of fire; its glare revealed a man wrapped in a heavy coat, detaching himself from the others, walking toward the train, and entering a car.

In this car Admiral Kolchak sat. For the first time in weeks his face did not twitch. He hardly looked up when the man burst into his compartment. He heard a few words in broken, heavily accented Russian. He could not quite understand all of the Czech-Russian gibberish, but one word meant "detention." He saw lights flickering outside and wondered about a torch parade, but soon he noticed that the paraders were tough characters carrying rifles, fixed bayonets, and cartridge bandoleers.

The visitor snorted and left. Kolchak waited.

Minutes limped past. Kolchak heard shuffling steps, muffled voices, and doors softly closing inside his train. He did not get up to look. He could well guess what went on.

His ship, leaking since the start, was at last sinking.

Fifty officers had still been with him at 7:00 P.M. Ten were left at 8:20. The others had sneaked away, in legion garb. One major tiptoed into Kolchak's compartment. He wore a legion corporal's blouse and tendered the Admiral the tunic of a legion sergeant.

"Oh no, not *that* way," the major later quoted Kolchak as having said. And he also insisted that the Admiral had laughed, a horrible laughter, his first expression of hilarity the major could remember, and certainly Kolchak's last.

The major could not stay on. The deadline, of which tunic-selling legionnaires had told them, was at hand. Already doors were bolted.

At 8:30 the visitor with the Czech accent appeared again. Trailing him, Kolchak saw a huge, bearded man. The first roared that the extradition was herewith carried out; the other said rather softly in clear Russian that Admiral Kolchak was under arrest. He called him Admiral, not Adventurer, even though he was the representative of the Political Center. The roaring man was a recently appointed Czech Vice-Consul, the only Allied representative present when a deal was put into effect: free departure of the legion in exchange for extradition of Admiral and bullion.

As Kolchak rose and reached for his coat, the representative of the Political Center motioned to waiting armed men, but they did not have to use prepared snares to keep the "nervous" Admiral from attempting suicide. The Admiral did not act like a nervous man.

His captors took him to the dungeon that Kalatshnikov had shown Allied personnel. On the following morning the Political Center formally turned Kolchak, and title to the gold, over to the Revolutionary Committee, and constituted itself as Cheka of Irkutsk, the Red Secret Police.

The Extraordinary Investigation Commission, appointed by the Revolutionary Committee to handle the Admiral's case, included two socialists, who aped and echoed the communist members.

Almost five years later K. A. Popov, Vice-Chairman of the Investigation Commission, disclosed that Lenin himself had ordered the commission "to reconstruct not only the history of the Kolchak regime, but also the biography of Kolchak, to give a picture of this leader of the counterrevolutionary offensive against the young Soviet Republic." This done, the prisoner was to be shipped to Moscow for public trial. The Admiral's person, debased by the previous procedures, should be exposed against the background of a world-wide conspiracy to destroy the Soviet Republic, and with it "the people's hope for freedom, social progress, and destruction of tyranny in every form."

The investigators assembled in a hall of the jail building, with nobody else but the Admiral and a sloppy guardsman present. Kolchak denounced the commission as a Bolshevik decoy and, turning to the guard, he appealed to him to combat "the hell-born Bolsheviks, whose very breath is violence and despotism." The guard stared at the chief investigators and did not seem to hear the Admiral's words.

Kolchak was asked to disclose details of the Allied anti-Russian conspiracy. He ignored the question. He was given to understand that by co-operating he would improve his lot. But the Admiral also ignored the hint. Investigators changed tactics and bombarded him with repetitious questions about his marital status. Wasn't he, in fact, not legally wed to the alleged Madame Kolchak, and wasn't their nine-year-old boy, who lived with his mother in Paris, illegitimate?

The Admiral replied coolly that he had been legally wedded to Sofia Fjodorovna Anirova in 1904.

"Have you always been a sadist?"

Kolchak was silent. Members of the commission took turns reading a bill of accusations of physical violence allegedly committed against workers and, in particular, the flogging of a woman teacher. There were many names, all of which the Admiral heard for the first time. Pressed to reply, he said that he had no knowledge of such acts, many of which had occurred in regions under Semenov's control. He did not acknowledge responsibility for acts of depravity committed by the ataman's men and not even for those charged to individuals described as his own followers.

The hearing dragged on, but its growing minutes gave no debasing picture of the Admiral and no evidence of an Allied conspiracy against the Russian people, as it could be used to incite Western liberals against their governments.

"He is a political nonentity," commission members protested, "and so are all his men."

But Kolchak was not shipped to Moscow. General Kappel, and yet another general, had established road blocks along the railroad. Their forces were small in number, but investigators were afraid that they would free the Admiral.

On February 7, 1920, Kolchak was led into a courtyard. He saw a pole rammed into the snow, a few soldiers with rifles ready, and three unarmed men. The unarmed men hurled themselves against the Admiral, who was dazzled by the sunlight. They tied him to the pole. He made a brisk gesture of defiance when they attempted to blindfold him. "Not that way . . ." The men desisted. "I want a priest." The men said that they did not believe in religion. "Read the sentence," Kolchak demanded. There was no reply; there had been no sentence. The soldiers took aim. The Admiral stiffened to rigid attention, holding his head high, eyes fixed on the muzzles, in an attitude of supremely unavailing valor, the ultimate sequence to his throw of the saber. . . .

"He died courageously," the commission recorded, and before sending the documentation to Moscow they padded the record by adding accounts of the accused's verbose denunciations of the Allies, which, however, differed in style from anything Kolchak had said.

Lenin called the investigators stupid, foolish, and vulgar. Nobody ever assumed official responsibility for the extradition of Kolchak, but Vice-Chairman Popov said, ". . . the Czechoslovaks betrayed him, of course, with connivance of the self-same Allied powers that had put him at the head of counterrevolution."

Colonel Fukuda of the Japanese military mission wrote later: "The day after Kolchak's arrest I went to see Syrovy and told him that my men would protect the Admiral after the Czechs rescued him from prison." The Japanese did not have enough soldiers to raid the jail. But Syrovy replied that he did not want to expose his men to "reprisals by workers and miners."

Still General Janin could have interfered. But the deal had been made, and the Frenchman reminisced, "At Mohilev [in 1917] my colleagues and myself wanted to protect our faithful ally, Nicholas II, but our ambassadors disapproved of it." Disgusted, haunted by the specter of censure for what others had planned, Janin did nothing. By saving one man he could not have saved the cause of Russia, nor that of a freedom that became ever more nebulous as its newest and worst enemies styled themselves its champions and were often believed by dupes.

The peoples who had won the war wanted peace; and if their statesmen had no workable conception of true peace, they would accept substitutes, slogans, and compacts, even if combined they formed the Trojan horse for worse conflagrations to come. Nowhere did veterans want to don uniforms again for the sake of Siberia.

General Janin was still in Irkutsk when Kolchak fell before the firing squad. "In the beginning, the Admiral was rather poorly accommodated," the French General noted. "Later, however, he was lodged in a comfortable cell. The Moscow government had ordered that he be not mistreated. He was subject to various interrogations, in the course of which, according to the Soviet investigator, they seemed to have agreed on various issues."

The final Soviet account of the investigation did not indicate that there had been such agreements, but Janin's notes dispersed the slightest doubt that may have existed about the Allies at Irkutsk not being aware of the fact that the so-called local non-Bolshevik government to which Kolchak had been delivered was taking orders from Moscow.

Kalatshnikov, who seems to have told Janin about Kolchak's comfortable cell, also told him that the Admiral had wanted to organize railroad sabotage along Lake Baikal. "A neuropath," Janin allegedly replied.

General Ogata, scion of a Japanese Samurai family, also was in Irkutsk on the day of the execution. He talked to Kalatshnikov and promised to withdraw all support from Semenov. That promise was kept.

And all the time the main Red forces advanced. They were clad in British uniforms destined for Kolchak's forces, and they added 1500 machine guns of Allied make to their equipment. Along the line of their advance railroad workers and miners began to stage walkouts in protest against mistreatment. The Bolsheviks did not argue; they let machine guns sputter. Commissar Smirnov, an appointee from Moscow, decreed that daily working hours be increased from nine to twelve, Sundays were abolished, nominal wages reduced by 90 per cent. Talking or smoking during working hours was penalized; abandoned *plenni* camps were crowded with discontented workers.

The bullion from Kolchak's train reached the coffers of Irkutsk with no loss through looting. The Revolutionary Committee, obviously upon Moscow's orders, decreed that it be shipped beyond the border for safekeeping, or more likely, for clandestine operations abroad.

Early in 1920 a mysterious woman was seen about Irkutsk. She was tall, overwhelmingly curvaceous, heavily perfumed, and painted with grotesque vulgarity. She wore a dark sable coat and was trailed by officers in fancy uniforms. Masha, one of Semenov's favorite odalisques, had run over to Irkutsk for the lucrative business of handling gold. She knew her way around the border, and she knew a few more things that even Bolsheviks appreciated.

Masha held a diplomatic passport and traveled back and forth between Irkutsk and Harbin. Once Chinese customs officials ransacked her car. Masha threw her aggressive 200 pounds and her savage vocabulary into the brawl, shoving two men bodily off the car and calling the others crossbreeds between 500 generations of dogs, swine, and vultures; 1550 pounds of gold were at stake. It is not established who eventually forwarded the treasure to the local black market: the amazon, her escorts, or the Chinese. But several tons of bullion reached Japan.

Firecrackers of travesty dimly flashed through bolts of tragic lightning in which Siberia went down to the most opaque darkness in aeons. The infernal northern vault, of which the shamans had taught, engulfed the entire vastness. It drained the quick of their will to resistance, destroyed all vestiges of hope, all expectancies but those of subjecting the entire planet to similar tribulations.

The free peoples of the world were beguiled by funny firecrackers and undaunted by the infernal vault. Masha was a character, and Bolshevism might not be as bad as some said. Bolshevism should not be contagious if you kept at a safe distance. Siberia was far away, and a happy end of the Siberian venture seemed at hand.

Two weeks after Kolchak died Janin moved to Chita, and from there to Harbin, where the Japanese entrenched themselves for future expansion. American transportation experts distinguished themselves all along the track from Chita to Vladivostok by keeping trains rolling under trying conditions.

From Moscow arrived assertations that Siberia would be granted provincial autonomy. One Janson, in charge of propaganda, distributed a declaration to Allied ranking officers to the effect that the Soviets wanted nothing but peace, reconstruction of a powerful Russia with access to the sea, and that the Allies would be well advised to assist the Soviets in their endeavors.

The partisans from Transbaikalia, the Maritime Province, Kamchatka, and Sakhalin were incorporated into the Red Army. Even this had a touch of piquancy. The supervisor of military amalgamation was the niece of a Tsarist general, a girl of twenty-three with a record of colorful love affairs.

By April 1, 1920, the evacuation of U.S. intervention forces was completed. Captain John F. Stevens, superefficient jack-of-all-trades on the Trans-Siberian, had achieved this aim well ahead of other Allied forces.

The embarkation of non-Japanese foreign troops lasted until September 10, 1920: 67,700 Czechoslovaks, 1025 Latvians, 1500 Serbs, 2300 Rumanians, and a small number of Poles went aboard ship in Vladivostok.

The last that was heard of General Kappel's small band indicated that it had joined the human flotsam of Eastern Siberia. The Bolsheviks did not report on their struggle, but apparently the last of these outlaws perished somewhere near the Pacific coast in the summer of 1923. It cannot be established whether they succumbed to Red police, the elements, or four-legged wild beasts.

Temporarily the Far Eastern branch of the Communist party styled itself *Dalbureau*. Ubiquitous Mr. Krasnotshokov became its head and the organ of Siberian Sovietization.

Janin went to Paris from Harbin, via China. An angry Clemenceau hissed that Kolchak had been assassinated and that there should be an investigation. But soon thereafter the aged "tiger" and his cabinet resigned. Janin was sent to Prague to receive high honors from President Masaryk and to present a repatriated Syrovy with the French Legion of Honor.

For the better part of 5000 years of surmised, intimated, and recorded history Siberia had groped its sinister path, from time to time engulfing other parts and peoples of the world in its flaring-up caldron. Siberia, abandoned by the foreigners, again groped its path, the caldron blazing under a thin cover of deception—hot, growing hotter, sheer unextinguishable, insatiable in its voracious appetite for fuel.

A new cycle of history had begun.

EPILOGUE Siberia, and its associates, their faces set against the outside world, are engulfing the lands and polluting the minds of those who have neither bars nor gates to shield themselves.

The cycle still has to run its course, and the news that emanates from the sprawling empire of Magog has not yet coagulated into history.

As in the distant past, when history was drafted by the subservient chroniclers of the victors, while the vanquished were deprived of life and liberty to present their side, the Soviet Gogs have monopolized the drafting of history. But unlike Temudshin, who did not know whether he had been right and did not care for the opinion of men, those who now lay claim to all lands under the eternal sky pose as paragons of righteousness and want to convince all peoples not yet engulfed of the desirability of subjugation.

The subjugated keep vegetating. From them will come the other side of recent Siberian history, after the cycle has run its course.

The author traveled through Siberia in the spring of 1941.

The land was eloquent in its sanctification of the Creator, but the people were uncommunicative. Sealed were the lips of those who, in chains, squatted in the rail yards of Irkutsk; who, in chains, were marched through the streets of Vladivostok; who trudged through the gates of a Transbaikalian camp. Their faces expressed the absolute dullness that nothing but absolute despair can create. And the faces of perished prisoners, dumped on the tracks in Birobidzan, were dull, even in death. Most of the quick, who wore no visible chains, had lost the habit of talking about anything but the trivialities of a life dedicated to the service of their masters, megalomaniacal officials, whose vociferousness was no more elucidating than the reading of a regimented publication would have been.

To shape all mankind in the likeness of their Siberian chattels is the design of the modern Gogs. Their law cannot tolerate the survival of the unshackled mind and its perennial incentive to rebellion against tyranny.

But the Lord is against Gog. No tyranny has ever survived.

Someday the victims will speak up.

I cannot hope to live to see that day, or to hear the resurrected present their side. But I do hope that enlightened chroniclers will write the full, unbiased history of the holocaust that flared up at the time my book ends.

INDEX

Abaka, Khan, 190–91
Abu Said, Khan, 196–98
Abyssinia, 43
Acre, Barons of, 188–89
Aden (Eudaemon), 17–18
Adhemar, Bishop, 90
Adrianople, 64
Aegean Sea, 83, 91
Aëtius, 55–56
Afghanistan, Afghans, 92–93, 122, 124, 153, 195, 197, 214, 218–19, 233, 239–40, 673
Agalak Island, 455
Agrippaei, 19–20
Ahmed, Sultan, 191–92
Aigun, 573–74, 578–79, 588
Ainus, 586 (*see also* Japan)
Akmolinsk, 647
Alakshak. *See* Alaska
Alans (Alanis), 49, 125
Alaric, King of the Visigoths, 51
Alaska (Alakshak), 9, 384, 431–34, 457–64, 466, 468, 470, 475ff., 574, 600, 644–45
Alaxa Island, 453
Albasin, 401, 403–5
Aldan River, 356, 370, 373
Alekseev, Fjodor, Ataman, 381, 383, 412
Aleksei, Tsar, 374–75, 389–90
Alekseiev, Jevgeni, Admiral, 624–27, 629–30
Aleppo, 154, 188, 229
Aleutians, 428, 433, 448ff., 455, 474, 478, 486–87, 498, 579, 701
Alexander Archipelago, 461, 474
Alexander, King of Poland, 255
Alexander Nevsky, Prince, 186
Alexander III ("The Great"), King of Macedonia, 17, 20, 31, 38, 84, 209
Alexander, Grand Duke of Vladimir, 200, 203
Alexander I, Tsar, 482–85, 488–91, 497, 500, 504–6, 509–17, 522, 525–26, 541–43, 549
Alexandria, 17, 21
Alexios, Emperor, 90
Altai (Mountains, district), 1, 10, 12, 18, 20, 22, 25, 39, 61, 68–69, 73, 94, 103, 117, 338, 349, 529, 534, 642, 674, 740
Altin, Khan, 359, 361, 363
Altaulovitch. *See* Mehmet Kul
Amchitka Pass, 455
America, 2, 8–9, 21–22, 28, 339, 351, 382, 384, 415–18, 420, 423–24, 427–34, 439–41, 452–53, 456, 458–61, 463–83, 485, 488–92, 495–500, 510, 526, 562, 717, 725–26 (*see also* United States)
American Company, 464, 469, 471
Amlak Island, 455
Amoy, 563
Amu Darja River, 120, 215, 217
Amur River, 1, 16, 77, 79, 242, 352, 370–71, 378–86, 388–96, 401–2, 406, 416, 442, 446, 556, 566ff.,

754

585–90, 598–600, 607, 622, 638, 641, 648, 662, 670, 703, 707, 712–14
Amur Company, 578, 587–88
Anadyr Peninsula, 381–83, 411–12, 420, 422, 424, 433, 474, 483
Anatolia Province, 72
Andreanof (Andrew) Islands, 455
Andrej, Prince, 200
"anegkok," 21
Anirova, Sofia F., 749
Aniva Gulf, 572, 574
Ankara, 229
Annam, 164
Antes, 59
Antioch, 188
Antung, 621, 670
A-pao-ki (chieftain), 77–78
Aphasians, 601
Apraxin, Gen. Admiral, 417, 419
Arabia, Arabs, 9, 17–18, 41, 43, 84, 95, 118, 184, 579
Aral Sea, 11, 61, 83, 118–19, 201, 216
Argun, Khan, 192–94
Argun River, 406
Ariq-Bögä, Prince, 164–67, 170
Arimaspi, 19
Aristas of Preconnensus, 19–20
Arkhangelsk, 244, 684, 711, 722, 729, 737
Arkoos, 702–4
Armenia (ns), 83, 92–94, 122, 135, 186–88, 197, 225, 449
Arnulf, German Emperor, 86
Arpad, Prince, 86
Asan, 611–12
Assassins (Hashishins), 154, 191
Astashev, Van, 536
Astor, John Jacob, 491–92
Astrakhan, 270, 283
Atchou, Prince, 168
Atlassov, Vladimir, 409–15, 417
Atshanis, 386–87
Atshu Island, 455
Attila, 52–59, 86, 234
Aubon, Ponce d', 147
Aukudinov, Gerafin, Ataman, 381, 383
Austria, 50, 54–55, 60, 67, 86, 91, 146–48, 265, 441, 452, 489, 501, 512, 571, 610, 615, 620, 653–55, 657–58, 666–67, 673–74, 679,
682–84, 710, 726, 734
Avacha, 420, 428, 431, 435–36, 464
Avacha Bay, 574
Awars, 28, 58–67, 82–84, 93
Ayagh Island, 455
Azerbaijan, 176, 198, 217
Azov, Sea of, 19–20, 49, 85, 125–26, 208, 216, 227

Babinov, Artemi, 353
Bactria, 38
Bagdad, 84, 118, 120, 125, 165, 186–87, 197, 225, 229
Bahadours (guards), 210, 212
Baibars, 189
Baichu, 154
Baidar, Prince, 142, 144, 146
Baidon, Afanas von, 404–6
Baikal (Lake, region, village), 1, 8, 10, 16, 18, 31, 35, 71, 80, 100, 102, 179, 234, 368, 370, 377, 395, 401, 405, 599, 602–3, 605–6, 609, 615, 618, 623, 628, 633, 636, 662, 688, 708, 725, 728–29, 747, 750
Baikal Circular Line (railroad), 602
Bai-Yulgen (deity), 25–27
Bajazet Islair, 211
Bakuntun (chieftain), 454
Balamir (Balamber), 49
Balboa, Vasco Núñez de, 373
Baldjouna, Baldjounists, 102–3, 107, 116
Balfour, Lord Arthur, 694, 697
Balkans, 50–51, 59, 62, 64, 146, 206, 226, 630
Balkh, 214
Balkhash, Lake, 12, 61, 68, 125, 130, 163, 212, 238
Baltic (Sea, region), Balts, 88, 138, 186, 206, 246–47, 251–52, 283–84, 287, 312, 331, 425, 472, 483, 542, 632, 634, 657, 660, 682, 716
Bangersky, Capt., 681–82
Baraba Steppe, 439
Baronov, Aleksei, 473ff., 485–95, 498
Barber, Capt., 481–82
Barents Sea, 244, 354, 660
Bar Hebracus, Metropolite of Aleppo, 188
Barnaul, 534, 648

755

Bar Nor, Lake, 101
Batavia, 493
Batory, Stephen, King of Poland, 305
Batu, Khan, 130, 135–39, 143–44, 148–53, 159–64, 176, 182, 186, 188, 198–200, 216, 224, 238, 244
Bavaria, 24, 54, 86, 148
Bayan, Khan, 60ff., 168, 171, 181
Béla IV, King of Hungary, 137, 141, 143, 146–48
Belgium, 578, 770
Beljavsky, 515, 519
Beloi Island, 354
Benedict, Friar, 151, 153–54, 156
Bengals, 594
Beneš, Eduard, 684, 723
Berenice, 17
Beresov, 350–51, 507
Beresovka, 663
Bering, Vitus, 9, 384, 415, 419ff., 450–51, 453
Bering Island, 439, 448, 452
Bering Sea, 382, 448, 450, 452–53, 461, 463–64
Bering Strait, 9, 433, 460, 492
Berké, Prince, 161, 182, 188–89, 200, 202
Bernadotte, Jean Baptiste, 511
Bessarabia, 65
Bestushev, Capt., 547–58
Bethlehem Steel Corp., 670
Betsharov, Dimitry, 467
Biddle, James, Commodore, 581
Bielov, Gen., 736
Bigler, John, Governor of California, 571
Billing, Capt., 463, 468
Birodidzan, 753 (see also Blagoveshchensk)
Birussa River, 533
Bismarck, Von, Gen., 540
Black Sea, 41, 58, 87, 163, 207, 216, 227, 233, 246–47, 716
Blagoveshchensk, 648, 700, 704 (see also Birobidzan)
Bleda, King of the Huns, 52
Blumberg (army commander), 727
Bogortshu, 96
Bohemia, 83, 141–43, 146, 391
Bohemund VI, King, 188–89
Bokhara, 38–39, 120, 124, 245, 275, 281, 310, 312, 317, 322–23, 336, 365, 404, 445, 505
Boleslav, King of Poland, 141–43
Bolkhovsky, Prince Simeon, 312–13, 316
Bolsheretsk, 450
Bolsheviks (communists, Maximalists), bolshevism, 10, 15, 269, 377, 601, 629–30, 646, 651–52, 667, 676ff., 695, 697, 699ff., 744ff.
Bombay, 470
Boretsky, Dmitri, 252
Boretsky, Isaak, Boyar, 250
Boretsky, Martha, 250–54
Börté, 96
Bosporus, 66, 87
Boston Tea Party, 489
Boumin, Khan, 62–64, 68
Bowes, Sir Jerome, 306–7
Boxer Rebellion, Boxers, 617–18, 620–21
Brandström, Elsa, 654, 659, 665
Bräsgä, Bogdan, Sotnik, 310–12
Brazil, 500
Brest Litovsk, 741
Bries, Von, Capt., 589
British East India Company, 464, 469, 556–58
British Isles, 51 (see also England)
Bruce, James, Ambassador, 593
Brusilov, Aleksei A., Gen., 678, 716
Bryant, William, 594
Buchanan, James, President of the United States, 592
Buda, 140, 142, 146
Budapest, 67
Budberg, Gen., 691
Budini, 19
Bug River, 549
Bulan, Khagan, 84
Bulat, Ssain. See Simeon, Tsar of Russia
Bulgaria, Bulgars, 61, 64–65, 83, 86–87, 127, 137, 186, 653
Bura, 442
Bureya River, 589
Büri, 138–39
Burma, 11, 17, 170, 490, 556–57
Bursa, Capt., 379–81
Buryaets, 22–23, 359, 368–70, 376–77, 643, 662, 667, 715, 747
Byzantium (Eastern Rome), 43, 51ff., 83–91, 229, 234, 258

756

California, 337, 490, 570–71, 589
Cambay, Gulf of, 177
Canada, 423, 429, 445, 461, 463, 491, 574, 711–12, 725, 738
Canadian Pacific Railroad, 608
Canton(ese), 176, 397, 446, 469–70, 479, 483, 489, 499, 555ff., 581, 591–92, 695
Canton River, 397
Carniolians, 55
Carnuntum, 51
Carpathian Mountains, 139
Carpin, Plan (Piano Carpini), Friar, 107, 109, 151–57, 176, 178
Caspian Sea, 11, 38, 48–49, 61, 87, 125, 177, 200, 225–27, 240, 247, 337, 722, 726–27, 729
Castries Bay, 572, 577
Catalaunian (fields), 55
Cathay. *See* China
Catherine I, Empress of Russia, 417–20, 440, 453
Catherine II ("The Great"), Empress of Russia, 441, 446, 452–53, 465ff., 477–78, 505, 541, 655
Cattaro, 146–47
Caucasus, Caucasian, 49, 84, 125, 198, 226, 467, 579, 729
Cécille, Admiral, 581
Celts, 55
Central Siberian Railway, 602
Ceylon, 17, 43, 176
Chabarov, Jerofei, 377–79, 384–89
Chabarovsk, 390
Chang Ch'ien, Ambassador, 37–40
Changchun, 699
Chang Tso-lin, Marshal, 695
Chanyang. *See* Mukden
Chapdelaine, Father, 592
Charlemagne, King of the Franks, 67, 83, 86
Charles Philip, Prince, 334
Cha-t'o, 76–78
Cheiban, 238–39
Che-kin-t'an, Emperor of China, 77
Cheljabinsk, 602–3, 608, 730, 734–35, 739
Chernigovsky, Nikifor, 401–4
Chien-k'un. *See* Uigurs
Chihli Province, 670
Chile, 470, 489
China (Cathay, Ki-tai, Nikan), Chinese, 4, 8–9, 11–21, 29–48, 55, 68ff., 163ff., 215, 227ff., 261, 267, 350, 352, 356, 362, 364–72, 375, 377, 379, 382, 386ff., 424–25, 433, 440ff., 453, 461, 469–70, 479, 483, 489–91, 499, 506–7, 534–35, 553ff., 602, 605ff., 632, 637, 642, 649, 662, 666, 670–71, 687, 693ff., 707, 718–19, 743, 751–52
Chinkiang, 562–63
Ch'in Shih Huang-ti. *See* Huang-ti
Chita, 77, 102, 589, 603, 607, 648, 663, 704, 706, 708, 713, 715, 720, 725–26, 741
Chmielnik, 143
Chou-Chou, 61–62, 68
Chouen-tshe, Emperor of China, 242
Chripunov, Jakow, Governor, 369, 375
Chuckchi Sea, 382
Chunchuse, 627
Chusan Island, 561
Chutski, 9, 382, 423–24, 433–34, 459, 474–75, 644–45
Cilicians, 135
Cimmerians, 19
Clavijo, Ruy Gonzales de, 230
Clemenceau, Georges, Prime Minister of France, 692, 697, 723, 727, 752
Clemens of Alexandria, 21
Cleopatra, Queen of Egypt, 17
Clermont-Ferrand, 90
Cochin China, 594, 635
Collins, P., 570
Coloane Island, 397
Columbia River, 491–92
Columbus, Christopher, 18, 177
Commander Islands, 439
Communists. *See* Bolsheviks
Condinia, 278–79, 282
Constantine, Tsar, 543–54
Constantinople, 53, 56, 89, 91, 247, 566
Controller Bay, 460, 479
Cook, James, Capt., 460–61, 463, 470
Cook Inlet, 460, 476
Copper Islands, 452–53
Cos Island, 43
Cossacks (Casaks), 247, 249, 281–82, 285–90, 293, 297–302, 309, 311, 313–14, 325–26, 333, 337,

757

340, 342–43, 346–47, 350–52, 355–69, 376, 379–81, 384, 388, 391, 401, 410, 412, 416, 421–22, 641, 660, 667, 700, 705, 707, 718–20, 725, 735, 757, 746
Coxe, William, 443, 445
Cracow, 143, 152
Crimea(n), 61–62, 91–92, 176, 201, 216, 247, 256, 262, 270, 283–84, 288, 318, 479, 572, 576, 579, 582, 591, 640, 726
Croatia, Croats, 67, 146, 682, 734
Croyère, Louis Delisle de la, 431
Crusades, 90–92, 188
Cuadra, Juan Francisco de Bodega y, 461
Cushing, Caleb, 564
Cyprian, Archbishop, 343–45
Cyril, St., 4, 85
Czartoryski, Adam, Prince, 549
Czechoslovakia, Czechs, 83, 542, 680, 682–84, 688, 691, 697, 708–12, 721ff., 740–41, 744, 747–48, 750, 752

Dacia, 48
Dagestan Province, 226
Dairen, 670
Dalmatia, 146
Dalny, 625
Damascus, 188, 193, 229
Damiette, 91
Dandolo, Enrico, Doge of Venice, 90
Danube River, 51–52, 54, 57–59, 64–65, 86, 579
Dappled Ordu, 338, 349
Dardanelles, 87
Darius, King of Persia, 123
Dawria, Dawriens, 371–72, 378–79, 385–86, 388, 390, 392–94, 565, 567, 569
Dekabrists, 541, 547–49, 636, 650, 675
Delatov, 464
Delhi, 122, 134, 228
Dengizieh, 57
Denikin, Alexander I, 681
Denikin, Anton, Gen., 726, 741, 746
Denmark, 260, 419–20
Dent, Launcellot, 559–60
Derbent, 225
Derby, Lord, 592
De-shima, 580–81

Deshnev, Simon, 381–84, 388, 401, 412, 423, 460
Devlet Hirei, Khan, 283–84
Diomede Islands, 9
Diterichs, Gen., 741
Divarnenko, 732–33, 739
Djagatai, Prince, 119, 130, 139, 160–61, 166–67, 170, 180, 196
Djani-beg, Khan, 198, 206
Djébé, Gen., 117, 121, 125–28, 136
Djelal ed Din Manguberti, 134
Djenghis Khan. *See* Temudshin
Djenghiskhanides, 129–30, 138, 142, 149, 155, 159–60, 165–67, 170, 172, 174, 178, 190, 192–93, 198, 200, 209, 215–18, 221ff., 234, 238, 298, 331, 404, 566, 594
Djoetchi, 119, 128, 130
Djürchäts, 79–80, 113–14
Dmitri, Grand Duke of Muscovy ("Donskoy"), 207–8, 216
Dmitri, "False," 331–33, 338
Dmitri, Prince of Vladimir, 200–1
Dmitri Ivanovitch, 328–32, 334
Dnieper River, 201, 217, 226, 247, 255
Dniester River, 50–51, 58
Dogger Bank, 634
Dolgoruki, Prince, 442
Don River, 19, 49, 84–85, 87, 176, 202, 208, 216, 226, 287
Dostojevsky, Fjodor, 663
Duchoborians, 642
Dui, 572
Dutch. *See* Holland
Dutch East India Company, 397, 580
Dutch West India Company, 382
Dutcheri, 372, 386
Dutov, Gen., 688–89, 727
Dvina (River, Bay), 259–64, 275
Dzungaria, 10, 16, 170

Eastern Chinese Railway, 603, 607–8, 615, 619–20, 624, 689, 698–99, 702, 718, 736
Ebbet, Capt., 491
Edgecumbe, Mt., 461
Edward I, King of England, 193
Edward VI, King of England, 274
Egypt(ians), 17–18, 21, 33, 43, 90, 92, 118, 137, 176, 177, 188–91, 201–2, 225–26, 229

Ekaterinburg (Sverdlovsk), 598, 601, 603, 721, 724, 726–27, 738–39
Eldjigidai, 162
Elgin, Lord, 570, 584, 592–96
Elizabeth I, Empress of Russia, 440–41, 451
Elizabeth I, Queen of England, 274–75, 282, 285–86, 306–7
Ellac, 57
Elliot, Charles, Admiral, 559–62, 576
Elmsley, Gen., 725
Emeket (deity), 23
England (Great Britain), English, 88, 90–91, 137–40, 190, 196, 260, 274–77, 279, 282, 285–86, 306–8, 311, 315, 350, 390, 397, 425, 445, 450, 460–63, 466–67, 469–70, 474–77, 480–84, 489–90, 495–99, 524–25, 534, 548, 554ff., 568, 572ff., 591–97, 601, 606, 609, 614–16, 620–21, 630, 634–38, 647, 666, 669–71, 673, 692–93, 698–99, 711–12, 717–20, 723, 725–26, 731, 737, 740, 744
Eric the Red, 9
Erlik (deity), 22ff., 177
Ermak, 287ff., 304, 307–14, 316, 319, 333, 340, 345, 350, 506
Eskimos, 9, 21, 463
Estonians, 657
Esztergom, 148
Etches, John, 466
Ethiopians, 17–18
Ettiger (Jediger), Khan, 267, 275, 281
Eudaemon, 17–18
Ezekiel, 4
Ezzelino, Friar, 154

Falkland Islands, 470
Farnum, Russel, 492
Federov, Prince, 285–86
Fedotov, 412, 415
Fergana, 38, 41–42
Fillmore, Millard, President of the United States, 582
Finland, Finns, 9, 12, 21–22, 85, 248, 251, 266, 541–42
Firando, 580
Fischer, J. E., Prof., 262, 352

Fjodor, Tsar of Russia, 331, 540
Fjodor, Tsarevitch, 305, 316 (*see also* Theodore Ivanovitch)
Fletcher, Giles, 245
Foch, Ferdinand, Marshal, 723, 735–38
Foochow (Foutshou), 184, 563, 670
Formosa (Tai-Wan), 387, 401, 592, 606, 614
Fort St. Mikhail, 480
Fortune Bay, 577
Fox Islands, 435, 462
France, French, 55–56, 90–91, 136, 141–42, 147, 178, 183, 186, 188, 190, 193, 196, 220, 254, 397, 423, 431, 445, 460–62, 489, 501, 511–12, 541–42, 548, 565–66, 568, 572, 578, 581, 584, 592–97, 607, 609, 616, 620, 670, 684, 692, 696–97, 699, 711–12, 719–20, 722–23, 725–35, 738, 740, 744, 752, 754–56
Franks, 55, 67
Frederick II, ("The Great"), King of Prussia, 441
Freemasonry, Freemasons, 540–42, 548
Friedrich II, German Emperor, 92, 136–37, 146–47
Friuli Province, 65
Fukuda, Col., 750
Fulcher of Orleans, 90
Foutshou. *See* Foochow

Gaetano, 460
Gagarian, Gen., 502
Gaikatu, Khan, 193–94
Gaiseric, King of the Vandals, 51
Gajda, Radola, Gen., 684, 735, 738–39
Galicia Province, 152, 653, 658
Ganges River, 18, 228
Gapon, 635
Gaul, 51, 55
Geadke, Col., 629
Genoa, Genoese, 91–93, 177, 183–85, 193, 201–2, 216, 226–27
Georgia Province, 92–94, 122, 125, 187, 225
Gepids, 57, 60
Germany, Germans, 55, 60–61, 64, 86, 89–90, 92, 101, 136–37, 141–42, 147, 152, 206, 247, 254, 260,

274, 288, 331, 349, 391, 401, 404, 408, 428, 467, 502, 511, 534, 549, 588–89, 601, 603, 607–8, 610, 613–18, 620, 635, 640, 647, 653–58, 661–62, 664, 666–67, 670–73, 681–82, 684, 689, 693, 697, 710–11, 722, 726–27, 734, 741, 746
Gersevanov, 504
Ghazan, Khan, 194–96
Gilaeks, 372–73, 386, 392, 394, 586
Gishigin (district), 585
Glotov, Stephen, 462–63
Gluchov, Ivan, Golova, 312–13, 316, 321
Gobi Desert, 10–11, 14, 69, 94, 102, 166
Godunov, Boris, Tsar of Russia, 284–86, 303, 305, 315–16, 320ff.
Gog, 4, 15, 529, 753
Golden Ordu, 149, 163, 182, 198, 200–2, 204, 206–7, 216, 223–24, 227, 234, 239, 259, 262, 303
Golikov, Ivan, 470–74
Golizyn, A. N., Prince, 442, 543
Golovin, Admiral, 425
Golovin, Capt., 491–92
Golovin, Fjodor, Ambassador, 403–7
Golovin, Peter, Governor of Yakutsk, 385–86, 388, 390–91, 394, 420
Goor Khan. *See* Temudshin
Goorgandj, 119
Gorbitsa River, 406
Gorlice, 674
Gortshakov, Prince, 325–26
Goshi (shaman), 81–82
Goths, 50–51
Gough, Sir Hugh, 562
Grand, Sir Hope, 595
Great Britain. *See* England
Great Canal, 176, 670
Great Wall, 33ff., 117, 129, 234, 240, 392
Greece, Greeks, 12–13, 15–21, 38, 44, 53–54, 89, 93, 187, 247, 449
Greenland, 463
Gregory IX, Pope, 141, 147
Gregory X, Pope, 178
Grippenberg, Gen., 633
Grochow, 549
Grodek (Radkow), 674
Grondijs, Ludovic, 707

Gros, Baron, 596
Gurganj, 177
Gurkhas, 594
Gustavus II Adolphus, King of Sweden, 334
Gvodzev, Michael, 459

Hadji Berlas, 211
Hagemeister, 493–94, 499
Hague Convention, 654, 658–60
Hakodate, 583–84
Halicz, 126, 138, 152
Haller, Gen., 734
Han (Dynasty), 36–37, 40
Han River, 168
Han Wou-ti, 69
Hankou, 184
Hanna, Capt., 470
Hanoi, 17
Hanseatic League (Hansa), 196, 251, 264, 274
Hara, Takashi, Prime Minister of Japan, 694, 696
Harbin, 80, 608, 624, 670, 689, 698–706, 718, 736, 751–52
Harun-al-Rashid, Khalif of Bagdad, 84
Hashishins. *See* Assassins
Hastings, Mary, Lady, 306–7
Hawaii, 574 (*see also* Sandwich Islands)
Hedenstrom, 515, 519
Heilungkiang, *see* Tsisihar
Helen of Troy, 17
Henry, Duke of Silesia, 141–44
Henry II, German Emperor, 87
Henry III, King of England, 136
Hephatites, 61
Heraclius, 65–66
Herat, 233
Hermanaric, Duke of the Ostrogoths, 49
Herodotus, 19–20
Hetum, King of Armenia, 186
Heüan-ti, Emperor of China, 46
Hienfong, Emperor of China, 593
Himalayas, 1, 228, 233
Himyarites, 18, 40
Hindenburg, Paul von, Field Marshal-Gen., 741
Hindu Kush Mountains, 118, 124
Hindustan, 176–77, 579
Hiogo (Kobe), 584

Hiroshima, 614
Hitler, Adolf, 223, 348, 549, 682, 722
Hiung-nu. *See* Huns
Hoffman, Von, Gen., 741
Hofmann, Ernst, 535–38
Hojo Tomi Kune, Shogun, 169
Hokkaido (Jesso) Island, 382, 424, 553
Holland, Dutch, 260, 267, 275, 350, 380, 382, 387, 390, 397, 417, 425, 580–81, 666
Holy Roman Empire, 67, 108, 261
Homs, 190, 192, 196
Ho-nan Province, 164
Hong Kong, 559, 563, 571, 576, 584, 588, 591–93
Hong Siutsinen, 569–70
Honolulu, 588, 711–12
Honoria, Princess, 56–57
Honorius IV, Pope, 192
Hope, Admiral, 593
Hormos, 17
Horvath, Gen., 689, 698–707, 715, 717–18
Hosein, Prince, 211–15
Houang-ti, 69
Housi-tsong, Emperor of China, 79–80
Huang-ti, Emperor of China, 15, 30ff.
Hu-chich, 19
Hudson's Bay Company, 461, 574
Hulägu, Khan, 163–65, 176, 185–90, 192, 196–97
Hunas, 48
Hungary, Hungarians, 50–51, 57, 64–65, 85–88, 137, 139–48, 155–56, 158, 653–55, 658, 662, 666, 682–84, 734, 746
Huns (Hiung-nu), 16, 19, 28, 31–32, 35–39, 41, 46–58, 61, 82–84, 93
Hutchins, John, 466
Hu-te, 19
Huzules, 682
Hyde, Thomas, 21
Hyperboreans, 19–20

Ibn-al-Athir, 134
Ignatiev, Nikolai, Gen., 596–97
Igor, Prince, 87
I-Ho-Tuan. *See* Boxer Rebellion
Ikishima Island, 169
Ildico, Damsel, 57
Ilshak (taigon), 467
Ilyas, Prince, 212
Inchon, 627
India, 11, 17, 20, 39, 40, 44, 48, 69, 92–93, 118, 123, 176, 184, 210, 227–28, 233, 362, 490, 555–56, 579, 595, 637, 673
Indian Ocean, 584, 632, 635
Indians (American), 9, 21–22
Indigirka River, 338
Indo-China, 170
Indus River, 11, 17, 44, 122
Innocent III, Pope, 91
Innocent IV, Pope, 151, 154–57
Iran, 75, 120
Iraq, 188
Irkutsk, 24, 447, 450, 463, 470–75, 477–80, 489, 492, 501–4, 514–15, 517ff., 533–36, 538, 552, 585, 589, 597, 601–2, 606, 614, 618, 624, 647–48, 659, 667, 676, 689, 701–2, 710, 726, 734, 736–39, 744–48, 750–51, 753
Irkutsk Baikal Railroad, 602
Irrawaddy River, 170
Irtysh River, 12, 18, 20, 73, 87, 89, 116, 119, 130, 223, 244, 258, 291, 298, 300–1, 309–11, 313, 345, 349, 641
Iser River, 322, 343
Ishii, Kikujiro, Viscount, 694–95
Isker, 3, 245, 268, 276, 293–95, 301–2, 307, 309, 311, 322
Ismaelites, 190–91
Ismaelov, Gerassim, 467
Ispahan, 218
Issedones, 19
Issyk-Kul, 94, 160–62
Istämi, Emperor, 62, 68
Italy, Italians, 2, 60, 65, 146, 152, 183, 190, 193, 398, 620, 708, 726, 734
Ito, Admiral, 612–13
Iurcea, 19
Ivan I, Grand Duke of Vladimir, 205–6
Ivan III, Grand Duke of Muscovy, 234, 247–49, 252–57
Ivan IV ("The Formidable"), Tsar of Russia, 266ff., 293, 295–96,

761

299, 303ff., 327, 334, 349, 654, 707, 737
Ivan V, Tsar of Russia, 403
Ivan, Tsarevitch, 305
Ivanov, Kubat, Capt., 376–77
Ivanov-Rynov, Gen., 724
Ives, Isbrand, 407

Jablonsky, Prince, 541–42
Jacobi, Lt. Gen., 463–64, 470–77, 483, 486, 501
Jadrinzev, N., 527
"jamstshiki," 347ff., 391, 507–8
Janin, Pierre, Gen., 680, 684, 691, 697, 700, 716, 722ff., 750–52
Japan(ese), 169–70, 190, 382, 398, 413, 415–17, 422, 427, 433, 446, 450, 478, 483–84, 488–89, 553, 567, 571, 574, 576, 579–84, 591, 594, 599, 602, 605ff., 640, 670–73, 689–90, 692–701, 704–15, 717–20, 722–26, 728, 731, 733, 740, 742, 744–45, 750–52
Java, 170, 176, 398
Jediger. See Ettiger
Jehol Province, 77, 95, 237–38
Jelezkoj, Prince, 338, 349, 357
Jenkinson, 245
Jepansae, 293–96
Jergunov, Archpriest, 507
Jerusalem, 89–92, 193
Jesso. See Hokkaido
Johnson, Richard, 89
Justinian, Emperor of Byzantium, 43

Kadan, Prince, 147–48
Kaichan, Emperor of China, 180–81
Kaidu, Gen., 142, 144, 146, 165–66, 170–71, 180
Kai-fong, 79–80, 114
Kaira-Khan (deity), 26
Kalatshnikov, 746–48, 750–51
Kaldoun, Mt., 129
Kalil, 233
Kalita, Ivan. See Ivan I
Kalmucks, 341, 357–62, 404–5
Kalpak, Prince, 249, 255–56
"Kam." See Shamanism, Shamans
Kama River, 279, 741
Kamarskoy, 393–94
Kamchadals, 412–13, 416, 422, 424, 430, 433–34, 440–42, 456
Kamchatka, 1, 241, 414–16, 419–21, 424–32, 435–36, 438–39,

448, 450–51, 453, 456, 462, 464, 478, 483, 492, 566, 572, 574–76, 599, 704, 740, 752
Kamchatka River, 412, 414–15, 441, 449
Kamehameha, King of the Sandwich Islands, 495–99
Kamenev, Col., 688
Kamenev, Lev, 651
Kamenshtshiki, 510
Kämpfer, Engelbert, 21
Kanaga Island, 455
Kanagawa, 584
Kanagists. See Konaghi
Kandikh, 25, 591
Kang-hsi, Emperor of China, 556–57
Kappel, Gen., 731, 735, 737, 749, 752
Kara Ki-tai, 94, 116–18, 130
Kara Sea, 12, 244, 248, 354
Kara Shurlu (deity), 27
Karafuto. See Sakhalin
Karakhanov, 689–90
Karakorum, 133, 135, 138–39, 142–43, 149–57, 159–66, 171, 178, 182, 186, 197, 199, 234–35
Karatsha, 312–14
Karelia, 22
Kars, 218, 579
Kashgar Province, 43, 94
Kashmir, 673
Kashovsky, Lt., 546, 548
Kato, Takaskina, Ambassador, 742, 744
Kauai Island, 495–98
Kaulbars, Gen., 633
Kaye Island, 430
Kazakstan, 170, 212
Kazan, 262–63, 270, 283
Kébék, Khan, 180
Kennan, George, 600
Kenteï, Mt., 105–6
Keraits, 89, 96–98, 100, 102
Kerch, 209–10, 214
Kerensky, Alexander F., 675
Kerman, 218
Kerts, 197
Kerulen River, 95
Khabarovsk, 603, 607–8, 648, 672, 700, 703–4
Khalmikov, Ataman, 724
Khara Gyrgan, 22
Kharkov, 680

762

Khartoum, 669
Khazars, 81, 84–87
Khingan Mountains, 69
Khirgizes, 16, 19, 71, 76–77, 89, 104, 341, 357–61, 363, 641–43, 652, 662
Khorasan, 218
Khorim, Gen., 688
Khorine, Gen., 727
Khoutlouk, Khagan, 71
Khwarezm, 118–24, 130, 133–34, 153
Kia Seen-tao, 167–68
Kiachow, Bay of, 607
Kiakhta (River, town), 442ff., 469–70, 483, 572, 579, 649
Kian. *See* Yangtse River
Kiang-ti, Emperor of China, 403
Kibutka, Gen., 189
Kiev, 87–89, 126, 138, 152, 374, 535, 660, 683
Kin (Dynasty), 94–95, 97, 99, 102, 104–6, 109–16, 121, 123–24, 132–33, 164, 181
Kin (tribe), 81–82
"King David," 91–94, 187
Kiptchaks (Komani, Kumans), 87, 92, 125–26, 139–40, 145, 186, 189, 196, 198
Kiselov, 733
Ki-tai. *See* China
K'i-tan, 72, 77–80
Kitchener, Horatio Herbert, Field Marshal Earl, 669
Knight, Austin M., Admiral, 697
Knox, Gen., 699, 720, 725–27, 731, 738–40, 743
Koa-tson, Emperor of China, 30
Kobe. *See* Hiogo
Kocho Tsaidam, 69
Kodar, 3
Kodiak, 462–66, 474–75, 481
Kola Peninsula, 255
Kolchak, Aleksandr V., Admiral, 691, 707, 715ff.
Koliuskis, 467–68
Koloman, Prince, 145–46
Koloshes, 480–82, 486–88, 490
Kolyma (River, district), 381–82, 638
Kolzo, Ivan, 286–87, 291–92, 307–12
Komani. *See* Kiptchaks
Konaghi (Kanagists), 463–66, 468

Konai (Gulf, peninsula), 461, 479
Konovalev, 475–76
Kopylov, 370–71
Korea(ns), 16, 21, 77, 80, 85, 133, 154, 170, 365, 579, 590–91, 598–99, 604, 606–8, 611–12, 614–15, 620–28, 637, 662
Korjak Mountains, 411–15
Korjaks, 411–15, 432, 434
Kornilov, Lavr G., Gen., 674, 678–81, 716
Kosodavlov, 523–24
Kostiajev, Col., 727
Kötchü (shaman), 104–5
Kotyan, 139
Kotzebue, Otto von, 484, 494, 499
Koutashev, Prince, 717
Kowloon Peninsula, 596
Krajevsky, 712
Krasnojarsk, 2–3, 366–68, 490, 533–36, 538, 648, 650, 664, 726, 734, 739, 744
Krasnotshokov, 703–4, 707, 713, 752
Krenitzin, Capt., 453, 455, 458
Kronstadt, 483, 586, 602
Kroom, Khan, 83
Kroupensky, Ambassador, 717–20
Krusenstern, Lt., 482–84, 490
Kuangsi, 557
Kuangtung, 557
Kubilai (She-tsu), 163–79, 182ff., 190, 192, 244
Kuibyshev. *See* Samara
Kular, Lake, 309
Kulikovo, 208
Kul-tégin, Khagan, 74
Kumans. *See* Kiptchaks
Kung Jesin, Prince, 595–96
Kunkantshei, Khan, 364
Kurakin, Ivan S., Governor of Tomsk, 366
Kurakin, Prince, 511
Kurbsky, Ssemjon, Prince, 256–57
Kurds, 194
Kurgan, 647
Kurile Islands, 424, 426–27, 472–73, 478, 488, 571, 576, 582, 590
Kuroki, 629–30
Kuropatkin, Aleksei N., Gen., 602, 605, 624–31, 633–34
Kursk, 471
Kusnezk Province, 360, 363, 366
Kütchlüg, 117–18

763

Kutchum, Khan, 275–77, 281–82, 288, 290, 293ff., 310, 312–14, 316–19, 349, 721
Kutd-ud-din, 93
Kut-el-Amara, 673
Kutluk Shah, Gen., 196
Kutuchta, Primate, 363
Kutuz, Sultan, 188–89
Kutuzov, Marshal, 511
Kuyuk, Prince, 138–39, 150–51, 155–61
Kuzgan, Emir, 210–12
Kvast, Capt., 382
Kwang Tshou-wang, 614
Kwangsi Province, 564, 592
Kwangtung Province, 564, 614, 637
Kyrov, Lt., 437
Kyushu Island, 169–70

Labrador, 460, 463
Labuan, 584
Lahoutan, Baron, 432
Langobards. *See* Lombards
Lansing, Robert, U. S. Secretary of State, 694
La Pérouse, Capt., 461
Lapps (Lopars), 21–22
Latvia(ns), 657, 681–82, 722, 734, 752
Lawkai, Prince, 378
Lebedev-Lastoshkin, 474–76
Lech (Slavonic chieftain), 83
Lech Valley, 86
Lee, Higginson & Co., 670
Leitha River, 147
Lena (River, district), 9, 355–56, 370, 373, 376, 378–80, 382, 390, 406–7, 410, 413, 442, 526, 622, 644–46, 650
Lenin, Nikolai, 650, 748, 750
Leningrad, 689–90 (*see also* Petrograd)
Leo I, Pope, 56
Leo IX, Pope, 89
Lesghiens, 125
Lesiva River, 325
Leskutov, 517–19, 522
Levashev, Lt., 453
Liaotung Peninsula, 606, 612, 614
Liaoyang, 612, 628–32, 634
Liegnitz, 143–44, 146
Li-lien-ying, 618
Lin, 19
Linevitsh, Gen., 630, 633–34, 636

Lin-tse-siu, 558–60, 563
Li-sé, 32–33, 36
Lisiansky, Capt., 484–87, 489–90
Li-tai-po, 70
Lithuania(ns), 141, 186, 206–7, 217, 226–27, 246–48, 251, 255, 263, 288, 334, 349, 418, 679, 734
Loire River, 55
Lombards (Langobards), 59–60, 65
London, 286, 397, 446, 492, 669
London Trading Company, 245
Loo-ye (idol), 444
Lopars. *See* Lapps
Lopuchin, I. W., 541
Louis VII (Ludovic), King of France, 90
Louis IX ("The Saint"), King of France, 136, 147, 178, 186
Louis XVI, King of France, 461
Louis ("The Child"), Emperor of the Franks, 86
Lvov, George E., Prince, 675
Luzon, 398

Macao Peninsula, 397, 555, 558–60, 571
Macedonia(ns), 17, 20, 31, 84
Machikatuna, Queen, 245
Mackenzie, Alexander, 461
Madagascar, 635
Maesnov, Ivan, 321
Magog, 4, 15, 529, 753
Magyars, 28, 85–87, 93, 502
Maimatchin, 444–46
Main River, 55
Maja River, 373
Makarov, Admiral, 626–27, 631
Malabar, 177
Malacca, Straits of, 17
Mamai, Khan, 207, 216
Mamelouks, 188–91, 196, 201–2, 225, 229
Manchouli, 608
Manchu Dynasty, 37, 242–43, 386–88, 393, 400, 408, 556, 565, 569, 619
Manchukuo, 571
Manchuria, Manchus, 10, 16, 61, 68, 80, 95, 128, 171, 241–42, 352, 378, 385–87, 392, 394, 400–2, 442, 445, 561–62, 567, 569–71, 573, 578, 585–86, 598–99, 603, 606–8, 611–12, 614, 618ff., 637,

641, 648, 651, 662, 667, 670, 689, 695, 698ff., 710, 747
"Mangansee," 249, 267, 278–80, 282, 285, 292, 321, 326–27, 335, 339, 350, 354
Maniakh, 63
Manichaeus, Manes, 75–76
Manichaeans, 75–76
Manila, 398, 636
Mansirov, Ivan, 316, 319–21
Maragha, 194
Maranov, Count, 542
Marcarius, 344
March River, 147
Marchand, Etienne, 461, 470
Margus, 52
Maria Theresa, Empress of Austria, 441
Marienbad, 590
Marinsk, 569, 576, 744
Maritime Province, 77, 241–42, 585, 590, 599–600, 624, 627, 630, 646, 661, 672, 695, 700, 704, 707, 713, 736, 752
Mariupol, 126
Marx, Karl, 459, 651, 674, 682
Marxist, 459, 650–52
Masaryk, Tomáš G., 684, 697, 723, 729, 738, 741–42, 752
Massachusetts, 461
Massagetae, 19
Maxim, Hiram, 610
Maximalists. *See* Bolsheviks
Maximov Islands, 354
Maximus, Tyrant, 51
Maydell, Baron, 2
Ma-yun-kun, Gen., 612
Mecca, 124, 214, 221
Media, 52
medicine men, 21
Mehmet Kul (Altaulovitch), 276–77, 288, 290, 292–96, 298, 300–1, 309–10, 313, 318
Mendoza, Juan Gonzáles de, 399
Meng, Gen., 695–96, 701, 703, 718
Mennonites, 588–89
Menshikov, Alexander, Prince, 418–19
Merkits, 95
Mesopotamia, 8, 11, 165, 168, 189–90, 225, 228–29, 673, 717
Methodius, St., 85
Mexico, 461–62
Michael (Romanov), Tsar of Russia, 334, 342, 361, 363–64
Middendorf, Alexander von, 568
Middle Ordu, 237–40, 262
Miechov, Mathias de, 245
Migration of People, 33, 40
Mikhail Aleksandrovitsh, Grand Duke, 675
Mikhailov, Vice-Premier, 736–37
Mikhailowsky, V. M., Prof., 22
Milnikov, 478
Miloradovitch, Mikhail A., Gen. Count, 543, 546
Ming Dynasty, 181–82, 229, 235–36, 242, 400
Ming-cha-chan, 73
Mingrelians, 601
Minin, Kosmo, 333, 335
Mistislav, Prince, 126, 138
Mithridates VI, King of Pontus, 39
Mizuki, 169
Mniszek, Marina, 332–33
Modo, Khan, 35–36
Mohammed, King, 118–22
Mohi, 145
Mohilev, 750
Mo-kin-liu, Khagan, 74
Moldavia, 65, 137, 572
Molokanes, 642
Molotov. *See* Perm
Mongka, Khan, 160–64, 178, 186, 188–89
Mongolia, Mongols, 8–10, 12–16, 18, 20–21, 28, 31, 35–36, 45–46, 61, 68–69, 82, 85, 89, 94ff., 179ff., 211ff., 233ff., 256ff., 270, 276, 283–84, 290, 298, 303, 324–25, 330, 334, 346, 359, 361, 363–65, 374–78, 404, 408–9, 445–48, 466, 510, 556, 566–67, 586, 594, 597, 601, 605, 611, 643, 662, 713, 715, 747; Inner Mongolia, 401; Outer Mongolia, 401, 649
Mongonsees, 88
Montagu Island, 460, 466
Montauban, Gen., 595
Mookooli, Gen., 116–17
Morai Sanctuary, 499
Moravia, 48, 50, 83, 87, 141–43, 146, 579, 684
Morris, Roland S., U. S. Ambassador to Japan, 697
Morrison, Horn & Sleigh, 589
Morse, Samuel F. B., 587
Mortier, Marshal, 548

Moscow, 49, 274, 279, 282–83, 307, 312, 343, 364, 367–68, 389–91, 393, 395–96, 402–4, 406–7, 412–13, 415, 474, 500–1, 549, 589, 616, 642, 654, 660–61, 701, 735–36, 739, 748–52 (*see also* Muscovy [city])
Moskwa River, 283, 304
Mo-tsh'o, Khagan, 71–74, 76
Mo-yen-tsho, Emperor of China, 74
Mozafferides, 197
Mozhaisk, 216
Muh-tsung, Emperor of China, 246
Mukden (Chanyang), 241–42, 608, 614, 620–21, 628, 631, 633–34, 637
Mukden-Antung Railroad, 670
Muenchhausen, Baron, 482
Mungals, 245
Muraviev, A. N., Col., 542
Muraviev-Amursky, Nikolai N., Lt. Gen., 566–79, 585–91, 593, 596–97, 602
Murmansk, 684, 711, 722
Murmansk Railroad, 660
Muscovy (principality), Muscovites, 3, 162, 208, 216, 225–27, 234, 245–61, 264–67, 282, 328, 334, 348, 642
Muscovy (city), Muscovites, 138, 205, 217, 262–63, 267, 270, 273, 277, 284, 296, 305, 311–13, 320–24, 333ff., 349, 355, 361, 363–65, 367, 374, 377, 381, 391, 394 (*see also* Moscow)
Mysovaya, 605

Nagasaki, 484, 581–82, 584, 700
Nagata, 584
Naimans, 89, 94, 98, 101, 103–4
Naktanis, 370
Nanking, 80, 182, 562–63
Napier, Lord Robert C., 557–58
Napoleon I, Emperor of the French, 100–1, 223, 489, 499, 501, 509, 511–12, 540–41, 547
Napoleon III, Emperor of the French, 574, 595, 692
Narym, 349
Nassir, Sultan, 202
Natkis, 372
Nebogatov, Vice-Admiral, 635–36
Nedsheli Lake, 645
Nemi, Prince, 357–58

Nenez, 243–44
Nepal, 556
Nerchinsk, 395–96, 405–8, 410, 413, 424–25, 442, 548, 566–67, 570, 578, 607
Nesselrode, Count Karl R., Russian Chancellor, 581–82
Neva River, 409
New York, 491–92, 723
New Zealand, 460
Newfoundland, 460
Nicholas I, Tsar of Russia, 525, 543–49, 581
Nicholas II, Tsar of Russia, 601, 633, 635, 651–53, 656–57, 661, 674–78, 681–82, 692, 721, 750
Niciphorus, Emperor of Byzantium, 83
Nicolas IV, Pope, 193
Niemen River, 511, 549
Nietzsche, Friedrich, 677
Nikan. *See* China
Nikolajevsk, 569–70, 576, 587–88, 602, 712
Nikolsk Ussurijsk, 603
Nikon, Patriarch, 401
Nile River, 8, 91, 188, 229
Ningpo, 562–63
Nirsk, 741
Nishapur, 121–22
Nizhni Novgorod, 333, 589
Nizhni Tagil, 533
Nizhni Udinsk, 745
Nogai (district), 336
Nogai, Gov., 200–1
Nogi, Maresuke, Gen. Count, 627, 629, 632–33
Northeast Passage, 382, 384, 423, 425, 460
Northumberland, 634
Noruz, Prime Minister, 194–95
Norway, 9
Novaja Zemlja, 354
Novgorod(ians), 88–89, 138, 206, 243–44, 246, 248ff., 272, 343, 544, 547
Novi Kamchatskoi, 451
Novo-Arkhangelsk, 488, 490–95
Novo Nikolajevsk, 648, 664, 726, 737, 743–44
Novodsikov, Capt. Michael, 449
Nozu, Gen., 630
Nubians, 18

Nurkatsi, Emperor of Manchuria, 242

Oahu Island, 499
Ob River, 18, 244, 249, 257, 310–11, 319–20, 326–27, 330, 349–50, 598, 602, 644
Obdoria(ns), 248–49, 257, 267, 277–78
Obdorsk, 326
Obolensky, Prince, 544–46, 548
Oder River, 143
Oelun-Eke, 94, 104–5, 111
Ogödai, Khan, 119, 130ff., 142, 149–50, 155–56, 160–61, 165, 180, 182
Oirats, 95, 236–38, 240
Oka River, 263, 369
Okhotsk (Sea, Gulf of, region, town), 352, 372–73, 390, 406, 420, 424, 446, 449, 468, 476, 483, 489–90, 492, 566, 568, 572, 577, 622, 704
Oku, Yasukata, Gen., Count, 630, 632–33
Okuma, Shigenobu, Marquis, 694
Oldjatou, Khan, 196
Olomouc, 146
Omsk, 3, 647, 663–64, 689–91, 702, 719–21, 725–27, 730–33, 736, 739–43
Omyakon, 2
Öngüt, 109, 112
Onon River, 50, 95, 104, 130
Oppeln, 141–42
Orda, Prince, 202
Ordos (River, region, tribe), 31, 34–5, 47
Orenburg, 727, 735
Orkhon River, 8–10, 14, 70, 74, 76–77, 79–80, 95, 97, 127
Orleans, 55, 90
Orlov, Lt., 569
Ormouz, 177
Orokes, 586
Osaka, 610
Oshima, Gen., 612
Osmans, 64
Ostjak, 311
Ostjaks, 12, 23, 257, 316, 319–20, 325–26, 350, 353, 357, 644, 652
Ostrogoths, 43, 49
Ostroleka, 549
Ostrovsky, 602, 604

Otano, Gen., 725
Otrepjew, Grigory, 331
Otto I, German Emperor, 86
Ottomans, 197, 229, 234, 240, 247, 283
Otvar, 119
Oughouzes, 87
Oumai (deity), 64
Oumeda, Col., 713
Ouriquans, 71
Oyama, Marshal, 613–14, 630–31, 634, 636
Oyster Bay, New York, 723

Pai River, 593
Palestine, 190
Palibothra (Patna), 17
Palmerston, Lord, 560, 591, 593
Pamir, 11, 16, 20, 31, 153
Panama, 373
Pannonia, 51–52, 57, 59–60
Panov & Kisselev, 474
Pan-Slavism, 542, 682
Paris, 91, 193, 501, 567, 585, 710, 723, 752
Parker, Sir William, Admiral, 562
Parkes, Consul, 591
Parthia(ns), 39, 41, 44
Pashkov, Gov., 394–96
Patna. *See* Palibothra
Paul, Tsar of Russia, 467, 478–79, 482, 540–41
Pavia, 86
Pearl Harbor, 613
Pechora River, 244, 257
Pedro I, Emperor of Brazil, 500
Pegolotti, Francesco Balducci, 177
Peking, 71–74, 78–81, 94, 97, 99, 112–15, 171–72, 176, 180–81, 184, 192, 230, 242, 246, 365, 397–98, 405, 407–8, 442–43, 446–48, 556, 559, 562–66, 570, 577, 579, 585, 592–96, 602, 612, 618–19, 695, 711
Pelym, 325, 329, 334, 338, 342
Penda, Corporal, 354–56
Pensa, 512–13, 515–16
Pérez, Juan, 461
Perm (Molotov), 262, 270, 598, 727, 735, 741
Perry, Matthew C., Commodore, 582–84, 610
Persia, 11, 17, 20, 31, 38, 43, 48,

52, 62–63, 65–66, 69, 84, 86, 92, 118, 123–24, 155–56, 163, 165, 176, 178, 187–98, 206, 213, 219, 238–40, 286–87, 555, 579, 598, 666, 673, 708
Pescadores Islands, 614
Pestel, Col., 541, 544, 548
Pestel, Gov. Gen., Senator, 503, 513–14, 521–22
Petchenegs, 85–87, 93
Peter I ("The Great"), Tsar of Russia, 270, 350, 384, 403, 407ff., 452
Peter II, Tsar of Russia, 419, 424, 440–41
Peter of Amiens, 90
Peters, William, Capt., 464
Petrograd, 654, 669, 671, 673ff., 692, 717
Petropavlovsk, 420, 574–76, 602
Petrov, Ivan, Capt., 363–66, 368
Philip ("The Fair"), King of France, 178, 193
Philippines, 397–98, 489
Pir-Mohammed, Prince, 233
Pishma River, 322
Plymouth Rock, 384
Po River, 60
Pointes, De, Admiral, 575
Pojarkov, Vassilj, 371–74
Pokrovskoj, 343
Poland, Poles, 88–89, 140–43, 152, 206, 227, 246, 251, 254, 263, 285, 288, 305, 331–33, 341, 349, 374, 401, 404, 441, 452–53, 511, 540–43, 549, 642, 653, 656, 722, 726, 734, 752
Polk, James K., President of the United States, 565
Polo, Maffeo, 182–83
Polo, Marco, 170, 182–85, 396
Polo, Niccolò, 182–83
Poltava, 217
Pompey, 39
Pontus, 39
Popov, Fedot, 536
Popov, Ivan, 448
Popov, K. A., 748, 750
Port Arthur, 606–15, 622, 624–33, 635, 637, 648, 670, 717
Port Etches, 475
Port Imperial, 572, 577
Portsmouth, New Hampshire, 637–38, 640, 649

Portugal, Portuguese, 350, 390, 397, 425, 555–56, 558, 580, 635
Poshabov, Ivan, 377
Posharsky, Dmitri M., 333–35
Possjet, Cabinet Minister, 553
Potemkin, Grigori Aleksandrovich, Prince, 471
Pottinger, Sir Henry, 562–63
Pradt, Dominique de, Abbé, 523
Preconnensus, 19
Price, David, Admiral, 574
Prince of Wales Island, 461
Prince William Sound, 460, 466
Priscus, Gen., 64–65
"promyshleniki," 351ff., 360, 367, 369–70, 377, 380, 401, 422, 459, 469, 534
Prussia, 101, 440, 445, 452, 501, 512, 549, 588
Pshaves, 601
Pskov, 98, 206, 255, 272, 333
Ptolemaïs, 91–92
Ptolemy I, King of Egypt, 17–18
Pusan, 612, 625, 627
Putilov, 618
Putjatin, Admiral, 572, 575–76, 578–79, 582, 584–85
Pyongyang, 612

Quara Balgassoun, 74
Quardikhan, 69
Quotcha, Prince, 161

Rab, Island of, 147
Radkow. *See* Grodek
Ragusinsky, Sava V., Count, 442
Rashid-ed-Din, Prime Minister of Persia, 195–96
Raskolniki, 401, 510
Razin, Stenka, 401
Red Sea, 17–18, 177, 229
Redl, Alfred, Col., 655
Reinsch, Paul S., 695–96
Rezanov, Jakim, 533
Rezanov, Nikolai, 477, 482–84, 488–90, 494
Rhine River, 51, 54–55, 141
Ricci, Matteo, 398–99
Richelieu, Cardinal, Armand, 423
Román, Gerónimo, 397
Roman, Bishop, Ivan, 334
Romanov Dynasty, 270, 334, 342, 350, 365, 374–75, 543 (*see also* Michael, Tsar of Russia)

Romanov, Andrej, 334
Romanov, Koshka, 334
Romanov, Philaret, 342-45
Romanov rubles, 705, 743
Romanov, Vassilj, 334
Rome, Romans, 4, 15, 17-18, 36, 39, 41-45, 48-56, 58, 83, 88-91, 93-94, 108, 178, 193, 220, 347, 397; Eastern Rome (*see* Byzantium) Western Rome, 52, 58
Roosevelt, Theodore, President of the United States, 636, 723-24
Rosen, Andreas Baron, 549
Rosen, Roman R., Baron, 636
Rostovskoy, Prince Ivan Ivanovich Lebanov-, 390-94
Rovinsky, 526
Rozhestvensky, Admiral, 634-36
Rubrouck, Guilleaume de, 178, 186, 199
Rugulas, King of the Huns, 51-52
Rumania, 722, 724, 752
Rurik, Prince, 87-88, 162, 246, 266
Russell, Lord John, 594
Russian-American Company, 461, 471, 478, 483, 485, 488, 490-92, 495-500, 568-70, 574, 578
Russian Trade Company, 275
Ruthenians, 639
Ryazan, 138, 255
Ryuku Islands, 579

Saad-ed-Daloué, 192-94
Sabbathists, 642
St. Lawrence Island, 423
St. Petersburg, 266, 383, 409, 419-20, 424-25, 427, 430, 440ff., 463, 468, 470-71, 477-79, 481, 483, 489-90, 492-94, 499-500, 503-4, 509-10, 512, 517, 521-23, 529, 534, 536, 540, 542-44, 546, 565ff., 585ff., 596-97, 605-7, 615-16, 618ff., 632, 634-36, 646, 649, 654-55, 658, 660, 669 (*see also* Petrograd)
Sàjo River, 145
Sakhalin (Karafuto), 372, 488, 553, 572, 574, 582, 586, 599, 637, 740, 752
Saladin, Sultan of Egypt, 90
Salem, Massachusetts, 583
Samara (Kuibyshev), 200, 223-24
Samarkand, 118, 120, 210, 214, 227-31, 664
Samojeds, 12, 23, 88, 243-45, 257, 261, 267, 277, 281, 289, 291-93, 301-4, 316, 325, 327, 350-51, 353-54, 526, 600
Samurzakanes, 601
San Francisco, 490, 500, 571, 575, 588
Sandepu, 633-34
Sandomiercz, 143
Sandwich Islands, 495ff. (*see also* Hawaii)
Sandwich, Lord, 460
Sangari, Isaak, 84
Sankhaiwan-Taku Railroad, 620
Sankolinsin, Gen., 594, 597
Sans Avoir, Walter, 90
Saracens, 92, 136-37, 153
Sarajevo, 653
Saratov, 659
Sarkel, 84-85, 87
Sarmats, 125
Sassanide Dynasty, 62, 65
Sassulitsh, Gen., 628-30
Satanism, 28
Sauma, Rabban, 192-93
Sauromatae, 19
Sayan Mountains, 533
Scandinavia(ns), 8, 87-88, 206
Schaeffer, Dr., 494ff.
Scott, Walter, 549
Scythians (Skolotes), 12-13, 19-20
Seidak (Sejid-jak), Khan, 317, 321-24
Selenginsk, 454
Seleucids, 41
Seljuk (Seldjouk), 89-90, 92, 118, 135, 154, 197
Semenov, Grigory, Ataman, 705-9, 713-15, 717-19, 721, 725, 728, 731, 745-46, 749, 751
Semenovzi, 714
Semipalatinsk, 648
Seoul, 611-12, 625
Serai, 200-2, 207, 227
Seraphim, Metropolitan, 546-47
Serbia, Serbs, 670, 726, 734, 752
Serbo-Croats, 542
Seres, 20
Sevastopol, 716
Shamanism, shamans, 21-29, 59, 67, 75-76, 89, 95, 100-5, 111-12, 115-17, 131, 159, 182, 241-

769

43, 294, 319–20, 325–26, 360, 410, 586, 652
Shamsha, Khan, 385
Shanghai, 562–63, 571, 594, 636, 717
Shansi Province, 670
Shantung Province 617, 670
Shelekov, Grigory Ivanovitsh, 464–65, 469–75, 477–78
Shelekova, Natalia, 477–79, 482, 493
She-tsu, Emperor of China. *See* Kubilai
Shilinsk, 572
Shilka River, 352, 371, 402, 406
Shimoda, 583
Shimonoseki, 606, 614
Shobolov, Gov. Gen. of Siberia, 504–5
Shtshapov, 504, 526
Shuisky, Prince Vassilj, 333, 338
Shumagine Islands, 432, 434
Sibir-Isker. *See* Isker
Sibirskoy, Princes of, 318
Sidon, 189
Sidorka, Isidor. *See* Dmitri, "False"
Siegbert, German Emperor, 60, 64
Sigismund, King of Poland, 331
Si-Hia(s), 108, 128–29
Sikhs, 594
Silesia (ns), 141–44, 152
Si-ling, Empress of China, 15
Silva River, 289
Simeon (adviser), 135
Simeon (Ssain Bulat), Tsar of Russia, 286
Sinai Peninsula, 188
Singapore, 560
Sinkiang Province, 20, 614
Sinoviev, Dmitri, 389, 391–92
Sitka, 459, 479–82, 485–88, 493
Skliandsky, 689–90
Skolotes. *See* Scythians
Skopzi (Sectarians), 642
Skrajaba, Vassilj, 249
Skuratov, Maria, 284
Slavonia, 82–83, 85
Slavs, Slavic, 85, 137, 682–83
Slovaks, 542, 682
Slovenes, 59, 542, 682, 734
Smirnov, 689–91, 703, 751
Smolensk, 126, 255, 334, 374
Sofisk, 585
Sokolov, 676

Sol-Wueshegodska, 264–67, 274, 276ff., 294, 298, 300, 303–5, 308, 311–12, 320–23, 326–27, 337, 350, 352
Som-go-tu, Prince, 405–6
Song (Sung) Dynasty, 79, 82, 94, 100, 104, 108, 110–11, 115–16, 123, 133–34, 163–64, 167, 181
Sorgaqtani, 160–61
Sosva River, 325
Soter, Ptolemy, Gen. *See* Ptolemy I
South China Sea, 397
Soviets, 220, 335, 663, 675, 752
Spain, 2, 51, 230, 339, 390, 397–98, 433, 460–62, 467, 479, 489
Spalato, 146
Spannberg, Lt., 420, 423–27
Spaskoj, 343
Speranski, Mikhail, 510–25
Spice Islands, 176
Spring-Rice, Cecil, 636
Sretensk, 603
Ssermjaga, 506–7
Stakelberg, Gen., 630
Stalin, Josef, 348, 549, 650, 689, 696, 722
Stalingrad (Tsaritsyn), 127, 226, 667, 727
Standard Oil Company, 670
Stanovoi Mountains, 406, 599
Stark, Admiral, 626
Stefanik, Milan, 684, 723, 726–27, 729–30, 735
Steller, Georg Wilhelm, 428–39, 441, 453
Stengel, Baron, 464
Stepanov, Onufrej, 392–96
Stephen I, King of Hungary, 87
Sterling, Admiral, 584
Sterlitamak, 741
Sternberg, Count Yaroslav of, 146
Stevens, Col. John, 700, 750
Stoessel, Gen., 627, 632–33
Stroganoff, Anikita, 258, 265–68, 273–82, 304, 317, 337, 339, 350, 352, 439
Stroganoff, Dmitri, 320–21
Stroganoff, Fjodor, 264
Stroganoff, Grigory, 279–82, 285
Stroganoff, House of, 259–67, 273ff., 306–12, 320ff., 336, 346, 350, 352, 368, 654
Stroganoff, Jakow, 280, 282, 285
Stroganoff, Luka, 260–64

Stroganoff, Maxim, 286–88, 290–91, 300, 302–3
Stroganoff, Spiridon, 260
Stroganoff, Ssemjon, 288, 290–91
Subotai (Subugutai), Gen., 101, 103–4, 121–22, 125–28, 132–33, 136–38, 141–51, 159, 164, 184, 238
Sudak, 92–94
Suebi, 51
Suez (Canal, Gulf of), 177, 188, 635
Sukin, Vassilj, 321
Suleiman, Sultan, 247
Sumatra, 17, 398
Sunblad, Gen., 727
Sung. See Song Dynasty
Sungari River, 392–93, 395–96
Surgut, 349
Sutter, Johann August, 337
Sverdlovsk. See Ekaterinburg
Sviatopolk, Prince of Moravia, 86
Sviatoslav, Prince of Kiev, 87
Sweden, Swedes, 9, 141, 251, 260, 331, 334, 374, 409, 501, 511–12, 654, 709, 717
Sylvester II, Pope, 87
Syr Darja River, 119, 221, 224, 231, 239
Syria, 39, 41, 43, 90, 135, 154, 165, 187, 190, 192–93, 225, 229
Syrjane Road, 248, 266
Syrovy, Jan, 682, 724, 727, 730, 741–42, 744–45, 750, 752

Tabriz, 176
Taganrog, 20, 543
Tagil River, 291
Tahiti, 574
Taidjuts, 95
Taidu, 172–73
Tai-Ming Dynasty, 365
Taipa Island, 397
Taiping, 570, 591, 594, 597
T'ai-tsong, Emperor of China, 69
Tai-Wan. See Formosa
Talyshins, 601
Tamerlane. See Timur
Tana, 226–27
Tanaka, Güchi, Gen. Baron, 718–20, 724, 731
T'ang Dynasty, 74, 77
Tangouts, 79
Tängri (deity), 64, 98, 100, 104–6, 112, 116, 119, 127, 149, 202, 221

Taoism, Taoists, 123–25
Tao-kwaang, Emperor of China, 563
Tara, 336, 341, 343, 508
Tarnow, 674
Tatars (Tatas), 16, 21, 28, 71, 79, 82, 97–100, 106, 141, 144, 146–47, 150–52, 157, 178, 181, 184, 283–85, 301–4, 309, 311, 314, 316, 318, 337, 357, 360, 601
Tatarskaja, 726
Ta-t'ong Province, 79–80
Ta Ts'in. See Rome
Taurida, 588–89
Tavda (Tawda) River, 297, 322, 325
Taymyr Peninsula, 382
Taz River, 327
Tchernigov, 126
Tchitcherin, Gen., 502
Telenguts, 341
Temudshin, (Djenghis Khan, Goor Khan), 94–131, 142, 149–50, 155ff., 171, 177, 180, 187, 198, 209, 216–17, 219, 221, 225, 233–34, 238–40, 244, 267, 275, 280, 303, 317, 356, 375, 753
Temür, Emperor of China, 179–82
Tenkonder. See Ahmed, Sultan
Teragai, 209–10
Terauchi, Gen. Seiki, 693–94
Terek River, 226
Tetschik, Prince, 249, 255–56
Thailand, 11
Theodore Ivanovitch, Tsar of Russia, 316, 318, 327–29 (see also Fjodor, Tsar of Russia)
Theodoric, King of the Visigoths, 55
Theodosius II, Emperor of Byzantium, 51, 56
Thrace, 50, 66
Thuringia, 60
Thyssagatae, 19
Tibet(ans), 15, 30, 37, 45, 75–76, 79, 164, 181, 235, 362, 365, 401, 556, 620, 671
Tientsin, 561, 579, 588, 593–94, 596
Tierra del Fuego, 470
Tikou-nai, Emperor of China, 81–82
Tilsit, 511
Timofeitch, Ermak. See Ermak
Timur (Tamerlane, Timur Lenk), 208–35, 239, 247

Ting, Admiral, 612-13
T'ing Che-hou, Khagan, 70
Tinghai Island, 560
Ting-ling, 19
Tisza River, 145
Tobol Ostrog, 323
Tobol River, 223, 238, 291, 296-98, 300, 322, 741
Tobolsk, 322, 326, 334, 336, 338, 341-43, 449, 507-8, 516, 526, 616-17, 664
Toghluk, Khan, 211-12
Toghon, Prince, 170
Togo, Heihachiro Admiral, 626-27, 635-36
Togrul, 96-98, 100-2
Tojan (Chieftain), 330
Toktamish, Khan, 215-18, 220-27, 229
Toktu, Khan, 201-2
Tö-kuang, Khan, 78
Tokugawa Dynasty, 583
Tokyo, 625, 636, 718, 721 (*see also* Yedo)
Tokyo Bay, 696
Tolbuzin, Mil. Gov., 402-5
Tolkatchev, 533
Toll, Count Eduard, 546
Tolstyk, Andrew, 454-55
Tomari, King of Kauai, 495, 497-99
Tomsk, 330, 338-39, 341, 357ff., 446, 508, 525-26, 534-36, 538-39, 616-17, 647
T'ong Che-hou, Khagan, 69-70
Tonghon, Prince, 236-38, 240
Ton-t'song, Emperor of China, 167-68
Ton-you-cook, 74-77
Tou-kine, 61
Toula Bouqua, Khan, 201
Toului, Prince, 130, 160
Trajan's Wall, 48, 50
Transbaikalia, 99, 568, 600, 602, 605, 641, 661, 672, 687, 695, 709, 711, 728, 738, 745, 752-53
Transbaikal Railway, 603, 622
Transoxiana, 209, 211ff.
Trans-Siberian Railroad, 348, 589, 598ff., 615-16, 620, 622, 628, 636, 649, 668, 671-72, 675, 684, 687, 689, 697-98, 702, 708-9, 722, 724, 728, 737-38, 740, 752
Transylvania, 60, 86, 144, 146

Trau, Island of, 148
Treskin, Anija Fjodorana, 514ff.
Treskin, Lt. Gov. Gen., 514ff.
Tripoli, 2
Trochaniotov, Prince, 325-26
Trotsky, Leon, 651, 681-82, 703
Troyzkoi, 343
Trubetzkoy, Prince, 333, 542, 544-45, 548
Tsaritsyn. *See* Stalingrad
Tschon-kau-ai, Emperor of China, 78
Tseretelli, 676
Tsetshina Island, 455
Tshaidse, 675-76
Tshaldones, 640-41, 652
Tshäpar, Prince, 180
Tshapu, 562
Tshech, 83
Tsherkesses, 125
Tshernitshev, Count, 541
Tshinhai, 562
Tshino, 16
Tshinkai, 131, 158, 162
Tshirikov, Lt., 423-28, 440, 451
Tshopan, Emir, 196, 198
Tshormakan, Gen., 134-35
Tshou Wen (bandit leader), 76
Tshou Yuang-tshan, Emperor of China, 181
Tshudov Monastery, 331
Tshugatsk, 466
Tshulkov, 321, 323-24, 341
Ts'in-che, 69
Tsingtao, 607, 614, 670
Tsitsihar, 608, 620
Tsu Hsi, Empress of China, 618
Tsushima Island, 169, 635-36
Tsushima Straits, 625-27
Tshussova River, 282, 289, 291
Tuan, Ch'i-jui, 695-96
Tuan, Prince, 618
Tumen, 336, 341, 648
Tümen Sasaktou, Khan, 242
Tumenez, Ataman, 359-63
Tunguses, 12, 21-22, 77 79, 241, 356, 370, 373, 468, 510, 526, 567, 569, 645
Tunguska River, 3, 369-70
Tunisia, 137
Tunulgassen, 454-55
Tunus, 343-45, 347
Tura River, 291, 293, 296, 322
Turakina, Empress, 150ff.

772

Turcs. *See* Türküt
Turgenev, Nikolai, 542
Turisk, 343–45, 347
Turkestan, 180, 187, 211, 213, 221, 239, 281, 404, 556, 630, 720
Turkey, Turks, 234, 283, 374, 555, 566, 572, 598, 653, 657, 673
Türküt (Tu-küeh), Turcs, 16, 21, 31, 61–64, 68–74, 83–85, 97–98, 109, 186, 192, 209, 211, 221
Turukhansk, 354–55, 509, 515
Tver, Tverites, 138, 203–6
Tyler, John, President of the United States, 564

Udsk, 585
Ufa, 689, 697, 700, 722–24, 726–27, 735, 741
Uglich Monastery, 328–30
Ugolinus, Bishop, 144–46
Ugria(ns), 12, 85, 348–50, 255–57, 261, 266–67, 278, 316
Uigurs (Chien-k'un), 12, 19, 74–76, 106, 124, 130, 240
Ukko (deity), 22
Ukraine, Ukrainians, 138–39, 152, 206, 217, 374, 530, 540, 542, 549, 657, 680, 726, 729
Ulbeja River, 373
Umaks, 341–42
Unalaska, 453, 456–60, 462
Unimak, 453–54, 457–58
Union Pacific Railroad, 608
United States, 259, 355, 459–61, 474, 489–90, 499, 523, 526, 560, 564–66, 570–75, 578, 581–84, 588–93, 598, 600–1, 603, 608–10, 615–16, 620–21, 625, 636–37, 644–46, 649, 654, 664, 666, 670–72, 687, 690ff., 709, 711–13, 717–20, 723–26, 731–33, 735–36, 739–40, 744, 752
Ural (Mountains, district), 3, 8, 12–13, 20, 39, 48, 83, 176, 198, 216, 223, 227, 239, 244–45, 249–50, 256–57, 261–62, 264, 266–67, 278, 282, 289, 303, 312, 316, 322, 324, 334, 337, 353, 355, 436, 516, 522, 534, 540, 548–50, 597, 602, 628, 652, 687, 689–90, 721–24, 727, 729–31, 734–35, 737
Urban II, Pope, 89–90
Urga, 18, 572

Uruga, 582
Urup Island, 571–72, 579
Urus, Khan, 215–16
Uspenskoj, 343
Ussuri River, 79, 446, 578, 585–86, 608, 630, 641, 712, 718, 724
Usuli River, 372
Usun, 105–6, 111
Uzbeg, Khan, 202, 205–6
Uzbeks, 233, 239–40, 317

Vagai River, 314
Vaganov, 568
Valens, Roman Emperor, 50
Valentinos, 59, 61–63
Vancouver, Canada, 575
Vancouver, George, 461, 477
Vandals, 51, 55
Vartan, 187
Vassilj I, Grand Duke of Muscovy, 225
Vassilj II ("The Blind"), Grand Duke of Muscovy, 247–48, 256, 262–63, 290
Vassilj III Grand Duke of Muscovy, 255
Vassilj, "Simple," 273
Velitshko, A. P., 550
Venice, 90–91, 146, 170, 177, 182–85, 195, 202
Verkhne Kamchatsk, 414
Verkhneudinsk, 704, 726
Verkhojansk, 2, 241, 380
Verkholensk, 405
Verkhoturie, 341–42, 348, 507
Victoria, Queen of England, 559–60, 584, 596
Victoria Bay, 587
Vienna, 51, 146, 512, 655
Visigoths, 49–50, 51, 55, 57
Viskovaty, Ivan, Prince, 273
Vistula River, 142–43, 549
Vitry, Jacques de, Bishop, 91–92
Vivaldo, Ugolino de, 177
Viviani, André, 694
Vladimir, 138, 200–1, 203–6, 216, 259
Vladivostok, 587, 596, 599, 601–3, 608, 615–16, 624, 626, 628, 631, 634, 636, 648, 652, 671–72, 684, 688, 697–98, 700, 710–12, 720, 724–26, 728, 744, 752–53
Volga River, 35, 49, 57, 83, 87, 130, 137, 150, 161, 176, 200–1, 207,

216, 225, 227, 263, 287, 598, 655–56, 689, 726, 735–36
Volga Germans, 348, 589, 640, 655
Volkonsky, Prince, 541
Vorotinsky, Michael, Prince, 284
Vries, Capt., 382

Waldersee, Gen. Count, 618
Walker, Robert J., U. S. Secretary of Treasury, 565
Wallachia, 57, 65, 87, 137, 572, 579
Wang Mau, Emperor of China, 46–47
Wanghia, 564–65
Ward, Mr. (British M.P.), 738
Ward, John (American Envoy Extraordinary to China), 592
Warsaw, 543, 549, 656
Washington, George, 549, 721
Waxel, Lt., 432, 435–37, 439
Wei-hai-wei, 613–14
Wellington, Duke of, 548, 560
Wenceslaus, King of Bohemia, 141–43, 146, 152
Wendes, 59
Wen-ti, Emperor of China, 69
Western Siberian Railway, 602
Whampoa, 565, 592
White Order, 202–3, 207, 213, 215–16, 223, 227, 234, 239, 262
White Sea, 255, 260
Wilhelm II, German Kaiser, 607, 656, 681–82, 741
William II, King of Holland, 581
Willoughby, Sir Hugh, 380
Wilson, Woodrow, President of the United States, 692, 697, 723, 727
Witte, Count Sergej, 602, 620
Woguls, 257, 293, 316, 325
Wood, Leonard, Gen., 724
Woo Too-po, Emperor of China, 113–14
Wou-lo, Emperor of China, 82
Wou Tsö-tien, Empress of China, 72–73
Wrangel, Peter, 681
Wu-i, 19
Wusong, 562
Wu-ti, Emperor of China, 37–42, 44

Yakutat, 479, 485
Yakutat Bay, 466–67

Yakut(s), 2, 9, 22–23, 355–56, 370, 569, 644, 695, 715
Yakutsk, 371, 373ff., 410ff., 420, 450, 460, 554, 648–49, 677–78
Yalu River, 79–80, 528–29, 611–12, 621–22, 625–26
Yamagate, Aritomo, Field Marshal, Prince, 612, 614, 724
Yana River, 2, 378–81, 410
Yangtse (Kian) River, 81–82, 168, 181, 184, 562
Yaroslavl, 138
Yayuchi (deity), 27
Yedo, 581–84. (*See also* Tokyo)
Yeliu-tch'ou-t'sai, Prince, 115–18, 121, 123ff., 136, 139, 142, 150–51, 158, 167, 185, 258, 267, 280
Yellow River, 80, 117, 128
Yellow Sea, 626
Yentai Mines, 631
Yesogai, 94–95, 99
Yenisei (River, district), 2–3, 12–13, 68, 76, 89, 165, 243–44, 325, 327, 345, 354, 509, 535, 622, 644, 661
Yeniseisk, 363, 369–71, 375, 377, 394, 447, 526, 554, 566
Yesoui, 129–30
Ying-tsong, Emperor of China, 237–38
Yokohama, 583
Yong-lo, Emperor of China, 220
You-ts'ai, 19
Yuan Dynasty, 169, 171, 176, 178, 180–82, 230
Yue-tshi, 38–39
Yugof, Emilian, 450–52
Yugoslavia, 722
Yukagiris, 379, 412–13
Yulgen. *See* Bai-Yulgen
Yu-nan, 164
Yund-shin, Emperor of China, 442
Yuriel, 216
Yustyug(ians), 248–50, 256

Zaharoff, Sir Basil, 624
Zarutsky, Ataman, 333
Zeelandia Castle, 387
Zemarchos, 63–64
Zeyer, Mr., 515–16, 520–21
Zoë, Princess, 258
Zurukaitu, 445